14th INTERNATIONAL SYMPOSIUM ON PROCESS SYSTEMS ENGINEERING

VOLUME 1

COMPUTER-AIDED CHEMICAL ENGINEERING, 49

14th INTERNATIONAL SYMPOSIUM ON PROCESS SYSTEMS ENGINEERING

VOLUME 1

Edited by

Yoshiyuki Yamashita
Professor and Chair of Department of Chemical Engineering
Tokyo University of Agriculture and Technology (TUAT), Tokyo, Japan
yama_pse@cc.tuat.ac.jp

Manabu Kano
Professor, Department of Systems Science
Kyoto University, Kyoto, Japan
manabu@human.sys.i.kyoto-u.ac.jp

ELSEVIER

Amsterdam – Boston – Heidelberg – London – New York – Oxford
Paris – San Diego – San Francisco – Singapore – Sydney – Tokyo

Elsevier
Radarweg 29, PO Box 211, 1000 AE Amsterdam, Netherlands
The Boulevard, Langford Lane, Kidlington, Oxford OX5 1GB, UK
50 Hampshire Street, 5th Floor, Cambridge, MA 02139, USA

British Library Cataloguing in Publication Data
A catalogue record for this book is available from the British Library

Library of Congress Cataloging-in-Publication Data
A catalog record for this book is available from the Library of Congress

ISBN (Volume 1): 978-0-443-18724-7
ISBN (Set) : 978-0-323-85159-6
ISSN: 1570-7946

For information on all Elsevier publications visit our website at https://www.elsevier.com/

Publisher: Susan Dennis
Acquisition Editor: Anita Koch
Editorial Project Manager: Lena Sparks
Production Project Manager: Paul Prasad Chandramohan
Designer: Greg Harris

Typeset by STRAIVE

Contents

Contributed Papers: Process Dynamics and Control

Contributed Papers: Scheduling and Planning

Contributed Papers: Supply Chain Management and Logistics

Contributed Papers: Process Intensification

Preface

This book contains papers presented at the 14th International Symposium on Process Systems Engineering (PSE 2021+), held at Kyoto University in Kyoto, Japan, June 19-23, 2022. The PSE series is a triennial conference which has been held since 1982, organized on behalf of the international PSE Executive Committee with representation from countries in Asia-Pacific, Europe, and the Americas. The goal is to create an academic and industrial dialogue, a critical assessment of existing enabling technologies, a discussion on research, education, and industrial needs, and an international forum for new directions, challenges, and opportunities in process systems engineering.

The PSE symposium bring together researchers, educators, and practitioners to discuss the latest developments in the field of Process Systems Engineering (PSE), including applications of methods, algorithms, and tools to solve a wide range of problems as well as provide the venue for discussion of new scientific challenges in our field. This symposium will feature more than 371 presentations including invited plenary and keynote lectures, as well as contributed papers (both oral and poster) encompassing a large number of core and cross-cutting PSE themes.

Among the PSE series, PSE 2021+ is special, because the first PSE symposium was held in Kyoto, Japan, in 1982. For this reason, and in light of the challenges facing our society, we chose the main theme of PSE 2021+ as "PSE for Smart & Sustainable Society: perspectives from the origin."

The PSE themes include:

- Process and Product Design/Synthesis
- Process Dynamics and Control
- Scheduling and Planning
- Supply Chain Management and Logistics
- Process Intensification
- Integration of Process Operations and Design/Synthesis
- Modeling, Analysis, and Simulation
- Optimization Methods and Computational Tools
- Process Monitoring and Safety
- Cyber-Physical Systems and Security
- Machine Learning and Big Data
- Energy, Food and Environmental Systems
- Pharma and Healthcare Systems

This book includes 10 invited papers and extended abstracts as well as 361 contributed papers. All papers have been reviewed by the International Programming Committee (IPC). We are very grateful to the IPC members for their assistance and constructive feedback during the review process. We would also like to thank the Elsevier editorial team, particularly Ms. Lena Sparks and Ms. Anita Koch for their support on this project, which provides an archival and fully indexed record of the conference.

The 14th Symposium on Process Systems Engineering (PSE 2021) was originally planned for July 2021. In view of the situation associated with the COVID-19 pandemic, the National Organizing Committee has approved the recommendation of the Executive Committee to postpone the symposium to June 2022. To clarify the postponement, the symposium is written as "PSE 2021+".

We hope PSE 2021+ will foster constructive interaction among thought leaders from academia, industry, and government and that this book will serve as a useful reference for the latest research in all areas of process systems engineering.

Yoshiyuki Yamashita and Manabu Kano

PSE 2021+ General Chairs

International Program Committee

Conference Chairs

Yoshiyuki Yamashita	Tokyo University of Agriculture and Technology
Manabu Kano	Kyoto University

Member

Thomas Adams	McMaster University
Claire Adjiman	Imperial College London
Rakesh Agrawal	Purdue University
Iftikhar Ahmad	National University of Sciences and Technology
Sharifah Rafidah Wan Alwi	Universiti Teknoogi Malaysia
Suttichai Assabumrungrat	Chulalongkorn University
Parisa Bahri	Murdoch University
Michael Baldea	University of Texas at Austin
Ana Paula Barbisa-Póvoa	Universidade de Lisboa
Lorenz Biegler	Carnegie Mellon University
David Bogle	University College London
Fani Boukouvala	Georgia Institute of Technology
Giulia Bozzano	Politecnico di Milano
Arief Budiman	Universitas Gadjah Mada
Ian Cameron	The University of Queensland
Pedro Castro	University of Lisbon
Tianyou Chai	Northeastern University
Chuei-Tin Chang	National Cheng Kung University
Nishanth Chemmangattuvalappil	University of Nottingham – Malaysia
Cheng-Liang Chen	National Taiwan University
Xi Chen	Zhejiang University
Leo Chiang	Dow Inc.
I-Lung Chien	National Taiwan University
Min-Sen Chiu	National University of Singapore
Shoukat Choudhury	Bangladesh University of Engineering and Technology
Luis Cisternas	Universidad de Antofagasta
Selen Cremaschi	Auburn University
Prodromos Daoutidis	University of Minnesota
Maria Soledad Diaz	Universidad Nacional del Sur
Alexander Dowling	University of Notre Dame
Helen Durand	Wayne State University
Mario Richard Eden	Auburn University
Mahmoud El-Halwagi	Texas A&M University

Fadwa Eljack	Qatar University
Sebastian Engell	TU Dortmund University
Antonio Espuña	Technical University of Catalonia
Dominic Foo	University of Nottingham – Malaysia
Ferenc Friedler	The University of Győr
Rafiqul Gani	PSE for SPEED
Furong Gao	The Hong Kong University of Science and Technology
Salvador García-Muñoz	Eli Lilly and Company
Michail Georgiadis	Aristotle University of Thessaloniki
Chrysanthos Gounaris	Carnegie Mellon University
Ignacio Grossmann	Carnegie Mellon University
Martin Guay	Queen's University
Ravi Gudi	IIT Bombay
Takashi Hamaguchi	Nagoya Institute of Technology
Renanto Handogo	Institut Teknologi Sepuluh Nopember
Iiro Harjunkoski	ABB Power Grids Research
M.M. Faruque Hasan	Texas A&M University
Gabriela Henning	Universidad Nacional del Litoral
Seongmin Heo	Dankook University
Diane Hildebrandt	University of South Africa
Mohamed Azlan Hussain	University Malaya
Marianthi Ierapetritou	University of Delaware
Nevin Gerek Ince	AVEVA
Arturo Jimenez	Instituto Tecnológico de Celaya
Xavier Joulia	Université de Toulouse
Niket Kaisare	Indian Institute of Technology Madras
Iftekhar Karimi	National University of Singapore
Yoshiaki Kawajiri	Nagoya University
Soorathep Kheawhom	Chulalongkorn University
Christopher Kieslich	Auburn University
Yasunori Kikuchi	The University of Tokyo
Sanghong Kim	Tokyo University of Agriculture and Technology
Naoki Kimura	Kyushu University
Paisan Kittisupakorn	Chulalongkorn University
Zdravko Kravanja	University of Maribor
Jay H Lee	KAIST
Jong Min Lee	Seoul National University
Moonyong Lee	Yeungnam University
Grégoire Léonard	University of Liège
Jinghai Li	Chinese Academy of Sciences
Zukui Li	University of Alberta
Hankwon Lim	UNIST

Fernando V. Lima	West Virginia University
Patrick Linke	Texas A&M University – Qatar
Liu Liu	Jiangnan University
Vladimir Mahalec	McMaster University
Thokozani Majozi	University of the Witwatersrand
Zainuddin Abd Manan	Universiti Teknologi Malaysia
Flavio Manenti	Università degli Studi di Milano
Seyed Soheil Mansouri	Technical University of Denmark
Christos Maravelias	Princeton University
Mariano Martin	University of Salamanca
Hideyuki Matsumoto	Tokyo Institute of Technology
Ruth Misener	Imperial College London
Alexander Mitsos	RWTH Aachen University
Ludovic Montastruc	INP-ENSIACET
Il Moon	Yonsei University
Iqbal Mujtaba	University of Bradford
Cláudio Augusto O Nascimento	University of São Paulo
Masaru Noda	Fukuoka University
Costas Pantelides	Imperial College London & Process Systems Enterprise Ltd.
Stavros Papadokonstantakis	Chalmers University of Technology
Lazaros Papageorgiou	University College London
Stratos Pistikopoulos	Texas A&M University
Joe Qin	City University of Hong Kong
G. V. Rex Reklaitis	Purdue University
Lakshminarayanan Samavedham	National University of Singapore
John Siirola	Sandia National Laboratories
Sigurd Skogestad	Norwegian University of Science and Technology
Ken-Ichiro Sotowa	Kyoto University
Rajagopalan Srinivasan	Indian Institute of Technology Madras
Hongyu Su	Zhejian University
Hirokazu Sugiyama	The University of Tokyo
Christopher Swartz	McMaster University
Kazuhiro Takeda	Shizuoka University
Raymond Tan	De La Salle University
Ana I. Torres	Universidad de la República
Anjan Tula	Zhejiang University
Metin Turkay	Koc University
Petar Varbanov	Brno University of Technology
Dimitrios Varvarezos	Aspen Technology
Xiaonan Wang	National University of Singapore
Yuan Yao	National Tsing Hua University
Fengqi You	Cornell University

Xigang Yuan	Tianjin University
Lei Zhang	Dalian University of Technology
Jinsong Zhao	Tsinghua University
Teng Zhou	Max Planck Institute, Magdeburg
Edwin Zondervan	University of Twente
Danielle Zyngier	Hatch

Proceedings of the 14th International Symposium on Process Systems Engineering – PSE 2021+
June 19-23, 2022, Kyoto, Japan
http://dx.doi.org/10.1016/B978-0-323-85159-6.50001-4

Actions toward carbon-neutral society with fuel cell technology

Yoshihiko Hamamura

Fuel Cell Business Field., Toyota Motor Corporation, Aichi 471-8571, JAPAN
yoshihiko_hamamura@mail.toyota.co.jp

Abstract

In recent years, many countries have announced the declarations and policies toward a carbon-neutral society in response to global warming. The entire industries must tackle with the issues and it is necessary not only to develop zero CO_2 emission vehicle, but also to reduce CO_2 emission during the process of vehicle manufacturing, disposal, and fuel production in case of the automotive industry. Hydrogen is considered to be an important energy toward carbon-neutral society because of portability, storability, and producibility from various renewable energies such as solar and wind. Toyota is challenging toward the wide expansion of fuel cell applications by communicating with the customers and utilizing the fuel cell system for the various applications around the world as well as the 2nd-generation MIRAI, the fuel cell electric vehicle (FCEV). Toyota is also proposing the fuel cell system modules for the efficient packaging so that every customer can deploy them to their system products without a large effort and time. Further collaboration and communication from a wide range of perspectives will be essential with every stakeholder in the fuel cell industry and research field because there are many technical hurdles toward the promotion of the application of the fuel cell systems. The strength of PSE, which specializes in system integration and optimization, is strongly demanded to solve such interdisciplinary and complex issues surrounding the fuel cell technologies.

Keywords: Carbon neutrality; Hydrogen; Fuel cell; System application

1. The world trend of carbon neutrality and hydrogen energy

Carbon neutrality and decarbonization are gathering attention, especially after the Kyoto Protocol (United Nation, 1997) and the Paris Agreement (United Nation, 2015), for the prevention of global warming. Table 1 shows the recent world trend surrounding carbon neutrality and hydrogen energy. In 2018, 1st. International Conference on Hydrogen was held in Japan and the roadmaps for the promotion of hydrogen utilization were announced. In 2019, many countries declared high numerical targets toward carbon neutrality and decarbonization as follows: deployment of 8 million fuel cell electric vehicles (FCEVs) and 400 - 1000 hydrogen fueling stations by 2050 in E.U.; 10 million FCEVs and hydrogen fueling stations in every 10 km on the roads within next 10 years in Japan; 1.2 million FCEVs and hydrogen fueling stations by 2030 in U.S.A. In 2020, large scale investments were announced from many countries all over the world as follows: Investment of 750 billion Euro in total for a 'Green Deal' was announced by the E.U. targeting the recovery from the COVID-19 crisis, in which 30 % is shared to climate control related purposes; U.K. set the target of decarbonization by 2050 and the prohibition of sales of gasoline and diesel internal combustion engine vehicles after 2030; and Japan declared the achievement of carbon neutrality by 2050. In 2021, The U.S.A government announced the recovery to the Paris Agreement, the investment of 2 trillion

U.S. Dollars for the environmental and infrastructural industries, and the target of carbon neutrality by 2050. The features of hydrogen in storability and portability of energy allow it to function well with a variety of renewable energy sources such as solar and wind, thus making hydrogen an essential energy source for achieving carbon neutrality (Daud et al., 2017).

Table 1. The world trend surrounding carbon neutrality and hydrogen energy

Year	Country	Policy / Event
2018	Netherlands	Hydrogen Roadmap
	U.S.A	DOE Hydrogen and fuel cell Program Overview
	E.U.	Hydrogen initiative
	Japan	International Conference on Hydrogen
	Australia	National Hydrogen Roadmap
2019	Republic of Korea	Hydrogen Economy Promotion Roadmap
	E.U.	FCH-JU Hydrogen Roadmap
	Japan	Hydrogen and Fuel Cell Roadmap
		International Conference on Hydrogen
	France	Hydrogen Roadmap
	Australia	Renewable Hydrogen Strategy
	U.S.A	FCHEA Roadmap
		California FC-Bus Roadmap
	Saudi Arabia	Renewable Energy Strategy
2020	E.U.	European Green Deal
	Republic of Korea	Green New Deal
	Japan	Carbon Neutrality in 2050
	U.K.	Green Industrial Revolution
2021	U.S.A	Green revolution
	Japan	Decarbonization Supply-Chain among Japan, Australia, and India

2. Fuel cell development for various applications and usages

The 1st-generation MIRAI was launched in 2014 as the world's first mass-production fuel cell electric vehicle (FCEV). In addition to the improvement in many aspects of the system performance, the 2nd-generation MIRAI was designed to achieve a significant improvements in fundamental vehicle features. It has not only high environmental performance, but also responsive acceleration, superior handling and vehicle control, reliable cruising range, an increased number of passengers, and a stylish exterior design as shown in Fig.1. It is expected that the role of the 1st-generation MIRAI is the 'starting point for popularization' and the 2nd-generation MIRAI is 'accelerating to popularization'.

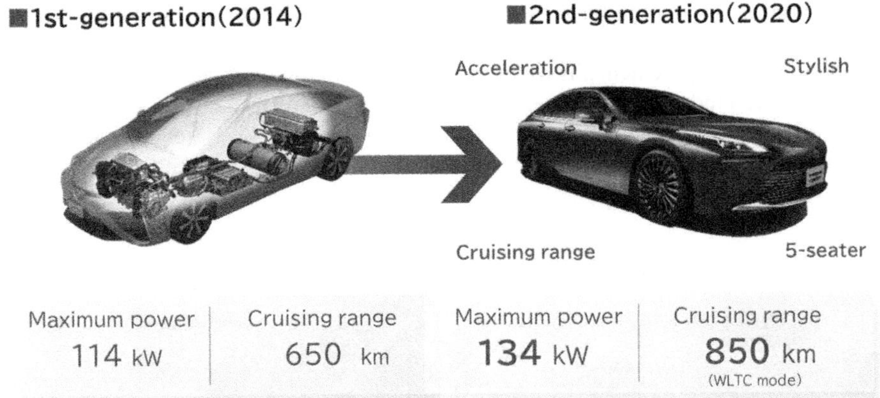

Fig. 1. MIRAI, fuel cell electric vehicle (FCEV) from TOYOTA

MIRAI's fuel cell system was not developed exclusively for MIRAI. The implementation of the 1st-generation fuel cell system to a variety of applications in addition to passenger vehicles, such as commercial vehicles of buses and tracks, stationary power generators, forklifts, and ships, has been investigated since 2014. In the process of developing these applications, it became obvious that significant time and effort were required until the completion of system integration for each application.

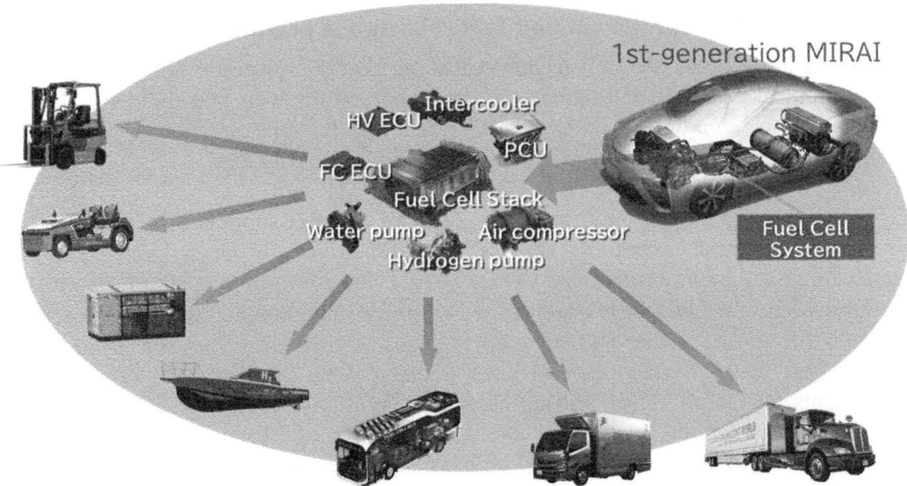

Fig. 2. The lineup of the different geometries of the fuel cell system modules

To overcome the problem described above, the system-modularization concept was adopted for 2nd-generation fuel cell system development. Vertical, horizontal and compact fuel cell system modules have been developed, where the same 2nd-generation system components such as fuel cell stack, air compressor, hydrogen pump, water pump, intercooler, engine control units (ECUs), and power control units (PCU) are efficiently repackaged. In addition, the interfaces between the fuel cell system and the applied system are gathered in one mounting surface in a rectangular package for ease of integration. Customers can choose suitable fuel cell system modules from the lineup according to their application requirements. It is expected that these products reduce the barrier to entry into the fuel cell industry with benefits for the customers and users. Actually, our partners are accelerating the development of the fuel cell powered trucks, buses, stationary power generators, ships, and construction machinery by utilizing these fuel cell system modules as shown in Fig. 3.

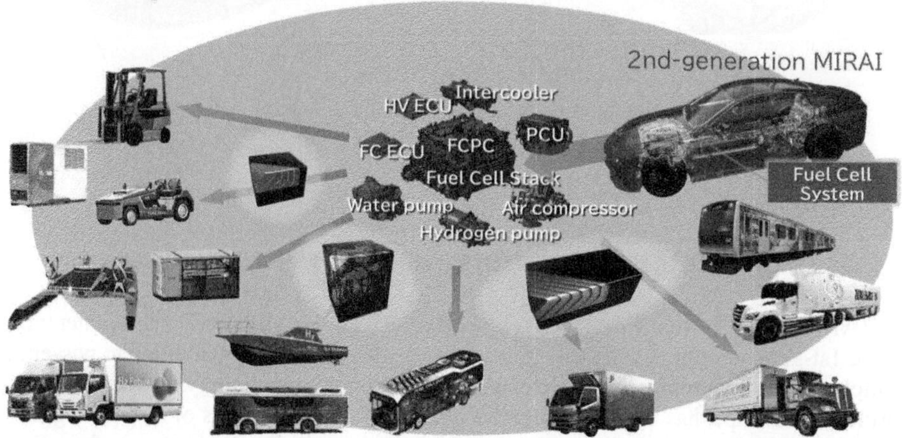

Fig. 3. The implementation of the fuel cell system to a variety of purposes

3. Collaboration for developing fuel cells and expectations for PSE

Though hydrogen and fuel cell technologies are steadily spreading around the world, many technical issues are still remaining. It is important for every stakeholder in the fuel cell industry to communicate with each other, move in the same direction in addition to a proper competition, and make the fuel cell technology easier to use.

Fig. 4 is a conceptual drawing of the 'FC-Platform' project supported by NEDO, New Energy and Industrial Technology Development Organization of Japan, as an example of the recent research consortium (FC-Cubic, 2021). This consortium is acting as a role of platform where the fuel cell researchers with various important and detailed knowledge can gather from universities and technical colleges across Japan. They are investigating the complex fuel cell reactions and mass transport with the high resolution analysis instruments for the physicochemical phenomena in atomic scale. The government and fuel cell manufacturers can share their specific issues, discuss the research and development roadmap with them, and collaborate and communicate with each other in the consortium.

PSE is the academic field which specializes in the system modeling, process synthesis/aggregation, and decomposition/analysis (Klatt et al., 2009). Since the fuel cell technology is highly interdisciplinary technical fields where the wide range of physics in various scale from nano to meter must be considered, the role of PSE will be more important as an interface of the variety of technical fields. The author encourages PSE engineers and researchers to join the fuel cell industry and research activities.

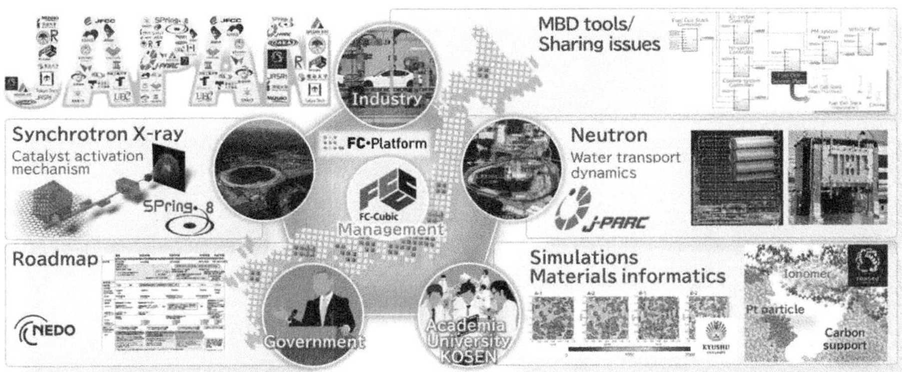

Fig. 4. The conceptual drawing of the 'FC-Platform' project in Japan as an example of the recent fuel cell research consortium

Conclusions

The role of hydrogen energy and fuel cells were discussed by describing the world trend surrounding carbon neutrality. The 2nd-generation fuel cell electric vehicle MIRAI and a fuel cell system module comprised of the MIRAI fuel cell components were shown. The fuel cell system module facilitates the development of fuel cell applications such as commercial vehicles of buses, tracks, and marine. Finally, the expectation for PSE researchers and engineers from the fuel cell industry were discussed. The author encourages PSE engineers and researchers to join the fuel cell industry and research activities.

References

FC-Cubic, 2021,
https://www.fc-cubic.or.jp/,
Jan. 26th, 2022, accessed

K. U. Klatt, W. Marquardt, Perspective for process systems engineering – Personal view from academia and industry, *Computers and Chemical Engineering*, 33(3), 2009, Pages 536-550

Toyota Motor Corporation, 2022,
https://www.toyota.co.jp/fuelcells/en/technology.html,
Jan. 26th, 2022, accessed.

Toyota Motor Corporation, 2022,
https://www.toyota.co.jp/fuelcells/en/applications.html,
Jan. 26th, 2022, accessed.

United Nations, Kyoto Protocol to the United Nations Framework Convention on Climate Change, 1997,
http://unfccc.int/resource/docs/convkp/kpeng.pdf,
Jan. 26th, 2022, accessed

United Nations, Paris Agreement, 2015,
http://unfccc.int/files/essential_background/convention/application/pdf/english_paris_agreement.pdf,
Jan. 26th, 2022, accessed

W.R.W. Daud, R.E. Rosli, E.H. Majlan, S.A.A. Hamid, R. Mohamed, T. Husaini,
PEM fuel cell system control: A review, *Renewable Energy*, Volume 113, 2017, Pages 620-638,

Proceedings of the 14th International Symposium on Process Systems Engineering – PSE 2021+
June 19-23, 2022, Kyoto, Japan
http://dx.doi.org/10.1016/B978-0-323-85159-6.50002-6

Challenges and Opportunities for Process Systems Engineering in a Changed World

Rafiqul Gani[a*], Xi Chen[b], Mario R. Eden[c], Seyed S. Mansouri[d], Mariano Martin[e], Iqbal M. Mujtaba[f], Orakotch Padungwatanaroj[g], Kosan Roh[h], Luis Ricardez-Sandoval[i], Hirokazu Sugiyama[j], Jinsong Zhao[k], Edwin Zondervan[l]

[a]*PSE for SPEED Company, Ordup Jagtvej 42D, DK-2920 Charlottenlund, Denmark*
[b]*Department of Control Science & Engineering, Zhejiang University, Hangzhou, China*
[c]*Department of Chemical Engineering, Auburn University, Auburn, AL 36849, USA*
[d]*Department of Chemical Engineering, Technical University of Denmark, DK-2800 Lyngby, Denmark*
[e]*Dep artment of Chemical Engineering,, University of Salamanca, Plz. Caídos 1-5, 37008 Salamanca, Spain*
[f]*Department of Chemical Engineering, University of Bradford, Yorkshire BD7 1DP, UK*
[g]*PSE for SPEED Company, 294/65 RK Office Park, Romklao Rd., Bangkok, Thailand*
[h]*Department of Chemical Engineering and Applied Chemistry, Chungnam National University, 34141 Daejeon, Republic of Korea*
[i]*Department of Chemical Enginering, University of Waterloo, N2L 3G1, Canada*
[j]*Department of Chemical Systems Engineering,, The University of Tokyo, 113-8656 Tokyo, Japan*
[k]*State Key Laboratory of Chemical Engineering, Tsinghua University, Beijing, China*
[l]*University of Twente, Faculty of Science and Technology, Enschede, The Netherlands*

**rgani2018@gmail.com*

Abstract

Changes have always been taking place on earth. However, the latest changes related to the climate, the COVID-19 pandemic, natural resources, pollution, to name a few, have changed our world and a new normal is emerging. The energy-water-environment-food-health nexus is becoming more complex. These challenges, however, also provide opportunities to tackle them and make scientific and engineering advances. PSE is well-placed through its core and expanding domain as well as its ability to apply a systems approach to meet current and future challenges. Many opportunities exist for the PSE community to take the lead in managing this complexity. This paper will provide an overview on some of the key challenges and opportunities where PSE could make immediate as well as long lasting impacts by developing sustainable and innovative solutions. Focus will be placed on the choice of problems to solve and the solution approaches that could make an impact and help to define the new normal for future generations.

Keywords: Process Systems Engineering; Climate; COVID-19; Resources; Pollution; Opportunities

1. Introduction

The effects of climate change, COVID-19 infections, inefficient resources utilization and uncontrolled pollution, to name a few, have changed the world and now urgent actions are needed to not only minimize their impact but also to find novel and innovative solutions that are environmentally-friendly and allow the sustainable development of society. These problems are global and their solutions no doubt need a multi-disciplinary approach. As defined by Pistikopoulos *et al.* (2020), Process Systems Engineering (PSE) is the scientific discipline of integrating scales and components describing the behaviour of a physicochemical system, via mathematical modelling, data analysis, design, optimization and control. PSE provides the 'glue' within scientific chemical engineering (and other related engineering domains), and offers a scientific basis and computational tools towards addressing contemporary and future challenges such as in energy, environment, the 'industry of tomorrow' and sustainability. As Sargent (2004) pointed out, "PSE is all about the development of systematic techniques for process modelling, design and control - some formulate their synthesis, design and/or control problem, or some useful simplification of it, in precise mathematical terms, and then seek to exploit the mathematical structure to obtain an effective algorithm, while others seek insight on the problem structure from physical intuition". Therefore, to address the challenges currently faced by society, the PSE community has the opportunity to play an important role (Grossmann and Harjunkoski, 2019) by helping to find novel and innovative solutions that can not only arrest the undesired trends but also guide us towards achieving the well-established goals of sustainable development (UN, 2021).

Figure 1 shows plots of effect X under *business as usual* and *controlled actions* as a function of time, where X could be any one of the challenges with respect to climate, COVID-19, resources utilization, pollution, sustainability and many more. Figure 1 also points out Earth's capacity to absorb the negative results of effect X, which means the *business as usual* curve needs to be flattened with *controlled actions* before it is too late. Note that although one plot is shown to highlight the concept, the actual curves and earth's capacity are different for different effects. The energy-water-environment-health-food nexus (Al-Ansari *et al.*, 2015; Mujtaba *et al.*, 2018; Slorach *et al.*, 2020) indicate however, that the individual items cannot be considered in isolation from each other because they have intrinsic interactions. The biocapacity of earth, which is a measure of its natural resources against its activities has reduced to 1.7 (Global Footprint Network, 2016) and must not become negative.

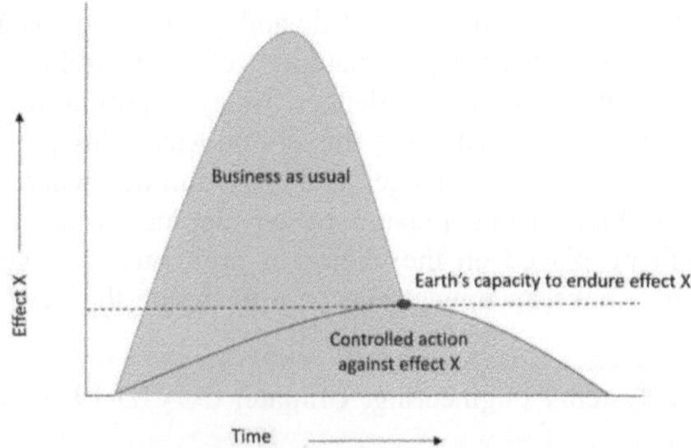

Figure 1: Business as usual versus control action against effect X (climate change, COVID-19 infections, resources utilization, pollution, sustainability, and many more)

Earth's natural resources for energy, water, biomass, minerals, etc., are not uniformly distributed but they are needed everywhere in different forms. According to Gani *et al.* (2020), a core activity of chemical and biochemical engineering is to convert these resources to products (various energy products, food products, health-care products, *etc.*), devices (car, television, phone, *etc.*) and/or services (electricity, fuels, fresh water, *etc.*) that society needs for its sustainability. The recent pandemic due to COVID-19 has shown that while the problem is global, their severity is different at different regions on earth. The same is true for global warming, resources utilization, pollution and major issues that impact society.

The objectives of this paper are to highlight selected focus areas representing current and future challenges on earth, the choices of problems to solve within them, and the systems approach-based solution methods that may be used to tackle them. The paper is organized as follows: a brief overview of the current status of PSE methods and associated computer-aided tools are given following the introduction; that is followed by a discussion on focus areas where PSE methods and tools can be applied together with a selected set of examples; and, ending with perspectives and concluding statements. The contents of the paper are the result of a discussion between the corresponding author and the co-authors on the following issues:

- In which of the problems can the PSE community make a significant contribution?
- What role should the PSE community play in tackling these problems?
- Which PSE methods and tools are best suited to tackle the problems?

This paper will also form the basis for the plenary lecture to be given by the corresponding author at the PSE2021 with material to be added.

2. PSE methods and tools

In the multi-layered view of PSE, Pistikopoulos *et al.* (2022) classified the PSE methods and associated tools in terms of the inner *fundamental* layer that involves process-product related activities where application of the fundamental concepts of PSE help to design, build and operate manufacturing processes that convert specific raw materials to desired products; the middle *expanding* layer that involves resources-efficiency related activities leading to the development of new technologies and more sustainable engineering solutions; the outer *unifying* layer that involves activities related to tackling of societal challenges leading to a more sustainable society. In this paper, some of the PSE methods and associated tools from all three layers are highlighted. See also Stephanopoulos and Reklaitis (2011) for a historic review of PSE activities and Grossmann and Harjunkoski (2019) for academic and industrial perspectives on PSE.

2.1. Methods

Three topics under methods are highlighted: modelling (because it is at the core of almost all PSE methods); numerical methods (which is necessary to solve the equations representing any model and are continuously updated to satisfy the demands from the expanding and unifying layers of PSE) and algorithms (since the schemes for integration and/or combination of models and numerical methods are needed to tackle the societal challenges from the unifying layer of PSE).

2.1.1. Modelling

A model (Hangos and Cameron, 2001) is a pattern, plan, representation, or description designed to show the structure or workings of an object, system, or concept; it could also be a study of a miniature of the actual; the model objectives need to be clearly defined. Modelling is the process of generating abstract or conceptual representation of a physical system, *i.e.*, representing reality in a virtual environment for a purpose. In systems approaches to problem solution, modelling is a core activity in the development of any model-based problem solution tool and requires a very good understanding of the system being investigated. As our understanding of the sub-systems whose problems we would like to solve, is incomplete, models based only on first principles cannot usually be obtained (or it is very time-consuming and resource demanding to obtain them). Therefore, knowledge related to the core fundamental layer of PSE is not sufficient, modelling options from the middle expanding layer of PSE, for example, systems identification or artificial intelligence (including machine learning, deep data learning, nature-inspired, *etc.*) need to be utilized (Lee *et al.*, 2018; Venkatasubramanian, 2019). Note that the modelling objectives are related to specific problems that need to be solved, giving rise to models of different complexities and forms. Therefore, to match and/or improve the numerical solver efficiency and reliability, local models (Chimowitz *et al.*, 1983), hybrid models (Chaffart and Ricardez-Sandoval, 2018), or surrogate models (Bhosekar and Ierapetritou, 2018) are being used. A few modelling related issues are highlighted below (not ordered in terms of priority):

- Development of predictive property models – more than 10 million chemicals have been identified but measured data are available for less than 50 thousand chemicals; properties such as toxicity, color, smell, *etc.*, need to be modelled.
- How to obtain new process (operation) models from generic models when new processes and/or operations do not have all required sub-system details; new process models such as intensified operations, fuel cells, medicine delivering devices.
- How to create plug and play options for links to external databases, solvers, models and/or new theory, data, computational resources in currently available computer-aided tools to expand their application range.

2.1.2. Numerical solvers

Models representing a system of interest, consisting of different combinations of equations (algebraic, ordinary differential, partial differential, symbolic, *etc.*) involving different types of variables (real, integer, Boolean, symbolic, *etc.*) require appropriate numerical solvers. According to Pistikopoulos *et al.* (2021), the two key tasks that PSE have focused on are *i)* optimization methods, comprising a variety of formulations, most notably mixed-integer linear and nonlinear programs, dynamic optimization (including optimal control) and hierarchical optimization (semi-infinite, bilevel, trilevel) and *ii)* simulation/optimization of dynamic systems with hybrid discrete-continuous (or in some case equivalently non-smooth) nature. Kronqvist *et al.* (2019) and more recently Nolasco *et al.* (2021) have reviewed optimization solvers. For a list of selected numerical solvers commonly used by the PSE community, see also Pistikopoulos *et al.* (2021). To improve the convergence and reliability of numerical solvers, symbolic computation methods, which directly use mathematical expressions for operations and derivations to identify the solution have been recently proposed by Zhang *et al.* (2021a, 2021b). Below, a few numerical solver related issues are highlighted (not ordered in terms of priority):

- Which criteria (*e.g.*, efficiency, reliability, and/or flexibility) should be used for numerical solver selection, when for similar problems more than one solver could be available.
- How to adapt currently available solvers to emerging modes of computation such as, quantum computing.
- Options to incorporate features such as machine learning, data analytics, etc. into the solver algorithm to make them intelligent.

2.1.3. Algorithms

Although algorithms also refer to the work-flow of numerical solvers, in this section, the term is used to refer to only synthesis, design and/or analysis of a wide range of process (chemical, petrochemical, biochemical, pharmaceutical, food, *etc.*) and/or chemicals-based products (solvents, refrigerants, fuel blends, paints, detergents, *etc.*), including devices (medicine delivery, power-supply, air-purifier, *etc.*). They are further classified in terms of available options (sustainable design, design under uncertainty, reverse design, flexibility and/or controllability analysis, *etc.*); type of approach (rule-based, process groups based, superstructure-based, *etc.*); and, application areas (process technology, product technology, analyser technology, etc.). The following selected articles provide an overview on the challenges and opportunities related to specific topics: Chen and Grossmann (2017) on process synthesis; Schilling *et al.* (2017) and Papathanasiou and Kontoravdi (2020) on product and process synthesis-design; Skiborowski *et al.* (2014) and Tula *et al.* (2017) on sustainable process design; Morari and Lee (1999), and, Yu and Biegler (2019) on process control, Diangelakis *et al.* (2017) and Rafiei and Ricardez-Sandoval (2020) on integrated process design and control optimization; Garcia and You (2015) on supply chain design and optimization, and, Maravelias and Sung (2009) on production planning and scheduling. Some algorithm related issues are briefly highlighted below (not ordered in terms of priority):

- Application range versus reliability versus flexibility.
- Detailed activity diagram (model) needed for software implementation.
- Adoption of hybrid approaches (interfacing of algorithms with computational resources).

2.2. Computer-aided tools

The PSE community continue to develop problem specific computer-aided tools for a wide range of applications. The most well-known PSE computer-aided tool is the process simulator, available in different versions, that is widely used for education as well as industrial practice. However, are the current versions of the various simulators able to solve the problems related to the energy-water-environment-food-health nexus? Also, as pointed out by Tula *et al.* (2019), process simulation is just one out of many tasks that needs to be performed for sustainable and innovative design. For example, tools for modelling are needed if the required model is not available in the simulator model library; or, a product design tool is needed to design-select an appropriate chemical for solvent-based separation; or, a process synthesis tool is needed to generate a flowsheet if a reference flowsheet is not available; or, analysis tools (sustainability, safety and hazards, LCA, economics, etc.) are needed to verify the feasibility of the chemical process. Pistikopoulos *et al.* (2021) provides a list of the above-mentioned tools developed by the PSE community. Some issues related to computer-aided tools are briefly highlighted below (not ordered in terms of priority):

- Application range of the available models in the model libraries – are they problem specific according to application area?
- Can the models, data, algorithms be adopted from one sector to another?
- Are simulation and design (including synthesis and analysis) options available in the same tool?
- Can they serve as virtual reality simulators to provide users with real experience?

3. Challenges and roles of PSE

Table 1 lists selected data to highlight the challenges and issues. The energy-water-environment-food-health nexus is getting more complex in the changing world and an integrated solution approach is necessary to tackle better the interactions among the individual effects. For example, energy in the form of fuels and electricity is needed by industry, transportation and housing sectors, but the type of fuel and the electricity generation defines the amounts of green-house gas (GHG) emissions, which in turn is related to climate change. Supply chain factors as well as waste disposal and therefore, resource utilization and pollution are also related, particularly for the chemical, petrochemical and pharmaceutical sectors. With respect to COVID-19, the pandemic is still not under control (December 31st, 2021) even though the rates of hospitalizations and deaths appear to be slowing down (see Table 1). However, based on data on consumption of energy (see Table 1), the non-renewable resources that emit CO_2 still dominate energy supplies. Capture, utilization, and/or sequestration of CO_2 is a challenge where adopted PSE methods and tools can play an important role. Society's daily needs such as plastics for packaging; chemicals for drugs, cosmetics, detergents, *etc.*; rare earth metals for construction, equipment, cars, etc., are causing pollution of land, water and/or air upon disposal and through their end-of-life properties.

Table 1: Current status of selected effects

Effect	Data	Reference
Global warming	New estimates of the chances of crossing the global warming level of 1.5°C in the next decades indicate that unless there are immediate, rapid and large-scale reductions in greenhouse gas emissions, limiting warming to close to 1.5°C or even 2°C will be beyond reach	IPCC (2021)
COVID-19	Worldwide total infections have reached 285,231,011 with 5,442,088 deaths as of 31 December 2021	Worldometers (2021)
Resources (energy)	CO_2 emitting non-renewable resources still contribute nearly 85% of the energy (not electricity) and around 65% for generation of electricity	Vooradi *et al.* (2017); IEA (2021)
Resources (water)	97% of water on earth is salt water and only 3% is fresh water, out of which, 68.1% is ice-caps and glaciers, 30.1% is ground water, 0.3% is surface water and 0.9% is other); Globally, at least 2 billion people use contaminated drinking water source	WHO (2019); Greenlee *et al.* (2009)
Resources (biomass)	Currently biomass contributes 3.4% of the total transportation energy demand. It would require 2.4 times the amount currently devoted to all energy demands (or, more than 1.3 times earth's current biomass resources) to satisfy only the total energy demand for the transportation sector in 2030.	Energy (2021); WBA (2020); IRENA (2014); IEA (2016)
Pollution (plastic waste, water)	Projected plastic waste generation of the EU-27 is estimated to reach 17 Mt/y in 2030	Fan *et al.* (2022)
Pollution (GHG release)	The GWP of CH_4 and N_2O are around 27~29 and 273 (100-year time period), respectively.	IPCC (2021)

Where should the focus to tackle these challenges be, what should be the choice of problems to solve, and, which solution approaches should be applied that could make an impact and help to define the new normal for future generations are still open questions that need to be addressed. Guillén-Gosálbez *et al.* (2019) recently highlighted process systems engineering thinking and listed tools that could be applied to solve sustainability related problems. Bakshi (2019) reviewed the role of process systems engineering toward sustainable chemical engineering. Burre *et al.* (2020) discussed how process systems engineering can help address common challenges for Power-to-X technologies. Martin *et al.* (2022) the challenges and opportunities related to sustainable process synthesis, design and analysis. Avraamidou *et al.* (2020) highlighted the challenges and opportunities for PSE related to achieving circular economy.

3.1. Sustainable process networks

The production of clean energy is directly linked to avoiding the depletion of natural resources, even if this goal has a more general aim, as well as limiting the production of waste and avoiding polluting the environment. According to the carbon-neutral roadmap presented by each government, chemical and petrochemical industries must reduce their greenhouse gas emissions to achieve zero net emissions by 2050. In order to significantly reduce carbon emissions in such industries while maintaining the current business portfolio, adoption of new technologies that can directly utilize electricity originating from renewable energy resources such as solar and/or wind energy to produce chemical products is necessary (Rangel-Martinez *et al.*, 2021). Process integration at the different manufacturing and production levels will play a critical role to ensure efficient and sustainable operation of existing and emerging systems, and their corresponding integration (Burnak *et al.*, 2019; Rafiei and Ricardez-Sandoval, 2020). Figure 2 highlights the concept of integration of sub-networks of utilities (energy and water), process for conversion of optimal product(s), integrated with capture and utilization of captured CO_2. Decisions related to individual sub-networks need to be made such that the overall objectives of sustainable design are satisfied. The objective for sustainable design of networks could be, for example, to find a design with zero or negative CO_2 (preferably all GHG) that is economically feasible, operationally safe and environmentally acceptable. Choices of raw materials and products can represent any industrial sector while choices of resources for utilities need to be made such that net zero emission requirement can be satisfied. Note that in Figure 2, the processing of waste utilities (energy, water), waste material, by-products for recycle, re-insertion and/or utilization in the process thus promoting circular economy is not shown.

Using core PSE methods and associated tools Li *et al.* (2022) have developed a conceptual application example of such a superstructure based sustainable network synthesis. Roh *et al.* (2018) have developed a computer-aided tool (called ArKaTAC[3]) that allows to perform both superstructure-based process synthesis and multi-dimensional analyses (including techno-economic analysis and life cycle assessment) of carbon capture and utilization systems. Filippini *et al.* (2019) reported design and economic evaluation of solar-powered hybrid multi effect and reverse osmosis system for seawater desalination. Also, Sanchez *et al.* (2019) have shown the utilization of captured CO_2 hydrogenation with green hydrogen for methanol, ammonia and urea productions, while, Guerras *et al.* (2021) proposes that biomass as a renewable resource should be devoted for the production of added value products (for example, in the pharma, food additives, health sectors) and only wastes should be used for energy production. Evaluation of these new technologies should also consider operational flexibility (Mitsos *et al.*, 2018) as well as safety (Eini *et al.*, 2016).

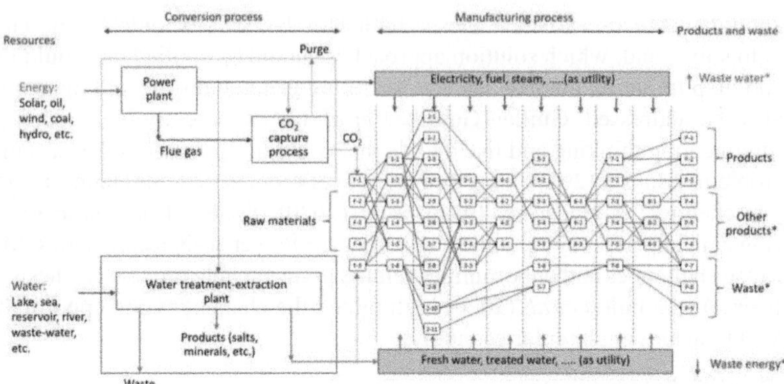

Figure 2: Superstructure for optimal integrated net zero emission network to achieve circular economy (note: * indicates they will need additional processing for recycle, re-insertion and/or utilization).

3.2. Chemical process safety

Even though the chemical industry has achieved a very impressive improvement in occupational safety, the reduction in major process accidents (on a global basis) has been less impressive and the insured losses due to major accidents in the chemical industry have not reduced in the last 30 years. It is estimated that 70% of the chemical accidents were caused by human errors. These incidents also point to inefficient resource utilization. PSE should be able to play a key role in developing and deploying advanced artificial intelligence-based technologies that assist operators in estimating and/or identifying all potential risks in the complex and dynamic chemical industrial operations and to make correct and consistent decisions. Interesting developments that could be evaluated for potential deployment are method for fault detection and diagnosis (see Fig. 3) based on transfer learning (Wu and Zhao, 2020), automatic frequency estimation of contributory factors for confined space accidents, natural language processing (Wang and Zhao, 2022), and, inherent safety and cognitive engineering as well as operator training (Srinivasan *et al.*, 2019).

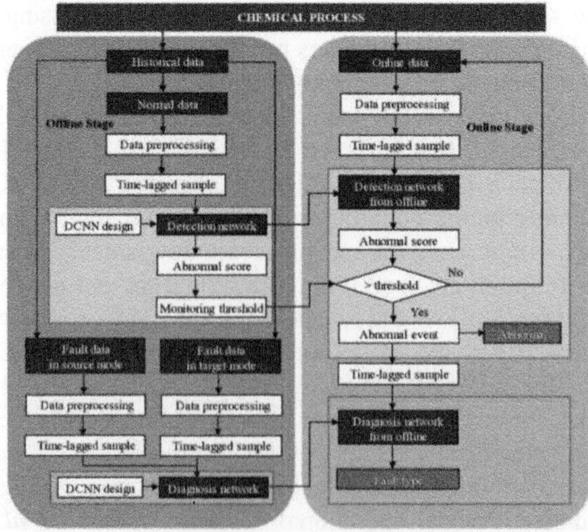

Figure 3: Framework for fault detection and diagnosis (Wu and Zhao, 2020).

3.3. Health and pharma sector

In the pharma sector, a principal challenge is to develop model (including data) based computer aided systems for synthesis, design, monitoring, control, as in chemical and petrochemical industries. Nevertheless, systems approach coupled with PSE methods and associated tools have made important contributions during the last decade, for example, in conversion from batch to continuous manufacturing (Ierapetritou *et al.*, 2016), development of process analytical technologies, and data-driven approaches for active pharmaceutical ingredients (API) syntheses and design of powder-/bio- processes (*e.g.*, Kim *et al.*, 2021). Advances in development of health-care products (Fuentes-Garí et al., 2015) and their manufacturing processes such as monoclonal antibody drugs and stem cells have been reported (*e.g.*, Hayashi *et al.* 2021). In sustainability and healthcare, COVID-19 has revealed the need for a systematic approach for vaccine/medicine development and supply chain. The urgent supply was mandated on top of maintaining the existing treatment capability. Besides COVID-19, R&D of innovative therapies, *e.g.*, regenerative medicine, is ongoing. These therapies tend to be expensive while the economic aspect is becoming critical in many countries. Analyses and discussions towards sustainable healthcare society (*e.g.*, Sugiyama *et al.*, 2021) can be further expanded as a topic of the PSE community. Figure 4 highlights the challenges and opportunities for adoption of PSE methods and tools to prepare for future pandemics. Four potential problems to solve are highlighted together with the issues and needs that need to be addressed.

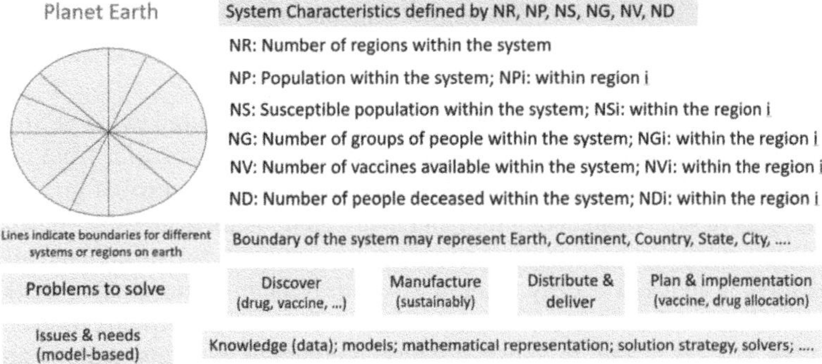

Figure 4: Visual plan to prepare for the next pandemic through PSE methods and tools

3.4. Chemicals based products and their substitution

In our changed world, we are living with chemicals that are in our food products, clothes, furniture, appliances, toys, cosmetics, medicines and many more. Society, for its existence anywhere on earth, needs to use a variety of products and/or means that are directly or indirectly connected to chemicals. Currently, more than one million chemicals can be found on planet earth and thousands of new chemicals-based products are entering the global market every year. Over 95 percent of all manufactured goods rely on some form of industrial chemical process (ICCA, 2019). As the number of chemicals grows rapidly, understanding their implications on human health and environment is increasingly becoming an issue. An important and urgent challenge is not only to identify the chemicals, which may have harmful effects, but also to substitute or control their use (Syeda *et al.*, 2022). As demand for safer alternatives in products is increasing, regulatory authorities, such as EU REACH (EU, 2021), US EPA (EPA, 2021) and Occupational Safety and Health Administration (OSHA, 2021) have taken up substitution of chemicals harmful to human health and environment as one of the central elements of their policies. As the pioneers of techniques such as computer-aided molecular design (CAMD) for chemical product design, the PSE community is well placed to assist and actively collaborate with the authorities to tackle this urgent problem. CAMD and different variations of it (Zhang *et al.*, 2020, Adjiman *et al.*, 2021), can easily be adopted for analysis of chemicals-based products and substitution of chemicals if hazardous chemicals are identified in the product. The chemical substitution problem and the possible solution steps are highlighted in Figure 5.

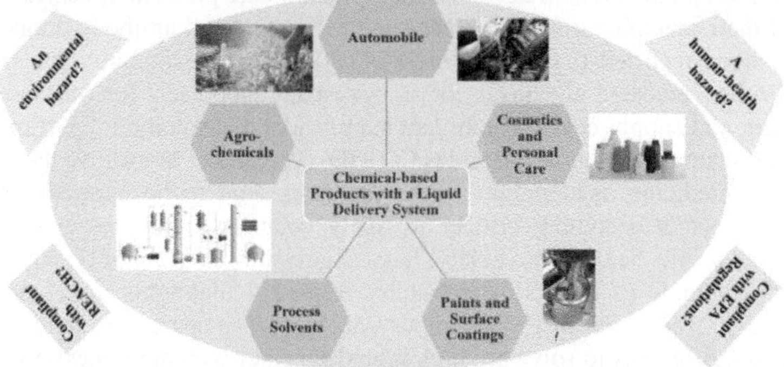

1. Identify contaminant; **2.** Analyze function of contaminant; **3.** Find alternative chemicals that offer similar (or improved) performance properties but without properties that promote pollution; **4.** Verify the functions; **5.** Confirm improved sustainability

Figure 5: Chemical substitution problem and suggested solution steps.

4. Perspectives (Opportunities)

A "systems thinking" or "systems integration" approach is required, where PSE provides the glue (architecture for consistent, efficient, and smooth data transfer from one tool to another) for integration of energy supply, water management, control of greenhouse gas emissions, process safety and economics and many other major issues that impact society and earth. PSE methods and associated tools can be adopted for sustainable and secure access to food, water and energy, leading to achievement of sustainable development goals, to develop and evaluate new technologies for carbon capture, utilization and sequestration (CCUS), and to close circular production systems with near-zero or minimum waste. Simultaneously, computer-aided molecular design (CAMD) techniques could be adopted for pollution control of water caused by plastics, including disposable personal protective equipment (PPE), *etc.*; pollution of air caused by GHGs, *etc.*; and pollution of land caused by disposed chemicals-based products.

In order to tackle the challenges of our changed world, the opportunity exists to not only adopt but also to develop new methods and tools as and when necessary. As models, modelling and data are at the core of all systems-based problem solution approaches, more effort is needed to understand systems that are outside our domain knowledge. It is important to use correct and consistent models and associated decision support tools for analysing the involved complex phenomena (*e.g.*, powder processing, biological reactions, cell behaviour, solid solubility, toxicity, *etc.*) in such a way that the decisions related to process and products (*e.g.*, production scale and mode, design space determination, process-operation specification, *etc.*) can be made.

Recognizing that resources in earth are not uniformly distributed, nevertheless, the concept of integrated networks could be applied for desalination to obtain fresh water using solar and/or wind energy sources where these can be harnessed. In regions where there is fresh water in abundance, technologies already available to combine hydrogen obtained through electrolysis of water with captured CO_2 to produce methanol (as an intermediate chemical from which other high-value chemicals could be synthesized), with N_2 from air to produce ammonia (as a hydrogen carrier), and, methanol and ammonia to produce urea (as a fertilizer). The analysis of competing interests as well as the presentation of feasible/optimal solutions under uncertainty (*i.e.*, societal design) would be another important contribution from PSE.

Stable and sustainable coupling of chemical industry and power generation sectors by exploiting operational flexibility, optimal integration of design, operation, and control of power-intensive chemical plants that already exist and also should be newly developed. Implementation of new technologies, such as intensified equipment and/or hybrid combination of distillation and membrane, for targeted reduction of energy consumption as a short-term solution need to be promoted through bench-mark problem solutions.

Lessons learnt from the pandemic with respect to the challenges posed to the supply chain and development of novel schemes and policies that can potentially reduce the impact of current and future pandemics should be considered as a global supply chain system. With the expertise and experience of the PSE community in the supply chain sector, an optimal vaccine allocation system that is region specific to immunize the population at the fastest rate could be developed and distributed to the appropriate agencies. Recognition of healthcare as an element of the energy-water-environment-food-health nexus will help re-designing the manufacturing processes and beyond. PSE can contribute to help prepare for the next pandemic with, for example, vaccine allocation software (to be made available globally to all countries) to reach herd immunity at the shortest time and with the minimum loss of life.

5. Conclusions

Process systems engineering as a multi-disciplinary field of research has many opportunities to tackle some of the greatest challenges faced by today's society. This opportunity is provided by the rich literature and many ongoing current and future activities to provide integrated solutions within water-energy-food-waste-health nexus. However, more efforts are needed to understand and develop models, tools and solutions strategies to address those major challenges. This can result in developing new technologies and process systems by means of predictive models. These predictive models should be able to address short-term necessities while laying the foundations for long-term solutions over a time horizon to help alleviate the current and future challenges to address different global objectives, such as the UN sustainable development goals. However, all the efforts would be wasted if the demands (due to increased growth and promising economy) cannot be limited; circular economy with zero waste and ability to sustain changes will be impossible if resources disappear because of increased demand. Thereby, a systems thinking approach is essential to not lose the opportunities within rather narrow windows to address global issues, such as global warming and the COVID-19 pandemic.

References

C. S. Adjiman, N. V. Sahinidis, D. G. Vlachos, B. Bakshi, C. T. Maravelias, C. Georgakis, 2021, Process systems engineering perspective on the design of materials and molecules, *Industrial & Engineering Chemistry Research*, 60(12), 5194-5206.

T. Al-Ansari, A. Korre, Z. Nie, N. Shah, 2015, Development of a life cycle assessment tool for the assessment of food production systems within the energy, water and food nexus, *Sustainable Production & Consumption*, 2, 52-66.

S. S. Avraamidou, G. Baratsas, Y. Tian, E. N. Pistikopoulos, 2020, Circular economy - a challenge and an opportunity for process systems engineering, *Computers & Chemical Engineering*, 133, 106629.

B. R. Bakshi, 2019, Toward Sustainable Chemical Engineering: The Role of Process Systems Engineering, *Annual Review of Chemical and Biomolecular Engineering*, 10, 265-288.

A. Bhosekar, M. Ierapetritou, 2018, Advances in surrogate based modeling, feasibility analysis, and optimization: A review, *Computers & Chemical Engineering*, 108, 250-267.

B. Burnak, N.A. Diangelakis, E.N. Pistikopoulos (2019), Towards the grand unification of process design, scheduling, and control—utopia or reality?, *Processes*, 7, 461.

J. Burre, D. Bongartz, L. Brée, K. Roh, A. Mitsos, 2020. Power-to-X: Between Electricity Storage, e-Production, and Demand Side Management, *Chemie Ing. Tech.* 92, 74–84. (https://doi.org/10.1002/cite.201900102).

D. Chaffart, L. Ricardez-Sandoval, 2018, Optimization and control of a thin film growth process: A hybrid first principles/artificial neural network based multiscale modelling approach, *Computers and Chemical Engineering*, 119, 465-479.

E. H. Chimowitz, T. F. Anderson, S. M. Macchietto, L. F. Stutzman, 1983, Local models for representing phase equilibriums in multicomponent, nonideal vapor-liquid and liquid-liquid systems. 1. Thermodynamic approximation functions, *Industrial & Engineering Chemistry Process Design and Development*, 22, 217-225.

S. Eini, H. Shahhosseini, N. Delgarm, M. Lee, A. Bahadori, 2016. Multi-objective optimization of a cascade refrigeration system: exergetic, economic, environmental, and inherent safety analysis, *Applied Thermal Engineering*, 22, 168-186.

EPA, 2021, (http://www.epa.gov/chemical-research/program-assisting-replacementindustrial-solvents-paris-iii).

Energy, 2021, (https://www.energy.gov/eere/bioenergy/biomass-resources).

EU, 2021, European Chemicals Agency (https://echa.europa.eu/).

Y. V. Fan, P. Jiang, R. R. Tan, K. B. Aviso, F. You, X. Zhao, C. T. Lee, J. J. Klemeš, 2022, Forecasting plastic waste generation and interventions for environmental hazard mitigation, *Journal of Hazardous Materials*, 424, 127330.

G. Filippini, M. A. Al-Obaidi, F. Manenti, I. M. Mujtaba, 2019, Design and economic evaluation of solar-powered hybrid multi effect and reverse osmosis system for seawater desalination, *Desalination*, 465, 114-125

M. Fuentes-Garí, E. Velliou, R. Misener, E. Pefani, M. Rende, N. Panoskaltsis, 2015, A systematic framework for the design, simulation and optimization of personalized healthcare: making and healing blood, *Computers and Chemical Engineering*, 81, 80-93.

R. Gani, J. Bałdyga, B. Biscans, E. Brunazzi, J. C. Charpentier, E. Drioli, et al., 2020, A multi-layered view of chemical and biochemical engineering, *Chemical Engineering Research and Design*, 155, 133-145. (https://doi.org/10.1016/j.cherd.2020.01.008)

D. J. Garcia, F. You, 2015, Supply chain design and optimization: Challenges and opportunities, *Computers & Chemical Engineering*, 81, 153-170.

Global Footprint Network, 2016, (https://data.footprintnetwork.org/?_ga=2.81569751.1924591506.1641417907-308979742.1641417907#/)

L. F. Greenlee, D. F. Lawler, B. D. Freeman, B. Marrot, P. Moulin, 2009, Reverse osmosis desalination: Water sources, technology, and today's challenges, *Water Research*, 43, 2317–2348.

I. E. Grossmann, I. Harjunkoski, 2019, Process systems engineering: academic and industrial perspectives, *Computers & Chemical Engineering*, 126, 474-484.

L. Guerras, D. Sengupta, M. Martín, M. El-Halwagi, (2021) Multi-layer approach for product portfolio optimization: Waste to added value products, *ACS Sustainable Chemical Engineering*, 9, 18, 6410–6426.

G. Guillén-Gosálbez, F. You, A. Galán-Martín, C. Pozo, I. E. Grossmann, 2019, Process systems engineering thinking and tools applied to sustainability problems: current landscape and future opportunities, *Current Opinion in Chemical Engineering*, 26, 170-179.

K. Hangos, I. T. Kameron, 2001, Process modelling and model analysis, Academic Press, USA.

Y. Hayashi, M. Kino-oka, H. Sugiyama, 2022. Hybrid-model-based design of fill-freeze-thaw processes for human induced pluripotent stem cells considering productivity and quality, *Computers & Chemical Engineering*, 156, 107566.

ICCA, 2019, (https://icca-chem.org/wp-content/uploads/2020/10/Catalyzing-Growth-and-Addressing-Our-Worlds-Sustainability-Challenges-Report.pdf).

IEA, 2016, (https://www.eia.gov/outlooks/ieo/pdf/transportation.pdf).

IEA, 2021, (https://www.iea.org/reports/world-energy-balances-overview).

M. Ierapetritou, F. Muzzio, G.V. Reklaitis, 2016, Perspectives on the continuous manufacturing of powder-based pharmaceutical processes, *AIChE Journal*, 62 (6), 1846-1862.

IPCC, 2021 (https://www.ipcc.ch/assessment-report/ar6/).

IRENA, 2014, (https://www.irena.org/-/media/Files/IRENA/Agency/Publication/2014/IRENA_REmap_2030_Biomass_paper_2014.pdf).

J. Kim, H. Yonekura, T. Watanabe, S. Yoshikawa, H. Nakanishi, S. Badr, H. Sugiyama, 2021. Model-based comparison of batch and flow syntheses of an active pharmaceutical ingredient using heterogeneous hydrogenation, *Computers and Chemical Engineering*, 156, 107541.

J. Kronqvist, D. E. Bernal, A. Lundell, I. E. Grossmann, 2019, A review and comparison of solvers for convex MINLP, *Optimization Engineering*, 20(2), 397–455.

J. H. Lee, J. Shin, M. J. Realff, 2018, Machine Learning: Overview of the Recent Progresses and Implications for the Process Systems Engineering Field, *Computers & Chemical Engineering*, 114, 111-121.

Y. Li, J. Wei, Z. Yuan, B. Chen, R. Gani, 2021, Sustainable Synthesis of Integrated Process, Water Treatment, Energy Supply, and CCUS Networks Under Uncertainty, *Computers & Chemical Engineering*, 157, 107636.

C. T. Maravelias, C. Sung, 2009, Integration of production planning and scheduling: Overview, challenges and opportunities, *Computers & Chemical Engineering*, 33, 1919-1930.

M. Martin, R. Gani, I. M. Mujtaba, 2022, Sustainable process synthesis, design and analysis: Challenges and opportunities, *Sustainable Production & Consumption*, (https://doi.org/10.1016/j.spc.2022.01.002)

A. Mitsos, N. Asprion, C.A. Floudas, M. Bortz, M. Baldea, D. Bonvin, A. Caspari, P. Schäfer, 2018. Challenges in process optimization for new feedstocks and energy sources, *Computers & Chemical Engineering*, 113, 209–221.

I. M. Mujtaba, R. Srinivasan, N. Elbashir, 2018, The water-food-energy nexus: Processes, Technologies and Challenges, CRC Press, USA.

N. Nolasco, V. S. Vassiliadis, W. Kähm, S. D. Adloor, R. Al Ismaili, R. Conejeros, T. Espaas, N. Gangadharan, V. Mappas, F. Scott, Q. Zhang, 2021, Optimal control in chemical engineering: Past, present and future, *Computers and Chemical Engineering*, 155, 107528.

OSHA, 2021, (http://www.osha.gov/dsg/safer_chemicals/why_transition.html).

M. M. Papathanasiou, C. Kontoravdi, 2020, Engineering challenges in therapeutic protein product and process design, *Current Opinion in Chemical Engineering*, 27, 81-88.

E. N. Pistikopoulos, A. Barbosa-Povoa, J. H. Lee, R. Misener, A. Mitsos, G. V. Reklaitis, V. Venkatasubramanian, F. You, R. Gani, 2021, Process Systems Engineering–The Generation Next?, *Computers & Chemical Engineering*, 147, 107252.

M. Rafiei, L.A. Ricardez-Sandoval, 2020, New frontiers, challenges, and opportunities in integration of design and control for enterprise-wide sustainability, *Computers & Chemical Engineering*, 132, 106610.

D. Rangel-Martinez, K. D. P. Nigam, L. A. Ricardez-Sandoval, 2021, Machine learning on sustainable energy: A review and outlook on renewable energy systems, catalysis, smart grid and energy storage, *Chemical Engineering Research and Design*, 174, 414-441.

K. Roh, H. Lim, W. Chung, J. Oh, H. Yoo, A. S. Al-Hunaidy, H. Imran, J. H. Lee, 2018, Sustainability analysis of CO2 capture and utilization processes using a computer-aided tool, *Journal CO2 Utilization*, 26, 60–69.

A. Sanchez, L.M. Gil, M. Martín, 2019, Sustainable DMC production from CO2 and renewable ammonia and methanol, *Journal of CO2 Utilization*. 33, 521-531.

R. W. H. Sargent, 2004, 25 years of progress in process systems engineering, *Computers & Chemical Engineering*, 28, 437–439.

J. Schilling, D. Tillmanns, M. Lampe, M. Hopp, J. Gross, A. Bardow, 2017, From molecules to dollars: integrating molecular design into thermo-economic process design using consistent thermodynamic modeling, *Molecular Systems Design & Engineering*, 2 (3), 301-320.

M. Skiborowski, A. Harwardt, W. Marquardt, 2014, Conceptual design of distillation based hybrid separation processes, *Annual Review of Chemical and Biomolecular Engineering*, 4(1), 45.

P. C. Slorach, H. K. Jeswani, R. Cuéllar-Franca, A. Azapagic, 2020, Environmental sustainability in the food-energy-water-health nexus: A new methodology and an application to food waste in a circular economy, *Waste Management*, 113, 359–368.

R. Srinivasan, B. Srinivasan, M. U. Iqbal, A. Nemet, Z. Kravanja, 2019, Recent developments towards enhancing process safety: Inherent safety and cognitive engineering, *Computers and Chemical Engineering*, 128, 364–383.

G. Stephanopoulos, G. V. Reklaitis, 2011, Process systems engineering: From Solvay to modern bio- and nanotechnology.A history of development, successes and prospects for the future, *Chemical Engineering Science*, 66, 4272–4306.

H. Sugiyama, N. Harada, E. Amasawa, M. Hirao, N. Yahagi, 2021, A prototype method for selecting reduction countermeasure against unused medicine considering patient characteristics, *J. Chemical Engineering of Japan*. 54, 152–161.

S. R. Syeda, E. A. Khan, O. Padungwatanaroj, N. Kuprasertwong, A. K. Tula, 2022, A perspective on hazardous chemical substitution in consumer products, *Current Opinion in Chemical Engineering*, 36, 100748.

A. K. Tula, D. K. Babi, J. Bottlaender, M. R. Eden, R. Gani, 2017, A computer-aided software-tool for sustainable process synthesis-intensification, *Computers & Chemical Engineering*, 105, 74–95.

A. K. Tula, M. R. Eden, R. Gani, 2019, Hybrid method and associated tools for synthesis of sustainable process flowsheets, *Computers & Chemical Engineering*, 131, 106572

UN (2021) Sustainable development Goals. (https://www.un.org/sustainabledevelopment/).

V. Venkatasubramanian, 2019, The promise of artificial intelligence in chemical engineering: Is it here, finally?, *AIChE Journal*, 65 (2), 466-478.

R. Vooradi, M. -O. Bertran, R. Frauzem, S. B. Anne, R. Gani, 2018, Sustainable chemical processing and energy-carbon dioxide management: Review of challenges and opportunities, *Chemical Engineering Research and Design*, 131, 440-464.

B. Wang, J. Zhao, 2022. Automatic Frequency Estimation of Contributory Factors for Confined Space Accidents, *Process Safety and Environmental Protection*, 157, 193-207.

WBA, 2020 (http://www.worldbioenergy.org/uploads/201210%20WBA%20GBS%202020.pdf).

WHO, 2019 (https://www.who.int/news-room/fact-sheets/detail/drinking-water).

Worldometers (https://www.worldometers.info/coronavirus/).

H. Wu, J. Zhao, 2020, Fault detection and diagnosis based on transfer learning for multimode chemical Processes, *Computers & Chemical Engineering*, 135, 106731.

Z. J. Yu, L. T. Biegler, 2019, Advanced-step multistage nonlinear model predictive control: Robustness and stability, *Journal of Process Control*, 84, 192–206.

L. Zhang, H. Mao, Q. Liu, R. Gani, 2020, Chemical product design–recent advances and perspectives, *Current Opinion in Chemical Engineering*, 27, 22-34.

S. Zhang, C. Zheng, X. Chen, 2021a, SyPSE: A Symbolic Computation Toolbox for Process Systems Engineering Part I-Architecture and Algorithm Development, *Industrial and Engineering Chemistry Research*, 60 (45), 16304–16316.

S. Zhang, F. Zhao, C. Zheng, L. Zhu, X. Chen, X., 2021b, SyPSE: A Symbolic Computation Toolbox for Process Systems Engineering Part II-Design for PSE Applications, *Industrial and Engineering Chemistry Research*, 60 (45), 16317–16329.

Proceedings of the 14th International Symposium on Process Systems Engineering – PSE 2021+
June 19-23, 2022, Kyoto, Japan
http://dx.doi.org/10.1016/B978-0-323-85159-6.50003-8

PSE Tools and Challenges in the Development of Advanced Pharmaceutical Manufacturing

Yingjie Chen[a], Pooja Bhalode[b], Yang Ou[b], Marianthi Ierapetritou[a,*]

[a]*Department of Chemical and Biomolecular Engineering, 150 Academy St, Newark, DE 19716, USA*
[b]*Department of Chemical and Biochemical Engineering, Rutgers University, 98 Brett Rd, Piscataway, NJ 08854, USA*
[*]*Corresponding author – mgi@udel.edu*

Abstract

Following the Industry 4.0 revolution, pharmaceutical industry is progressing towards embracing its principles for smart manufacturing. Industry 4.0 encourages the application of a robust, integrated data framework to connect physical components to virtual environment. It enables an accurate representation of the physical parts in digitized space, leading to the realization of Digital Twins (DTs). In this work, our effort on developing process systems engineering (PSE) tools towards the development of a DT for advanced pharmaceutical manufacturing are presented. These tools are demonstrated through applications in the areas of solid-based drug manufacturing and biologics production.

Keywords: Industry 4.0; Digital twin; System analysis; Pharmaceutical manufacturing; Biologics production.

1. Introduction

Driven by the Industry 4.0 revolution and the vision to develop agile, robust, and flexible manufacturing process to produce high quality drugs, the pharmaceutical industry is adopting this digitalization move (O'Connor et al., 2016, Chen et al., 2020). Efficient process monitoring, prediction, and analysis are realized using process analytical technologies (PAT), data collection and processing, Internet of Things (IoT), and big data analytics. The framework allows for the establishment of a virtual representation of the physical process with information communications, resulting in a DT capable to enhance process robustness and facilitate process design and operations (Chen et al., 2020). For DTs, maintaining precise virtual representations of processes and conducting detailed analyses are two crucial tasks. These tasks are challenging for pharmaceutical manufacturing as multi-scale information, ranging from powder and cell properties to bulk flow of materials, needs to be integrated with complex reaction networks and transport phenomena. These components lead to complex model development and high computational costs, limiting the implementation of DT in advanced pharmaceutical manufacturing.

To address these challenges, we propose the use of PSE tools focusing on modeling and analysis approaches. From a modeling perspective, mechanistic models for particle and cell level modeling, surrogate and hybrid modeling for model reduction, adaptive modeling for model updates, and flowsheet models for process integration are developed. For process analyses, efficient tools in sensitivity and feasibility analysis, techno-economic analysis (TEA), life cycle assessment (LCA), and optimization are applied. The development and application of these methods will be illustrated for solid-based drug manufacturing and biological production.

2. Application in solid-based drug and biologics manufacturing

The in-silico design, analysis, and optimization methods provide a basis for digital manufacturing, which support resolving the bottleneck of the pharmaceutical industry in improving productivity and quality. Mechanistic models enable the incorporation of process details and material properties, providing a comprehensive digital replication of the unit. These models include discrete element modelling (DEM) to simulate dynamic powder flow in solid-based drug manufacturing (Bhalode and Ierapetritou 2020), and computational fluid dynamics (CFD) with kinetic models to capture cellular activities for biologics manufacturing (Yang and Ierapetritou, 2021). However, these models can be computationally intensive. To address such challenge, surrogate and hybrid models that combine data and process knowledge in different scales are utilized (Bhalode and Ierapetritou, 2021, Chen and Ierapetritou, 2020, Metta and Ierapetritou, 2019). Dynamic algorithms and adaptive strategies based on moving windows are used to capture time-variant process behaviours, supporting the development of DTs (Bhalode et al., 2022). Models in solid-based drug manufacturing and monoclonal antibody (mAb) production will be presented as case studies (Ding and Ierapetritou, 2021, Yang and Ierapetritou, 2021, Chopda et al., 2021).

Along with unit operation models, flowsheet models are constructed with appropriate information transfer, which facilitate early-stage design, evaluation, and decision making. To improve process understanding, PSE tools such as regression and variance-based sensitivity analysis, feasibility analysis with adaptive sampling, and deterministic optimization are performed for identification of critical process parameters, design space, and optimal operating conditions, respectively. Cases in direct compaction of solid-based drugs (Wang et al., 2017a, Metta et al., 2020, Bhalode et al., 2020) and continuous chromatography of biologics (Ding and Ierapetritou, 2021) will be demonstrated.

TEA tools are integrated with flowsheet models to analyse the cost and energy effectiveness of the process and to identify the benefits of continuous operations over traditional batch or semi-batch operation alternatives. Applications in both wet granulation for the production of solid-based drugs (Sampat et al., 2022), and mAb production will be discussed (Yang et al., 2019). To assess the sustainability potential of advanced pharmaceutical manufacturing processes, LCA tools (Luo and Ierapetritou, 2020) are utilized to obtain important environmental indicators including the global warming potential of the product. With information on sustainability and process economics, multi-objective optimization is performed to strive for a balance between the two and guide process design and operations. To reduce sampling cost, maintain process feasibility, and find accurate Pareto solutions, a two-stage optimization framework based on Wang et al. (2017b) is proposed. The feasibility stage identifies the feasible regions with promising values for all objectives, followed by the optimization stage to find the Pareto within the feasible regions. The surrogate-based feasibility-driven multi-objective optimization algorithm will be shown for wet granulation route of solid-based drug manufacturing.

Acknowledgement

The authors acknowledge funding from U.S. Food and Drug Administration through grants DHHS-FDA-U01FD006487, R01FD006588, and FDABAA-20-00123.

References

P. Bhalode, M. Ierapetrittou, 2020, Discrete element modeling for continuous powder feeding operation: Calibration and system analysis, Int J Pharm, 585, 119427.

P. Bhalode, M. Ierapetritou, 2021, Hybrid multi-zonal compartment modeling for continuous powder blending processes, Int J Pharm, 602, 120643.

P. Bhalode, Y. Chen, M. Ierapetritou, 2022, Hybrid modelling strategies for continuous pharmaceutical manufacturing within digital twin framework, Proceedings of the 14th International Symposium on Process Systems Engineering, Paper 306.

P. Bhalode, N. Metta, Y. Chen, M. Ierapetritou, 2020, Efficient Data-based Methodology for Model Enhancement and Flowsheet Analyses for Continuous Pharmaceutical Manufacturing, Comput Aided Chem Eng, 48, 127-132.

Y. Chen, M. Ierapetritou, 2020, A framework of hybrid model development with identification of plant-model mismatch, AIChE Jounal, 66, 10, e16996.

Y. Chen, O. Yang, C. Sampat, P. Bhalode, R. Ramachandran, M. Ierapetritou, 2020, Digital Twins in Pharmaceutical and Biopharmaceutical Manufacturing: A Literature Review, Process, 8, 9.

V. Chopda, A. Gyorgypal, O. Yang, R. Singh, R. Ramachandran, H. Zhang, G. Tsilomelekis, S. Chundawat, M. Ierapetritou, 2021, Recent advances in integrated process analytical techniques, modeling, and control strategies to enable continuous biomanufacturing of monoclonal antibodies, J Chem Technol Biotechnol.

C. Ding, M. Ierapetritou, 2021, A novel framework of surrogate-based feasibility analysis for establishing design space of twin-column continuous chromatography, Int J Pharm, 609, 121161.

Y. Luo, M. Ierapetritou, 2020, Comparison between Different Hybrid Life Cycle Assessment Methodologies: A Review and Case Study of Biomass-based p-Xylene Production, Ind Eng Chem Res, 59, 52, 22313-22329.

N. Metta, R. Ramachandran, M. Ierapetritou, 2019, A Computationally Efficient Surrogate-Based Reduction of a Multiscale Comill Process Model, J Pharm Innov, 15, 424-444.

N. Metta, R. Ramachandran, M. Ierapetritou, 2020, A novel adaptive sampling based methodology for feasible region identification of compute intensive models using artificial neural network, AIChE J, 67, 2, e17095.

T. O'Connor, L. Yu, S. Lee, 2016, Emerging technology: A key enabler for modernizing pharmaceutical manufacturing and advancing product quality, Int J Pharm, 509, 1-2, 492-498.

C. Sampat, L. Kotamarthy, P. Bhalode, Y. Chen, A. Dan, S. Parvani, Z. Dholakia, B. Glasser, M. Ierapetritou, R. Ramachandran, Enabling energy-efficient manufacturing of pharmaceutical products by implementing a smart manufacturing platform, J Adv Manuf Process.

Z. Wang, M.S. Escotet-Espinoza, M. Ierapetritou, 2017a, Process analysis and optimization of continuous pharmaceutical manufacturing using flowsheet models, Comput Chem Eng, 107, 77-91.

Z. Wang, M.S. Escotet-Espinoza, R. Singh, M. Ierapetritou, 2017b, Surrogate-based Optimization for Pharmaceutical Manufacturing Processes, Comput Aided Chem Eng, 40, 2797-2802.

O. Yang, M. Ierapetritou, 2021, mAb Production Modeling and Design Space Evaluation Including Glycosylation Process, Processes, 9, 2, 324.

O. Yang, M. Qadan, M. Ierapetritou, 2019, Economic Analysis of Batch and Continuous Biopharmaceutical Antibody Production: A Review, J Pharm Innov, 14, 1-19.

Proceedings of the 14th International Symposium on Process Systems Engineering – PSE 2021+
June 19-23, 2022, Kyoto, Japan
http://dx.doi.org/10.1016/B978-0-323-85159-6.50004-X

Experience and Perspectives on our Journey towards Deep Decarbonization

Iftekhar A Karimi* and Shamsuzzaman Farooq*

Department of Chemical & Biomolecular Engineering, National University of Singapore, 4 Engineering Drive 4, Singapore 117585
cheiak@nus.edu.sg and chesf@nus.edu.sg

Abstract

The enormity of mankind's decarbonization challenge precludes a simple monolithic solution. Its unprecedented scale and complexity affect every nation without exceptions. Ideally, our mission should be to fully replace the fossil fuels with zero-carbon renewable alternatives, but the path to that end is long and challenging. In this talk, we discuss our experience and perspectives on some decarbonization pathways with concrete examples (efficiency improvements, novel processes for CO2 utilization, non-polluting energy sources, ...), where successful translational outcomes can be accelerated by continuous guidance from process systems engineering tools and techniques.

Keywords: carbon emissions, decarbonization, hydrogen, carbon utilization, carbon capture, supply chain.

1. Introduction

Economic development and per capita energy consumption of a nation are strongly correlated. Rising world population with a desire for better living has increased energy demand exponentially, which is mostly met with easy-to-use hydrocarbon fuels with little concern for a backlash from abusing the nature and despite warnings flagged by many scientific studies. The consequence is an unprecedented rise in the atmospheric CO2 levels. In the meantime, global warming is already showing early signs of catastrophic consequences all around the world. From Kyoto Protocol in 1997 through Paris Agreement in 2015 to Glasgow COP26 in 2021, it took 23 years for the world to fully wake up to the urgency of the situation and take decarbonization seriously. Fortunately, the scientific community was fully committed well ahead of the political consensus on this matter, and has compiled a significant body of work on decarbonization. These contributions, spanning a broad spectrum of issues, can be classified into three themes: reduce, recycle/reuse, and replace carbon; which are widely known as 3Rs. In most countries, the journey towards decarbonization has involved the 3Rs in the same sequence.

Decarbonizing existing systems require addressing inherently large-scale problems. Consequently, our collective 3R-driven decarbonization journey has witnessed a resurgence of the need to apply the classical Chemical and Process Systems Engineering (PSE) concepts and methods. Parallelly, low carbon technology innovations are required for capturing carbon emissions and producing power, chemicals, and fuels. We believe that their industrial success requires mission oriented translational work, and constant guidance from PSE right from the beginning can benefit them greatly.

In this talk, we present our perspectives on the 3Rs for our journey from high-carbon present to no-carbon future with examples from our work at the National University of Singapore that illustrate the central role of PSE in this urgent and critical mission.

2. Reduce

Reducing CO2 emissions from the power and industry sectors by increasing energy efficiency is a low hanging fruit, hence the obvious first target for many countries and research. Our work has yielded several observations.

Much literature has used energy or exergy as a KPI (Key Performance Index) for many problems. In our opinion, annualized total cost (TAC) should be the preferred KPI, as minimum-TAC solutions can be significantly different from minimum-energy/exergy solutions (Rao et al., 2016; Rao & Karimi, 2018). Furthermore, no doubt a sound theoretical concept, exergy is inadequate for economic industrial decisions in practice.

Rigorous simulation-based optimization has been quite useful for us. Our work (Dutta et al., 2018; Rao & Karimi, 2017) required detailed rigorous simulations of industrial facilities with realistic thermodynamic properties. It proved easier and more accurate to use them directly versus deriving analytical correlations for the conventional algebraic optimization. Hamedi et al. (2020) have identified several pitfalls of the latter.

Saleem et al. (2018) developed a computational fluid dynamics (CFD) model for an industry-scale LNG storage tank and showed that surface evaporation predominates, and nucleate boiling is unlikely. Furthermore, the static pressure delays internal circulation and complete mixing. Sundaram & Karimi (2021) were able to predicts pressure transients using a simpler model and their results matched both the CFD model real tank data. LNG recirculation is a major cause of BOG losses (hence power use in reliquefaction) from these tanks. Using a validated dynamic simulator, we (Karimi et al, 2019) proposed a modified recirculation scheme, a new operations schedule for BOG compressors, and a lower recondenser pressure to reduce power use by nearly 40%.

Heat integration has hugely benefitted the process industry. We addressed several key areas. First, Nair et al. (2019) developed a novel stageless superstructure that offers complete flexibility in network configuration and is seamless for both grassroots and retrofit synthesis. Second, Nair et al. (2016) showed that inter-plant (versus intra-plant) heat integration can offer substantial energy savings, but at the cost of several significant complexity, safety, control, logistics, ownership, and collaboration challenges. Capital costs become much more crucial. Third, integrating work along with heat (Hamdi et al., 2020) offers additional carbon reduction. Fourth, Rao & Karimi (2017) and Rao et al. (2019) addressed the flowsheet and operation optimizations of processes with multi-stream exchangers. Fifth, Christopher et al. (2017) used vapor recompression and self-heat recuperation to decrease energy use by 45% for propane/propylene separation.

LNG regasification terminals worldwide waste LNG's cold energy. Dutta et al. (2018a) showed that a well-configured organic Rankine cycle (ORC) can recover this energy and produce 0.5−12.9 kW/t-LNG of power with an NPV of $2.45-6.87 million at an operating regasification terminal. Furthermore, Dutta et al. (2018b) proposed an integrated regasification-production process to produce valuable heavy hydrocarbons (ethane, LPG) from rich/medium LNG by exploiting the cold energy. In fact, such a process can generate 7-10% profit for the terminal.

We have implemented process data-based pump and insulation health monitoring at the same terminal. While estimating the remaining useful life (RUL) to schedule timely preventive maintenance, the user interface also tracks increasing CO2 emission from deteriorating health. Thus, it is possible to account for environmental impact (carbon tax) to schedule maintenance.

Our above discussion illustrates how PSE methodologies for design, simulation, integration, and optimization can reduce carbon emissions in real industrial processes.

3. Recycle / Reuse

While renewable energy sources are a priority, hydrocarbons will remain in use during the transition to a zero-carbon economy. Hence, carbon capture and concentration (CCC) from various stationary emission sources for sequestration and utilization (CSU) will be important and unavoidable during the transition. CO2 recycle/ utilization can be achieved in two ways. The conventional way is to capture it from the existing processes and produce useful chemicals via green hydrogen. The alternative is to radically change the way we produce power and chemicals today by integrating their productions to achieve zero net CO2 emissions.

Our studies (Khurana & Farooq, 2017, 2019) on CCC have led to the following perspectives. First, the scale and footprint of a CCC plant, irrespective of the technology, are far larger than the largest chemical plant known today. Second, adsorption-based CCC processes (VSA, TSA, etc) do not show any significant cost advantage compared to the established industrial amine processes. Third, the cost reduction from designing both adsorbent and process simultaneously (process inversion) by considering adsorbent attributes also as optimization variables was minimal. This implies that process rather than material innovation is more promising. The idea of process inversion can help other R&DD efforts such as catalysts for CO2 utilization (CU).

In order to gain a broader understanding of the prospects and challenges of CO2 reuse, we (Dutta et al., 2017) conceptualized a zero-emissions scheme (Figure 1) to integrate both power and chemicals production. All CO2 produced was recycled internally and reused to produce useful fuels and chemicals. All reaction and separation operations along with heat and power integration were also built within the scheme. Using the scheme as a surrogate to achieve zero net carbon emissions made us quickly realize that an abundant supply of green renewable hydrogen is a prerequisite. If the scheme was used to meet the current global demands of all chemicals, CO2 avoidance would be at most 59% of 2013 emissions. This implies that CU must produce fuels to increase CO2 avoidance. Furthermore, CU products must be cost-competitive and profitable.

Our recent study (Vo et al., 2021) on the feasibility of producing transportation fuels, methanol and 1-propanol from CU shows that only 1-propanol is competitive at the present levels of carbon tax, CO2 cost, and green hydrogen price. Our proposed scheme for producing 1-propanol from CO2 utilization is a three-step process. Even though this process is economically profitable and emits less CO2 than the current commercial process, a novel catalyst allowing a single step process may seem more attractive intuitively. However, our technoeconomic study based on preliminary data from a single-step catalyst shows contrary results. The first problem is low selectivity towards propanol versus non-alcoholic by-products. The second problem is the high H2 burden arising from the oxygen molecules introduced with each mole of CO2. This is an excellent illustration of how a complete process study at an early stage of catalyst development can guide further materials research. In view of the current high green H2 cost, its higher consumption in CO2 utilization compared to the conventional routes deserves further study.

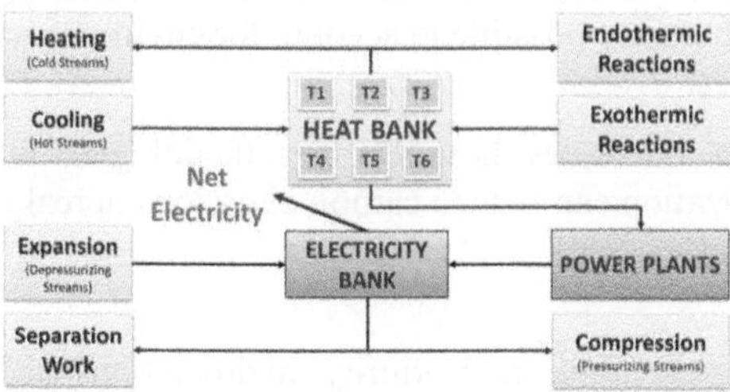

Figure 1: Scheme for the integrated production of power and chemicals with zero net carbon emissions.

4. Replace

The grand vision for deep decarbonisation foresees the emergence of an energy landscape based on global hydrogen supply chains (HSCs, Figure 2). While much effort is underway on technologies (e.g. water electrolysis) to produce green hydrogen via renewable electricity, it will take time before such green H2 is cost competitive with the blue hydrogen produced from NG with CCS. Other material and equipment hurdles along with the lack of infrastructure will keep both NG and CCSU critically relevant for the foreseeable future. In other words, HSCs will be inseparable from NG/LNG and CO2 supply chains. Several countries (e.g. EU, USA, Korea, Australia, Japan) have developed roadmaps for how H2 could develop in specific regions. Since some countries (e.g. Singapore) with high energy needs have few renewable energy resources, export/import of H2 via global transport routes will be a key aspect of HSCs with low density of H2 as a significant hurdle. Hence, countries are asking three main questions: what are the technoeconomic and environmental costs of producing, importing, and transporting H2?

Fully funded by and in collaboration with ExxonMobil USA, we are working on a hydrogen roadmap for ASEAN (Association of South East Asian Nations) under the umbrella of Singapore Energy Center. We conducted a holistic study of various options for producing and transporting hydrogen from both technoeconomic and environmental perspectives, and are analysing various scenarios for the planning of HSCs in ASEAN from now to 2050. For this, we (Hong et al., 2021) have developed a multiperiod mixed-integer nonlinear programming model for geographically distributed SC capacity planning, and a tool called HEART (Hydrogen Economy Assessment & Resource Tool). HEART enables the long-term design and planning of H2 production and import, and computes the cost of producing and transporting H2. In the near future, we will also be collaborating with Chiyoda and Mitsubishi Japan to plan and optimize the local distribution of H2 in Singapore, when MCH (Methyl CycloHexane) is used as a carrier for importing H2.

Using data from various H2 reports, we developed simplified analytical correlations for the cost of producing H2 from NG, coal, biomass, and water electrolysis at various locations in ASEAN. We (Hong et al., 2021) then analysed four options for transporting hydrogen, namely methyl cyclohexane (MCH), liquid hydrogen (LH2), compressed hydrogen (CH2), and liquid ammonia (LNH3) and computed the landed cost of H2 as a function of various technoeconomic and geographic parameters. Our study showed that HSC costs are comparable to production costs, hence both require careful attention for

H2 economy. H2 produced via steam reforming with CCS and supplied via pipelines is the cheapest option for distances within 2000 km. The next best option is the direct use of NH3 instead of H2 for power generation. MCH and liquid NH3 showed comparable landed costs for H2, and using green H2 is essential for achieving >80% carbon avoidance. Liquid H2 has the highest energy penalty. Contrary to the misgiving that direct NH3 burning will increase NOx emissions, our recent comparative study (Saleem et al., 2022) of literature data on burning hydrogen, ammonia, and natural gas shows that NOx generation from H2 combustion is more than that from an equivalent amount of NH3.

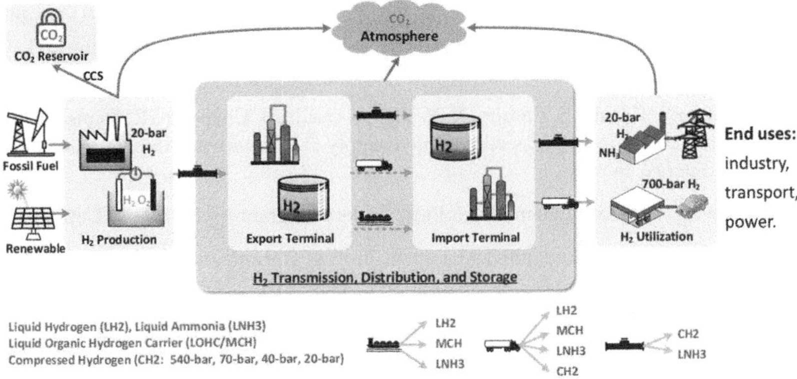

Figure 2: Schematic of hydrogen supply chain and its key elements. (Hong et al., 2021)

5. Conclusions

Various branches of chemical engineering and related sciences have sufficiently progressed where we can have high confidence in simulation-based prediction of a process performance obtained via PSE tools and techniques. In this paper, we have demonstrated with examples drawn from our work how that can play important roles in all three Rs to arrest our existential threat from global warming.

We strongly advocate a paradigm shift where PSE would be the guiding vector for materials research from the beginning in order to provide timely feedback necessary to ensure that what looks exciting at a small scale meets the requirements of a successful commercial translation. This new paradigm has the potential to maximize resource utilization and shorten development times.

Acknowledgements

This work was funded by grants from National University of Singapore, Singapore Energy Center, ExxonMobil Research & Engineering, and Energy Market Authority of Singapore and National Research Foundation of Singapore under their Energy Innovation Research Program.

References

C. Christopher, A. Dutta, S. Farooq, I. Karimi, 2017, Process synthesis and optimization of propylene/propane separation using vapor recompression and self-heating recuperation, Ind. Eng. Chem. Res., 56, 49, 14557-14564.

A. Dutta, S. Farooq, I. Karimi, S. Khan, 2017, Assessing the potential of CO2 utilization with an integrated framework for producing power and chemicals. J of CO2 Utilization, 19, 49-57.

A. Dutta, I. Karimi, S. Farooq, 2018a, Heating Value Reduction of LNG (Liquefied Natural Gas) by Recovering Heavy Hydrocarbons: Technoeconomic Analyses Using Simulation-Based Optimization, Ind. Eng. Chem. Res., 57, 17, 5924-5932.

A. Dutta, I. Karimi, S. Farooq, 2018b, Economic feasibility of power generation by recovering cold energy during LNG (Liquefied Natural Gas) regasification. ACS Sustainable Chemistry & Engineering, 6, 8, 10687-10695.

H. Hamedi, I. Karimi, T Gundersen, 2020, Simulation-based approach for integrating work within heat exchange networks for sub-ambient processes. Energy Conv & Management, 203, 112276.

X. Hong, V. Thaore, I. Karimi, S. Farooq, X. Wang, A. Usadi, B. Chapman, R. Johnson, 2021, Techno-enviro-economic analyses of hydrogen supply chains with an ASEAN case study, Int J of Hydrogen Energy, in press.

I. Karimi, S. Farooq, L. Samavedham, 2019, Final Report for grant NRF2014EWT-EIRP003-008.

M. Khurana, S. Farooq, 2017, Integrated Adsorbent-Process Optimization for Carbon Capture and Concentration Using Vacuum Swing Adsorption Cycles, AIChE Journal 63 (7), 2987–2995.

M. Khurana, S. Farooq, 2017, Integrated Adsorbent-Process Optimization for Carbon Capture and Concentration Using Vacuum Swing Adsorption Cycles, AIChE Journal 63 (7), 2987–2995.

A. Saleem, S. Farooq, I. Karimi, R. Banerjee, 2018, A CFD simulation study of boiling mechanism and BOG generation in a full-scale LNG storage tank, Comp. Chem. Eng., 115, 112-120.

S. Nair, Y Guo, U Mukherjee, I. Karimi and A Elkamel, 2016, Shared and Practical Approach to Conserve Utilities in Eco-Industrial Parks. Comp. Chem. Eng., 93, 221-233.

S. Nair, I. Karimi, 2019, Unified Heat Exchanger Network Synthesis via a Stageless Superstructure". Ind. Eng. Chem. Res., 58, 15, 5984-6001.

H. Rao, I. Karimi, 2017, A Superstructure-based Model for Multistream Heat Exchanger Design within Flowsheet Optimization, AIChE J, 63, 9, 3764-3777.

H. Rao, I Karimi, 2018, Optimal design of boil-off gas reliquefaction process in LNG regasification terminals, Comp Chem Eng, 117, 171-190.

H. Rao, S. Nair, I. Karimi, 2019, Operational Optimization of Processes with Multistream Heat Exchangers". Ind. Eng. Chem. Res., 58, 15, 5838-5850.

H. Rao, K Wong and I Karimi, 2016, Minimizing Power Consumption Related to BOG Reliquefaction in an LNG Regasification Terminal. Ind. Eng. Chem. Res., 55, 27, 7431-7445.

A. Saleem, I. Karimi, S. Farooq, 2022, Estimating NOx emissions of useful two-fuel blends from literature data, Fuels, in press.

A. Sundaram, I. Karimi, 2021, State Transients in storage systems for energy fluids, Comp. Chem. Eng., 144, 107128.

C. Vo, C. Mondelli, H. Hamedi, J. Pérez-Ramírez, S. Farooq, I. Karimi, 2021, Sustainability Assessment of Thermocatalytic Conversion of CO2 to Transportation Fuels, Methanol, and 1-Propanol, ACS Sustainable Chem & Eng, 9, 10591−10600.

Proceedings of the 14th International Symposium on Process Systems Engineering – PSE 2021+
June 19-23, 2022, Kyoto, Japan
http://dx.doi.org/10.1016/B978-0-323-85159-6.50005-1

Surrogate Modeling and Surrogate-Based Optimization with Stochastic Simulations

Samira Mohammadi[ǂ], Bianca Williams[ǂ], Selen Cremaschi*

Department of Chemical Engineering, Auburn University, Auburn, AL, United States
**selen-cremaschi@auburn.edu*
[ǂ]Authors contributed equally

Abstract

In recent years, high-fidelity simulation models have become widespread to study, design, and optimize engineering systems. However, the complexity of the models often requires computational power beyond what is feasible. One common way to reduce computational cost is to use surrogate/meta models, simplified approximations of more complex, higher-order models, and map input data to output data. Many techniques have been developed for surrogate modeling; however, there remains a need for a systematic method for selecting suitable techniques. In addition, surrogate models built using traditional methods do not accurately represent the outputs of high-fidelity stochastic simulations, e.g., simulations with uncertain parameters. This work describes a new framework that combines PRESTO (Predictive REcommendations of Surrogate models To Optimize), a surrogate model selection tool, with a novel technique, PARIN (PARameter as INput-variable), for building accurate surrogate models of stochastic simulations. We applied the framework to two stochastic test functions with one uncertain parameter. The results reveal that the framework yielded lower normalized root mean square errors than stochastic kriging in predicting the mean and standard deviation of the test function outputs.

Keywords: surrogate model, stochastic simulation, surface approximation, process design/optimization

1. Introduction

In recent years, high-fidelity simulation models have become widespread to study, design, and optimize engineering systems (e.g., (Burnak et al., 2019; Al et al., 2020; Marvi-Mashhadi et al., 2020; Wang et al., 2020)). However, in many cases, the complexity of the models requires computational power beyond what is available for applications like sensitivity analysis or optimization studies. One common way to reduce computational costs is to use surrogate/meta models. Surrogate models, also known as response surfaces, black-box models, metamodels, or emulators, are simplified approximations of more complex, higher-order models and map input data to output data (Jiang et al., 2020).

With all the surrogate modeling techniques currently available, there is a need for a systematic procedure for selecting the appropriate technique. Recent works (Cui et al., 2016; Garud et al., 2018; Jia et al., 2020) have made progress in generalizing the selection of a surrogate model to approximate a design space by using meta-learning approaches avoiding expensive trial-and-error methods. However, selecting surrogate models for surrogate-based optimization remains an open challenge. Furthermore, surrogate models built using traditional techniques do not accurately represent the outputs of high-fidelity stochastic simulations, e.g., simulations with uncertain parameters (Staum, 2009). High-fidelity simulations may contain different sources of uncertainty, including uncertain inputs, parameters, and model form (Ankenman et al., 2008). The existing machine learning (ML) methods are mainly built for deterministic problems, and they usually fail in representing the stochastic simulation outputs properly (Staum, 2009). The current ML techniques can be used to model outputs of stochastic simulation only when the source of uncertainty is the inputs. A surrogate model is built using an appropriate ML technique with the input/output data generated using the deterministic simulation. Then, the input uncertainty may be propagated to the ML model outputs using uncertainty propagation methods (Kim, 2016).

Three current approaches to model the stochastic simulations with uncertain parameter(s) are 1) fixing the value of the uncertain parameters (Hüllen et al., 2019), 2) using a subset of realizations of the uncertain parameters (Hüllen et al., 2019), and 3) stochastic kriging (Ankenman et al., 2008). Using the first method leads to a deterministic output and the loss of uncertainty. The second method requires training several surrogate models to estimate the output and its uncertainty. Applying stochastic kriging limits the ML technique to kriging; however, it has been shown that the best ML technique for building a surrogate model depends on the data characteristics, which is a function of the underlying phenomena the model represents (Williams and Cremaschi, 2021).

In this paper, we propose a new framework to address the shortcomings of the previous methods and build surrogate models of simulations with uncertain parameter(s). The approach combines our recently developed surrogate model recommendation tool (PRESTO - Predictive REcommendations of Surrogate models To Optimize) with a novel approach, PARIN (PARameter as INput-variable), for building accurate surrogate models of stochastic simulations with uncertain parameters (Section 2). Computational studies use two test functions with different dimensions to evaluate the new framework (Section 3). The training data set is generated using Sobol sampling methods, and then the output for each given input point is calculated. The resultant training data set is fed to the PRESTO to obtain a set of recommended ML techniques for the data set. The recommended models are trained for each of the test functions. The performance of the new framework is compared to stochastic kriging (Section 3). Normalized root mean square error is used as the metric to compare the accuracy of the mean and standard deviation estimations of the test function outputs (Section 3). The comparisons reveal that the mean and standard deviation estimates obtained by the new framework are closer to their true values than the ones obtained using stochastic kriging. These results are presented and discussed in Section 4, followed by conclusions in Section 5.

2. Framework for Training Surrogate Models for Stochastic Simulations

The framework (Figure 1) starts by collecting input/output data, i.e., the training data set, from the stochastic simulation using a space-filling design. PARIN, PARameter as INput-variable, converts the stochastic simulation into a deterministic one by extracting its uncertain parameters and considering these parameters as additional inputs to the simulation (Section 2.2). Therefore, the input data set also includes the uncertain parameters. PRESTO (Section 2.1) selects the best surrogate modeling technique given the training data set, and a surrogate model is trained using the selected technique. The parameter uncertainty is incorporated into the surrogate model outputs utilizing an appropriate uncertainty propagation method (Section 2.2).

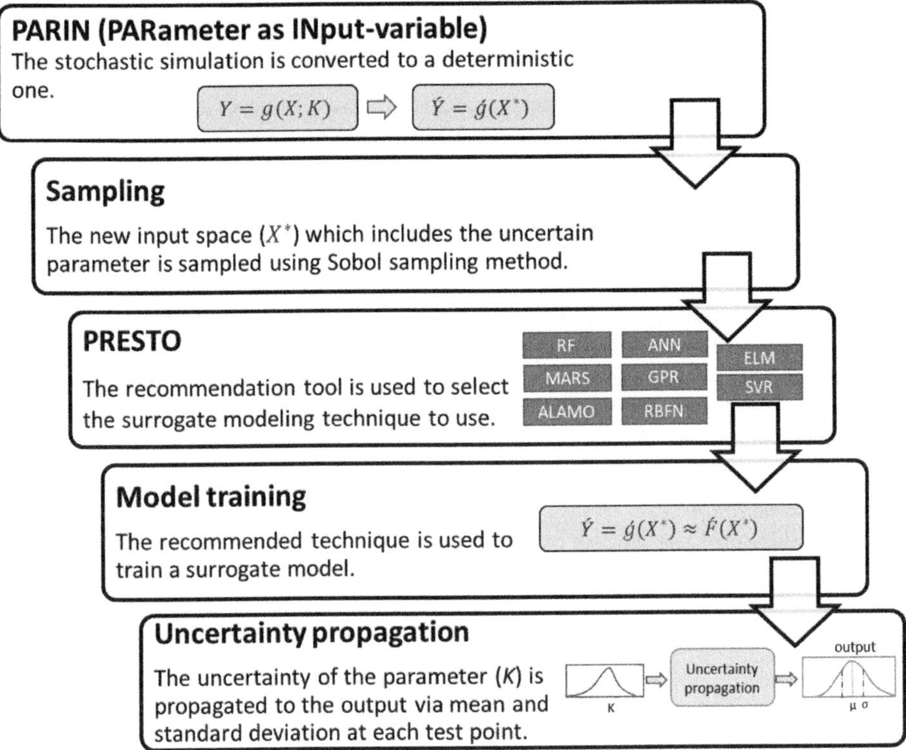

Figure 1 – Workflow of the new framework

2.1. PRESTO - Predictive REcommendations of Surrogate models To approximate and Optimize

PRESTO is a random forest-based framework for selecting appropriate surrogate modeling techniques (Williams et al., 2021). Given a dataset of input-output values, it provides a list of surrogate models predicted to give the most accurate surface approximation of the underlying model of the given input-output pairs. In order to collect the data required to construct PRESTO, data sets were generated using test functions from the optimization test suite of the Virtual Library of Simulation experiments (Surjanovic and Bingham, 2013) at various input dimensions and sample sizes. Surrogate models were trained for each generated data set using a set of candidate surrogate modeling techniques. The calculated performance of each model was used to determine if a surrogate model was appropriate ("recommended") or not ("not recommended") for modeling a particular data set. This information was used to train random forest classifiers using data set characteristics as inputs and the assigned recommendation class as outputs (Williams et al., 2021).

PRESTO recommends models based on the prediction of their performance for adjusted-R^2. The formula for calculating adjusted-R^2 ($\hat{R}^2$) is shown in Eq. (1).

$$\hat{R}^2 = 1 - (1 - R^2)\left[\frac{n-1}{n-(k+1)}\right] \tag{1}$$

In Eq. (1), R^2 is the R-squared regression coefficient, n is the number of data points in the training set, and k is the number of model parameters (or hyperparameters). The adjusted-R^2 takes into account both the surrogate model accuracy and complexity. Taking complexity into account is important in preventing overfitting of the model as overfit models do not generalize well to data outside of the training set. R^2 values typically fall between zero and one, with an R^2 of one indicating an exact fit to the original, more complex model data. However, with the adjustment for model size, adjusted-R^2 values can become negative.

PRESTO calculates characteristics, or attributes, of the underlying model using only the available input-output information. These attributes include calculations related to the location and distribution of the data points and estimations of the gradients of the surface. Based on the values of the data set attributes, PRESTO classifies each of a set of candidate surrogate model forms as being either "recommended" or "not recommended" for that data set (Williams et al., 2021).

2.2. PARIN - PARameter as INput-variable: A novel approach for surrogate modeling of stochastic simulations

PARIN builds surrogate models of stochastic simulations by considering the uncertain parameter(s) as additional inputs to the system. Suppose we are given a stochastic simulation, $Y = g(X; K)$, where X is the input vector, K is the uncertain parameter, and Y is the stochastic output (Figure 2). PARIN converts the stochastic simulation to a deterministic one, $Y' = \acute{g}(X^*)$, where the vector X^* now also includes the uncertain parameter K (Figure 2), and the output of the deterministic model is denoted Y'. A surrogate model, $\widehat{Y'} = F'(X^*)$, is trained to predict the deterministic simulation output, Y', with data generated from the deterministic simulation, $Y' = \acute{g}(X^*)$. Different surrogate modeling techniques can be employed to train $F'(X^*)$. We select the surrogate modeling technique using PRESTO (Section 2.1). Then, the stochastic output of the original simulation model is estimated by propagating the uncertainty of the parameter K to the surrogate model output. Here, again, a number of uncertainty propagation methods can be employed.

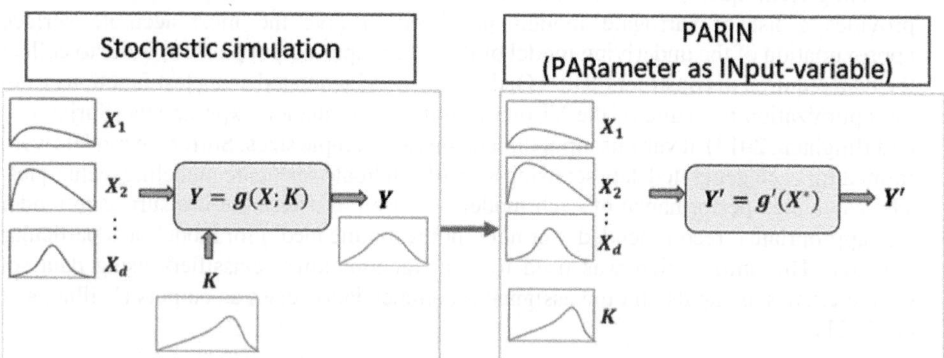

Figure 2 – PARIN (PARameter as INput-variable) - A novel approach for building surrogate models of stochastic simulations

3. Computational Experiments

We evaluate the performance of the framework via computational experiments using two test functions, Griewank and Rastrigin functions given in Eqs. (2) and (3), from the

Virtual Library of Simulation Experiments optimization test suite (Surjanovic and Bingham, 2013). Each test function includes one uncertain parameter and one, two, or four inputs. A normal distribution is assumed for the uncertain parameter (p) of each function. Variable d in both functions denotes the input dimension, which can be changed. The dimension is increased from one to four geometrically to investigate the impact of the input dimension on the performance of the proposed framework.

$$f(x) = \sum_{i=1}^{d} \frac{x_i^2}{p} - \prod_{i=1}^{d} cos\left(\frac{x_i}{\sqrt{i}}\right) + 1 \quad (2)$$

where,

$$p \sim Normal(4000, 400)$$

$$f(x) = pd + \sum_{i=1}^{d} \left[x_i^2 - p\left(cos(2\pi x_i)\right)\right] \quad (3)$$

where,

$$p \sim Normal(10, 1)$$

The training data set for each test function included the inputs, the uncertain parameter, and the corresponding function values for 1000 evaluations generated using Sobol sampling (Sobol', 1967). We used Sobol sampling because it has been shown to yield robust results in comparative studies of uncertainty propagation methods (Mohammadi and Cremaschi, 2019). PRESTO is used to select the best surrogate modeling technique for each training data set. A surrogate model is trained using the selected technique. During training, the hyperparameters of the models are optimized using 5-fold cross-validation (Wong, 2015).

The performance is evaluated using 10,000 test points sampled using Halton method (Halton, 1960). The parameter uncertainty is propagated to the output of each of these test points using a simulation-based method using Halton sampling. With $m = 1000$ points sampled from the uncertain parameter distribution, the mean (μ_l) and standard deviation (σ_l) of the lth test point is calculated using Eq. (4) and Eq. (5), respectively.

$$\mu_l = E[F'(X_l^*)] \approx \frac{1}{m}\sum_{j=1}^{m} h(x_j) \quad (4)$$

$$\sigma_l^2 = (E[F'(X_l^*)^2] - E[F'(X_l^*)]) \approx \frac{1}{m}\sum_{j=1}^{m} h(x_j)^2 - \mu^2 \quad (5)$$

3.1. Metric for evaluating framework's performance

The metric used to evaluate the performance of the new framework is the normalized Root Mean Squared Error (nRMSE), shown in Eq. (6). The metric is calculated using 10,000 test points generated by the Halton sampling method (Halton, 1960). The framework's ability to estimate the mean and standard deviation of the stochastic simulation output is assessed using nRMSE for each test function.

$$nRMSE = \left(\sqrt{\frac{\sum_{i=1}^{N}(Y_i - \hat{Y}_i)^2}{N}} \bigg/ Y_{max} - Y_{min} \right) \tag{6}$$

In Eq. (6), Y_i and $\hat{Y}_i$ are the true and predicted values of the desired moments (mean/standard deviation), respectively, for i^{th}test point. N is the total number of test points. Y_{max} and Y_{min} are the maximum and minimum values of the true moment values within the test set, respectively.

3.2. Stochastic kriging

Among three existing approaches for building surrogate models of stochastic simulations, fixing the value of the uncertain parameter does not provide information about the output uncertainty. The second approach, building multiple surrogate models, each built using a value from a select subset of parameter values, requires training multiple models, which introduces additional uncertainty, and may become computationally expensive as the number of surrogate models increases. Hence, here, the accuracy of the proposed framework is only compared to that of stochastic kriging, described briefly below. The performance metric, nRMSE, is also used to assess the stochastic kriging model's ability to estimate the mean and standard deviation of the stochastic simulation output.

Stochastic kriging (SK) (Ankenman et al., 2008), which extends classic kriging (Rasmussen and Williams, 2005), was initially proposed to account for the intrinsic variance in addition to the extrinsic one. The prediction of an SK model, $\hat{\mathbf{y}}$, can be represented by Eq. (7), where $\sum_M$ is the covariance matrix across all sample points, $\sum_M (x,.)$ is the covariance vector consisting of the covariance of the point x and other points, and $\sum_\varepsilon$ is the diagonal covariance matrix of the intrinsic uncertainty. β_0 is the unknown parameter estimated by the maximum likelihood.

$$\hat{\mathbf{y}} = \boldsymbol{\beta}_0 + \textstyle\sum_M (\boldsymbol{x},.)^T [\sum_M + \sum_\varepsilon]^{-1} (\bar{\mathbf{y}} - \boldsymbol{\beta}_0 \mathbf{1}_k) \tag{7}$$

The training data set for SK included 1000 input/output pairs for each test function at each input dimension. The set is constructed by evaluating the test functions for 100 input values at ten samples from the uncertain parameter distribution. Both input values and the samples from the distribution were determined using Sobol sampling.

4. Results and Discussion

4.1. Selected Surrogate Modeling Techniques by PRESTO

The candidate surrogate model techniques considered in this study included single hidden layer artificial neural network (ANN) models (Haykin, 2009), extreme learning machines (ELM) (Huang et al., 2006), Gaussian process regression (GPR) (Rasmussen and Nickisch, 2010), multivariate adaptive regression splines (MARS) (Friedman, 1991), random forests (Breiman, 2001), and support vector regression (Smola and Scholkopf, 2004). The models selected for the test functions at each studied input dimension are listed in Table 1.

Figures 3 and 4 show the average adjusted-R^2 value for the trained surrogate models that PRESTO recommended compared to the average adjusted-R^2 value of the models that PRESTO did not recommend for the Griewank and Rastrigin functions. The models trained using the recommended techniques for both functions have higher adjusted R^2

values and thus better predictive capability than the not recommended ones. The difference is more pronounced for higher dimensions and the Rastrigin function than the Griewank function.

Table 1 – PRESTO selected models for Griewank and Rastrigin functions

	Recommended Surrogate Models		
	1D	2D	4D
Griewank	ANN ELM **GPR** MARS	ANN ELM **GPR** MARS	**GPR** MARS
Rastrigin	GPR **MARS**	GPR **MARS**	**MARS**

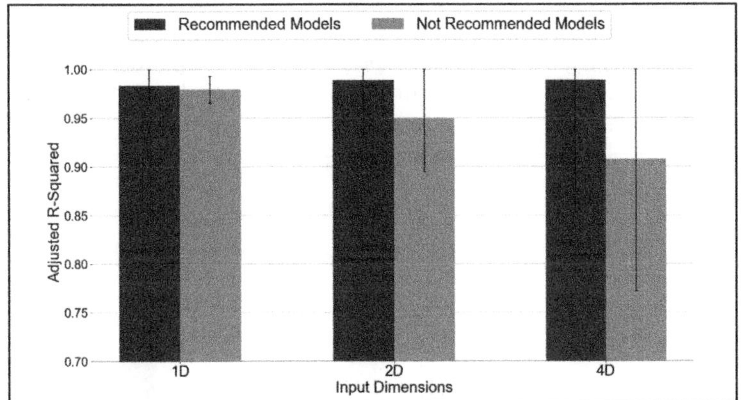

Figure 3 – Average Adjusted R^2 values for Griewank Function. Error bars represent +/- one standard deviation.

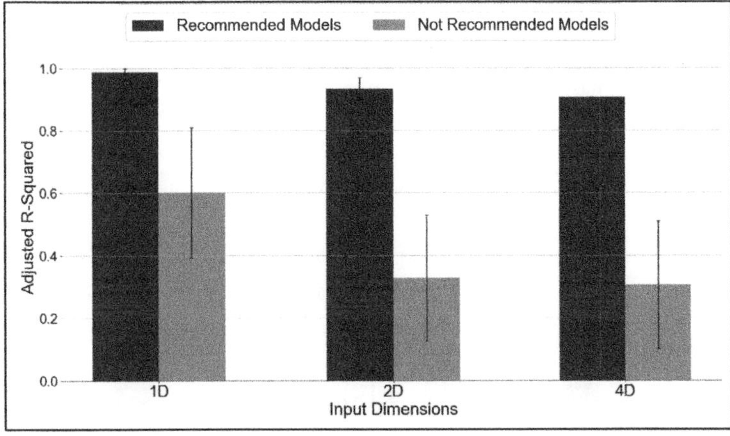

Figure 4 – Average Adjusted R^2 values for Rastrigin Function. Error bars represent +/- one standard deviation.

4.2. Surrogate modeling of stochastic simulations using PARIN

We selected GPR and MARS techniques (both recommended by PRESTO, bold in Table 1) for training surrogate models for deterministic Griewank and Rastrigin functions at each input dimension. The deterministic functions are obtained by including the uncertain parameter as an additional input for each function. We also trained SK models for the test functions. The mean and standard deviation of the test points are estimated using the GPR and MARS surrogate models with Halton-sampling-based uncertainty propagation (Section 3) and the SK models (Section 3.1). Then, the nRMSEs of the mean and standard deviation are calculated via Eq. (6). The results are summarized in Figures 5 and 6.

Figure 5 includes bar plots of the nRMSE obtained using the new framework and SK models for estimating the mean of the two test function outputs. For the Grienwank function, the nRMSE obtained by the new framework for estimating the mean is lower than the nRMSE obtained by SK models for all dimensions (Figure 5). However, the nRMSE yielded for the mean estimates by the SK models for one and two inputs are lower than the nRMSE yielded by the new framework for the Rastrigin function though the difference is relatively small (Figure 5). As shown in Figure 5, the trend is reversed for the Rastrigin function with four inputs with the new framework yielding a significantly lower nRMSE value for estimating the mean of the output.

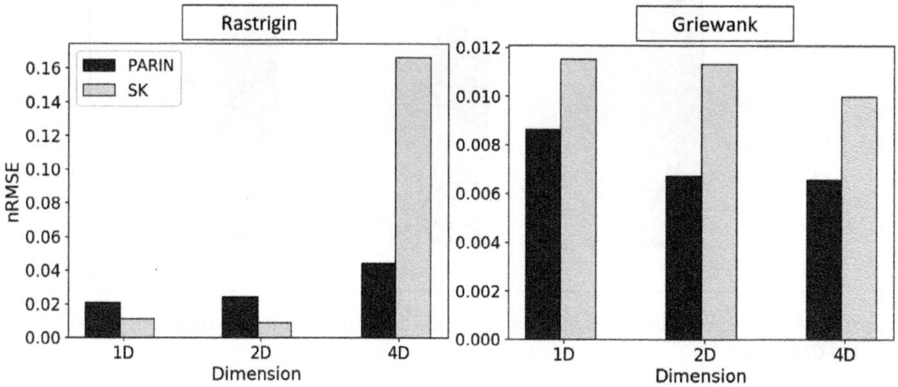

Figure 5 - Bar plots of nRMSE for predicting mean of the two test function outputs using the new framework and stochastic kriging (SK)

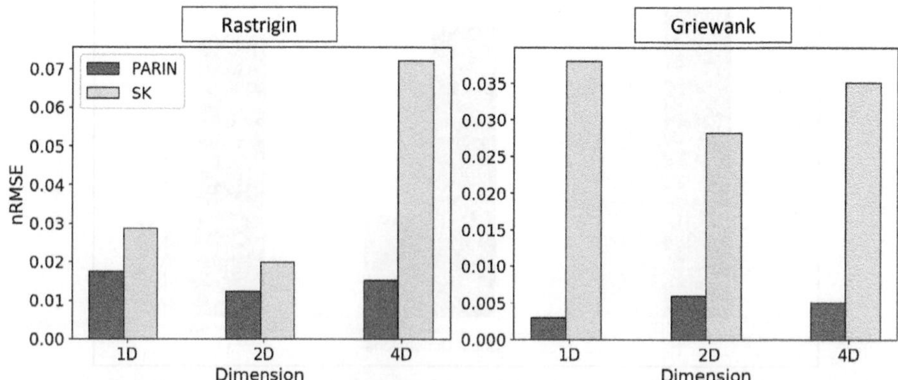

Figure 6 - Bar plots of nRMSE for predicting standard deviation of the two test function outputs using the new framework and stochastic kriging (SK)

Figure 6 presents similarly-formatted bar plots of the nRMSE for estimating the standard deviation of the test function outputs. As shown in Figure 6, for both functions and input dimensions, the nRMSEs of the standard deviation estimates obtained by the new method are lower than those obtained by the SK models. Figure 6 reveals that the difference is larger for the Grienwank function and at higher dimensions for both functions.

Overall, these results suggest that the new framework generates closer mean and standard deviation estimates of the output to the true values (i.e., the stochastic simulation outputs) compared to the same obtained by SK. Furthermore, it is better than SK in capturing the uncertainty of the output due to parameter uncertainty.

5. Conclusions

High-fidelity simulations are complicated and expensive to run. Surrogate models are used to represent these simulations with cheaper to evaluate functions. However, most of the existing surrogate modeling techniques cannot model the stochastic simulation outputs with high accuracy, and the current methods do not capture the uncertainty of the output. This study introduces a new framework to build surrogate models of stochastic simulations where the source of stochasticity is the uncertain model parameters. The framework converts the stochastic simulation to a deterministic one by incorporating uncertain parameters as model inputs (PARIN - PARameter as INput-variable) and uses PRESTO, Predictive REcommendations of Surrogate models To Optimize, to select the best modeling technique for training surrogate models. Comparing the new framework to stochastic kriging, the most popular method to train surrogate models for stochastic simulations, revealed that the framework yielded output mean and standard deviation estimates closer to the true values than those obtained by SK.

References

Al, R., Behera, C.R., Gernaey, K.V., and Sin, G. (2020). Stochastic simulation-based superstructure optimization framework for process synthesis and design under uncertainty. Computers & Chemical Engineering 143. doi: ARTN 10711810.1016/j.compchemeng.2020.107118.

Ankenman, B., Nelson, B.L., Staum, J., 2008. Stochastic kriging for simulation metamodeling. Proc. - Winter Simul. Conf. 362–370. https://doi.org/10.1109/WSC.2008.4736089

Breiman, L. (2001). Random forests. Machine Learning 45(1), 5-32. doi: Doi 10.1023/A:1010933404324.

Burnak, B., Diangelakis, N.A., Katz, J., and Pistikopoulos, E.N. (2019). Integrated process design, scheduling, and control using multiparametric programming. Computers & Chemical Engineering 125, 164-184. doi: 10.1016/j.compchemeng.2019.03.004.

Cui, C., Hu, M.Q., Weir, J.D., and Wu, T. (2016). A recommendation system for meta-modeling: A meta-learning based approach. Expert Systems with Applications 46, 33-44. doi: 10.1016/j.eswa.2015.10.021.

Friedman, J.H. (1991). Multivariate Adaptive Regression Splines - Rejoinder. Annals of Statistics 19(1), 123-141. doi: DOI 10.1214/aos/1176347973.

Garud, S.S., Karimi, I.A., and Kraft, M. (2018). LEAPS2: Learning based Evolutionary Assistive Paradigm for Surrogate Selection. Computers & Chemical Engineering 119, 352-370. doi: 10.1016/j.compchemeng.2018.09.008.

Halton, J.H., 1960. On the efficiency of certain quasi-random sequences of points in evaluating multi-dimensional integrals. Numer. Math. 2, 84–90. https://doi.org/10.1007/BF01386213

Haykin, S. (2009). Neural Networks and Learning Machines. Upper Saddle River, New Jersey: Pearson Education, Inc.

Huang, G.B., Zhu, Q.Y., and Siew, C.K. (2006). Extreme learning machine: Theory and applications. Neurocomputing 70(1-3), 489-501. doi: 10.1016/j.neucom.2005.12.126.

Hüllen, G., Zhai, J., Kim, S.H., Sinha, A., Realff, M.J., Boukouvala, F., 2019. Managing Uncertainty in Data-Driven Simulation-Based Optimization. Comput. Chem. Eng. 106519. https://doi.org/10.1016/j.compchemeng.2019.106519

Jia, L.Y., Alizadeh, R., Hao, J., Wang, G.X., Allen, J.K., and Mistree, F. (2020). A rule-based method for automated surrogate model selection. Advanced Engineering Informatics 45. doi: ARTN 10112310.1016/j.aei.2020.101123.

Jiang, P., Zhou, Q., and Shao, X. (2020). Surrogate Model-Based Engineering Design and Optimization. Surrogate Model-Based Engineering Design and Optimization, 1-240. doi: 10.1007/978-981-15-0731-1.

Marvi-Mashhadi, M., Lopes, C.S., and LLorca, J. (2020). High fidelity simulation of the mechanical behavior of closed-cell polyurethane foams. Journal of the Mechanics and Physics of Solids 135. doi: ARTN 10381410.1016/j.jmps.2019.103814.

Mohammadi, S., Cremaschi, S., 2019. Efficiency of Uncertainty Propagation Methods for Estimating Output Moments, in: Muñoz, S.G., Laird, C.D., Realff, M.J. (Eds.), Proceedings of the 9th International Conference on Foundations of Computer-Aided Process Design, Computer Aided Chemical Engineering. Elsevier, pp. 487–492. https://doi.org/https://doi.org/10.1016/B978-0-12-818597-1.50078-3

Rasmussen, C.E., and Nickisch, H. (2010). Gaussian Processes for Machine Learning (GPML) Toolbox. Journal of Machine Learning Research 11, 3011-3015.

Smola, A.J., and Scholkopf, B. (2004). A tutorial on support vector regression. Statistics and Computing 14(3), 199-222. doi: Doi 10.1023/B:Stco.0000035301.49549.88.

Sobol', I.M., 1967. On the distribution of points in a cube and the approximate evaluation of integrals. Zhurnal Vychislitel'noi Mat. i Mat. Fiz. 7, 784–802.

Staum, J., 2009. Better Simulation Metamodeling: The why, what, and how of Stochastic Kriging 119–133.

Surjanovic, S., and Bingham, D. (2013). Virtual Library of Simulation Experiments [Online]. Simon Fraser University. Available: http://www.sfu.ca/~ssurjano. [Accessed 2018].

Wang, L.N., Chen, X.Y., Kang, S.K., Deng, X.W., and Jin, R. (2020). Meta-modeling of high-fidelity FEA simulation for efficient product and process design in additive manufacturing. Additive Manufacturing 35. doi: ARTN 10121110.1016/j.addma.2020.101211.

Williams, B., and Cremaschi, S. (2021). Selection of surrogate modeling techniques for surface approximation and surrogate-based optimization. Chemical Engineering Research & Design 170, 76-89. doi: 10.1016/j.cherd.2021.03.028.

Williams, B., Otashu, J., Leyland, S., Eden, M., and Cremaschi, S. (2021). PRESTO: Predictive REcommendation of Surrogate models To approximate and Optimize. Chemical Engineering Science. doi: https://doi.org/10.1016/j.ces.2021.117360.

Wong, T.T., 2015. Performance evaluation of classification algorithms by k-fold and leave-one-out cross validation. Pattern Recognit. 48, 2839–2846 https://doi.org/10.1016/j.patcog.2015.03.009

Proceedings of the 14th International Symposium on Process Systems Engineering – PSE 2021+
June 19-23, 2022, Kyoto, Japan
http://dx.doi.org/10.1016/B978-0-323-85159-6.50006-3

Application of PSE into social changes: biomass-based production, recycling systems, and regional systems design and assessment

Yasunori Kikuchi[a,b,c*]

[a] *Institute for Future Initiatives, The University of Tokyo, Tokyo 113-8654, Japan*
[b] *Presidential Endowed Chair for "Platinum Society", The University of Tokyo, Tokyo 113-8656, Japan*
[c] *Department of Chemical System Engineering, The University of Tokyo, Tokyo 113-8656, Japan*
ykikuchi@ifi.u-tokyo.ac.jp

Abstract

Towards the goal of zero fossil-based greenhouse gas emissions, a trend is growing to change the raw materials for energy and materials to those derived from renewable sources. When considering the introduction of any technology, the basics of PSE, i.e., mathematical modelling and simulation of changes to understand the impact on mass and heat balances, are essential for appropriate technology and system assessments including life cycle assessment (LCA). In this study, the role of PSE is discussed through case studies in the assessment of several technologies and systems under consideration, such as cellulose nanofibers reinforced plastics (CNFRP), recycling of lithium-ion batteries (LIB), and regional material and energy systems design in Tanegashima. Although the technology options for those issues are under development, the performances of systems applying them are necessitated for current decision making. The data for LCA, however, is not sufficiently collected due to their low technology readiness levels. Prospective LCA for such emerging technologies is employed in the filling of data gaps and interpretation of assessment results with uncertainties. PSE can be applied into such assessments and have an important role of design of systems.

Keywords: life cycle assessment, technology readiness level, sociotechnical analysis, socioeconomical analysis, technoeconomic analysis.

1. Introduction

Towards the goal of zero fossil-based greenhouse gas emissions, a trend is growing to change the raw materials for energy and materials to those derived from renewable sources. When considering the introduction of any technology, the basics of PSE, i.e., mathematical modelling and simulation of changes to understand the impact on mass and heat balances, are essential for appropriate technology and system assessments including life cycle assessment (LCA).

In this study, the role of PSE is discussed through case studies in the assessment of several technologies and systems under consideration, such as cellulose nanofibers reinforced plastics (CNFRP), recycling of lithium-ion batteries (LIB), and regional material and energy systems design in Tanegashima. The related previous literatures are briefly reviewed. The applicability of PSE basics is discussed considering the requirements for the technology and systems design and assessments towards social changes. Although the technology options for those issues are under development, the performances of systems applying them are necessitated for current decision making. The data for LCA, however, is not sufficiently collected due to their low technology readiness levels (TRLs).

2. Reviews on application of PSE

2.1. CNFRP production from lignocellulosic biomass (Kanematsu et al., 2021)

Cellulose nanofibers (CNF) can be produced from plant-derived renewable resources and have advantage of mechanical properties in lightness and strength when it was applied as the filler of the composites. Acetylated cellulose nanofiber-reinforced plastics (AcCNF-RP) have been developed as substitutes for conventional structural materials (Eichhorn et al., 2010). CAPE tools enabled simulation-based life cycle inventory analysis to reveal the environmental and economic performance of AcCNF-RP considering the future scale-up of production processes. CAPE tools have huge potentials for systems design and assessment adopting emerging technologies, which are necessitated towards carbon neutral society. Especially in chemical production, biomass-derived production can become one of the production routes with sustainable feedstocks. Not only conversion routes, but also the acquisitions of feedstocks from agriculture or forestry are now under development and construction. Before their huge installation, CAPE tools should be combined with prospective LCA to visualize the performances of such low TRL emerging technologies.

2.2. LiB recycling systems (Kikuchi et al., 2021)

When designing the target recycling systems, best mixture of physical segregation and chemical treatment should be pursued considering the specific characteristics of respective components. The recycling of cathode particles and aluminum (Al) foil from positive electrode sheet (PE sheet) dismantled from spent LiBs was experimentally demonstrated by applying a high-voltage pulsed discharge (Tokoro et al., 2021). This separation of LIB components by pulsed discharge was examined by means of prospective LCA (Kikuchi et al., 2021). The indicators selected were life cycle greenhouse gas (LC-GHG) emissions and life cycle resource consumption potential (LC-RCP). CAPE tools can become methods applicable for acquiring data for prospective assessments. Prospective LCA should be applied into the technology assessment that employs modelling tools which focus on potential environmental impacts arising from various technologies even still at the R&D stage, i.e., low technology readiness level. With CAPE tools, the inventory data for prospective LCA can be connected with the design methods for optimizing the throughputs of unit operations, analyzing the upscaled process systems, and conducting the quantification of environmental loads with plausible process systems design.

2.3. Regional systems design in Tanegashima (Kikuchi et al., 2020)

Well-coordinated, multifaceted actions, including a shift from imported fossil to locally available renewable resources and empowering of rural areas are vital in tackling the social challenges such as resource security, sustainable food production, and forest management. Co-learning approach to practice the multifaceted actions with a case study on Tanegashima, an isolated Japanese island, was applied to move the society towards sustainability. In these actions, thorough understandings in the feasible technologies, the locally available resources and the socioeconomic aspects of the local community should be shared among the stakeholders to acquire the momentum for a change. In addition to the technoeconomic analysis, several other analyses were conducted to reveal the concerns of respective stakeholders, share the understandings on the possibilities of technology options, and their socioeconomic implications on local sustainability. Tools such as the life-cycle assessment, input–output analysis, and choice experiments based on questionnaire surveys on the residents' preferences are used for the analyses. The stakeholders were provided with the results. These opportunities gradually converted the concerns of the local stakeholders on their future regional energy systems into expectations and yielded constructive alternatives in technology implementation that can use the locally available resources. PSE basics were employed in the simulation and visualization of the possible future visions achieved by feasible technologies and available resources.

3. Application of PSE into social changes

3.1. Arguments for social changes

3.1.1. Design and assessment considering TRL

Novel technologies, including processes, systems, and ways of thinking, are expected to play a critical role in transforming regional societies to become revitalized and sustainable. However, technology development has the "valley of death" in the transfer to society, as is often seen for various energy technologies (e.g., Weyant 2011). Although many types of subsidies are designed to bridge the valley by accelerating technology development based on the TRL (e.g., Debois et al. 2015), the public may perceive that an insufficiently mature technology, or the new installation of existing technology even if it has previous implementation examples in other regions, could have unpredicted consequences associated with its implementation in their regional societies, resulting in the creation of a difficult obstacle to overcome for innovative change in social systems (Weyant 2011).

MOE-TRL Phases	RISTEX-phase	Phases of implementation into society		
8. Industrialization/ Deployment	Effect deployment	Reuse for other purpose	M	Death valley 2
		Reuse for other sites	L	
		Building networks	K	
		Implementation analysis	J	
7. Field test (Implementation)	Implementation	Specification of owners	I	Death valley 1
	Social experiment	Fund raising for implementation	H	
6. Field test		Field demonstration test	G	
5. Practical use	Test	Demonstration test of T&S	F	
4. Practical use demonstration	Test demonstration	Systematic analysis on T&S	E	
3. Applied research (Experiment)	Specification of concept, model, and technology	Development of T&S	D	
2. Applied research (Report, analysis)		Requirement definition on technology and systems (T&S)	C	
1. Fundamental study		Procure required elements	B	
	Preparation	Structuring rationales of problems	A	

Ministry of Environment, Japan: Technology Readiness Level

Kaya, Okuwada, Shakai Gijutsu Ronbunshu, 12, (2015) 12-22

Death valley 1: Owners of business
Death valley 2: Reuse for other purpose

Figure 1 Phases of social implementation considering the TRLs adopted in government subsidized projects towards decarbonization in Japan (Ministry of Environment Japan, 2014) and surveyed on the projects funded by RISTEX (Research Institute of Science and Technology for Society, Japan Science and Technology Agency) (Kaya and Okuwada, 2015).

Figure 1 shows the phases of social implementation considering various types of TRLs. Especially in energy-related technologies that mitigate fossil resource consumption, decentralized and multiple-generation technologies are often seen as promising, but the barriers in progressing to demonstration tests are often too high, hindering the implementation of such technologies. Although technology road-mapping has become a method to address such obstacles by making the effects of technology implementation qualitatively or quantitatively transparent, technology road-mapping has limited roles in practical technology implementation. Appropriate technology and systems design and assessments could support the progressing phases of social implementation.

3.1.2. Prospective LCA for emerging technology

Conventional LCA does not take into account changes in technology level, because it refers to information on the current technology level and specifically estimates the environmental impacts of each process related to the provision of products and services. The significance of conducting a strategic LCA of emerging technologies for the 30-year time horizon up to the target year of 2050 arose regarding the issues on the climate change. Emerging technologies, as defined by Rotolo et al. (2015), are characterized as "innovative", "rapid growth", "consistent", "significant impact" and "uncertain", which makes technology assessment difficult due to lack of existing data and knowledge. Four main issues were identified as needing to be addressed in conducting prospective LCAs of emerging technologies (Thonemann et al., 2020; Moni et al., 2020). (1) comparability of technologies; (2) availability and quality of data; (3) scale-up challenges; and (4) uncertainty of assessment results. Process modeling and simulation are effective in estimating the missing process inventories in industrial scale production, because these technologies are under development in lab or pilot scale.

3.1.3. Technoeconomic, socioeconomic, and sociotechnical analyses

Elements of technology assessment that have been proposed for implementation include the shift in social systems such as the relationships between the socio-, econo-, and techno- spheres through transformation in aviation systems (Kikuchi et al., 2020b). Economic aspects of technology implementation have been examined in technoeconomic (TE) analyses to clarify the relationships between the characteristics of technologies and various economic indicators, such as direct and indirect costs, fixed capital investment, and product price. Socioeconomic (SE) analysis has also become an essential method for analyzing the impacts of technology implementation on SE systems. The benefits should be analyzed within a sociotechnical (ST) approach to ensure that society benefits from the technology implementation.

3.1.4. Social changes with process systems design and assessments

Geels and Schot (2007) argue that transitions occur through interactions among niche innovations, sociotechnical regimes, and the sociotechnical landscape. The seeds of niche innovations were generated by university researchers, e.g., AcCNF-RP for structural materials, a high-voltage pulsed discharge as physical separation methods for products, and energy systems applying regionally available renewables. The windows of opportunity for such seeds of niche innovation are created by the destabilization of regimes such as the policy/regulation, market, infrastructure, industrial network and ecosystem as the specific conditions for technologies and systems. The landscape, such as the public movements towards carbon neutral society, may have placed pressure on the regimes. To grow the seeds of niche innovation, niche actors should be involved and motivated by technology assessments by university researchers, triggering adjustments in existing systems (Geels et al. 2017).

The social embeddedness of emerging technology options should be addressed through the holistic application of scientific technology assessments into co-learning. The main questions are whether systematic technology assessments could contribute to the bridging of the valley of death between research development and actual implementation, how the settings of assessment, i.e., boundary, indicators, and raw data, could be defined through co-learning for mitigating concerns of stakeholders, and how the assessment results could become informative for the stakeholders to understand the necessity of the implementation of the technology options. The TRLs of potential technologies may be lab-scale demonstration, where the process inventory data required for LCA was not sufficiently obtained from the experimental demonstration considering their upscaling. For such technology, modeling and simulation can be employed to fill the gap of foreground data (Tsoy et al., 2020), which can take into account the future potential of the technology and aim to predict the environmental impacts on the technology under development (Arvidsson et al., 2018; Moni et al., 2020; Thonemann et al., 2020).

4. Conclusions

Prospective assessments for novel technology options are employed in the filling of data gaps and interpretation of assessment results with uncertainties. PSE can be applied into such assessments and have an important role of design of systems. The basics of PSE, i.e., mathematical modelling and simulation of changes to understand the impact on mass and heat balances, are essential for appropriate technology and system assessments. The obtained information applying PSE can become the essential information for the social changes which involve various stakeholders. The elaborated interpretation for those who are not experts in PSE is needed to accurately convey the quantitative and qualitative essences clarified by PSE.

Acknowledgement

This work was supported by MEXT/JSPS KAKENHI Grant Number JP21H03660, JST-Mirai Program Grant Number JPMJMI19C7, and JST COI-NEXT JPMJPF2003. Activities of the Presidential Endowed Chair for "Platinum Society" at the University of Tokyo are supported by the KAITEKI Institute Incorporated, Mitsui Fudosan Corporation, Shin-Etsu Chemical Co., ORIX Corporation, Sekisui House, Ltd., the East Japan Railway Company, and Toyota Tsusho Corporation.

References

R. Arvidsson, A.M. Tillman, B.A. Sandén, M. Janssen, A. Nordelöf, D. Kushnir, S. Molander. 2018, Environmental assessment of emerging technologies: recommendations for prospective LCA. J Ind Ecol, 22(6), 1286-1294.

S. Debois, T. Hildebrandt, M. Marquard, T. Slaats, 2015. Bridging the valley of death: a success story on Danish funding schemes paving a path from technology readiness level 1 to 9. Software Engineering Research and Industrial Practice (SER&IP), 2015 IEEE/ACM 2nd International Workshop 54–57.

S.J. Eichhorn, A. Dufresne, M. Aranguren, N.E. Marcovich, J.R. Capadona, S.J. Rowan, C. Weder, W. Thielemans, M. Roman, S. Renneckar, W. Gindl, S. Veigel, J. Keckes, H. Yano, K. Abe, M. Nogi, A.N.. Nakagaito, A. Mangalam, J. Simonsen, A.S. Benight, A. Bismarck, L.A.. Berglund, T. Peijs. 2010. Review: Current International Research into Cellulose Nanofibres and Nanocomposites. J. Mater. Sci., 45, 1–33.

F.W. Geels, J. Schot, 2007. Typology of sociotechnical transition pathways. Res. Policy, 36, 399–417.

F.W. Geels, B.K. Sovacool, S. Sorrell, 2017. Sociotechnical transitions for deep decarbonization. Science, 357, 1242–1244.

Y. Kanematsu, Y. Kikuchi, H. Yano. 2021. Life Cycle Greenhouse Gas Emissions of Acetylated Cellulose Nanofiber-reinforced Polylactic Acid Based on Scale-up from Lab-scale Experiments, ACS Sustainable Chem. Eng., 9(31), 10444-10452

A. Kaya, K. Okuwada, 2015. Investigating the courses of implementation by describing resarch perfomance, Shakai Gijutsu Ronbunshu, 12, 12-22.

Y. Kikuchi, M. Nakai, Y. Kanematsu, K. Oosawa, T. Okubo, Y. Oshita, Y. Fukushima, 2020a. Application of technology assessments into co-learning for regional transformation: A case study of biomass energy systems in Tanegashima, Sustain. Sci., 15, 1473-1494.

Y. Kikuchi, A. Heiho, Y. Dou, I. Suwa, I.C. Chen, Y. Fukushima, C. Tokoto, 2020b. Defining Requirements on Technology Systems Assessment from Life Cycle Perspectives: Cases on Recycling of Photovoltaic and Secondary Battery, Int. J. Autom. Technol., 14(6), 890-908.

Y. Kikuchi, I. Suwa, A. Heiho, Y. Dou, S. Lim, T. Namihira, K. Mochidzuki, T. Koita, C. Tokoro, 2021, Separation of cathode particles and aluminum current foil in lithium-ion battery by high-voltage pulsed discharge Part II: Prospective life cycle assessment based on experimental data, Waste Manage., 132, 86-95.

Ministry of Environment Japan, 2014. User manual of TRL setting tool, https://www.env.go.jp/earth/ondanka/biz_local/26_01/trl_manual.pdf

S.M. Moni, R. Mahmud, K. High, M. Carbajales-Dale. 2020. Life cycle assessment of emerging technologies: A review. J Ind Ecol, 24, 52-63.

D. Rotolo, D. Hicks, B.R. Martin. 2015. What is an emerging technology? Res. Policy, 44(10), 1827-1843.

N. Thonemann, A. Schulte, D. Maga. 2020. How to Conduct Prospective Life Cycle Assessment for Emerging Technologies? A Systematic Review and Methodological Guidance. Sustainability, 12(3), 1192.

C. Tokoro, S. Lim, K. Teruya, M. Kondo, K. Mochizuki, T. Namihira, Y. Kikuchi, 2021, Separation of cathode particles and aluminum current foil in Lithium-ion battery by high-voltage pulsed discharge part I: Experimental investigation, Waste Management, 125, 58-66.

N. Tsoy, B. Steubing, C. van der Giesen, J. Guinée. 2020. Upscaling methods used in ex ante life cycle assessment of emerging technologies: a review. Int. J. Life Cycle Assess. 25, 1680-1692.

J.P. Weyant, 2011. Accelerating the development and diffusion of new energy technologies: beyond the "valley of death". Energ. Econ. 33, 674-682.

Proceedings of the 14th International Symposium on Process Systems Engineering – PSE 2021+
June 19-23, 2022, Kyoto, Japan
http://dx.doi.org/10.1016/B978-0-323-85159-6.50007-5

Q-MPC: Integration of Reinforcement Learning and Model Predictive Control for Safe Learning

Tae Hoon Oh[a], Jong Min Lee[a*]

[a]School of Chemical and Biological Engineering, Institute of Chemical Processes, Seoul National University, Seoul, 08826, Republic of Korea
jongmin@snu.ac.kr

Abstract

Model-free reinforcement learning (RL) learns an optimal control policy by using the process data only. However, simple application of model-free RL to a practical process has a high risk of failure because the available amount of data and the number of trial runs are limited. Moreover, it is likely that state constraints are violated during the learning period. In this work, we propose Q-MPC framework, an integrated algorithm of RL and model predictive control (MPC) for safe learning. The Q-MPC learns the action-value function in an off-policy fashion and solves a model-based optimal control problem where the trained action-value function is assigned as the terminal cost. Because the Q-MPC utilizes a model, the state constraints can be respected during the learning period. For simulation study, Q-MPC, MPC, and double deep Q-network (DDQN) were applied with varying prediction horizons. The results show the advantages of Q-MPC that outperforms MPC by reducing the model-plant mismatch and shows much fewer constraint violations than DDQN.

Keywords: Reinforcement Learning; Model Predictive Control; Optimal Control; Safe Learning

1. Introduction

As the digitalization of manufacturing processes progresses, an unprecedented amount of operational data are measured and stored. Accordingly, there is a growing interest in developing data-based methods that can improve the existing process performance. Model-free reinforcement learning (RL) is a data-based optimal control method that aims to learn an optimal control policy in the absence of a process model. Model-free RL can be applied to any discrete-time system as long as the system has the Markov property. Therefore, optimal control policies for a wide range of complex systems characterized by nonlinearity, discrete events, and stochasticity can be obtained if one can secure a sufficient amount of data. In addition, the online computation of trained control policy is much less than that of the model-based control such as model predictive control (MPC). In line with these advantages, several studies conduct apply model-free RL methods to chemical processes, such as simulated moving bed (Oh et al. 2021), microfluid (Dressler et al. 2018), polymerization (Ma et al. 2019), polishing, and photo-product bioprocesses (Petsagkourakis et al. 2020).

However, using model-free RL to obtain an optimal control policy of the manufacturing process may pose several practical challenges. First, the amount of data required to learn an optimal control policy may not be practical to obtain even for a digitalized process. Also, the data should be generated with a certain degree of explorations that may do harm to the process performance. Finally, the model-free RL does not have any model for the state transition, which cannot guarantee the satisfaction of state constraints. More specifically, model-free RL cannot explicitly ensure the state constraints, but it can consider the constraints implicitly by modifying either the optimality criterion such as adding penalty terms or the exploration procedure with the guidance of a risk metric (Garcia and Fernandez 2015). Therefore, the model-free RL can learn the state constraint only after it experiences the constraint violation. This is a major drawback as the state constraints are typically imposed for safety reasons.

In most cases, a model built on *a priori* knowledge of system dynamics is available. This model may not be precise, but it can provide the information of correlation between the state and input and can be used to ensure the safety constraints with a sufficient margin. Therefore, using data to improve the existing model-based control can be a more practical approach instead of completely ruling out the model like model-free RL. We propose an algorithm that integrates RL and MPC, referred to as Q-MPC. Q-MPC improves the performance of existing MPC by incorporating the advantage of data-based learning of RL. We first formulate a double deep Q-network (DDQN) optimization problem on the continuous action space, which uses gradient-based numerical optimization. This method is an off-policy algorithm where only the critic is approximated by a deep neural network. Then, the actor, originally represented as the optimizer of the trained action-value function, is extended to an open-loop model-based optimal control problem. This model-based optimal control problem predicts the states and costs up to the prediction horizon with a model and assigns the action-value function as a terminal cost. Therefore, the Q-MPC is a generalization method of MPC as the actor implements the control input by solving the optimization problem in a receding horizon fashion. Furthermore, Q-MPC becomes equivalent to DDQN in continuous action space by setting the prediction horizon length to 0. The Q-MPC can explicitly impose the state constraints and explicitly schedule the exploration. In addition, it can improve the control policy with a much less amount of data than the model-free RL methods. For the simulation study, MPC, Q-MPC, and DDQN are applied, where the length of the prediction horizon is scheduled. The simulation results show that Q-MPC outperforms MPC by learning and can guarantee the satisfaction of state constraints even during the learning period. DDQN also outperforms MPC after sufficient learning, but it violates the state constraints much more frequently than Q-MPC during the learning period.

2. Q-model predictive control

Suppose that the dynamic model and constraints are represented as $\dot{x} = f(x, u)$ and $g(x, u) \leq 0$. In addition, let the path-wise and terminal cost of the system be $L(x, u)$ and $\phi(x, u)$, respectively. Even though the system dynamics is given as continuous time, the control input is assumed to be implemented on the system in a discrete-time manner with zero-order hold. The time interval between control inputs is denoted as Δt and is fixed as a constant value. Let the system be terminated at a finite time step N_T. Then, the total cost is given by

$$J(x_{0:N_T}, u_{0:N_T}) = \phi(x_{N_T}, u_{N_T}) + \sum_{k=0}^{N_T-1} L(x_k, u_k). \tag{1}$$

Suppose that the system is controlled by a control policy $u(\cdot)$. The value function, $V^l_{u(\cdot)}(x)$ associated with this control policy $u(\cdot)$ is defined as

$$V^l_{u(\cdot)}(x_0) = E\left[\phi(x_{N_T}, u(x_{N_T})) + \sum_{k=l}^{N_T-1} L(x_k, u(x_k)) \mid x_l = x_0\right], \tag{2}$$

where the integer $l \in [0, \ldots, N_T]$ denotes the time step. Similarly, the action-value function (Q-function) is defined as

$$Q^l_{u(\cdot)}(x_0, u_0) = E\left[\phi(x_{N_T}, u(x_{N_T})) + \sum_{k=l}^{N_T-1} L(x_k, u(x_k)) \mid x_l = x_0, u_l = u_0\right]. \tag{3}$$

The optimal control policy $u^*(\cdot)$ is defined as a control policy that gives the minimal return, $V^l_{u^*(\cdot)}(x) \leq V^l_{u(\cdot)}(x)$, for all feasible x and l. Suppose that an optimal control policy exists, then the value function with $l = 0$ is equal to the optimal value. In addition, once the optimal action-value function is given, then the optimal control policy can be obtained without the information of system dynamics by

$$u^*(x) \in \underset{u}{\operatorname{argmin}}\, Q^l_{u^*(\cdot)}(x, u). \tag{4}$$

Therefore, learning the action-value function implies learning an optimal control policy, and the Q-learning based RL aims to approximate the optimal action-value function without any knowledge of state dynamics.

The Q-learning based RL is classified as an off-policy algorithm, that is the action-value function can be learned from any data obtained from the system. Therefore, all the data obtained from the system can be stored in a single data set, and learning can proceed with the data randomly sampled from this set (Van Hasselt et al, 2016). This random sampling helps to break the correlations in the measured sequence and smooth over changes in the data distribution. The Bellman equation states that the optimal action-value function satisfies the following recursive equation (Sutton and Barto 2018)

$$Q^l_{u^*(\cdot)}(x_l, u_l) = E\left[L(x_l, u_l) + \min_u Q^{l+1}_{u^*(\cdot)}(x_{l+1}, u)\right]. \tag{5}$$

The Bellman equation (5) breaks the sequence of costs into a single time step by using the principle of optimality. Then, the input choice made from the behaviour policy for the next time step is replaced by the target policy which enables to update the actor in an off-policy fashion.

To prevent the selection of the under-estimated value (over-estimated for maximization) in (5), two function approximators can be used to approximate the action-value function. This algorithm is called Double Deep Q-Network (DDQN). The target deep neural networks is denoted as $Q_{\theta_t}(x, u)$ and the online deep neural networks is denoted as $Q_{\theta_{on}}(x, u)$, respectively. The target network is only utilized to evaluate the minimal value of action-value function in (5) to learn the online network. In this case, the squared error for a single list tuple $D = [x_l, u_l, L(x_l, u_l), x_{l+1}]$ is given as

$$Error(\theta_{on}, \theta_t, D) = E\left[Q_{\theta_{on}}^{l}(x_l, u_l) - L(x_l, u_l) - \min_{u} Q_{\theta_t}^{l+1}(x_{l+1}, u)\right]. \quad (6)$$

Let $B = \{D_1, D_2, \ldots, D_n\}$ be the batch data set which is the set of several data lists randomly sampled from the data set. Then, the online network is updated by applying the one-step gradient descent with the appropriate learning rate α as

$$\theta_{on} \leftarrow \theta_{on} + \alpha \nabla_{\theta_{on}} \frac{1}{|B|} \sum_{D \in B} Error(\theta_{on}, \theta_t, D). \quad (7)$$

The target network can be updated by

$$\theta_t \leftarrow (1 - \tau)\theta_t + \tau\theta_{on}. \quad (8)$$

where $\tau \in [0, 1]$ is the update rate. Then, DDQN selects the control input u_l associated with the state x_l by solving the following simple optimization problem:

$$u_l = \operatorname*{argmin}_{u} Q_{\theta_{on}}^{l}(x_l, u). \quad (9)$$

The input of DDQN is totally determined by the learned action-value function Q_{on}. This implies that the control performance of DDQN can be degraded, and the constraints can be violated with inaccurate action-value function. This is a common but crucial problem for all model-free RL that the constraints can be learned only after they are violated.

Instead of using (4) to calculate control input, the Q-MPC solves the following open-loop optimal control problem:

$$\min_{u} Q_{\theta_{on}}\left(x_{l+N_p}, u_{l+N_p}\right) + \sum_{k=l}^{l+N_p-1} L(x_k, u_k) \quad (10)$$

subject to

x_l is given, $x_{k+1} = f(x_k, u_k)$ and $g(x_k, u_k) \leq 0$

where N_p denotes the prediction horizon and the continuous system is converted into its discrete-time counterpart. If the prediction reaches the terminal time, then the exact terminal cost ϕ is assigned to (10) instead of action-value function. Note that, solving the optimization problem (10) gives the open-loop control trajectory $u_l, \ldots, u_{l+N_p}$ but only u_l is implemented to the system.

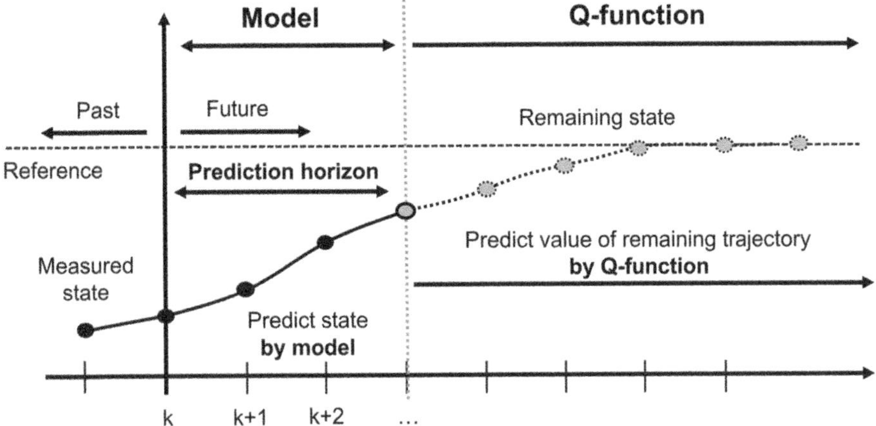

Figure 1: The scheme of Q-MPC.

The scheme of Q-MPC is presented in Figure 1. Compared with nominal MPC, the terminal cost of Q-MPC is replaced by the trained action-value function. Because the action-value function Q learns the value from the data, Q-MPC can adapt the system dynamics. Compared with DDQN, the actor of Q-MPC is also presented as an optimization problem formulated as a mathematical program such as the quadratic program (10). However, the model is used to predict the state transition and associated cost for N_p time step. The use of the model helps to satisfy the constraints and dramatically reduces the required amount of data to improve the control policy. The receding horizon control makes it easy to satisfy the constraints even with a short prediction horizon.

The prediction horizon of Q-MPC determines how long model is involved in prediction. For example, if the length of prediction horizon is 0, then the Q-MPC is equivalent to DDQN in the continuous domain. In this case, the model is completely excluded in determining control policy. On the other hand, if the prediction reaches the terminal time, the action-value function is excluded in calculating control inputs, and Q-MPC becomes equivalent to nominal MPC. Therefore, the performance of Q-MPC is directly affected by the length of prediction horizon which is another tuning parameter. We suggest setting the prediction horizon much smaller than the whole batch operation because even for the short prediction horizon length, the input is highly affected by the model. In addition, we suggest setting relatively long prediction horizon at the early stage of learning where the accuracy of action-value function is low.

3. Simulation studies

A simple photo-production system having 3 states ($x_1, x_2, and\ x_3$) and 2 inputs ($u_1\ and\ u_2$) is considered where the system dynamics are given as (Petsagkourakis et al. 2020)

$$\frac{dx_1}{dt} = 1, \tag{11}$$

$$\frac{dx_2}{dt} = -(u_1 + 0.5u_1^2)x_2 + \frac{0.5u_2}{(x_2 + x_3 + 0.1)}, \tag{12}$$

$$\frac{dx_3}{dt} = u_1 x_2 - 0.2u_2 x_2, \tag{13}$$

where the first state denotes the time. The time interval is selected as 0.05 and system is assumed to be terminated at 1. Therefore, the system contains 20 horizons. Note that because the system terminates in finite steps, the time should be included in the state.

The lower and upper bounds for all states are 0 and 1, respectively, and the bounds for inputs are 0 and 5, respectively. In addition, the second state has additional lower bound presented as

$$x_2 \geq 0.45. \tag{14}$$

The path-wise cost and terminal cost is given as

$$L(x, u) = 0.01\left(\frac{u_1}{25}\right)^2, \text{and} \tag{15}$$

$$\phi(x, u) = 3(1 - x_3), \tag{16}$$

and the penalty $\max(0,\ 0.45 - x_2)$ for violating constraint (*) is added to the cost.

The surrogate model that Q-MPC used is given as

$$\frac{dx_1}{dt} = 1, \tag{17}$$

$$\frac{dx_2}{dt} = -(u_1 + 0.55u_1^2)x_2 + \frac{0.5u_2}{(x_2 + x_3 + 0.5)}, \tag{18}$$

$$\frac{dx_3}{dt} = u_1 x_2 - 0.1u_2 x_2. \tag{19}$$

The Q-MPC solves the following optimization problem

$$\min_u V\left(x_{N_p}\right) + \sum_{k=0}^{N_p - 1} L(x_k, u_k)$$

$$\text{subject to} \tag{20}$$

$$\text{(4), (5), (6), and } x_2 \geq 0.45 \text{ for k} = 0, \ldots, N_p.$$

The action-value function is approximated by deep neural networks that is consisted of three layers. The number of nodes for each layer are 16, 4, and 1, respectively. The following smooth activation function is utilized to optimize the deep neural network by IPOPT method

$$A(x) = \log(1 + x^2). \tag{21}$$

The online network was trained for every episode, and the target network was updated for every 5 episodes. The learning and updating rates were selected as 0.02 and 0.01, respectively. The batch size |B| was selected as 64. Each method was applied to the system for 1,000 episodes, but the first 10 episodes were simulated with random control inputs for comparison. The prediction horizon of Q-MPC was set to 20 for episodes 10 to 30, 5 for episodes 30 to 200, and 1 for episodes 500 to 1,000.

The simulation results are presented in Figures 2 and 3. Figure 2 shows the optimal total cost and total cost obtained by Q-MPC, MPC, and DDQN. Because the model in MPC does not change throughout the simulations, the total cost of MPC is kept constant. The Q-MPC cannot outperform MPC with a prediction horizon of 5, as the mismatch between the model and action-value function can worsen the performance. In addition, the total cost increases around 200 episodes because the prediction horizon of Q-MPC is changed from 5 to 3. Then, the total cost gradually decreases to that of MPC by learning. The first episode that Q-MPC outperforms MPC is the 297th episode. DDQN also successfully learns the system dynamics and eventually outperforms MPC, but the first episode that outperforms MPC is the 718th episode. Figure 2 clearly shows that Q-MPC improves the control policy much faster than DDQN. Figure 3 shows the number of constraint violations. Because the number of horizons for a single episode is 20, the maximum possible number of violations is 20. Q-MPC never violates the constraint throughout learning, whereas DDQN violates the constraint even if the learning is nearly finished. Note that the violations in the early stage are made by randomly implemented input and not by Q-MPC. Figure 3 shows the advantages of Q-MPC that it can safely learn the system dynamics and improve the existing control policy.

4. Conclusions

We proposed a novel Q-MPC algorithm to learn the system safely. Q-MPC is a generalization method of both DDQN and MPC, where each method can be recovered by adjusting the length of the prediction horizon. The simulation results showed that Q-MPC could improve the control policy by satisfying the state constraint. In addition, Q-MPC requires much less amount of data to improve the control policy than DDQN.

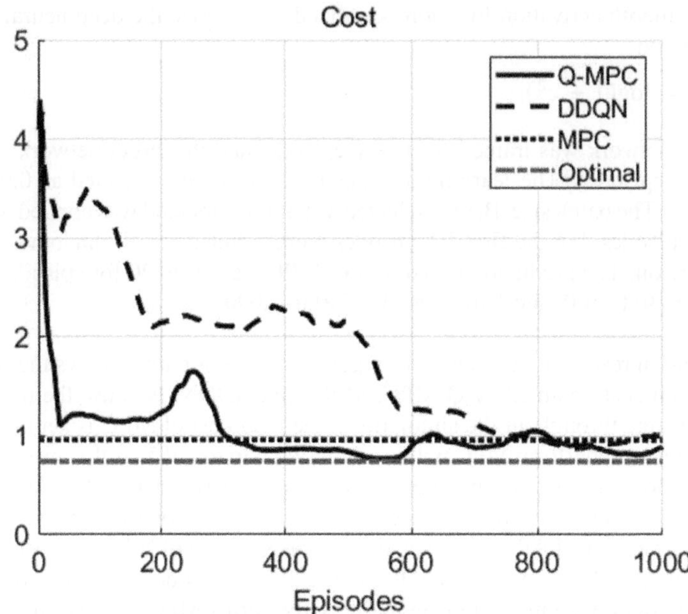

Figure 2: The moving averaged value of total cost with 50 samples.

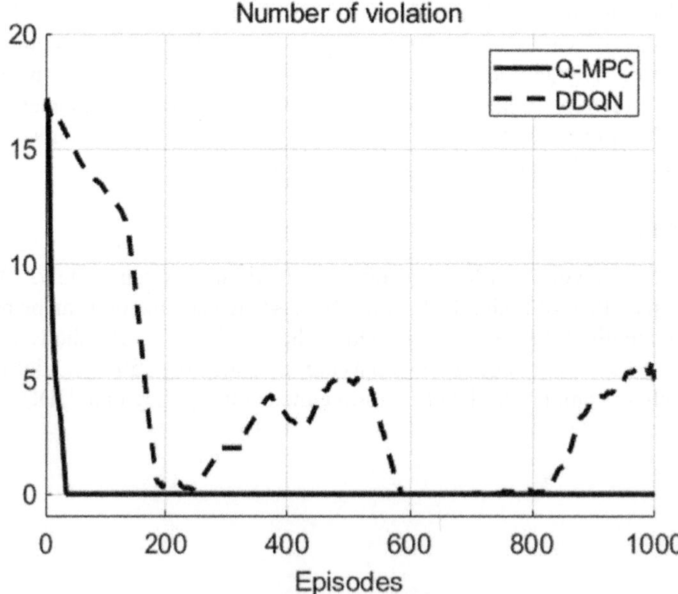

Figure 3: The number of constraint violations.

References

T. H. Oh, J. W. Kim, S. H. Son, H. Kim, K. Lee, and J. M. Lee, 2021, Automatic control of simulated moving bed process with deep Q-network, Journal of Chromatorgraphy A, 1647, 462073.

O. J. Dressler, P. D. Howes, J. Choo, and A. J. deMello, 2018, Reinforcement learning for dynamic microfulidic control, ACS omega, 3, 8, 10084 – 10091.

Y. Ma, W. Zhu, M. G. Michael, and J. Romagnoli, 2019, Continuous control of a polymerization system with deep reinforcement learning, Journal of Process Control, 75, 40 – 47.

P. Petsagkourakis, I. O. Sandoval, E. Bradford, D. Zhang, and E. A. del Rio-Chanona, 2020, Reinforcement learning for batch bioprocess optimization, Computers & Chemical Engineering, 133, 106649.

J. Garcia, and F. Fernandez, 2015, A comprehensive survey on safe reinforcement learning, Journal of Machine Learning Research, 16, 1, 1437 – 1480.

H. Van Hasselt, A. Guez, and D. Silver, 2016, Deep reinforcement learning with double q-learning, Proceedings of the AAAI conference on artificial intelligence, 30, 1.

R. S. Sutton, and A. G. Barto, 2018, Reinforcement learning: An introduction, MIT press.

Proceedings of the 14th International Symposium on Process Systems Engineering – PSE 2021+
June 19-23, 2022, Kyoto, Japan
http://dx.doi.org/10.1016/B978-0-323-85159-6.50008-7

Presentation abstract: Optimization formulations for machine learning surrogates

Francesco Ceccon[a*], Jordan Jalving[b*], Joshua Haddad[b], Alexander Thebelt[a], Calvin Tsay[a], Carl D Laird[c+], Ruth Misener[a+]

[a]*Department of Computing, Imperial College London, 180 Queen's Gate, SW7 2AZ, UK*
[b]*Center for Computing Research, Sandia National Laboratories, Albuquerque, NM 87123, USA*
[c]*Department of Chemical Engineering, Carnegie Mellon University, Pittsburgh, PA 15213, USA*
[*]*Contributed equally,* [+]*Contributed equally*
claird@andrew.cmu.edu, r.misener@imperial.ac.uk

Abstract

In many process systems engineering applications, we seek to integrate surrogate models, e.g. already-trained neural network and gradient-boosted tree models, into larger decision-making problems. This presentation explores different ways to automatically take the machine learning surrogate model and produce an optimization formulation. Our goal is to automate the entire workflow of decision-making with surrogate models from input data to optimization formulation. This presentation discusses our progress towards this goal, gives examples of previous successes, and elicits a conversation with colleagues about the path forward.

Keywords: neural networks, gradient-boosted trees, Pyomo, optimization formulations

1. Main Text

The optimization and machine learning toolkit (https://github.com/cog-imperial/OMLT, OMLT 1.0) is an open source software package enabling optimization over high-level representations of neural networks (NNs) and gradient-boosted trees (GBTs). Optimizing over trained surrogate models allows integration of NNs or GBTs into larger decision-making problems. Computer science applications include maximizing a neural acquisition function (Volpp et al., 2019) or verifying neural networks (Botoeva et al., 2020). Engineering applications of grey-box optimization (Boukouvala et al., 2016) hybridize mechanistic, model-based optimization with surrogate models learned from data. OMLT 1.0 supports GBTs through an ONNX (https://github.com/onnx/onnx) interface and NNs through both ONNX and Keras interfaces. OMLT transforms these pre-trained machine learning models into the algebraic modeling language Pyomo (Bynum et al., 2021) to encode optimization formulations.

OMLT is a general tool incorporating both NNs and GBTs, many input models via ONNX interoperability, both fully-dense and convolutional layers, several activation functions, and various optimization formulations. The literature often presents these different optimization formulations as competitors, e.g. our partition-based formulation competes with the big-M formulation for ReLU NNs (Kronqvist et al., 2021; Tsay et al., 2021). In

OMLT, competing optimization formulations become alternatives: users can switch between the formulations and find the best for a specific application.

References

Elena Botoeva, Panagiotis Kouvaros, Jan Kronqvist, Alessio Lomuscio, and Ruth Misener. Efficient verification of ReLU-based neural networks via dependency analysis. In Proceedings of the AAAI Conference on Artificial Intelligence, volume 34, pages 3291–3299, 2020.

Fani Boukouvala, Ruth Misener, and Christodoulos A. Floudas. Global optimization advances in Mixed-Integer Nonlinear Programming, MINLP, and Constrained Derivative- Free Optimization, CDFO. European Journal of Operational Research, 252(3):701 – 727, 2016.

Michael L Bynum, Gabriel A Hackebeil, William E Hart, Carl D Laird, Bethany L Nicholson, John D Siirola, Jean-Paul Watson, and David L Woodruff. Pyomo—Optimization Modeling in Python, volume 67. Springer Nature, 2021.

Jan Kronqvist, Ruth Misener, and Calvin Tsay. Between steps: Intermediate relaxations between big-M and convex hull formulations. In International Conference on Integration of Constraint Programming, Artificial Intelligence, and Operations Research, pages 299– 314. Springer, 2021.

Artur M Schweidtmann and Alexander Mitsos. Deterministic global optimization with artificial neural networks embedded. Journal of Optimization Theory and Applications, 180(3):925–948, 2019.

Calvin Tsay, Jan Kronqvist, Alexander Thebelt, and Ruth Misener. Partition-based formulations for mixed-integer optimization of trained ReLU neural networks. In Advances in Neural Information Processing Systems, 2021.

Michael Volpp, Lukas P Fröhlich, Kirsten Fischer, Andreas Doerr, Stefan Falkner, Frank Hutter, and Christian Daniel. Meta-learning acquisition functions for transfer learning in Bayesian optimization. In International Conference on Learning Representations, 2019.

Proceedings of the 14th International Symposium on Process Systems Engineering – PSE 2021+
June 19-23, 2022, Kyoto, Japan
http://dx.doi.org/10.1016/B978-0-323-85159-6.50009-9

Pharma PSE: a multiscale approach for reimagining pharmaceutical manufacturing

Hirokazu Sugiyama

Department of Chemical system Engineering, The University of Tokyo, 7-3-1, Hongo, Bunkyo-ku, Tokyo 113-8656, Japan
sugiyama@chemsys.t.u-tokyo.ac.jp

Abstract

Confronted with the global challenges including COVID-19, pharmaceutical manufacturing needs to simultaneously achieve long-term efficiency and short-term resilience. Process systems engineering (PSE) can provide scientific basis here, and in fact, PSE researchers have made significant contributions to pharma in the last decade. The author, after having worked for a global pharmaceutical company, initiated research on pharmaceutical process systems engineering: Pharma PSE. The research tackles different challenges in small molecules, biopharmaceuticals, and regenerative medicine, at the scales of molecules/cells, processes, and the society. This paper first introduces the viewpoint of Pharma PSE, followed by showcasing a research example that involved a range of computer-aided analyses at different scales. The multiscale approach of Pharma PSE can provide a new horizon to "reimagine" pharmaceutical manufacturing processes and beyond, towards establishment of a sustainable healthcare society.

Keywords: Pharmaceuticals, Regenerative medicine, Process modelling, Process design, Sustainable healthcare society.

1. Introduction

The relevance of pharmaceuticals is more apparent than ever before. The Sustainable Development Goals (SDGs; United Nations Development Programme, 2021) defined the achievement of the "access to safe, effective, quality and affordable essential medicines and vaccines for all" as a part of Goal No. 3. Long-term efficiency is critical for manufacturing while the development pipeline of new drugs needs to be enhanced further. Another mandate for manufacturing is to cope with pandemics, especially COVID-19, by dealing with the short-term surges in demand and disruptions in the supply chain. The pharmaceutical industry needs to establish a system where long-term efficiency and short-term resiliency are achieved at the same time.

In the last decade, the community of process systems engineering (PSE) have been introducing and practicing systems approaches in the design, operation, and control of pharmaceutical production processes. The previous studies have covered various topics in the manufacture of active pharmaceutical ingredients (APIs) as well as dosage forms (e.g., tablets and injectables). Continuous manufacturing and process analytical technologies (PATs) have been intensively researched (e.g., Badr and Sugiyama, 2020; Bhalode et al., 2021; Diab et al., 2021, Ghijs et al., 2021; Hong et al., 2021). Furthermore, advanced model-based approaches for quality assurance (e.g., Ochoa et al., 2021) and the subjects related to personalized healthcare (e.g., Içten et al., 2015; Wang et al., 2018; Papathanasiou et al., 2020) have been investigated.

Table 1. Characteristics and research opportunities in the pharmaceutical domain

Small molecules	Biopharmaceuticals	Regenerative medicine
• Large quantity in supply • Most conventional form of medicine (e.g., tables) • Intensive research performed on "flow chemistry" & "continuous manufacturing" • Rigorous modeling needed for the G/L/S interfaces in flow chemistry • Difficulty in modeling heterogeneity in powder processing	• Market rapidly growing • Monoclonal antibodies (mAbs) and vaccines attracting recent attentions • Intensive research performed on host cells, media, manufacturing technologies and equipment, and measurement devices • Challenges in modeling biological behavior (e.g., heterogeneity, dynamics, and impurities)	• Future therapy based on stem cells • Clinical trials intensively performed • Need to establish manufacturing processes as well as supply chain • High cost of R&D and manufacturing raising social attentions • Models required for describing cell behavior, process performance, supply chain, and cost-effectiveness

In a world of ever-increasing demand for advanced pharmaceuticals, there is a need for increasing efficiency, flexibility, and production capacity. At the same time, there are innovations that span all categories of pharmaceutical products. Table 1 shows the characteristics of different product categories, and the associated modeling challenges. Innovations here include the introduction of novel therapeutics, materials, and shifts in production scales especially for personalized medicine. Such innovations create a need and an opportunity to "reimagine" pharmaceutical manufacturing to better accommodate the changes and developments in the industry and in society.

The author, after having worked for a global pharmaceutical company, launched a research group on pharmaceutical process systems engineering: Pharma PSE. The research tackles challenges in small molecules, biopharmaceuticals, and regenerative medicine from a multiscale viewpoint. The research aims to expand PSE into a critical domain in society by incorporating the systems approach into the development of new products and processes. This paper first introduces the multiscale viewpoint of Pharma PSE, followed by a case study on regenerative medicine. This paper serves as the basis for the keynote lecture at PSE2021+ with more materials to be added.

2. Multiscale research viewpoint

Figure 1 describes the multiscale viewpoint of Pharma PSE. At the molecule/cell level, elements of a manufacturing process are investigated such as the choice of host cells, nutrition media, or protective agents are considered. At the process level, alternatives regarding manufacturing technologies, equipment specification, and operation strategy in manufacturing processes are investigated. Higher level assessments are conducted up to the level of the healthcare society.

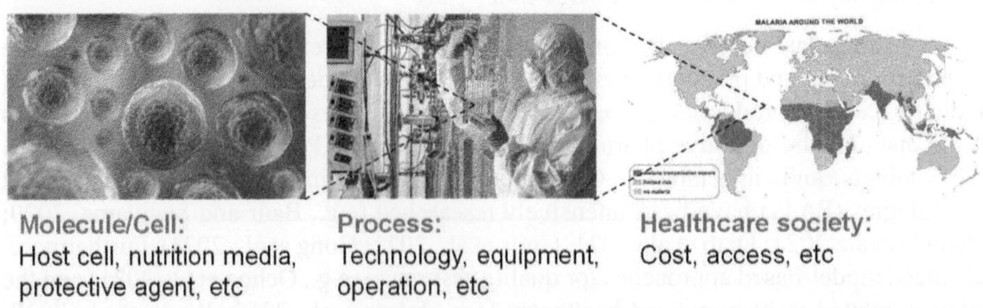

Figure 1 The multiscale viewpoint in Pharma PSE research.

Recognizing the entire system as in Figure 1 would facilitate bottom-up analyses that allow for the comprehensive assessment of impacts of lower-level modifications on higher-level targets. For example, the performance of novel host cells (cell level) could be assessed regarding lead time (process level), and supply agility (society level). Top-down analyses could also be enabled for determining promising alternatives at lower levels given higher levels goals. In conducting Pharma PSE research, such "zoom-in and zoom-out" is supported by the appropriate consideration/use of modeling strategy (first-principle, data-driven, or hybrid), simulation methods, objective function(s), design and operational alternatives, and physical- and cyber-space information.

3. Research example on cryopreservation of hiPS cells

This paper introduces design of cryopreservation processes for hiPS cells as an example.

3.1. Molecule/cell level: computational screening of cryoprotective agents

As a study at the molecule/cell level, this work (Hayashi et al., 2021a) investigated cryoprotective agents (CPAs) that are used in the cryopreservation of cells including hiPS cells. A computational screening was performed for candidate compounds using quantum chemistry and molecular dynamics (MD) simulations. The motivation was to search for an alternative CPA to dimethyl sulfoxide (DMSO), which is currently widely used but is known to be toxic to cells. Figure 2 shows the overview of the work. For forty compounds, the solvation free energy and partition coefficient, and the root mean square deviation (RMSD) of a phospholipid bilayer which composes a cell membrane, were calculated by quantum chemistry simulation and by MD simulation, respectively. These three indicators were used to assess osmoregulatory ability, affinity with a cell membrane, and ability to stretch a cell membrane, respectively. The quantum chemistry simulation revealed that trimethylglycine, formamide, urea, thiourea, diethylene glycol, and dulcitol were better than DMSO, regarding either or both of the indicators considered. Further analysis with the MD simulation suggested formamide, thiourea, and urea as promising candidates within the simulated conditions.

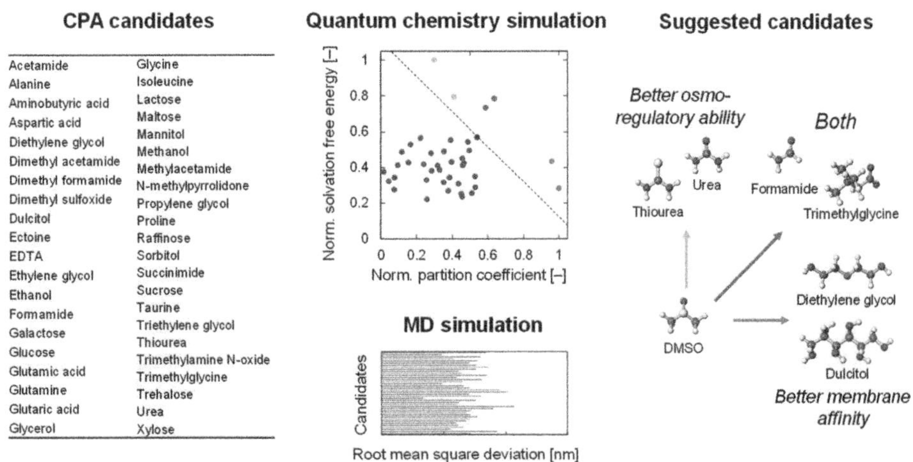

Figure 2 Computational screening of CPA candidates using quantum chemistry and MD simulations (Hayashi et al., 2021a)

3.2. Process level: model-based assessment of temperature profiles in slow freezing

As a study at the process level, this work (Hayashi et al., 2021b) presented a model-based assessment of temperature profiles in slow freezing for hiPS cells. Figure 3 shows the summary. The basis here was our previously developed single-cell model (Hayashi et al., 2020) that consists of heat transfer, mass transfer, and crystallization models. The three models can quantify temperature distribution in a vial, cell volume change through transmembrane water transport, and intracellular ice formation during freezing, respectively. These first-principle models was then extended to cover the cell survival rate through data-driven modeling. Experiments using hiPS cells provided the necessary parameter values of the multivariate regression model. The newly developed hybrid single-cell model can, given a temperature profile of freezing, estimate the cell survival rate and required freezing time as the quality and productivity indicators, respectively. As a case study, the model was used to assess ca. 16,000 temperature profiles. The simulation results suggested that fast-slow-fast (i.e., non-linear) cooling in the dehydration, nucleation-promoting, and further cooling zones, respectively, as a promising profile.

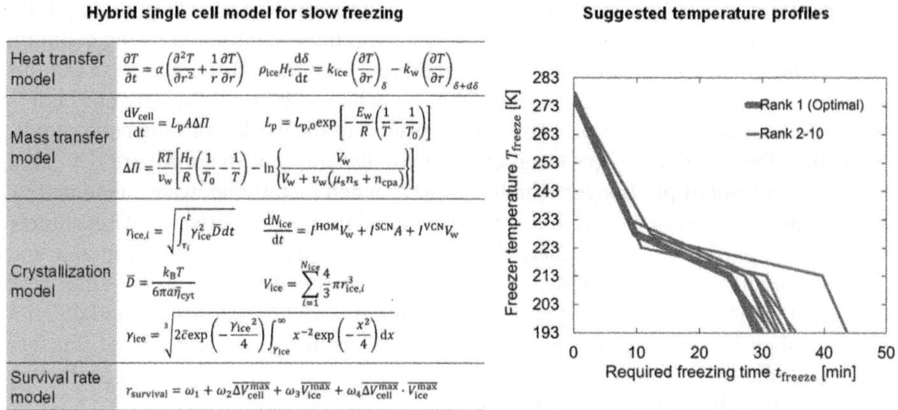

Figure 3 Model-based assessment of freezing temperature profiles (Hayashi et al., 2021b)

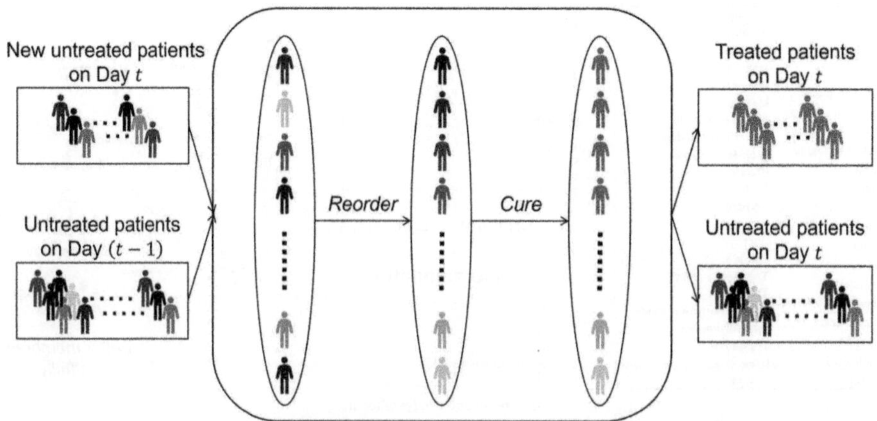

Figure 4 Agent-based model for analyzing cost-effectiveness in the manufacture of allogeneic hiPS cells in Japan (Hayashi et al., 2022)

3.3. Society level: cost-effectiveness analysis in the manufacture of allogeneic hiPS cells in Japan

Finally as a study at the society level, this work (Hayashi et al., 2022) proposed an agent-based model (ABM) for cost-effectiveness analyses in the manufacture of allogeneic hiPS cells in Japan. The ABM (see Figure 4) was set up for estimating the disability-adjusted life years (DALYs) of each patient and the total required cost for manufacturing allogeneic hiPS cells. The DALYs and the total required cost for manufacturing were used as the indicators of effectiveness and cost, respectively. Cryopreservation was considered as a part of the manufacturing processes. The developed ABM can calculate these two indicators, given the disease, the annual number of treated patients, and the treatment mode. The developed model was then applied to analyze therapy for two diseases using allogeneic hiPS cells, which are currently undergoing clinical studies in Japan. A case study suggested that the treatment mode (i.e., treating patients from the youngest to the oldest) would affect the cost-effectiveness significantly.

4. Lessons learnt towards future research

The interconnections between each of the above studies across different scales are visible by taking the multiscale view shown in Figure 1. For example, the choice of CPA can influence the extracellular condition during freezing, which can affect the process duration, and thus the supply performance. Taking a multiscale approach requires the use of flexible modelling strategies, e.g., in this case the use of models spanning quantum chemistry and agent-based modelling with different degrees of detail. The approach also requires taking the position of multiple stakeholders, such as varying the research viewpoint form experimental investigator (for CPA) to process practitioner (for freezing unit), and further to manufacturers and the government (for cell supply). Similar characteristics could be observed in other workpieces in small molecule (e.g., Matsunami et al., 2020) and biopharmaceuticals (e.g., Badr et al., 2021). Recognition of these characteristics can provide new research opportunities such as multiscale scenario analyses and optimization, investigation of appropriate model resolution considering cross-scale interconnections, and multiobjective decision-making. The multiscale approach can provide a richer insight for "reimagining" the manufacturing processes and the associated systems of pharmaceuticals.

5. Conclusions

This paper presented the research viewpoint of Pharma PSE, which aims to cover topics in different drug categories at various scales in one frame. As an example, a study on cryopreservation of hiPS cells was showcased, which involved various simulation-based analyses. The observation indicated that the multiscale approach of Pharma PSE can provide a new horizon to "reimagine" the manufacturing processes and beyond, towards establishment of a sustainable healthcare society.

Acknowledgement

The author would like to thank Mr. Yusuke Hayashi, Dr. Sara Badr and Dr. Isuru Udugama at Sugiyama Lab in The University of Tokyo for the support in preparing the paper, and all lab members of for the hard work and innovation. All research partners and the funding supports (currently: Japan Society for the Promotion of Science (JSPS) [grant No. 21H01699 and 20K21102]; Japan Agency for Medical Research and Development (AMED) [grant No. JP21ae0121015AMED]) are sincerely appreciated.

References

S. Badr, H. Sugiyama, 2020. A PSE perspective for the efficient production of monoclonal antibodies: Integration of process, cell, and product design aspects. Curr. Opin. Chem. Eng. 27, 121–128.

S. Badr, K. Okamura, N. Takahashi, V. Ubbenjans, H. Shirahata, H. Sugiyama. 2021. Integrated design of biopharmaceutical manufacturing processes: Operation modes and process configurations for monoclonal antibody production. Comput. Chem. Eng. 153, 107422.

P. Bhalode, H. Tian, S. Gupta, S. M. Razavi, A. Roman-Ospino, S. Talebian, R. Singh, J.V. Scicolone, F.J. Muzzio, M. Ierapetritou. 2021. Using residence time distribution in pharmaceutical solid dose manufacturing–A critical review. Int. J. Pharm. 610, 121248.

S. Diab, M. Raiyat, D.I. Gerogiorgis, 2021. Flow synthesis kinetics for lomustine, an anti-cancer active pharmaceutical ingredient. React. Chem. Eng. 6, 1819–1828

M. Ghijs, B. Vanbillemont, N. Nicolaï, T. DeBeer, I. Nopens. 2021. Two-dimensional moisture content and size measurement of pharmaceutical granules after fluid bed drying using near-infrared chemical imaging. Int. J. Pharm. 595, 120069

Y. Hayashi, I. Horiguchi, M. Kino-oka, H. Sugiyama, 2020. Slow freezing process design for human induced pluripotent stem cells by modeling intracontainer variation. Comput. Chem. Eng. 132, 106597.

Y. Hayashi, Y. Nakajima, H. Sugiyama, 2021a. Computational screening of cryoprotective agents for regenerative medical products using quantum chemistry and molecular dynamics simulations. Cryobiol. 100, 101–109.

Y. Hayashi, I. Horiguchi, M. Kino-oka, H. Sugiyama, 2021b. Model-based assessment of temperature profiles in slow freezing for human induced pluripotent stem cells. Comput. Chem. Eng. 144, 107150.

Y. Hayashi, K. Oishi, H. Sugiyama, 2021. An agent-based model for cost-effectiveness analysis in the manufacture of allogeneic human induced pluripotent cells in Japan. Comput. Aided Chem. Eng. (Proceedings of PSE2021+), Paper ID 143, in submission.

M.S. Hong, A.E. Lu, R.W. Ou, J.M. Wolfrum, S.L. Springs, A.J. Sinskey, R.D. Braatz, 2021. Model-based control for column-based continuous viral inactivation of biopharmaceuticals. Biotechnol. Bioeng. 118, 3215–3224.

E. Içten, A. Giridhar, L.S. Taylor, Z.K. Nagy, G.V. Reklaitis. 2015. Dropwise additive manufacturing of pharmaceutical products for melt-based dosage forms. J. Pharm. Sci. 104, 1641–1649.

K. Matsunami, T. Nagato, K. Hasegawa, H. Sugiyama. 2020. Determining key parameters of continuous wet granulation for tablet quality and productivity: A case in ethenzamide. Int. J. Pharm. 579, 119160.

M.P. Ochoa, S. García-Muñoz, S. Stamatis, I.E. Grossmann. 2021. Novel flexibility index formulations for the selection of the operating range within a design space. Comput. Chem. Eng. 149, 107284.

M.M. Papathanasiou, Ch. Stamatis, M. Lakelin, S. Farid, N. Titchener-Hooker, N. Shah. 2020. Autologous CAR T-cell therapies supply chain: challenges and opportunities? Cancer Gene Ther. 27, 799–809.

United Nations Development Programme (UNDP), Sustainable Development Goals, https://www.undp.org/sustainable-development-goals#good-health (accessed January 04, 2022)

X. Wang, Q. Kong, M.M. Papathanasiou, N. Shah, 2018. Precision healthcare supply chain design through multi-objective stochastic programming. Comput. Aided Chem. Eng. 44, 2137–2142.

Proceedings of the 14th International Symposium on Process Systems Engineering – PSE 2021+
June 19-23, 2022, Kyoto, Japan
http://dx.doi.org/10.1016/B978-0-323-85159-6.50010-5

Artificial Intelligence and Process Systems Engineering

Raghunthan Rengaswamy[a,b*]

[a]*Department of Chemical Engineering, Indian Institute of Technology, Madras*
[b]*Robert Bosch Center for Data Science and AI*
raghur@iitm.ac.in

Abstract

Process systems engineering is a thriving field within chemical engineering. PSE deals with several design and operational tasks that allow process systems to work efficiently and safely. There is a large intersection between PSE tools and Artificial Intelligence (AI) algorithms, recognized for decades now. With unprecedented availability of various forms of data and significant improvement in computational prowess, AI techniques have started to address large and meaningful engineering problems. In this talk, we will explore the relevance and importance of AI techniques in the next generation process systems engineering applications. Various aspects of PSE and the impact of AI cross-cutting these aspects will be described as outlined below. The focus of this talk will be on the most recent developments and industrial applications that the author has been involved in.

PSE as an area has implications in process modelling, process design, process optimization and process operations. Computer-aided tools are at the centre of all modelling activities. With the advent of AI, automated model building tools are being increasingly researched. Assembling first principles models in a purely data-driven manner is a promising area. Of course, process design is a key aspect of PSE. Design is an inverse problem, where a set of requirements are provided and designs that can satisfy the requirements are desired. As a result, any data-driven modelling tool can also be used in design if there are many exemplar designs that are available for training. As the result, the strength of AI in modelling can be leveraged for this inverse modelling problem. Natural evolution inspired techniques such as genetic algorithms also continue to play an important part in addressing complicated inverse design problems. Recently, reinforcement learning has also been used in solving design problems.

The use of AI techniques in optimization is another exciting area of research. Many core AI algorithms themselves use optimization techniques in their development; use of learning approaches in optimization is an interesting synergy between the two fields. Convex representations using neural networks that allow convex optimization approaches to be used in optimization is an emerging area of research. Other convenient representations from an optimization viewpoint are likely to pursued. An example of such a representation is the difference of convex representation.

The biggest impact of AI in PSE is in the area of process operations. With the ability of systems to collect data at an unprecedented level and the possibility of collecting variegated datatypes, AI algorithms can now be comprehensively explored for various process operations tasks. In process monitoring and operator training, natural language processing ideas have a large role to play. Further, data from different types of sensors such as vision, noise and so on, over and above the standard sensor data, is likely to revolutionize the way process monitoring and fault detection and diagnosis tasks are performed. This is particularly powerful when data from different plants are centralized allowing for the possibility of transfer learning to occur.

Standard data rectification and gross error detection techniques that used to rely on process models are now being addressed by purely data driven approaches. This brings in several important questions that need to be satisfactorily addressed by the machine learning techniques. Interestingly, sensor placement for data reconciliation, fault detection and diagnosis algorithms that used to rely on process models are also being reimagined as data driven problems.

Work on the use of neural networks and knowledge-based systems in control has been around for more than three decades. However, with renewed interest in AI, these approaches are being explored again with better architectures and larger computational power. Reinforcement learning is a natural approach to address several learning-based control problems. There has been a flurry of activity in this area, and one would expect this area to progress quite rapidly. There are several challenges related to inclusion of constraints, robustness and so on that need to be addressed comprehensively.

Looking forward, two important streams of work can be identified. One of those is the hybridization of existing knowledge with the data driven AI systems. This will be a very profitable area of research and will bring in systems that are explainable, robust and more deployable in engineering problems. Another avenue that will assume significance is moving towards purely unsupervised learning. Many successful applications use supervised and/or semi-supervised learning approaches. However, in the future, several concepts for unsupervised learning will be explored. This, we believe, will lead to truly intelligent process systems that are safe, efficient and robust to inherent variations that cannot be controlled.

Keywords: PSE, AI, ML.

1. Christoph Thon, Benedikt Finke, Arno Kwade and Carsten Schilde

Proceedings of the 14th International Symposium on Process Systems Engineering – PSE 2021+
June 19-23, 2022, Kyoto, Japan
http://dx.doi.org/10.1016/B978-0-323-85159-6.50011-7

Reinventing the Chemicals/Materials Company: Transitioning to a Sustainable Circular Enterprise

George Stephanopoulos[a,c,*], Bhavik R. Bakshi[a,b], and George Basile[a]

[a]*The Global KAITEKI Center, Arizona State University, Tempe, AZ 85257, USA*
[b]*Department of Chemical Engineering, The Ohio State University, Columbus, OH 43210, USA*
[c]*Department of Chemical Engineering, Massachusetts Institute of Technology, Cambridge, MA 02139, USA*
geosteph(@mit.edu

Abstract

Decarbonization of the Chemicals/Materials Industry (CMI) is feasible, even though technical and economic hurdles exist. However, given the prevailing constraints (economics, green electricity, available biomass), and weak decoupling of GDP from resource utilization, it is clear that the industry cannot achieve the Paris Agreement targets without transforming itself to a Sustainable Circular Enterprise. Such transformation will have deep and broadly-based ramifications on the economy, the structure of CMI and the character of CMI-companies, which need to reinvent themselves. In this paper we will offer data and arguments to substantiate the above statements, and will outline the questions that need to be answered by academic research.

Keywords: Climate change; Circular economy; Sustainability; Process/product redesign; Energy, Environmental systems.

1. The Chemicals and Materials Industry (CMI)

Industrial activities create all the physical products (e.g., cars, agricultural equipment, fertilizers, building construction materials, transportation vehicles, electronic devices, textiles, household items, food, health and security related products, etc.), whose use delivers the services that satisfy specific human needs. In this paper we consider industrial activities over the whole supply chain, from extraction of primary materials (e.g., ores, coal, petroleum, natural gas) or recycling of waste materials, through chemicals-materials-products manufacturing, to the services these products offer and the demand that such services satisfy. For the purposes of this paper, the Chemicals and Materials Industry (CMI) includes the classical chemical/petrochemical industry (organic, inorganic), the cement industry, the iron and steel industry, the non-ferrous materials industries (aluminium, magnesium, copper, and others), and a variety of industrial activities producing smaller amounts of a broad array of chemicals and materials.

Figure 1 shows the complete supply chain of what we consider as the CMI's position in the economy. The supply chain is composed of the following components: (a) *Raw Materials*: Earth stock of ores, minerals, petroleum, coal, natural gas, raw biomass. (b) *Extractive Industry*: Extracts the Raw Materials from the earth stock of raw materials and generates the Feedstocks. For example, natural deposits of petroleum contain gases and solids, which are separated, before the petroleum satisfies the specs to be a feed in a petroleum refinery. Similar extractive processing is required for the preparation of mined coal, minerals, and natural gas. (c) *Feedstocks*: The form and state of Raw Materials, which satisfy the required specs for feeds to the Processing Industry, in order to produce the Materials that the Manufacturing Industry needs. (d) *Processing Industry*: The set of activities that converts the Feedstocks to Materials. Examples include the conversion of coal, petroleum, or natural gas to fuels and chemicals; iron ore to various grades of iron and steel; conversion of clay, marl, lime, sand, into cement; raw biomass into grades of lignin, sugars, proteins. (e) *Materials*: All chemicals and materials generated by the Processing Industry, which are used for the manufacturing of the various Products the market needs. Examples include: all polymers; various grades of iron and steel; various grades of cement; various types of pulp and paper; etc. (f) *Products*: Buildings, roads, general infrastructure, automobiles, airplanes, electronic devices, pharmaceuticals, household items, etc. (g) *Services*: The satisfaction of the specific need that a product satisfies, such as: housing, clothing, transportation, food, therapeutics, entertainment, security, etc.

In all activities of the supply chain in Figure 1, scrap/wastes are generated and are processed by the "Waste Industry". The corresponding wastes can be reused, repaired, remanufactured, recycled, discarded (landfilled), or destroyed (incinerated).

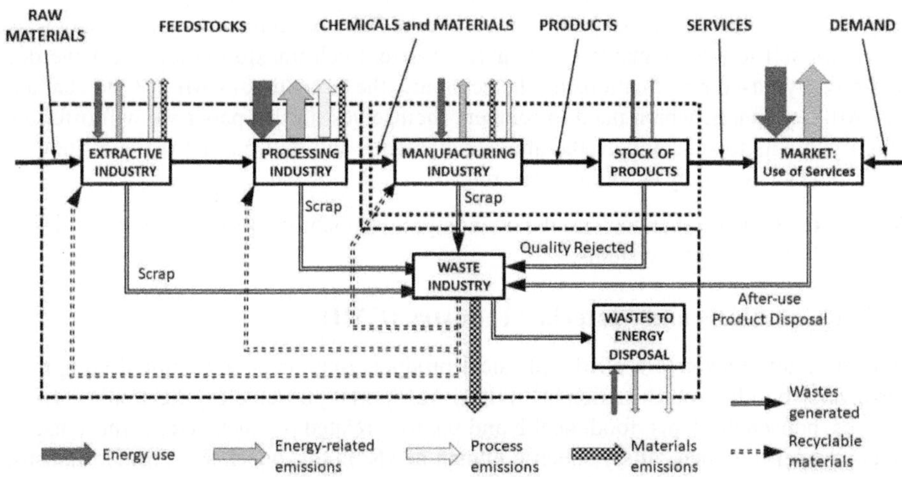

Figure 1. Complete supply chain of the *Chemicals and Materials Industry* (enclosed by the dashed and dotted envelops) from *Raw Materials* to *Services* that satisfy human needs.

2. GHG and Materials Emissions from CMI

Nearly 3/4 of Green House Gas (GHG) emissions (i.e. 73.2%) come from energy use, and 1/3 of it (24.2%) is attributed to industrial use of energy. Adding 5.2% of process-related GHG emissions (primarily from chemicals and cement), we take 30% of total emissions stemming from CMI. When compared with the emissions from transportation (16%), buildings (17.5%, heating, cooling, lighting), and agriculture, forestry and land use (18.4%), we realize that industry is the largest contributor of GHG emissions. The largest contributors of industrial GHG emissions are: iron and steel (24%), cement (19%), chemicals (18%), aluminium (6%), pulp and paper (3%). For the chemicals industry, the largest contributors are; ammonia, olefins (ethylene, propylene), methanol, and aromatics (benzene, toluene, xylenes).

As indicated above, from a strict accounting point of view (i.e. see dashed envelop in Figure 1), the CMI accounts for 30% of global GHG emissions; CO_2, CH_4, N_2O, and F-gases. However, within the scope of CMI's complete supply chain of production and consumption activities, as shown in Figure 1 (i.e. append the activities in the dotted envelop), the GHG emissions corresponding to "chemicals/materials handling and use" are much higher, and account for about 70% of the total GHG emissions. In the extreme case, these emissions include all emissions, except passenger mobility and energy use for residential purposes (space, water heating, and lighting). For example, GHG emissions related to freight transport are not "energy related", because they serve material needs, i.e. move consumer goods around.

In addition, CMI produces large amounts of materials emissions with possible adverse effects on the environment; e.g. 0.5 Gt/yr of plastics with ~40% going to landfills (where carbon is sequestered for hundreds of years) and ~ 20% leaking to the environment with disastrous health effects.

During the period 1990-2016, the global GHG emissions from industry increased by 175%, while the global GDP increased by 110%. Emissions from other sectors were far lower: transport 70%, manufacturing 50%, agriculture 20%, buildings 5%. Furthermore, we note that over the 20-year period of 1998-2018 despite the fact that the share of industry in global GDP has declined, and the annual per cent growth of manufacturing's value added has remained roughly constant, around 2%, the rate of growth of emissions from industry has far outpaced the emissions from any other sector of the world economy (https://data.worldbank.org/indicator/NV.IND.MANF.KD.ZG). The conclusion is clear and inescapable: *Industry's emissions are closely related to the rates of GDP growth.*

The relationship between GDP and GHG emissions has been the subject of many studies and is characterized by the *absolute* and *relative decoupling* between GDP and resource utilization or emissions, which are defined as follows:

$$\begin{aligned} \text{Absolute Decoupling} &= \frac{\Delta(\text{Resource Utilization})}{\Delta(\text{GDP})} < 0 \\ \text{Relative Decoupling} &= \frac{\Delta(\text{Resource Utilization})}{\Delta(\text{GDP})} < 1 \end{aligned} \tag{1}$$

Analysis of nearly 900 studies, based on empirical data on levels of emissions versus levels of consumption and production per capita, have led to important observations, which frame the scope of analysis for the transition of the Chemicals and Materials Industry to a net-zero fossil carbon industry, and can be summarized as follows (Haber, et al., 2020; Mir and Storm, 2016): (i) There is econometric evidence which supports the Carbon-Kuznets-Curve (CKC) hypothesized pattern (see Figure 2), between CO_2-eq emissions production or consumption, and GDP per capita. Such pattern would lead to absolute decoupling after the turning point. (ii) The turning point, for a production-based CKC curve, has been estimated to lie in the range of 50 to 100 $GtCO_2$-eq, which is far beyond the COP21 emissions reduction goals. (iii) Examples of consumption-based absolute decoupling are very rare. (iv) Relative decoupling is frequent for material use as well as GHG and CO_2 emissions, but not for useful exergy. From the above observations we reach two important conclusions: (i) Absolute decoupling, i.e. reduction of resource (energy, materials) utilization and GHG emissions per unit of GDP growth, cannot be achieved through observed decoupling rates. (ii) To reach the Paris Agreement goals by 2050, efforts to decouple resource utilization from GDP growth are necessary conditions but not sufficient. Sufficiency-oriented strategies must include strict enforcement of absolute targets.

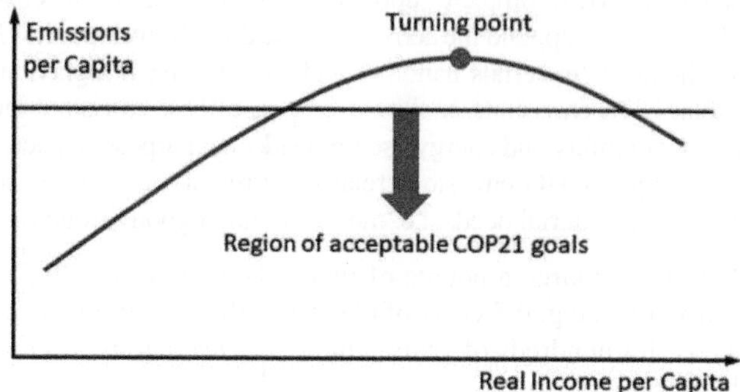

Figure 2. The Carbon-Kuznets-Curve (CKC) relationship between CO2-eq emissions and real income.

3. Towards the Circularization of CMI

The following formula offers a simple way for computing GHG emissions. It also identifies the points where major interventions would lead to emissions reductions.

$$G = \frac{G}{E} \times \frac{E}{M} \times \frac{M}{Pr} \times \frac{Pr}{S} \times S \tag{2}$$

G, GHG emissions. *G/E*, Emissions Intensity; GHG emissions per unit of energy used. *E/M*, Energy Intensity; energy used per unit of material. *M/Pr*, Materials Intensity; materials used per unit of product to create the product and maintain stock of the product. It depends both on the design of the product and on the scrap discarded during its production. *Pr/S*, Product-Service Intensity; it determines the level of service provided by a product, and depends on whether the product is consumable or durable. *S*=Total Service Demand=(Population)×(GDP/capita); the total global demand for service. Traditional programs of Continuous Improvement (KAIZEN) and process optimization can reduce the values of the first three factors, *G/E*, *E/M*, and *M/Pr*, with potential reduction of emissions by 25% - 40%. The remaining must come from the following sources: (i) Renewable energy supplies and major technological breakthroughs, such as: carbon capture sequestration and/or use. (ii) Major reductions in Materials Intensity (*M/Pr*), Product-Service Intensity (*Pr/S*), and Total Service Demand (*S*). *S* is directly related to GDP/capita and we discussed earlier. (iii) Introduction of Circular practices: reuse, repair, remanufacturing, recycle products, wastes or scraps. The conclusion is inescapable: *To meet the Paris Agreement goals we must do the following:* (1) *Change the focus from the energy sector to the chemicals/materials sector.* (2) *Enhance circularization of all supply chain activities (processing, manufacturing, distributions, sales, recovery, reuse, reprocessing, remanufacturing).* (3) *Reduce virgin material demand by extending the percent utilization of all material products (housing, mobility, nutrition, communications, consumables).*

A series of obstacles prevents the full and idealized circularization of the CMI. These obstacles are: (a) *Products may be too complex* to recycle, reuse, or remanufacture. The large-scale use of synthetic materials makes the closing of the cycle nearly impossible. Furthermore, the recycling of synthetic materials (e.g. polymers) invariably produces inferior materials. Redesign of products with easily assembled and disassembled material components, as well as extensive use of biomass-based, degradable materials, could address these concerns to a large degree. (b) *How do you recycle fossil fuels?* A large part of fossil materials is used to provide energy for heating and electricity, leading to exhaust streams, whose useful energy has diminished and is unusable. Two options are open: Shift to progressively larger amounts of renewable energy, and optimize the process of capturing and sequestering or/and using CO_2. (c) *Growing human needs.* Continuous growth of material human needs leads to the extraction of continuously larger amounts of natural resources. By increasing the amount of materials recycled, we may be able to establish steady state. However, in order to achieve this, we ned to have a holistic approach to the circular economy that involves the complete life cycle of materials; something that many advocates of the circular economy fail to account for, by focusing on limited segments of the whole. (d) *Accumulation of natural resources.* A significant portion (about 30-35%) of processed natural resources remains in the economy and accumulates in the form of buildings, infrastructure, and consumer products; it is not recycled, destroyed, or disposed in a landfill. Therefore, the circular economy is not truly a steady state situation, but one which continues to be extractive economy, with increasing inventory of materials over various time horizons. (e) *Recycling and reuse are not enough.* The economy needs to adjust to the above limitations, by increasing the percent utilization of all material goods. For example, we cannot have a sustainable circular economy with cars unused more than 90% of the time, office buildings used only 60% of the time, or more than 30% of food wasted.

4. The Research Scope of Sustainable Circular CMI (S-CCMI)

So far, the prevailing discussion on circular economy has been driven by the following simple definition of the sustainable circular CMI (S-CCMI): It is an economic model, focused on designing and manufacturing products, components and chemicals/materials for reuse, remanufacturing and recycling. However, the S-CCMI must sustain economic growth, and this definition is not sufficient to delineate its actionable scope. While the specific characteristics of S-CCMI can differ for different sectors of CMI, they must be driven by a simple principle: *The resource inputs and recycled materials should maintain dynamic material balances of "wastes" at the sustainably highest allowable materials-accumulation levels.* Pure "steady state" requirements are impossible; materials accumulate in the economy continuously. For example, carbon extracted from earth is equal to the amount of carbon returned to the earth, while the amount of carbon accumulated in the system remains below the sustainably highest level. The "sustainably highest level" allowance is determined by climate change (GHG emissions) and environmental impact (materials emissions) constraints.

Design elements of the S-CCMI. The above simple principle has a broad range of implications for all activities in the "materials handling and use" network of Figure 1. At The Global KAITEKI Center (TGKC) of Arizona State University, we have undertaken an extensive research program, which addresses all questions related to the transition of CMI to S-CCMI, such as: (i) Reduction in the input and use of non-renewable material resources. (ii) Reduction in the generation of wastes and emissions (GHG and materials). (iii) Increase in inner materials use and recycle up to the sustainably highest level of materials use. (iv) Redesign of products and associated components, materials, and chemicals to facilitate recycle, and reuse. (v) Development of new technologies for the capture, sequestration and use of carbon.

Transformation of CMI companies to S-CCMI companies. Aspects of the research program evaluate the following implications on the structure and operations of the CMI companies, as they transform to S-CCMI companies: (1) Transition from centralized and vertically integrated, open-chain large-scale processing and manufacturing systems, to smaller-size, decentralized, distributed and locally managed processing and manufacturing activities. (2) Economies of scale, which have dominated the large-scale processing in CMI will no longer be the drivers for large-scale investments. Materials, transportation, logistical services, and financial costs will drive the structure of S-CCMI. (3) Redefinition of the scope of the business activities, with the CMI companies transforming themselves from producers of virgin chemicals and materials, to producers of integrated components and products, and suppliers of technical services to support the life-cycle of their products.

The economics of transition from CMI to S-CCMI. The economic benefits of such transformation S-CCMI companies have been estimated to be very attractive: (1) Significantly higher returns on investment. (2) Reduction in volatility between supply and demand, due to effective recycling and self-regulating system, leading to resilient economic growth. (3) Stronger market position and competitive differentiation for the companies, which espouse the future of S-CCMI. This will be particularly true for the companies, which are presently strong and have strong R&D, engineering, and supply-chain market positions.

Societal and human adjustments during the transition from CMI to S-CCMI. The consumers will need to adjust their behavior away from "owning physical products" towards "using services of physical products", but the benefits are many and attractive: (i) The transition *from "owning, using and disposing" to "using and returning"* will force improvement of service quality, durability and reliability of products. (ii) This transition will foster the appearance of new emerging trends of sharing, lending, swapping etc. that will benefit the consumers. (iii) The companies of present CMI employ very few people per dollar of asset values. The S-CCMI will increase these numbers significantly and fuel more predictable and sustainable demand of products and services at higher levels. (iv) The demands of S-CCMI can only be met by human resources of significantly higher education and skills. This will be in-line with historical expectations.

5. Conclusions

The transition of the CMI to a Sustainable Circular CMI is a necessary (and possibly sufficient) condition for industry to maintain under control the growing mountains of environmental "wastes"; GHG emissions and discarded materials. The implications are broad and deep and require restructuring of CMI, reinvention of the CMI companies and realignment of human behavioural traits in the new market place. The question is not whether to transition to S-CCMI or not, but how; the scope of research at TGKC.

Acknowledgements

The authors gratefully acknowledge the support from "The Global KAITEKI Center" at Arizona State University (ASU), a university-industry partnership between ASU and The KAITEKI Institute of Mitsubishi Chemical Holdings Corporation.

References

M. Brudermüller, 2020, How to build a more climate-friendly chemical industry, World Economic Forum, Annual meeting.

H. Haber, et al., 2020, A systematic review of the evidence on decoupling of GDP, resource use and GHG emissions, part II: synthesizing the insights, Environ. Res. Lett. 15 065003

G. Mir and S. Storm, 2016, Carbon Emissions and Economic Growth: Production-based versus Consumption-based Evidence on Decoupling, Working Paper No. 41, Institute for New Economic Thinking.

Proceedings of the 14th International Symposium on Process Systems Engineering – PSE 2021+
June 19-23, 2022, Kyoto, Japan
http://dx.doi.org/10.1016/B978-0-323-85159-6.50012-9

Value Chain Optimization of a Xylitol Biorefinery with Delaunay Triangulation Regression Models

Nikolaus I. Vollmer[a*], Krist V. Gernaey[a], Gürkan Sin[a]

[a]Process and Systems Engineering Center (PROSYS), Department of Chemical and Biochemical Engineering, Technical University of Denmark, Søltofts Plads, Building 228A, 2800, Kgs. Lyngby, Denmark
nikov@kt.dtu.dk

Abstract

The presented work focuses on the value chain optimization of a conceptually designed biorefinery, considering the plant capacity and other logistic and design constraints. An existing framework is used to create surrogate models, which are then used to reformulate the underlying optimization problem for performing value chain optimization. The used Delaunay triangulation regression surrogate model performs well and is a suitable candidate for value chain optimization. The results indicate an apparent effect of the economics of scale, and the market conditions mainly constrain the designed value chain.

Keywords: Biorefinery, Surrogate Modelling, Delaunay Triangulation, Mixed-Integer Linear Program, Value Chain Optimization

1. Introduction

A key approach in expediting the transition towards a bio-based economy is the conceptual design and implementation of value chains based on integrated second-generation biorefineries. Although these biorefineries have been investigated for several decades, and despite their vast potential regarding a sustainable production of fuels and chemicals, the major challenge remaining concerns their economic viability (Ubando et al., 2020). Among other factors that influence the economic viability, the capacity and location of the plant and the design of suitable feedstock and product supply chains are essential considerations to take (Gargalo et al., 2017). What is classically referred to as economies of scale can improve the economic key performance indicators (KPIs) of a plant up to a certain point, as the capital expenditures do not increase proportionally with the plant capacity. In contrast, additional necessary equipment, as well as increased operational costs for logistics, can thwart this effect.

Hence, it is crucial to conceptually design both the biorefinery process and the entire value chain in which the biorefinery will be embedded. Vollmer et al. (2021) have recently developed a framework (S3O) that allows for the conceptual design of biorefinery processes based on mechanistic modeling for all unit operations in the process. The framework utilizes flowsheet simulations and different types of surrogate models to perform a superstructure optimization to determine candidate process topologies. This procedure is applied to eliminate nonlinearities, which are inherent to all unit operation models and constitute the superstructure optimization as a mixed-integer nonlinear optimization problem (MINLP) (Vollmer et al., 2021b). The surrogate models aim either at linearizing the original model or eliminating the integer variables.

Similarly, in value chain optimization, nonlinear models are commonly linearized with piecewise linear approaches (Krämer et al., 2021).

In the scope of this work, the S3O framework is extended by using the already present Delaunay Triangulation Regression (DTR) surrogate model to perform value chain optimization based on a conceptually designed process through the framework. By flowsheet sampling with the process flowsheet with relevant input and output variables for the value chain optimization, piecewise linear DTR surrogate models are created. The value chain optimization is set up and constituted as a mixed-integer linear program (MILP), using the DTR surrogate model and solved with a suitable solver. This solution is benchmarked with a Gaussian Process Regression (GPR) surrogate model, which is equally incorporated in the S3O framework. The solution is analyzed and compared to the initial base case process design to conclude how to design an optimal value chain.

2. Methodology

2.1. Mechanistic Process Models

The basis of the work in this manuscript is a running flowsheet simulation model created in the first step of the S3O framework. Each flowsheet model consists of various unit operation models. All unit operation models are mechanistic models, consisting of mass and energy balances and a kinetic description of the respective reaction or transfer process. Based on the mass and energy balance calculations, the fixed capital investment for each unit operation is calculated by a plant capacity ratio based on a report by the National Renewable Energy Laboratory (NREL) regarding a similar biorefinery setup. Based on the fixed capital investment and other report data, capital expenditures and operational expenses (CAPEX and OPEX) and different KPIs, e.g., the net present value (NPV) of the plant, are calculated. Input parameters for the flowsheet simulation can be operational variables and the feedstock mass, and other setup parameters. Output variables can be all mass and energy flows, as well as design parameters, e.g., vessel sizes, or economic variables referring to CAPEX or OPEX, or ultimately the KPIs of the plant. All flowsheet simulations are performed through the S3O framework as it is implemented in MATLAB.

2.2. Delaunay Triangulation Regression

DTR is based on a triangulation of points as a logical extension of piecewise linear regression in any dimension (Vollmer et al., 2021b). In a two-dimensional case, a triangulation consists of triangles or 2-simplices. For any dimension n, the triangulation hence consists of n-simplices. Each n-simplex itself is constituted by n+1 vertices. Within each simplex, each point can be described as a linear affine combination of the vertices. In this manuscript, the vertices are assigned to be the sampling points of the flowsheet simulations. The DTR utilizes Delaunay triangulation, which imposes the criterion to each simplex not to contain any other vertex of another simplex within the circumcircle – or its pendant in other dimensions – of the simplex. For a more detailed description, the reader is referred to Vollmer et al. (2021b). The results show an excellent functionality of the DTR surrogate for superstructure optimization applications within the S3O framework, despite impaired validation metrics. Furthermore, DTR has been used in other research works for performing operations optimization (Obermeier et al., 2021). In this work, the DTR surrogate model is created with functions provided through the scipy library for Python.

2.3. Gaussian Process Regression

Another very popular type of surrogate model is a GPR model, a machine learning model with a broad variety of possible applications (McBride and Sundmacher, 2019). The model itself harvests its potential through a stochastic process – the eponymous Gaussian Process – which correlates the given input and output data, in this case, the flowsheet samples (Vollmer et al., 2021b). Also, using GPR surrogate models for process design applications within the S3O frameworks shows good functionality with good validation metrics (Vollmer et al., 2021a). In this work, the GPR functionalities of the Statistics & Machine Learning Toolbox in MATLAB are used.

2.4. Value Chain Optimization

The original value chain optimization in this manuscript is an MINLP of the form given in Eq. (1).

$$MINLP: \quad \begin{array}{c} \max z = f(x,y) \\ s.t. \;\; g(x,y) \leq 0 \\ h(x,y) = 0 \\ x \in X, \;\; y \in [0,1] \end{array} \tag{1}$$

The functional relation $f(x,y)$ denotes the flowsheet simulation, including continuous input variables x and binary input variables y. The objective z is equally one of the model outputs. Inequality constraints are represented by $g(x,y)$ and equality constraints are represented by $h(x,y) = 0$. Both inequality and equality constraints can describe conditions regarding logistics, markets, plant capacity, location, and supply and demand for the biorefinery. When utilizing the DTR surrogate model, the MINLP converts into a MILP due to eliminating the nonlinearities by the piecewise linear approach. When using the GPR surrogate model, the MINLP converts into a set of nonlinear programs (NLP), with each element of the set representing one realization of the combinations of all binary variables that need to be solved separately. The MILP can be solved with the GUROBI solver, whereas each NLP is solved with the fmincon solver in MATLAB while employing a multi-start procedure to guarantee global optimality.

3. Application

3.1. Case Study

The biorefinery in this case study is a multi-product biorefinery that converts wheat straw into xylitol, succinic acid, and heat. The latter is used for process integration purposes in the downstream processing of the former two products. It consists of a biomass pretreatment unit, a unit for enzymatic hydrolysis, two evaporation units in the upstream process, two fermentation units for the production of xylitol and succinic acid, two evaporation units, four crystallization units, and one combustion unit for the lignin.

3.2. Optimization Problem

The original biorefinery is designed for an annual feedstock mass of $m = 150.000\,t$ designed for being located in Denmark, corresponding to approximately 3% of the nationally harvested amount of wheat straw (Danish Agriculture & Food Council, 2015). In order to see a significant effect of the economies of scale, the capacity of the biorefinery could be potentially increased up to $m = 600.000\,t$, as practiced in the mentioned report of the NREL (Humbird et al., 2011). However, as wheat straw is harvested and centrally collected, a higher amount of feedstock correlates with a longer transportation distance. Per each full additional 150.000 t of feedstock, it is considered to increase the transportation distance stepwise by 100km, with a transportation price of $0.05\ \$/(t \cdot km)$. As this increases the costs for transportation, a potential option is to not install one plant with a capacity of bigger than $m = 300.000\ t$, but to install two plants with the ability to be able to process $m = 600.000\ t$ in a decentralized manner which alleviates the economic impact (Galanopoulos et al., 2020). This is expressed by a binary variable y_p as part of the optimization problem. Lastly, as fermentation processes need equipment for inoculation, a higher capacity than the original one requires an additional fermentation tank, which increases the CAPEX of the plant. The costs of the additional tank scale linearly with the feedstock mass. The capacity itself, however, is calculated through the capacity ratio. For the flowsheet simulations, the operational variables, as well as the feedstock mass and the plant number y_p are used. The effects of all three mentioned aspects are calculated in the flowsheet simulation. As output, the NPV of the plant and the mass of produced xylitol and succinic acid are calculated. The objective in the optimization is set to be the NPV of the plant, and the mass of xylitol and succinic acid are constrained to be $g_1 = m_{xyo} \in [5,33]\%$ and $g_2 = m_{xyo} \in [20,50]\%$ of the global production of the respective substance. The lower limits are imposed to assure a minimal production, whereas the upper limits are imposed to avoid decreasing market prices, which would negatively influence the plant profitability due to the comparatively small market size of both products.

3.3. Results

For illustrative purposes, the NPV as the objective function of the feedstock mass with fixed operational conditions is displayed in Figure 1.

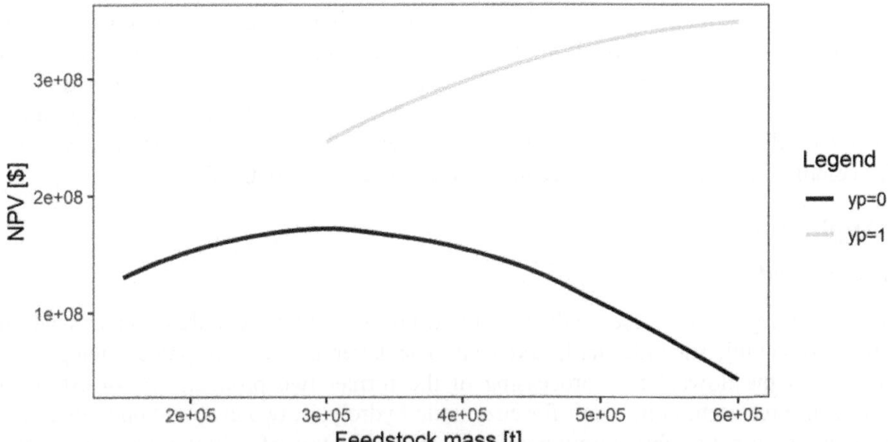

Figure 1: Plot of the objective function with the feedstock mass as a variable for $y_p = 0$ and $y_p = 1$

The effect of the economies of scale, the constraining effects of increased costs for logistics and equipment, and the reduction of the expenses through decentralized production are visible. For the value chain optimization, the process flowsheet model is sampled with N=1000 simulation samples for all five operational variables, the feedstock mass, and the binary variable y_p with two sets of the sample size sampled by Latin Hypercube sampling for each realization of y_p. The DTR and the GPR surrogate models are fitted to the sampling data and cross-validated. The results of the cross-validation for both models are presented in Table 1.

Table 1: Results of the surrogate model validation for the NPV as output variable

	DTR		GPR	
	$y_p = 0$	$y_p = 1$	$y_p = 0$	$y_p = 1$
R^2_{train}	1	1	1	1
R^2_{test}	0.552	0.408	0.957	0.937
$RMSE_{train}$	0	0	$3.19 \cdot 10^5$	$1.04 \cdot 10^5$
$RMSE_{test}$	$3.07 \cdot 10^8$	$2.97 \cdot 10^8$	$9.48 \cdot 10^6$	$1.57 \cdot 10^5$

It becomes evident that the DTR surrogate metrics are impaired compared to the ones of the GPR. Particularly for the case of $y_p = 1$, the DTR surrogate model does fail to predict accurately, while the GPR shows improved metrics compared to the case of $y_p = 0$. The optimization problem for the value chain optimization is set up as described in section 2.4 with all variables, the objective function, and the constraints as described in section 3.2. The results are presented in Table 2.

Table 2: Results of the value chain optimization with the optimization result (left) and the validation simulation result (right) for each binary decision and surrogate model

	DTR				GPR			
	$y_p = 0$		$y_p = 1$		$y_p = 0$		$y_p = 1$	
M_{feed} $[10^3 \cdot t]$	302		293		292		292	
$\boldsymbol{NPV}$ $[\mathbf{10^8 \cdot \$}]$	**1.96**	**2.47**	**2.93**	**3.29**	**7.1**	**3.56**	**5.8**	**2.60**
M_{xyo} $[10^3 \cdot t]$	19.8	20.4	22.1	22.2	29.1	22.4	21.8	20.2
M_{suc} $[10^3 \cdot t]$	35.9	38.0	35.9	35.1	35.9	35.9	35.9	35.9

Primarily, the result from both the optimization with the DTR and the GPR surrogate shows that the effect of the economics of scale is visible, and the feedstock capacity is increased to a maximally feasible limit, which is imposed by the market saturation bounds. The effects of increased transportation costs and additional equipment do not influence the objective to the same degree. In other studies investigating products as bioethanol with higher market volumes, these effects become more significant (Galanopoulos et al., 2020). Furthermore, the operational conditions were not significantly influenced. Also, the results of both optimization problems with the different surrogate models agree, indicating that the DTR model is a suitable candidate for value chain optimization despite insufficient validation metrics, since it performs better in predicting the objective function and the constraints. The differences in prediction with the GPR surrogate model for the case of $y_p = 1$ and $y_p = 0$ can be explained by the different fit of each model, which is reflected by the validation metrics. The differences in prediction for the DTR surrogate model can be equally attributed to the different fit expressed by the validation metrics. This indicates a potential increase in prediction quality for both models by using larger sampling sizes. It is noted that the economic metrics are calculated with fixed price considerations for feedstock and products. Hence the emphasis is on the trend of NPV rather than its absolute value. Further studies of uncertainties that will yield a distribution of NPV are needed as the volatility in the market prices for feedstock and products, as well as the market demand uncertainty, will affect the nominal values presented here.

4. Conclusion

Based on a conceptually designed process for an integrated second-generation biorefinery, this study aimed to design an optimal value chain with the given process design by taking into account a varying feedstock mass and other logistic and design constraints for the plant. The value chain optimization was performed using two surrogate models to transform the underlying MINLP into either a MILP or a set of NLPs. The results from solving the optimization problems show results in agreement with each other. This proves the suitability of DTR surrogate models for the use in value chain optimization problems, and this despite impaired validation metrics of the surrogate model, which has been addressed before (Vollmer et al., 2021a; Vollmer et al., 2021b) With regards to the actual value chain, it becomes evident that the economics of scale positively influence the KPIs of the biorefinery. The limitations for economic resilience are found in the actual market sizes of the products rather than in the additional costs for increased CAPEX and OPEX of a larger biorefinery. These results are essential and contribute to facilitating the further design and implementation of biobased value chains to create more sustainable production patterns in the future.

Acknowledgments

The research project is part of the Fermentation-Based Biomanufacturing Initiative funded by the Novo Nordisk Foundation (Grant no. NNF17SA0031362).

References

Danish Agriculture & Food Council, 2015, Facts and Figures: Denmark – a Food and Farming Country, 1-56

C. Galanopoulos et al., 2020, An integrated methodology for the economic and environmental assessment of a biorefinery supply chain, Chemical Engineering Research and Design, 160, 199-215.

C.L. Gargalo et al., 2017, Optimal Design and Planning of Glycerol-Based Biorefinery Supply Chains under Uncertainty, Industrial & Engineering Chemistry Research, 56, 41, 11870-11893

D.Humbird et al., Process design and economics for biochemical conversion of lignocellulosic biomass to ethanol: dilute-acid pretreatment and enzymatic hydrolysis of corn stover, No. NREL/TP-5100-47764, National Renewable Energy Laboratory, Golden (CO), United States

A. Kämper et al., 2021, AutoMoG: Automated data-driven Model Generation of multi-energy systems using piecewise-linear regression, Computers & Chemical Engineering, 145, 107162

K. McBride and K. Sundmacher, 2019, Overview of surrogate modeling in chemical process engineering, Chemie Ingenieur Technik, 91, 3, 228-239

A. Obermeier et al., 2021, Generation of linear-based surrogate models from nonlinear functional relationships for use in scheduling formulation, Computers & Chemical Engineering, 146, 107203

A.T. Ubando et al., 2020, Biorefineries in circular bioeconomy: A comprehensive review. Bioresource Technology, 299, 122585

N.I. Vollmer et al., 2021a, Benchmarking of Surrogate Models for the Conceptual Process Design of Biorefineries, Computer Aided Chemical Engineering, 50, 475-480

N.I. Vollmer et al., 2021b, Synergistic optimization framework for the process synthesis and design of biorefineries, Frontiers of Chemical Science and Engineering, 1-23

Proceedings of the 14th International Symposium on Process Systems Engineering – PSE 2021+
June 19-23, 2022, Kyoto, Japan
http://dx.doi.org/10.1016/B978-0-323-85159-6.50013-0

Evaluating the Impact of Model Uncertainties in Superstructure Optimization to Reduce the Experimental Effort

Stefanie Kaiser[a*], Sebastian Engell[a]

[a] *Department of Chemical Engineering, TU Dortmund University, Emil-Figge-Str. 70, 44227 Dortmund, Germany*
stefanie2.kaiser@tu-dortmund.de

Abstract

Optimization-based process design can be an efficient tool for finding synergies between process units, but it strongly relies on accurate process models. Hence, experiments for model refinement may be necessary. We present an optimization-based methodology to enhance the process development by integrating superstructure optimization under uncertainties and optimal design of experiments. In this manner, experiments for model refinement can be focussed on the parameters which are critical for discrete design decisions. These parameters are identified by a local discrimination analysis followed by a computation of the partial dependence or the permutation feature importance. The methodology is applied to the hydroaminomethylation of 1-decene. It is shown that it reduces the number of experiments needed for the decision between alternative process structures.

Keywords: Superstructure Optimization, Process Design, Optimal Design of Experiments, Linear Discrimination Analysis.

1. Introduction

Superstructure optimization has been developed as a tool to support design decisions in process development by the optimization of discrete and continuous parameters of a superstructure that describes a range of process alternatives. The formulation of the superstructure and the solution of the resulting large mixed-integer optimization problems have been widely studied ((Chen & Grossmann, 2017), (Skiborowski et al., 2014)). However, the prerequisite of the application of the approach is the availability of models that describe the chemical and physical phenomena in the different pieces of equipment as well as the necessary investments and the costs of operation accurately. Since the models that are available for process design are usually uncertain in the early process design phases, where nonetheless often important structural decisions are taken, these uncertainties should be considered in the optimization. Steimel and Engell (2016) proposed a two-stage formulation for superstructure optimization under uncertainty where the uncertainty is modelled by discrete scenarios and the design degrees of freedom are identical for all scenarios but the operational degrees of freedom are adapted to the realization of the uncertainties, i.e. the real behavior of the plant. However, often there will be several process structures that are optimal for different scenarios, and the uncertainty should be reduced by experimental work to obtain a unique solution. In order to identify the optimal design with the smallest experimental effort, the authors proposed an integrated methodology that combines superstructure optimization under uncertainty,

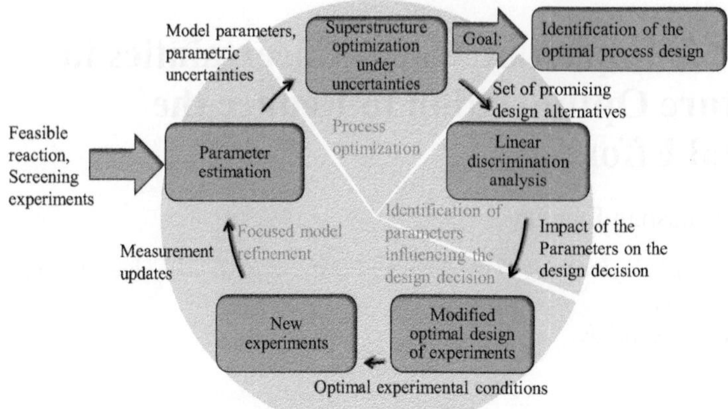

Figure 1: Schematic representation of the integrated methodology.

sensitivity analysis, and optimal design of experiments ((Kaiser & Engell, 2020), (Kaiser et al., 2021)). The parameters with the highest impact on the process cost for the most promising design are identified using a sensitivity analysis. A modified optimal design of experiment is used to plan experiments that focus on determining these parameters.

Our earlier work showed that the process design could be accelerated, but it did not yet take the impact of the uncertain parameters on the structural decisions into account. We improve the methodology by evaluating the impact of the model parameters on the discrete design decisions and planning experiments that are targeting to determine the parameters that influence the discrete design decisions the most. In the following, we will describe the methodology and apply it to the hydroaminomethylation of 1-decene.

2. Methodology

The idea is to integrate superstructure optimization under uncertainty, the identification of relevant parameters, the design of focused experiments, and parameter estimation as can be seen in Figure 1. By this, efficient experiments can be planned for model refinement that are focused on determining the parameters that have the highest impact one the discrete design decisions. The single steps are explained in the next section.

2.1. Superstructure optimization under uncertainty

For superstructure optimization under uncertainty Steimel and Engell (2016) proposed to formulate a two-stage mixed integer optimization problem.

$$\begin{aligned} \min_{y_d, y_c, x_\omega} \; & G(y_d, y_c) + \sum_{\omega=1}^{\Omega} \pi_\omega F_\omega(y_d, y_c, x_\omega, z_\omega) \\ \text{s.t.} \; & h(y_d, y_c, x_\omega, z_\omega) = 0 \\ & g(y_d, y_c, x_\omega, z_\omega) \le 0 \end{aligned} \tag{1}$$

The objective function (1) consists of two terms. The first term accounts for the cost when fixing the discrete (y_d) and continuous (y_c) design degrees of freedom, which cannot be adapted to the realization of the uncertainties. The second term is the weighted sum of the scenario dependent costs for the Ω discrete scenarios of the uncertain parameters. The operational degrees of freedom x_ω are assumed to be adapted to the realization of the uncertainty and are therefore optimized separately for each scenario.

2.2. Linear discrimination analysis

To identify the effect that the uncertainties have on the design decision, the outputs are divided into g classes K_l– here the best design decisions – depending on the values of the uncertain parameters. By a linear discrimination analysis, the features that separate the classes can be identified. A realization x_i of a feature carrier $\boldsymbol{e}$ is assigned to the class K_l for which the value of the discrimination function is maximum (Rinne, 2008):

$$d_{l*}(x_i) = \max_{1 \le l \le g} d_l(x_i) \Rightarrow x_i \in K_{l*}. \tag{2}$$

Supposing that a number or realizations (samples) x_i have been classified, arbitrary values of $\boldsymbol{e}$ can be assigned to the classes under the assumption that the features are independent, Gaussian distributed, and have an equal feature-independent variance

$$\boldsymbol{\Sigma}_l = \sigma^2 \boldsymbol{I} \; \forall \, l. \tag{3}$$

A realization with vector $\boldsymbol{x}$ is assigned to the class with the minimum Euclidean distance between the class center $\boldsymbol{\mu}_l$ and $\boldsymbol{x}$. The linear discrimination function is defined as:

$$d_l(\boldsymbol{x}) = -\frac{1}{2\sigma^2}\boldsymbol{\mu}_l'\boldsymbol{\mu}_l + \frac{1}{\sigma^2}\boldsymbol{\mu}_l'\boldsymbol{x}. \tag{4}$$

$\boldsymbol{\mu}_l$ is computed as the average of the classified samples that belong to class l.
The relationship between the features and the predicted class can be represented by the partial dependence (PD) as described by (Greenwell, 2017). It is computed as the average probability of the output belonging to the different classes when the value of this feature is varied, averaged over the values of all other features. The assignment of the class for a value of the feature is based on (4) and the averaging is done over the set of the classified realizations of the parameter vector (samples). This gives the fractions of the predictions of each design decision being the optimum one depending on the values of the individual features (parameters in our case). If $\boldsymbol{x}^s$ is the feature of interest and $\boldsymbol{X}^c$ is its complement (i.e. all other features), the partial dependence of the output f at $\boldsymbol{x}_s$ is defined as:

$$f^s(\boldsymbol{x}^s) = E_C[f(\boldsymbol{x}^s, \boldsymbol{X}^c)] = \int f(\boldsymbol{x}^s, \boldsymbol{X}^c) p_c(\boldsymbol{X}^c) d\boldsymbol{X}^c \tag{5}$$

The results of the PD are compared to the permutation feature importance (PFI) that also capture interaction effects (Fisher et al., 2019). For each feature, the values are exchanged with values from a different sample to generate a new feature matrix X^{perm}. The classification of the discrimination model of X^{perm} is then compared to the true optimal discrete design as indicated in the training data and the number of wrong classifications is compared for all features. If permuting one feature leads to a wrong classification, it implies that this feature as a large influence on the model output.

2.3. Optimal design of experiments

To design an experiment to determine the parameters that influence the design decision, an optimal design of experiment (ODoE) is used. In ODoE a metric of the inverse of the Fisher information matrix (FIM) is minimized (Franceschini & Macchietto, 2008).

$$\boldsymbol{FIM} = \sum_{\tau=\tau_1}^{\tau_N} \boldsymbol{Q}^T(\boldsymbol{u}_\tau) \mathbf{diag}^{-1}(\sigma_1^2, \dots, \sigma_{ny}^2) \boldsymbol{Q}(\boldsymbol{u}_\tau) \tag{6}$$

with $\boldsymbol{Q}(\boldsymbol{u}_\tau)$ being the matrix of the derivatives of the model outputs with respect to the parameters of the experiment with the input $\boldsymbol{u}_\tau$. As only some of the parameters will have an impact on the design decision, as identified by PD and PFI, only these are included in the ODoE. Here an A-optimal design of experiments is used which minimizes the trace of the inverse of the FIM.

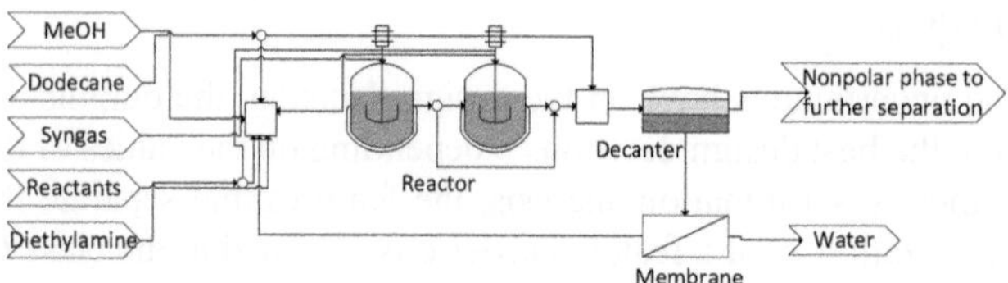

Figure 2: Superstructure of the process.

3. Case study

The presented methodology is applied to the homogeneously catalysed hydroamino-methylation of 1-decene in a thermomorphic solvent system of methanol and dodecane. In this process, long-chain amines are produced and water is formed as a by-product. Thermomorphic solvent systems are single phase at reaction temperature and separate into two phases when cooled down which enables a recycling of the expensive catalysts. The reaction can either be performed as a tandem reaction (HAM) in one reactor or in two subsequent steps, thus performing the two subsequent reactions hydroformylation (HYFO) and reductive amination (RA) in different reactors. The superstructure is depicted in Figure 2. The process consists of three steps: reaction, separation and removal of water. Kinetic models for the two reactions steps can be found in (Hentschel et al., 2015) and (Kirschtowski et al., 2021). The HAM was modelled by combining both model structures and fitting the parameters to twelve experiments. The gas solubilities as well as the phase separation are predicted using the equation of state PC-SAFT. As the iterative solution of the PC-SAFT equations is not feasible in the optimization, surrogate models were trained as proposed in (Nentwich & Engell, 2019). The membrane separation is modelled using a solution-diffusion model. The uncertainties considered in this case study are the pre-exponential factors and the activation energies of all reaction rates resulting in 31 uncertain parameters. The binary design degrees of freedom are the choices whether the tandem reaction or the subsequent reactions are used and whether the nonpolar solvent dodecane is fed before or after the reaction, and the continuous design decisions are the volumes of the reactors and the area of the membrane. As recourse variables, the temperatures in the reactors and the decanter, the partial pressures of syngas, the solvent ratio and the catalyst concentration are optimized. The cost function is the production cost per kg of product for a constant capacity of 10.000 t/a.

3.1. Application of the integrated methodology

The superstructure optimization was performed for the four structurally different process alternatives. For each alternative, the predicted costs for the best designs are shown in Figure 3 (left). Each line in the figure represents one scenario of uncertain parameters. Initially, design 1 is optimal for most but not for all scenarios. As one cannot make a design decision based on this result, a further model refinement is necessary. As a next step, we analyzed which parameters influence the design decision. Therefore, a linear discrimination analysis was performed. Designs 2 and 4 are not optimal for any scenario and therefore, only designs 1 and 3 are considered. The influence of the parameters on the class allocation was analysed via PD and PFI. The partial dependence plots are shown in Figure 4, where the scores of all 31 parameters are presented. One can see that

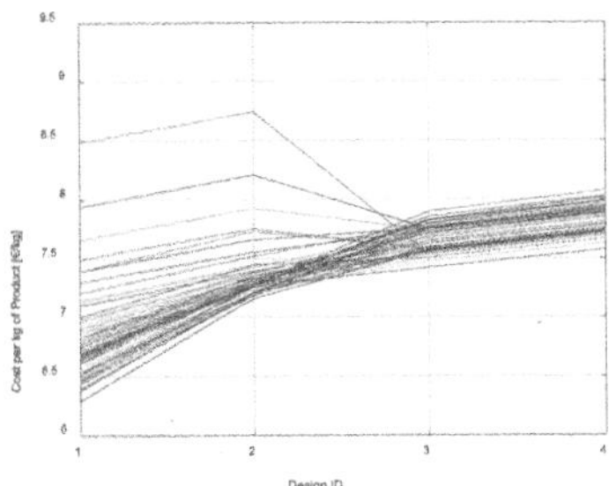

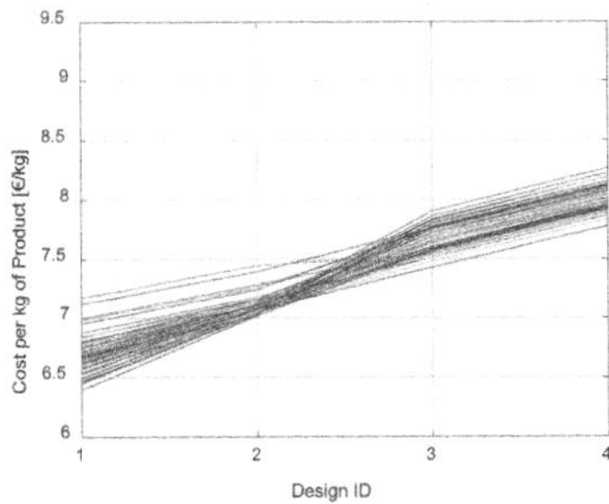

Figure 3: Predicted costs for the four best structurally different designs for 50 scenarios of the uncertain parameters after the initial superstructure optimization (left) and after 7 iterations. The design IDs indicate the structurally different designs. Design 1 and design 2 correspond to the tandem reaction with a dodecane feed after and before the reaction respectively and design 3 and 4 to the two subsequent reactions with a dodecane feed after and before the reaction.

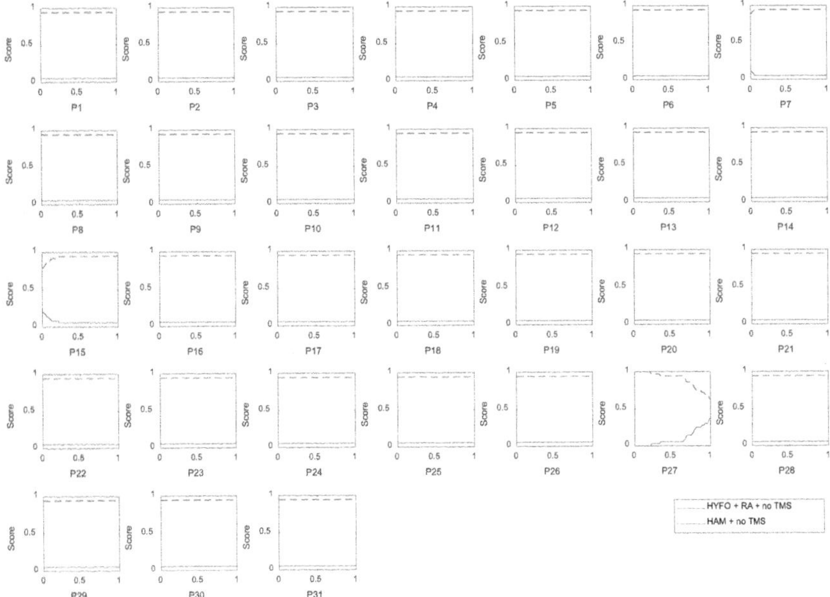

Figure 4: Partial dependence plots for the two discrete designs that were identified as optimal for at least one of the different scenarios considered.

parameter P27 (the activation energy of the side reaction to from n-decene to iso-decene) determines the decision the most. The same result was obtained by PFI where only changing this parameter shows an effect on the predicted class.

Hence, the optimal design of experiments was restricted to determining this parameter. The reaction temperature, the total pressure, the syngas ratio, the catalyst concentration and the sampling times were optimized for one batch experiment. The experiment was replaced by a simulation of the reaction with the nominal values of the parameters corrupted with added white noise with a standard deviation of 5 %. After one simulation experiment, the parameters were updated and the procedure was repeated. After seven iterations, one design could be identified as optimal for all scenarios as it can be seen in Figure 3 (right). In contrast, by a full factorial design with 32 additional experiments one cannot identify one design as optimal for all scenarios. Therefore, the proposed methodology shows an advantage over established techniques for model refinement.

4. Conclusion and Outlook

We presented an integrated methodology that accelerates the process development process by reducing the number of required experiments to find the optimum discrete design decisions. Using a superstructure optimization under uncertainties followed by a discrimination analysis, the parameters that influence the design decision the most can be identified. Hence, efficient experiments can be planned by optimal design of experiments that focus only on determining these parameters until the model is accurate enough to make a design decision. In the case study, we could identify one parameter as strongly influencing the design decision. Simulation studies showed that designing experiments for this parameter can reduce the number of experiments compared to a full-factorial design. In the future, we plan to expand the methodology to uncertain parameters in different process units.

Acknowledgement

Gefördert durch die Deutsche Forschungsgemeinschaft (DFG) - TRR 63 "Integrierte chemische Prozesse in flüssigen Mehrphasensystemen" (Teilprojekt D1) - 56091768. Funded by DFG in the context of the Transregio SFB InPROMPT.

References

Chen, Q. & Grossmann, I. E. (2017). Recent Developments and Challenges in Optimization-Based Process Synthesis. *Annual Review of Chemical and Biomolecular Engineering*, *8*(1), 249–283.

Fisher, A., Rudin, C. & Dominici, F. (2019). All models are wrong, but many are useful: Learning a variable's importance by studying an entire class of prediction models simultaneously. *Journal of Machine Learning Research*, *20*, 1–81.

Franceschini, G. & Macchietto, S. (2008). Model-based design of experiments for parameter precision: State of the art. *Chemical Engineering Science*, *63*(19), 4846–4872.

Greenwell, B. M. (2017). pdp: An R package for constructing partial dependence plots. *R Journal*, *9*(1), 421–436.

Hentschel, B., Kiedorf, G., Gerlach, M., Hamel, C., Seidel-Morgenstern, A., Freund, H. & Sundmacher, K. (2015). Model-based identification and experimental validation of the optimal reaction route for the hydroformylation of 1-dodecene. *Industrial and Engineering Chemistry Research*, *54*(6), 1755–1765.

Kaiser, S. & Engell, S. (2020). Integrating Superstructure Optimization under Uncertainty and Optimal Experimental Design in early Stage Process Development. *Computer Aided Chemical Engineering*, *48*, 799–804.

Kaiser, S., Menzel, T. & Engell, S. (2021). Focusing experiments in the early phase process design by process optimization and global sensitivity analysis. *Computer Aided Chemical Engineering*, *50*, 899–904.

Kirschtowski, S., Jameel, F., Stein, M., Seidel-Morgenstern, A. & Hamel, C. (2021). Kinetics of the reductive amination of 1-undecanal in thermomorphic multicomponent system. *Chemical Engineering Science*, *230*, 116187.

Nentwich, C. & Engell, S. (2019). Surrogate modeling of phase equilibrium calculations using adaptive sampling. *Computers and Chemical Engineering*, *126*, 204–217.

Rinne, H. (2008). *Taschenbuch der Statistik* (4th ed.). Verlag Harri Deutsch.

Skiborowski, M., Wessel, J. & Marquardt, W. (2014). Efficient optimization-based design of membrane-assisted distillation processes. *Industrial and Engineering Chemistry Research*, *53*(40), 15698–15717.

Steimel, J. & Engell, S. (2016). Optimization-based support for process design under uncertainty: A case study. *AIChE Journal*, *62*(9), 3404–3419.

Proceedings of the 14th International Symposium on Process Systems Engineering – PSE 2021+
June 19-23, 2022, Kyoto, Japan
http://dx.doi.org/10.1016/B978-0-323-85159-6.50014-2

Retrosynthesis Pathway Design Using Hybrid Reaction Templates and Group Contribution-Based Thermodynamic Models

Wang W., Liu Q., Zhang L.*, Dong Y., Du J.

Institute of Chemical Process Systems Engineering, School of Chemical Engineering, Dalian University of Technology, Dalian 116024, CHINA
keleiz@dlut.edu.cn

Abstract

Organic synthesis plays an essential role in the pharmaceutical industry. Traditionally, knowledge-based methods are used for the design of synthesis route, which is expensive and time-consuming and thus hinders the high-throughput design of the synthesis route. In this article, a retrosynthetic analysis framework is established using hybrid reaction templates and Group Contribution (GC)-based thermodynamic models. First, a hybrid database consisting of partial atom-mapping and full atom-mapping reaction templates is constructed utilizing well-studied organic reactions from literature. Second, numerous virtual reactions are generated from reaction templates with respect to target molecule, and reaction thermodynamic models based on the GC method are developed to validate the effectiveness of virtual reactions in a timely fashion. Finally, Breadth-First Search (BFS) algorithm is employed to search candidate retrosynthesis pathways which are thermodynamically feasible. In this procedure, five quantitative criteria are used to identify the top-ranked routes, including Fathead Minnow 96-hr LC_{50} ($LC_{50}FM$), flash point (Fp), Natural Product-likeness Score (NPScore), Synthesis Accessibility Score (SAScore), and Synthesis Complexity Score (SCScore). With the help of the developed framework, synthesis routes considering thermodynamic feasibility can be obtained. Two case studies involving Aspirin and Ibuprofen are presented to highlight the feasibility and reliability of the proposed framework.

Keywords: Retrosynthesis pathway design; Reaction template; Reaction equilibrium constant; Group contribution method; Breadth-First Search algorithm

1. Introduction

Organic synthesis is one of the most crucial components of the modern pharmaceutical industry. Traditionally, knowledge-based methods are applied to design synthesis routes for different pharmaceutical products. Nowdays, Computer-Aided Synthesis Design (CASD) techniques have enabled in-silico retrosynthesis and thus received considerable attention from chemists (Law et al., 2008; Szymkuc et al., 2016; Schwaller et al., 2020). Various searching algorithms have been successfully applied to optimize different objectives of synthesis route design. A crucial step in retrosynthetic analysis is to find a method that constructs explicit or implicit relations between reactants and products. Corey and Wipke are forerunners in retrosynthesis for their efforts in introducing the Logic and Heuristics Applied to Synthetic Analysis (LHASA) in the 1960s (Corey & Wipke, 1969). In their work, reaction templates (a certain type of sub-molecular pattern that maps atom connectivity) were used as a bridge linking up reactants with products.

Route Designer (Law et al., 2008) employed extended reaction templates to ensure the validity of synthesis routes. Syntaurus (Szymkuc et al., 2016) used more than 20,000 explicitly defined reaction rules to avoid obtaining absurd synthesis routes. The developers of Chematica (Szymkuc et al., 2016) have manually encoded more than 10,000,000 molecules and reactions to form synthesis networks. Among these methods, the reaction template is more favorable for its concise form in representing chemical reactions. Reaction templates are manually encoded by chemists who are experienced in organic synthesis. Gradually, chemists pay more and more attention to algorithms that automatically extract features as well as generate templates from the known reactions in commercial databases owned by pharmaceutical companies and non-commercial databases like USPTO (Lowe, 2014) and Reaxys (Goodman, 2009). So far, extraction algorithms have made significant progress in theory and practice. Law et al. (2008) focusing on extending the reaction cores to necessary chemical environments. Coley et al. (2017) used a heuristics-driven algorithm to extract reaction templates from the USPTO database. Reaction templates cannot work alone in retrosynthesis. Specialized algorithms written by expert chemists are used to cooperate with reaction templates. As the Artificial Intelligence (AI) develops, many researchers have found that Machine Learning (ML) can solve retrosynthesis when reaction templates are applied. Segler and Waller (2017) proposed a model for retrosynthesis using neural-symbolic ML and 103 hand-coded reaction templates, while Coley et al. (2017) applied ML and rigid reaction templates for the reversed problem. Template-free method is developing rapidly thanks to the new advancement in NLP (Natural Language Process) technology. Reactions written in SMILES (Simplified Molecular-Input Line-Entry System) (Weininger, 1998) notations are used to train RNN (Recurrent Neural Network) or Transformer model. The well-known template-free architecture is Molecular Transformer (Schwaller et al., 2019), which reads the mixed (or separated) strings of reactants, solvents, catalysts, and reagents as the inputs to predict possible product strings.

Although retrosynthesis analysis has been studied for several decades, there are remaining problems unsolved. Increasing the depth of a neural network or applying newly raised neural network architecture may allow us to get more satisfying results for prediction, but the relation between input and output becomes hard to be understood. Other aspects, such as process safety, environmental friendliness of reagents, and the price of raw materials, should also be considered during the process of synthesis route design. This paper presents a retrosynthetic analysis framework using hybrid reaction templates and GC-based thermodynamic models. The curated reaction templates are manually encoded according to available literature (Smith & March, 2001) to ensure the validity. In Section 2, the proposed three-steps framework is discussed in detail. In Section 3, two case studies are presented to highlight the feasibility and reliability of the proposed framework.

2. Retrosynthetic analysis framework using hybrid reaction templates and GC-based thermodynamic models

The proposed retrosynthetic analysis framework is divided into three parts: (1) Generate virtual routes; (2) Verify virtual routes; (3) Rank valid routes, as shown in Figure 1.

2.1. Step 1: Generate virtual routes

Reaction template is a sub-molecular pattern that maps atom connectivity. SMARTS strings are used to encode reaction templates in this framework since they are fully supported in RDKit (Landrum, 2016). Chemical reactions written in SMARTS strings are reversible by simply switching reactants and products. SMARTS strings are classified into two categories according to the completeness, called partial atom-mapping and full atom-mapping. Partial atom-mapping SMARTS strings have asymmetric numbers labeling, while full atom-mapping SMARTS strings have symmetric numbers labeling. The most of the SMARTS strings in the well-known USPTO 1976-2016 database (Lowe, 2014) are partial atom mapping and thus hardly useful for our framework. As a result, the reaction template database is established manually according to available literature (Smith & March, 2001). In our reaction template database, 347 different reaction templates covering the most used reactions are established. These reaction templates are classified into nine categories. Some partial atom-mapping reaction templates (9.7% of total reaction templates) in our reaction template database are kept maintaining the diversity of the reaction template database.

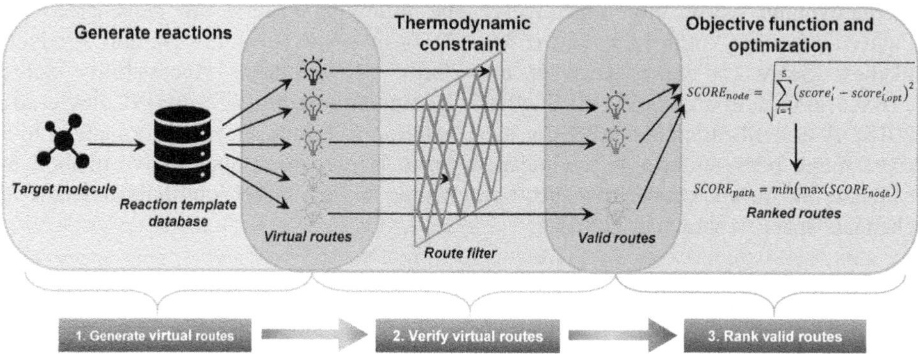

Figure 1. A three-step retrosynthesis analysis framework using hybrid reaction templates and GC-based thermodynamic models

2.2. Step 2: Verify virtual routes

Chemical equilibrium theory provides a convenient way to evaluate whether a reaction is able to occur or not under a given temperature. For isothermal and isobaric reaction, the reaction equilibrium constant is correlated with the change of standard molar Gibbs free energy of the reaction $\Delta_r G_m^\theta$, ideal gas constant R and reaction temperature T, as shown in Eq.(1).

$$K = \exp\left(-\Delta_r G_m^\theta / RT\right) \tag{1}$$

A more flexible formula for calculating reaction equilibrium constant using standard molar Gibbs free energy is expressed as Eq.(2), which is derived under a rational assumption as per the textbook "Principles of Modern Chemistry (7th Ed)" (Oxtoby et al., 2011).

$$\Delta_r G_m^\theta(T) = \sum_j \upsilon_j \Delta_f H_{m,j}^\theta(298.15\text{ K}) - T \sum_j \upsilon_j S_{m,j}^\theta(298.15\text{ K}) \tag{2}$$

Here, $\Delta_f H_{m,j}^\theta$ and $S_{m,j}^\theta$ represent the standard molar enthalpy of formation and the standard molar entropy for compound j, respectively; υ_j is the stoichiometric coefficient of compound j. Existing databases such as Lange's Handbook of Chemistry (Speight, 2005) contain thermodynamic parameters at 298.15 K for most common molecules. However, molecules involved in retrosynthesis pathway design are usually intermediates whose thermodynamic parameters are not readily available from the databases. Therefore, GC methods are introduced here as an alternative way to calculate relevant thermodynamic parameters and other properties that are involved in retrosynthesis pathway design. The relevant data used in GC methods come from our previous work in solvent design (Liu et al., 2019). BFS algorithm is widely used in solving problems like shortest path problems and minimum steps problems. Pre-set reaction equilibrium constant K_0 is used as a criterion to keep the BFS algorithm focusing on the most promising reaction routes. An online database of market-buyable molecule is introduced to improve computational effectiveness and accelerate convergence.

Step 3: Rank valid routes

In this step, a quantitative evaluation system is developed to rank routes that pass the thermodynamic verification objectively. The following criteria are considered: (1) Fathead Minnow 96-hr LC_{50} ($LC_{50}FM$); (2) flash point (Fp); (3) Natural Product-likeness Score (NPScore) (Ertl et al., 2008); (4) Synthesis Accessibility Score (SAScore) (Ertl et al., 2009); (5) Synthesis Complexity Score (SCScore) (Coley et al., 2018). A normalization is applied for each criterion to ensure they are normalized to a fixed range between 0 to 1. Euclidean distance is used as a quantitative method to calculate the distance between a specific molecule and the target (optimal) molecule in chemical space as shown in Eq.(3).

$$SCORE_{node} = \sqrt{\sum_{i=1}^{5}\left(score_i' - score_{i,opt}'\right)^2} \tag{3}$$

In a multi-step synthetic problem, the node with the highest value of $SCORE_{node}$ is deemed to be the synthesis-determining step. After finding all the synthesis-determining steps of corresponding routes, their scores are ranked in ascending order to find out the optimal synthesis route as shown in Eq.(4).

$$SCORE_{path} = \min\left(\max(SCORE_{node})\right) \tag{4}$$

The $SCORE_{path}$ in Eq.(4) is defined as the score of a full synthesis route, representing the synthetic features of the synthesis route. If any additional criterion needs to be considered in the future, Eq.(3) is extensible while Eq.(4) remains valid.

3. Case studies

3.1. Synthesis route design for Aspirin

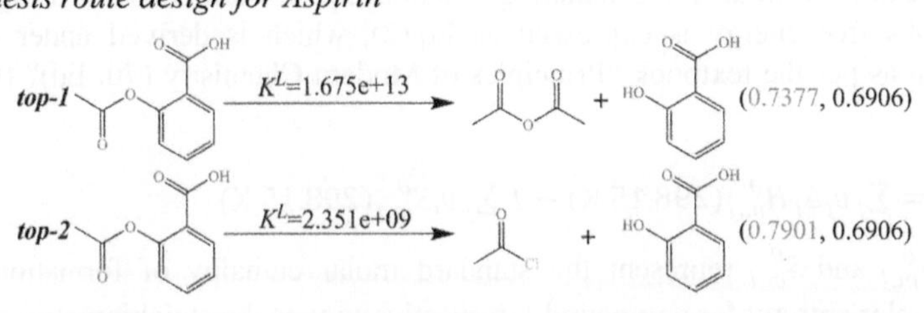

Figure 2. The results of synthesis route design for Aspirin

The SMILES of Aspirin is required, which is CC(=O)OC1=CC=CC=C1C(=O)O. Here, K_0 was set to 100 and search depth was set to 2. The reaction temperature was set to

298.15 K in order to search reactions that are feasible at room temperature. The results of synthesis route design for Aspirin are shown in Fig. 2.

According to Eq. (4), the optimal synthesis route for Aspirin is to use acetic anhydride reacting with salicylic acid, which is consistent with the industry practice. Acetyl chloride gets a higher overall score for its low flash point and thus ranked second.

3.2. Synthesis route design for Ibuprofen

The SMILES of Ibuprofen is required, which is CC(C)CC1=CC=C(C=C1)C(C)C(=O)O. All synthesis constraints were the same as Aspirin except for the search depth which was set to 3. The design results for Ibuprofen are shown in Fig. 3.

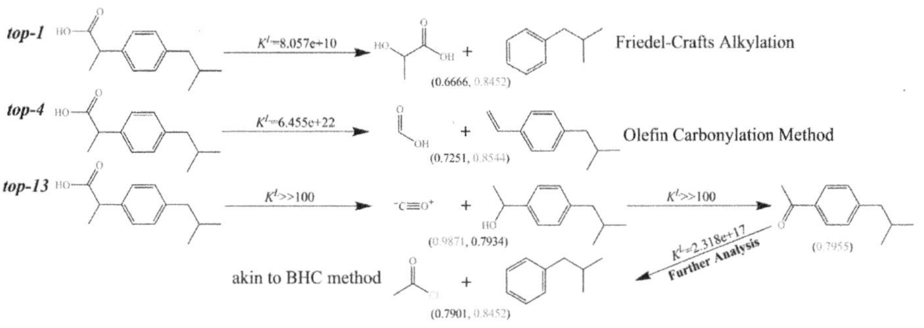

Figure 3. The results of synthesis route design for Ibuprofen

The top-1 route is Friedel-Crafts alkylation which tends to produce multi-substituted products. The catalysts with high shape-selectivity are needed to make this route practical. The well-known olefin carbonylation method is found and ranked 4 while a method alike to BHC method is found and ranked 13.

4. Conclusions

In this paper, a retrosynthetic analysis framework using hybrid reaction templates and GC-based thermodynamic models is proposed. First, a hybrid reaction template database is used to generate various possible routes. Then, reaction equilibrium constant is used to verify the thermodynamic tendency of virtual routes while BFS algorithm is applied to the searching process. Finally, model criteria are proposed as a quantitative and efficient method to evaluate different synthesis routes. The constructed hybrid reaction templates database is reliable and can be updated manually. During the process of ranking synthesis routes, the concept of "synthesis-determining step" is introduced and integrated with the ranking system, and more attentions ought to be paid to the synthesis-determining steps. The synthesis route design results for Aspirin and Ibuprofen are satisfactory and thus highlight the feasibility and effectiveness of the proposed framework. The limitations are clear due to the using of thermodynamic models which only provide the tendency of reaction. Reaction kinetics should also be considered and work together with the thermodynamics. Considering reaction kinetics requires the knowledge of precise kinetic equations which could be a major obstacle for developing reaction kinetics-based models in retrosynthesis. In conclusion, the proposed framework provides a new solution for a rational retrosynthesis by utilizing reaction thermodynamics.

References

Coley, C. W., Barzilay, R., Jaakkola, T. S., Green, W. H., Jensen, K. F., 2017. Prediction of Organic Reaction Outcomes Using Machine Learning. ACS Cent. Sci. 3, 434-443.

Coley, C. W., Rogers, L., Green, W. H., Jensen, K. F., 2018. SCScore: Synthetic Complexity Learned from a Reaction Corpus. J. Chem. Inf. Model. 58, 252-261.

Corey, E. J., Wipke, W. T., 1969. Computer-Assisted Design of Complex Organic Syntheses. Science. 166, 178-192.

Ertl, P., Roggo, S., Schuffenhauer, A., 2008. Natural Product-likeness Score and Its Application for Prioritization of Compound Libraries. J. Chem. Inf. Model. 48 (1), 68-74.

Ertl, P., Schuffenhauer, A., 2009. Estimation of synthetic accessibility score of drug-like molecules based on molecular complexity and fragment contributions. J. Cheminform. 1, 8.

Goodman, J. 2009. Computer Software Review: Reaxys. J. Chem. Inf. Model. 49 (12), 2897-2898.

Landrum, G., 2016. RDKit: Open-source cheminformatics; http://rdkit.org, (accessed March 15, 2020).

Law, J., Zsoldos, Z., Simon, A., Reid, D., Liu, Y., Khew, S. Y., Johnson, A. P., Major, S., Wade, R. A., Ando, H. Y., 2009. Route Designer: A Retrosynthetic Analysis Tool Utilizing Automated Retrosynthetic Rule Generation. J. Chem. Inf. Model. 49, 593-602.

Lowe, D. M., 2014. Patent reaction extraction: downloads. https://bitbucket.org/dan2097/patent-reaction-extraction/downloads, (accessed November 6, 2019).

Liu, Q., Zhang, L., Tang, K., Feng, Y., Zhang, J., Zhuang, Y., Liu, L., Du, J., 2019. Computer-aided reaction solvent design considering inertness using group contribution-based reaction thermodynamic model. Chem. Eng. Res. Des. 152, 123-133.

Oxtoby, D. W., Gillis, H. P., Campion, A., Helal, H. H., Gaither, K. P.,2011. Principles of Modern Chemistry, 7th Ed. CENGAGE Learning, Belmont.

Schwaller, P., Laino, T., Gaudin, T., Bolgar, P., Bekas, C., Lee, A. A., 2019. Molecular Transformer: A Model for Uncertainty-Calibrated Chemical Reaction Prediction. ACS Cent. Sci. 5 (9), 1572-1583.

Schwaller, P., Petraglia, R., Zullo, V., Nair, V. H., Haeuselmann, R. A., Pisoni, R., Bekas, C., Luliano, A., Laino, T., 2020. Predicting retrosynthetic pathways using a combined linguistic model and hyper-graph exploration strategy. Chem. Sci. 11, 3316-3325.

Segler, M. H. S., Waller, M. P., 2017. Neural-Symbolic Machine Learning for Retrosynthesis and Reaction Prediction. Chem. Eur. 23, 5966-5971.

Smith, M. B., March, J., 2001. March's Advanced Organic Chemistry, 5th Ed. John Wiley & Sons, New Jersey.

Speight, J. G., 2005. Lange's Handbook of Chemistry, 16th Ed. McGraw-Hill, New York.

Szymkuc, S., Gajewska, E. P., Klucznik, T., Molga, K., Dittwald, P., Startek, M., Bajczyk, M., Grzybowski, B. A., 2016. Computer-Assisted Synthetic Planning: The End of the Beginning. Angew. Chem. Int. Ed. 55, 5904-5937.

Weininger, D., 1998. SMILES, a Chemical Language and Information System 1. Introduction and Encoding Rules. J. Chem. Inf. Comput. Sci. 28, 31-36.

Proceedings of the 14th International Symposium on Process Systems Engineering – PSE 2021+
June 19–23, 2022, Kyoto, Japan
http://dx.doi.org/10.1016/B978-0-323-85159-6.50015-4

Optimization-based Design of Product Families with Common Components

Chen Zhang[a], Clas Jacobson[a], Qi Zhang[b], Lorenz T. Biegler[c], John C. Eslick[d,e], Miguel A. Zamarripa[d,e], David Miller[d], Georgia Stinchfield[c], John D. Siirola[f], Carl D. Laird*[c]

[a]*Carrier Global Corporation, Palm Beach Gardens, Florida 33418*
[b]*Dept. of Chem. Eng. and Materials Science, U. of Minnesota, Minneapolis, MN 55455*
[c]*Carnegie Mellon University, 5000 Forbes Ave, Pittsburgh, PA 15213, United States*
[d]*National Energy Technology Laboratory, Pittsburgh, Pennsylvania, USA*
[e]*NETL Support Contractor, Pittsburgh, Pennsylvania, USA*
[f]*Sandia National Laboratories, P.O. Box 5800, Albuquerque, NM 87123, United States*

**claird@andrew.cmu.edu*

Abstract

For many industries addressing varied customer needs means producing a family of products that satisfy a range of design requirements. Manufacturers seek to design this family of products while exploiting opportunities for shared components to reduce manufacturing cost and complexity. We present a mixed-integer programming formulation that determines the optimal design for each product, the number and design of shared components, and the allocation of those shared components across the products in the family. This formulation and workflow for product family design has created significant business impact on the industrial design of product families for large-scale commercial HVAC chillers in Carrier Global Corporation. We demonstrate the approach on an open case study based on a transcritical CO_2 refrigeration cycle. This case study and our industrial experience show that the formulation is computationally tractable and can significantly reduce engineering time by replacing the manual design process with an automated approach.

Keywords: product family design, discrete optimization, product manufacturing

1. Introduction

For many industries, addressing global markets and varied customer needs means producing a family of products that are able to satisfy a range of design requirements. For example, commercial chiller systems for HVAC sold in different regions of the world are subject to different operating and boundary conditions, customer cost and performance expectations, and efficiency regulations. This requires the design and manufacturing of a family of products to meet requirements of different geographical regions and customer needs. Optimizing each of the products independently results in significantly increased manufacturing cost and complexity since each design will include unique sizing for all of the sub-components, ignoring the potential for sharing these components across multiple products within the family. Therefore, manufacturers seek to design the entire family of products simultaneously, determining the optimal design for each product, the designs of common components, and the assignment of these components to each of the products in the family. This is a highly-combinatorial problem, that is typically performed with heuristics and ad-hoc approaches, takes significant engineering time, and results in sub-optimal designs. Many industries need effective design of product families that can exploit shared components, and this is an active area of research in manufacturing where various heuristics and optimization strategies have been applied (Simpson et al. 2014). Some examples of optimization-based approaches have focused on definition and optimization of a commonality index or degree of commonality (Thonemann & Brandeau 2000) and application of genetic algorithms (Liu et al. 2011). Integer programming techniques have also been used in, for example, the integration of the supply chain with the product family design (Baud-Lavigne et al. 2016). These concepts have applicability to chemical process design. In particular, for decentralized applications where many instances of similar processes with different performance specifications are required, the benefits of well-designed product families allow for significant reduction in engineering and construction costs.

In this paper, we present an mixed-integer programming formulation for product family design with common sub-components developed in collaboration with researchers at Carrier Global Corporation. Instead of manufacturing uniquely specified (e.g., sized) components for each product, we seek to manufacture a small number of component designs and share these across multiple products. The formulation determines the cost optimal designs for each of the products, the optimal sizing for the shared components, and the allocation of these components for each of the products. This formulation and workflow for product family design has created significant business impact on the industrial design of product families for large-scale commercial HVAC chillers in Carrier Global Corporation. In one application, the product family design workflow selected common compressors for a global family of over 200 products, leading to significant direct cost savings (material and labor), indirect cost savings (prototype design, build, and test), and an order of magnitude reduction in R&D time associated with this task. This process is being used and extended within Carrier across several product lines.

We demonstrate the product family design formulation on an open case study considering a family of HVAC products based on a CO_2 refrigeration cycle described in Li & Groll (2005). The model for the system is built using the IDAES process modeling platform (Lee et al. 2021) and the product family design problem is implemented in Pyomo (Bynum et al. 2021). The approach is shown to be computationally tractable for real-world systems, with significantly reduced engineering time, replacing the manual design process with an automated, optimization-based approach.

2. Product Family Design Formulation

We assume that the set of products P and their performance requirements have already been specified (e.g., from market analysis). Product requirements may be captured as boundary conditions that must be matched exactly or as inequalities that provide bounds on the product performance. The set of components where there is opportunity for utilizing shared designs across multiple products is given by C, and the set of candidate designs for each component c is given by S_c. Our goal is to optimally design all of the products $p \in P$ while reducing the overall manufacturing costs by utilizing a (hopefully small) subset of the candidate component designs in these products.

For each product p we consider a set of design alternatives. For each alternative, we specify which candidate component designs are to be utilized in the product. For the initial set of design alternatives, we typically consider all combinations of candidate designs for each of the components (i.e., the Cartesian product of all S_c for all $c \in C$). Then, for each of these alternatives, we can perform simulations (or optimizations) and identify the alternatives that meet the required performance specifications. We define this set of all feasible alternatives for product p as A_p. The set Q_a is a tuple set that captures the specific candidate component designs used within each alternative a.

The proposed formulation for optimal design of product families with common components is shown in Equations (1-6). The binary variables z_{cs} identify which candidate designs s are selected for each component c, and x_{pa} captures which alternative is selected for product p. Equation (1) is the objective function, and the first term captures the expected cost associated with the family design where w_p is the expected sales (or sales fraction) for each product, and α_{pa} is the annualized cost if alternative a is selected for product p. The second term captures the cost required to develop the manufacturing process for each unique component selected. In many industrial examples, the cost of this manufacturing complexity is difficult to capture, and we can also constrain the number of candidate component designs selected with Equation (2).

$$\min_{x,z} \sum_{p\in P} w_p \sum_{a\in A_p} \alpha_{pa} x_{pa} + \sum_{c\in C} \sum_{s\in S_c} \beta_{cs} z_{cs} \tag{1}$$

s.t.

$$\sum_{s\in S_c} z_{cs} \leq N_c \qquad \forall\, c \in C \tag{2}$$

$$\sum_{a\in A_p} x_{pa} = 1 \qquad \forall\, p \in P \tag{3}$$

$$x_{pa} \leq z_{cs} \qquad \forall\, p \in P, a \in A_p, (c,s) \in Q_a \tag{4}$$

$$0 \leq x_{pa} \leq 1 \qquad \forall\, p \in P, a \in A_p \tag{5}$$

$$z_{cs} \in \{0,1\} \qquad \forall\, c \in C, s \in S_c. \tag{6}$$

Equation (3) ensures that only one alternative is selected for each product, and Equation (4) allows alternative a for product p only if the required components have been selected.

3. Process Case Study

For our case study, we consider the design of a family of products for commercial HVAC applications based on the transcritical CO_2 refrigeration cycle described in Li & Groll (2005). The process flow diagram is shown in Figure 1. We developed an IDAES model for this process using the standard unit model library with the exception of the ejector which required a custom model. The compressor model includes an efficiency curve to capture the drop in efficiency when it is operating away from the design flowrate. IDAES also includes a costing framework that was used to capture the equipment capital costs.

We consider two performance criteria when specifying the products P. The cooling capacity is the primary criterion determining the size of the components in the refrigeration

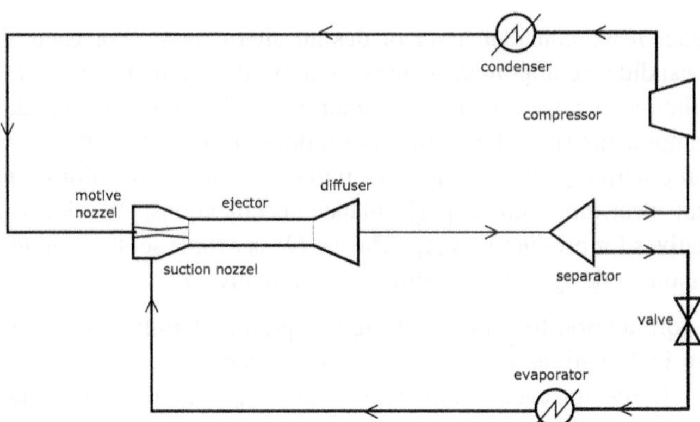

Figure 1: Process flowsheet for CO2 refrigeration cycle. This model was based on Li & Groll (2005)

cycle and can vary significantly based on customer needs. The outside air temperature varies significantly by region, and different units are designed for different conditions.

Here, we consider capacities of CAP=$\{80, 100, 120, 140, 160, 180, 200\}$ tons of refrigeration and outside air temperature specifications of OAT=$\{28, 29, 30, 31, 32, 33, 34, 35\}$ degrees Celsius. With these specifications, we have a total of 56 different products to consider, identified as the Cartesian product of all values in CAP and OAT.

The opportunities we consider for shared components across the products include the evaporator, the condenser, and the compressor, defining C=$\{\text{Evap}, \text{Cond}, \text{Compr}\}$. We consider five sizes of evaporator labeled A through E in order of increasing size, seven sizes of condenser labeled A through G in order of increasing size, and four sizes for the compressor, labeled A through D, also in order of increasing size. This gives us a total of 140 alternatives to consider for each product defined by the Cartesian product of the different candidate components specified as, $S_{\text{Evap}} = \{\text{A, B, C, D, E}\}$, $S_{\text{Cond}} = \{\text{A, B, C, D, E, F, G}\}$, and $S_{\text{Compr}} = \{\text{A, B, C, D}\}$.

We performed simulations for each of these alternatives across all the products (with CAP and OAT specified as boundary conditions) for a total of 7840 simulations. Of these, 3708 were infeasible and not able to meet the desired performance specifications. The feasible alternatives were used to define the remaining data required in the optimization formulation along with recorded capital and operating costs from the IDAES model.

The product family design problem (1-6) was formulated in Pyomo (Bynum et al. 2021) and solved using Gurobi (Gurobi Optimization, LLC 2021). We set the maximum number of candidate components to 2 for each of the evaporator, condenser, and compressor. Gurobi was able to solve this problem in under one second. Results showing the optimal designs are illustrated in Figure 2. The figure on the left shows the solution considering capital cost only (materials and construction). In this case, the optimization selected evaporators C and D, condensers A and B, and compressors A and B for manufacturing. The colors on the figure show unique designs, and the legend on the right indicates which selected components were matched with each design. The optimization selected a larger

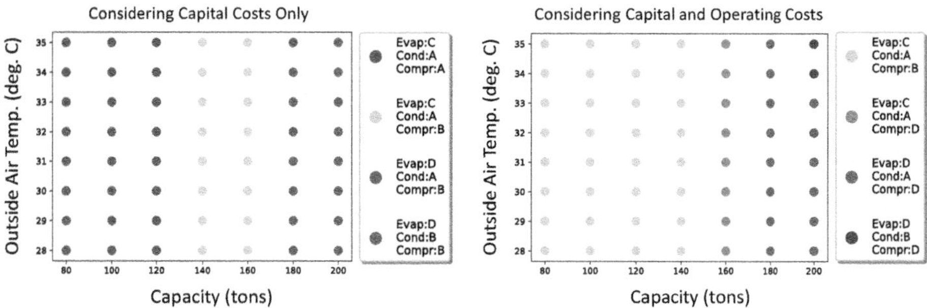

Figure 2: Optimal design of the product family with capital costs only on the left and capital plus operating costs on the right.

compressor when moving from 120 to 140 tons of capacity, and a larger evaporator when moving from 160 to 180 tons. As well, we see a change to a larger condenser for the higher outside air temperatures at the largest capacity. In this case, since we considered capital costs only, the optimization has selected the smallest compressors that are able to guarantee feasibility across the products. However, for most of these products, these compressors are operating off of their design flowrates and not achieving peak efficiency.

The figure on the right shows the optimal product family design considering both capital and operating costs. Here, we notice that the optimization did not select the smallest compressors, but has selected larger compressors so that they are operating closer to their design flowrate for improved operating efficiency.

4. Conclusion

In this paper, we have presented a formulation for optimal product family design. This formulation determines optimal designs across a set of products from a number of defined alternatives while reducing manufacturing costs by exploiting the opportunity for shared components across multiple products. This approach has been used industrially at Carrier Global Corporation with significant reduction in both costs and engineering time. The approach is also easily extended to support optimization of non-shared components by replacing the simulations with optimization problems for each of the alternatives considered.

This formulation can be efficiently solved for large data sets with commercial mixed-integer linear programming solvers. The computational bottleneck is the large number of simulations or optimizations that are required to gather the input data. It can be beneficial to use engineering knowledge to reduce the set of alternatives, and consequently, the total number of simulations that need to be performed.

It is important to note that there are a number of chemical process applications that can benefit from distributed operation of smaller, intensified, modular processes (Baldea et al. 2017). Any application that requires a large number of similar processes with variation in specific process requirements is an excellent candidate for the approaches outlined in this paper. This includes, for example, applications in water treatment, carbon capture from smaller localized sources, direct air capture, and other environmental processes. The concepts of product family design can be utilized to shift from one-off unique designs for each application to the definition of a suite of products that span the design space while reducing manufacturing costs with shared components.

References

Baldea, M., Edgar, T. F., Stanley, B. L. & Kiss, A. A. (2017), 'Modular manufacturing processes: Status, challenges, and opportunities', *AIChE journal* **63**(10), 4262–4272.

Baud-Lavigne, B., Agard, B. & Penz, B. (2016), 'Simultaneous product family and supply chain design: An optimization approach', *International Journal of production economics* **174**, 111–118.

Bynum, M. L., Hackebeil, G. A., Hart, W. E., Laird, C. D., Nicholson, B. L., Siirola, J. D., Watson, J.-P. & Woodruff, D. L. (2021), *Pyomo—Optimization Modeling in Python*, Vol. 67, Springer Nature.

Gurobi Optimization, LLC (2021), 'Gurobi Optimizer Reference Manual'.
URL: *https://www.gurobi.com*

Lee, A., Ghouse, J. H., Eslick, J. C., Laird, C. D., Siirola, J. D., Zamarripa, M. A., Gunter, D., Shinn, J. H., Dowling, A. W., Bhattacharyya, D. et al. (2021), 'The idaes process modeling framework and model library—flexibility for process simulation and optimization', *Journal of Advanced Manufacturing and Processing* p. e10095.

Li, D. & Groll, E. A. (2005), 'Transcritical co2 refrigeration cycle with ejector-expansion device', *International Journal of refrigeration* **28**(5), 766–773.

Liu, Z., San Wong, Y. & Lee, K. S. (2011), 'A manufacturing-oriented approach for multiplatforming product family design with modified genetic algorithm', *Journal of Intelligent Manufacturing* **22**(6), 891–907.

Simpson, T. W., Jiao, J., Siddique, Z. & Hölttä-Otto, K. (2014), 'Advances in product family and product platform design', *New YorN: Springer* .

Thonemann, U. W. & Brandeau, M. L. (2000), 'Optimal commonality in component design', *Operations Research* **48**(1), 1–19.

Acknowledgements and Disclaimer: Neither the United States Government nor any agency thereof, nor any of their employees, nor the support contractor, nor any of their employees, makes any warranty, express or implied, or assumes any legal liability or responsibility for the accuracy, completeness, or usefulness of any information, apparatus, product, or process disclosed, or represents that its use would not infringe privately owned rights. Reference herein to any specific commercial product, process, or service by trade name, trademark, manufacturer, or otherwise does not necessarily constitute or imply its endorsement, recommendation, or favoring by the United States Government or any agency thereof. The views and opinions of authors expressed herein do not necessarily state or reflect those of the United States Government or any agency thereof. Sandia National Laboratories is a multimission laboratory managed and operated by National Technology and Engineering Solutions of Sandia, LLC., a wholly owned subsidiary of Honeywell International, Inc., for the U.S. Department of Energy's National Nuclear Security Administration under contract DE-NA-0003525. This paper describes objective technical results and analysis. Any subjective views or opinions that might be expressed in the paper do not necessarily represent the views of the U.S. Department of Energy or the United States Government. The authors acknowledge contributions of Dr. Rui Huang who assisted with the problem formulation and workflow definition.

Proceedings of the 14th International Symposium on Process Systems Engineering – PSE 2021+
June 19-23, 2022, Kyoto, Japan
http://dx.doi.org/10.1016/B978-0-323-85159-6.50016-6

Economic evaluation and analysis of electricity and nano-porous silica productions from rice husk

Semie kim[a], and Young-Il Lim [a*]

[a]*CoSPE, Department of Chemical Engineering, Hankyong National University, Gyeonggi-do, Anseong-si, Jungang-ro 327, 17579 Republic of Korea*
limyi@hknu.ac.kr

Abstract

Techno-economic analysis (TEA) was performed for the production of electricity or nano-porous silica (NPS) from 50 t/d of rice husk (RH). The process for electricity generation from RH had a net electricity efficiency of 15%. Using the same amount of RH (approximately 2 t/h), 278 kg/h of NPS was produced. The electricity production process was not profitable because of negative return on investment (ROI). In the case of producing NPS from RH, the total investment cost (TCI) and total production cost (TPC) were 13.7 M$ and 1.5 M$/y, respectively. The ROI and payback period (PBP) were predicted to be 3.7%/y and 17.5 y, respectively.

Keywords: Rice husk; Rice husk ash (RHA); Nano-porous silica (NPS); Electricity production; Techno-economic analysis (TEA)

1. Introduction

About 782 million tonnes of paddy rice were produced in the world in 2020. Asia accounts for 90% (705 million tonnes) of global production (FAO, 2020). During the milling process of paddy rice, rice husk is produced as an agricultural by-product (Peerapong and Limmeechokchai, 2009). 1,000 kg of paddy rice produces 220 kg of rice husk (Mor et al., 2017). 1,000 kg of rice husk (RH) produces 480~1,000 kW_e of electricity (Steven et al., 2021). Along with electricity generation, about 18~20 % of rice husk remains ash (Subbukrishna et al., 2007). The ash is mainly composed of silica (>90%) (Liu et al., 2011; Nayak et al., 2019). Silica with the purity of 95 wt% is used in industrial fields such as reinforced rubber additives (tire), materials (zeolite and polymer), concrete, and semi-conductor (Prasara-A and Gheewala, 2017; Steven et al., 2021). In general, Silica is produced from sand and sodium carbonate at 1400-1500 °C (Munasir and Triwikantoro, 2013). Sodium silicate (SS) is produced from RH ash burned at 650~850 °C (Kim and Kim, 2020). The nano-porous silica (NPS) is finally synthesized from a polymerization of SS in H_2SO_4 solution (Pode, 2016). Therefore, eco-friendly electricity and nano-porous silica (NPS) can be produced using rice husk, which is considered as a carbon-neutral biomass (Bergqvist et al., 2008; Pode, 2016).

In this study, two process flow diagrams (PFDs) were constructed for electricity and nano-porous silica (NPS) productions from rice husk using a commercial process simulator (ASPEN Plus, ASPEN Tech, USA). Based on the PFDs, the economic feasibility of the electricity and NPS production processes was compared using an equal amount of rice husk.

2. Process description

The rice husk (RH) used in this study is a by-product of paddy rice produced in Vietnam. Table 1 shows the proximate and ultimate analyses of RH containing 41.0 wt% carbon, 5.5 wt% hydrogen, 34.9 wt% oxygen, 0.7 wt% nitrogen, 0.1 wt% sulfur, and 17.8 wt% ash. The ash includes 94.20 wt% SiO_2, 0.75 wt% P_2O_5, 2.88 wt% K_2O, 0.97 wt% CaO, and 1.20 wt% others.

Table 1. Proximate and ultimate analyses of rice husk (RH) in this study.

Proximate analysis (wt%)		Ultimate analysis (wt%, dry basis)		Ash	
Moisture	10.00	C	41.0	SiO_2	94.20
Volatile matter	68.30	H	5.5	P_2O_5	0.75
Fixed carbon	13.68	O	34.9	K_2O	2.88
Ash	16.02	N	0.7	CaO	0.97
		S	0.1	others	1.20
		Ash	17.8		
Total	100.00		100.0		100.00
HHV (MJ/kg)	14.80				

To compare the economic values of the electricity or NPS production process, the same amount of RH (50 t/d) was used as a raw material. Two processes using RH were considered: Case 1 (electricity), and Case 2 (NPS).

Case 1 is the electricity production power plant from RH, as shown in Figure 1. The RH is burned with 50% excess air at 750 °C (see Eq. (1)).

$$Rice\ husk + O_2 \rightarrow H_2O + CO_2 + SiO_2 + others \quad (1)$$

The steam turbine generates electricity at 400 °C and 25 bar using the heat of combustion. The cyclone to remove fly-ash, bag-filter and bird blue scrubber to remove fine dust were used.

In Case 2, the NPS is produced using RHA (see Figure 2). RHA reacts with sodium carbonate to produce sodium silica (SS) in the hydrothermal synthesis reactor as shown in Eq. (2).

$$Na_2CO_3 + SiO_2 \rightarrow Na_2O \cdot 3.4SiO_2 + CO_2 \quad (2)$$

The activated carbon (AC), which is an unconverted carbon, is separated in the ultrafiltration. SS reacts with sulfuric acid to produce NPS (see Eq. (3)). Finally, NPS containing 6% moisture is produced through filtering and drying.

$$Na_2O \cdot 3.4SiO_2 + H_2SO_4 \rightarrow Na_2SO_4 + SiO_2 + H_2O \quad (3)$$

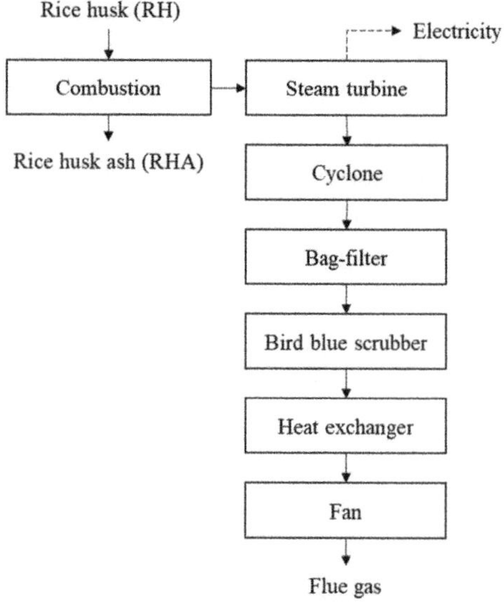

Figure 1. Block flow diagram (BFD) of electricity production from rice husk

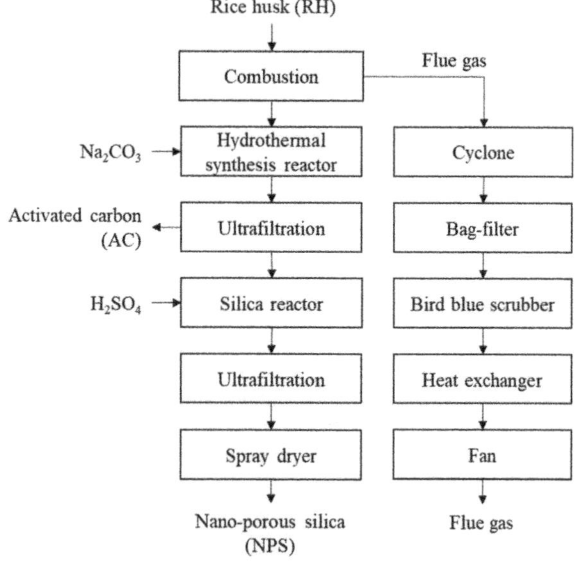

Figure 2. Block flow diagram (BFD) of NPS production from rice husk

3. Methodology of techno-economic analysis

The techno-economic analysis (TEA) is a method for determining the economic feasibility of a process (Do et al., 2014; Lim et al., 2016). The TEA used in this study investigates the technical feasibility of the process by calculating mass and energy balance using thermodynamic models and equations of state. In addition, the economic values such as the total investment cost (TCI), total production cost (TPC), return on investment (ROI), and payback period (PBP) are examined in the TEA (Kim and Lim, 2021; Kim et al., 2021).

Table 2 shows the assumptions used in economic evaluation. The prices of raw electricity and cooling water are the same as Vu et al. (Vu et al., 2020). For the raw material price, the 2019 market price was applied. The prices of RH, AC and NPS were assumed to be 10, 1,000, and 1,500 \$/t, respectively.

Table 2. Economic assumptions for electricity or NPS plants from rice husk.

Parameter		Assumption	Unit
Debt ratio (λ)		0.7	
Plant availability		8000	h/y
Startup time (50% plant performance)		4	month
Plant lifetime (L_p)		20	y
Inflation rate (α)		2	%/y
Corporation tax rate (β)		20	%/y
Interest rate (γ)		6	%/y
Raw material and product price	Rice husk	10	\$/t
	Na_2CO_3	200	\$/t
	H_2SO_4	143	\$/t
	Activated carbon	1,000	\$/t
	Nano-porous silica	1,500	\$/t
Utility price	Electricity	0.098	\$/kWh
	Liquefied natural gas	0.5	\$/kg
	Cooling water	0.273	\$/m^3

4. Results

The performance and economic feasibility of the electricity or NPS production process from RH were compared.

4.1. Process performance

The process simulation was performed for the two processes to produce electricity and NPS, respectively. Table 3 shows the process performance for the two processes. In Case 1, electricity was 1,343 kW_e from 2,083 kg/h (50 t/d) rice husk. The 90 kW_e was consumed for steam turbine, flue gas treatment, and air compression. The net electricity was 1,254 kW_e, which was a net electricity efficiency of 15% . Case 2 produced 278 kg/hr NPS and 40 kg/hr AC with the same amount of rice husk as Case 1. An electricity of 90.5 kW_e was consumed in NPS production.

Table 3. Process performance for electricity or NPS plants from rice husk.

	Case 1	Case 2	Unit
Feed (Rice husk) flow rate	2,083.3	2,083.3	kg/h
Product			
Nano-porous silica	-	278.1	kg/h
Activated carbon	-	39.5	kg/h
Electricity	1,343.2	-	kW_e
Electricity consumption	88.9	90.5	kW_e
Net electricity	1,254.3	-	kW_e
Net electricity efficiency	14.9	-	%

4.2. Economic values (TCI, TPC, POI, and PBP)

Table 4 shows the economic values of the processes for electricity or NPS production from rice husk. The TCI for electricity generation (Case 1) including combustion, flue gas treatment, and steam turbines was 13,447 k$. In Case 2 including hydrothermal synthesis reactor, filter, and dryer for NPS production, TCI was 13,705 k$. The TPCs of Case 1 and Case 2 were 998 and 1,476 k$/y.

Case 1 was not economically feasible because of negative ROI. The ROI and PBP of Case 2 were 3.7 %/y and 17.5 y, respectively.

Table 4. Economic values for electricity or NPS plants from rice husk.

Economic values	Case 1	Case 2	Unit
Total capital investment (TCI)	13,446.9	13,705.1	k$
Total production cost (TPC)	997.9	1,476.1	k$/y
Return on investment (ROI)	-	3.7	%/y
Payback period (PBP)	-	17.5	y

5. Conclusions

The agricultural by-products are produced from crop production, and an eco-friendly process is required to treat the by-products. In this study, the economic feasibility of electricity or NPS production process was compared using the same amount of rice husk (50 t/d). The electricity production plant included a combustor and steam turbine. The NPS plant included a combustor, reactor, filter, and dryer. An electricity of 1,254 kW_e were produced with a net electrical efficiency of 14.9%. The 278 kg/h NPS was produced using the same amount of RH. The TCI and TPC of the electricity production plant were13,447 k$ and 998 k$/y, respectively, which was not profitable. Those of the NPS production plant were13,705 k$ and 1,476 k$/y, respectively. The ROI was 3.7%/y, which may be attractive as a carbon-neutral technology.

References

M.M. Bergqvist, K. Samuel Wårdh, A. Das, E.O. Ahlgren, 2008, A techno-economic assessment of rice husk-based power generation in the Mekong River Delta of Vietnam, International Journal of Energy Research, 32, 12, 1136-1150.

T.X. Do, Y.-i. Lim, H. Yeo, Y.-t. Choi, J.-h. Song, 2014, Techno-economic analysis of power plant via circulating fluidized-bed gasification from woodchips, Energy, 70, 547-560.

FAO, 2020, World Food and Agriculture - Statistical Yearbook 2020.

J.G. Kim, J.Y. Kim, 2020. Method for Manufacturing Water Glass Using Rice Husk or Rice Husk Ash, no. 10-2097728.

S. Kim, Y.-I. Lim, 2021, Heat Integration and Economic Analysis of Dry Flue Gas Recirculation in a 500 MW e Oxy-coal Circulating Fluidized-bed (CFB) Power Plant with Ultra-supercritical Steam Cycle, Korean Chemical Engineering Research, 59, 1, 60-67.

S. Kim, Y.I. Lim, D. Lee, M.W. Seo, T.Y. Mun, J.G. Lee, 2021, Effects of flue gas recirculation on energy, exergy, environment, and economics in oxy-coal circulating fluidized-bed power plants with CO2 capture, International Journal of Energy Research, 45, 4, 5852-5865.

Y.-I. Lim, J. Choi, H.-M. Moon, G.-H. Kim, 2016, Techno-economic comparison of absorption and adsorption processes for carbon monoxide (CO) separation from Linze-Donawitz gas (LDG), Korean Chemical Engineering Research, 54, 3, 320-331.

Y. Liu, Y. Guo, Y. Zhu, D. An, W. Gao, Z. Wang, Y. Ma, Z. Wang, 2011, A sustainable route for the preparation of activated carbon and silica from rice husk ash, Journal of hazardous materials, 186, 2-3, 1314-1319.

S. Mor, C.K. Manchanda, S.K. Kansal, K. Ravindra, 2017, Nanosilica extraction from processed agricultural residue using green technology, Journal of cleaner production, 143, 1284-1290.

S. Munasir, Z. Triwikantoro, 2013, Book Synthesis of silica nanopowder produced from Indonesian natural sand via alkalifussion route, 1555, Issue, 28-31.

P.P. Nayak, S. Nandi, A.K. Datta, 2019, Comparative assessment of chemical treatments on extraction potential of commercial grade silica from rice husk, Engineering Reports, 1, 2, e12035.

P. Peerapong, B. Limmeechokchai, 2009, Thermodynamic and Economic Analysis of 1.4 MWe Rice-Husk Fired Cogeneration in Thailand, Journal of Renewable Energy and Smart Grid Technology, 4, 2, 35-46.

R. Pode, 2016, Potential applications of rice husk ash waste from rice husk biomass power plant, Renewable and Sustainable Energy Reviews, 53, 1468-1485.

J. Prasara-A, S.H. Gheewala, 2017, Sustainable utilization of rice husk ash from power plants: A review, Journal of Cleaner production, 167, 1020-1028.

S. Steven, E. Restiawaty, Y. Bindar, 2021, Routes for energy and bio-silica production from rice husk: A comprehensive review and emerging prospect, Renewable and Sustainable Energy Reviews, 149, 111329.

D. Subbukrishna, K. Suresh, P. Paul, S. Dasappa, N. Rajan, 2007, Book Precipitated silica from rice husk ash by IPSIT process, Issue, 7-11.

T.T. Vu, Y.-I. Lim, D. Song, T.-Y. Mun, J.-H. Moon, D. Sun, Y.-T. Hwang, J.-G. Lee, Y.C. Park, 2020, Techno-economic analysis of ultra-supercritical power plants using air-and oxy-combustion circulating fluidized bed with and without CO2 capture, Energy, 194, 116855.

Proceedings of the 14th International Symposium on Process Systems Engineering – PSE 2021+
June 19-23, 2022, Kyoto, Japan
http://dx.doi.org/10.1016/B978-0-323-85159-6.50017-8

Future biofuels: A Superstructure-Based Optimization Framework Integrating Catalysis, Process Synthesis, and Fuel Properties

Juan-Manuel Restrepo-Flórez[a], Christos T. Maravelias[b,c*]

[a] Department of Chemical and Biological Engineering, University of Wisconsin–Madison, 1415 Engineering Drive, Madison, 53706, USA
[b] Department of Chemical and Biological Engineering, Princeton University, 50-70 Olden St, Princeton, 08540, USA
[c] Andlinger Center For Energy And Environment, Princeton University, 86 Olden St, Princeton, 08540, USA
maravelias@princeton.edu

Abstract

In this work, we present a process systems engineering framework that allows the integration of catalysis, process synthesis, and fuel property modelling enabling the systematic design of fuels with tailored properties and the biorefineries able to produce them. Methodologically, the proposed framework relies on a superstructure-based formulation in which three hierarchical decisions are made: what chemical products will undergo chemical transformations? what chemistries will be used to transform these chemical products? and which specific catalyst and processes will be used? This optimization framework is coupled with a fuel property model such that the decisions made at the process synthesis level are constrained by the desired fuel properties. We apply this framework to the problem of ethanol upgrading with an emphasis on three specific problems: First, we show how we can design biorefineries for the production of fuels (gasoline, diesel, or jet fuel) with specific properties. Second, we study the interplay between fuel properties and profit, and we show how the constraints imposed on the fuel properties impact both the optimal biorefinery designed and its economics. Finally, we show how the studied framework can be used to find the optimal biorefinery associated with a specific chemistry or catalyst. The results presented constitute the first systematic and comprehensive study of ethanol upgrading in which the simultaneous process and product design are considered.

Keywords: Biorefineries; superstructure; process synthesis; biofuels; product design.

1. Introduction

In the last twenty years, ethanol has been established as the dominant biofuel. However, ethanol has significant limitations: first, it can only be blended at a maximum 10% level with gasoline; and second, it is a poor replacement for middle distillates (Eagan et al., 2019a). These limitations are becoming increasingly problematic. At the same time, it is likely that in the near future there will be a surplus of ethanol, provided that the demand for blending at 10% is satisfied, and the consumption of gasoline will decrease as electric and fuel cell vehicles penetrate the market (Eagan et al., 2019a, 2019b; Fasahati and Maravelias, 2018). These challenges have prompted the search for technologies enabling the chemical transformation of ethanol into more fungible components. With this goal in mind numerous chemistries, catalysts, and processes have been developed (Eagan et al., 2019a; Sun and Wang, 2014). At first, research was focused on designing ethanol upgrading strategies yielding fuel products with properties similar to those of currently used fossil fuels. In recent years, however, we have come to realize that this vision is short-sighted (König et al., 2020). The diversity of chemistries associated with ethanol, which is known for been a platform chemical, can be exploited to design fuel products with properties not only equal but better than currently used fossil fuels. The realization of this vision requires the integration of such diverse areas as catalysis, process synthesis, and fuel property modelling (Restrepo-Flórez and Maravelias, 2021).

In this work we develop a superstructure-based framework for the automated design of biorefineries for ethanol upgrading. This framework is conceived such that we can simultaneously consider the design of processes (biorefineries) and fuels. Thus, enabling the design of biofuels with tailored properties. We apply this framework three problems (1) the identification of the optimal refinery to produce gasoline, diesel, and jet fuel (2) the characterization of the relation between fuel properties and profit, and (3) the identification of the optimal technology associated with a specific chemistry.

2. Superstructure description

An upgrading strategy can be defined as a sequence of chemical transformations leading to the production of products with desired properties. There are at least three decisions associated with the design of an upgrading strategy (1) which molecules will undergo transformation (2) which chemistries will be used to transform these molecules, and (3) which processes (reaction-separation system) will be used such that these chemical transformations can be accomplished. To represent this sequence of nested decisions we propose a hierarchical superstructure (Figure 1) containing three levels, each of which is associated with one of the aforementioned decisions (1) technology group, (2) technology and (3) module.

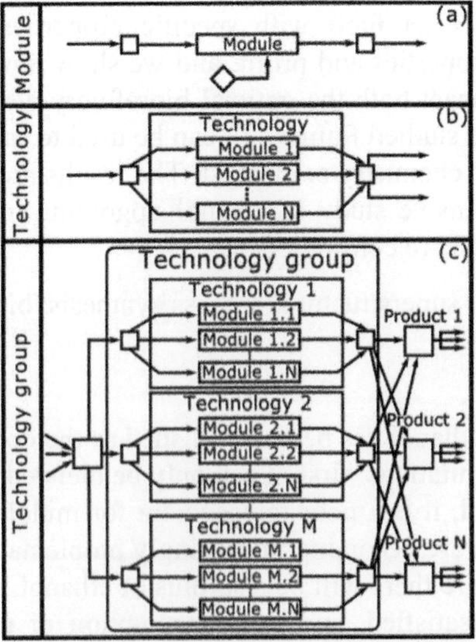

Figure 1. Superstructure architecture proposed and the three decision levels represented (a) Module (b) Technology (c) Technology group

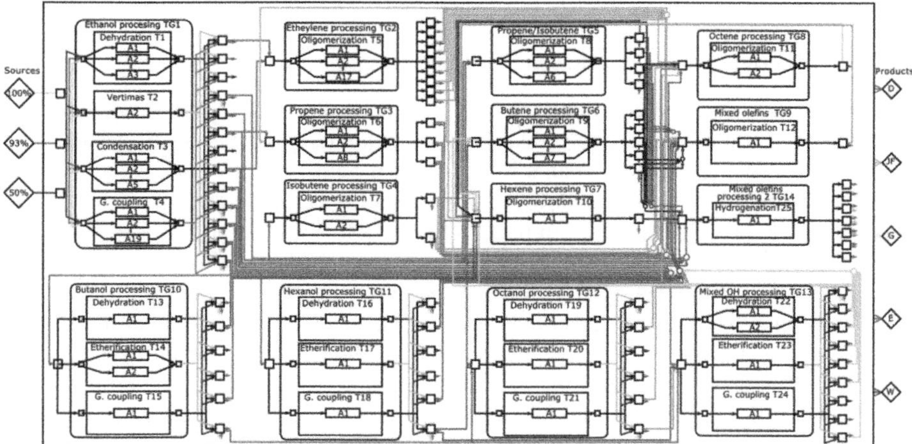

Figure 2. Ethanol upgrading superstructure containing the chemistries that can be used as well as feedstocks and final products. D: Diesel, JF: Jet fuel, G: Gasoline, E: Electricity, W: Waste.

In the case of ethanol, we use the architecture inf Figure 1 to build a comprehensive superstructure capturing the multiple chemistries available for ethanol upgrading (Figure 2). This superstructure is designed to consider three ethanol sources with different purity (50%, 93%, and 99.9%), and five products: gasoline, jet fuel, diesel, electricity, and waste. The superstructure is comprehensive because (1) it contains a representative set of the chemical reactions available for ethanol upgrading, and (2) it is richly connected, allowing to capture all feasible sequences of upgrading steps.

3. Mathematical model

The problem of finding the optimal sequence of upgrading steps to produce a given fuel can be represented as a mixed inter non-linear program (MINLP) model. The simplified mathematical representation is shown in Eq. (1). To write the model, we define three types of binary variables to account for the discrete decisions made at each of the superstructure levels (1) Y_i^{TG} $(\forall i \in \mathbf{I}^{\mathrm{TG}})$ (2) Y_i^{T} $(\forall i \in \mathbf{I}^{\mathrm{T}})$ and (3) Y_i^{M} $(\forall i \in \mathbf{I}^{\mathrm{M}})$, where $\mathbf{I}^{\mathrm{TG}}$ is the set of technology groups considered, $\mathbf{I}^{\mathrm{T}}$ the set of technologies, and $\mathbf{I}^{\mathrm{M}}$ the set of modules. The equations in the mathematical model can be grouped in (1) Process equations, used to model the selection of technology groups, technologies, and catalyst; represent mass balances for the different superstructure units; calculate capital and operating costs associated with the selected units; and enforce the superstructure connectivity (2) A fuel property model, used to estimate the values of the most relevant fuel properties.

$$Max(\text{Profit}) \qquad (1)$$
$$s.t. \begin{cases} \text{Process equations} \\ \text{Fuel property model} \end{cases}$$

The fuel property model consists of: Linear blending rules used to estimate the value of viscosity (υ), density (ρ), cetane number (CN), and octane number (RON) as a function of the fuel composition; a model of the distillation profile constructed based on the true boiling point approximation, according to which the components of a blend boil sequentially based on their boiling points; and a set of constraints limiting the amount of certain components (olefins, aromatics, and ethanol) in the final fuel blend.

4. Results

Optimal refineries to produce gasoline, jet fuel and diesel

The framework that we developed can be used to find the optimal sequence of upgrading operations required to produce a fuel with similar properties to gasoline, jet fuel, or diesel. We show these results by means of a Sankey diagram in Figure 3 (a-c). Additionally, we show the breakdown of capital and operating costs for each of these refineries in Figure 3(d-f). The simplest refinery also yielding the higher economic benefit is the one used to produce gasoline (Figure 3(a)). In this case, a Guerbet coupling module, followed by a hexanol dehydration module is enough to produce a blend satisfying the imposed constraints. In the case of jet fuel, the optimal biorefinery consists of an ethanol Guerbet coupling module followed by a butanol dehydration module and a sequence of oligomerization reactions. Additionally, the refinery also contains a small etherification module, and a hydrogenation module aimed at reducing the olefin content in the final fuel. Finally, in the case of diesel, the optimal biorefinery consists of a Guerbet coupling module, followed by a butanol dehydration module and a sequence of oligomerizations. This biorefinery also contains a hydrogenation unit. We note that in all cases the most important economic driver is the cost of the feedstock. This implies that to improve the biorefinery economics it is important to find strategies to reduce the cost of ethanol, or alternatively to increase the biorefinery's yield.

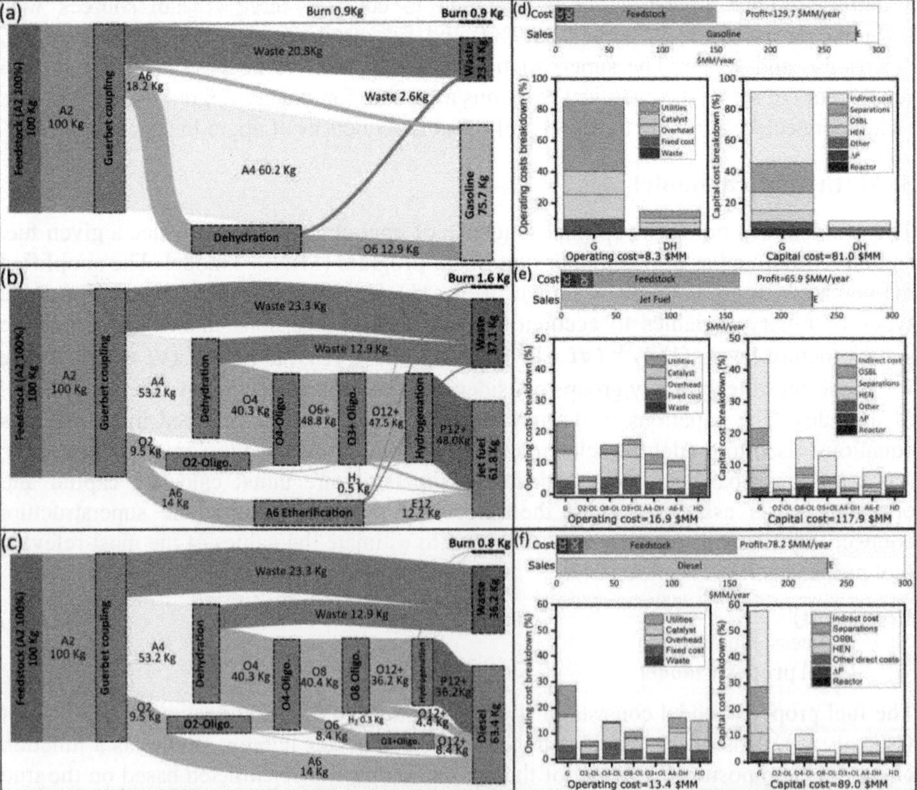

Figure 3. (a)(b)(c) Sankey diagram with the mass flows in the optimal biorefineries. (d)(e)(g) Capital and operating costs breakdown in these biorefineries.

The role of complexity

In Figure 4, we show the relation that exist between the biorefinery complexity, measured as the number of modules, and the profit and fuel composition in a diesel production biorefinery. Increasing complexity leads to a higher profit, but at the same time increases the operational challenges of the system. Understanding this relation is fundamental in the design stage of upgrading refineries.

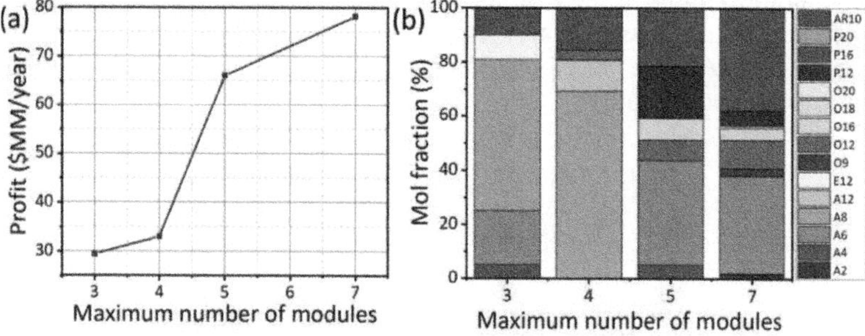

Figure 4. Effect of complexity on (a) profit and (b) fuel composition

The role of properties on the biorefinery economics

The production of high-quality fuels from ethanol is an exciting opportunity that opens the door to a new paradigm in biofuel research. In Figure 5, we study the role of fuel properties on the biorefinery economics (Figure 5(a)) and fuel composition (Figure 5(b)). Particularly, we study the effect cetane number on a diesel production biorefinery. Cetane number (CN) has been identified as a key property to mitigate NO_x emissions. Having a biofuel with high CN can serve two purposes: first, such a fuel burns cleaner; second, it can be used in blends with fossil diesel to raise the overall quality of the fuel. From Figure 5(a), we see that producing fuels with higher CN impacts the refinery economics, the higher the CN the lower the profit. In terms of fuel composition (Figure 5(b)), we note that as the CN increases so does the fraction of ethers (known for having a high CN) in the fuel. It is important to highlight that finding strategies to produce these fuels while simultaneously considering their properties was only possible because we used a framework able to capture the complexity of the problem.

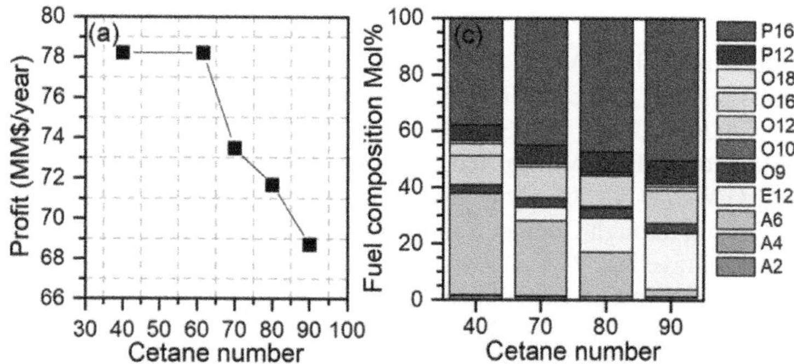

Figure 5. Effect of cetane number on (a) process economics and (b) fuel composition. Components are labelled using a character to identity of the functional group (P: paraffin, O: olefin, E: ether, A: alcohol), and a number to denote the number of carbons in the molecule.

Identification of optimal technologies

Another capability of the developed framework consists in providing insights as to the optimal strategy that can be used to produce a specific fuel by using a specific chemistry. For example, in Figure 6, we show the optimal biorefinery for diesel production obtained when we force the system to use ethanol dehydration. The strategy selected consist in dehydrating ethanol to ethylene, and then use a sequence of oligomerization reactions to increase the molecular weight. A final hydrogenation unit to reduce the olefin content is also employed. This kind of approach is useful to researchers working in the development of a specific chemistry to identify how their work fits into a broader context.

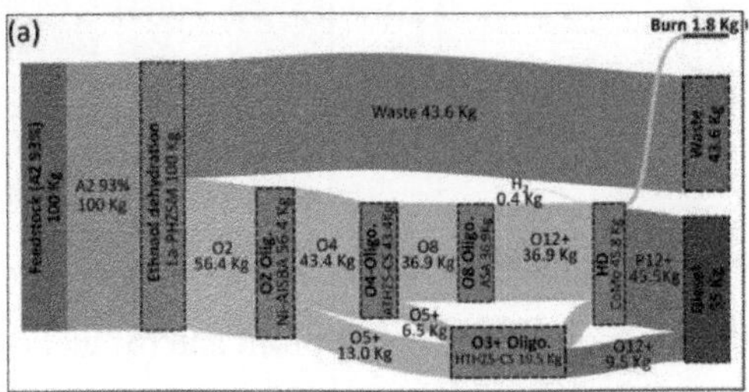

Figure 6. Sankey diagram showing the optimal refinery compatible with ethanol dehydration to produce diesel fuel

4. Conclusions

In this work, we developed a superstructure optimization approach to study the problem of ethanol upgrading toward fuels with tailored properties. We showed optimal ethanol upgrading strategies for the production of gasoline, jet fuel, and diesel. The most important cost driver in all cases was the cost of feedstock. We studied the relation between profit and biorefinery complexity and showed that increasing complexity may lead to improvements in the process economics. Additionally, we explored the relation between fuel properties and profit in the context of a diesel production biorefinery. We proved that it is possible to upgrade ethanol toward diesel fuel with high cetane number, with a superior quality than its fossil counterpart. This contrasts with typical approaches for biofuel production, focused on finding fuels with the same quality than fossil fuels.

References

Eagan, N.M., Kumbhalkar, M.D., Buchanan, J.S., Dumesic, J.A., Huber, G.W., 2019a. Chemistries and processes for the conversion of ethanol into middle-distillate fuels. Nat. Rev. Chem. 3, 223–249.

Eagan, N.M., Moore, B.J., McClelland, D.J., Wittrig, A.M., Canales, E., Lanci, M.P., Huber, G.W., 2019b. Catalytic Synthesis of Distillate-Range Ethers and Olefins from Ethanol through Guerbet Coupling and Etherification. Green Chem. 1–12.

Fasahati, P., Maravelias, C.T., 2018. Advanced Biofuels of the Future: Atom-Economical or Energy-Economical? Joule 2, 1915–1919.

König, A., Neidhardt, L., Viell, J., Mitsos, A., Dahmen, M., 2020. Integrated design of processes and products: Optimal renewable fuels. Comput. Chem. Eng. 134.

Restrepo-Flórez, J.M., Maravelias, C.T., Advanced fuels from ethanol – a superstructure optimization approach. Energy Environ. Sci., 2021, **14**, 493-506

Sun, J., Wang, Y., 2014. Recent advances in catalytic conversion of ethanol to chemicals. ACS Catal. 4, 1078–1090.

Proceedings of the 14th International Symposium on Process Systems Engineering – PSE 2021+
June 19-23, 2022, Kyoto, Japan
http://dx.doi.org/10.1016/B978-0-323-85159-6.50018-X

Superstructure Optimization of Biodiesel Production from Continuous Stirred Tank and Membrane Reactors

Thien An Huynh[a*], Vincent Reurslag[a], Maryam Raeisi[a], Meik B. Franke[a] and Edwin Zondervan[a]

[a]*Sustainable Process Technology, Faculty of Science and Technology, University of Twente, Meander, kamer 216, Postbus 217, 7500 AE Enschede, the Netherlands*
t.a.huynh@utwente.nl

Abstract

This work presents a superstructure model with the objective to maximize the total profit of biodiesel production by reducing the production cost and increasing the value of the by-product glycerol. The heat integration of the superstructure model is a novel feature which allows further reduction of utility costs and energy consumption of the biodiesel separation. The superstructure model is used to optimize two biodiesel production scenarios from a conventional continuous stirred tank reactor (CSTR) and a membrane reactor (MR). The superstructure optimization is solved with Advanced Interactive Multidimensional Modeling System (AIMMS) software. The annual profit of the new optimized production pathway for the conventional reactor is 840,606 $. The biodiesel production pathway with the membrane reactor consumed 70% less energy than the conventional reactor. However, the production cost of the MR is nearly two times higher than the CSTR due to the low biodiesel yield of the membrane reactor. The results show the potential to improve traditional biodiesel production and make intensified production methods more viable with the superstructure optimization.

Keywords: Biodiesel, Superstructure, Optimization, AIMMS, Process, Design.

1. Introduction

Biodiesel is a biofuel which is mainly obtained from chemical reactions between vegetable oil or animal fat with alcohol in the presence of a catalyst (Knothe et al., 2010). Biodiesel has become a potential solution for reducing greenhouse gas (GHG) because it has a lower net carbon dioxide (CO_2) emission than fossil fuels. CO_2 released from biodiesel engines is absorbed by plants which will be the feedstock for biofuel production making this a circular process (Hanaki and Portugal-Pereira, 2018). However, biodiesel is more expensive than fossil fuels, which poses a significant challenge for integrating the biofuel into GHG reduction strategies.

The cost of biodiesel can be reduced by optimizing its production which consists of reaction and purification processes. Intensified reactor designs which combine reaction and separation into one operation unit have been developed to improve biodiesel conversion and purity. A membrane reactor is a process intensification option which integrates a membrane separation into a cross-flow reactor to produce higher quality biodiesel than conventional reactors (Cao et al., 2008). Besides the reaction, the purification process plays an important role in biodiesel production as it accounts for 60-80% of the total production cost (Atadashi et al., 2011). Therefore, the optimization of a biodiesel purification process has become an important research topic. For example, several biodiesel purification scenarios have been simulated and analysed to identify the optimal biodiesel production process from soybean oil (Myint and El-Halwagi, 2009).

To design an optimal biodiesel production process, two methods are commonly used: the heuristic approach and the superstructure-based approach. The heuristic approach is based on rules derived from experience and understanding of unit operations while the superstructure approach is based on optimization algorithms and mathematical models to identify the optimal process from all possible alternatives (Tula et al., 2017). However, a disadvantage of the heuristic approach is that the interaction between different process stages and levels of detail are difficult to capture. The superstructure approach solves design problems simultaneously as a mathematical programming problem and therefore does not have this disadvantage (Mencarelli et al., 2020).

Superstructure optimization has become more popular in recent researches of biochemical process design. AlNouss et al. (2019) used superstructure optimization to develop an economic and environmentally friendly gasification process, which produces fuels, fertilizers, and power from multiple biomass sources. Galanopoulos et al. (2019) developed a superstructure framework for optimizing the design of an integrated algae biorefinery which can reduce the cost of biodiesel production up to 80%. However, superstructures for biodiesel production are usually generalized with a minimum numbers of operating units and a simplified glycerol purification process.

Therefore, this work proposes a superstructure model for biodiesel production that includes a wide range of operating units, a detailed glycerol purification section and heat integration functions. The model is used to optimize two biodiesel production processes from: a) continuous stirred tank reactor and b) membrane reactor. The results are compared with a conventional biodiesel production process (Zhang et al., 2003a,b).

2. Superstructure development

2.1. Problem statement

Given are the composition of feedstock and products from the transesterification reactor and options of processing equipment which are grouped into tasks and stages, and the technical and economic specifications of processing options. Under conditions that: 1) The possible processing routes are represented by logical constraints where each processing option is associated with a logical decision variable. 2) The flow rates in and out of an option complies with mass balance constraints. 3) The energy requirements are calculated based on the flowrates. 4) A heat integration function which is capable of matching hot and cold streams is integrated for further reduction of heating and cooling requirements. 5) The investment and operating costs are calculated according to according to the flowrates and energy requirement. The superstructure optimization problem decides the optimal biodiesel processing route while complying with logical, mass and energy constraints, and ASTM standards of biodiesel product (Zhang et al., 2003a), while maximizing the total profit of the biodiesel refinery.

2.2. Superstructure topology

The superstructure of the biodiesel purification section has 28 technical options which are relating to 28 binary decision variables and grouped into different tasks including phase separation, methanol removal, neutralization, washing and purification. By grouping similar options into tasks, the superstructure can be defined easier. The possible processing routes which are combinations of different options over 5 consecutive stages are presented in Figure 1. The input stream of the superstructure is the product stream of the transesterification reactor which converts vegetable oil into biodiesel. The main output is the biodiesel stream with purity of 99.65% according to ASTM standards. The glycerol output of phase separation tasks becomes the input of glycerol treatment superstructure.

In Figure 2, the glycerol superstructure is useful in deciding the numbers of treatment stages depending on the initial purity of glycerol input and the final grade of glycerol output. The final glycerol grades are waste glycerol (~ 50% - 85% wt. glycerol), crude glycerol (~85% - 98%) and technical glycerol (~98% - 99.5%) (Bart et al., 2010).

2.3. Mathematical model

The mathematical model includes mass balances of component k in each option j as shown in Eq.(1) and Eq.(2).

$$m_{j,k}^{P} = m_{j,k}^{F} \cdot SF_{j,k} \cdot y_i \tag{1}$$

$$m_{j,k}^{W} = m_{j,k}^{F} \cdot (1 - SF_{j,k}) \cdot y_i \tag{2}$$

where $m^{F}_{j,k}$, $m^{P}_{j,k}$ and $m^{W}_{j,k}$ are mass flow rates of feed (kg/h), product and waste streams of component k in and out option j, respectively. $SF_{j,k}$ is the split factor which indicates how much of component k going to product stream from the feed stream. y_j is the binary decision variable which is 1 if the option is selected and 0 if the option is not selected. The product stream of an option will be the feed stream of the next option on the same process route. The equipment cost (USD) of a technical option, EC_j, is presented in Eq.(3) (Seider et al., 2016).

$$EC_j = EC_j^{Ref,year} \cdot \left(\frac{m_j^F}{m_j^{F,Ref}}\right)^E \cdot \left(\frac{CE^{2020}}{CE^{year}}\right) \cdot y_j \tag{3}$$

where $EC^{Ref,year}{}_j$, $m^{F,Ref}$ and CE^{year} are the reference cost of the equipment, the reference capacity and the Chemical Engineering Index of the reference year, respectively. The total capital investment (TCI) is shown in Eq.(4) (Seider et al., 2016).

$$TCI = 1.05 \cdot f_{L,TCI} \cdot \Sigma_j(EC_j) \tag{4}$$

where 1.05 is the delivery cost of equipment to the plant location and $f_{L,TCI}$ is the Lang factor with value of 5.93 (Seider et al., 2016). The total annualized capital investment ($TACI$) is calculated with interest rate (IR) (0.1) and total project lifetime (LT) (20 years) as shown in Eq.(5).

$$TACI = TCI \cdot \frac{IR \cdot (IR+1)^{LT}}{(IR+1)^{LT}-1} \tag{5}$$

The objective function is to maximize the total annualized profit (TAP) as follows.

$$\max TAP = BDS + GLS - TACI - TAOP \tag{6}$$

where the total annual operating costs (*TAOP*), the annual biodiesel sales (*BDS*) and glycerol sales (*GLS*) are defined from the mass flow rate of the superstructure.

Heat integration of the superstructure optimization model is a function based on Pinch Technology to minimize the heating and cooling requirements of the biodiesel production. First, a series of heat intervals defined from the temperature differences of the product streams which are designated as hot streams or cold streams depending on their heating or cooling requirements. Second, the function selects hot and cold streams based on the decision variable in each product stream. Third, the hot and cold streams are matched with each other according to their temperature to calculate the total heat load of heat intervals and set up the heat cascade. Finally, the minimum hot and cold utility requirements can be predicted by balancing the negative heat interval of the infeasible heat cascade. To reduce the complexity of the model, the heat exchanger network and investment costs are not considered in the heat integration function.

The mathematical model is implemented in the software AIMMS, version 4.82.3.29 64-bit. The AIMMS solver is the Outer Approximation Algorithm, which is an algorithm using CPLEX 20.1 as MIP solver and CONOPT 4.1 as NLP solver. The model includes 1,602 constraints and 1,629 variables with 43 binary variables. The optimization problem is solved in an average of 1.83 s with a CPU Intel(R) Core(TM) i5-8265U CPU @ 1.80 GHz and 8.00 RAM.

3. Results and discussion

The superstructure model is applied for two base cases of biodiesel produced from CSTR and MR. The feedstock is rapeseed oil, infeed flowrate 1000 kg/h. The costs are calculated based on the price of biodiesel, feedstock, chemical and equipment in 2020.

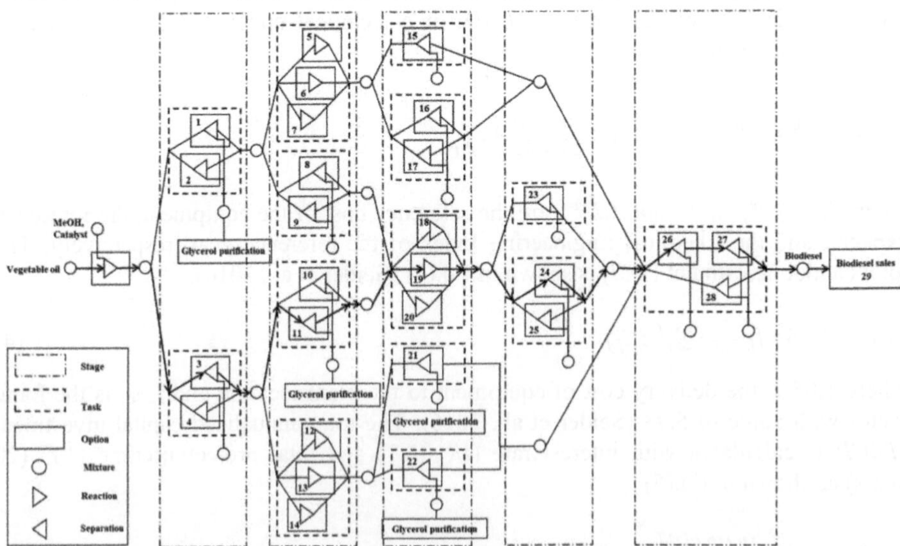

Figure 1: Superstructure of biodiesel purification from the transesterification of vegetable oil. The optimal processing route is the arrow line.

For the case of biodiesel produced in a CSTR, the optimal processing route is presented by the arrow line in Figure 1 and 2. The separation of methanol and glycerol at the first and second stages increases methanol recycle and reduces downstream equipment costs.

The third stage is neutralization of the base catalyst with H_2SO_4, then dry washing the product stream with magnesol. Finally, water, methanol and unreacted oil are removed from the biodiesel stream with vacuum flash evaporators to achieve the purity standard. The glycerol stream from second stage goes through neutralization and decanter to increase the glycerol content to 95%. The glycerol is sold as crude glycerol.

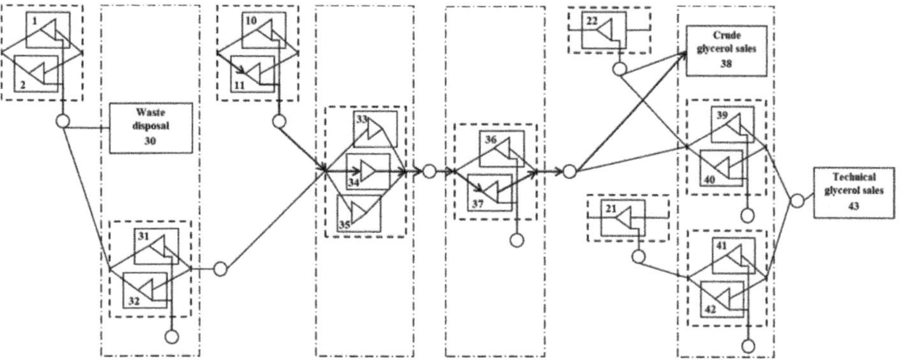

Figure 2: Superstructure of treatment routes for the glycerol separated from biodiesel production process. The arrows show the optimized glycerol processing route.

Options 1, 10, 22 and 36 are centrifuges; 2, 11 and 37 are decanters; 3, 8 and 31 are flash evaporators; 4, 9, 27, 32, 40 and 42 are vacuum distillation columns; 5, 12, 18 and 33 are neutralization with H_3PO_4; 6, 13, 19 and 34 are neutralization with H_2SO_4; 7, 14, 20 and 35 are neutralization with HCl; 15, 21 are 23 are water washing; 16 and 24 are dry washing with magnesol; 17 and 25 are dry washing with ion exchange resins; 26, 27, 39 and 41 are vacuum flash evaporators. Option 30 is treatment of waste glycerol with counting as expense of the process. Options 29, 38 and 43 are selling biodiesel, crude and technical glycerol, respectively.

The total annualized profit of the optimal process is 840,606 $ which is higher than the process proposed by Zhang (2003b). The explanation for finding different profits is that the optimal process has lower production costs by using magnesol dry washing instead of water washing, a system of flash evaporators instead of distillation columns and heat integration to reduce energy consumption.

For the case of MR, the superstructure model gives the same optimal processing route as the case of the CSTR. The difference is within the final purification stage where the MR case uses only one vacuum flash evaporator to remove methanol and water, because the membrane reactor removes the unreacted oil. Therefore, the energy requirement is 70% lower than the case of CSTR. However, the membrane reactor has only 56% biodiesel yield of the conventional reactor making the annualized profit of the process of membrane reactor negative, -2,126,584 $.

4. Conclusions

A superstructure model for optimizing the biodiesel production has been developed. The superstructure can be developed faster and expanded easier by grouping similar options into processing tasks. With a novel heat integration function, the proposed model can be used to identify the best processing route which minimizes the production cost and the energy requirement. The optimization results show the potential for improvement of biodiesel production in terms of economic and environment indicators. The optimized process of the CSTR shows a good profit and the case of MR has better energy consumption. However, the superstructure only considers one feedstock and two types of reactor. The superstructure will be extended to cover a large range of feedstock and different reaction technologies to further reduce the cost of biodiesel production.

References

A. AlNouss, G. McKay, T. Al-Ansari, 2019, Superstructure Optimization for the Production of Fuels, Fertilizers and Power using Biomass Gasification, Computer Aided Chemical Engineering, 46, 301-306, doi: 10.1016/B978-0-12-818634-3.50051-5.

A.K. Tula, D.K. Babi, J. Bottlaender, M.R. Eden, R. Gani, 2017, A computer-aided software-tool for sustainable process synthesis-intensification, Computers & Chemical Engineering, 105, 74-95, doi: 10.1016/j.compchemeng.2017.01.001.

C. Galanopoulos, P. Kenkel, E. Zondervan, 2019, Superstructure optimization of an integrated algae biorefinery, Computers & Chemical Engineering, 130, doi: 10.1016/j.compchemeng.2019.106530.

G. Knothe, J. Krahl, J.V. Gerpen, 2010, The biodiesel handbook 2nd ed., Urbana: Academic Press and AOCS Press.

I.M. Atadashi, M.K. Aroua, A.R. Abdul Aziz, N.M.N. Sulaiman, 2011, Refining technologies for the purification of crude biodiesel, Applied Energy, 88, 12, 4239-4251, doi: 10.1016/j.apenergy.2011.05.029.

J.C.J. Bart, N. Palmeri, S. Cavallaro, 2010, chap 13 - Valorisation of the glycerol by-product from biodiesel production, Biodiesel Science and Technology, Biodiesel Science and Technology, Woodhead Publishing, Cambridge, UK, 571-624, doi: 0.1533/9781845697761.571.

K. Hanaki, J. Portugal-Pereira, 2018, The Effect of Biofuel Production on Greenhouse Gas Emission Reductions, Biofuels and Sustainability: Holistic Perspectives for Policy-making, Springer Japan, 53-71, doi: 10.1007/978-4-431-54895-9_6.

L.L. Myint, M.M. El-Halwagi, 2009, Process analysis and optimization of biodiesel production from soybean oil, Clean Techn Environ Policy,11, 263–276, doi: 10.1007/s10098-008-0156-5.

L. Mencarelli, Q. Chen, A. Pagot, I.E. Grossmann, 2020, A review on superstructure optimization approaches in process system engineering, Computers & Chemical Engineering, 136, doi: 10.1016/j.compchemeng.2020.106808.

P. Cao, M.A. Dubé, A.Y. Tremblay, 2008, High-purity fatty acid methyl ester production from canola, soybean, palm, and yellow grease lipids by means of a membrane reactor, Biomass and Bioenergy, 32, 11, 1028-1036, doi: 10.1016/j.biombioe.2008.01.020.

T.A. Huynh, E. Zondervan, 2021, Dynamic modeling of fouling over multiple biofuel production cycles in a membrane reactor, Chemical Product and Process Modeling, doi: 10.1515/cppm-2020-0093.

W.D. Seider, D.R. Lewin, J.D. Seader, S. Widagdo, R. Gani, K.M. Ng, 2016, Product and Process Design Principles: Synthesis, Analysis and Evaluation - 4th Editiony, John Wiley & Sons Inc., New York, USA.

Y. Zhang, M.A. Dubé, D.D. McLean, M. Kates, 2003a, Biodiesel production from waste cooking oil: 1. Process design and technological assessment, Bioresource Technology, 89, 1, 1-16, doi: 10.1016/S0960-8524(03)00040-3.

Y. Zhang, M.A. Dubé, D.D. McLean, M. Kates, 2003b, Biodiesel production from waste cooking oil: 2. Economic assessment and sensitivity analysis, Bioresource Technology, 90, 3, 229-240, doi: 10.1016/S0960-8524(03)00150-0.

Proceedings of the 14th International Symposium on Process Systems Engineering – PSE 2021+
June 19-23, 2022, Kyoto, Japan
http://dx.doi.org/10.1016/B978-0-323-85159-6.50019-1

Process Design and Techno-Economic Analysis of Biomass Pyrolysis By-Product Utilization in the Ontario and Aichi Steel Industries

Jamie Rose, Thomas A. Adams II*

McMaster University, 1280 Main Street West, Hamilton, Ontario, Canada, L8S 4L7
**Corresponding Author: tadams@mcmaster.ca*

Abstract

Iron- and steel-making companies throughout the globe have been aiming to reduce emissions. One method to do so is to replace pulverized coal used in blast furnaces with biochar, but biochar is currently far more expensive than coal. To increase the value of biochar, by-products of pyrolysis can be combusted to generate heat and offset fossil fuel usage. In this study, pyrolysis by-product combustion was studied using Aspen Plus and process cost models to offset fuels in both Ontario, Canada, and Aichi, Japan. It was found that each tonne of biochar made produces by-products which save 130 USD and 1.47 t CO_2-e of emissions in Ontario, while in Aichi 96 USD and 2.44 t CO_2-e are saved.

Keywords: Biochar, Pyrolysis, Pulverized Coal Injection, Iron, Steel

1. Introduction

Steel production currently accounts for about 8% of annual anthropogenic carbon emissions (Worldsteel Association, 2021a). One method of reducing emissions is replacing coal used in pulverized coal injection in blast furnaces with biocarbon produced from the pyrolysis of biomass (Ye et al., 2019). However, widespread biochar usage has several hurdles, one of which is that it is prohibitively expensive at present. There is currently little published information on wholesale biochar prices, and the few data points available are not particularly recent. For example, in values of USD_{2021}, wholesale prices were 2400 USD/t (metric tonne) in 2015 (Campbell et al., 2018). Research has suggested production costs may drop to 870 USD/t with small scale production (Keske et al., 2020) or 240 USD/t in a large-scale production facility designed for an economy that uses biochar heavily (Project Drawdown, n.d.). In comparison, steam coal is typically only 70 USD/t(U.S. Energy Information Administration, 2021). Therefore, there is incentive to reduce the net cost of using biochar to match or even go below that of coal.

Another issue with biomass pyrolysis is that it also produces by-products, which are often considered to be waste and are difficult to handle due to toxicity (Bridgwater et al., 1999). The by-products of biomass pyrolysis are separated into two phases, including bio-oil, also known as tar, and light gases (Dunnigan, Ashman, et al., 2018). The light gases generally consist of CO, CO_2, CH_4, H_2, and low carbon fuel gases, while the tar phase consists of water and volatile organic compounds (VOCs) (Amini et al., 2019).

To tackle both of these issues, it is worthwhile to investigate the value of utilization of the by-products of biomass pyrolysis. Although there are studies which looked at tire pyrolysis by-product value (Czajczyńska et al., 2017), usage of by-products for self-sustaining pyrolysis (Xu et al., 2011), the economic value of bio-oil specifically (Badger et al., 2011), and the heating value of biomass pyrolysis by-products (Dunnigan, Morton, et al., 2018), there have not been any comprehensive techno-economic analyses which cover environmental and economic benefits of the utilization of biomass pyrolysis by-products. Given that the products mostly consist of combustible hydrocarbons, one of the simplest potential methods to use these by-products is heat generation through combustion. This heat can be used for processes such as steam generation, iron production, or even biomass drying and pyrolysis. This allows for fossil fuel usage to be offset, thereby reducing purchase and emission costs, which increases the value of biochar. This value can be used to close the gap between biochar and coal prices.

For this analysis, Aspen Plus chemical process simulation software was used to calculate the thermodynamics and products of combustion of pyrolysis by-products based on experimental compositions and conditions. These results were then compared to fuel and carbon prices used in iron- and steel-making facilities in two locations. The locations investigated were Aichi Prefecture in Japan, which is in the third largest steel producing country in the world (Worldsteel Association, 2021b), and the province of Ontario in Canada. These locations were chosen because Aichi and Ontario both produce a similar amount of steel, at about 10,000,000 t annually (Aichi Prefectural Government, 2017), (Cheminfo Services Inc., 2019), but use different fuels for heat generation. Relevant data were readily available for the most commonly used heating fuels both locations, allowing for a complete cost comparison.

Collaboration with and data sharing from ArcelorMittal Dofasco, Natural Resources Canada (NRCan), and CHAR Technologies has allowed for a realistic determination of the value and feasibility of pyrolysis by-product usage. ArcelorMittal Dofasco is aiming to replace up to 40,000 t of pulverized coal with biochar per year, so this value was used for design calculations.

2. Methods

To determine the financial and environmental value of pyrolysis by-product combustion, the heat generated from combustion was considered to be used to offset the currently most-used non-renewable fuels in local iron- and steel-making facilities. According to data from ArcelorMittal Dofasco, natural gas is generally the only fuel that is purchased for heat generation in their plant. Therefore, by-product value was determined based on offsetting natural gas in the Ontario case. However, in Japan, iron- and steel-making companies tend to use both natural gas and steam coal, but approximately four times more heat is generated with steam coal than natural gas (Japan Iron and Steel Federation, 2020). Therefore, in the Aichi case, steam coal will be assumed to be the main fuel that is offset with by-product combustion. Since the pyrolysis was done with biomass, emissions from by-product combustion are carbon neutral if it is assumed that the biomass would not otherwise be used for carbon sequestration. Therefore, emissions reductions from offsetting fossil fuels with pyrolysis by-product combustion were considered to be direct reductions.

Data on the composition of by-products were received from NRCan's lab-based experiments from the pyrolysis of construction and demolition wood at 600 °C. These data include the ratio of biochar, bio-oil, and light gas produced from pyrolysis, as well as bio-oil and light gas compositions. The distribution of products from wood pyrolysis is shown in Table 1. These ratios are similar to others in literature (Amini et al., 2019).

Table 1: Product distribution of pyrolysis of wood on a dry, ash-free basis

Pyrolysis Product	Mass % of Initial Feedstock
Light Gas	27.6
Bio-oil	44.8
Biochar	27.6

In regards to data used for simulation, the composition of the light gas is given in Table 2, while the composition and ultimate analysis of the bio-oil are given in Table 3 and Table 4, respectively. Although the bio-oil composition given in this paper includes only general categories of compounds, the actual data set used for simulation includes approximately 30 specific compounds. Also, it is common for pyrolysis to be done in a nitrogen-rich atmosphere, but the method used by CHAR Technologies creates positive pressure in the chamber shortly after pyrolysis begins, preventing combustion. This means that the by-products do not contain any nitrogen gas. CHAR Technologies also noted that the pyrolysis process can be considered to be steady state.

Table 2: Composition of light gas by-product of pyrolysis on a dry basis

Light Gas Component	Composition (Volume %)
H_2	9.4
CO	26.2
CO_2	43.0
CH_4	17.2
C_2H_6	1.3
C_2H_4	0.6
Other Light Hydrocarbons	2.3

Table 3: Composition of the bio-oil by-product of pyrolysis

Bio-oil Component	Composition (Mass %)
Water	56.6
Acids	9.6
Other Oxygenates	8.9
Methanol	7.6
Phenols	3.6
Furans	1.6
Other Condensable Compounds	12.1

Table 4: Ultimate analysis of the bio-oil on a wet basis

Ultimate Analysis Element	Mass %
Carbon	26.6
Hydrogen	9.5
Oxygen	63.9

The pyrolysis by-products contain many VOCs, which are gaseous at the 600 °C pyrolysis process outlet temperature but can begin to condense at temperatures below 450 °C, as per data from CHAR Technologies. Therefore, it was imperative that the process was designed so that the by-products can be combusted without condensation. Although it is typical to use thermal oxidizers to destroy gaseous VOCs while recovering a portion of the heat of combustion, thermal oxidizers are used for flue gases which contain up to only 10,000 ppmv organic compounds, with the rest being air (Wang et al., 2020). For destruction of streams without oxygen and that contain VOCs in higher concentrations, a vapour combustor, also known by other names such as enclosed flare (Anguil, n.d.), should be used instead (Gulf Coast Environmental Systems, n.d.). A vapour combustor is essentially a small flue gas stack with the option to recover the heat of combustion, and related operating and capital costs were found for annual usage of 40 kt of biochar using published correlations (United States Environmental Protection Agency, 1980). A diagram of the process design is shown in Figure 1.

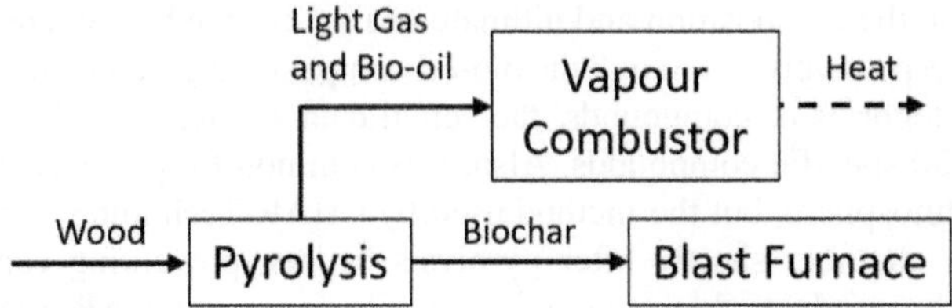

Figure 1: A system based on pyrolysis by-products which generates heat with a vapour combustor

The products of by-product combustion were predicted using an RGIBBS block in Aspen Plus, which calculates the products and enthalpy change of a reaction through minimizing Gibbs free energy based on the parameters and composition of the reactants used. In the model, pyrolysis by-products at 600 °C and 1.01325 bar in a gaseous phase were mixed with air at 25 °C and 1.01325 bar so that the products contained 2 % oxygen by volume after combustion, as per guidelines from ArcelorMittal Dofasco. The property method used was the Peng-Robinson-Boston-Mathias (PR-BM) model, which has been shown in literature to work well for mixtures of CO_2 and hydrocarbons (Li et al., 2019). Peng-Robinson-based methods have also been shown to predict CO_2-H_2O well (Zhao & Lvov, 2016). This simulation model was also used to determine that the by-products are within the flammability envelope when mixed with up to 30 % excess air, as per the calculated adiabatic flame temperature method (Hansel et al., 1992). Aspen Plus was also used to calculate higher and lower heating values of the by-product stream. This was done by adding the known lower heating values of the reactants for the LHV and then adding to this heat of vaporization of product water to determine the HHV.

Cost savings gained from by-product combustion in each location were calculated based on local fuel costs and carbon prices. Specific values used for each situation as well as the equation used for cost calculation are available in the supporting document (Rose & Adams, 2021).

3. Results

Results for the calculated HHV and LHV of the light gas, bio-oil, and weighted by-product mixture are given in Table 5.

Table 5: Calculated heating values for the pyrolysis by-products

By-Product Stream	LHV (MJ/kg)	HHV (MJ/kg)
Light Gases	10.0	10.9
Bio-Oil	10.7	11.4
Mix	10.5	11.2

Given the pyrolysis product ratios in Table 1 and these heating values, it was found that each tonne of biochar made also creates enough by-products to produce 29.4 GJ HHV or 27.4 GJ LHV of heat through combustion. Also, for a vapour combustor system that uses 40 kt of biochar per year, capital and operating costs were found to be 912,000 USD_{2021} total and 271,000 USD_{2021} per year, respectively. Assuming a 20-year project lifetime, these values were then used to calculate specific future value cost savings and carbon emissions reductions from offsetting fossil fuels through vapour combustion, as shown in Table 6. At a rate of 1 tonne of pulverized coal used per 10 tonnes of metal produced (U.S. Department of Energy, 2000), if all pulverized coal for 10 Mt of metal production were to be replaced with biochar, there would be an annual emissions reduction of 1.50 Mt CO_2-e in Ontario or 2.44 Mt CO_2-e in Aichi, equivalent to taking 625 thousand or one million cars off the road, respectively (Wynes & Nicholas, 2017).

Table 6: Cost savings per tonne of biochar produced from offsetting fossil fuels with by-product combustion in a vapour combustor

Location	Cost Savings/t Biochar 2022 Case	Cost Savings/t Biochar 2030 Case	Emissions Reductions (t CO_2-e/t Char)
Ontario	135 USD_{2021}	280 USD_{2021}	1.50
Aichi	96 USD_{2021}	350 USD_{2021}	2.44

4. Conclusions

Combustion of pyrolysis by-products has been shown to be a viable method for increasing the value of biochar as a replacement for pulverized coal in blast furnaces. Even with the purchase and operation of new equipment, by-product combustion can increase the value of one tonne of biochar by anywhere from 96 to 350 USD_{2021} in Aichi, Japan, and 135 to 280 USD_{2021} in Ontario, Canada. The greater difference in Aichi is due a greater reduction in carbon emissions with a similar increase in carbon taxes. These reductions are up to 1.50 tCO2-e/t char used in Ontario and 2.44 tCO2-e/t char used in Aichi, applicable for up to one million tonnes of biochar used per year in each location.

References

Aichi Prefectural Government. (2017). *全国からみた愛知県の工業 [Industry in Aichi Prefecture as Compared to the Whole of Japan]* (pp. 1–16).

Amini, E., Safdari, M. S., DeYoung, J. T., Weise, D. R., & Fletcher, T. H. (2019). Characterization of pyrolysis products from slow pyrolysis of live and dead vegetation native to the southern United States. *Fuel*, *235*(June 2018), 1475–1491. https://doi.org/10.1016/j.fuel.2018.08.112

Anguil. (n.d.). *Vapor Combustor Unit (VCU)*. https://anguil.com/air-pollution-control-solutions/vapor-combustor-unit-vcu/

Badger, P., Badger, S., Puettmann, M., Steele, P., & Cooper, J. (2011). Techno-economic analysis: Preliminary assessment of pyrolysis oil production costs and material energy balance associated with a transportable fast pyrolysis system. *BioResources*, *6*(1), 34–47. https://doi.org/10.15376/biores.6.1.34-47

Bridgwater, A. V., Meier, D., & Radlein, D. (1999). An overview of fast pyrolysis of biomass. *Journal of Inorganic Biochemistry*, *Organic Ge*, 1479–1493.

Campbell, R. M., Anderson, N. M., Daugaard, D. E., & Naughton, H. T. (2018). Financial viability of biofuel and biochar production from forest biomass in the face of market price volatility and uncertainty. *Applied Energy*, *230*(June), 330–343. https://doi.org/10.1016/j.apenergy.2018.08.085

Cheminfo Services Inc. (2019). *Economic Assessment of the Integrated Steel Industry*. https://canadiansteel.ca/files/resources/Final-Report-Economic-Assessment-of-the-Integrated-Steel-Industry.pdf

Czajczyńska, D., Krzyżyńska, R., Jouhara, H., & Spencer, N. (2017). Use of pyrolytic gas from waste tire as a fuel: A review. *Energy*, *134*, 1121–1131. https://doi.org/10.1016/j.energy.2017.05.042

Dunnigan, L., Ashman, P. J., Zhang, X., & Kwong, C. W. (2018). Production of biochar from rice husk: Particulate emissions from the combustion of raw pyrolysis volatiles. *Journal of Cleaner Production*, *172*, 1639–1645. https://doi.org/10.1016/j.jclepro.2016.11.107

Dunnigan, L., Morton, B. J., Ashman, P. J., Zhang, X., & Kwong, C. W. (2018). Emission characteristics of a pyrolysis-combustion system for the co-production of biochar and bioenergy from agricultural wastes. *Waste Management*, *77*, 59–66. https://doi.org/10.1016/j.wasman.2018.05.004

Gulf Coast Environmental Systems. (n.d.). *Vapor Combustor Unit.* http://www.gcesystems.com/air-pollution-control/vapor-combustor-unit.html

Hansel, J. G., Mitchell, J. W., & Klotz, H. C. (1992). Predicting and controlling flammability of multiple fuel and multiple inert mixtures. *Plant/Operations Progress*, *11*(4), 213–217. https://doi.org/10.1002/prsb.720110408

Japan Iron and Steel Federation. (2020). *鉄鋼業における発電設備運用の実態 [Actual Conditions of Power Generation Equipment Operation in the Steel Industry]*. https://www.meti.go.jp/shingikai/enecho/denryoku_gas/denryoku_gas/sekitan_karyoku_wg/pdf/002_07_00.pdf

Keske, C., Godfrey, T., Hoag, D. L. K., & Abedin, J. (2020). Economic feasibility of biochar and agriculture coproduction from Canadian black spruce forest. *Food and Energy Security*, *9*(1), 1–11. https://doi.org/10.1002/fes3.188

Li, C., Gao, Y., Xia, S., Shang, Q., & Ma, P. (2019). Calculation of the Phase Equilibrium of CO2–Hydrocarbon Binary Mixtures by PR-BM EOS and PR EOS. *Transactions of Tianjin University*, *25*(5), 540–548. https://doi.org/10.1007/s12209-019-00194-y

Project Drawdown. (n.d.). *Biochar Production*. https://drawdown.org/solutions/biochar-production/technical-summary

Rose, J., & Adams, T. A. II (2021). *Supplemental Data for "Process Design and Techno-Economic Analysis of Biomass Pyrolysis By-Product Utilization in the Ontario and Aichi Steel Industries."* http://psecommunity.org/LAPSE:2021.0800

U.S. Department of Energy. (2000). *Blast Furnace Granulated Coal Injection System Demonstration Project: A DOE Assessment*. *June*, 46.

U.S. Energy Information Administration. (2021). *Quarterly Coal Report April–June 2021*. https://www.eia.gov/coal/production/quarterly/pdf/qcr-all.pdf

United States Environmental Protection Agency. (1980). *Organic Chemical Manufacturing Volume 4: Combustion Control Devices*. https://nepis.epa.gov/Exe/ZyPDF.cgi/2000MF11.PDF?Dockey=2000MF11.PDF

Wang, F., Lei, X., & Hao, X. (2020). Key factors in the volatile organic compounds treatment by regenerative thermal oxidizer. *Journal of the Air and Waste Management Association*, *70*(5), 557–567. https://doi.org/10.1080/10962247.2020.1752331

Worldsteel Association. (2021a). *Climate change and the production of iron and steel*. https://www.worldsteel.org/en/dam/jcr:228be1e4-5171-4602-b1e3-63df9ed394f5/worldsteel_climatechange_policy%2520paper.pdf

Worldsteel Association. (2021b). *Global crude steel output decreases by 0.9% in 2020*. https://www.worldsteel.org/media-centre/press-releases/2021/Global-crude-steel-output-decreases-by-0.9--in-2020.html

Wynes, S., & Nicholas, K. A. (2017). The climate mitigation gap: education and government recommendations miss the most effective individual actions. *Environmental Research Letters*, *12*(7), 74024. https://doi.org/10.1088/1748-9326/aa7541

Xu, R., Ferrante, L., Hall, K., Briens, C., & Berruti, F. (2011). Thermal self-sustainability of biochar production by pyrolysis. *Journal of Analytical and Applied Pyrolysis*, *91*(1), 55–66. https://doi.org/10.1016/j.jaap.2011.01.001

Ye, L., Peng, Z., Wang, L., Anzulevich, A., Bychkov, I., Kalganov, D., Tang, H., Rao, M., Li, G., & Jiang, T. (2019). Use of Biochar for Sustainable Ferrous Metallurgy. *Jom*, *71*(11), 3931–3940. https://doi.org/10.1007/s11837-019-03766-4

Zhao, H., & Lvov, S. N. (2016). Phase behavior of the CO2-H2O system at temperatures of 273-623 K and pressures of 0.1-200 MPa using Peng-Robinson-Stryjek-Vera equation of state with a modified Wong-Sandler mixing rule: An extension to the CO2-CH4-H2O system. *Fluid Phase Equilibria*, *417*, 96–108. https://doi.org/10.1016/j.fluid.2016.02.027

Proceedings of the 14th International Symposium on Process Systems Engineering – PSE 2021+
June 19-23, 2022, Kyoto, Japan
http://dx.doi.org/10.1016/B978-0-323-85159-6.50020-8

Optimal design of solar-aided hydrogen production process using molten salt with CO_2 utilization for ethylene glycol production

Wanrong Wang, Nan Zhang, and Jie Li*
Department of Chemical Engineering, The University of Manchester, Manchester M13 9PL, UK
jie.li-2@manchester.ac.uk

Abstract

In this work, a machine-learning based optimisation framework is proposed for optimal design of solar steam methane reforming using molten salt (SSMR-MS) with CO_2 capture and utilisation. The computational results demonstrate that significant profit in TAC can be made compared with the existing SSMR-MS. With ethylene glycol (EG) production, the optimal Levelised cost of Hydrogen Production (LCHP) is 0.00 \$ kg^{-1} which is largely reduced compared to the existing process with LCHP of 2.40 \$ kg^{-1}. The captured CO_2 using the amine-based solution is utilized to produce around 33.59 kt y^{-1} EG.

Keywords: Hydrogen; Solar energy; CO_2 utilization; Machine learning

1. Introduction

Hydrogen is an important energy carrier in the transportation sector and essential industrial feedstock for petroleum refineries, methanol, and ammonia production. The global demand for hydrogen is expected to increase 10-fold by 2050, clearly indicating its significant role in the future (Wang et al., 2021). Conventional hydrogen production primarily utilises natural gas and oil-based feedstock for steam reforming, which results in considerable greenhouse gas emissions mainly CO_2, thus contributing to global warming (Voldsund et al., 2016). The damaging consequences of global warming deem further investigation into clean and affordable hydrogen production process using renewable energy sources to be crucial. Meanwhile, research is also ongoing into CO_2 capture and utilisation technology which considers CO_2 as a viable alternative carbon source for the chemical supply chain (Alper et al., 2017) to obtain value-added products such as methanol, ethylene carbonate and ethylene glycol (Yang et al., 2021).

Solar energy for hydrogen production has received significant attention in recent years due to its primary abundance as an energy source (Koumi Ngoh et al., 2012). To effectively use solar energy for large-scale hydrogen production, an optimal design of solar steam methane reforming using molten salt (SSMR-MS) which shows great potential has been studied to reduce TAC and CO_2 emission (Wang et al., 2021). However, the optimal Levelised Cost of Hydrogen Production (LCHP) is still much higher than that of the conventional methane steam reforming. Furthermore, in their work CO_2 removal model is represented using a simple separation block with a constant separation efficiency, which could lead to inaccurate account of annualized cost of CO_2 capture. To further reduce LCHP and improve the model accuracy, an integrated rate-based CO_2 removal model in SSMR-MS along with CO_2 utilization for ethylene glycol (EG) production is investigated in this work. This is the main novelty of this work.

In this work, an optimization framework from (Wang et al., 2021) is extended for such optimal design of SSMR-MS with integration of CO_2 capture and utilization. The artificial neural network (ANN) is employed to establish relationships of total annualised cost (TAC), hydrogen production rate, molten salt duty and gas flowrates from CO_2 capture unit with thirteen independent input variables in SSMR-MS. A hybrid global optimisation algorithm is employed to solve the developed optimisation problem and generate the optimal design, which is then validated in Aspen Plus V8.8 and SAM. The computational results demonstrate that TAC of the SSMR-MS process can be compensated by the profit of selling EG and CO_2 emissions reduction by 68.92 % can be achieved compared to the existing SSMR-MS process in Wang et al. (2021). Captured CO_2 can produce around 33.59 kt yr^{-1} EG.

2. Problem description

Figure 1 illustrates a schematic diagram of integrated system including SSMR-MS for large-scale hydrogen production, CO_2 capture, and EG production. A detailed description of the SSMR-MS process has been made in Wang et al. (2021). The pre-reformer is non-adiabatic and molten salt transfers concentrated solar energy in heat to pre-reformer. The flow scheme in the pre-reformer is in co-current. The process is to produce F_{H_2} hydrogen with η_{H_2} purity to satisfy hydrogen demand in an oil refinery. A rate-based CO_2 removal model using methyl diethanolamine (MDEA) as the solution is built in Aspen Plus V8.8. The reaction for CO_2 absorption and MDEA regeneration process using MDEA are listed in Moioli et al. (2016). The capture CO_2 with coke oven gas is used to produce EG.

The objective is to minimize total annualized cost (TAC) of the integrated system, which includes total annualized capital cost and operating cost.

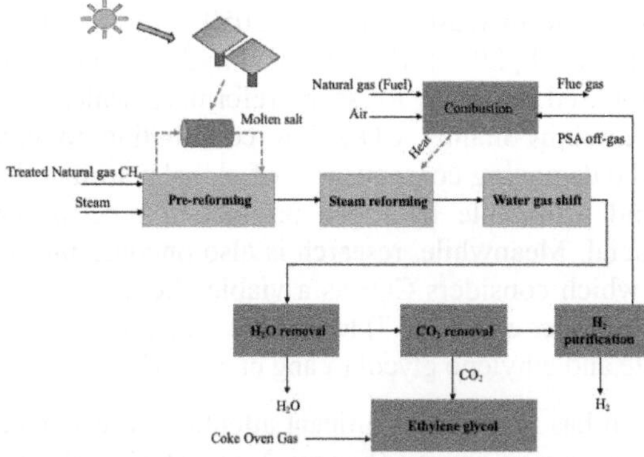

Figure 1: Block diagram of the SSMR-MS process (Adapted from Wang et al., 2021)

3. Mathematical formulation

The integrated process can be modelled using rigorous models in Aspen Plus V8.8. The optimisation problem using these rigorous models is often highly complex. To reduce the complexity of the problem, surrogate model is developed based on machine learning techniques. ANN is used to create surrogate models of the rate-based CO_2 removal process and the entire process. A major advantage of ANN over other statistical techniques is the ability to correlate multiple inputs to multiple outputs, leading to compact models that can be implemented in an optimisation environment with ease (Ibrahim et al., 2018).

In this work, a surrogated model for the CO_2 capture process is firstly developed and integrated within SSMR-MS process in Aspen Plus V8.8. This is because when the rigorous rate-based CO_2 removal model for CO_2 capture is integrated with the SSMR-MS process in Aspen Plus V8.8, the simulation of the integrated system is extremely difficult to converge. The input variables for the CO_2 capture process include the inlet stream component flowrate of CH_4, H_2O, CO, CO_2, H_2 which are denoted as $F_{in,CH_4,MDEA}$, $F_{in,H_2O,MDEA}$, $F_{in,CO,MDEA}$, $F_{in,CO_2,MDEA}$ and $F_{in,H_2,MDEA}$, respectively and temperature ($T_{in,MDEA}$) obtained from hydrogen production process. In other words,

$$\mathbf{z} = [F_{in,CH_4,MDEA}, F_{in,H_2O,MDEA}, F_{in,CO,MDEA}, F_{in,CO_2,MDEA}, F_{in,H_2,MDEA}, T_{in,MDEA}]^T.$$

The outlet stream flowrates of CH_4, H_2O, CO, CO_2 and H_2 in the CO_2 removal process are predicted using ANN surrogate models respectively, as shown in Eqs.1-5.

$$F_{out,CH4,MDEA} = ANN_1(\mathbf{z}) \tag{1}$$

$$F_{out,H2O,MDEA} = ANN_2(\mathbf{z}) \tag{2}$$

$$F_{out,CO,MDEA} = ANN_3(\mathbf{z}) \tag{3}$$

$$F_{out,CO2,MDEA} = ANN_4(\mathbf{z}) \tag{4}$$

$$F_{out,H2,MDEA} = ANN_5(\mathbf{z}) \tag{5}$$

These surrogate models are then integrated with the rigorous models of SSMR-MS by using user model within Aspen Plus interface with Excel Link (Fontalvo, 2014) for sample generation. Then a new surrogate model representing the entire integrated process is constructed through extending the optimisation framework of Wang et al. (2021). There are usually three steps for the development of a surrogate model, including data generation (i.e., sampling), construction of the surrogate model and construction of feasibility constraints using a support vector machine (Wang et al., 2021). Samples generated using the Latin hypercube sampling method are used as input in Aspen Plus V8.8 to get values for the corresponding output variables.

In the integrated process, the independent input variables including molar flowrate of natural gas into pre-reformer F_{NG}, steam to methane ratio $\gamma_{S/C}$, operating temperature of reformer T_R, high-temperature water gas shift (HWGS) reactor T_{HWGS}, low-temperature water gas shift (LWGS) reactor T_{LWGS}, tube length of pre-reformer L_{PR}, reformer L_R, HWGS reactor L_{HWGS} and LWGS reactor L_{LWGS}, tube number in pre-reformer N_{PR}, reformer N_R, HWGS reactor N_{HWGS} and LWGS reactor N_{LWGS} vary between lower and upper bounds. A vector **x** is used to denote all these variables. In other words,

$$\mathbf{x} = [F_{NG}, \gamma_{S/C}, T_R, T_{HWGS}, T_{LWGS}, L_{PR}, L_R, L_{HWGS}, L_{LWGS}, N_{PR}, N_R, N_{HWGS}, N_{LWGS}]^T.$$

$$x^L \leq \mathbf{x} \leq x^U \tag{6}$$

The objective function TAC can be calculated as follows,

$$TAC = Ccapital \cdot ACCR + Cproduction \tag{7}$$

where $Ccapital$ is total capital investment. $ACCR$ is annual capital charge ratio. $Cproduction$ is the total production cost per year.

The optimisation problem using the surrogate models is stated as follows,

$$\begin{aligned}
(PS) \quad & Min \quad && TAC = TAC_1 + TAC_{solar} \\
& s.t. && TAC_1 = ANN_6(\boldsymbol{x}) + ANN_7(\boldsymbol{x}) \\
& && TAC_{solar} = f(Q_{MS}) \\
& && \mathrm{Q_{MS}} = \mathrm{ANN_8}(\mathbf{x}) \\
& && F_{H_2} = ANN_9(\boldsymbol{x}) \geq F_{H_2}^{TA} \\
& && Eq.\ (6)
\end{aligned}$$

where TAC_1 is non-solar related cost, TAC_{solar} is the solar related cost. $ANN_6(\boldsymbol{x})$ is CO_2 removal process related cost. ANN_7 is the non-solar related cost excluding MDEA unit. $\mathbf{x}$ is the set of independent variables in hydrogen production process, Q_{MS} is molten salt duty. The relationship of solar-related equipment cost, and molten salt duty is described using an algebraic linear function $f(Q_{MS})$. The surrogate model comprises 4 artificial neural networks as indicated above in the optimization problem *PS* and a linear regression model $f(Q_{MS})$. F_{H_2} denotes the predicated flowrate of hydrogen.

4. Solution algorithm

A hybrid optimisation algorithm similar to that of (Wang et al., 2021) is employed to solve the optimisation problem PS, as shown in Figure 2. This hybrid algorithm combines the advantages of the stochastic optimisation algorithm and the deterministic optimisation method. We employ different platforms and data are transferred between them to exploit their strength and reduce the computational complexity. In sample generation process, Matlab is used as the core platform to interact with other programs. Sample points are imported to Aspen Plus. Within Aspen Plus, the process contains a user model which calls Visual Basic Application (VBA) in Excel (Fontalvo, 2014) as a bridge to transfer data between Aspen Plus user model and Matlab (ANN model for composition prediction in CO_2 removal process). The hybrid algorithm is implemented in MatLab R2019a.

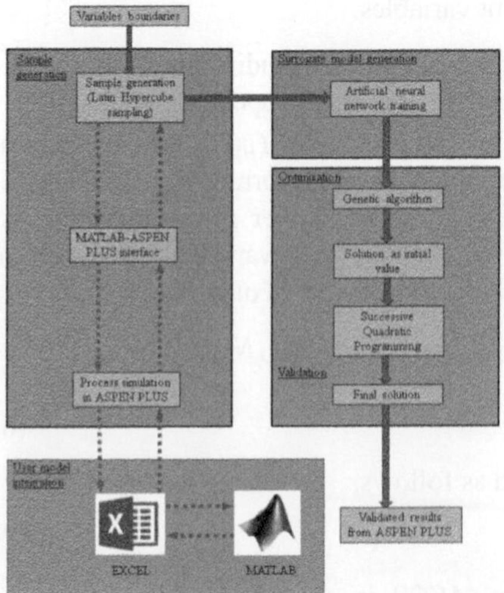

Figure 2: Flowchart of the extended design methodology

5. Computational studies

The extended optimisation framework is used to generate the optimal design of the SSMR-MS process with integration of CO_2 capture and utilisation. The hydrogen production rate is 2,577 kmol h^{-1}. The desired hydrogen purity is 99.9 vol%. Other data can be referred to Wang et al. (2021). The results are given in Table 1. It can be seen that the optimal TAC is 166.50 M\$ y^{-1}. The optimal steam to carbon ratio is 2.7.

Table 1: Optimisation results for SSMR-MS from surrogate models

Item	Optimal value
$\gamma_{S/C}$	2.7
T_R (°C)	962.3
T_{HWGS} (°C)	421.1
T_{LWGS} (°C)	200.7
L_{PR} (m)	11.2
L_R (m)	12.0
L_{HWGS} (m)	4.8
L_{LWGS} (m)	4.3
N_{PR}	4,031
N_R	55
N_{HWGS}	1367
N_{LWGS}	2624
F_{NG} (kmol h^{-1})	781.9
Q_{MS} (MW)	14.54
F_{H_2} (kmol h^{-1})	2,577
TAC (M\$ y^{-1})	166.50

The optimal values of independent variables in Table 1 are used as input in Aspen Plus V8.8 to generate values of all dependent variables. The validated results for Q_{MS}, F_{H_2} and TAC are 14.31 MW, 2577.2 kmol h^{-1}, 165.22 M\$ y^{-1} respectively. The largest difference between actual results and predicted results from the ANN surrogate models is within 1 %, indicating the ANN model has high prediction accuracy.

Then heat integration is conducted to further reduce energy consumption. The final results are provided in Table 2. It can be observed after heat integration, TAC is 155.05 M\$ y^{-1}, which is reduced by 6.2 % compared to that before heat integration (165.22 M\$ y^{-1}). What is striking is that, with the integration of EG production, the whole hydrogen production process cost can be compensated with a large profit.

We also compare our optimal results with the best results from Wang et al. (2021) and the conventional steam methane reforming (denoted as CSMR), as shown in Table 2. It can be observed that without EG production, TAC in this work is higher than that from Wang et al. (2021) due to CO_2 capture cost increased using the rate-based CO_2 removal model. With an annual production of 33.59 kt EG, LCHP decreases from 2.40 \$ kg^{-1} to 0

$ kg^{-1} due to high profit from EG. CO_2 emission reduces by 68.92 %. What is more important is that LCHP (0.00 $ kg^{-1}) is extremely economic attractive and CO_2 emission is reduced by 73.80 % compared to that of CSMR. The economic and environmental benefit obtained by using solar energy and applying CO_2 utilization process show the optimal case in this work is very promising for industrial hydrogen production.

Table 2: Comparative optimization results

Item	Optimal Case	Wang et al. (2021)	CSMR
Q_{MS} (MW)	14.31	10.20	20.00
F_{H_2} (kmol h^{-1})	2,577.2	2577.3	2,577.0
TAC without EG production (M$ y^{-1})	155.05	122.30	90.90
TAC with EG production (M$ y^{-1})	-21142.24	-	-
LCHP ($ kg^{-1})	0.00	2.40	2.00
CO_2 emission (kt y^{-1})	131.74	423.90	502.90
EG (kt y^{-1})	33.59	0.00	0.00

6. Conclusion

In this paper, the existing optimisation-based framework using machine learning techniques is extended for optimal design of solar steam methane reforming using molten salt (SSMR-MS) integrated with CO_2 capture and utilization for large-scale H_2 production. The computational results show that TAC was reduced largely with significant profit generated compared to the existing SSMR-MS. By considering CO_2 conversion, around 33.59 kt EG is produced per year. In the future, more process options for different pre-reformer operating conditions are expected to evaluate.

References

Alper, E. and Yuksel Orhan, O., 2017, CO_2 utilization: Developments in conversion processes. Petroleum, 3, 109-126.

Fontalvo Alzate, J., 2014. Using user models in Matlab® within the Aspen Plus® interface with an Excel® link. Ingeniería e Investigación, 34(2), pp.39-43.

Ibrahim, D., Jobson, M., Li, J. & Guillén-Gosálbez, G., 2018, Optimization-based design of crude oil distillation units using surrogate column models and a support vector machine, Chem. Eng. Res. Des., 134, 212-225.

Koumi Ngoh, S. & Njomo, D., 2012, An overview of hydrogen gas production from solar energy, Renewable and Sustainable Energy Reviews, 16, 6782-6792.

Moioli, S., Pellegrini, L., Picutti, B. and Vergani, P., 2013, Improved Rate-Based Modeling of H_2S and CO_2 Removal by Methyldiethanolamine Scrubbing. Industrial & Engineering Chemistry Research, 52, 2056-2065.

Voldsund, M., Jordal, K. & Anantharaman, R., 2016, Hydrogen production with CO_2 capture, International Journal of Hydrogen Energy, 41, 4969-4992.

Wang, W., Ma, Y., Maroufmashat, A., Zhang, N., Li, J. and Xiao, X., 2021, Optimal design of large-scale solar-aided hydrogen production process via machine learning based optimisation framework. Applied Energy, 305, 117751.

Yang, Q., Zhang, J., Chu, G., Zhou, H. and Zhang, D., 2021b, Optimal design, thermodynamic and economic analysis of coal to ethylene glycol processes integrated with various methane reforming technologies for CO_2 reduction. Energy Conversion and Management, 244,114538.

Proceedings of the 14th International Symposium on Process Systems Engineering – PSE 2021+
June 19-23, 2022, Kyoto, Japan
http://dx.doi.org/10.1016/B978-0-323-85159-6.50021-X

Design of a novel hybrid process for membrane assisted clean hydrogen production with CO_2 capture through liquefaction

Donghoi Kim[ab*], Zhongxuan Liu[b], Rahul Anantharaman[a], Luca Riboldi[a], Lars Odsæter[a], David Berstad[a], Thijs A. Peters[c], Jonathan M. Polfus[c], Harald Malerød-Fjeld[d], and Truls Gundersen[b]

[a]*SINTEF Energy Research, Trondheim 7465, Norway*
[b]*Department of Energy and Process Engineering, Norwegian University of Science and Technology (NTNU), Trondheim 7491, Norway*
[c]*SINTEF Industry, Oslo 0314, Norway*
[d]*CoorsTek Membrane Sciences AS, 0349 Oslo, Norway*
donghoi.kim@sintef.no

Abstract

This work introduces a novel hybrid concept to produce H_2 from natural gas by using the protonic membrane reformer (PMR) with liquefaction based CO_2 capture system. For process intensification, recycling of the off-gas from the capture process and a water gas shift reactor for the retentate gas from the PMR are applied to the hybrid configuration. The suggested concept achieves around 99 % of system H_2 and CO_2 recovery rates even when the PMR is operated at relatively low hydrogen recovery, resulting in energy efficient H_2 production with a low carbon intensity.

Keywords: Low emission hydrogen production, proton conducting membrane, membrane reactor, CO_2 capture, hybrid process.

1. Background

Hydrogen is a clean fuel and is thus expected to play an important role in a future decarbonized energy scenario. Currently, 48 % of the world's hydrogen is produced by steam reforming (Voldsund et al., 2016), where natural gas and steam react to form hydrogen rich syngas. The focus on low-carbon hydrogen production from natural gas has been predominantly on CO_2 separation technologies. However, CO_2 separation does not contribute significantly to the energy penalty of the process (Voldsund et al., 2016). The largest losses are in the reforming of natural gas to hydrogen and subsequent separation to produce high purity hydrogen. The key focus area for cost-efficient low emission hydrogen production is an intensified process for hydrogen production and separation from natural gas with suitable CO_2 separation technology. Here we investigate an innovative hybrid technology for H_2 production with CO_2 capture combining H_2 production from natural gas by a protonic membrane reformer (PMR) technology with subsequent CO_2 separation by liquefaction in a novel integrated process. The technology enables a high carbon capture rate with high purity CO_2 and H_2 and a hydrogen cost comparable to conventional technologies without CO_2 capture.

The PMR technology produces high-purity hydrogen from steam methane reforming (SMR) in a single-stage electrochemical membrane reactor process with near-zero energy loss (Malerød-Fjeld et al., 2017). The tubular membrane reformer comprises a BaZrO3-based proton-conducting electrolyte deposited as a dense film on a porous Ni composite electrode with a dual function as a reforming catalyst. Methane is steam-reformed to CO and H_2 over Ni particles inside the ceramic tube. Hydrogen is electrochemically transported as protons to the outer side, and CO is thereby converted to CO_2 as the water gas shift (WGS) equilibrium is shifted due to the extraction of H_2. The hydrogen produced is of high purity and electrochemically compressed in situ. The H_2 recovery in the PMR is proportional to the electricity input (Malerød-Fjeld et al., 2017). At high hydrogen recovery, the outlet composition is mainly CO_2 and steam. The retentate gas from the PMR has a relatively high fraction of CO_2, which makes CO_2 separation by liquefaction the most competitive technology for this application (Berstad et al., 2013). Liquefaction based CO_2 capture technologies have also been well tested for a wide range of syngas compositions with hydrogen (Kim et al., 2020).

Thus, in this work, different process configurations are developed in an analytical manner to combine the two technologies. One of the process concepts considers the appropriate placement of recycle streams to improve overall H_2 and CO_2 recovery when the PMR is operated at low H_2 recovery of around 90 % (for example reduced current density) for less energy intensive unit operation. Such operating conditions are also expected to lower stress on the material leading to prolonged life. Detailed process models of the different unit operations including the protonic membrane reactor are included in the hybrid system to analyse the different process options.

2. Hybrid process concepts

High recovery rates of H_2 and CO_2 are required on the plant level to achieve energy efficient low carbon hydrogen production for the PMR based system. This requires the development of optimal integration between the PMR and CO_2 liquefaction processes where additional process steps are considered. Figure 1 shows one of the process concepts for the PMR based hydrogen production with carbon capture. In this configuration, natural gas and water are heated by the hot temperature H_2 product and the retentate gas from the PMR. The mixture of natural gas and steam is then sent to a pre-reformer to convert heavier hydrocarbons in natural gas to hydrogen, CO, and CO_2 to supply a pre-reformed feed to the PMR. The pre-reformer outlet stream is set to have a fixed steam carbon ratio.

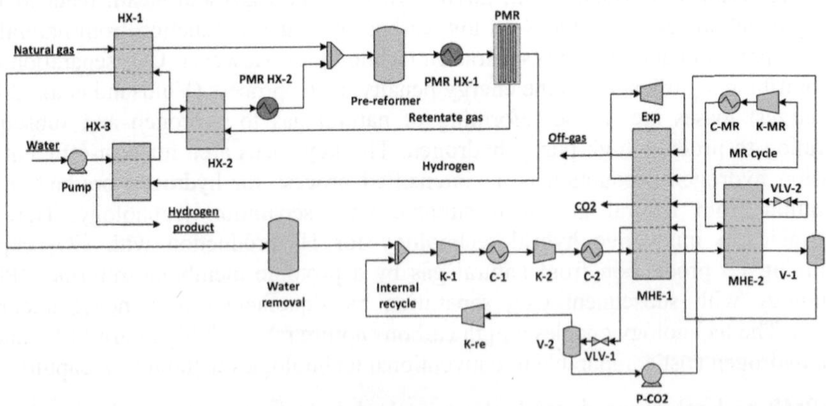

Figure 1. Process flow diagram of the simplified hybrid system for clean hydrogen production.

The temperature of the PMR feed is further increased to the operating temperature of the PMR by using the heat produced from the PMR, which is assumed to be operated isothermally. Then, the compressed pure hydrogen and the retentate gas are produced from the PMR. The SMR and WGS in the PMR result in a net endothermic reaction. However, the heat requirement can be covered by the heat generated by electricity used for the separation and compression of H_2 in the membrane, which is also enough to increase the temperature of the feed streams via PMR HX-1 and 2. The remaining PMR heat after the heat integration could be further used to produce steam.

The retentate gas from the heat recovery unit is fed to the CO_2 liquefaction process, after dehydration, to capture high purity liquid CO_2 while removing impurities in the liquid product through off-gas venting. In the CO_2 capture process (CCP), the dehydrated retentate gas is compressed before being liquefied by a hydrocarbon based mixed refrigerant (CH_4, C_2H_6, C_3H_8, and C_4H_{10}). The cold energy of the incondensable gas (off-gas) from the liquefier (MHE-2) is then used to pre-cool the compressed retentate gas. The off-gas from the pre-cooler is further utilized to supply the cold duty of heat exchanger MHE-1 by depressurizing it via a turbo expander. The liquid CO_2 product from the liquefier is also sent to the pre-cooler to cover the cold duty after being pressurized to the transport pressure. The off-gas leaving the CO_2 capture process could be vented or used as fuel to produce steam in the system.

Hydrogen production of this configuration is, however, dependent on the performance of the PMR as it is the only place where H_2 is extracted. If the hydrogen recovery rate (HRR) of the PMR is low with reduced electric power input, a considerable amount of H_2 left in the PMR is sent to the liquefaction process through the retentate gas. Since the hydrogen is not condensed in the CCP, it is lost through the off-gas, resulting in a low system HRR. Thus, when the PMR is operated at lower hydrogen recovery, the system HRR is also reduced, showing limited flexibility of the process. Another issue of the simplified concept with the PMR operating at low hydrogen recovery is the relatively high CO fraction in the retentate gas that causes poor performance of the CO_2 liquefaction system. The high fraction of CO in the feed to the CCP results in a deeper purification of the liquid CO_2 to achieve high purity. For the purification of the liquid CO_2, a larger amount of off-gas is produced, containing traces of CO_2, hence reducing the system carbon capture rate (CCR). The large flow rate of the off-gas stream will also require an extra facility to treat the CO and H_2 mixture. The high CO fraction, and thus a lower CO_2 fraction in the retentate gas, also means larger power consumption for the liquefaction process where the energy efficiency of the system is proportional to the CO_2 purity of feed gas (Kim et al., 2020).

To maintain H_2 production performance high at a low HRR of the PMR, the off-gas from the liquefaction system can be recycled (see Figure 2). This recycle allows collecting the valuable H_2 in the off-gas through the PMR, achieving a high system HRR. However, some off-gas venting will still be required to avoid N_2 accumulation in the system, which is assumed to be 10 % in this work. The off-gas recycle, however, will not reduce the CO fraction in the retentate gas, resulting in poor carbon capture performance of the hybrid concept. The improvement of the CCP can be achieved by a WGS reactor for the retentate gas as illustrated in Figure 2. The WGS reactor will convert the CO in the retentate gas to CO_2 and H_2, giving a low CO content and simultaneously increasing CO_2 content in the feed to the liquefaction process. Thus, this configuration can achieve high HRR and CCR while producing liquid CO_2 with negligible impurities even when the PMR is operate at low hydrogen recovery.

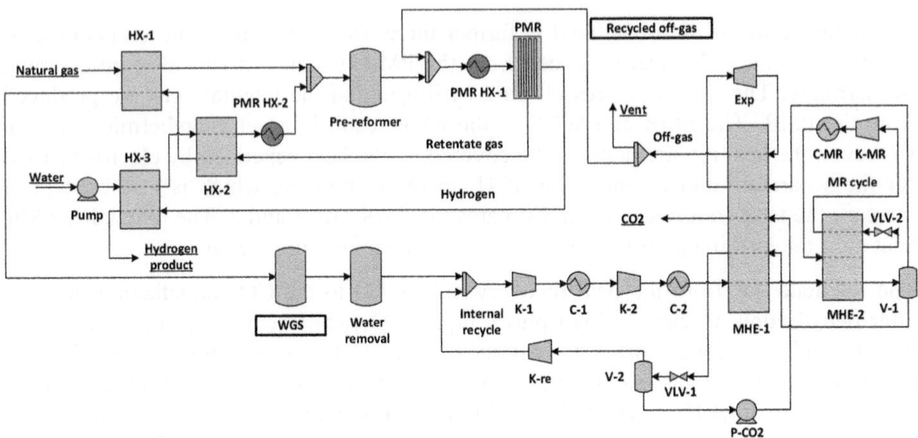

Figure 2. Process flow diagram of the modified hybrid system with off-gas recycle and a WGS reactor for the PMR operating at a low H_2 recovery (See text boxes for the modifications).

3. Modelling approach and design basis

In order to simulate the hybrid system, the PMR is modelled in C to represent the data from Malerød-Fjeld et al. (2017) and connected to Aspen HYSYS where all the other process units are built. In this work, the two process concepts neither include a vent gas utilization nor a steam cycle for the PMR surplus heat left after the heat integration. The PMR operating conditions that give 91 % of HRR are selected for the comparison of the two hybrid configurations assuming the membrane reformer is operated at relatively low H_2 recovery. However, it is worth mentioning that the PMR operating conditions such as temperature and current density will certainly impact process performance. While this has been analysed as part of this work, is not included in the paper. The hybrid system is assumed to have a natural gas feed rate of 3,000 kmol/h (lower heating value of 50 MJ/kg) to produce about 500 t/d hydrogen. CO_2 is assumed to be delivered at 150 bar with 99 mol% purity while allowing CO level lower than 0.5 vol%, assuming pipeline transport (Harkin et al., 2017). Other design conditions are listed in Table 1.

Table 1. Design basis for the PMR and the CO_2 capture process.

Parameters	Unit	Value
PMR feed steam to carbon ratio	-	2.5
PMR operating pressure	bar	26
PMR operating temperature	°C	800
PMR current density	A/m^2	7000
PMR H_2 product and retentate pressure	bar	26
PMR H_2 product and retentate temperature	°C	800
Pre-reformer inlet temperature	°C	450
WGS reactor inlet temperature	°C	200
ΔT_{min} for gas/gas heat exchanger	°C	30
ΔT_{min} for gas/liquid heat exchanger	°C	20
ΔT_{min} for low temperature heat exchanger	°C	3
Isentropic efficiency of compressor	%	80
Isentropic efficiency of gas expander	%	85
Isentropic efficiency of pump	%	75

4. Key performance indicators (KPIs)

Various key performance indicators are selected to evaluate the thermodynamic performance of the hybrid systems, such as specific power consumption (SPC) of the PMR, the CO_2 capture process, and the overall system. The SPC of the PMR is based on the electricity input to the PMR per unit mass of hydrogen produced. The SPC of the CCP is the net power consumption in the CCP per unit mass of CO_2 captured. The SPC of the hybrid system is estimated by the total net power consumption per unit mass of H_2 produced. The CCR of the CCP is the molar flow rate of the CO_2 captured per unit molar flow rate of CO_2 in the retentate gas. The system CCR is defined as the molar flow rate of CO_2 captured divided by the total molar flow rate of carbon in natural gas. Other KPIs such as hydrogen recovery rate (HRR) are as follows (it is worth mentioning that CH_4 conversion of the PMR is always kept high in this work):

$$HRR_{\mathrm{PMR}} = \frac{\dot{n}_{\mathrm{H_2,product}}}{\dot{n}_{\mathrm{H_2,PMR\ feed}} + \dot{n}_{\mathrm{H_2,generated\ in\ PMR}}} \quad (1)$$

$$HRR_{\mathrm{sys}} = \frac{\dot{n}_{\mathrm{H_2,product}}}{\dot{n}_{\mathrm{H_2,produced\ \ in\ pre-ref}} + \dot{n}_{\mathrm{H_2,produced\ in\ PMR}} + \dot{n}_{\mathrm{H_2,produced\ in\ WGS}}} \quad (2)$$

5. Results and discussion

The simulation results in Table 2 indicate that compared to the simplified hybrid concept, the process with off-gas recycle and a WGS reactor has a larger H_2 production capacity and a lower system SPC. Besides, the configuration with the off-gas recycle gives very high system HRR and CCR at around 99 %, verifying that this concept can produce H_2 with a low carbon intensity even when the PMR operating conditions are set for a relatively low HRR (91 %). As presented in Table 2, due to the recycle of the H_2 rich off-gas, the HRR and the hydrogen production rate of the PMR are improved compared to the simplified hybrid system. The recycled stream also makes the PMR feed richer in hydrogen, and it is advantageous to extract and compress H_2 in the membrane reformer, reducing its SPC. Besides, the WGS reactor effectively shifts CO to CO_2 in the retentate gas, increasing the CO_2 content of the feed to the liquefaction process and the efficiency of the CO_2 capture system (higher CCR and lower SPC).

The simplified hybrid concept has a low system carbon capture rate although the process has a similar CCR in the CCP compared to the hybrid process with off-gas recycle. This is because only a part of the natural gas supplied to the system is shifted to CO_2 in the PMR while the rest becomes CO, which is not captured through the liquefaction process. Thus, significant amounts of carbon are lost through the CO rich off-gas from the CO_2 capture process. However, the hybrid concept with off-gas recycle has a WGS reactor where almost all CO in the retentate gas is shifted to CO_2, thus allowing the liquefaction system to reduce the carbon loss via the vented off-gas.

It is worth noting that the heat from the PMR is more effectively utilized in the hybrid concept with off-gas recycle as it has a smaller amount of heat left from the PMR compared to the simplified hybrid system. Although the remaining of the PMR surplus heat is assumed to be used to produce electricity and supplied to the hybrid concepts with a 50 % conversion rate, the configuration with off-gas recycle will still have a lower system SPC (43.0 MJ/kg H_2) compared to the simplified scheme (45.6 MJ/kg H_2).

Table 2. Performance of the two hybrid concepts for clean hydrogen production with the PMR.

Parameter	Unit	Simplified hybrid	Modified hybrid
PMR H_2 production	t/d	475	560
PMR heat leftover	MW	29.38	13.00
SPC_{PMR}	MJ/kg H_2	46.39	42.19
HRR_{PMR}	%	91.06	93.99
$x_{CO2,CCP\ feed}$	(dry basis)	0.53	0.65
$x_{CO,CCP\ feed}$	(dry basis)	0.22	0.01
Captured CO_2	t/d	1965	3374
SPC_{CCP}	MJ/kg CO_2	0.45	0.30
CCR_{CCP}	%	83.44	89.27
HRR_{sys}	%	91.06	98.75
CCR_{sys}	%	57.80	99.30
SPC_{sys}	MJ/kg H_2	48.26	43.99

6. Conclusions

In this work, a novel hybrid concept is developed to produce H_2 from natural gas using an innovative proton membrane reformer followed by a liquefaction based CO_2 capture system. The hybrid concept with off-gas recycle and a WGS reactor effectively recovers H_2 produced in the PMR while capturing almost all CO_2 from the process even when the PMR is operated at relatively low H_2 recovery with less energy input. Thus, this hybrid scheme will be a promising option for H_2 production with a low carbon intensity. This process design can be further improved by optimal heat integration with the PMR surplus heat and the utilization of the vent stream as fuel.

Acknowledgements: This work was performed within the CLIMIT-KPN MACH-2 project (294629) with support from the NCCS Centre, performed under the Norwegian research program Centres for Environment-friendly Energy Research (FME). The authors acknowledge the following partners for their contributions: Aker Solutions, Ansaldo Energia, Baker Hughes, CoorsTek Membrane Sciences, EMGS, Equinor, Gassco, Krohne, Larvik Shipping, Lundin, Norcem, Norwegian Oil and Gas, Quad Geometrics, Total, Vår Energi, and the Research Council of Norway (257579).

References

D. Berstad, R. Anantharaman, P. Nekså, 2013, Low-temperature CO2 capture technologies – Applications and potential, International Journal of Refrigeration, 36, 5, 1403-1416.

T. Harkin, I. Filby, H. Sick, D. Manderson, R. Ashton, 2017, Development of a CO2 Specification for a CCS Hub Network, Energy Procedia, 114, 6708-6720.

D. Kim, D. Berstad, R. Anantharaman, J. Straus, T. Peters, T. Gundersen, T, 2020. Low Temperature Applications for CO2 Capture in Hydrogen Production, Computer Aided Chemical Engineering, 48, 445-450.

H. Malerød-Fjeld, D. Clark, I, Yuste-Tirados, R. Zanón, D. Catalán-Martinez, D. Beeaff, S.H. Morejudo, P.K. Vestre, T. Norby, R. Haugsrud, J.M. Serra, C. Kjølseth, 2017, Thermoelectrochemical production of compressed hydrogen from methane with near-zero energy loss, Nature Energy, 2, 12, 923-931.

M. Voldsund, K. Jordal, R. Anantharaman, 2016, Hydrogen production with CO2 capture, International Journal of Hydrogen Energy, 41, 9, 4969-4992.

Proceedings of the 14th International Symposium on Process Systems Engineering – PSE 2021+
June 19-23, 2022, Kyoto, Japan
http://dx.doi.org/10.1016/B978-0-323-85159-6.50022-1

Analysis and design of integrated renewable energy and CO_2 capture, utilization, and storage systems for low-cost emissions reduction

Mohammad Lameh, Dhabia M. Al-Mohannadi, Patrick Linke*

Department of Chemical Engineering, Texas A&M University at Qatar, Education City, PO Box 23874, Doha, Qatar
patrick.linke@qatar.tamu.edu

Abstract

CO_2 capture, utilization, and storage (CCUS) as well as renewable energy (RE) technologies are key options for the decarbonization of economies. The high cost of such pathways makes it important to develop a strategic screening approach that yields the optimal implementation of CO_2 reduction pathways while ensuring the economic viability of such projects. This work proposes a Process Systems Engineering approach to develop minimum cost CO_2 reduction pathways. The approach implements a systematic analysis methodology to understand key decisions of the optimal design. After that, a detailed network portfolio can be obtained by solving a reduced optimization problem. The method is demonstrated in a case study which shows how the high-level analysis can be used to guide the detailed design of CO_2 reduction networks, resulting in an efficient systematic planning.

Keywords: cost-optimal CO_2 reduction, marginal abatement cost, economic analysis, optimization.

1. Introduction

Process Systems Engineering methods have been developed to optimize the planning of CO_2 emissions mitigation (Manan et al., 2017). The general process engineering approach consists of analysing the problem to develop high-level insights and targets based on which the designs of integrated systems are assessed (Klemes, 2013). The early applications of such approach were focused on developing pinch analysis methodologies for optimizing heat integration (Linnhoff et al., 1979). The minimum heating and cooling targets developed allowed the validation and the understanding of optimal designs of heat exchanger networks (Linnhoff & Hindmarsh, 1983). The problem of cost-optimal CO_2 reduction has been addressed through designing an integrated system considering all available CCUS and RE options that achieve the desired CO_2 emissions reduction at the lowest possible cost (Al-Mohannadi et al., 2020). The solution is obtained through implementing an optimization model which yields the integrated processing system with the minimum cost. However, such solutions are not usually easily understood, and they require further analysis and interpretation. Recently, a cost analysis methodology for CO_2 reduction pathways was developed based on the Marginal Abatement Cost (MAC) of the different considered options (Lameh et al., 2021). This methodology allows the development of low-cost CO_2 reduction solutions using basic high-level information about the reduction technologies, but it lacks the level of detail that the design optimization models have.

To our knowledge, none of the exiting studies show a comprehensive Process Systems Engineering approach with analysis and design methodologies that systematically identify optimal pathways for CO_2 reduction. This work addresses the gap by presenting a two-step approach to support the decisions of planners and policy makers to achieve optimal CO_2 reduction. In the first step, the analysis method uses technical and economic factors of the different possible CO_2 reduction pathways to develop quick insights into the minimum cost solutions based on high level overview of the defined problem. These insights would simplify the optimization so that a global optimal solution is achieved. In the second step, the integrated CCUS-RE network optimization is performed to design a detailed CO_2 reduction configuration through physical CO_2 emissions processing and storage, and through applying renewable energy technologies. The solution of the optimization problem can then be understood based on the high-level insights obtained from the analysis tool applied in the first step. A case study is presented to illustrate the application of the method.

2. Methods

The aim of the proposed approach is to identify cost-optimal transitions to achieve a set target for CO_2 reduction. Different CO_2 emitting sources exist, among which are fossil-based energy production plants that cover a defined demand. The set target for CO_2 emissions reduction can be achieved by implementing a CO_2 abatement network which consists of CCUS and RE pathways. In the CCUS pathways, the emissions from the sources are captured and allocated to CO_2 sinks which can either store the CO_2 or utilize the emissions to produce value-added products. The RE pathways involve the implementation of renewable energy options to replace some of the existing fossil-based energy sources to cover the demand. The problem is addressed at two stages: analysis and design. At the first stage, CO_2 reduction analysis is conducted to determine the expected cost of the optimal CO_2 abatement network which achieves a set level of reduced emissions (Figure 1 (a)). This approach allows the identification of major insights corresponding to the total cost of CO_2 reduction through a simple illustrative procedure. The detailed design of the optimal network that achieves the CO_2 reduction target is addressed in the second stage in which the exact layout of the network with the flowrates and allocations is identified (Figure 1(b)). The analysis is conducted through developing the marginal abatement cost (MAC) curve considering the different available options (Lameh et al., 2021).

$$MAC_{CCUSij} = \frac{C_{si} - R_{dj}}{\eta_{dj} - \gamma_{si}} \tag{1}$$

$$MAC_{Eij} = \frac{C_{ej} - C_{exi}}{\varepsilon_{ei} - \varepsilon_{exj}} \tag{2}$$

Each CCUS option is characterized by the cost (C_{si}) of CO_2 supply from each source (capture, compression, and transport), the profit (R_{dj}) generated by each sink, the secondary emissions associated with supplying CO_2 from the sources (γ_{si}), and CO_2 fixation efficiency of each sink (η_{dj}). The MAC for the CCUS options can be calculated as shown in equation (1). The RE options are considered as energy-shifting pathways which are characterized by the cost of the RE source (C_{ei}), the cost of the existing source that is phased out (C_{exi}), and their corresponding emissions levels (ε_{ei} and ε_{exi}).

The MAC for the RE options can be determined as shown in equation (2). The CO_2 reduction potential for each option is determined based on prioritizing the cheapest pathways. The different options in the CO_2 abatement network are demonstrated on a minimum MAC (mini-MAC) profile from which the cost of a set level of CO_2 reduction can be determined.

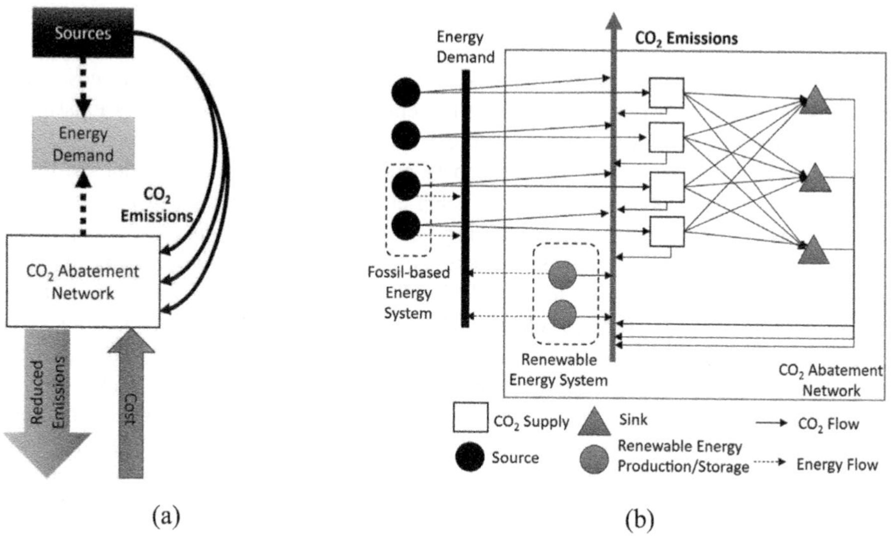

Figure 1 The CO_2 abatement network as considered through system analysis (a) and network design (a)

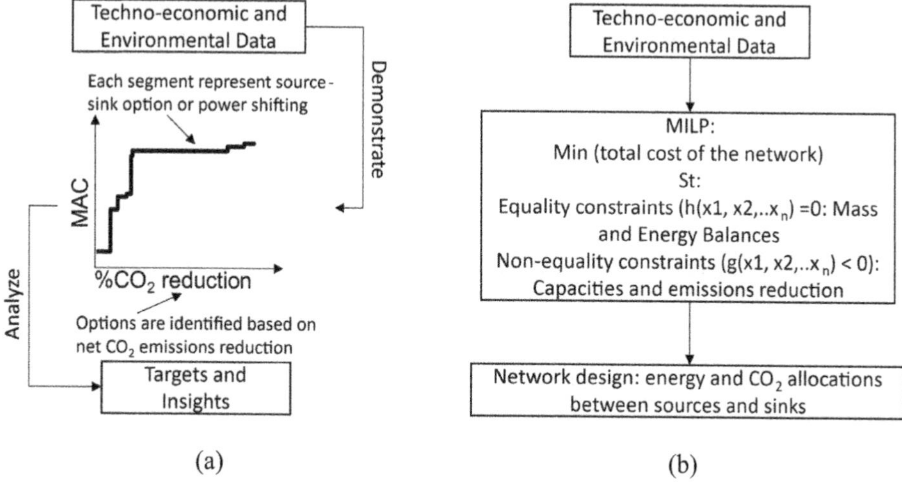

Figure 2 The framework applied in the analysis (a) and design (b) of the CO_2 abatement network

The network optimization problem is decomposed in a two-step approach (Al-Mohannadi et al., 2020) with the main network synthesis problem being formulated as a mixed integer linear program (MILP). The MILP determines the overall design of the CO_2 reduction portfolio which corresponds to the minimum cost for the set level of CO_2 reduction. The model is formulated by setting the equations for the energy and mass balances and the costs for the different components in the system (CO_2 capture, compression, piping, sinks, and RES). The optimization problem is defined by setting an objective function (minimizing the total cost of the system), and the constraints that ensure that the capacities of the CO_2 abatement technologies are not exceeded, and the set CO_2 emissions reduction is achieved. Figure 2 describes the methodologies followed in conducting the analysis and design of the CO_2 reduction network.

3. Case Study

The system studied in this work consists of four major CO_2 emitting sources which emissions flowrates is estimated based on the energy and industrial sectors existing in Qatar (Alfadala & El-Halwagi, 2017). Table 1 shows the data used to characterize each of the considered sources. The capture costs and secondary emissions are estimated based on Metz et al. (2005) and von der Assen et al. (2016). The cost of transportation is based on linearized compression, pumping, and piping cost models (Al-Mohannadi et al., 2020). Four potential CO_2 sinks are considered for implementation as CO_2 utilization and storage technologies (Table 2). The data is estimated based on existing technoeconomic studies (Hepburn et al., 2019) for enhanced oil recovery (EOR) , CO_2 storage (GCCSI, 2011), chemicals (Pérez-Fortes et al., 2016), and fuels (Tremel et al., 2015). For the renewable energy contribution, the demand for electric power can be covered either by an existing natural gas power plant (NG PP) or by introducing solar photovoltaic system (Solar PV). The solar PV can cover up to 13% of the electric power demand without requiring energy storage. The levelized cost of electricity for the solar PV is assumed to be 0.017 $/kWh (BELLINI, 2020). The cost of operating the NG PP was neglected (assuming very low cost of natural gas).

Table 1 The data for the sources

Source	CO_2 Produced ($MtCO_2/y$)	Capture Cost ($/$tCO_2$)	Transportation Cost ($/$tCO_2$)	Secondary emissions ($tCO_2/tCO_{2\text{-captured}}$)
High Concentration	8.32	0.00	3.00	0.01
Combustion	48.65	31.12	3.48	0.24
Cement	1.99	56.85	3.15	0.24
NG PP	25.88	27.33	3.27	0.24

Table 2 The data for the sinks

Sink	Capacity ($MtCO_2/y$)	CO_2 Breakeven Cost ($/$tCO_2$)	CO_2 Fixation Efficiency ($tCO_2/tCO_{2\text{-utilized}}$)
EOR	1	45	1
Storage	15	-20	1
Chemicals	4	-280	0.92
Fuels	17	-440	0.6

The collected data was used to analyze the cost of economic CO_2 reduction by generating the mini-MAC profile of the considered options (Figure 3 (a)). The mini-MAC profile identifies the promising pathways for economic CO_2 reduction: these are the pathways represented by the segments forming the MAC curve. The total cost of CO_2 reduction can be determined by integrating the mini-MAC profile (area under the curve) as shown in Figure 3 (b). This outcome can guide the network design by showing the expected total cost for different levels of CO_2 reduction. Each single point on the total cost profile corresponds to an optimal network design that can achieve the CO_2 reduction target with minimum cost. Instead of generating random designs through an exhaustive procedure of running the optimization model multiple times, key targets from the total cost profile can be determined. The high-level analysis shows that the maximum CO_2 reduction potential that can be achieved is 26.2 $MtCO_2$/y, which is around 31% of the considered emissions (84.8 $MtCO_2$/y). This is due to the limited capacity of the considered options (the capacity of the sinks is 37 $MtCO_2$/y), and to the secondary emissions associated with CO_2 supply and CO_2 sinks. The analysis identifies a cost neutral CO_2 reduction with a flowrate of 2.8 $MtCO_2$/y (11% of the maximum reduction potential). The mini-MAC profile shows a high cost for the options that require CO_2 supply from NG PP and combustion for utilization in chemicals and fuels production. Implementing a hybrid network consisting of renewable energy (shifting to solar) and CO_2 integration (capturing from high concentration sources and NG PP and allocating the emissions to EOR and storage) can reduce the emissions by 17.4 $MtCO_2$/y (66% of the maximum reduction potential) at a relatively low cost (35.6 \$/tCO_2). Beyond that abatement level, the expensive pathways are required, and the average MAC would rise to 374 \$/tCO_2 at the maximum achievable level of CO_2 reduction.

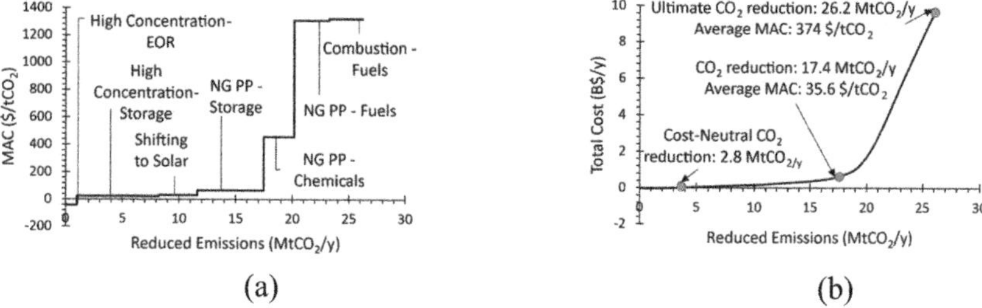

Figure 3 The mini-MAC profile (a) and the estimated cost of optimal CO_2 reduction (b)

To verify the results of the analysis, the design is performed for: a network that achieves a cost-neutral CO_2 reduction, a network corresponding to the maximum CO_2 reduction before the aggressive rise in the cost, and a network with the ultimate CO_2 reduction that can be achieved with the considered options. The CO_2 reduction levels for the three different targeted networks were determined from the total cost profile, and they were used as the CO_2 reduction constraints in the described optimization model. The optimization model minimizes the cost by determining the optimal CO_2 allocation between sources and sinks and the energy contribution of each power option. The design results for the three targeted systems are shown in Figure 4. The costs of the detailed designs for the three cases validated the results obtained from the analysis, with a slight marginal error (up to 2%). Hence, the proposed approach provides a systematic methodology for identifying cost-optimal CO_2 reduction by implementing simple high-level analysis to determine the expected costs, and to plan the designs of the optimal networks, and validate their outcomes.

4. Conclusions

This work presented a comprehensive Process Systems Engineering approach for planning and designing cost-optimal CO_2 abatement networks considering CCUS and RE options through analysis and design. The application of the method to a case study showed how the analysis of the system can be used to validate the results obtained from the design procedure and to understand the optimization solutions in the context of achieving affordable CO_2 emissions reduction. Future work will analyze the errors and deviations in both approaches and their impact under various uncertainties.

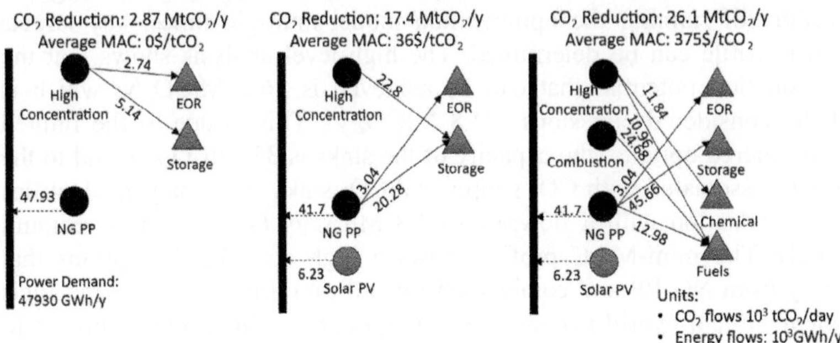

Figure 4 Three designs for the CO_2 abatement network with different levels of CO_2 reduction

References

Al-Mohannadi, D. M., Kwak, G., & Linke, P. (2020). Identification of optimal transitions towards climate footprint reduction targets using a linear multi-period carbon integration approach. Computers & Chemical Engineering, 140, 106907.

Al-Mohannadi, D. M., Kwak, G., & Linke, P. (2020). Identification of optimal transitions towards climate footprint reduction targets using a linear multi-period carbon integration approach. Computers & chemical engineering, 106907.

Alfadala, H. E., & El-Halwagi, M. M. (2017). Qatar's chemical industry: Monetizing natural gas. Chemical Engineering Progress, 113, 38-41.

BELLINI, E. (2020). Qatar's 800 MW tender draws world record solar power price of $0.01567/kWh. In (Vol. 2021): PV Magazine.

GCCSI. (2011). The costs of CO2 storage: post-demonstration CCS in the EU, Global CCS Institute. In: Global CCS Institute.

Hepburn, C., Adlen, E., Beddington, J., Carter, E. A., Fuss, S., Mac Dowell, N., Minx, J. C., Smith, P., & Williams, C. K. (2019). The technological and economic prospects for CO 2 utilization and removal. Nature, 575, 87-97.

Klemes, J. J. (2013). Handbook of process integration (PI): minimisation of energy and water use, waste and emissions: Elsevier.

Lameh, M., Al-Mohannadi, D. M., & Linke, P. (2021). Minimum marginal abatement cost curves (Mini-MAC) for CO 2 emissions reduction planning. Clean Technologies and Environmental Policy, 1-17.

Linnhoff, B., & Hindmarsh, E. (1983). The pinch design method for heat exchanger networks. Chemical Engineering Science, 38, 745-763.

Linnhoff, B., Mason, D. R., & Wardle, I. (1979). Understanding heat exchanger networks. Computers & Chemical Engineering, 3, 295-302.

Manan, Z. A., Nawi, W. N. R. M., Alwi, S. R. W., & Klemeš, J. J. (2017). Advances in Process Integration research for CO_2 emission reduction–A review. Journal of cleaner production, 167, 1-13.

Metz, B., Davidson, O., & De Coninck, H. (2005). Carbon dioxide capture and storage: special report of the intergovernmental panel on climate change: Cambridge University Press.

Pérez-Fortes, M., Schöneberger, J. C., Boulamanti, A., & Tzimas, E. (2016). Methanol synthesis using captured CO2 as raw material: Techno-economic and environmental assessment. Applied Energy, 161, 718-732.

Tremel, A., Wasserscheid, P., Baldauf, M., & Hammer, T. (2015). Techno-economic analysis for the synthesis of liquid and gaseous fuels based on hydrogen production via electrolysis. International Journal of Hydrogen Energy, 40, 11457-11464.

von der Assen, N., Müller, L. J., Steingrube, A., Voll, P., & Bardow, A. (2016). Selecting CO2 Sources for CO2 Utilization by Environmental-Merit-Order Curves. Environmental Science & Technology, 50, 1093-1101.

Proceedings of the 14th International Symposium on Process Systems Engineering – PSE 2021+
June 19-23, 2022, Kyoto, Japan
http://dx.doi.org/10.1016/B978-0-323-85159-6.50023-3

Techno-economic-environmental assessment for optimal utilisation of CO_2 in the Fischer-Tropsch gas-to-liquid process

Ali Attiq Al-Yaeeshi, Ahmed AlNouss and Tareq Al-Ansari*

College of Science and Engineering, Hamad Bin Khalifa University, Qatar Foundation, Doha, Qatar
*talansari@hbku.edu.qa

Abstract

Considering the un-declining emissions of CO_2, which is a major contributor to global warming, carbon capture and utilisation (CCU) has been promoted as a potential CO_2 reduction pathway, generating economic benefits and reduced environmental burdens. The integration of CCU with power plants and chemical industries drives the potential of adapting a CO_2 capture and utilisation scheme. Chemical synthesis such as gas-to-liquids (GTL) process using the Fischer-Tropsch technology is a promising pathway in this configuration. The objective of this study is to assess the techno-economic-environmental viability of maximising the production of wax, diesel, gasoline and LPG in an FT-GTL plant, while optimizing the utlisation of different variables such as steam, oxygen, CO_2, and the syngas recycle to purge ratio. The effect of reforming techniques and syngas recycle ratio on the production capacity are analysed upon supplementing the process with additional CO_2 at a range of 1000-2000 t/d. The methodology is based on the maximum production of syngas in the reforming units, which include steam-based methane reforming (SMR) and oxygen/steam-based auto-thermal reforming (ATR). Aspen HYSYS is used to model the GTL production flowsheets. The results demonstrate a significant improvement in the total refined products capacity for all scenarios based on variable function of raw material flow rate of CO_2, steam, oxygen and split ratio of syngas to the purge. The sensitivity analyses demonstrate the feasibility of the ATR and SMR options to provide significant enhancement when integrated with CO_2. The total refined product of hydrocarbons increase significantly when the decision variables are optimized.

Keywords: SMR, ATR, CO_2 Utilisation, GTL, CAPEX, OPEX, Optimisation

1. Introduction

Greenhouse gas (GHG) emissions are one of the most considerable environmental concerns of the recent era and are a leading cause for global warming, where CO_2 is a major contributor (IEA, 2018). The concentration of CO_2 in the atmosphere can be reduced through applying carbon capture and utilisation (CCU) processes. The Gas-to-Liquid (GTL) process is one example of an application that can accept CO_2 as a feedstock to enhance its product output (Al-Yaeeshi et al., 2020). Incidentally, McGregor (2019) stated that the CO_2 can replace the CO product in Fischer–Tropsch synthesis within the GTL process. Although, there are challenges for the introduction of CO_2 as feedstock in the FTS process, there are economic and environmental benefits in utilising the otherwise waste CO_2.

The main function of the GTL process is the conversion of natural gas (NG) into liquid refined products using the intermediate carbon monoxide (CO) and hydrogen (H_2) rich syngas. The long chain hydrocarbon products from the FT reactor include wax, diesel, gasoline and LPG at a reduced aromatic and sulphur content, thereby enhancing environmental compliance. Therefore, the synthetic fuels are considered a relatively more environmentally friendly array of products (Shell, 2019). The GTL production line comprises of five major units: pre-reforming, reforming, FT synthesis, product upgrading and fractionation. It begins by converting the natural gas into synthesis gas via various possible reforming reactions. The long chain hydrocarbons are then synthesised in the FT reactor, and subsequently treated in the upgrading section using H_2. Finally, in the fractionation column the refined products are separated. The economics of the GTL plant is high due to the costs of the FTS, and the efficiency required to produce a high stability ratio of H_2 and CO (syngas) (Al-Sobhi et al., 2021).

The CO_2 can be introduced as a feedstock or as recycled stream to influence the chemical equilibrium in the reforming unit and enhance syngas quality. Accordingly, the key parameters required in an optimisation problem include; reactor model design, operating conditions, and the total feed of CO_2 quantity, where by each component directly contributes to the enhancement of the product and the syngas H_2:CO ratio. Ekwueme et al. (2019) assessed the economics of a GTL plant considering an autothermal reforming model (ATR) and a steam/CO_2 reforming model, demonstrating positive economics of GTL process relative to other gas conversion technologies. Moreover, the steam/CO_2 reforming model is better performing from an economic perspective than the ATR in a small scale plant. Marchese et al. (2021) assessed the economic performance of direct air capture to the FT model, and maximised CO_2 conversion into synthetic chemicals, with a focus on wax. Furthermore, the recirculation of the FT off-gas was studied to enhance the performance, demonstrating a high system efficiency with a maximum carbon dioxide conversion at approximately 68.3 %.

CO_2 utilisation within GTL process has been studied by Al-Yaeeshi et al. (2019) and Al-Yaeeshi et al. (2020) to evaluate the efficiency of integrating the CO_2 into the steam methane reformer (SMR) and Auto-Thermal reformer (ATR). With the objective of maximising the production of wax, diesel, gasoline and LPG, this study analyses from a techno-economic-environmental perspective, the effect of reforming techniques, steam and oxygen demands and syngas recycle to purge ratio on the production capacity upon supplementing the FT-GTL process with CO_2 at the range of 1000-2000 t/d. A model is developed to assess different ATR and SMR reforming techniques within the GTL process. The CO_2 sink considered in this study is the Oryx GTL plant located in state of Qatar, which is configured with an ATR reformer with a natural gas feed of 330,000 cubic feet per day (QP, 2018). The feedstock consists of natural gas and steam with oxygen in the case of ATR and steam only in the case of SMR. The oxygen enters a Gibbs reactor, where natural gas is reformed to mainly CO and H_2. The purification process of syngas occurs prior to the FT unit to ensure high production of hydrocarbon molecules. Further purification is applied for the effluent from the FT unit to separate water and reprocess the unreacted CO and H_2. Subsequently, the hydrocarbon flow is sent to the upgrading unit, in which hydrogen is used to crack the longer-chain carbon molecules into smaller-chain hydrocarbons. Finally, the hydrocarbons are fractionated into wax, diesel, gasoline and LPG while the remaining stream is recycled to hydrocracking section.

2. Methodology

This study introduces a simulation flowsheet of the FT-GTL process integrated with CO_2 as a feedstock to maximise the production of wax, diesel, gasoline and LPG. It assumes the raw feed CO_2 is pure at the required operating parameters of GTL plant. The model is developed based on the raw data and ranges listed in Table 1 by using Aspen HYSYS-V9.

Table 1. Model raw data

Parameter	**NG Feed**	**CO_2**	**O_2 (ATR)**	**Steam (ATR)**	**Steam (SMR)**
Flow (T/d)	1.54×10^4	$1\text{-}2 \times 10^3$	$1.5\text{-}2 \times 10^4$	$2\text{-}5 \times 10^3$	$1\text{-}9 \times 10^4$
T (C)	25	150	144	500	500
P (bar)	1	25	25	25	25
	Hydrocracking	**FT**	**Reformer**	**Fractionator**	**Split Ratio**
T (C)	345	250	1050	Top P: 1 bar	(0.7-1)%
P (bar)	80	25	23	Bottom P :1.5 bar	

Various scenarios are studied depending on the GTL plant capacity, reformer type and CO_2 feedstock rate. The plant capacity is designed to process 15372 ton/d of NG feedstock to produce 34000 bbl/day of liquid hydrocarbons through dual trains. The molar oxygen to carbon ratio (O_2/C) is 0.6, and steam to carbon ratio (S/C) is 0.4 in the ATR reformer base scenario. In the case of the SMR reformer, the steam to carbon ratio is 3. The feed rate range of CO_2 for both reformers is varied between 1000-2000 ton/d to demonstrate the enhancement profile in the production of liquid hydrocarbons. Aspen HYSYS is used to assess the variations in each operating parameter. Results of the sensitivity analyses are used to construct regression models relating total refined products and H_2:CO ratio in syngas to changes in each operating parameter. The functions of the total refined products and H_2:CO ratio in syngas for each operating parameter are employed, where the weighted average of these functions is calculated to characterise the objective functions of the proposed optimisation model. The singular objective function of total refined products and H_2:CO ratio in syngas is then maximised to produce the optimal decision variables for each objective.

Variables:

$\dot{m}_{Total}$: Total hydrocarbons production rate (t/d)
$\dot{m}_{LPG}$: LPG production rate (t/d)
$\dot{m}_{Gasoline}$: Gasoline production rate (t/d)
$\dot{m}_{Diesel}$: Diesel production rate (t/d)
$\dot{m}_{Wax}$: Wax production rate (t/d)
$\frac{H_2}{CO}$: Molar ratio of hydrogen to carbon monoxide (°C)

Decision variables:

$\dot{m}_{steam}$: Steam flowrate (t/d)
$\dot{m}_{Oxygen}$: Oxygen flowrate (t/d)
$\dot{m}_{CO_2}$: CO_2 flowrate (t/d)
SR: split ratio of syngas to the purge (%)

Objective function:

$$\textit{Maximise: } \dot{m}_{Total} = \dot{m}_{LPG} + \dot{m}_{Gasoline} + \dot{m}_{Diesel} + \dot{m}_{Wax} \quad (1)$$

$$\textit{Maximise: } \frac{H_2}{CO} \quad (2)$$

Constraints: *As illustrated in Table 1*

3. Results

The output of sensitivity analyses demonstrates a variation in the rates of refined products with the changes in CO_2, O_2, steam, and recycle ratio. Figure 1 illustrates the effect of steam variation for ATR and SMR cases. The total refined products decreases with the increase in steam rate indicating optimum values at 21,500 and 2500 t/d for SMR and ATR, respectively while the H_2:CO ratio increases.

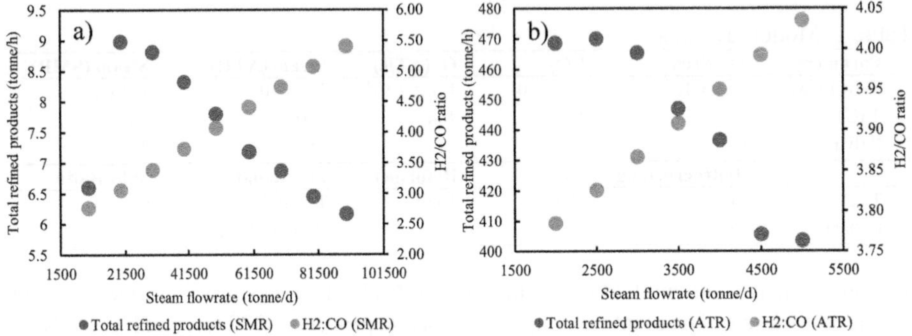

Figure 1: Effect of steam on total refined products and H_2:CO ratio for (a) SMR and (b) ATR.

The effect of CO_2 injection rate illustrated in Figure 2, demonstrates that the total refined products increases with the increase in CO_2 injection rate indicating an optimum value at 1900 t/d for ATR and continuous increasing trend for SMR, while the H_2:CO ratio decreases indicating more generation of CO through the equilibrium shift reaction.

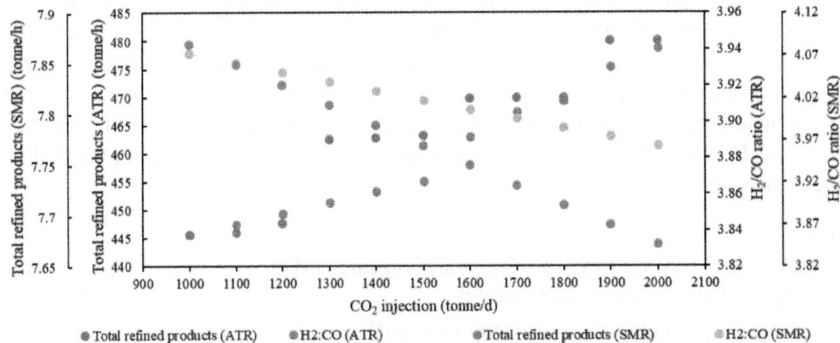

Figure 2: Effect of CO_2 injection on total refined products and H_2:CO ratio for SMR and ATR.

The variation of the split ratio of syngas recycle to FT reactor and purge stream illustrated in Figure 3a indicates that the total refined products are maximised at around 0.95 ratio with no pressure build up issues. The variation on oxygen rate (Figure 3b) applicable to the ATR indicates an optimum value at 18,000 t/d.

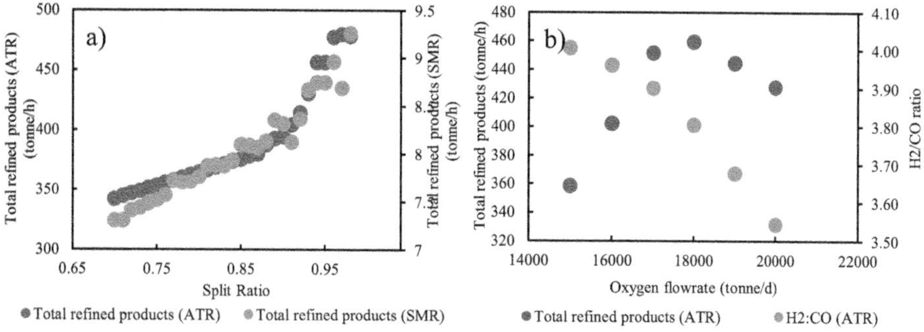

Figure 3: Trends of (a) split ratio variation for SMR and ATR and (b) oxygen flowrate for ATR.

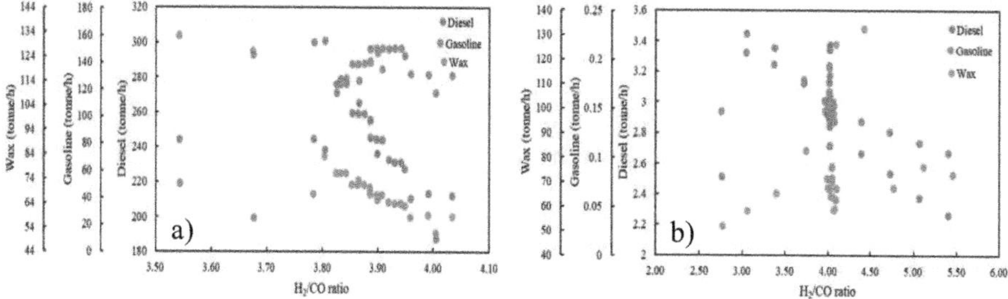

Figure 4: Optimal CO_2 source-sink allocation for (a) scenario 3 and (b) scenario 4.

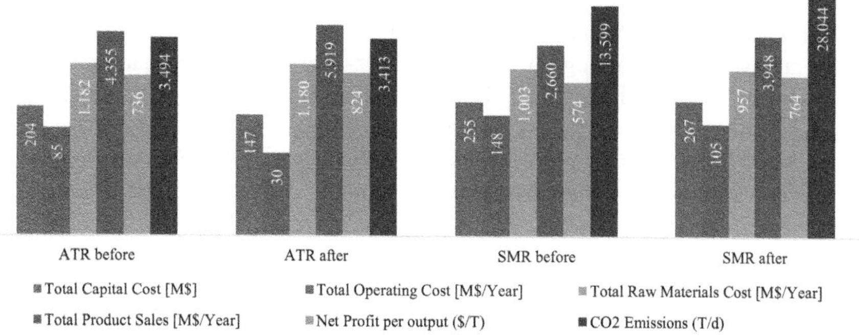

Figure 5: Results of the techno-economic-environmental assessment.

Plotting the two competing functions together as in Figure 4 indicates a high production for gasoline at higher H_2:CO ratio of approximately 3.9-4 compared to 3.8 for diesel and wax in the ATR case. Whereas, the SMR case revealed different schemes where the wax is maximised at a higher H_2:CO ratio of approximately 3.9-4.5 compared to 3 for diesel and gasoline. In summary, the optimization problem for the ATR case indicates an oxygen requirement rate of 18000 t/d, steam rate of 2500 t/d, CO_2 injection rate of 1900 t/d, a 21 bar FT pressure and a 0.97 split ratio. Whereas, in the case of the SMR, the optimization problem reveals a steam rate requirement of 20000 t/d, continuously increasing CO_2 injection trend, a 25 bar FT pressure, and a 0.98 split ratio. Furthermore, in both the ATR and SMR, the steam rate has a significant impact on the system. The techno-economic-environmental assessment demonstrates an improvement in the net profit per products for both ATR and SMR cases, and a reduction in the environmental emissions for the ATR case as illustrated in Figure 5 compared to the study conducted by Al-Yaeeshi et al.

(2020). This is associated with a slight increase in the capital cost due to the increased capacity and a reduction in operating costs, thus indicating a reduction in the requirement of utilities. This provides a substantial assessment to enhance the entire process efficiency and optimise the total capacity of refined products.

4. Conclusions

The assessment in this study is applied to two different GTL reforming technologies, which are the ATR and SMR. The integration of captured CO_2 with the FT-GTL process demonstrates a significant enhancement in the production of refined products. The results of the sensitivity analysis demonstrate that the wide range of variables impact the total refined hydrocarbon products, namely LPG, Gasoline, Diesel, and Wax. The variables applied in the assessment are steam, CO_2, oxygen, and split ratio of syngas recycle to FT reactor and purge stream for the ATR and SMR cases. The output in both cases detail optimal operating values that result in the significant enhancement in the final hydrocarbon production. The highest impact in both cases is with steam injection. Future studies should include the computation of the energy output / input, impact of CO_2 price on the techno-economic recycle of hydrogen and economic viability of hydrogen integration from different sources.

References

S.A. Al-Sobhi, A. AlNouss, and M. Alhamad, 2021, Techno-economic and environmental assessment of Gasoline produced from GTL and MTG processes, Computer Aided Chemical Engineering, 50, 1827-32.

A.A. Al-Yaeeshi, A. AlNouss, G. McKay, and T. Al-Ansari, 2019, A Model based analysis in applying Anderson–Schulz–Flory (ASF) equation with CO2 Utilisation on the Fischer Tropsch Gas-to-liquid Process, Computer Aided Chemical Engineering, 46, 397-402.

A.A. Al-Yaeeshi, A. AlNouss, G. McKay, and T. Al-Ansari, 2020, A simulation study on the effect of CO2 injection on the performance of the GTL process, Computers & Chemical Engineering, 136, 106768.

S. Ekwueme, I. Nkemakolam Chinedu, U. Julian, A. Kerunwa, N. Ohia, J. Princewill, and O. Emeka, 2019, Economics of Gas-to-Liquids (GTL) Plants, Petroleum Science and Engineering, 3, 85-93.

IEA, 2018, Global Energy & CO2 Status Report 2018 - The latest trends in energy and emissions in 2018, https://iea.blob.core.windows.net/assets/23f9eb39-7493-4722-aced-61433cbffe10/Global_Energy_and_CO2_Status_Report_2018.pdf

M. Marchese, G. Buffo, M. Santarelli, and A. Lanzini, 2021, CO2 from direct air capture as carbon feedstock for Fischer-Tropsch chemicals and fuels: Energy and economic analysis, Journal of CO2 Utilization, 46, 101487.

J. McGregor, 2019, 21. Fischer–Tropsch synthesis using CO2, Volume 2 Transformations, 413-32.

QP, 2018, Subsidiaries and join venture details Accessed 14/11/2018, https://www.qp.com.qa/en/QPActivities/Pages/SubsidiariesAndJointVenturesDetails.aspx?aid=3

Shell, 2019, Shell qatar project and sites, https://www.shell.com.qa/en_qa/about-us/projects-and-sites.html

Proceedings of the 14th International Symposium on Process Systems Engineering – PSE 2021+
June 19-23, 2022, Kyoto, Japan
http://dx.doi.org/10.1016/B978-0-323-85159-6.50024-5

Machine Learning-based Hybrid Process Design for the Recovery of Ionic Liquids

Yuqiu Chen*, Xiaodong Liang, Georgios M. Kontogeorgis

Department of Chemical and Biochemical Engineering, Technical University of Denmark, Lyngby, DK-2800, Denmark
yuqch@kt.dtu.dk

Abstract

Recycling ionic liquids (ILs) from dilute aqueous solutions is essential for their applications in both labs and industries. In this work, an efficient hybrid process scheme that combines aqueous two-phase extraction (ATPE) and distillation operating at their highest efficiencies is proposed for the recovery of ILs from dilute aqueous solutions. To find high performance salting-out agents for ATPE, an optimal IL-based aqueous biphasic systems (ABS) design method is employed. In this optimal design method, a machine learning (ML)-based model, i.e., artificial neural network (ANN)-group contribution (GC) model, is applied to predict the phase equilibrium behaviours of IL-based ABS. As a proof of the concept, results of the recovery of two hydrophilic ILs from their aqueous solutions are presented.

Keywords: IL recovery, Hybrid process scheme, ATPE, Machine learning, ABS.

1. Introduction

Ionic liquids (ILs) as innovative fluids have received wide attention in both academia and industries due to their unique properties such as negligible vapor pressure, non-flammability, wide electrochemical windows, excellent catalytic activities. Great efforts have been made to facilitate their applications in industry. However, currently there are little industrial processes employing ILs mostly because their relatively high costs in comparison with conventional solvents and our limited understanding of their environmental impacts. For example, large volumes of dilute aqueous IL solutions will be produced during the dissolution and regeneration of cellulose when using ILs as solvents. The disposal of these aqueous IL solutions will directly cause the loss of these high value solvents and this may even result in severe environment issues due to the toxicity and degradation of the disposed ILs. Both economic and environmental concerns of using ILs can be offset to some extent if they are efficiently recycled.

To date, various technologies including distillation, extraction, adsorption, membrane separation, aqueous two-phase extraction (ATPE), crystallization, electrodialysis and external force field separation have been proposed for the recovery/recycling of ILs after their application (Zhou et al., 2018). Each separation technology described above has its own advantages and shortcomings. Currently, distillation and extraction are two of the most widely studied separation approaches for the recovery/recycling of ILs. Due to the fact that most ILs have very low volatility, distillation is usually used for the recovery of ILs from volatile substances, while extraction is preferred in the case of separating ILs from non-volatile or thermally sensitive components. When recovering ILs from dilute aqueous solutions, however, distillation method has an extremely low thermal efficiency since large volumes of water need to be evaporated, while extraction approach demands a large amount of solvent for achieving a high recovery yield. On the other hand, ATPE that based on the formation of the aqueous biphasic systems (ABS), provides an alternative pathway for recovering ILs from dilute aqueous solutions. This is due to the fact that it allows the ILs to be efficiently concentrated or recovered in the IL-rich phase with the addition of a small amount of salting-out agent (Ventura et al., 2017). However, further purification process such as distillation is generally still required after aqueous two-phase extraction due to the fact that the IL purity in the IL-rich phase is not high enough. On the other hand, hybrid process schemes, which combine processing units operating at their highest efficiencies to perform one or more process tasks, are being considered as promising innovative and sustainable processing options (Chen et al., 2018). With this concept, a hybrid process scheme combining ATPE and distillation method is proposed for the recovery of ILs from their dilute aqueous solutions. In this hybrid process scheme, salting-out agents with high ABS forming ability are identified for ATPE through an optimal design method integrating a machine learning (ML)-based model into the computer-aided design technique. Results of two case studies are presented to highlight the hybrid process design method proposed in this work.

2. Design method

2.1. ANN-GC model

The ability to predict phase equilibrium behaviours of IL-based ABS is essential for its early design. However, thermodynamic models that can provide such predictions are still not available for these aqueous systems due to their high complexity. Fortunately, a machine learning-based nonlinear model proposed in our recent work provides the possibility of describing IL-based ABS (Chen et al., 2021a). This model combines the artificial neural network (ANN) algorithm and the group contribution (GC) method. Together with the system's' temperature and the mass fraction of IL, 34 IL functional groups and 37 salting-out agent functional groups are used as inputs (size of 73 x 1) in this ANN-GC model. The input layer reads the structure information of IL-ABS and then the hidden layer transfers and delivers this input information to the output layer where the phase composition of IL-based ABS is quantified, as shown in Figure 1. A combination of tansig transfer function (Eq. (1)) in the hidden layer and purelin transfer function ((Eq. (2)) in the output layer was applied.

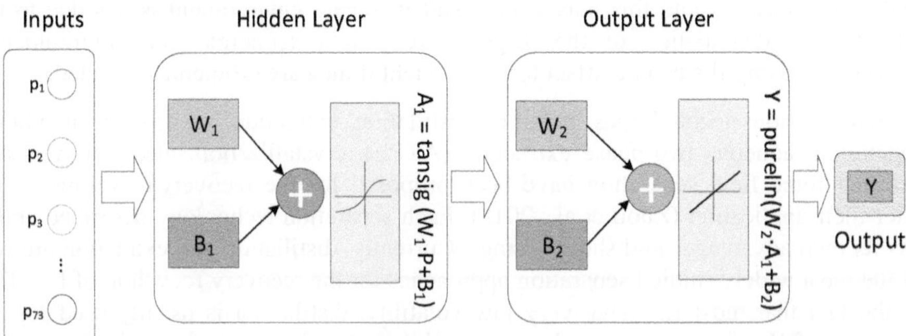

Figure 1. Structure of the three-layer artificial neural network (ANN) with an input vector size of 73 x 1.

$$f_1(x)=\frac{2}{1+e^{-2x}}-1 \tag{1}$$

$$f_2(x)=x \tag{2}$$

To train and test this ANN-GC model, 17,449 experimental data points covering 171 IL-based ABS at different temperatures (278.15K-343.15K) from numerous literatures were collected. This ANN-GC model gives a mean absolute error (MAE) between the experimental and model-calculated mass fraction of salting-out agent of 0.0175 and a coefficient of determination (R^2) of 0.9316 for the 13,789 training data points, and for the 3,660 test data points they are 0.0177 and 0.9195, respectively. These results show that this ANN-GC model can well describe the IL-based ABS.

2.2. Optimal salting-out agent design

The separation performance of an ATPE largely depend on the ABS forming ability of the used salting-out agents. The formation and stability of IL-based ABS is not only dependent on the structures of ILs such as cation types, lengths of alkyl chain and the anions, they are also highly associated with the type of salting-out agents.36 ABS with different ILs and salting-out agents at different temperature generally present different phase behaviors, it is challenging to find optimal ABS for the recovery of various ILs. Due to the number of potential IL-ABS being so large, it would be time consuming and expensive to use the trial-and-error approach to search for the optimal ABS. On the other hand, the optimal design of compounds/systems through manipulating properties at the molecular level is often the key to considerable scientific advances and improved process systems performance (Alshehri et al., 2020). For IL-based ABS , the optimal design method that integrates the ANN-GC model into the computer-aided design technique proposed in our most recent work is ideally suited as salting-out agents with high ABS forming ability can be rapidly and reliably identified for different IL aqueous solutions (Chen et al., 2021b).

When tailoring an ABS for the recovery of ILs from aqueous solutions, the IL should be as much as possible to be concentrated in the IL-rich aqueous phase, while the salting-out agent and water should be at the other phase. As we know, the closer to the axis origin a binodal curve is, the greater is the ability of a salting-out agent to phase split, the tie-line length (*TLL*) and slope of the tie-lines (S_{TL}) are able to verify trends in the partition coefficients or recovery efficiencies of ABS.

$$TLL=\sqrt{\left(x_S^T-x_S^B\right)^2+\left(x_{IL}^T-x_{IL}^B\right)^2} \tag{3}$$

$$S_{TL}=\frac{x_{IL}^T-x_{IL}^B}{x_S^T-x_S^B} \tag{4}$$

where the supercrits T and B designate the top phase (IL-rich phase) and the bottom phase (salt-rich phase), respectively, while the subscripts S and IL denote the mass fraction x of the salting-out agent and of the IL.

With the use of an objective function combining TLL and S_{TL}, the optimal design of IL-based ABS is formulated as a MINLP optimization problem mathematically descried by Eq. (5). In IL-based ABS, the specific IL is denoted by a vector $H^{IL} = [H_1^{IL}, H_2^{IL} ... H_{34}^{IL}]$. The first 5 elements $H_{1\text{-}5}^{IL}$ are integer variables describing the number of cation substituents. and the rest elements $H_{6\text{-}34}^{IL}$ are binary variables denoting the existence of cations and anions. On the other hand, each generated salting-out agent is represented by a vector $y = [y_1, y_2 ... y_{37}]$. The first 26 elements $y_{1\text{-}26}$ are binary variables describing the existence of salt anions, carbohydrates, amino acids. The other elements $y_{27\text{-}37}$ are integer variables denoting the number of salt cations. The best performance salting-out agent and its inputs can be determined for specific IL aqueous solutions (e.g., specific temperature T^{as}, IL structure H^{IL} and IL mass fraction in IL-water mixture G^{as}) by maximizing f $(z, y, T^{as}, H^{IL}, G^{as})$ that subjects to a series of constraints on salting-out agent structure, mass balance and phase equilibria.

$$\max_{z,y} TLL \cdot (-S_{TL})^r = f\left(z, y, T^{as}, H^{IL}, G^{as}\right)$$

$$\begin{aligned} s.t. \quad & \text{salting-out agent structural constraints} \\ & \text{mass balance constraints} \\ & \text{phase equilibria constraints} \end{aligned} \tag{5}$$

where vector z represents a continuous variable describing the ratio of added salting-out agent to the original IL-water mixture and r is an adjustable parameter describing the degree of influence from TLL and S_{TL}.

2.3. Hybrid recovery process scheme

The novelty of a hybrid process scheme is that each involved processing unit can operate at their highest efficiencies. The result is same task performed at much less energy inputs and/or lower cost. As mentioned above, distillation method has an extremely low thermal efficiency for recovering ILs from their dilute aqueous solutions, while ATPE approach cannot meet the final product specification. In such a case, hybrid process scheme combining ATPE and distillation is ideally suited as most water can be easily removed by adding a certain amount of salting-out agents and the rest of water can be distilled with a low energy input, as shown in Figure 2.

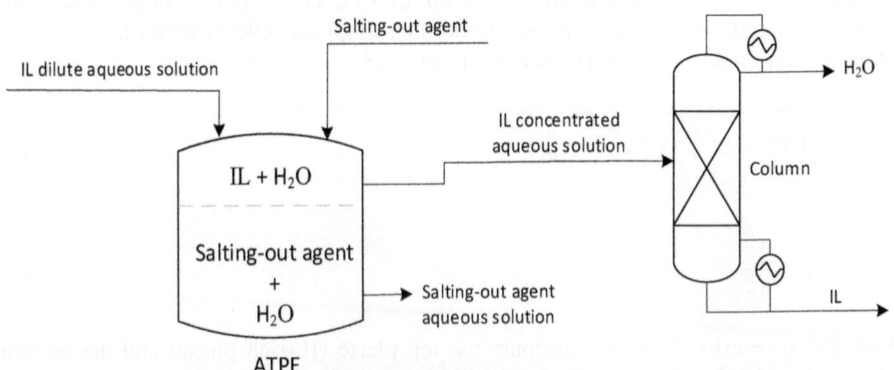

Figure 3: Hybrid process scheme for the recovery of ILs from dilute aqueous solutions.

3. Case studies

1-butyl-3-methylimidazolium chloride ([C_4mIm][Cl]) is a highly efficient direct solvent for the dissolution and regeneration of cellulose and large volumes of dilute IL aqueous solutions are produced during the precipitation of the regenerated cellulose.12,13 Therefore, efficient recycling of [C_4mIm][Cl] from these aqueous solutions is a critical step for the commercialization of this IL-based pretreatment technology. n-butylpyridinium trifluoromethanesulfonate ([C_4Py][TfO]) is another well-known hydrophilic IL that has potential industrial applications and it's also important to recover them from aqueous solutions during these applications. In this section, the proposed hybrid process design method will be used to recover [C_4mIm][Cl] and [C_4Py][TfO] from their aqueous solutions. First, two salting-out agents $NH_4)_2SO_3$ and KH_2PO_4 are, respectively, identified for [C_4mIm][Cl]- and [C_4Py][TfO]-based ABS formation by solving the MINLP problems in the modelling system GAMS 24.4.6, where a deterministic global optimization solver, Lindoglobal, is applied. As shown in Figure 3a and 3b, both $(NH_4)_2SO_3$ and KH_2PO_4 have better ABS forming ability than their counterparts K_2CO_3 (Zafarani-Moattar et al., 2010) and $(NH_4)_2SO_4$ (Guo et al., 2020) reported in the literature, indicating the availability of this optimal salting-out agent design method.

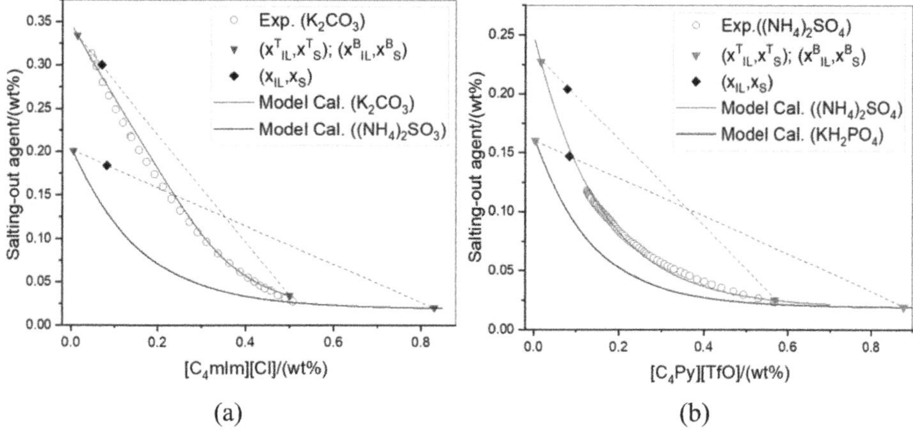

(a) (b)

Figure 3: Ternary phase diagrams for ABS composed of (a) [C_4mIm][Cl]-H_2O-K_2CO_3/$(NH_4)_2SO_3$ and (b) [C_4Py][TfO]-H_2O-$(NH_4)_2SO_4$/KH_2PO_4.

For the recovery of 10 wt% [C_4Py][TfO] from aqueous solutions, the ABS of [C_4mIm][Cl]-H_2O-$(NH_4)_2SO_3$ gives an IL recovery efficiency of 95.0 wt% and a salting-out agent input of 2.36 kg/kg IL recovery, and for the ABS of [C_4Py][TfO]-H_2O-KH_2PO_4 they are 95.6 and 1.81, respectively.

After removing most water by APTE, the IL concentrated aqueous solution is sent to the distillation column, where purified IL can be obtained at the bottom and the rest of water is distilled from the top. In this work, the detailed process simulations of distillation column are performed in Aspen Plus. By far, ILs are still not included to the component database in Aspen Plus and therefore they should be defined as pseudo-components. To do this, properties of ILs such as molecular weights, physical properties and critical properties need to be specified. Likewise, information of the thermodynamic method for the IL containing system should also be specified. In this work, the physical property models are taken directly from our previous work (Chen et al., 2019) and critical properties are calculated from the fragment contribution-corresponding states method proposed by Huang et al. (2013). On the other hand, UNIFAC model is selected as the thermodynamic method and model parameters including group volume parameters, surface area parameters and interaction parameters are taken from the published works (Song et al., 2020). Table 1 presents the process performance of both hybrid process scheme (Scheme 1) and pure distillation process (Scheme 2). Clearly, the hybrid process scheme demands much less energy input than that of the pure distillation process. However, a certain amount of salting-out agent is needed for ATPE in the hybrid process scheme. Nonetheless, the hybrid process scheme provides a good alternative for recovering ILs from dilute aqueous solutions due to its excellent energy performance.

Table 1: Energy performance of hybrid process scheme and pure distillation process.

IL aqueous solutions	$[C_4mIm][Cl]$ solution		$[C_4Py][TfO]$ solution	
Process scheme	Scheme 1	Scheme 2	Scheme 1	Scheme 2
Salting-out agent input (kg/kg IL recovery)	2.36	0	1.18	0
Energy input (kW/kW IL recovery)	0.16	6.86	0.082	6.62

4. Conclusions

A hybrid process scheme that combines ATPE and distillation method has been proposed for the recovery of hydrophilic ILs from their dilute aqueous solutions. In this hybrid process scheme, salting-out agents with high ABS forming ability are identified for ATPE through an optimal design method integrating the ANN-GC model into the computer-aided design technique. Two case studies are performed to test this hybrid design method. In both cases, the salting-out agents identified by the optimal design method have better ABS forming ability than their counterparts reported in the literature, and the hybrid process scheme present much better energy performance than the recovery process only using distillation unit.

References

A.S. Alshehri, R. Gani, F.You, 2020, *Computers & Chemical Engineering*, 141 (4), 107005.

J. Guo, S. Xu, Y. Qin, Y. Li, X. Lin, C. He, S. Dai, 2020, *Fluid Phase Equilibria*, 506 (15), 112394.

J. Zhou, H. Sui, Z. Jia, Z. Yang, L. He, X. Li, 2018, *Rsc Advances*, 8 (57), 32832-32864.

M.T. Zafarani-Moattar, S. Hamzehzadeh, 2010, Journal of Chemical & Engineering Data, 55 (4), 1598-1610.

S.P. Ventura, F.A. e Silva, M.V. Quental, D. Mondal, M.G. Freire, J.A. Coutinho, 2017, *Chemical reviews*, 117 (10), 6984-7052.

Y. Chen, E. Koumaditi, J.M. Woodley, G.M. Kontogeorgis, R. Gani 2018, *Computer Aided Chemical Engineering. Elsevier*. 43, 851-856.

Y. Chen, E. Koumaditi, R. Gani, G.M. Kontogeorgis, J.M. Woodley, 2019, *Computers & Chemical Engineering*, 130 (2), 106556.

Y. Chen, X. Liang, J.M. Woodley, G.M. Kontogeorgis, 2021a, *Chemical Engineering Science*, 247 (16), 116904.

Y. Chen, X. Meng, Y. Cai, X. Liang, G.M. Kontogeorgis, 2021b, *Industrial & Engineering Chemistry Research,* 60 (43), 15730-15740.

Y. Huang, H. Dong, X. Zhang, C. Li, S. Zhang, 2013, *AIChE Journal*, 59 (4), 1348-1359.

Z. Song, T. Zhou, Z. Qi, K. Sundmacher, 2020, *AIChE Journal*, 66 (2), e16821.

Proceedings of the 14th International Symposium on Process Systems Engineering – PSE 2021+
June 19-23, 2022, Kyoto, Japan
http://dx.doi.org/10.1016/B978-0-323-85159-6.50025-7

A Short-Cut Method for Synthesis of Solvent-based Separation Processes

Shuang Xu[a], Toby Crump[a], Selen Cremaschi[a], Mario R. Eden[a] and Anjan K. Tula[b]*

[a]*Department of Chemical Engineering, Auburn University, Auburn, AL, 36849, USA*
[b]*College of Control Science & Eng., Zhejiang University, Hangzhou 310027, China*
anjantula@zju.edu.cn

Abstract

In the process industry, non-ideal mixtures are mainly separated by solvent-based separation, such as extraction, extractive distillation, and azeotropic distillation. For these separation methods, the separation barrier is overcome by adding an external component (solvent/entrainer) to the system. Much effort has been devoted to optimally design/select the solvent through screening different solvents' physical properties. It is also necessary to account for separation process properties such as energy consumption, number of stages, etc., during solvent selection. In this work, a short-cut evaluation model that can quickly assess the solvents' physical/mixture properties and process properties has been applied for designing an optimal separation-based process. Four case studies (acetone/chloroform, acetone/methanol, benzene/cyclohexane, and methanol/methyl acetate) have been considered. The results reveal that given a list of potential solvents, the short-cut evaluation model can correctly predict the process performance.

Keywords: Solvent-based separation; optimization; solvent selection.

1. Introduction

Solvent-based separation is a class of processes where non-ideal mixtures are purified based on their solubility difference (extraction) or vapor-liquid equilibrium difference (extractive distillation and azeotropic distillation). Typically, a third component (solvent/entrainer) is added to bypass the separation barrier and facilitate the separation. The effectiveness of this separation is highly dependent on the solvent. Different solvents lead to different process designs and eventually influence the overall capital/operating cost. Many solvent selection methods have been proposed to select the optimal solvent. Shen *et al.* (2015) proposed a solvent evaluation and ranking algorithm, which selects the solvents based on the summation of five important physical properties, such as boiling point, selectivity, molecular weight, etc. Cignitti *et al.* (2019) presented an optimization model to design the solvent by maximizing the separation driving force. Kossack *et al.* (2008) pointed out that solvent screening based on physical properties alone may result in unfavorable solvent choices. A more comprehensive solvent selection method, rectification body method (RBM), was proposed by Kossack *et al.* (2008), which can accurately calculate the process properties, like minimum solvent flowrate and minimum energy demand. However, this method is computationally demanding.

It is necessary to develop a fast and reliable solvent selection method so that a large number of solvents can be evaluated efficiently. A short-cut solvent evaluation model is presented in this paper, which takes both solvent physical properties and separation process properties such as minimum energy consumption, the minimum number of stages, etc., into account during solvent selection. Given a list of potential solvents, the model can quickly evaluate the performance of the different solvents and give recommendations on the best option. The paper includes two parts: 1) solvent evaluation, 2) evaluation results validation. In the solvent evaluation, the model is applied to rank a list of solvents. The ranking results are validated by rigorous process simulation models where the operating/design variables are identified via derivative-free optimization.

2. Methodology

2.1. Solvent short-cut evaluation method

The solvent evaluation model aims to quickly and reliably assess different solvents based on various performance indicators. This model considers both the process properties and physical properties in the evaluation process. Firstly, a short-cut calculation model, which is based on Underwood and Fenske equations, is applied to calculate the process properties like minimum reflux ratio and the number of stages of a column. The Underwood and Fenske equations assume that the system has constant relative volatility. A typical extractive distillation system includes two columns, where the second column is simply solvent recovery distillation. Therefore, for the second column, the Underwood and Fenske equations can be applied to calculate the minimum number of stages and reflux ratio. However, these two equations cannot be directly applied to the extractive distillation column. Figure 1 shows the vapor-liquid equilibrium curve across the extractive distillation column. The extractive distillation column is divided into three sections: rectification, extraction, and stripping, and the relative volatility is different for each section, which means this change in relative volatility across the sections has to be accounted for. Here, we assume that the relative volatility is constant for each section, so the Fenske equation can be used in each section separately to calculate the minimum number of stages. The minimum reflux ratio is calculated when the operating line intersects with the VLE curve. In this way, the column minimum reboiler duty can be calculated by using the stage enthalpy balance. The extractive distillation column is described by Equations (1) – (6), where Equation (1) is only applied for ternary systems that do not have a separation boundary (Gerbaud and Rodriguez-Donis, 2014). For ternary systems with a separation boundary, such as the acetone/chloroform/ethylene glycol system, one can assume the distillate/bottom composition and calculate the minimum solvent flowrate through mass balance.

$$\left(\frac{F_E}{F_{AB}}\right)_{min} = \frac{(RR+1)D}{F_{AB}} \times \frac{(x_{PA}-y^*_{PA})}{(x_E-x_{PA})} + \frac{D(x_D-x_{PA})}{F_{AB}(x_E-x_{PA})} \tag{1}$$

$$N_{min,i} = \frac{lg[(x_{i,l}/x_{i,h})/(x_{i+1,l}/x_{i+1,h})]}{\lg(\alpha_{lh,i})}, i = 0,1,2 \tag{2}$$

$$N_{min} = \sum_{i=0}^{2} N_{min,i} \tag{3}$$

$$R_{min,j} = \frac{F_E x_{j,l} + D(x_D - y_{j,l})}{D(y_{j,l} - x_{j,l})}, j = 1,2 \tag{4}$$

$$R_{min} = max\{R_{min,1}, R_{min,2}\} \tag{5}$$

$$Q_{reboiler,min} = (R_{min}+1)DH_{D,V} + WH_W - H_E F_E - H_{AB}F_{AB} - R_{min}DH_{D,L} \tag{6}$$

In the model, F_E is the solvent/entrainer flowrate, F_{AB} is the raw material flowrate, RR is the predefined reflux ratio for solvent flowrate calculation. D and W are the distillate and bottom flowrates. x_D and x_W are the distillate and bottom compositions. x_E is the inlet solvent composition. x_{PA} is the minimum solvent composition that breaks the azeotropes after adding the solvent, and component A is the lightest component in the system. $y_{PA}{}^*$ is the vapor composition in equilibrium with x_{PA}. $N_{min,i}$ is the minimum number of stages in the ith section. $x_{i,l}$ and $x_{i,h}$ are the light and heavy component compositions in the ith section. $\alpha_{lh,i}$ is the geometric relative volatility of the ith section. $x_{j,l}$ and $y_{j,l}$ are the light compound liquid and vapor compositions at the first (j=1) and last (j=2) stage of the extractive section. R_{min} is the minimum reflux ratio. $H_{D,V}$ are $H_{D,L}$ are the vapor and liquid enthalpies of the distillate product. H_E and H_{AB} are the enthalpies of entrainer and binary raw materials. The inlet is assumed to be at boiling point (q= 1). After analyzing different extractive distillations systems, $x_{1,E}$ is usually between 60 % to 80%, $x_{2,E}$ is close to $x_{1,E}$, and the difference is in the range of 5%.

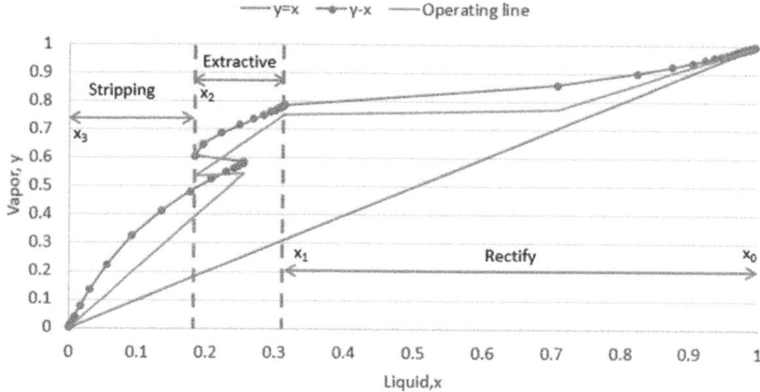

Figure 1. VLE plot of acetone/methanol/water extractive distillation. (x_0, x_1, x_2, x_3 – boundary composition in each section).

For each solvent, we calculate the minimum reboiler duty, number of stages, and reflux ratio by applying the proposed calculation method. Eight properties, including six process properties, e.g., the minimum number of stages, reboiler duty and reflux ratio, and two physical properties, e.g., solvent flowrate and boiling point, are considered in the evaluation model. These properties are selected because they directly influence the process capital and/or utility cost. Given N number of potential solvents, for each property, a value from one to N is assigned (where one is given to the best solvent with that property). Finally, the solvents are ranked based on summation scores, and the best solvent has the overall lowest score.

2.2. Validation model

To validate the rankings given by the solvent evaluation method, simulation-based optimization is employed to optimally design the extractive distillation setups. The total annualized cost, which considers both capital and utility costs, is the objective function. The number of stages, inlet stage, and solvent flowrate are the decision variables. A generalized form of the optimization problem solved by the simulation-based optimization algorithms is given in Equations (7)-(15).

$$min: TAC = \frac{i(i+1)^n}{(i+1)^n - 1} \times IC + AUC \tag{7}$$

$$st. IC = \sum_j Cost_j(q_{s,j}) \tag{8}$$

$$AUC = 24 \times 300 \times \sum_j Utility_j(q_{o,j}) \tag{9}$$

$$q = \Theta(F_S, N_k, N_{k,feed}, N_{1,S}), k = 1, 2 \tag{10}$$

$$x_m \geq purity \tag{11}$$

$$F_{S,L} \leq F_S \leq F_{S,U} \tag{12}$$

$$N_{k,feed,L} \leq N_{k,feed} \leq N_{k,feed,U} \tag{13}$$

$$N_{k,L} \leq N_k \leq N_{k,U} \tag{14}$$

$$N_{1,S,L} \leq N_{1,S} \leq N_{1,S,U} \tag{15}$$

Here, TAC is the total annualized cost, IC is the investment cost, AUC is the annualized utility cost, i is interest, n is plant life (n=5 is used in this model), $Cost_j$ is the investment cost of equipment j, $Utility_j$ is the utility cost of equipment j, $q_{s,j}$ is the sizing variable for equipment j, $q_{o,j}$ is the operating variable for equipment j, x_m is the product purity of component m, $\Theta(F_S, N_k, N_{k,feed}, N_{1,S})$ is the process simulation model, F_S is the solvent flowrate rate, N_k is the number of stages of column k, $N_{k,feed}$ is the materials feed stages of column k, $N_{1,S}$ is the solvent feed stage of the first column, and L and U represent the lower and upper bounds.

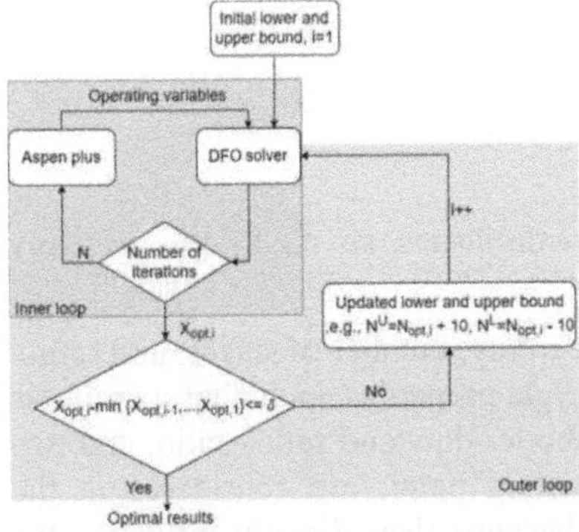

Figure 2. DFO solving algorithm for validation model.

To generate stable results that are not influenced by the initial lower and upper bounds, an algorithm (Figure 2) is developed to solve the optimization problem. The algorithm has two parts: 1) inner loop: given the initial upper and lower bounds of the decision variables, the inner loop runs the process simulation, and using a derivative-free optimization (DFO) solver, the best design parameters are identified. 2) outer loop: according to the identified best design parameters from the inner loop, the lower and upper bounds are updated and sent back to the inner loop. The process terminates after reaching a stable objective value.

3. Results and Discussion

Four separation systems, acetone/chloroform, acetone/methanol, benzene/cyclohexane, and methanol/methyl acetate, with their potential solvents, were selected from the review paper by Gerbaud *et al.* (2019). The short-cut evaluation model and DFO results are listed in Table 1. The identified design parameters of the best solvent are listed in Table 2.

Table 1. Tested evaluation and DFO results.

Solvents	Score	TAC, 10^6\$	Solvents	Score	TAC, 10^6\$
Acetone/Chloroform			Acetone/Methanol		
EG	16	0.77	Water	20	3.32
DMSO	14	0.66	2-Proponal	35	7.6
o-Xylene	28	1.05	Ethanol	27	6.64
Benzene	33	1.29	DMSO	14	2.87
Chlorobenzene	29	0.94	EG	24	4.63
Benzene/Cyclohexane			Methanol/Methyl Acetate		
Dimethyl phthalate	22	0.95	DMSO	13	1.05
NMP	24	0.76	EG	18	1.11
Aniline	34	0.97	2-Methoxyethanol	17	0.98
Sulfolane	19	0.69	-	-	-
Furfural	21	0.72	-	-	-

For acetone/chloroform separation, the short-cut evaluation method ranks the five solvents in the following order: DMSO (Dimethyl sulfoxide) > EG (ethylene glycol) > chlorobenzene > o-xylene > benzene. The DFO gave a similar TAC order except for chlorobenzene and o-xylene. This is because the system has a separation boundary, and we have to approximate this separation boundary using calculated residue curves from process simulation software. The solvent flowrate of o-xylene is 1.22 times larger than chlorobenzene, but it is 1.61 times larger from the DFO results. So, the o-xylene system has higher reboiler duty and higher TAC value. The short-cut and DFO results give the same order: DMSO > water > EG > ethanol > 2-proponal for acetone/methanol separation. For the benzene/cyclohexane case, the short-cut model predicts the following order: sulfolane > furfural > dimethyl phthalate > N-Methyl-2-pyrrolidone (NMP) > aniline, but the DFO results show that the NMP has better performance than dimethyl phthalate. Although the evaluation model correctly represents that the dimethyl phthalate system has a lower number of stages, but its high boiling point results in higher column temperatures, which requires a furnace. Due to this, the capital cost of dimethyl phthalate system is higher than the NMP system. For the methanol/methyl acetate case study, only three solvents were selected because of the lack of experimental phase equilibrium data. Among these three solvents, the short-cut evaluation method predicts that DMSO has the best performance, but the DFO results show that 2-methoxyethanol has better performance. The evaluation model shows that the 2-methoxyethanol has a smaller number of stages for the extractive column and a higher number of stages for the second column, which results in similar capital costs. However, the predicted minimum reboiler duty does not correctly represent the utility cost. Two reasons may cause this deviation: 1) Boiling point, DMSO has higher boiling point than 2-methoxyethanol, so different types of utilities have to be used. However, in this model, we rank the properties only based on their relative heat duty, and the different types of utilities are not considered. 2) Boundary composition (x_1, x_2). The boundary composition influences the sections' relative volatility and thus influences the calculated reboiler duty. The same $x_{1,E}$ value is used in all cases, but DFO proves that DMSO $x_{1,E}$ is equal to 60%, while 2-methoxyethanol, EG has similar $x_{1,E}$ values around 70%.

Table 2. Design parameters of the identified best solvent for the four separation systems.

		Acetone/ chloroform	Acetone/ methanol	Benzene/ cyclohexane	Methanol/ methyl acetate
Best identified solvent		DMSO	DMSO	Sulfolane	2-methoxyethanol
F_{AB} (equimolar), kmol/h		100	540	100	100
T1	N_1	36	41	25	49
	$N_{1,f}$	13	27	13	37
	$N_{1,s}$	3	3	2	6
T2	N_2	13	19	13	23
	$N_{2,f}$	4	14	4	8
F_s, kmol/h		111	399.6	88	263

4. Conclusions

Solvents can alter the relative volatility of mixtures and therefore the selection of the optimal solvent impacts extractive distillation design and operation. The best solvent has to balance the process capital and utility cost so that the annualized cost is minimized. This work presents a simple and reliable short-cut evaluation method to assist in solvent selection for solvent-based distillation. The proposed method was applied to four different extractive distillation systems. By including the process properties in the solvent ranking algorithm, the solvent with the best process performance (lower capital/utility cost) is identified. The evaluation results were validated by a rigorous design approach where the key operating parameters are optimally designed. Both the solvent evaluation and the optimized process results demonstrated that DMSO, DMSO, sulfolane, are the best solvents for separating acetone/chloroform, acetone/methanol, and benzene/cyclohexane azeotrope systems, respectively. The methanol/methyl acetate azeotrope system results indicated that the solvent boiling point and the choice of boundary composition might highly impact the ranking results, so the ranking algorithm will need to be further improved by taking these factors into account. The proposed approach can be applied as a first screening of potential solvents with low computational cost and decent screening results.

References

Cignitti, S., Rodriguez-Donis, I., Abildskov, J., You, X., Shcherbakova, N. and Gerbaud, V., 2019. CAMD for entrainer screening of extractive distillation process based on new thermodynamic criteria. *Chemical Engineering Research and Design*, 147, 721-733.

Gerbaud, V. and Rodríguez-Donis, I., 2014. Extractive distillation. In *Distillation* (pp. 201-245). Academic Press.

Gerbaud, V., Rodriguez-Donis, I., Hegely, L., Lang, P., Denes, F. and You, X., 2019. Review of extractive distillation. Process design, operation, optimization and control. *Chemical Engineering Research and Design*, 141, 229-271.

Kossack, S., Kraemer, K., Gani, R. and Marquardt, W., 2008. A systematic synthesis framework for extractive distillation processes. *Chemical Engineering Research and Design*, 86(7), 781-792.

Shen, W., Dong, L., Wei, S. A., Li, J., Benyounes, H., You, X., & Gerbaud, V. (2015). Systematic design of an extractive distillation for maximum-boiling azeotropes with heavy entrainers. *AIChE Journal*, 61(11), 3898-3910.

Proceedings of the 14th International Symposium on Process Systems Engineering – PSE 2021+
June 19–23, 2022, Kyoto, Japan
http://dx.doi.org/10.1016/B978-0-323-85159-6.50026-9

Modeling and Optimization of Ionic-Liquid-Based Carbon Capture: Impact of Thermal Degradation Kinetics

Kyeongjun Seo[a], Zhichao Chen[a], Thomas F. Edgar[a], Joan F. Brennecke[a], Mark A. Stadtherr[a], Michael Baldea[a*]

[a]*McKetta Department of Chemical Engineering, The University of Texas at Austin, Austin, Texas 78712, United States*

mbaldea@che.utexas.edu

Abstract

Ionic liquids (ILs) have recently been considered as alternatives to conventional amine-based absorbents in post-combustion CO_2 capture processes. However, solvent losses by IL thermal degradation could be more significant than in the case of conventional amine solvents. In this paper, we propose an advanced process design that uses a thin-film unit under vacuum to minimize the thermal degradation of solvent during regeneration. We employ rigorous thermodynamics and rate-based mass transfer models, with robust simulation and optimization capabilities implemented using a pseudo-transient modeling technique. The impact of solvent thermal degradation on the economic performance of the IL-based carbon capture process is studied. A comparison to a conventional process design is presented.

Keywords: carbon capture, flowsheet optimization, ionic liquids, process design, thermal degradation kinetics

1. Introduction

Recently, ionic liquids (ILs) have gained attention as promising solvents for post-combustion carbon capture due to desirable properties such as negligible volatility, high CO_2 absorption capacity and low heat of regeneration (Aghaie et al., 2018).

In this work, we consider triethyl-(octyl)phosphonium 2-cyanopyrrolide ([P_{2228}][2-CNPyr]) as an IL chemical absorbent for CO_2 capture because of its high CO_2 absorption capacity, moderate reaction enthalpy, superior reversibility, and relatively low viscosity (Seo et al., 2014). Although it is a promising candidate IL for carbon capture in terms of these properties, its thermal stability should also be considered because solvent (thermal) degradation could result in economic losses as well as operational problems (Rao and Rubin, 2002). Our experiments indicate that the thermal degradation rate of [P_{2228}][2-CNPyr] is comparable to or greater than that of monoethanolamine (MEA), a conventional amine-based solvent. In addition, given that the bulk price of ILs is expected to be higher (estimated \$10/kg) than that of conventional amine solvents (e.g., MEA at \$1.5-2/kg) (Ramdin et al., 2012), the cost associated with solvent loss is particularly important.

Solvent thermal decomposition occurs mainly during solvent regeneration, where the solvent is exposed to high temperatures. A conventional solvent regeneration system (stripper and reboiler) has a relatively long liquid residence time (5-10 minutes) (Walters et al.,

2016; Jung et al., 2018), exposing the solvent to high temperatures for prolonged periods of time. The thermal degradation of the solvent can be reduced by using a short residence time with a small liquid hold-up (Alhusseini et al., 1998) at the regeneration temperature. Thin-film technology can replace such a conventional regeneration system, diminishing residence times and thus the thermal degradation issue. When thin film units are operated under vacuum pressure, the regeneration temperature can be lowered even further.

Based on these considerations, we propose a novel flowsheet design for an IL-based carbon capture process. We then perform economic optimization of the proposed process flowsheet using a pseudo-transient optimization framework (Pattison and Baldea, 2014) with a focus on the economic impact of solvent thermal degradation. The regeneration temperature and associated liquid residence time are reduced using a thin-film column integrated with a vacuum compressor. This can significantly reduce the thermal degradation of IL absorbent and the associated make-up costs compared to the conventional regeneration system using a reboiler.

2. Flowsheet description

Figure 1 shows the proposed process design for IL-based CO_2 capture. The conventional regeneration system that consists of a stripper and reboiler is replaced with a thin-film unit. A thin-film unit is composed of a bundle of tubes in a shell. A liquid film flows downward on the interior vertical surface of each tube and the tube walls are heated by steam on the shell side. This unit can provide high heat and mass transfer rates due to the large surface area created by the liquid film. In the case of the proposed carbon capture plant, the liquid is the rich (i.e., high CO_2 concentration) IL solvent. The CO_2 is desorbed from the liquid and leaves at the top of the unit.

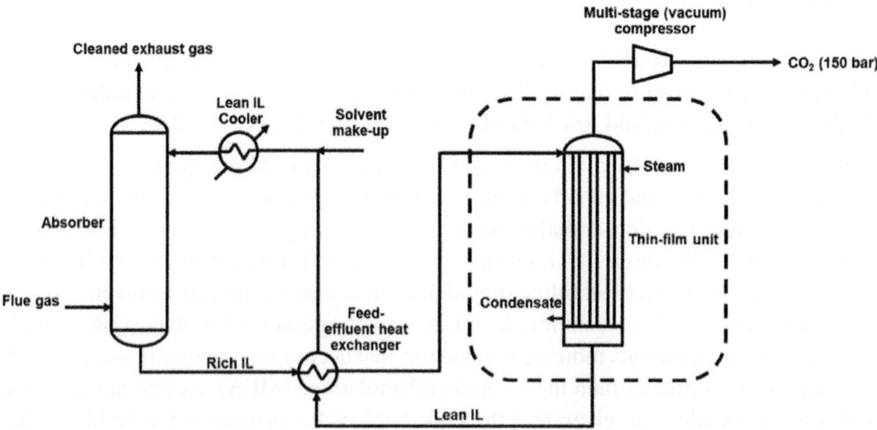

Figure 1: Proposed IL-based carbon capture process flowsheet. A conventional system stripper and reboiler system is replaced with a thin-film unit (shown by the dashed line) for solvent regeneration.

The CO_2 absorption model and other physical properties for the IL solvent used in this work ($[P_{2228}][2\text{-CNPyr}]$) are presented in our previous work (Seo et al., 2020). The experimentally measured thermal degradation of this IL solvent can be described by apparent zero-order kinetics, with an Arrhenius temperature dependence of the rate constant:

$$\frac{m(t)}{m(0)} = 1 - \left(k_0 \exp\left(-\frac{E_a}{RT}\right)\right) t \tag{1}$$

where $m(0)$ is the initial mass of solvent and $m(t)$ is the mass after time t. The pre-exponential factor k_0 and activation energy E_a are estimated from experimental data to be $k_0 = 305.5\ \mathrm{h}^{-1}$ and $E_a = 41.8$ kJ/mol.

We use a rate-based mass transfer model to describe kinetically limited transport phenomena. A detailed description of the rate-based model for the absorber column and the related material and energy balances can be found in our previous work (Seo et al., 2020). However, we modify the mass transfer coefficient and effective area correlations (Song et al., 2018) to be more suitable for viscous IL solvent flow. For the thin-film unit, the same rate-based model is used with some modifications. The liquid phase mass transfer coefficient is estimated using the correlation of Yih and Chen (1982). The mass transfer resistance in the vapor phase is assumed to be negligible. The mass transfer area per volume is calculated by dividing the total tube surface area by the overall thin-film column volume. For the heat transfer rate in the thin-film unit, an additional heat transfer term between the steam and liquid film is introduced. The heat exchanger model is also based on Seo et al. (2020). However, the overall heat transfer coefficient and the associated pressure drop models are modified to use empirical correlations for viscous liquids (Talik et al., 1995). The flooding point for the thin-film unit is determined using an empirical correlation from Mouza et al. (2005). Finally, the liquid residence time for each unit (only residence times in the heat exchanger and the regeneration unit where the solvent operates at high temperature are considered) is estimated from the ratio of the total hold-up volume to the liquid flowrate.

3. Process economic optimization

The optimization problem is formulated as:

$$\begin{aligned} \min_{\pi} \quad & \phi(\chi, \pi, \xi) \\ \text{s.t.} \quad & f(\chi, \pi, \xi) = 0 \\ & c(\chi, \pi, \xi) \leq 0 \end{aligned} \tag{2}$$

where the objective function, ϕ, is the sum of the annualized capital cost (for the absorber, heat exchanger, compressor, cooler, gas blower, solvent pump, and thin-film unit) and the operating cost (for heating, cooling, electricity, and solvent make-up) of the IL-based CO_2 capture process, f is the flowsheet model described above, and c are process operating constraints. π are process decision variables, χ are process state variables, and ξ are process parameters. The decision variables and constraints are summarized in Table 1. The resulting CO_2 capture process flowsheet model is difficult to solve because of its large size and coupled nonlinear equations. We improve the initialization and convergence of this complex flowsheet optimization problem using a pseudo-transient modeling technique (Pattison and Baldea, 2014).

Table 1: Decision variables and process constraints for process optimization

Component	Relevant variables and equations
Decision variables[a]	$F^L, L, D, L_T, D_T, T_{\text{absorber,in}}, T_{\text{thin-film,in}}, T_{\text{steam}}, P_T$
Process constraints[b]	$\frac{F^V_{CO_2,\text{in}} - F^V_{CO_2,\text{out}}}{F^V_{CO_2,\text{in}}} \geq 0.9$
	$\Delta T_{\text{appr, min}} \geq 1\,°\text{C}$
	$T_S \leq 150\,°\text{C}$
	$0.08\,\text{bar} \leq P_T \leq 1\,\text{bar}$
	$\text{Fr}_V \leq 0.8\text{Fr}^*_V$

[a] F^L is IL solvent circulation flowrate, L and D are height and diameter of the absorber, L_T and D_T are height and diameter of the thin-film unit, $T_{\text{absorber,in}}$ and $T_{\text{thin-film,in}}$ are inlet temperatures of the absorber and thin-film unit, T_{steam} is regeneration steam temperature, and P_T is pressure of the thin-film unit.

[b] The CO_2 removal rate is constrained to be at least 90%, the minimum approach temperature of heat exchanger is constrained to be not lower than 1 °C, the suction pressure of the vacuum is limited to equal or greater than 0.08 bar, and the thin-film unit is restricted to operate below 80% of the flooding point.

Figure 2 shows a comparison of optimal process costs between the proposed (thin-film unit operated under vacuum pressure) and conventional (stripper with a reboiler system operated under atmospheric pressure) regeneration systems. The flue gas conditions correspond to a natural gas combined cycle power plant (case B31B in James et al. (2019)). The same cost correlations are used for both systems. In the conventional process, the residence times in the stripper and reboiler are assumed to be 0.1 and 5 minutes, respectively (Walters et al., 2016).

The absorber cost of the conventional system ($74.4 M/year) is higher than that of the thin-film system ($38.7 M/year). Also, the optimal absorption temperature is 15 °C for the conventional system whereas it is 30 °C for the proposed system. This is because a smaller mass transfer area for CO_2 absorption and higher absorption temperature would be sufficient to capture the same level of CO_2 since the solvent regeneration is more effective under reduced pressure. The optimal operating pressure for the proposed regeneration system is found to be 0.41 bara. Therefore, the compressor equipment cost is much higher for the thin-film case ($51.0 M/year) compared to the conventional case ($18.4 M/year) because a larger compressor is required to accommodate increased CO_2 gas volume at the reduced operating pressure. However, the CO_2 loading in the regenerated IL solvent can be much lower for the proposed system (0.097 CO_2/mol IL) compared to the conventional system (0.161 mol CO_2/mol IL).

A key comparison in the operating costs is the solvent replacement cost. The residence time in the regeneration system is much smaller in the proposed configuration (thin-film: 1.2 min vs. conventional: 5.1 min). This can be attributed to a small liquid hold-up volume in the thin-film unit. As a result, the solvent make-up cost related to thermal degradation is significantly reduced (thin-film: $31.7 M/year vs. conventional: $90.2 M/year). Electric-

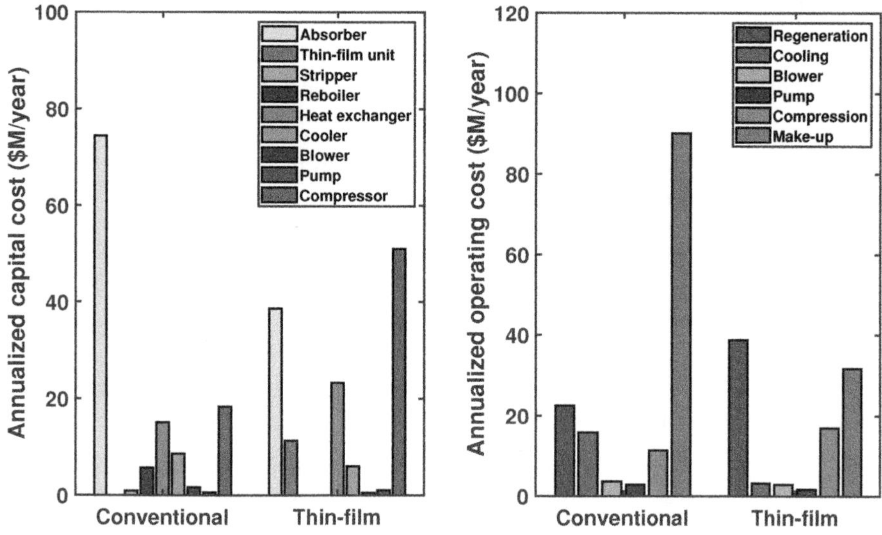

Figure 2: Comparison of process economics between proposed and conventional systems.

ity cost for the compression would be higher for the thin-film system because of operating under vacuum (thin-film: $16.9 M/year vs. conventional: $11.3 M/year). However, the solvent cooling cost is higher for the conventional system because of lower absorption temperature (thin-film: $3.2 M/year vs. conventional: $15.8 M/year). Overall, the process economic cost is significantly reduced for the proposed system ($227.3 M/year) relative to the cost for the conventional setup ($271.6 M/year).

4. Conclusions

Solvent thermal degradation can be a significant concern in an IL-based CO_2 capture process. In this work, we propose a flowsheet configuration that utilizes a thin-film solvent regeneration unit under vacuum for reducing the regeneration temperature and the associated liquid residence time. We determine the optimal annualized process cost of this advanced IL-based carbon capture process (for a a natural gas combined cycle power plant) and find a significant reduction in process cost (in particular, the solvent make-up cost associated with thermal degradation is reduced by about a factor of three) compared to the conventional case, in which a stripper and reboiler are used for the solvent regeneration.

5. Acknowledgments

This work was supported by the University of Texas Energy Institute under the Fueling a Sustainable Energy Transition program. Partial support from ExxonMobil is acknowledged with gratitude.

References

M. Aghaie, N. Rezaei, S. Zendehboudi, 2018, A systematic review on CO_2 capture with ionic liquids: Current status and future prospects, Renew. Sustain. Energy Rev., 96, 502-525.

A. A. Alhusseini, K. Tuzla, J. C. Chen, 1998, Falling film evaporation of single component liquids, Int. J. Heat and Mass Transf., 41, 12, 1623-1632.

B. E. Gurkan, T. R. Gohndrone, M. J. McCready, J. F. Brennecke, 2013, Reaction kinetics of CO_2 absorption in to phosphonium based anion-functionalized ionic liquids, Phys. Chem. Chem. Phys., 15, 7796-7811.

R. E. James, D. Kearins, M. Turner, M. Woods, N. Kuehn, A. Zoelle, 2019, Cost and Performance Baseline for Fossil Energy Plants Volume 1: Bituminous Coal and Natural Gas to Electricity, NETL-PUB-22638.

H. Jung, D. Im, S. H. Kim, J. H. Lee, 2018, Dynamic modeling and analysis of amine-based carbon capture systems, IFAC-PapersOnLine, 51, 18, 91-96.

A. Mouza, M. Pantzali, S. Paras, 2005, Falling film and flooding phenomena in small diameter vertical tubes: The influence of liquid properties, Chem. Eng. Sci., 60, 18, 4981-4991.

R. C. Pattison, M. Baldea, 2014 Equation-oriented flowsheet simulation and optimization using pseudo-transient models, AIChE J., 60, 4104-4123.

M. Ramdin, T. Loos, T. Vlugt, 2012, State-of-the-art of CO2 capture with ionic liquids, Ind. Eng. Chem. Res., 51, 8149-8177.

A. B. Rao, E. S. Rubin, 2002, A technical, economic, and environmental assessment of amine based CO_2 capture technology for power plant greenhouse gas control, Environ. Sci. Technol., 36, 20, 4467-4475.

S. Seo, M. Quiroz-Guzman, M. A. DeSilva, T. B. Lee, Y. Huang, B. F. Goodrich, W. F. Schneider, J. F. Brennecke, 2014, Chemically tunable ionic liquids with aprotic heterocyclic anion (AHA) for CO_2 capture, J. Phys. Chem. B, 118, 21, 5740-5751.

K. Seo, C. Tsay, B. Hong, T. F. Edgar, M. A. Stadtherr, M. Baldea, 2020, Rate-based process optimization and sensitivity analysis for ionic-liquid-based post-combustion carbon capture, ACS Sustain. Chem. & Eng., 8, 10242-10258.

D. Song, A. F. Seibert, G. T. Rochelle, 2018, Mass transfer parameters for packings: Effect of viscosity, Ind. Eng. Chem. Res., 57, 2, 718-729.

A. C. Talik, L. S. Fletcher, N. K. Anand, L. W. Swanson, 1995, Heat transfer and pressure drop characteristics of a plate heat exchanger using a propylene-glycol/water mixture as the working fluid, 30th National Heat Transfer Conference, 83-88.

M. S. Walters, T. F. Edgar, G. T. Rochelle, 2016, Regulatory control of amine scrubbing for CO_2 capture from power plants, Ind. Eng. Chem. Res., 55, 16, 4646-4657.

S.-M. Yih, K.-Y. Chen, 1982, Gas absorption into wavy and turbulent falling liquid films in a wetted-wall column, Chem. Eng. Commun., 17, 1-6, 123-136.

Proceedings of the 14th International Symposium on Process Systems Engineering – PSE 2021+
June 19-23, 2022, Kyoto, Japan
http://dx.doi.org/10.1016/B978-0-323-85159-6.50027-0

Process Design of Formic Acid and Methanol Production from CO2 Promoted by Ionic Liquid: Techno-Economic Analysis

Taofeeq O. Bello*, Antonio E. Bresciani, Claudio A.O. Nascimento, Rita M.B. Alves

Department of Chemical Engineering, Escola Politecnica, Universidade de São Paulo, Av. Prof. Luciano Gualberto, travessa do Politécnico, n° 380, São Paulo 05508-010, Brazil
tbello@usp.br

Abstract

Carbon dioxide conversion technologies have been extensively investigated as a viable pathway for lowering greenhouse gas emissions. However, due to thermodynamic and product separation limitations, numerous routes have been proposed. This work presents a techno-economic study of the production of formic acid and methanol promoted by ionic liquid at a commercial scale. To that aim, Aspen Plus® V10 was employed to build a simulation that included the solubilization of CO_2 in 1-ethyl-2,3-dimethylimidazolium nitrite ([Edmim][NO_2]) ionic liquid (IL), synthesis of the CO_2-[Edmim][NO_2] adduct with hydrogen, product separation, and recycling of the IL. The CO_2 conversion (87 %) resulted in ~83 % and ~14 % yield of formic acid and methanol, respectively. This result is an improvement in previous conducted findings. Furthermore, it was discovered that a discount rate between 4-5 % (@ 0.78 USD/kg of formic acid) or 0.93-1 USD/kg (@ 10% discount rate) would make the project profitable.

Keywords: Carbon dioxide Conversion; Formic acid; Ionic Liquid; Methanol.

1. Introduction

Carbon dioxide (CO_2) utilization and conversion in the production of fuels, chemicals, and materials are potentially promising CO_2 abatement alternatives by lowering CO_2 emissions, reducing fossil fuel usage (Pérez-Fortes and Tzimas, 2016), and also providing a chemical storage alternative for intermittent renewable electricity (Schlögl, 2013). This approach can significantly contribute to the decarbonization of the energy system (Olah et al., 2009). Formic acid (FA) and methanol (MeOH) are typical examples of chemicals and liquid energy carriers. However, the hydrogenation of CO_2 to formic acid is endergonic in the gas phase (ΔG^{o}_{298} = +33 kJ/mol), hence, thermodynamically unfavorable (Wang & Himeda, 2012; Leitner, 1995). The thermodynamic limitation can be overcome by perturbing the reacting system with a secondary reaction or molecular interaction. One of the available strategies is the neutralization of the reaction with a weak base (tertiary amines or alkali/alkaline earth bicarbonates) to yield formamides (Xu et al., 2011; Jessop et al., 1999). However, there are concerns about the post-treatment of intermediates to get a pure formic acid. (Leitner, 1995; Su et al., 2015). Ionic liquids (ILs) play an essential role in solving these two problems due to their solvating and low volatility property (Zeng et al., 2017). In addition, ILs can fine-tune the properties of the solvent by altering the structure, catalyst immobilization (Ghavre et al., 2011; Kokorin, 2012; MacFarlane et al., 2017), and CO_2 activation (Wang et al., 2015). Hence, in this work, the economic implications of deploying a process plant for the hydrogenation of CO_2 to formic acid and methanol using IL ([Edmim][NO_2]) as the reaction media was examined. The evaluation to retrieve technical and process significant parameters was carried out with the Aspen Plus V10 process simulation software.

2. Process Description.

The process flow diagram of the CO_2 hydrogenation to FA acid and MeOH was developed and shown in Figure 1. The synthesis method is a two-step process comprising CO_2 solubilization and conversion in a column and reactor, respectively. The plant capacity was set at 33,000 t/y of FA and MeOH with a purity of 97.7 % and 99.99 %, respectively. The feedstocks for this process are CO_2 and hydrogen (H_2) and the ionic liquid, which serves as the reaction media. CO_2 and H_2) were assumed to be free from impurity. The [Edmim][NO_2] was initially heated to a temperature of 40 °C before entering the solubilization section together with compressed CO_2 at 80 bar. The CO_2 dissolves in the IL forming a CO_2-[Edmim][NO_2] adduct. The resulting adduct leaves the solubilization unit and enters the synthesis section together with a stream of compressed hydrogen gas. The reactor operates at 20 °C and 17 bar for CO_2 conversion. FA, MeOH, and water are the resulting products of the reaction, which, together with unreacted CO_2 and H_2, are sent to a separator to remove and recycle the [Edmim][NO_2], while the remaining compounds leave the column as vapor products. The products are cooled, and unreacted H_2 and CO_2 are separated using black-box separator units and recycled to the reactor and solubilization column, respectively. The stream of formic acid, methanol, and water are sent to the separation unit, where two distillation column units are employed. Methanol is separated at the first distillation column. The bottom product from the first column, an azeotropic mixture of FA and water, enters an extractive distillation using [Edmim][NO_2] as solvent. FA with 97.7 % w/w is recovered as the top product, while [Edmim][NO_2] and water are separated by a simple flash separation process. Table 1 presents the operating conditions for the main process equipment.

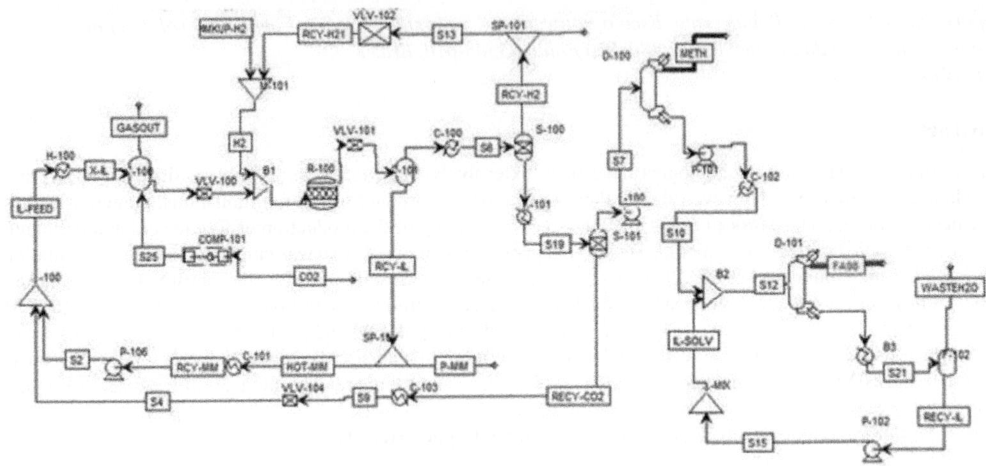

Figure 1: Proposed process flowsheet of CO_2 hydrogenation with [Edmim][NO_2] as reaction media

Table 1: Operating conditions for the main process equipment

Units		Operating Conditions
Compression	CMP-101	Pexit = 80 bar, Number of stages = 3
Solubilization Column	F-100	T = 20 °C; P = 80 bar
Separator	F-101	T = 150 °C; P = 0.1 bar
Reactor	R-100	T = 20 °C; P = 17 bar
Distillation Column	D-100	P = 1 bar; Stages = 22; Feed stage = 11; Reflux ratio = 4; Condenser: Full.
Extractive Distillation Column	D-101	P = 1 bar; Stages = 23; Feed stage = 2; Reflux ratio = 0.01; Condenser: full; Distillate to feed ratio = 0.69

3. Process Simulation.

The thermodynamic models for the CO_2 solubilization and synthesis sections are the conductor-like screening model for segment activity coefficient (COSMO-SAC) with Peng Robinson-Wong Sandler equation of state (ESPRWS). Due to the unavailability of experimental data of [Edmim][NO2], its thermodynamic properties were estimated by Conductor Like Screening Model for real solvents (COSMO-RS) as described in previous works (Bello et al., 2021a, 2021b). The reactor was modeled using RYield with two independent reactions (FA and MeOH formation) (Bello et al., 2021b). The solubilization column was modelled with a two-outlet flash using rigorous vapor-liquid equilibrium.. The distillation columns (D-100 and D-101) were modelled with a rigorous RADFRAC model in equilibrium mode. All the property methods were selected following the guidelines of Towler and Sinnott (2013) and taking into account the reaction system's temperature, pressure, and volatility. Multistage compressors were selected and modelled as isentropic with a fixed discharge pressure from the last stage. Heat exchangers were modelled by the shortcut method.

4. Techno-Economic Assessment

In any chemical project, estimating capital (CAPEX) and operational (OPEX) costs are critical components in determining the long-term viability of any chemical process. The CAPEX comprises costs such as equipment, land, and installation. Raw materials (CO_2 and H_2), reaction media [Edmim][NO_2], and utilities are all included in the OPEX. The equipment purchase and utility costs were estimated using the inbuilt Aspen Process Economic Evaluation (APEA). Aspen software's cost basis calculation is based on the first quarter of 2016. When compared to other cost correlations, this method can provide reasonably accurate cost estimates during the conceptual phase (Towler and Sinnott, 2012). The installation costs of the sized equipment were then calculated. After that, the total capital investment was determined utilizing several factors linked to the total installation costs. Revenues were calculated by multiplying each product's annual production by its market value. A discounted cash flow analysis was performed assuming a 15-year plant lifespan. The projected interest rate was 10%, the income tax rate was 45%, and depreciation was calculated using the straight-line technique for project years. The impact of the product price and discount rate on the project's Net Present Value (NPV) were evaluated.

5. Results and Discussion

5.1. Process Simulation Results

As seen in Table 2, the technical indicators presented are the per pass and overall CO_2 conversions, as defined by Eq.(1) and Eq.(2), and utility requirements. As depicted in Table 1, per pass CO_2 conversion of 86% was achieved in the presence of the [Edmim][NO_2] as reaction media. The unreacted CO_2-[Edmim][NO_2] adduct was recycled back to the reacting system, which allows nearly 100 % CO_2 conversion.

Table 2. Technical indicators of the CO_2 hydrogenation to formic acid and methanol process.

Indicators	Values	Units
Overall CO_2 conversion	100	%
Per Pass Conversion	87.5	%
Conversion factor (FA)	1.17	tCO2/t FA
Conversion factor (MeOH)	6.87	tCO2/t MeOH
MeOH Produced	0.46	t/h
FA Produced	2.68	t/h
Hot utility	1.35	MWh/t MeOH +FA
Cold utility	3.63	MWh/t MeOH +FA
Electricity	1.97	MWh/t MeOH +FA

$$CO_2ConvR = \left(\frac{CO_2in - CO_2out}{CO_2in}\right)_{Reactor} \tag{1}$$

$$CO_2ConvP = \left(\frac{CO_2in - CO_2out}{CO_2in}\right)_{Process} \tag{2}$$

5.2. Economic Result

Table 3 summarizes the economic breakdown of plant investment and operation cost. The raw material and utility constitute the larger shares of the OPEX. The utility cost is majorly influenced by the compression of H_2 and CO_2, which is required to fulfill the solubilization and synthesis requirements for CO_2 and H_2, respectively. The net present values at different discount rates and formic acid prices are presented in Figures 2 and 3, respectively. At a discount rate of 10%, the project is not economically viable. Hence, a sensitivity analysis of discount rate from 4% to 10% was carried out to determine the discounted cash-flow rate of return (DCFROR, when NPV =0). From the result, a discount rate between 4-5% makes the project profitable. At this discount rate, a free cost of CO_2 would improve the NPV as only H_2 is the major contributor to the raw material cost since the ionic liquid cost is estimated on a biannual basis (low volatility). In figure 3, the price of formic acid was varied to observe the behavior of the NPV at a 10% discount rate. At NPV =0, the selling cost of formic acid is 0.935 USD/kg, which makes it the minimum selling point for the project to be viable at a 10 % discount rate.

Table 3: Estimated CAPEX, OPEX and revenues of simulated process

CAPEX	USD	OPEX	USD	Revenue	USD/YR
Purchase Equipment Cost	11,775,700	Raw Material Cost	4,089,956	Formic Acid @ 0.78	16,715,161
ISBL	15,308,410	Utilities	4,157,864	Methanol @ 0.5	1,827,864
OSBL	1,837,009	Operating Labour Cost	1,483,442		
Indirect costs (IC)	15,259,423	Other Manufacturing Cost	3,051,827		
Project Contingency	3,240,484				
Process Contingency	1,620,242				
Fixed Capital Investment (FCI)	37,265,569				
Working Capital (WC)	4,471,868				
Cost of Land	2,000,000				
Total Capital Investment (TCI)	43,737,436				

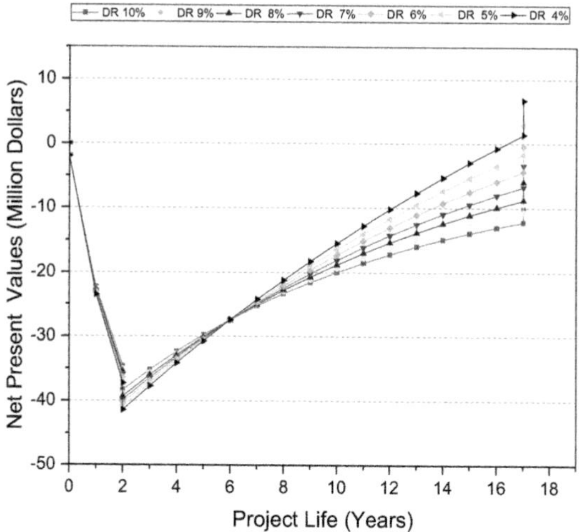

Figure 2: Cash flow diagram at different discount rates

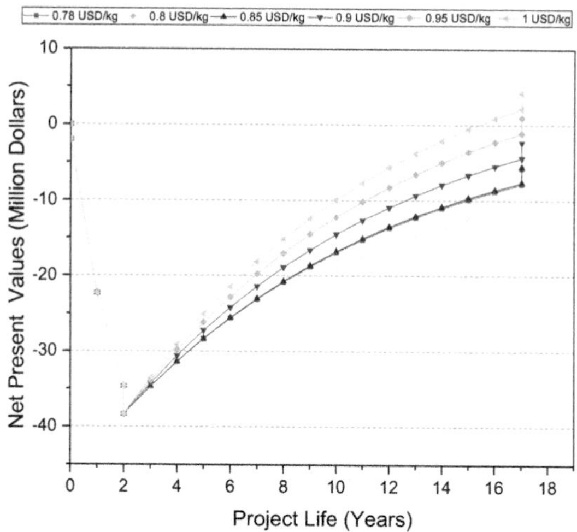

Figure 3: Cash flow diagram at different selling prices of formic acid

6. Conclusions

The techno-economic study based on process simulation has proven the economic feasibility of the hydrogenation of CO_2 promoted by [Edmim][NO_2] at a commercial scale. The results showed that the CAPEX and OPEX required are 43.9 MUSD and 12.7 MUSD, respectively. To ensure economic profitability, the calculated minimum selling cost of formic acid was 0.935-1 USD/kg. In addition, at the current 10% discount rate, the project is profitable with a carbon credit tax of 66 USD/tCO_2. The project's minimum payback time was calculated to be four years.

Acknowledgments

The authors gratefully acknowledge the support of the RCGI – Research Centre for Gas Innovation, hosted by the University of São Paulo (USP) and sponsored by FAPESP – São Paulo Research Foundation (2014/50279-4) and Shell Brazil. This study was financed in part by the Personnel Coordination of Improvement of Higher Level - Brazil (CAPES) - Finance Code 001

References

T.O. Bello, A.E. Bresciani, R.M.B. Alves, C.A.O. Nascimento, 2021a. Systematic Screening of Ionic Liquids for Hydrogenation of Carbon dioxide to Formic Acid and Methanol. Ind. Eng. Chem. Res.

T.O. Bello, A.E. Bresciani, C.A.O. Nascimento, R.M.B. Alves, 2021b. Thermodynamic analysis of carbon dioxide hydrogenation to formic acid and methanol. Chem. Eng. Sci. 242, 116731. https://doi.org/10.1016/j.ces.2021.116731

M. Ghavre, S. Morrissey, N. Gathergoo, 2011. Hydrogenation in Ionic Liquids. Ion. Liq. Appl. Perspect. https://doi.org/10.5772/14315

P. G. Jessop, T. Ikariya, R. Noyori, 1999. Homogeneous catalysis in supercritical fluids. Chem. Rev. 99, 475–494.

Kokorin, A., 2012. Ionic Liquids: Applications and Perspectives, Ionic Liquids: Applications and Perspectives. https://doi.org/10.5772/1782

W. Leitner, 1995. Carbon Dioxide as a Raw Material: The Synthesis of Formic Acid and Its Derivatives from CO<inf>2</inf>. Angew. Chemie Int. Ed. English 34, 2207–2221. https://doi.org/10.1002/anie.199522071

P.D.R. MacFarlane, D.M. Kar, D.J.M. Pringle, 2017. Fundamentals of Ionic Liquids Ionic Liquids in Biotransformations and Electrodeposition from Ionic Handbook of Green Chemistry – Green Solvents Electrochemical Aspects of Ionic Liquids , 2nd edition Nanocatalysis in Ionic Liquids.

G.A. Olah, A. Goeppert, G.K.S. Prakash, 2009. Chemical Recycling of Carbon Dioxide to Methanol and Dimethyl Ether: From Greenhouse Gas to Renewable, Environmentally Carbon Neutral Fuels and Synthetic Hydrocarbons. J. Org. Chem. 74, 487–498. https://doi.org/10.1021/jo801260f

M. Pérez-Fortes, E. Tzimas, 2016. Techno-economic and environmental evaluation of CO2 utilisation for fuel production. Synthesis of methanol and formic acid, Scientific and Technical Research Series. Luxembourg. https://doi.org/10.2790/89238

R. Schlögl, 2013. The Solar Refinery. In Chemical Energy Storage. Walter de Gruyter GmbH: Berlin, Germany, Boston, MA, USA.

J. Su, L.Yang, M. Lu, H. Lin, 2015. Highly efficient hydrogen storage system based on ammonium bicarbonate/formate redox equilibrium over palladium nanocatalysts. ChemSusChem 8, 813–816. https://doi.org/10.1002/cssc.201403251

G. Towler, R. Sinnott, 2013. Chemical Engineering Design Principles, Practice and Economics of Plant and Process Design, Second Edi. ed. Elsevier, Oxford. https://doi.org/10.1016/B978-0-08-096659-5.00022-5

G. Towler, R.K. Sinnott, 2012. Chemical engineering design: principles, practice and economics of plant and process design. Elsevier.

W. Wang, Y. Himeda, 2012. Recent Advances in Transition Metal-Catalysed Homogeneous Hydrogenation of Carbon Dioxide in Aqueous Media. Sch. Enviromental Sci. 250–264. https://doi.org/10.5772/48658

Y. Wang, M. Hatakeyama, K. Ogata, M. Wakabayashi, F. Jin, S. Nakamura, 2015. Activation of CO2 by ionic liquid EMIM-BF4 in the electrochemical system: a theoretical study. Phys. Chem. Chem. Phys. 17, 23521–23531. https://doi.org/10.1039/c5cp02008e

W. Xu, L. Ma, B. Huang, X. Cui, X. Niu, H. Zhang, 2011. Thermodynamic analysis of formic acid synthesis from CO2hydrogenation. ICMREE 2011 - Proc. 2011 Int. Conf. Mater. Renew. Energy Environ. 2, 1473–1477. https://doi.org/10.1109/ICMREE.2011.5930612

S. Zeng, X. Zhang, L. Bai, X. Zhang, H. Wang, J. Wang, D. Bao, M. Li, X. Liu, S. Zhang, 2017. Ionic-Liquid-Based CO<inf>2</inf> Capture Systems: Structure, Interaction and Process. Chem. Rev. 117, 9625–9673. https://doi.org/10.1021/acs.chemrev.7b00072

Proceedings of the 14th International Symposium on Process Systems Engineering – PSE 2021+
June 19-23, 2022, Kyoto, Japan
http://dx.doi.org/10.1016/B978-0-323-85159-6.50028-2

Synthesis of Distillation Sequence with Thermally Coupled Configurations Using Reinforcement Learning

Jaehyun Shim[a] and Jong Min Lee[a*]

[a]School of Chemical and Biological Engineering, Institute of Chemical Processes, Seoul National University, 1 Gwanak-ro, Gwanak-gu, Seoul 08826, Republic of Korea
buzzinga@snu.ac.kr
**Corresponding Author's E-mail: jongmin@snu.ac.kr*

Abstract

Distillation column is a representative chemical process unit, which is the most popular choice to separate a multicomponent mixture into pure substances. Since a typical industrial process involves multiple distillation columns, it is important to obtain an optimal sequence to optimize energy consumption and separation performance. For this a large number of candidates have to be investigated in the optimization problem, while the number of possible sequences becomes larger when thermally coupled configuration is considered. In this study, reinforcement learning algorithm is applied to find an optimal sequence to avoid the computational burden of exhaustive in solving such large scale problems. Reinforcement learning searches for a solution in an evolutionary fashion via value function approximation in a limited region of the solution space. Case studies demonstrate the efficacy of reinforcement learning to find a nearly optimal solution for distillation sequence synthesis problems. The objective of the case studies is to derive distillation sequence which minimizes the total annual cost for separating five component mixtures. The result is that total annual cost of the configurations of distillation sequence designed using reinforcement learning were only about 2.5% larger than the optimal result obtained from mixed-integer nonlinear programming. This shows that reinforcement learning can find a nearly-optimal structure without exhaustive search.

Keywords: design, distillation column, thermally coupled, reinforcement learning, optimization

1. Introduction

Distillation column is an essential unit operation for multicomponent separation and the efficiency of separating multicomponent depends on the configuration of distillation sequences. Therefore, it is important to design distillation sequences to obtain an optimal sequence with high efficiency and a large number of candidates have to be investigated to find an optimal distillation sequence. However, the size of the search space increases rapidly with the number of components to be separated and grows exponentially when thermally coupled (TC) configurations are considered (Shah, V. H. et al., 2010). Moreover, continuous variables such as liquid and vapor flowrate for mass balance in the distillation column should be determined while the configuration that is a discrete decision is chosen simultaneously, which means synthesis of distillation column is a mixed integer problem (Gooty, R. T. et al., 2019). Thus, the exhaustive search approach is not effective for large size multicomponent separation problems and reinforcement learning (RL) is proposed as an alternative framework to find an optimal distillation sequence in this study. RL approximates a value function of state via learning based on trial and error. Value function indicates how optimal the decision is and RL optimizes the objective function by outputs from value function. RL has two types of algorithm: value-based method and policy gradient method. Q-learning, SARSA, and deep Q network are well-known value-based methods and REINFORCE, actor critic, and deep deterministic policy gradient are representative policy gradient methods (Nian, R. et al., 2020). In this study, actor-critic algorithm is used to synthesize distillation sequences and case studies are implemented for 5 components separation problem including thermally coupled configurations. The objective of the problems is to minimize total annual cost of the distillation sequence. Finally, the results from RL are compared with those from mixed-integer nonlinear programming (MINLP) in order to analyze the ability of RL to optimize the distillation sequence.

2. Distillation sequence

If there exists difference between relative volatilities, a mixture having more than three components is separated through a train of several distillation columns. When it comes to mixture separation, types of split in a distillation column can be categorized into sharp and non-sharp splits. There are substances of which relative volatility is between that of light key (LK) component and heavy key (HK) component in a case of non-sharp split, whereas sharp split does not have such substances. For simplicity and clear presentation of the proposed concept, this study considers the sharp split only. TC configuration is also introduced to the optimization problem.

2.1. Thermally coupled configuration

Distillation process using conventional columns which includes heat exchangers such as condenser and reboiler shows an inherent inefficiency due to remixing an intermediate component which should be re-purified in the next column. Introducing TC configurations by removing heat exchangers, the inefficiency of the conventional columns can be improved with a side stream because it prevents remixing (Hernández, S. et al., 2003).

2.2. Fenske-Underwood-Gilliland method

Once a structure of distillation sequence is decided, the corresponding variables such as reflux ratio, column diameter, and flow rate of distillate and bottom stream are calculated via distillation system dynamics. In this study, Fenske-Underwood-Gilliland (FUG) method was used for calculating the variables instead of the rigorous method such as Aspen simulator. FUG method is based on the assumption that the relative volatility of the component is constant along the column and the molar overflow of the component is constant along the column. FUG method consists of Equations (1)-(4).

$$\sum_{i=1}^{N} \frac{\alpha_i f_i}{\alpha_i - \varphi} = F(1-q) \tag{1}$$

$$\sum_{i=1}^{N} \frac{\alpha_i \xi_i f_i}{\alpha_i - \varphi} = D(R_{min}+1) \tag{2}$$

$$N_{min} = \frac{\log\left[\left(\frac{\xi_{LK}}{1-\xi_{LK}}\right)\left(\frac{1-\xi_{HK}}{\xi_{HK}}\right)\right]}{\log(\alpha_i/\alpha_j)} \quad (3)$$

$$\frac{N_t - N_{min}}{N_{min}+1} = 0.75\left[1-\left(\frac{R-R_{min}}{R+1}\right)^{0.5668}\right] \quad (4)$$

where i indicates the component, α_i is the relative volatility, f_i is the feed flow rate, φ is the root of Underwood equation, F is the total feed flow rate of the column, q is the quality of the feed, ξ_i is the recovery fraction, D is the total distillate flow rate, R_{min} is the minimum reflux ratio, N_{min} is the minimum number of theoretical stages, N_t is the number of theoretical stages, and R is the actual reflux ratio. Eqs. (1) and (2) are Underwood equations, Eq. (3) is Fenske equation, and Eq. (4) is Gilliland equation (Fenske, 1932; Underwood, 1949; Gilliland, 1940).

2.3. Total annual cost

The objective of this study is to find the most economical distillation sequence and total annual cost (TAC) is used as a criterion for evaluating the economics. Therefore, the optimal distillation sequence has the minimum TAC. TAC consists of the capital cost and sum of the operation cost of distillation sequences. Operation cost includes column equipment investment, condenser equipment investment, and reboiler equipment investment. Column equipment investment is a function of D, R, and N_t, and condenser and reboiler equipment investment is a function of R and ξ_i. Therefore, TAC of a distillation sequence can be estimated with these parameters obtained from FUG method and its calculation formulas were referenced in Zhang, S. et al. (2018).

3. Reinforcement learning

RL refers to a family of algorithms that learns the optimal value function that satisfies the optimality equation of dynamic program using either simulation or operational data. A decision-making entity called an agent takes an action based on the current state, the environment is changed by the action, and it gives the agent a reward as a feedback of the action. As a result, the agent learns the value function and policy in the state space, and its corresponding control policy maps the current state to a nearly-optimal action. Among various RL algorithms, this study employs the actor-critic algorithm since it can make a discrete decision and learn the policy directly with policy gradient method. Given a current state, the actor calculates an action using the learned policy function and the critic evaluates how beneficial the action is. The actor learns policy based on the evaluation from the critic and critic updates evaluations by rewards from environment (Konda, V. R. et al., 2000). The main challenge in this approach is to formulate the problem and define state, action, and reward.

3.1. State

Separation matrix representation (SMR) (Shah, V. H. et al., 2010) was employed in order to convert the topology of distillation sequence into a mathematical form which can be used in the RL algorithm. SMR is an upper triangular matrix as shown in Figure.1 and each element of the matrix means the stream in the sequence correspond to feed, distillate, or bottom flow of each column. 1 is assigned to each element if there exists a reboiler or

$$\begin{bmatrix} ABC & AB & A \\ 0 & BC & B \\ 0 & 0 & C \end{bmatrix}$$

Figure 1. Separation matrix representation for separating 3 components mixture.

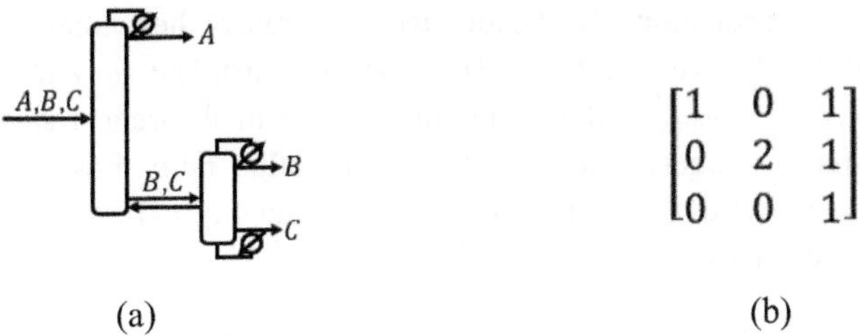

Figure 2. an example of separation matrix representation for separating 3 components mixture.

condenser in the stream, while 2 is assigned if TC configuration exists. For instance, the sequence shown in Figure.2 (a) is represented as the matrix in Figure.2 (b). Additionally, temperature and flow rate of each component in the stream are converted into the matrix form based on the SMR indicating the sequence. As a result, all matrices are stacked and used in the current state.

3.2. Action

A distillation sequence is determined by the choice of which components are separated at which column and where TC configurations are located. For each column, what material is separated and whether there is a TC structure become actions in each column. One of the actions is choosing a HK substance, and the other is deciding if there is a TC structure. Accordingly, a stage is defined as deciding a HK substance and TC structure of each column and a stage-wise reward is described in section.3.3.

3.3. Reward

Since the objective function is TAC of a distillation sequence, the return in RL formulation is also TAC of a sequence, i.e. sum of TAC of all distillation columns. Therefore, TAC of each distillation column in a sequence is set to a reward because sum of the all rewards equals to the return as definition. In addition, negative value of TAC is used as the reward in algorithm so as to minimize total TAC because RL algorithms basically learn in the direction of maximizing the reward.

4. Results and discussion

A case study was implemented for confirming the ability of RL to design optimal distillation sequence with an arbitrary multicomponent mixture. Through the case study, the sequence was found to minimize TAC for separating 5 components mixture. For simplifying explanation in the case study, the stream flowing through the distillation

Table 1. Components and feed composition.

Case study 1	
Component	Mole fraction
ethanol (A)	0.25
n-propanol (B)	0.15
i-butanol (C)	0.35
n-butanol (D)	0.10
phenol (E)	0.15
The flowrate of the feed mixture is 500.4 kmol/h	

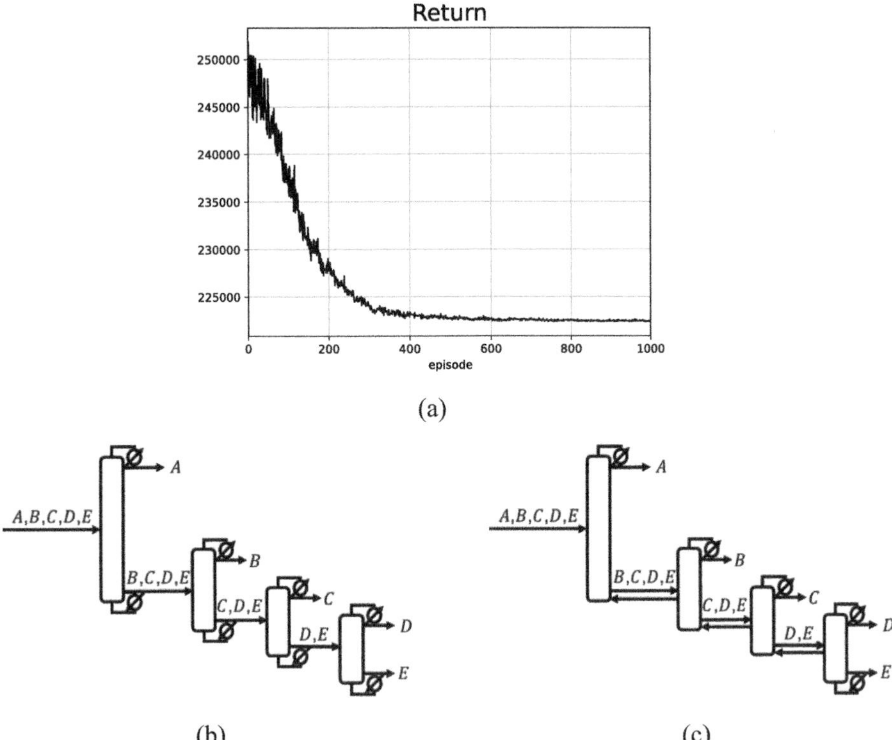

Figure 3. Return of RL and distillation sequences synthesized by RL and MINLP in case studies.

sequence is denoted as ABCDE, where each letter means a component in the stream and is assigned to a nature number to use in mathematical equations: A = 1, B = 2, ..., E = 5. The notation is arranged in order of relative volatility, for example, in a stream ABCDE, A is the most volatile component and E is the least volatile component. RL algorithm was carried out to find the distillation sequence minimizing TAC via trial and error as mentioned above, followed by comparing the result from learned RL and that from MINLP.

4.1. Case study

Components in the inlet mixture are ethanol, i-propanol, n-propanol, i-butanol, and n-butanol, corresponds to A, B, C, D, and E orderly, and their feed composition are presented in Table.1. Figure.3 (a) shows return, i.e. TAC of a designed distillation sequence, decreased as episode progresses and converged to a certain level after about a thousand iteration. A distillation sequence was determined using the learned RL agent as shown in Figure.3 (b) and its TAC is 222,258.15 $/y, whereas Figure.3 (c) is the optimal sequence found by MINLP and has TAC of 216,747.68 $/y. The separation order of the two structures is same, so the difference in TAC between the sequences comes from TC configuration. TC configuration should be adopted for efficient separation of mixture according to MINLP, but RL was learned in a direction that does not consider the TC configuration. Nonetheless, TAC of the sequence from RL is only about 2.5% higher than that from MINLP, which means RL found the near-optimal structure. Moreover, any superstructure is not required when solving the problem of finding an optimal distillation sequence using RL.

5. Conclusion

Through this study, it was demonstrated that a near-optimal structure can be determined without a superstructure or any prior knowledge except for the material properties of the desired mixture. This is more beneficial when solving a large-scale optimization problem since full search becomes near impossible and time consuming as the scale increases. It can be proved by applying RL algorithm to a larger design problem, for instance, a separation problem for more than 5 components mixture.

Acknowledgements

This study was supported by Hanhwa Solutions Corporation.

References

Fenske, M., 1932, Fractionation of straight-run Pennsylvania gasoline., Industrial & Engineering Chemistry, 24, 5, 482-485.

Gilliland, E. R., 1940, Multicomponent rectification., Industrial & Engineering Chemistry, 32, 8, 1101-1106.

Gooty, R. T., Agrawal, R., & Tawarmalani, M., 2019, An MINLP formulation for the optimization of multicomponent distillation configurations., Computers & Chemical Engineering, 125, 13-30.

Hernández, S., Pereira-Pech, S., Jiménez, A., & Rico-Ramírez, V., 2003, Energy efficiency of an indirect thermally coupled distillation sequence., The Canadian Journal of Chemical Engineering, 81, 5, 1087-1091.

Konda, V. R., & Tsitsiklis, J. N., 2000,. Actor-critic algorithms. In Advances in neural information processing systems, 1008-1014.

Nian, R., Liu, J., & Huang, B., 2020, A review on reinforcement learning: Introduction and applications in industrial process control. Computers & Chemical Engineering, 139, 106886.

Shah, V. H., & Agrawal, R., A matrix method for multicomponent distillation sequences, AIChE journal, 56, 7, 1789-1775.

Underwood, A. J. V. , 1949, Fractional distillation of multicomponent mixtures., Industrial & Engineering Chemistry, 41, 12, 2844-2847.

Zhang, S., Luo, Y., Ma, Y., & Yuan, X., 2018, Simultaneous optimization of nonsharp distillation sequences and heat integration networks by simulated annealing algorithm., Energy, 162, 1139-1157.

Proceedings of the 14th International Symposium on Process Systems Engineering – PSE 2021+
June 19-23, 2022, Kyoto, Japan
http://dx.doi.org/10.1016/B978-0-323-85159-6.50029-4

Optimal Design of Heat Integrated Reduced Vapor Transfer Dividing Wall Columns

Fanyi Duanmu and Eva Sorensen*

Department of Chemical Engineering, University College London (UCL), Torrington Place, London WC1E 7JE, United Kingdom
** Corresponding author: e.sorensen@ucl.ac.uk*

Abstract

A dividing wall column (DWC) is capable of saving capital costs and improving energy efficiency for ternary liquid separations. Alternative DWC structures have been proposed, termed Reduced Vapor Transfer DWC (RVT-DWC) in this work, which involves less difficult-to-control vapor transfer streams. The most interesting RVT-DWC structure, the LL structure, which has a dividing wall extending throughout the column and has no interconnected vapor transfer streams, is studied in this work. Three heat integrated designs of the LL structure, the LL structure with combined condenser and reboiler (LL-CCR), vapor recompression assisted LL structure (VR-LL), and vapor recompression assisted LL structure with combined condenser and reboiler (VR-LL-CCR), are introduced and compared to the standard DWC, standard LL structure, and vapor recompression assisted DWC (VR-DWC) designs, respectively. Although the LL-CCR structure shows only minor improvement in total annualized costs (TAC) when compared to the LL structure, its vapor recompression assisted design (VR-LL-CCR) has the lowest TAC among all the structures studied (17 % lower than LL-CCR, 4 % lower than VR-DWC, and 10 % lower than VR-LL). Moreover, the vapor recompression assisted structures have lower TAC than their corresponding base structures.

Keywords: Distillation, Dividing Wall Column, Optimization, Heat integration, Vapor recompression

1. Introduction

Process Intensification (PI) has received significant interest in recent years as a mean of achieving more energy efficient chemical processes. A prime example of PI is a dividing wall column (DWC) for the separation of ternary mixtures. Agrawal (2000) proposed several alternatives to a standard DWC, denoted as Reduced Vapor Transfer DWCs (RVT-DWCs) in this work, which involve less difficult-to-control vapor transfer streams, thus reducing the complexity of the unit. These RVT-DWCs have been claimed to be superior to a standard DWC in terms of controllability (Cui et al., 2020), and to have a similar economic performance (Agrawal, 2000) and almost identical energy demands (Waltermann et al., 2019), thus the RVT-DWCs can be considered as competitive alternatives to the standard DWC. Out of all the RVT-DWC structures, the LL structure (liquid-liquid structure, both thermal coupling streams replaced by liquid sidedraw streams, the dividing wall extended throughout the column, utilizing two condenser and two reboilers) has the most interesting structure, and is the structure that

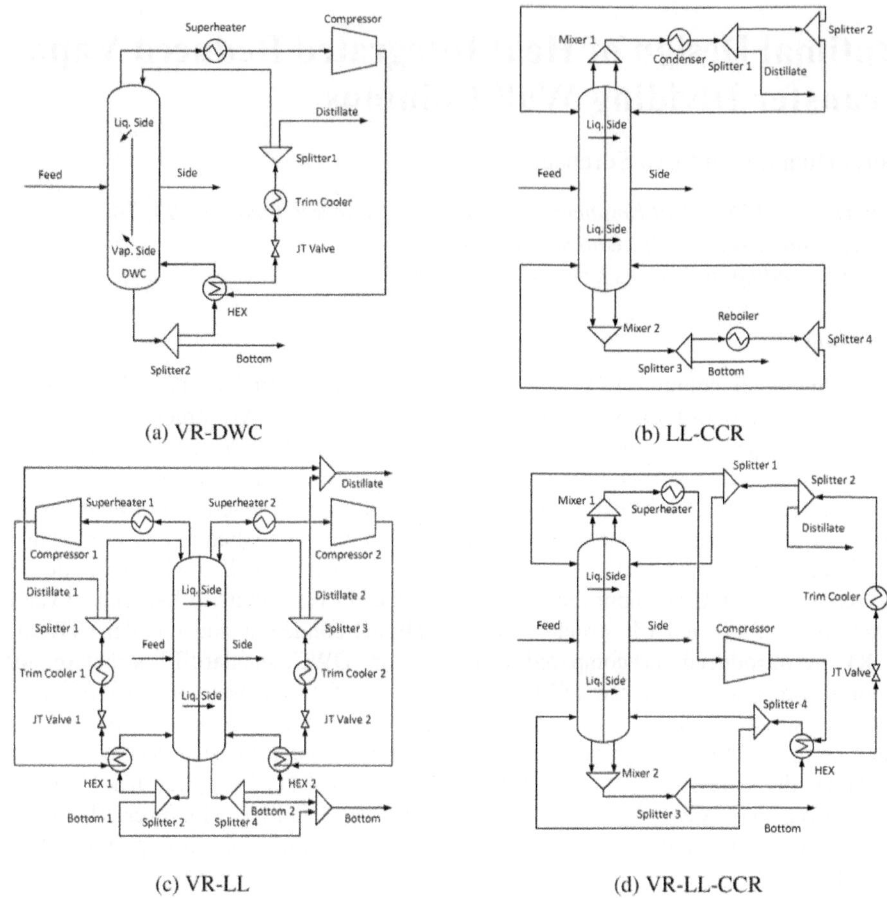

Figure 1: Flowsheets of (a) Vapor recompression assisted dividing wall column (VR-DWC), (b) LL structure with combined condenser and reboiler (LL-CCR), (c) vapor recompression assisted LL structure (VR-LL), and (d) vapor recompression assisted LL structure with combined condenser and reboiler (VR-LL-CCR).

will potentially provide the most improvement with heat integration. Heat integration by combining the condensers and reboilers in the LL structure may improve the economic performance (Ramapriya et al., 2014). Moreover, heat integration by vapor recompression can save both energy and cost, and its effectiveness for a standard DWC was considered by Xu et al. (2017), but its potential effectiveness for a RVT-DWCs has not yet been studied. This work therefore aims to investigate the economic performance of the LL structure by considering heat integration based on vapor recompression.

2. Methodology

In this work, six different structures are designed, optimized, and compared, which are the standard dividing wall column (DWC, not shown), vapor recompression assisted dividing wall columns (VR-DWC, Figure 1a), LL structure (LL, not shown), LL structure with combined condenser and reboiler (LL-CCR, Figure 1b), vapor recompression assisted LL structure (VR-LL, Figure 1c), and vapor recompression assisted LL structure with combined condenser and reboiler (VR-LL-CCR, Figure 1d). It should be noted that, unlike the structures proposed by Agrawal (2000), in all the LL structures studied in this work, the product streams (distillate and bottom streams) are combined into single product streams, which also reduces the number of product constraints for optimization. For all vapor recompression assisted structures, the same structure is utilized including a superheater installed just after the top vapor stream from the column to improve the efficiency of the heat integration design (Yang et al., 2019). The superheated vapor is compressed in an isentropic compressor with 85 % efficiency. Then, a counter-current shell and tube heat exchanger (HEX) is used to vaporize the boilup flow using the recompressed vapor stream. After that, a Joule-Thompson valve (JT valve) and a trim cooler are used to lower the stream pressure back to the column pressure and to condense the stream, respectively. Finally, a splitter is used to control the product and reflux flowrates. For LL-CCR and VR-LL-CCR, two additional splitters are used to control the flowrate (split ratio) of reflux and boilup streams into the prefractionator (left)/main column (right).

All rigorous simulations (equilibrium based) are performed in gPROMS ProcessBuilder version 1.4 (Process Systems Enterprise, 2020). As there is no built-in column libraries for DWC and LL structures, their corresponding Petlyuk designs are used instead. All designs are optimized using both stand-alone particle swarm optimization (PSO) and a combined stochastic/deterministic optimization method similar to the one proposed by Chia et al. (2021), but using PSO instead of Genetic Algorithm (GA). PSO is coded in MATLAB (The MathWorks Inc., 2019) while OAERAP is built-in within gPROMS ProcessBuilder, with gO:MATALAB (Process Systems Enterprise, 2019) used to transfer data between MATLAB and gPROMS ProcessBuilder. The objective function is the total annualized cost (TAC) based on the summation of annualized capital cost of all equipment and of the operating cost. The operating hour is set as 8400 $h\ y^{-1}$ and the payback period is 8 y. The sizing equations of the column are from Seider et al. (2016) and cost equations and installation factors are from Sinnott and Towler (2020). High pressure steam is used as the heating utility with a cost of 24 $€\ t^{-1}$ and for electricity a cost of 23.5×10^{-6} $€\ kJ^{-1}$. All prices are converted to US dollars at the end for comparison. The design with the lowest TAC from both optimization methods is taken as the final results to ensure a good optimal design and fair comparison. For all the designs, the column pressure is maintained at 1 *bar* and not optimized. For the optimization task, all design and operating variables are optimized simultaneously including the number of stages, feed/sidedraw locations, reflux/boilup ratios, distillate/bottom flowrate, splitter ratio (used in LL-CCR and VR-LL-CCR), temperature in the superheater, and outlet pressure in the compressor. In terms of optimization constraints, other than the three product specifications, the number of stages on both sides of the wall is considered the same for the LL structures (although does not have to be), the vapor fraction of the stream from the compressor should be equal to one, and the heat exchanger inlet temperature difference should be greater or equal to the minimum temperature approach.

3. Case Study

The comparison of the economic performance of the various structures are based on the separation of an equi-molar benzene/toluene/o-xylene (0.33/0.34/0.33) mixture, with

UNIQUAC as the thermodynamic model. The feed is supplied at 1000 *kmol* h^{-1} as a saturated liquid at 1 *bar*, which is the same as the operating pressure in the column with no pressure drop. Calculations are performed using an AMD Ryzen 9 3900X CPU with 3.79 GHz and 64 GB memory. For PSO, the parallel computing function in MATLAB was activated with 18 workers to speed up the optimization, and it takes about 1 to 3 hours to perform the optimization depending on the complexity of the model.

The key design and operating variables for all structures are shown in Table 1. In general, all structures have similar total number of stages (48-52). For the main column, the LL structures have lower reflux ratio compared with DWC structures as the majority of the light and heavy components are removed from the system from the prefractionator, which makes the separation in the main column easier. By comparing the vapor recompression assisted structures with their corresponding base designs, no significant changes of design and operating variables are found, which indicates that the retrofit of the base designs can easily be achieved without changing the column structures. Considering the energy usage of designs without vapor recompression, they have similar total reboiler/superheater and condenser/cooler duties. The LL-CCR structure does not improve the energy efficiency (LL duties similar to LL-CCR duties). The vapor recompression assisted designs require about 60 % less total energy (steam plus electricity), and there are significant savings in the reboiler/superheater and condenser/cooler duties (about 80 % and 70 %, respectively) when compared to the base designs. Out of the three vapor recompression assisted structures, VR-LL and VR-LL-CCR have similar energy consumption, slightly lower than the energy required by VR-DWC. It is worth noting that there are two vapor recompression systems in the VR-LL structure (one at each side of the wall, Figure 1c), but the equipment duties in VR-LL is very close to the VR-LL-CCR which has one vapor recompression system (Figure 1d). Breaking down the equipment duties in VR-LL (not shown), the equipment at the prefractionator side requires more energy (e.g., 1.75 *MW* for compressor on the prefractionator side vs 0.94 *MW* on the main column side) due to the removal of the majority of the light and heavy components in the prefractionator.

The cost information of all the designs is shown in Table 1. Compared to DWC and VR-DWC, all variations of LL structures have lower capital costs (CAPEX) for distillation columns (inclusive of column shell and trays) as the removal of products (distillate and bottom streams) from the prefractionator leads to a smaller column diameter. Considering the total CAPEX of each design, all vapor recompression assisted designs have significantly larger cost (e.g., VR-LL CAPEX is 2.61 times of LL CAPEX) due to the high compressor cost (e.g., in VR-LL structure, the compressors contributes 66 % of total CAPEX). It should be noted that, although VR-LL and VR-LL-CCR require similar total compressor duty, VR-LL uses two separate vapor recompressor systems (i.e., two compressors), thus the compressor CAPEX is higher (about 44 %). By considering the operating cost (OPEX) of each design, the OPEX for the vapor recompression assisted structures are about 40 % lower than their corresponding base structures. The comparison of the total annualized cost (TAC) shows that the standard DWC and standard LL structure have similar TACs (DWC 1 % more expensive). Compared with LL, LL-CCR (LL with combined condenser and reboiler) shows only very minor improvement (1 % lower). More importantly, all vapor recompression assisted structures achieved significant saving in TAC when compared with their corresponding base structures (15 % savings in VR-DWC, 8 % savings in

Table 1: Key design and operating parameters of all the structures

Items	**DWC**	**VR-DWC**	**LL**	**LL-CCR**	**VR-LL**	**VR-LL-CCR**
Prefractionator						
Total stages	26	30	52	49	52	48
Feed stage	14	14	29	24	28	27
Liq. sidedraw stages	-	-	11/38	9/36	10/40	9/37
Liq. side ($kmol\ h^{-1}$)	-	-	283/283	266/311	275/313	266/304
Distillate ($kmol\ h^{-1}$)	-	-	211	-	204	-
Molar reflux ratio	-	-	2.78	-	2.72	-
Main Column						
Total stages	48	48	52	49	52	48
Feed stages	8/35	7/38	9/40	8/36	8/38	8/35
Side prod. stage	21	18	25	20	21	19
Side prod. ($kmol\ h^{-1}$)	337	338	337	337	338	337
Liq. side ($kmol\ h^{-1}$)	231	239	-	-	-	-
Vap. side ($kmol\ h^{-1}$)	690	692	-	-	-	-
Distillate ($kmol\ h^{-1}$)	333	331	122	332	127	332
Molar reflux ratio	2.58	2.66	2.16	-	2.31	-
Mass Split Ratio to Main Column						
Reflux flowrate	-	-	-	0.36	-	0.35
Boilup flowrate	-	-	-	0.35	-	0.34
Vapor Recompression System - Pre/Main						
Superheater temp. (K)	-	-/409	-	-	413/404	-/410
Compressor pres. (bar)	-	-/5.22	-	-	5.21/5.12	-/5.16
Total Duty/Power (MW)						
Reboiler/Superheater	10.93	2.02	10.84	10.86	1.87	1.98
Condenser/Cooler	10.28	3.73	10.19	10.2	3.61	3.64
Compressor	-	2.78	-	-	2.69	2.71
CAPEX (M \$)						
Column	5.155	5.2007	4.7378	4.4081	4.7484	4.3047
Reboiler/Heater	1.4325	0.3363	1.6428	1.4245	0.4379	0.3318
Condenser/Cooler	1.5797	0.5602	1.5273	1.5669	0.6244	0.5468
Compressor	-	9.4839	-	-	13.5107	9.3629
Heat Exchanger	-	1.2427	-	-	1.2968	1.324
Total CAPEX	8.1672	16.8238	7.9079	7.3995	20.6182	15.8702
OPEX ($M\ \$\ y^{-1}$)						
Steam	5.242	0.9696	5.1995	5.2061	0.9487	0.9526
Electricity	-	2.2337	-	-	2.165	2.1746
Total OPEX	5.242	3.2033	5.1995	5.2061	3.1137	3.1272
TAC ($M\ \$\ y^{-1}$) *	6.2629	5.3063	6.1879	6.131	5.691	5.111

* Operating hours = 8400 $h\ y^{-1}$; Payback period = 8 y

VR-LL, and 17 % savings in VR-LL-CCR). The comparison between all vapor recompression assisted structures shows that the VR-LL-CCR design is the best (4 % and 10 % lower when compared to VR-DWC and VR-LL, respectively). It should be noted that the improvement of the vapor recompressor assisted structures is indeed a trade-off between the increased capital cost of compressor and energy saved, thus the improvement is dependent on the payback period (here assumed to be 8 years).

4. Conclusions

This work introduces three types of heat integrated reduced vapor transfer dividing wall designs (LL-CCR, VR-LL, and VR-LL-CCR) and compares them with the standard DWC, standard LL, and VR-DWC. It was found that the LL-CCR shows only minor improvement of Total Annualized Cost (TAC) compared with LL but its vapor recompression assisted design (VR-LL-CCR) has the lowest TAC (17 % lower than LL-CCR, 4 % lower than VR-DWC, and 10 % lower than VR-LL). Moreover, all vapor recompression assisted designs have lower TAC compared to their corresponding base designs. The improvement is, however, dependent on the payback period as it is a trade-off between the more expensive compressor and the energy saved from the vapor recompression system. It should be noted that the steam and electricity prices will affect the economic performances of the VR designs. A more comprehensive study which includes the sensitivity analysis of utility prices will be carried out in the future. Besides, the VR designs are more complex than the standard structures, which may be more difficult for operation. Thus, the controllability study will be performed as the future work.

References

Agrawal, R. (2000). Thermally coupled distillation with reduced number of intercolumn vapor transfers. *AIChE Journal*, 46(11):2198–2210.

Chia, D. N., Duanmu, F., and Sorensen, E. (2021). Optimal Design of Distillation Columns Using a Combined Optimisation Approach. In Turkay, M. and Gani, R., editors, *31st European Symposium on Computer Aided Process Engineering*, pages 153–158. Elsevier B.V.

Cui, C., Zhang, Q., Zhang, X., and Sun, J. (2020). Eliminating the vapor split in dividing wall columns through controllable double liquid-only side-stream distillation configuration. *Separation and Purification Technology*, 242(December 2019):116837.

Process Systems Enterprise (2019). gO:MATLAB.

Process Systems Enterprise (2020). gPROMS ProcessBuilder version 1.4.

Ramapriya, G. M., Tawarmalani, M., and Agrawal, R. (2014). Thermal coupling links to liquid-only transfer streams: A path for new dividing wall columns. *AIChE Journal*, 60(8):2949–2961.

Seider, W. D., Lewin, D. R., Seader, J. D., Widagdo, S., Gani, R., and Ng, K. M. (2016). *Product and Process Design Principles: Synthesis, Analysis and Evaluation*. Wiley, 4 edition.

Sinnott, R. and Towler, G. (2020). *Chemical Engineering Design*. Elsevier, 6 edition.

The MathWorks Inc. (2019). MATLAB R2019b version 9.7.

Waltermann, T., Sibbing, S., and Skiborowski, M. (2019). Optimization-based design of dividing wall columns with extended and multiple dividing walls for three- and four-product separations. *Chemical Engineering and Processing - Process Intensification*, 146(August):107688.

Xu, L., Li, M., Yin, X., and Yuan, X. (2017). New Intensified Heat Integration of Vapor Recompression Assisted Dividing Wall Column. *Industrial & Engineering Chemistry Research*, 56(8):2188–2196.

Yang, A., Jin, S., Shen, W., Cui, P., Chien, I.-L., and Ren, J. (2019). Investigation of energy-saving azeotropic dividing wall column to achieve cleaner production via heat exchanger network and heat pump technique. *Journal of Cleaner Production*, 234:410–422.

Proceedings of the 14th International Symposium on Process Systems Engineering – PSE 2021+
June 19-23, 2022, Kyoto, Japan
http://dx.doi.org/10.1016/B978-0-323-85159-6.50030-0

A Model-Data Driven Chemical Analysis System for Products and Associated Processes

Sultana Razia Syeda[a]*, Easir A Khan[a], Nichakorn Kuprasertwong[b], Orakotch Padungwatanaroj[b], and Rafiqul Gani[b,c]

[a]*Department of Chemical Engineering, Bangladesh University of Engineering and Technology,(BUET), Dhaka-1000*
[b]*PSE for SPEED Company, 294/65 RK Office Park, Romklao Rd., Bangkok, Thailand*
[c]*PSE for SPEED Company, Ordrup Jagtvej 42D, DK-2920 Charlottenlund, Denmark*
**syedasrazia@che.buet.ac.bd*

Abstract

Currently, more than one million chemicals can be found on planet earth and thousands of new chemicals-based products are entering the global market every year. Many of the chemicals used in these products serve specific functions and are therefore included in the synthesized product. Some of these chemicals, however, could have harmful hazardous effects, while for others, better functioning alternatives may be available. Therefore, an analysis-based method to identify and substitute chemicals that are classified as hazardous or may have lower economic potential is needed. This paper presents a model-data based chemical analysis method for chemicals-based products and their associated processes. A large database of chemicals has been developed to identify hazardous chemicals. A link to a library of property models has been established to fill out gaps in measured property data. A flexible work-flow for analysis has been developed to identify and substitute chemicals within the product and/or its associated process. The main concepts and tools are highlighted through two case studies.

Keywords: Chemical products; Hazardous chemicals; Chemical substitution; Health hazards, Environmental hazards, Physical hazards

1. Introduction

Today, we are living with chemicals that are in our food, clothes, furniture, appliances, toys, cosmetics and medicines. Society, for its existence anywhere on earth, needs to use a variety of products and/or means that are directly or indirectly connected to chemicals. For example, from the time one wakes up in the morning to the time one goes to sleep, one may use products that are directly connected to chemicals, such as tooth-paste, soap, drugs, preserved milk or juice, perfume, creams for skin-care, and many more. Other chemicals-based products (to be called chemical products) indirectly influence our activities, such as cooking oil, paint, gasoline, fuel for cooking, electricity, etc., while others affect our survival, such as, air we breathe, water we drink, water we use for cleaning, soil we use for various purposes, to name a few.

Over 95 percent of all manufactured goods rely on some form of industrial chemical processes (ICCA, 2019). Chemicals are also a significant contributor to our economies. World chemicals sales were valued at €3,669 billion in 2019. Nearly 500,000 chemical substances from CAS REGISTRY® cover areas of community interest and an estimated 40,000 to 60,000 industrial chemicals are found in commerce globally. As the number of chemicals grows rapidly, understanding their implications on human health and environment is increasingly becoming a problem. An important and urgent challenge is not only to identify the chemicals, which may have harmful effects but also to substitute and/or control their use. What is needed is an intelligent chemical analysis-substitution system. Note, however, while reducing the use of hazardous chemicals is a primary goal of this system, replacing substances without proper assessment of the alternatives can lead to regrettable substitutions (Hogue, 2013). Regulated chemicals subject to phasing out should be urgent candidates for substitution. For example, Per- and Polyfluoroalkyl Substances (PFAS) are restricted by EU POPs regulation due to their bio persistence and bio accumulative nature (Cousins *et al.*, 2019). In addition to regulations, consumer comfort, awareness or economics may also act as driving factors for the substitution of chemicals in many products. Every product or chemical is related to its manufacturing process and life cycle assessment could point to the need for substitution of hazardous chemicals also used in processing. In order to substitute hazardous chemicals in a process, the main functional role of the chemical in the process must be specified along with a complete process description and process operating parameters (Jhamb *et al.*,2018).

Demand for safer alternatives in products is increasing continuously and regulatory authorities, such as EU REACH (EU, 2021), US EPA (Harten, 2014) and Occupational Safety and Health Administration (OSHA, 2021) have taken up substitution of chemicals that are harmful to human health and environment as one of the central elements of their policies. Avoidance of hazardous chemicals in the processes is recommended by Control of Major Accident Hazards Regulations (HSE, 2015). Different international organizations, research institutes and state/provincial governments have proposed frameworks for the assessment of alternative substitute candidates in a product and/or process. These frameworks are mostly case specific and limited to prescribed classes of chemicals. Even though several databases are available, most of them are incomplete and have information gaps that need to be filled. An overview of assessment frameworks, methods and associated tools (such as databases) are discussed in Syeda *et al.* (2021). An important unresolved issue is the accessibility of the data needed to perform analysis for different types of chemical products.

In this paper, aspects of a systematic analysis method for chemical substitution related to chemical products and their associated processes are presented. The method is based on collected data stored in structured databases, a suite of property model libraries, and a work-flow applicable for a wide range of chemical substitution problems. Selected features of the chemical analysis method are highlighted through two case studies.

2. Database and Methodology

The developed (ChemSub) database consists of 3 knowledge sections (chemical product classes, chemical properties, hazard data). For each product class, examples of known products in terms of product classification (single molecule, blend-formulation, functional and device) along with chemical identity, compositions, chemical functions, etc., are also stored. Within each class, the products are further divided into sub-classes. Data of 189 product sub-classes, such as refrigerants, dyeing additives, solvents, adsorbents, etc., have been collected. In the chemical properties section, collected data is divided and stored in terms of pure component property, functional pure component property, functional mixture property and phase equilibrium related properties. For the hazard data section, chemicals are classified according to three types of hazardous effects. A simplified version of the ontology, implemented for knowledge representation in the created library of databases is highlighted in Figure 1, where the chemical identity is the link to each section of the database. This knowledge representation allows easy retrieval of all information (properties, hazardous effects, product classes) of an identified chemical. A reverse search, that finds, for example, chemicals according to their product class and then determines, which of them have unacceptable properties and/or hazardous effects is also allowed. Currently, as Fig 1 indicates, there are 919823 chemicals in all the databases, there are 3 hazardous effects as defined by Globally Harmonized System (GHS) hazard classes and associated hazard category, under which, there are 10 physical, 2 environmental and 9 health hazardous effects. Within pure component properties, 17 properties are covered (in addition to functional and mixture properties).

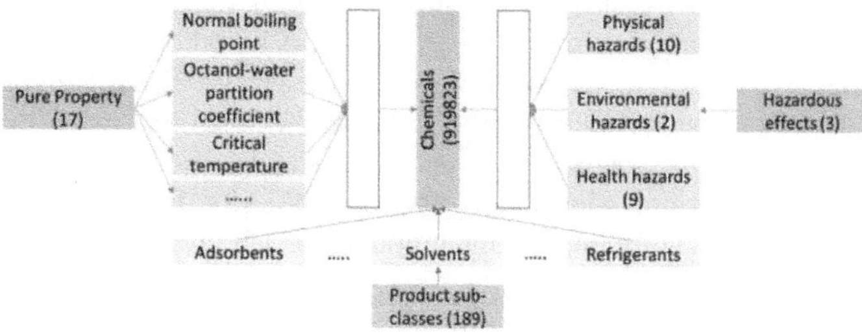

Figure 1: The ontology for knowledge representation in the database

The main steps of the work-flow for chemical substitution, developed from the experience of solving numerous substitution problems, are highlighted in Figure 2. The starting point (step-1) is problem definition, where details of the product are given in terms of product classification, product functions, the identity of chemicals involved, their compositions and many more. In step-2, the identified product is analysed in terms of important properties and their values. Here in-house property estimation models available in the ProCAPE toolbox (ChemSub, 2021) is used. In step-3, the chemical species are further analysed in terms of hazardous properties and/or effects, by retrieving the relevant hazardous effects data for each chemical through the ChemSub software (ChemSub, 2021). In steps 4-5, substitutes that match the desired target values for substitution are identified through the ProCAMD toolbox (Kalakul *et al.*, 2018). That is, chemicals that have the desired product function properties and do not have the undesired hazardous effects are identified. In step-6, the top ranked substitution candidates are listed for further verification of their properties and functions with experiments. An option for the design of experiments for selected products is also available. Note that each of the 6 steps requires its own specific computational methods and tools as highlighted in Fig 2.

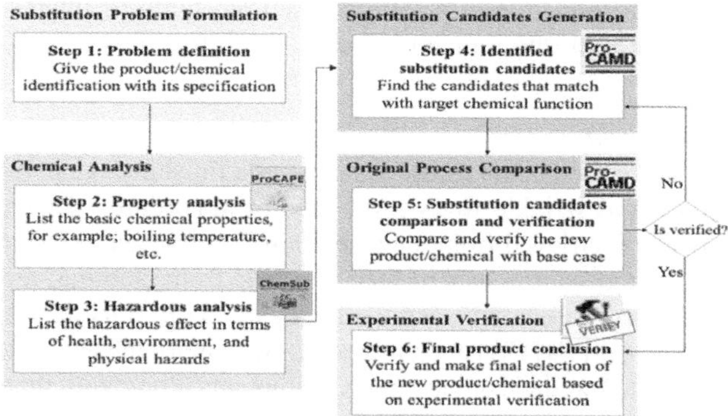

Figure 2: Work-flow for analysis based chemical substitution

3. Case studies

Results from two selected case studies are given below to highlight the main concepts of chemical substitution. These two case studies are selected because they exhibit features that are common to many chemical products. Note that the work-flow outlined in Fig 2 has been found to be applicable for a large number of products that have been analysed.

3.1. Mosquito Repellent

The mosquito repellent product is used to highlight the substitution of the active ingredient (N, N-Diethyl-meta-toluamide or diethyltoluamide, known as DEET), which is widely used in different versions of this product. DEET repels mosquitos by blocking the neuron to smell humans. Currently, insect repellents based on DEET are available in different product types; liquid formulations, lotions or sprays. Table 1 gives an example of the DEET based mosquito repellent product. It can be noted that in addition to DEET, a solvent is used to dissolve DEET, which is solid at standard conditions. Also, additives such as acidic acid (for pH adjustment) and Linalool (for fragrance) are used. The hazardous effects of each compound in the product are also given in Table 1.

Table 1: Typical formulation of a DEET based mosquito repellent product

Chemical	% Weight	Health hazard (Category)	Environmental hazard (Category)	Physical Hazards (Category)
DEET	10	Skin irritant (2), Eye irritant (2) Acute Toxicity (4)	Aquatic Chronic (3)	-
Acetic Acid	0.11	Skin Corrosive (1), Eye Damage (1)	-	-
Iso-propanol	41.8	Skin irritant (2), Specific Target Organ Toxicity STOT(SE) (3)	-	Flammable liquid (2)
Linalool	0.10	Skin irritant (2), Eye irritant (2), Skin Sensitizer (1)	-	-

Note: The category effect numbers in parenthesis range from 1 (very serious) to 4 (least serious)

From the analysis (step 3), it is found that DEET may cause irritation of the skin and eye. Search of the ChemSub database identifies picaridin, methyl nonyl ketone and ethyl 3-(N-butylacetamido) propionate as alternatives, which do not have any restriction from EU or US EPA. Natural compounds like Citronella oil and Eucalyptus oil extracted from plants are also found to be alternatives for DEET. The ChemSub database also helps to check the hazardous effects of the alternative active ingredients, which are listed in Table 2. From Table 2, Picaridin appears to be a safe alternative and is known to be very effective against mosquitoes by forming a vapor barrier on the skin surface leading to difficult landing. The formulation of picaridin based mosquito repellents contains 20% by weight of picaridin with the remaining being solvents and additives (Conte et al., 2011).

3.2. Textile finishing agent

Formaldehyde resins are used in the textile industry, as a finishing agent, to stiffen clothes and make fabrics, such as wrinkle-free cotton, rayon and corduroy. Different hazardous effects of formaldehyde retrieved from the ChemSub database are listed in Table 3. Due to the off-gassing and emission issues of formaldehyde from clothing, replacements are desired. Alternatives that are showing some efficacy in textile finishing include glyoxal, butane tetracarboxylic acid (BTCA) and citric acid. An important issue in the handling of these chemicals is related to their processing requirements along with their functionality in the product. Table 4 lists the limitations, hazardous effects, and processing requirements of some alternatives found in the ChemSub database. The most effective finishing agent among the three is found to be BTCA, which is less hazardous than formaldehyde but is more expensive as larger amounts are required. On the other hand, citric acid is a cost-effective and environment friendly alternative, but it impacts the fabric adversely. More candidates need to be investigated and needed data need to be measured.

Table 2: Hazardous effects of alternatives to DEET in mosquito repellents

Chemical	Health hazard (Category)	Environmental hazard (Category)	Physical Hazards (Category)
Picaridin	Acute Toxicity (4)	Slight aquatic toxicity (4)	Flammable liquid (3)
Methyl Nonyl Ketone	Dermal toxicity; eye and dermal irritation (3)	Aquatic Chronic (1)	Not classified
Ethyl-P	Eye irritant (2)	-	-
Citronella Oil	Skin irritant (2); Eye damage (1); Skin sensitizer (1)	Aquatic Chronic (2)	Flammable liquid (2)
Eucalyptus oil	Skin (2) & eye irritant (4); Aspiration (1); Skin sensitizer (1); Acute toxicity (4);	-	Flammable liquid (3)

Note: Ethyl-P is short for Ethyl 3-(N-butyl acetamido) propionate

Table 3 Hazardous effects Formaldehyde found in textile finishing agent

Chemical	Health hazard (Category)	Environmental hazard (Category)	Physical Hazards (Category)
Formaldehyde	Oral toxicity (3), Dermal toxicity (3), Skin Sensitization (1), Eye irritant (1), Inhalation toxicity (1), Respiratory Sensitization (1), Organ toxicity (3), Germ cell mutagenicity (2), Carcinogenicity (1), Reproductive toxicity (1)	Flammable substance (1), Compressed gas	Acute aquatic environment hazard (2), Long-term aquatic environment hazard (3)

Table 4: Alternative anti-crease finishing agents

Alternatives	Limitations/ disadvantages	Hazards (Category)	Processing requirements	Remarks
Glyoxal	Low mechanical strength; fabric discolouring	Skin irritant (2), Eye irritant (2), Skin sensitization (1), Germ cell mutagenicity (2), Respiratory tract irritation (3)	Aluminium sulphate is used as a catalyst and glycols are used as additives	Processing is expensive and may have corrosion issues
Butane tetracarboxylic acid (BTCA)	Low mechanical strength	Acute Toxicity (4), Skin irritant (2), Eye irritant (2)	Sodium hypophosphite (NaH_2PO_2) is used as additive	High anti-crease capacity, tensile strength; imparts satisfactory whiteness, high cost
Citric acid	Fabric discolouring, low resilience	Eye irritant (2)	Nitrogenous additives	Cost-effective; environmentally friendly

4. Conclusions

The main components of a data-model based analysis method for chemical substitution related to chemical products and their associated processes have been presented. Two examples are given as representatives of many similar problems studied to establish the method. For example, replacement of solvents in products as well as processes, refrigerants, additives as stabilizer, and many more. The implemented ontology in the ChemSub database, the property model library and the suite of algorithms for different steps define the application range, which is being extended continuously. Even though over 910000 chemicals are listed in the ChemSub database, actual measured property data exist for less than 10% of the chemicals. There is, therefore, a need to establish integrated and accessible databases based on reliable experimental data and accompanying property models to fill the gaps. Also, although the situation is improving, barriers to the implementation of green chemistry principles still exist (Matus *et al.*, 2012). An opportunity exists for the development of machine learning based property models with a wide application range as well as a new class of integrated computer-aided methods and associated tools (Pistikopoulos *et al.*, 2021). That is, an opportunity exists for the development of more intelligent search methods to identify better and safer alternatives. Product oriented knowledge representation in the ChemSub database and a framework for chemical substitution are proposed to overcome the case specific nature of existing tools. In case of substitution in processes, computer aided tools for chemical substitution need to be integrated with process simulators to generate necessary information on process parameters. Finally, disclosure of product components by manufacturers and traders is a precondition for successful chemical substitutions

References

ChemSub, 2021, Computer-aided tool for chemical substitution, PSE for SPEED Company Ltd., Bangkok, Thailand.

E. Conte, R. Gani, K. M. Ng, 2011, Design of formulated products: a systematic methodology, AIChE Journal, 57, 2431-2449.

I. T. Cousins, G. Goldenman, D. Herzke, R. Lohmann, M. Miller, C. A. Ng, S. Patton, M. Scheringer, X. Trier, L. Vierke, Z. Wang, J. C. DeWitt, 2019, The concept of essential use for determining when uses of PFASs can be phased out. Environmental Science: Processes & Impacts, 21, 1803-1815.

EU, 2021, European Chemicals Agency (https://echa.europa.eu/).

P. F. Harten, 2014, Program for Assisting the Replacement of Industrial Solvents (PARIS III), 18th Annual Green Chemistry & Engineering Conference, North Bethesda MD, June 17-19.

HSE, 2015, (https://www.hse.gov.uk/comah/background/comah15.htm).

C. Hogue, 2013, Assessing Alternatives to toxic chemicals: governments, businesses, and now the National Academy of Sciences consider how to avoid "regrettable substitution", Chemical Engineering News, 91, 19–20.

ICCA, 2019, (https://icca-chem.org/wp-content/uploads/2020/10/Catalyzing-Growth-and-Addressing-Our-Worlds-Sustainability-Challenges-Report.pdf).

S. Jhamb, X. Liang, R. Gani, G. M. Kontogeorgis, 2019, Systematic Model-Based Methodology for Substitution of Hazardous Chemicals, ACS Sustainable Chemical Engineering, 7, 7652–7666.

S. Kalakul, L. Zhang, Z. Fang, H. A. Choudhury, S. Intikhab, N. Elbashir, M. R. Eden, R. Gani, 2018, Computer aided chemical product design – ProCAPD & tailor-made blended products, Computers & Chemical Engineering, 116, 37-55.

K. J. M. Matus, W. C. Clark, P. T. Anastas, J. B. Zimmerman, 2012, Barriers to the Implementation of Green Chemistry in the United States, Environ. Sci. Technol. 46, 10892–10899.

OSHA, 2021, (https://www.osha.gov/safer-chemicals/why-transition).

E. N. Pistikopoulos, A. Barbosa-Povoa, J. H. Lee, R. Misener, A. Mitsos, G. V. Reklaitis, V. Venkatasubramanian, F. You, R. Gani, 2021, Process Systems Engineering–The Generation Next? Computers & Chemical Engineering, 147, 107252.

S. R. Syeda, E. A. Khan, O. Padungwatanaroj, N. Kuprasertwong, A. K. Tula, 2022, A perspective on hazardous chemical substitution in consumer products; Current Opinion in Chemical Engineering, 36, 100748.

Proceedings of the 14th International Symposium on Process Systems Engineering – PSE 2021+
June 19-23, 2022, Kyoto, Japan
http://dx.doi.org/10.1016/B978-0-323-85159-6.50031-2

Construction of Database and Data-driven Statistical Models for the Solubility of Nanomaterials in Organic Solvents

Junqing Xia* and Yoshiyuki Yamashita

Department of Chemical Engineering, Tokyo University of Agriculture and Technology, Naka-cho, Koganei City, Tokyo, 184-8588, JAPAN
xiajunqing@m2.tuat.ac.jp

Abstract

Nanomaterials have been put into practical use in many fields. Therefore, the ability to predict the properties of nanomaterials has gained utmost significance. In this study, we have presented a database of solubility of organically-modified and non-modified nanomaterials in organic solvents. Furthermore, we attempted to model the solubility of one collected nanoparticle using various data-driven statistical modeling techniques. The solubility prediction using data-driven models is more accurate than that of the conventional solute-solvent similarity method based on Hansen solubility parameters (HSPs). In addition, the modeling results exhibit that certain solvent features, such as dielectric constant and molar logP, also have a significant influence on the solubility of nanomaterials.

Keywords: process science; machine learning; organically-modified nanomaterial; nanomaterial database; nanomaterial solubility.

1. Introduction

A nanoparticle has been widely accepted as a particle of any shape with dimensions in the range of 1 and 100 nm (Vert et al., 2012). These nanometer-sized materials have been applied in various fields such as medicine, electronics, materials, and chemical engineering. To retain their unique physical and chemical properties, the nanoscale structures of individual nanoparticles must be protected from undesirable interactions with other substances, such as solvents or polymers. One of the many effective protection strategies involves modifying the surface of nanoparticles with organic substances (Tomai et al., 2021), which further introduces unique solubility and cohesiveness behaviors. Therefore, from an industry perspective, the ability to predict the physical and chemical properties of modified and non-modified nanoparticles is becoming increasing vital, as it significantly impacts the design, construction, and operations of the manufacturing processes.

Recently, machine learning techniques have been introduced in the research of molecular and material sciences, for designing new compounds and synthesis routes, as well as revealing new principles hiding behind phenomenon (Butler et al., 2018). To construct and evaluate such machine learning models, training data must be collected first. We believe that to estimate the solubility or cohesiveness of nanoparticles, features such as Hansen solubility parameters (HSPs), UV shift, and Z potential are equally relevant. However, such data have not been previously collected or organized.

In this study, we introduced a new database for the solubility of nanomaterials in various solvents, which is currently at its early development stage with limited data points. In addition, we applied several data-driven statistical techniques to model the relationship between solubility and solvent feature parameters for one nanoparticle.

2. Solubility database for nanomaterials

With the growing numbers of practical use of nanomaterials, various databases have been established to collect the unique properties of these materials, such as caNanoLab, Dortmund data bank (DDB) nanofluids, eNanomapper, NANoREG, NanoDatabank, NanoMILE, and PubVINUS. For example, DDB nanofluids contain experimental data on the thermophysical properties of nanofluids (Mondejar et al., 2021). eNanoMapper serves as a data infrastructure for managing the toxicity of engineered nanomaterials (Jeliazkova et al., 2015). PubVINUS provides physicochemical properties and bioactivities as well as descriptors of various nanomaterials (Yan et al., 2020). However, most of the existing databases are focused on the bioactivities and the environmental impact of nanomaterials; thus, only the solubility in water is included. To establish the correlations among the structure, functionality, and properties of nanomaterials related to process manufacturing (Figure 1), we have proposed a new database as its foundation for future development. Our ultimate goal includes establishment of correlation models among feature measurements/parameters (e.g. molar weight, size distribution), transformed features (e.g. solubility parameter, surface potential), and process properties of nanomaterials (e.g. solubility, cohesiveness), as shown in Figure 2.

2.1. Data collection

Currently, this database is focused on the solubility of nanomaterials. Research papers and reviews were screened for collecting data points. The keywords used for searching include, but are not limited to: colloids, dispersibility, HSPs, nanomaterial, nanoparticle, solubility, stability, and organic solvent. Nanomaterials such as 2D-nanomaterials and nanotubes were also collected, as particles with dimensions smaller than 500 nm, as well as tubular or fiber-like structures with two dimensions below 100 nm are also qualified as "nanoparticles" (Vert et al., 2012).

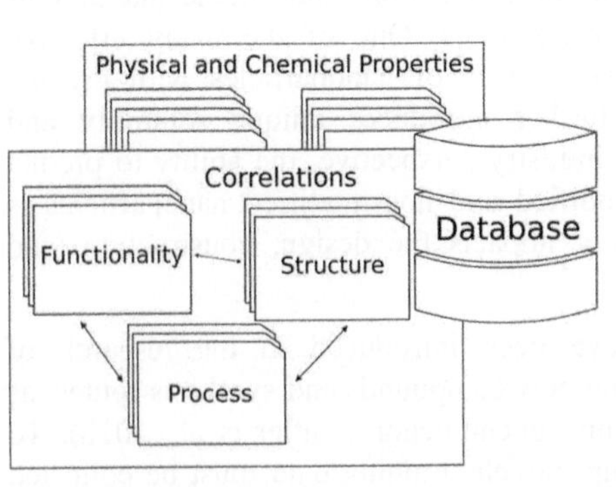

Figure 1 Layout of the database

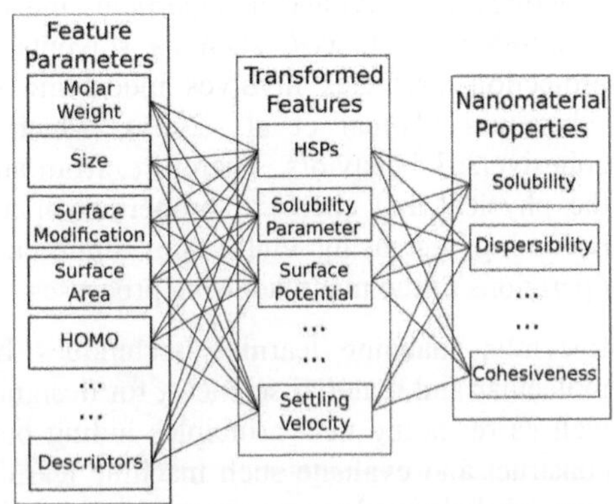

Figure 2 Illustration of correlation models

2.2. Features of the database

The current database contains approximately 1,200 solubility data points from 74 types of organically-modified and non-modified nanomaterials, including six types of nanotubes, 44 types of 2D-nanomaterials, and 38 types of nanoparticles. The core compositions of the collected nanomaterials and their percentages in this database are shown in Table 1. Furthermore, parameters related to solubility, such as the estimated HSPs of nanomaterials, sonification conditions (time, initial concentration, sonification power, temperature), and centrifugation conditions (revolutions per minute, time), were collected as well, depending on the applicability.
Approximately 250 pure, and 30 mixed solvents were collected. Among them, there were 23 frequently-utilized solvents, ranging from low polarity (such as hexane) to high polarity (such as dimethyl sulfoxide). In addition, approximately 53 % of all data points were originated from organically-modified nanomaterials. Decanoic acid, oleic acid, and acetic acid are currently the most commonly used organic modifiers in this database.

Solvents and organic modifiers were reorganized into their own auxiliary databases to enrich the information contained in the database, for modeling purposes. For each substance in its corresponding auxiliary database, more than 230 additional feature parameters were gathered from various sources: for example, surface tension and dielectric constants were collected from handbooks (Haynes et al., 2017), quantum chemical properties such as highest occupied molecular orbital were calculated using the Python package Psi4 (Psi4 project team, 2021), and molecular descriptors were acquired using the Python package RDKit (G. Landrum, 2021).

2.3. Data quality and discussions

The greatest challenge we experienced during data collection was the different formats of solubility in different reports. Only 28.9 % of the solubility data were reported as concentration measurements with the units of mg/mL or mg/mg, and 18.1 % of the data were expressed in terms of light absorption. Nearly 49.5 % of the data points were reported using descriptions such as "good" or "bad," and the rest can only be evaluated indirectly from photos. In addition, data that related to the preparation of nanomaterial solutions, such as sonification time, were often either unavailable or incomplete.

The quality of the data will certainly affect the quality of the prediction models. It also limits the direct comparisons among different nanomaterials. Therefore, it is crucial to form a standard format for recording experimental data in the future.

Currently, this database is at its early stages. More solubility data, features and properties of nanomaterials will be collected and reorganized in the future.

Table 1 Core composition of nanomaterials and their percentages in the database

ZrO_2	18.0 %	Al_2O_3	4.4 %	WS_2	3.7 %	$MoSe_2$	2.8 %
RGO[1]	11.7 %	ZnO	4.4 %	C_3N_4	3.2 %	MoS_2	2.5 %
C_{60}	7.8 %	Graphene	4.2 %	Germanane	3.2 %	$MoTe_2$	1.9 %
CNT[2]	6.0 %	GO[3]	4.0 %	CeO_2	2.9 %	Others	19.3 %

[1] RGO: reduced graphene oxide; [2] CNT: carbon nanotube; [3] GO: graphene oxide.

3. Selection of solvent features and data-driven solubility models

In previous studies, HSPs have often been used to predict the solubility of nanomaterials (Tomai et al., 2021). This prediction is based on the similarity between the solvent and solute, by calculating $R_s = (4\Delta\delta_D^2 + \Delta\delta_P^2 + \Delta\delta_H^2)^{0.5}$, where $\Delta\delta = \delta_{solvent} - \delta_{solute}$, and δ_D, δ_P, and δ_H are different HSPs that contribute to solubility (Hansen, 2007). When R_s is smaller than an experimental-determined threshold, it indicates that the solvent and solute are adequately similar, so that a stable solution can be formed. This method functions well for bulk materials. However, to reiterate the demonstration by various data points in our database, R_s does not predict well for nanomaterials, regardless of their surfaces being modified or not.

3.1. Feature selection

In this study, we attempted to obtain important solvent feature parameters and their correlations with the solubility of nanomaterials using data-driven statistical models. However, the quality of the data prevented us from creating a universal solubility model. Thus, the CeO_2 nanoparticle modified with decanoic acid (Tomai et al., 2021) was chosen as the modeling nanoparticle because of its typical diameter (5.2 nm) and tight size distribution.

To construct reliable data-driven statistical models, important solvent feature parameters governing the solubility of nanomaterials must be identified first before modeling. Instead of using feature extraction methods (for example, principle component analysis), feature selection methods are used to eliminate irrelevant solvent feature parameters. Feature selection methods are commonly categorized into three types: the filters rely on the correlation of candidate variables with the variable to predict regardless of models, the wrappers select best performed subsets of variables depending on chosen models, and the embedded methods select variable subsets and tune the model parameters simultaneously. In this study, recursive feature elimination (RFE) was used as the wrapper algorithm for several linear and nonlinear data-driven models listed in Table 2. Least absolute shrinkage and selection operator for logistic regression (LASSO-LR) was chosen as the embedded method. Both feature selection and modeling were conducted under the R-4.1.0 environment using "caret" and "glmnet" packages.

Table 2 Selected solvent features using RFE

Logistic Regression	BCUT2D_MWHI, dielectric constant, dipole moment, HOMO, δ_P, FpDensityMorgan1, LUMO, MaxEStateIndex, MinAbsEStateIndex, MinEStateIndex, molar volume, molar weight, QED, VSA_EState1
Random Forest, SVM[1] (linear), SVM (polynomial)	BCUT2D_MWHI, dielectric constant, dipole moment, EState_VSA1, FpDensityMorgan1, δ_P, MinAbsPartialCharge, molar logP, molar refractivity
SVM (radial), LDA[2], kNN[3]	dielectric constant, δ_P, δ_H, MaxPartialCharge, MinAbsPartialCharge, MinPartialCharge, molar logP, PEOE_VSA1, SlogP_VSA2

[1] SVM: support vector machine; [2] LDA: linear discriminant analysis;
[3] kNN: k-nearest neighbors.

Twenty-five solubility data points of the modified CeO_2 nanoparticles were divided into an 18-sample training dataset and a seven-sample test dataset. All test samples have missing values for solvent surface tension. Because no detailed measurement of solubility was reported, the nanoparticle solubilities in all solvents were categorized into two classes: samples with solubility larger than 0.01 wt% was labeled as "soluble," while the rest were labeled as "non-soluble." The results of the RFE from 230 solvent features using the training dataset are listed in Table 2. It can be observed that only two HSPs, δ_P and δ_H, were able to be selected as significant features. In addition, it is clear that other features might also play important roles in solubility prediction, such as the dielectric constant, dipole moment, and molar logP.

3.2. Data-driven modeling for solubility of nanomaterial

The selected features using RFE and LASSO were reorganized into combinations of feature data as the inputs for each corresponding modeling method. Any combination containing correlated features was removed. Owing to the small sample size of the training dataset, the leave-one-out cross-validation strategy was used for model training. The prediction performance of the models was tested using the test dataset. A few of the best-performed feature combinations for each model are listed in Table 3.

It can be observed that the solubility prediction performances using the data-driven models, especially the radial-kernel SVM, were much better as compared to using the similarity-based R_s. In addition, solvent features, such as dielectric constant, dipole moment, and molar logP, performed as good as, if not better than HSPs δ_P and δ_H. This coincides with the results obtained from the previous feature selections. However, it needs to be emphasized that these predictions are limited to only one nanoparticle, and further evaluation of the models is constrained by the small size of available data. Therefore, more research will be conducted on how to construct better solubility prediction models using various yet limited information from the entire database.

Table 3 Best-performed feature combinations for each data-driven model

Data-driven Model	Modeling Variables	Accuracy
Logistic Regression	dielectric constant, EState_VSA1, LUMO, MinEStateIndex	85.7 %
Random Forest	dielectric constant, EState_VSA1, MinAbsPartialCharge	85.7 %
SVM (linear)	dipole moment	71.5 %
SVM (polynomial)	dipole moment, EState_VSA1, molar logP	85.7 %
SVM (radial)	dielectric constant, EState_VSA1, MaxPartialCharge, SlogP_VSA2	100 %
LDA	dipole moment, FpDensityMorgan2, δ_H	85.7 %
kNN	dipole moment, molar logP, VSA_EState1	85.7 %
LASSO-LR	dipole moment, δ_P, NumAliphaticCarbocycles, QED, SlogP_VSA4	71.5 %
R_s	δ_D, δ_P, δ_H	42.9 %

4. Conclusions

In this study, we have presented a database for the solubility of organically-modified and non-modified nanomaterials in organic solvents. This database contains approximately 1,200 data points. Furthermore, we attempted to construct data-driven statistical models for solubility using the collected data of one nanoparticle. The data-driven solubility prediction models perform better than the R_s method based on the similarity of solute-solvent HSPs. These models demonstrated that in addition to HSPs δ_P and δ_H, solvent feature parameters, such as dielectric constant and molar logP, should also be viewed as important factors in predicting the solubility of nanomaterials.

Acknowledgement

This study is supported by the grants from Materials Processing Science project ("Materealize") of Ministry of Education, Culture, Sports, Science and Technology, Japan, Grant Number JPMXP0219192801.

References

K.T. Butler, D.W. Davies, H. Cartwright, O. Isayev, and A. Walsh, 2018, Machine Learning for Molecular and Materials Science, Nature, 559, 547–555

C.M. Hansen, 2007, Hansen Solubility Parameters: A User's Handbook, 2nd Edition, CRC Press, LLC, Boca Raton, USA

W.M. Haynes (Editor-in-Chief), 2017, CRC Handbook of Chemistry and Physics, 97th edition, CRC Press, LLC, Boca Raton, USA

N. Jeliazkova, C. Chomenidis, P. Doganis, B. Fadeel, R. Grafström, B. Hardy, J. Hastings, M. Hegi, V. Jeliazkov, N. Kochev, P. Kohonen, C.R. Munteanu, H. Sarimveis, B. Smeets, P. Sopasakis, G. Tsiliki, D. Vorgrimmler and E. Willighagen, 2015, The eNanoMapper database for nanomaterial safety information, Beilstein Journal of Nanotechnology, 6, 1609–1634

G. Landrum, 2021, RDKit: Open-source cheminformatics, http://www.rdkit.org

M.E. Mondejar, M. Regidor, J. Krafczyk, C. Ihmels, B. Schmid, G.M. Kontogeorgis, F. Haglind, 2021, An open-access database of the thermophysical properties of nanofluids, Journal of Molecular Liquids, 333, 115140

Psi4 project team, 2021, http://psicode.org

T. Tomai, N. Tajima, M. Kimura, A. Yoko, G. Seong, T. Adschiri, 2021, Solvent accommodation effect on dispersibility of metal oxide nanoparticle with chemisorbed organic shell, Journal of Colloid and Interface Science, 587, 574–580

X. Yan, A. Sedykh, W. Wang, B. Yan, H. Zhu, 2020, Construction of a web-based nanomaterial database by big data curation and modeling friendly nanostructure annotations, Nature Communications., 11, 2519

M. Vert, Y. Doi, K-H Hellwich, M. Hess, P. Hodge, P. Kubisa, M. Rinaudo, and F. Schué, 2012, Terminology for biorelated polymers and applications (IUPAC Recommendations 2012), Pure and Applied Chemistry, 84, 377–410

Proceedings of the 14th International Symposium on Process Systems Engineering – PSE 2021+
June 19-23, 2022, Kyoto, Japan
http://dx.doi.org/10.1016/B978-0-323-85159-6.50032-4

Fast, efficient and reliable problem solution through a new class of systematic and integrated computer-aided tools

Orakotch Padungwatanaroj[a*], Nichakorn Kuprasertwong[a], Jakkraphat Kogncharoenkitkul[a], Kornkanok Udomwong[a], Anjan Tula[b], Rafiqul Gani[a,c]

[a]*PSE for SPEED Company Limited, 294/65 RK Office Park, Romklao Rd., Bangkok, 10520, Thailand*
[b]*College of Control Science and Eng, Zhejiang University, Hangzhou 310027, China*
[c]*PSE for SPEED Company, Skyttemosen 6, DK-3450 Allerød, Denmark*
**orakotch@pseforspeed.com*

Abstract

Process systems engineering involves the use of systematic methods and tools to solve a wide range of problems. In this paper, the integration of a new class of computer-aided methods and their associated tools in a flexible software architecture is presented. Two problem specific software architectures are highlighted, one for sustainable process design and another for integrated product design and analysis. In each case, the core software components, which are extended versions of ProCAFD (software for sustainable process design) and ProCAPD (software for product design and analysis) are highlighted together with linked software-components, and, solutions from different case studies.

Keywords: Sustainable process design, Chemical product design, integrated software architecture, computer-aided methods

1. Introduction

To tackle the grand challenges of energy, water, environment, food and health that modern society is currently facing, opportunities exist for development and use of new methods and associated computer-aided tools that are not available in the currently available software tools, such as the well-known process simulators (Pistikopoulos et al., 2021). Synthesis and design of new, innovative and significantly more sustainable processes require implementation of hybrid methods that employ multiple models, data sources and solution algorithms. For example, validation and testing of novel hybrid energy efficient separation techniques require the integration of data, models, simulation and analysis at various levels of complexity and integration of operational tasks (Tula et al., 2020). For generation and verification of new intensified process options, models that can simulate new intensified operations are needed as well as methods for design of chemicals and materials, as in membrane-based hybrid separation schemes (O'Connell et al., 2019). Similarly, synthesis, design, analysis of chemical products needs large databases to identify and/or substitute potentially harmful or hazardous chemicals within the product being designed (Syeda et al., 2022). The verification of new products needs validated models of processes, which are normally not available in commercial software tools, while, implementation of their design methods requires new and innovative unit operations and/or materials, as in membrane-based separation, that may also not be known. In many of the product and/or process synthesis and/or design problems, thermodynamic properties play a more significant role than their conventional use in mass and energy balance-based process models. For example, synthesis and design of energy efficient and environmentally acceptable solvent-based separations or fluids for

refrigeration, need integrated solution strategies accounting for product and process design issues. Solution of these problems contribute to tacking the challenges facing modern society.
Based on the above, any computer-aided software tool needs a number of options, such as, an option for synthesis of processing routes as well as chemical products; an option for design and analysis of chemical processes and products so that targets for sustainable improvements can be identified; and, an option for innovation so that novel and more sustainable alternatives can be generated and verified. To provide the above options, in addition to the model-based process simulation option, a number of computer-aided methods and their associated software tools (to be called linked components) are needed: a versatile database of chemicals with respect to their properties, their use, their environmental impacts etc.; a versatile modelling toolbox, including options for generating new models through data analysis, machine learning as well as first principles, when the needed model is not available in the model library; a versatile toolbox of property estimation options; a toolbox for process synthesis and another for product synthesis based on different methods of solution; a toolbox for design and analysis including economics, sustainability, environmental impacts, etc., and many more.
The objective of this paper is to highlight two integrated software tools that allow the needs to be matched through flexible and integrated software architectures. Two specific software tools, ProCAFD (Tula et al. 2019) and ProCAPD (Kalakul et al., 2018), for sustainable process design and chemical product design, respectively, are presented in their extended versions. The extensions are mainly with respect to how different linked components are integrated to the original, thereby enabling them to solve a wider range of problems. The additional software components are, PSE for SPEED database with data on more than 75000 chemicals; HI-Opt toolbox for simultaneous heat integration and process optimization, ProREFD (Udomwong et al., 2020) for refrigerant design and verification; ChemSub for substitution of hazardous and less efficient chemicals, to name a few. Note that external tools like process simulators or numerical solvers needed for specific steps in different work-flows are available. Results from case studies highlighting selected features of the integrated software tools are also presented.

2. Methodology & Associated Tools

2.1 ProCAFD-Sustainable process design: The work-flow for sustainable process design implemented in ProCAFD consists of 12 steps within the 3-stages methodology of Babi et al., (2015). Figure 1a highlights the 12 steps of the work-flow. Figure 1b highlights the tools needed for the different steps of the work-flow. Starting at the centre, where the ProCAFD tool is located, the next level (shaded in blue) shows the component functions and the next outer level (shaded in light green) shows the actual linked-components available for the steps of the work-flow. This component-based architecture provides the flexibility to configure and generate customized integrated software tools tuned for specific application areas and/or problem needs. That is, it removes the options not needed for the problems of interest and allows to add and/or remove linked-components as and when necessary. Figure 1b also highlights that different tool-components are available different stages, for example, Super-O for process synthesis stage, ECON, LCSoft for design-analysis stage and HI-Opt for process innovation stage.

2.2 ProCAPD-Chemical product design: ProCAPD is a collection of linked components that are needed for various stages of the work-flow for design and/or analysis of different types chemical products. Figure 2a shows the work-flow steps of the design methodology, while Figure 2b shows the architecture of ProCAPD.

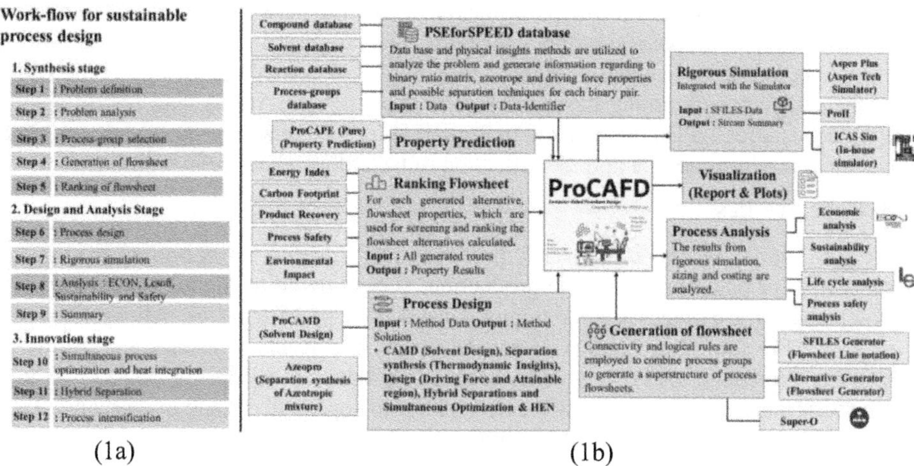

(1a) (1b)

Figure 1: Work-flow (1a) and architecture of ProCAFD (1b)

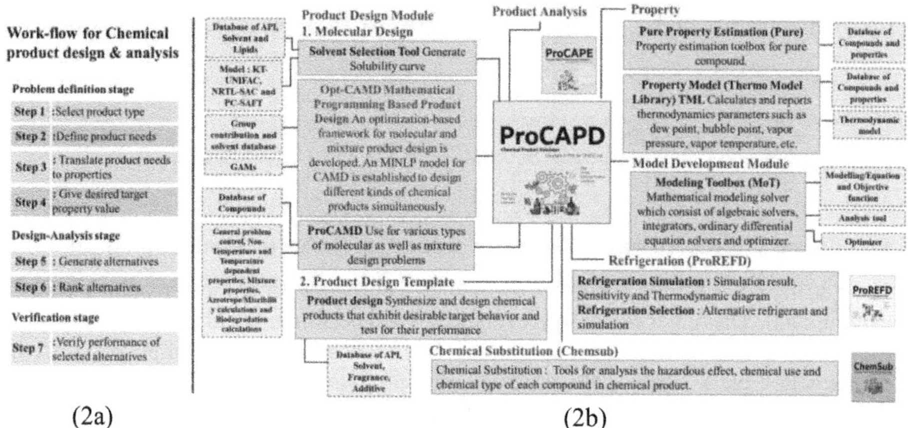

(2a) (2b)

Figure 2: Work-flow (2a) and architecture of ProCAPD (2b)

Note that design of chemical products, which are classified as single molecules, liquid blends, formulated liquid blends, formulated functional products and devices, need for each product type and within it, each product sub-type, different sets of data, models and computational algorithms, even though the steps of the work-flow of the methodology are the same. For example, design of single molecules involving small molecules (as in refrigerant design) or larger organic chemicals (as in organic solvent design) or complex molecules with ions and organic fragments (as in ionic liquids), may require similar properties but different data-sets and/or property models. On the other hand, liquid blends are mixtures of liquid compounds while formulated liquid blends have active ingredients that are usually solids to which solvents and additives are added to obtain a final liquid blended product. A large database of 24000 chemicals classified in terms of lipids, solvents, ionic liquids, active ingredients, etc., is available for selection of a product component. A database of 810000 chemicals help to identify potentially hazardous chemicals. The link to ProCAPE helps to analyse product and/or process functional properties. Since less than 10% of the chemicals in the different databases have measured property data, property prediction options in ProCAPE for pure component, mixture and phase equilibrium properties help to quickly fill-out the gaps in the required properties. Finally, different problem solution algorithms are available in ProCAPD for, selection of chemicals based on database search, computer-aided molecular design (ProCAMD), mathematical programming based molecular design (OptCAMD), and hybrid solution approaches. ProCAPD is also linked to ProREFD for refrigerant design and ChemSub for chemical product analysis and identification of hazardous chemicals in products.

3. Case Studies

3.1 Sustainable process design: The production of Cumene, an important intermediate substance for phenol and acetone production, is considered to highlight selected work-flow steps of the 3-stages methodology for sustainable process design. All steps and tools of ProCAFD shown in Figure 1 are used. Propylene reacts with benzene to produce cumene. Propylene also reacts with cumene to produce p-diisopropylbenzene as a by-product. Unconverted benzene is reacted with p-diisopropylbenzene in a second reactor to produce additional cumene. The synthesis toolbox generates a total of 8160 processing routes considering two reaction steps and all available process group options. Removing some of the membrane-based separation process groups, 2622 processing routes are obtained. Selecting only vapor-liquid distillation/flash process groups, 20 processing routes are obtained and one of these (Maity et al., 2013) is selected as the base case.

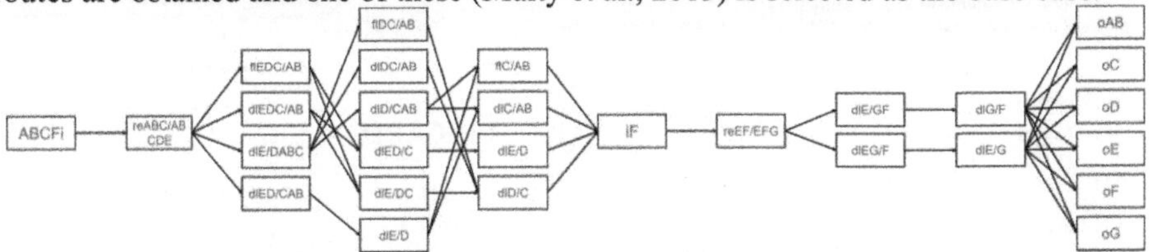

Figure 3: Reduced superstructure of processing routes for cumene production.

The starting point for the design-analysis stage is process simulation (results highlighted in Figure 4a). Driving force-based reverse design is performed (Tula et al. 2019) to obtain the design parameters of unit operations (such as distillation column, reactors, heat exchangers, etc.) that are needed for process simulation. AVEVA PROII (https://www.aveva.com/en/products/pro-ii-simulation/), which is linked to ProCAFD is used to perform steady state simulation and analysis tools such as ECON (cost estimation), LCSoft (life cycle assessment), Safety (inherent safety analysis) are used to identify the process "hotspots". As shown in Fig 4b, distillation columns 2 and 3 have the largest utility costs. This is also confirmed by the plots of the carbon footprints. The environmental impacts (not shown in Fig 4) indicate that the release of benzene, a carcinogenic chemical (also confirmed by ChemSub) leaves the process with the purge stream. Therefore, unlike the published design, the benzene feed is adjusted so that there is zero benzene purge, indicating that a small amount of by-product that has a lower price than the cumene will be produced as part of the more sustainable design. In stage 3, the targeted improvement in terms of decrease of energy demand is realized through simultaneous heat integration and process optimization (Duran and Grossmann, 1986), by adding an extended transhipment model to the optimizer in AVEVA PROII. Compared to the base case design, the profit is increased by 13.57%, the carbon footprint is reduced 78.65 % for the reboiler in DIST2. The ecological footprint is calculated to be 1.219. Detailed results for this sustainable process design can be obtained from the authors.

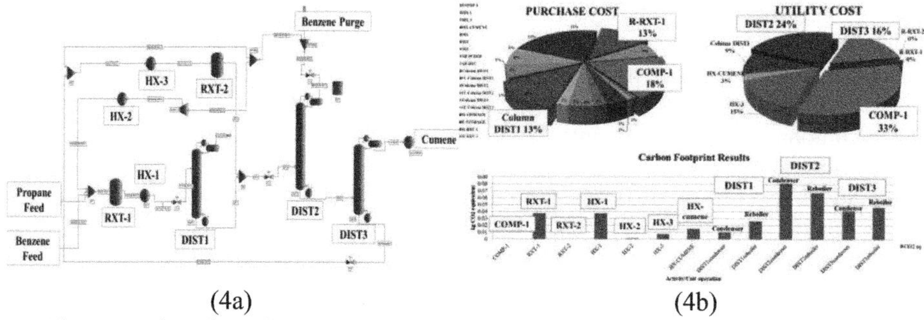

(4a) (4b)

Figure 4: Flowsheet for cumene production (4a) and selected analysis results (4b)

3.2 Chemical Product Design – Substitution Issues: Two chemical substitution problems related to chemical product design are highlighted. The first problem involves the replacement of refrigerants used in a two-cycle refrigeration process (Biegler et al., 1997) with alternatives that are more efficient and checked for safety issues through the hazards database. The refrigerants to be replaced are propylene (R290) and ethylene (R1150). ProREFD is used to find and verify the alternative refrigerants. One of the best alternatives for cycles 1 & 2 are listed in Table 1 together with refrigeration process performance results from ProREFD. In this example, ProCAPE, ProREFD and ChemSub have been used within ProCAPD. More solution details can be obtained from the authors.

Table 1 Performances of the best alternatives for cycles 1 & 2 & the reference

Cycle 1				Cycle 2				Overall
Comp	Qc kJ/hr	Qe kJ/hr	W kJ/hr	Comp	Qc kJ/hr	Qe kJ/hr	W kJ/hr	COP
R290	*67820*	*44867*	*22954*	*R1150*	*86098*	*54245*	*31853*	*0.99*
R1270/R1216 (38/62)	43279	23270	20009	Chemicals with similar boiling point could not be found.				

Note: The numbers in italic in the second row give the values of the reference refrigerants

The second example involves the improvement of a formulated liquid product (an insect repellent) by substituting its active ingredient (DEET, found in many commercial products), by another (Picaridin, found in some commercial products). The analysis shows that Picaridin has better functional properties against mosquitos, while Deet is more effective against other insects. Table 2 gives lists their known hazardous properties. Note that if the active ingredient is changed, the formula for the formulated liquid product also needs to be verified. The formulated liquid insect repellent with Deet has the following contents (in terms of weight percent): Deet = 10%; isopropanol = 41.8 %; water = 44.15%; and additives (acetic acid for pH control and linalool for fragrance) = 4.05%. For insect repellent based on Picaridin the formula is the following: Picaridin = 9.7%; 2-propanol = 42.3%; water = 43.95%; additives (acetic acid for pH control and linalool for fragrance) = 4.05%, which has been verified through experiments (Conte et al., 2012). In this example, Product template, ProCAPE, and ChemSub have been used within ProCAPD. More solution details can be obtained from the authors.

Table 2 Example of active ingredient used in mosquito repellent

Chemical	**State**	**Health hazard**	**Environmental hazard**	**Physical hazard**
Deet	Solid	Irritant-, skin (2), eye (2); Acute toxicity (4)	Aquatic chronic (3)	May damage plastic and leather
Picaridin	Solid	Acute toxicity (4)	Slight aquatic toxicity (4)	-

Note: The numbers in parenthesis indicate assigned category, where 5 indicates low hazard level and 1 indicates high hazard level.

4. Conclusions

A flexible software architecture that is capable to meeting the needs of sustainable process design and chemical product design and analysis has been presented. The architecture allows the linking of specific computer-aided methods and associated software tools as linked components for specific integrated software tools. Two integrated software tools one configured for sustainable process design and another for chemical product design and analysis have been presented. Through case studies, some of the features of the integrated software tools have been highlighted. The architecture of the integrated software tools allows linked components to be added or removed according to specific problem requirements. In this way, the changing specifications of methods and associated computer-aided tools needed to efficiently and reliably solve problems tackling the challenges of energy, water, environment, food and health can be matched. Current and future work is developing more case studies and testing the plug and play issues of linked components within problem specific software architectures to identify the desired more sustainable product and process alternatives. Flexible component-tools based architecture of software tools could be the answer for the need for computer-aided tools that are required to tackle the challenges of a changing earth.

References

D. K. Babi, J. Holtbruegge, P. Lutze, A. Gorak, J.M. Woodley, R. Gani, 2015, Sustainable Process Synthesis-Intensification, Computers & Chemical Engineering, 81, 218-44

E. Conte, R. Gani, Y. S. Cheng, K. M. Ng, 2012, Design of formulated products: experimental component, AIChE Journal 58 (1), 173-189

M. A. Duran, I. E. Grossmann, Simultaneous optimization and heat integration of chemical processes, 1986, AIChE J, 32, 123-138

S. Kalakul, L. Zhang, Z. Fang, H.A. Choudhury, S. Intikhab, N. Elbashir, M.R. Eden, R. Gani, 2018, Computer aided chemical product design – ProCAPD & tailor-made blended products, Computers & Chemical Engineering, 116, 37-55

D. Maity, R. Jagtap, N. Kaistha, 2013, Systematic top-down economic plantwide control of the cumene process, Journal of Process Control, 23, 1426-1440

J. P O'Connell, M. R. Eden, A. K. Tula, R. Gani, 2019, Retrofitting Distillation Columns with Membranes, *Chemical Engineering Progress,* 115 (12), 41-49

E. N. Pistikopoulos, A. Barbosa-Povoa, J. H. Lee, R. Misener, A. Mitsos, G. V. Reklaitis, V. Venkatasubramanian, F. You, R. Gani, 2021, Process Systems Engineering–The Generation Next? Computers & Chemical Engineering, 147, 107252

S. R. Syeda, E. A. Khan, O. Padungwatanaroj, N. Kuprasertwong, A. K. Tula, 2022, A perspective on hazardous chemical substitution in consumer products, Current Opinion in Chemical Engineering, 36, 100748

A. K. Tula, M.R. Eden, R.Gani, 2020, Computer-aided process intensification: Challenges, trends and opportunities, AIChE Journal, 66, e16819

A. K. Tula, M.R. Eden, R. Gani, 2019, Hybrid method and associated tools for synthesis of sustainable process flowsheets, Computers & Chemical Engineering, 131:2019, 106572

K. Udomwong, A. Robin, N. Kuprasertwong, O. Padungwatanaroj, A.K. Tula, L. Zhu, L. Zhou, B. Wang, S. Wang, R. Gani, 2020, ProREFD: Tool for Automated Computer-Aided Refrigerant Design, Analysis, and Verification, Computer Aided Chemical Engineering, 50, 457-462

A.W. Westerberg, I. E. Grossmann, L. Biegler, 1997, Chapters 4&5, Systematic Methods of Chemical Process Design, Wiley, USA

Proceedings of the 14th International Symposium on Process Systems Engineering – PSE 2021+
June 19-23, 2022, Kyoto, Japan
http://dx.doi.org/10.1016/B978-0-323-85159-6.50033-6

Design of Bio-Oil Solvents using Multi-Stage Computer-Aided Molecular Design Tools

Jia Wen Chong[a], Suchithra Thangalazhy-Gopakumar[a], Kasturi Muthoosamy[b], Nishanth G. Chemmangattuvalappil[a*]

[a]*Department of Chemical and Environmental Engineering, University of Nottingham Malaysia, Selangor 43500, Malaysia*
[b]*Nanotechnology Research Group, Centre of Nanotechnology and Advanced Materials, University of Nottingham Malaysia, Selangor 43500, Malaysia*
Nishanth.C@nottingham.edu.my

Abstract

Direct application of fast-pyrolysis bio-oil as biofuel is limited due to its undesirable attributes like low heating value, high viscosity, and storage instability. Solvent addition is a simple and practical method in upgrading pyrolysis bio-oil. In this work, a computer-aided molecular design (CAMD) tool was developed to generate the molecular structure of the solvent with desirable properties. Molecular signature descriptors were employed to represent property prediction models that comprise different classes of topological indices. Because of the differences in the structural details involved in different property prediction models, signatures of different heights were needed in formulating the design problem. However, the complexity of a CAMD problem increases with the height of signatures, due to the combinatorial nature of higher-order signatures. Thus, a multi-stage framework was developed by introducing a novel set of consistency rules that restrict the number of higher-order signatures. With the developed consistency rules, only relevant and consistent signatures were generated to keep the CAMD problem in a manageable size. Phase stability analysis was conducted after solvent candidates were identified to evaluate the stability and miscibility of the solvent-oil blend. As a result, a feasible solvent that fulfils the target properties with low environmental impact was identified.

Keywords: Computer-aided molecular design, bio-oil solvent, molecular signature descriptor.

1. Introduction

Biomass has received increased attention as a potential alternative fuel by converting into bio-oil via various conversion processes. Among the available biomass conversion processes, pyrolysis has the advantage of being a relatively simple and inexpensive technology. However, poor fuel properties of bio-oil from pyrolysis such as corrosiveness, high viscosity and low heating value limit its application as a biofuel. Solvent addition is one of the most popular bio-oil upgrading methods as it is relatively simple and economically viable. Conventionally, the design of solvents involves a trial-and-error process within a large set of candidates which is tedious, time-consuming, and costly. Unlike traditional search and optimisation techniques, a more efficient solvent design can be carried out by utilising CAMD (Computer-Aided Molecular Design) tools where molecules possessing desired properties are identified based on the pre-determined product requirements. CAMD is a reverse engineering approach in which the optimal molecules can be identified from a given set of molecular building blocks and a specified set of targeted properties. In the past, CAMD has been widely incorporated in designing solvents for biofuel additives. Previous research focused only on the functionality of the solvent itself that can be predicted using GC prediction models with 1st order group contributions. However, it is also important to include the environmental aspects into the design of bio-oil solvent to minimise the environmental impact. Moreover, incorporation of contributions from higher-order molecular groups in CAMD is crucial to account for the interactive effects of molecular groups (Marrero & Gani, 2001). In addition, the selected GC model may not have all the model parameters required for the estimation of property of a specific chemical (Hukkerikar et al., 2012). For this reason, TI (Topological Index) approaches can be applied as they are a function of the entire molecular graph, which reflect the entire nature of the molecular structure (Austin et al., 2016).

Different types of property prediction models can be modelled using either GC or TI approach. Different properties may be expressed with different TI as well. However, different TIs exhibit different mathematical expression, which pose challenges in combining and solving it simultaneously on a common platform (Chemmangattuvalappil & Eden, 2013). To overcome this issue, molecular signature descriptor was introduced, where various GC models and TIs can be expressed on a common platform (Visco et al., 2002). Molecular signature descriptor is one of the 2D fragment-based TI that systematically captures the structural information of a 2D structural formula. It describes the molecular atoms in terms of extended valencies up to a predefined height (Faulon et al., 2003). Owing to the fact that molecular signature descriptor is known as the canonical representation of a molecule, all other 2D classes of descriptors can be represented in terms of molecular signature (Visco & Chen, 2016).

Signatures of higher height were required for the coverage of TIs and higher-order GCs. Despite the high accuracy of estimation, the complexity of CAMD increases due to the combinatorial nature of higher-order signatures. Hence, the height of signatures must be lowered to be used in a CAMD formulation. However, not all the signatures considered in the CAMD problem are consistent with each other to form a feasible molecule. Thus, a consistency rule was developed in this work to reduce the size of CAMD problem by excluding irrelevant molecular signature at a lower height from the building block sets (Chong et al., 2021). Infeasible signatures (signature that do not fulfil the consistency rules) are systematically eliminated at different levels and this can help to keep a manageable problem size. After determining all the possible additives, the accuracy of the estimated higher heating value of solvent candidates were verified through a database search. Other than the thermodynamic properties, Gibbs free energy of mixing was estimated to evaluate the miscibility of solvent-oil blend. With the developed approach, an optimum solvent that improves the solvent-oil blend properties and stability was generated.

2. Methodology

This work presents a novel multi-stage solvent design methodology with consistency rule incorporated to reduce the size and complexity of the CAMD problem. The developed framework can be divided into 4 main stages as shown in Figure 1.

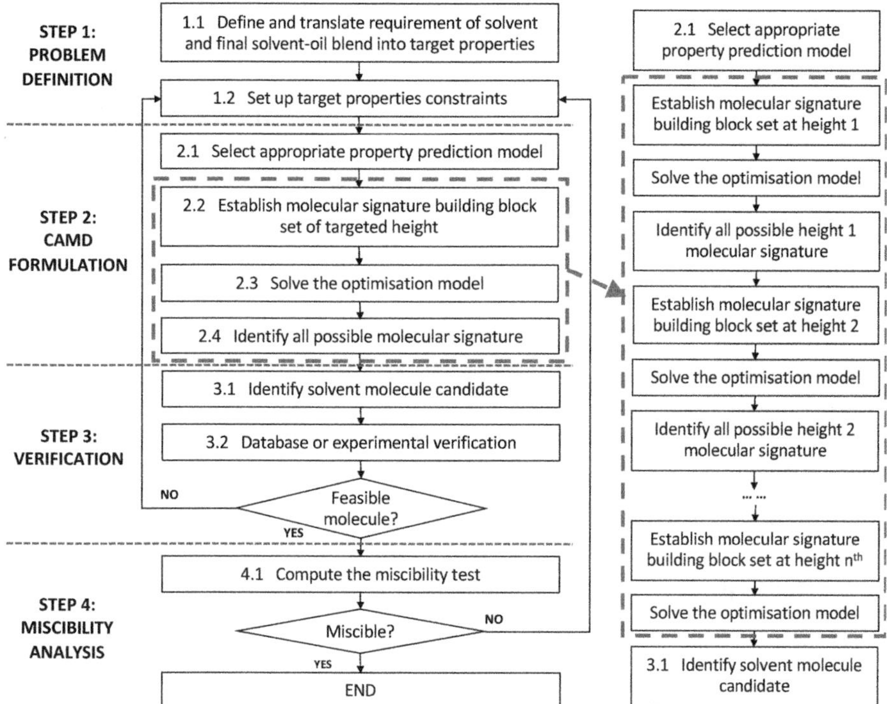

Figure 1 Framework for the development of CAMD model for the design of solvent

2.1. Problem Definition

Firstly, the problem definition was formulated, where the product needs were determined based on the requirements from regulations and specifications. In addition, environmental properties were considered to ensure that the generated solvent molecules have low environmental impact. The identified product requirements were then translated into measurable quantitative target properties. This is then followed by selection of suitable property prediction models to estimate the target properties of the solvent. In this work, property prediction models in terms of GC method and TI were considered and expressed as a function of the molecular signature descriptor. As shown in Eq. 1, the molecular signature descriptor of molecule *G*, *TI(G)* can be expressed as a dot product between two vectors, ${}^{h}\alpha_g$, the vector of occurrence number of atomic signatures of height *h*, and $TI\left(root\left({}^{h}\sum\right)\right)$, the vector of predicted values from the model computed for each of the atomic signatures.

$$TI(G) = k^{h}\alpha_g \cdot TI\left(root\left({}^{h}\sum\right)\right) \tag{1}$$

2.2. Consistency Rules

In the developed approach, signatures of height h were generated based on the collection of height $h-1$ signatures identified from the CAMD problem. The first layer of signature generated must contain one of the height $h-1$ signatures from the previous result. For example, assuming the signatures C1(C), C2(CC), C2(CO) and C3(CCO) were identified as the promising height 1 signature from the CAMD problem, the generated height 2 signatures based on C1(C) are shown as below:

1. C1(C2(CC))
2. C1(C2(CO))
3. C1(C3(CCO))

With this approach, the total number of generated height 2 signatures was reduced from 13 signatures to 3 signatures. In another example, taking the collection of height 2 signatures, the following set is obtained:

1. C1(C3(CCO)
2. C1(C2(CC))
3. C2(C1(C)C2(CC))
4. C2(C2(CC)C2(CC))
5. C2(C2(CC)C3(CCO))
6. C3(C1(C)C2(CC)O1(C))
7. O1(C3(CCO))

In this case, height 3 signatures generated based on the signature (3), C2(C1(C)C2(CC)) are listed as:

1. C2(C1(C2(CC))C2(C1(C)C2(CC)))
2. C2(C1(C2(CC))C2(C2(CC)C2(CC)))
3. C2(C1(C2(CC))C2(C2(CC)C3(CCO)))

2.3. Verification and Miscibility Analysis

To ensure that the molecules generated from previous steps are feasible and practical, verification step was conducted through database search from various platforms. On the other hand, phase stability test was conducted by computing the Gibbs tangent plane distance to avoid phase separation in the final solvent-oil blend.

3. Case Study

3.1. Problem Definition

The main objective of the designed solvent is to improve the physical properties of the bio-oil. Greater higher heating value (HHV) is preferable for better fuel combustion. Thus, the HHV of the designed solvent was maximized, which serves as the objective function. Table 1 summarized the constraints for each target properties identified. In this study, bio-oil derived via palm kernel shells (PKS), with moisture content of 16 wt.% and HHV of 19 MJ/kg, was used as the basis. The main components of the pyrolysis bio-oil include phenol, 2,6-dimethoxyphenol, 2-methoxyphenol, furfural, acetic acid and 1,2-benzenediol.

Based on the target properties identified, suitable property prediction models in terms of GC method and connectivity index were selected to estimate the properties of the designed solvents. In this case study, maximum signature height required in this problem was set at 4. The atoms that are commonly present in solvents (hydrogen, carbon, nitrogen, and oxygen) were chosen for the design of bio-oil solvent. The hydrocarbon groups considered in this study were limited to alkanes, alkenes, alcohol, carboxylic acid, ketones, aldehyde, esters, ethers, and nitriles which can be predominately found in solvents. Then, the molecular signatures descriptors up to height 4 were generated based on the selected atoms' type and chemical families, resulting in a total of 10,000 different molecular signature combinations. By applying the consistency rule, the signature set size was reduced to the final 21 height 4 signatures.

Table 1 Target properties and constraint for each identified product requirements.

Requirements/Needs	Targeted Properties	Constraints
Liquid state at room temperature	Normal boiling point / K	> 400.15
	Normal melting point / K	< 298.15
Combustion quality	Higher heating value	To maximize
Fuel flow consistency	Viscosity / mPa s	$1 > v > 6$
	Density / kg m^{-3}	$800 > \rho > 1000$
Environmental related properties and toxicology	Aquatic acute toxicity, LC50	> 100
	Aquatic acute toxicity, EC50	> 100
	Oral acute toxicity, LD50	> 100
	Bioconcentration factor	< 1000
	Soil-water partition coefficient / L kg^{-1}	< 31622
	Global Warming Potential	< 10
	Photochemical Oxidation Potential	< 10

3.2. Results and Discussion

Based on the database search conducted, the feasible solvent molecules were identified as 2-octanol, 2-heptanol, 2-hexanol and 2-pentanol, respectively. The higher heating value estimated in present work for the abovementioned solvent candidates were close to the actual higher heating value obtained from NIST database, with less than 1% differences. All the resulting molecules possess a higher heating value of at least 37.5 MJ/kg. It can be concluded that 2-octanol is the most suitable solvent candidate with the highest higher heating value at 40.89 MJ/kg. Figure 2 shows the Gibbs energy and tangent plot for 2-octanol and bio-oil blend. From Figure 2, the blend is stable and exhibit homogenous single-phase as the tangent line was plotted below the Gibbs curve.

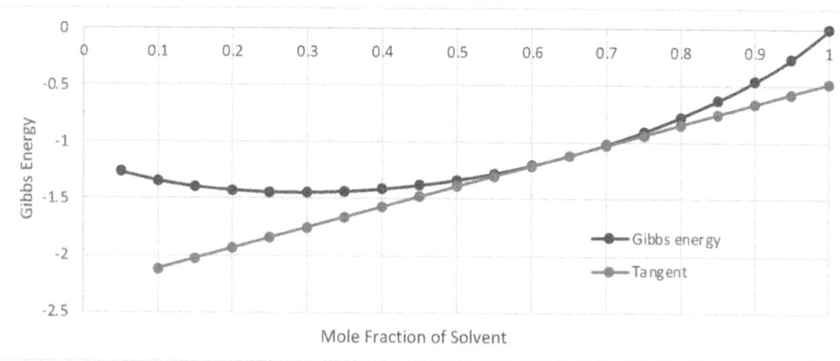

Figure 2 Gibbs energy and tangent plot for 2-octanol and bio-oil.

4. Conclusion

A multi-stage CAMD methodology was developed to design an optimal solvent that can upgrade bio-oil while possessing low environmental impact. The developed multi-stage approach was used to reduce the size of problem due to the combinatorial nature of higher-order signatures. Moreover, consistency rules were applied to ensure only relevant and consistent signatures are generated. The results from the case study shows that solvent generated can achieve good functionality while displaying promising environmental characteristics. To conclude, the developed methodology in this work can be applied in the design of molecules for any application. Further improvements can be made by considering the addition of emulsifiers and/or reactive solvents in the design of additives for bio-oil upgrading purposes.

Acknowledgements

The authors would like to express sincere gratitude to Ministry of Higher Education Malaysia for the realization of this research project under the Grant FRGS/1/2019/TK02/UNIM/02/1.

References

A.S. Hukkerikar, S. Kalakul, B. Sarup, D.M. Young, G. Sin & R. Gani, 2012, Estimation of environment-related properties of chemicals for design of sustainable processes: Development of group-contribution+ (GC +) property models and uncertainty analysis. Journal of Chemical Information and Modeling, 52(11), 2823–2839.

D.P. Visco & J.J. Chen, 2016, The Signature Molecular Descriptor in Molecular Design: Past and Current Applications. Computer Aided Chemical Engineering, 39, 315–343.

D.P. Visco, R.S. Pophale, M.D. Rintoul & J.L. Faulon, 2002, Developing a methodology for an inverse quantitative structure-activity relationship using the signature molecular descriptor. Journal of Molecular Graphics and Modelling, 20(6), 429–438.

J. Marrero & R. Gani, 2001, Group-contribution based estimation of pure component properties. Fluid Phase Equilibria, 183–208.

J.L. Faulon, D.P. Visco & R.S. Pophale, 2003, The Signature Molecular Descriptor. 1. Using Extended Valence Sequences in QSAR and QSPR Studies. Journal of Chemical Information and Computer Sciences, 43(3), 707–720.

J.W. Chong, S. Thangalazhy-Gopakumar, K. Muthoosamy & N.G. Chemmangattuvalappil, 2021, Design of bio-oil additives via molecular signature descriptors using a multi-stage computer-aided molecular design framework. Frontiers of Chemical Science and Engineering, https://doi.org/10.1007/s11705-021-2056-8.

N.D. Austin, N.V. Sahinidis & D.W. Trahan, 2016, Computer-aided molecular design: An introduction and review of tools, applications, and solution techniques. Chemical Engineering Research and Design, 116, 2–26.

N.G. Chemmangattuvalappil, & M.R. Eden, 2013, A Novel Methodology for Property-Based Molecular Design Using Multiple Topological Indices. Industrial & Engineering Chemistry Research, 52(22), 7090–7103.

Proceedings of the 14th International Symposium on Process Systems Engineering – PSE 2021+
June 19-23, 2022, Kyoto, Japan
http://dx.doi.org/10.1016/B978-0-323-85159-6.50034-8

Synthesis of azeotropic distillation processes without using a decanter

J. Rafael Alcántara-Avila*, Maho Okunishi, Shinji Hasebe

Department of Chemical Engineering, Kyoto University, Katsura Campus Nishikyo-ku, Kyoto 615-8510, Japan
jrafael@cheme.kyoto-u.ac.jp

Abstract

This work presents a synthesis method for deriving distillation process structures to separate a ternary mixture with a homogeneous azeotrope. First, the liquid composition space is divided into small subspaces, each of which is assigned to a distillation module. Then, all of the connections among the heating, cooling, feed, product, and distillation modules are contained in a superstructure. The relations expressed in the superstructure are mathematically reformulated as a linear programming problem in which the utility cost is minimized. The optimal solution shows the connection between modules that indicates the best structure. The optimal solution is interpreted and translated to a feasible and realistic distillation process at a post-optimization step.

The proposed method is applied to the separation problem of the mixture of acetone, chloroform, and benzene. The optimization result shows that the direct sequence of two columns is a possible candidate for the optimal structure. Moreover, this structure is derived without assigning any *a priori* knowledge of the process structure.

Keywords: Process Synthesis, Azeotropic Distillation, Process Optimization

1. Introduction

Distillation is the most widely used technique to separate liquid mixtures. However, it uses large amounts of energy because the vaporization of liquid streams is inevitable. Although distillation research is often regarded as a mature area, new design and/or operation discoveries renew the interest in distillation because such improvements can translate into huge economic benefits (Caballero and Grossmann, 2013).

Li, Demirel, and Hasan (2019) proposed a block-based phenomena methodology for the synthesis of distillation processes. The blocks with phase and material assignment assemble to represent various phenomena (e.g., mixing, reaction, phase contact, and phase transitions), which are typical in distillation processes. These blocks can connect to represent various distillation processes, including single columns, dividing wall columns, and reactive distillation columns. Although an MINLP formulation was presented, the proposed methodology can generate intensified distillation processes without any *a priori* enumeration of candidate distillation processes. The separation of a ternary zeotropic mixture was taken up as a case study, and the optimization result showed that the dividing wall column (DWC) was the best process.

Takase and Hasebe (2015) proposed a synthesis method for the separation of a ternary mixture. In their method, the composition space was discretized, and each discretized subspace was assigned to a distillation module. For each module, the liquid and vapor compositions and their molar enthalpies are uniquely determined. Thus, the synthesis problem was formulated as a linear programming (LP) problem. The vapor and liquid flow rates among modules were treated as optimization variables. The case study problem showed that the DWC was the best process to minimize operating costs.

It is known that even though a distillation boundary exists, in some cases, it is possible to separate a ternary mixture by using simple distillation columns (Biegler, Grossmann and Westerberg, 1997). The method proposed by Takase and Hasebe (2015) was applied to separating a ternary zeotropic mixture. However, this research extends their method because it considers separating a ternary mixture with an azeotrope and a distillation boundary. Thus, the separation is more difficult because a distillation boundary divides the composition space into two distillation regions.

2. Problem Statement

In this work, the synthesis problem for the separation of a ternary mixture containing a homogeneous azeotrope, based on the following assumptions, is formulated:

1. The ternary mixture forms a homogeneous azeotrope.
2. The feed is saturated liquid, and its flow rate and composition are given in advance.
3. All products are withdrawn as saturated liquids, and the purity specification of each product is given in advance as the lower bound of its key component.
4. The operating pressure is given in advance, and the pressure drop is negligible.
5. The process is at a steady-state.
6. The vapor leaving from a distillation stage is in equilibrium with the liquid on that stage.
7. Utility costs per unit amount of heating and cooling are given in advance.

Under these assumptions, the optimal process is derived without any structural assumption. The state-space discretization used in the IDEAS approach is adopted to formulate the material and heat balance equations (Drake and Manousiouthakis, 2002). A stage in any distillation column is treated as a distillation module. All possible flow connections among these modules are considered. Figure 1 represents the superstructure for the connections among modules.

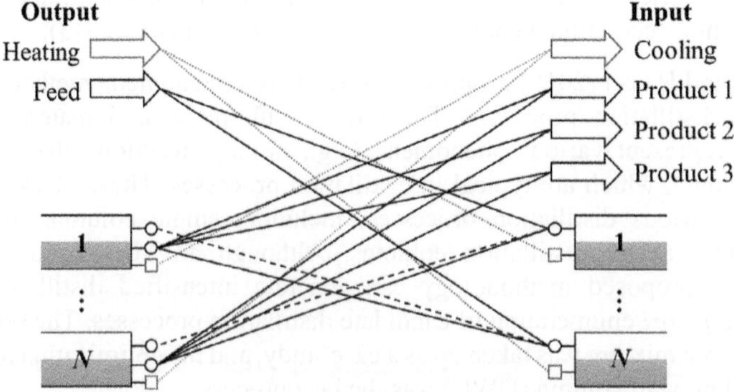

Figure 1. Superstructure representation for the separation of a ternary mixture

The squares numbered from 1 to N represent each distillation module. Each distillation module is further divided into input and output parts in which the same number is assigned.

Products 1 to 3 have only input flows, and the feed has only output flows. The heating and cooling utilities are also treated as modules. The solid, dashed, and dotted lines between modules represent feasible paths of liquid flows, vapor flows, and heat, respectively.

The proposed superstructure allows liquid and vapor flows among all distillation modules. The feed can be supplied to any distillation module. Each product module can accept liquid flows from any distillation module. Furthermore, heating and cooling are allowed in any distillation module.

3. Mathematical formulation

Based on the superstructure in Figure 1, the optimization problem which aims to minimize the utility cost (UC) is formulated by Eq. (1) to Eq. (6). Since the utility cost is the most relevant cost in distillation, the UC minimization is a valid assumption. Moreover, this research aims to derive novel distillation structures that do not depend on *any a priori* structural assumption rather than optimizing a predefined distillation structure.

Eq. (1) shows the objective function, Eq. (2) to Eq. (4) represent the material balance at each module, Eq. (5) represents the energy balance at each module, and Eq. (6) represents the purity constraint on each product

$$UC = \sum_{i \in S_M} (c_H Q_i^H + c_C Q_i^C) \tag{1}$$

$$\sum_{i \in S_M} L_{Fi} - L^F = 0 \tag{2}$$

$$\sum_{j \in S_M} (L_{ji} + V_{ji}) + L_{Fi} - \sum_{j \in S_M} (L_{ij} + V_{ij}) - \sum_{p \in S_P} L_{ip}^P = 0 \qquad i \in S_M \tag{3}$$

$$\begin{aligned} \sum_{j \in S_M} (L_{ji} x_{jk} + V_{ji} y_{jk}) + L_{Fi} x_k^F - \sum_{j \in S_M} (L_{ij} x_{ik} + V_{ij} y_{ik}) - \sum_{p \in S_P} L_{ip}^P x_{ik} \\ = 0 \qquad i \in S_M, k = 1,2 \end{aligned} \tag{4}$$

$$\begin{aligned} \sum_{j \in S_M} (L_{ji} h_j^L + V_{ji} h_j^V) + L_{Fi} h^F + Q_i^H - \sum_{j \in S_M} (L_{ij} h_i^L + V_{ij} h_i^V) - \sum_{p \in S_P} L_{ip}^P h_i^L \\ - Q_i^C = 0 \qquad i \in S_M \end{aligned} \tag{5}$$

$$x_k^P \sum_{j \in S_M} L_{jk}^P - \sum_{j \in S_M} L_{jk}^P x_{jk} \geq 0 \qquad k = 1,2,3 \tag{6}$$

where S_M and S_P are the sets of distillation module numbers and product numbers, respectively. c_H and c_C are the heating and cooling costs per unit amount of energy. Q_i^H and Q_i^C are the amounts of heat supply and removal at distillation module i. L_{Fi} is the feed liquid flow rate entering to module i and L^F is the feed flow rate. L_{ji} and V_{ji} are the liquid and vapor flow rates from module i to module j, respectively. L_{ip}^{P} is the liquid flow rate from module i to product p. x_{jk} and y_{jk} are molar fractions of the kth component in the liquid and vapor at module j, respectively. x_k^F is the molar fraction of the kth component in the feed stream. h_j^L and h_j^V are liquid and vapor molar enthalpy at module j. It is assumed that the purity specification of product k is given as the lower bound of the molar fraction of kth component and is given by x_k^P.

Eq. (1) to (6) are linear equations and inequalities for the optimization variables. Therefore, the optimization problem can be formulated as a linear programming (LP) problem. In plotting the result on a ternary distillation diagram, it is possible to recognize how the separation of the mixture with a distillation boundary is performed (Królikowski *et al.*, 2011). The result shown on the ternary distillation diagram is used to find the plausible process structure.

4. Case Study

The separation of acetone, chloroform, and benzene was taken as a case study (Biegler, Grossmann and Westerberg, 1997). The feed composition was 35 mol% of acetone, 25 mol% of chloroform, and 40 mol% of benzene, while the product specifications were 90 mol% for each product. This mixture forms a maximum temperature azeotrope between acetone and chloroform. The ternary diagram is separated into two distillation regions by a distillation boundary. The feed flow rate is 120 kmol/h, and the heating and cooling costs are 10 GJ/$ and 0.5 GJ/$, respectively. The NRTL method in Aspen HYSYS® V9 was used to estimate the physical properties.

5. Results and Discussions

5.1. Reference designs

Figure 2 shows the reference designs that meet the target 90 mol% compositions for all products. The designs were simulated in HYSYS® V9 for the sake of comparison. Design 1 has 50 stages in the first column (C1) and 60 stages in the second column (C2), while Design 2 has 45 stages in C1 and 50 stages in C2. The liquid composition profile of each design is shown in Figure 3. The utility cost for Design 1 was 130.60 $/h, while that for Design 2 was 152.20 $/h.

5.2. Optimization results

The composition space was discretized in increments of 0.025, and each discretized composition represents a subspace assigned to a distillation module. However, near the distillation boundary and above a benzene composition of 0.7, the composition space was discretized with increments of 0.005. As a result, 2,700 distillation modules were placed on the ternary composition diagram. Figure 4 shows the liquid flows between distillation modules obtained by solving the optimization problem. The squares in the figure represent the modules with liquid flows above 5 kmol/h, and the coordinates of each square represent the liquid composition assigned to the module. The solid grey lines represent the selected liquid path. The solid red squares near the benzene product mean that heating is necessary at each of those modules. In contrast, the solid blue squares near the acetone and chloroform products mean that cooling is needed. The utility cost was 129.3 \$/h, which is slightly lower than that of Design 1.

Since the composition space is discretized, the obtained process includes many secondary flows of small flow rate among the modules. However, extracting the dominant flows from the result shown in Figure 4 makes it possible to construct a simple and efficient process structure. In this case, the dominant flow paths in Figure 4 are similar to those in Figure 3. Thus, it can be said that the structure in Figure 2 is close to the optimal structure. As a result, the optimal structure's utility cost is close to that of Design 1. Though a new process structure was not created, the process structure was derived without inputting the structure information.

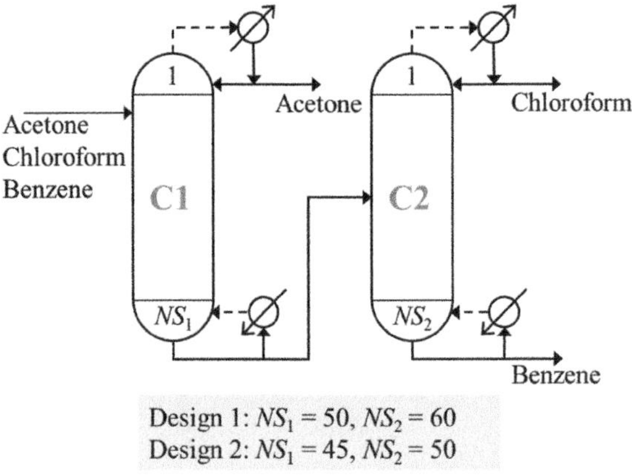

Figure 2. Reference designs

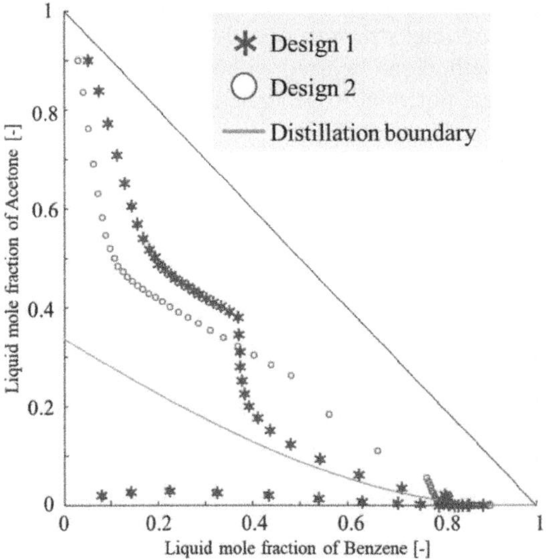

Figure 3. Liquid composition profile for each reference design

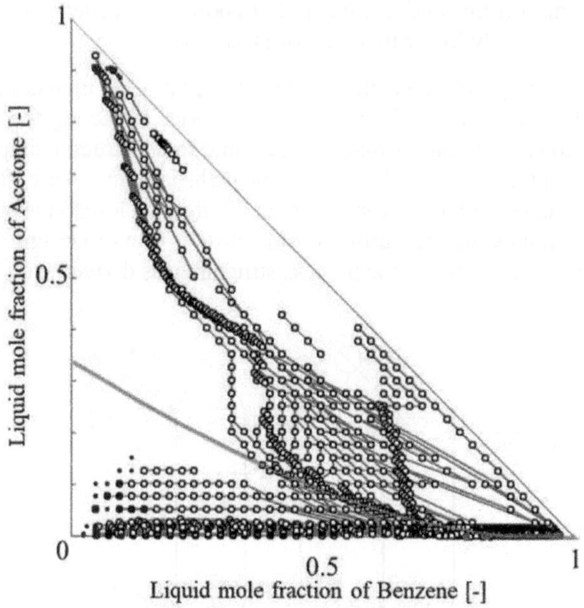

Figure 4. Liquid composition profile of the optimization result

6. Conclusions

A module-based synthesis method using the IDEAS approach was proposed for the separation of homogeneous azeotropic mixtures, which did not require a decanter. The method was applied to the separation problem of acetone, chloroform, and benzene, and the result showed that the optimal structure was close to the structure known as a direct sequence. The proposed method can be used without assuming the process structure in advance. Thus, it has a great potential to generate an original process structure that has not been used in the existing chemical plants.

References

Biegler, L. T., Grossmann, I. E. and Westerberg, A. W. (1997) *Systematic Methods of Chemical Process Design*. Prentice Hall.

Caballero, J. A. and Grossmann, I. E. (2013) 'Synthesis of Complex Thermally Coupled Distillation Systems Including Divided Wall Columns', *AIChE Journal*, 59(4), pp. 1139–1159.

Drake, J. E. and Manousiouthakis, V. (2002) 'IDEAS approach to process network synthesis: minimum utility cost for complex distillation networks', *Chemical Engineering Science*, 57, pp. 3095–3106.

Królikowski, A. R., Królikowski, L. J. and Wasylkiewicz, S. K. (2011) 'Distillation profiles in ternary heterogeneous mixtures with distillation boundaries', *Chemical Engineering Research and Design*, 89(7), pp. 879–893.

Li, J., Demirel, S. E. and Hasan, M. M. F. (2019) 'Systematic Process Intensification involving Zeotropic Distillation', *Computer Aided Chemical Engineering*, 47, pp. 421–426.

Takase, H. and Hasebe, S. (2015) 'Optimal Structure Synthesis of Ternary Distillation System', in *Computer Aided Chemical Engineering*. Elsevier B.V., pp. 1097–1102.

Proceedings of the 14th International Symposium on Process Systems Engineering – PSE 2021+
June 19-23, 2022, Kyoto, Japan
http://dx.doi.org/10.1016/B978-0-323-85159-6.50035-X

Reduce Environmental Impact and Carbon Footprint for Cost Competitive Process Plant Design: Integrating AVEVA™ Process Simulation with modeFRONTIER®

Yutaka Yamada[a*], Simone Genovese[b], Cal Depew[c], Ralph Cos[d], Hiroshi Kuwahara[e] and Taiga Inoue[f]

[a]*Product Development, AVEVA, Tokyo, 108-0023, JAPAN*
[b]*Project Management, ESTECO, Trieste 99 - 34149, ITALY*
[c]*Director, AVEVA, Lake Forest 92630, USA*
[d]*Principal SW Development, AVEVA, Garching 85748, Germany*
[e,f]*Simulation Technology, IDAJ, Kanagawa 220-8137, JAPAN*
yutaka.yamada@aveva.com

Abstract

There is a significant need in chemical and petrochemical industries for process synthesis tools to identify cost-competitive processes with low greenhouse gas emissions and environmental impact compared to existing designs, based on process-wide multi-objective optimization. Deadlines and human resources usually constrain the design process; however, only single-objective optimization for individual units is usually considered. To extend the optimization scope, AVEVA™ Process Simulation can be coupled with the multi-objective optimization software modeFRONTIER®. The integrated system allows solving multi-objective problems in a short time. This study demonstrates how a given industrial process can be optimized, ensuring stable and robust operation at low total annual cost (TAC) while reducing idle time and outperforming manual work. The proposed methodology is demonstrated using a case study of an ethanol distillation process plant. Designers and consultants can use this methodology to aid decision-makers in the design phase to identify robust, low-cost designs that deliver preferred performance in terms of environmental impact in the future operation.

Keywords: Multi-objective Optimization; Process Design; Process Simulation.

1. Introduction

Globally, governments are starting to impose regulations on greenhouse gas emission in addition to the existing regulations on water, and toxic pollution. Manufacturers are looking to make their operations greener and simulation can assist companies in their pursuit of greener production. Generative design, an iterative design process that uses simulation and machine-learning to mimic nature's evolutionary approach to design, offers the potential to boost sustainability across the manufacturing industry. Until now, generative design has been used primarily to optimize products, such as reducing the mass of products or costs while preserving functionalities. Currently generative design has shown capability and versatility to provide benefits in other applications, succeeding, for example, in construction industry's new challenges. This study will investigate if Generative Design has the potential ability to redesign larger manufacturing systems entirely. It must be emphasized that an ideal plant that is at the same time efficient, cost-effective, environment-friendly, and risk-free is hard to achieve. There are always some necessary trade-offs to be made to ensure optimal use of energy resources while limiting environmental, health impacts or operability as shown by L. Gerber (L. Gerber et al., 2013) or B. Brent (B. Brent et al., 2020).

When the fluid includes the azeotropic components and recycles, it's hard to determine the optimum design for total number of trays, feed stages, recycle flow rate, reflux ratio, operating pressures and heating/cooling medium. Also the detailed engineering data associated with unit operations are necessary to estimate operating, equipment costs and environmental burden. In this project, AVEVA™ Process Simulation has been used as the first-principles simulation tool that has the flexibility to change various specification and the functionality to calculate the COD (Chemical Oxygen Demand) in the wastewater (environmental load), the Capital Cost(CapEx), Operating Costs (OpEx) and Greenhouse gas (GHG) emissions. To support this design process, to get a better understanding of the model itself, and to reduce the number of evaluations to find the optimal solution, it has been coupled with modeFRONTIER, the desktop solution for process automation and optimization in the engineering design process.

2. Simulation model and Design condition

2.1. Base model for the case study

The separation of ethanol and water is complex because of the existence of azeotrope; several distillation sequences are described in the book of Seader (Seader et al., 2010). The distillation feed mixture is composed of 90% water and 10% ethanol. In this study, following the most common and classic distillation method, three-column sequences using benzene as entrainer have been selected. The first column, Preconcentrator concentrates most of the ethanol from the feed. From the bottom of the second column, Azeotropic column, ethanol with more than 99% purity is produced. The overhead of the azeotropic column is condensed and decanted. The effluent with a high concentration of entrainment and ethanol is recycled to the Azeotropic column with the fresh benzene as reflux from the L1 phase. The water-rich phase is sent to the Entrainer Recovery column. The third column, the Entrainer Recovery column, recovers the entrainer and ethanol from the overhead and recycles them to the Azeotropic column. The distillation processes were simulated in AVEVA Process Simulation software using NRTL physical property model with the default binary parameters.

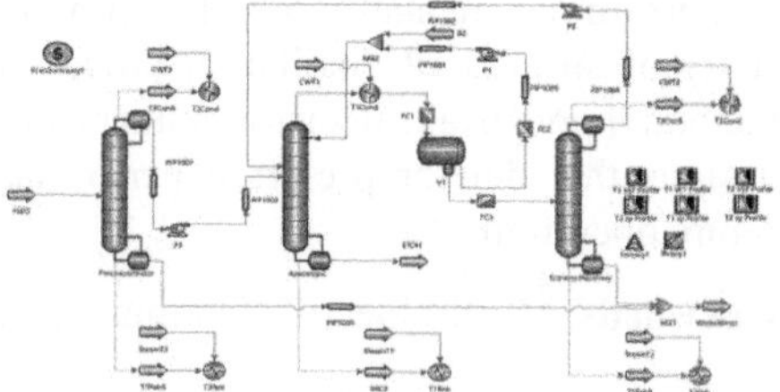

Figure 1: Flowsheet of the entire ethanol distillation process

2.2. Design conditions summary

The column diameter is set to keep the flooding factor = 0.7 and the height for each stage is fixed as 0.59m. The flooding factor is calculated using the Fair correlations. The Sieve tray is selected as the internals of the columns. The column efficiency is set as 0.6. Cooling water return temperature is set as 45C and U value is set as 1,000kcal/h-m2-K for all condenser. Steam outlet vapor fraction is set as 0 and U value is set as 5,000 kcal/h-m2-K for all reboiler. Counterflow heat exchange was applied for all heat exchanger. Pump efficiency is set as 0.7 and the elevation of each reflux drum is set as 10m for all pumps. The pipe length for the suction and discharge of the pump is set as

20m and the velocity is set as 2m/s for the liquid line. The preconcentrator column design condition is separately done from the entire optimization by creating NQ-curve using Python API because there are no recycles to this column. The Azeotropic column and the EntrainerRecovery column conditions are designed using modeFRONTIER as mentioned in section 4.3.

3. Objective function

3.1. Environmental impact

The environmental load is evaluated by the concentration of ethanol in the wastewater. In particular, the measure used to evaluate such concentration is the COD. Many governments impose strict regulations regarding the maximum chemical oxygen demand allowed in wastewater before it can be returned to the environment. For example, in Japan , a maximum oxygen demand of 160mg/l must be reached before wastewater or industrial water can be returned to the environment due to the Water Pollution Prevention Act. COD of the ethanol can be considered as 2.09 g COD/g ethanol from the following reaction: $C_2H_6O + 3O_2 \rightarrow 2CO_2 + 3H_2O$. The equation to calculate COD is implemented as a flowsheet equation.

3.2. Total annual cost (TAC)

AVEVA™ Process Simulation has the functionality to add the cost estimate model to each unit. The operational cost is based on the paper by Ulrich (Ulrich et al., 2006) as shown below. Each cost depends on two utility-specify coefficients (a, b), the current CEPCI, and $C_{s,f}$ (the cost of fuel in \$/GJ).

$$C_{S,u} = a(CEPCI) + b(C_{S,f}) \tag{1}$$

The price is based on the 2019 CEPCI (607.5) and the average wholesale price of No. 2 fuel oil in 2019 for the United States (\$12.83/GJ). Benzene cost is taken from 2015 ICIS. Operation time is considered as 8000hr/year. Installed cost is calculated based on the below equation from the book of James (James et al., 1988). As reported on Ethanol Producer Magazine (http://www.ethanolproducer.com), ethanol plants require stainless steel (SS) for most of the equipment hence it has been used for the cost calculations.

$$(Installed\ cost, \$) = C\left(\frac{M\&S}{280}\right)H^{n1}D^{n2}A^{n3}F_T \tag{2}$$

M&S index is calculated based on the below equation from the book of Zacharias (Zacharias et al., 2007).

$$M\&S = 1250 + 25(Year - 2005) \tag{3}$$

With SI units, the following equation is used for the cost of the column, internals, and heat exchanger.

$$(Column\ cost, \$) = (957.904)\left(\frac{M\&S}{280}\right)H^{0.802}D^{1.066}(2.18 + F_mF_p) \tag{4}$$

$$(Internal\ cost, \$) = (97.243)\left(\frac{M\&S}{280}\right)H^{1}D^{1.55}(F_s + F_t + F_m) \tag{5}$$

$$(HeatExchanger\ cost, \$) = (474.67)\left(\frac{M\&S}{280}\right)A^{0.65}(2.29 + (F_d + F_p)F_m) \quad (6)$$

The cost for the piping, electrical, buildings, and indirect costs are considered as double of the installed costs based on the rule of thumb. The wastewater treatment is not included in this cost model because the COD in the wastewater will be controlled to be under the regulation. The above equations are all included in the equipment cost submodel. The Total Annualized Cost (TAC) is calculated as a function of an annualized form of total capital cost in three years and the total operating cost. Cost escalation, interest, location factor is not considered here.

4. Optimization-driven design

4.1. Design exploration

Design Space Exploration is the process of finding a design solution (unique combinations of the settings of the independent variables) or solutions that best meet the desired design requirements from a space of tentative design points. One of the difficulties of the distillation process, especially azeotropic distillation process, is due to its high nonlinearity and number of variables to be considered. It's difficult to find the optimal number of stages, feed stage, reflux/boilup ratio and recycle flow rate as there are no analytical solutions. Also trying to analyse every possible design requires millions of case studies. This is a time-consuming method and due to the shortage of engineer's time, the case studies are usually stopped far before it gets the best solution. Process automation and machine learning algorithms are required to obtain optimal solutions with minimum computation and time. In this context, the engineer's know-how is fundamental while modeFRONTIER advanced data analysis and visualization tools allow to turn data into valuable insights and pick the best design solution.

4.2. Process Automation

To leverage modeFRONTIER's Machine Learning algorithms to optimize the process parameters in order to reduce the waste and the cost, an interface between the process simulation software AVEVA™ Process Simulation and modeFRONTIER® has been developed. The integration uses Python and communicates directly to AVEVA™ Process Simulation thanks to native Python APIs.

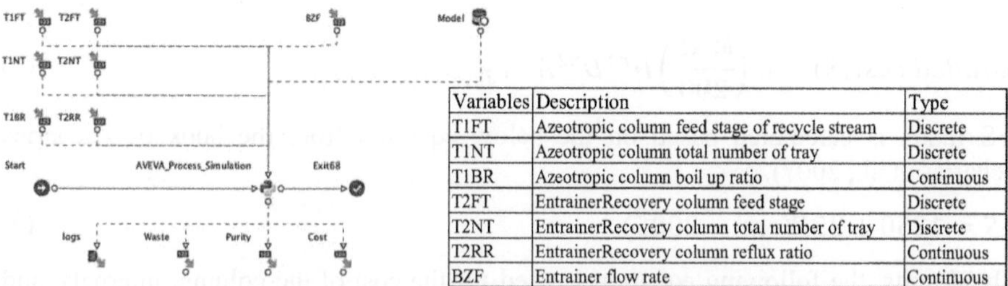

Variables	Description	Type
T1FT	Azeotropic column feed stage of recycle stream	Discrete
T1NT	Azeotropic column total number of tray	Discrete
T1BR	Azeotropic column boil up ratio	Continuous
T2FT	EntrainerRecovery column feed stage	Discrete
T2NT	EntrainerRecovery column total number of tray	Discrete
T2RR	EntrainerRecovery column reflux ratio	Continuous
BZF	Entrainer flow rate	Continuous

Figure 2: Workflow created by modeFRONTIER® and the input variables table

The studied model has seven Input variables and eight Output Variables. Increasing the recycle flow rate raises the product purity. On the other hand, it will cause a higher pump power consumption and the need for pipes with bigger diameters so TAC goes to increase. Increasing the number of stages, feed stage, and reflux/boil-up ratio improves product purity, but the CapEx and OpEx increase. So the trade-off relation between the wastewater, product purity and TAC can be expected by changing the above variables.

5. Case Study

5.1. Preliminary investigation using pilOPT

As a preliminary study, 400 case study using Uniform Latin Hypercube DOE(Design of Experiments) and 100 case study using pilOPT, autonomous optimization alogrithm, is done to explore the relatively wide range of the design space. This work provides some insight into this process optimization like the minimum T1BR, sensitivity of T1FT.

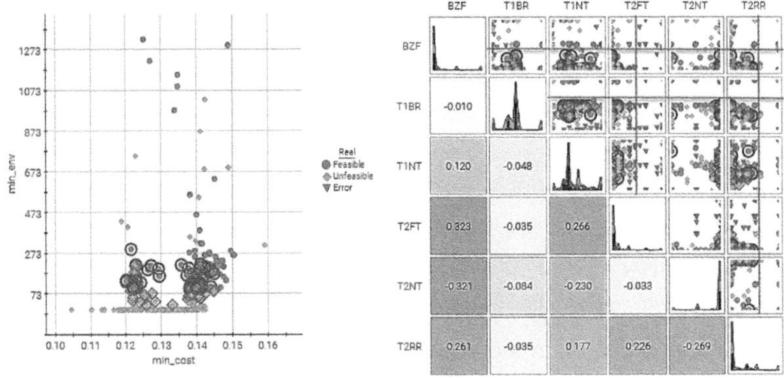

Figure 3: Scatter Matrix chart on Input Variables

5.2. Detailed study based on the above study

In order to reduce the domain of Input Variables, in the output domain, the designs of the most promising region, have been selected and this allowed to highlight their distribution in the space of inputs (Figure.3 Scatter Matrix chart on the right). From this study, the design space is narrowed down, shrinking the Upper Bound of T1BR and T2FT Variable. Few designs from the Pareto Front of this initial study have been selected and used as DOE for a second phase of optimization. Given the high nonlinearity of the model a Genetic Algorithm has been adopted. To speed up the optimization, we leveraged on two AVEVA™ Process Simulation running in parallel under the control of the same MOGA-II genetic algorithm. To run 900 designs it took little more than 25 hours and the resulting Pareto Front is visible at figure 4.

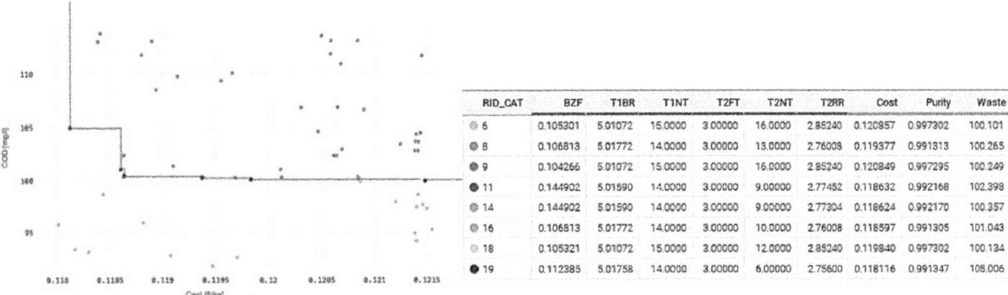

RID_CAT	BZF	T1BR	T1NT	T2FT	T2NT	T2RR	Cost	Purity	Waste
6	0.105301	5.01072	15.0000	3.00000	16.0000	2.85240	0.120857	0.997302	100.101
8	0.106813	5.01772	14.0000	3.00000	13.0000	2.76008	0.119377	0.991313	100.265
9	0.104266	5.01072	15.0000	3.00000	16.0000	2.85240	0.120849	0.997295	100.249
11	0.144902	5.01590	14.0000	3.00000	9.00000	2.77452	0.118632	0.992168	102.398
14	0.144902	5.01590	14.0000	3.00000	9.00000	2.77304	0.118624	0.992170	100.357
16	0.106813	5.01772	14.0000	3.00000	10.0000	2.76008	0.118597	0.991305	101.043
18	0.105321	5.01072	15.0000	3.00000	12.0000	2.85240	0.119840	0.997302	100.134
19	0.112385	5.01758	14.0000	3.00000	6.00000	2.75600	0.118116	0.991347	105.006

Figure 4: MOGA-II Pareto Front

6. Result

The Generative design approach produced a Pareto Front composed of eight designs (Figure.5), with a difference of ~3$/ton of produced ethanol between the minimum and maximum waste options. For each of these nominal designs (Figure. 4), to validate the robustness of each solution, a cloud of "Robust Designs" that follow a Gaussian distribution around the nominal design, has been generated automatically by modeFRONTIER® and validated with AVEVA™ Process Simulation.

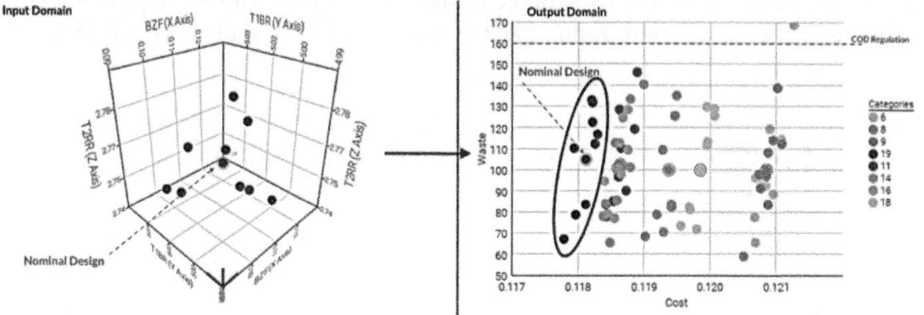

Figure 5: Robust design analysis

The result visible from Figure.5 is that even if very small noise is applied to BZF, T2RR and T1BR, it causes high variation in the Waste, while Cost and Purity are not affected so much. In particular, Design N. 6 has one Robust Design that reaches COD = 168 that is clearly out of regulation. Decision-makers should reject this design and select the N.19 instead that seems less sensitive to noise.

7. Conclusions

We have seen that several charts generated by modeFRONTIER® give some insights about the direction of the design and reduce the execution time of a parametric study thanks to its algorithms. Moreover, modeFRONTIER® identified several good designs that satisfy constraints and reduce environmental impact and total annual cost (TAC). We could reduce the COD by ~56% and the Cost of 21% with respect to the rough baseline design in just a few days. Furthermore, the project demonstrated that among several possible solutions feasible in a deterministic way, some of them may not satisfy requirements when considering noise affecting input variables. A probabilistic analysis helped to reject one of the eight designs present in the Pareto Front.

References

James Merrill Douglas, 1988, Conceptual Design of Chemical Processes, McGraw-Hill, 568-77

Ulrich, G.D.,Vasudevan, P.T., 2006, How to Estimate Utility Costs, Chemical Engineering, 66-69

Zacharias B. Maroulis, George D. Saravacos, 2007, Food Plant Economics, CRC Press, 95-97

L. Gerber, S. Fazlollahi, F. Maréchal, 2013, A systematic methodology for the environomic design and synthesis of energy systems combining process integration, Life Cycle Assessment and industrial ecology, Computers & Chemical Engineering, 59, 2-16

Brent Bishop and Fernando V. Lima, 2020, Modeling, simulation, and operability analysis of a nonisothermal, countercurrent, polymer membrane reactor, Processes, 8(1), 78

J. D. Seader, Ernest J. Henley, D. Keith Roper, 2010, Separation Process Principles with Applications using Process Simulators, Willey, 343-351

Proceedings of the 14th International Symposium on Process Systems Engineering – PSE 2021+
June 19-23, 2022, Kyoto, Japan
http://dx.doi.org/10.1016/B978-0-323-85159-6.50036-1

Reliability incorporated optimal process pathway selection for sustainable microalgae-based biorefinery system: P-graph approach

Juin Yau Lim[a], Akos Orosz[b], Bing Shen How[c], Ferenc Friedler[d], and ChangKyoo Yoo[a,*]

[a] *Integrated Engineering, Department of Environmental Science and Engineering, College of Engineering, Kyung Hee University, Republic of Korea*
[b] *Department of Computer Science and Systems Technology, Faculty of Information Technology, University of Pannonia, Hungary*
[c] *Biomass Waste-to-Wealth Special Interest Group, Faculty of Engineering, Computing and Science, Swinburne University of Technology, Jalan Simpang Tiga, 93350 Kuching, Sarawak Malaysia*
[d] *Széchenyi István University, H-9026 Győr, Egyetem tér 1, Hungary*
ckyoo@khu.ac.kr

Abstract

Biofuel from microalgae is one of the promising solutions on addressing climate change by its possibility of reducing the fossil fuel dependency. Till-date, the overall competitiveness of microalgae based biorefinery is the major concern due to its unique operational mechanism, especially the biological growth of microalgae that fluctuates towards the surrounding. Therefore, a novel graph-theoretic approach has been proposed to provide an optimization approach for identifying optimal process design with the consideration of three aspects that includes: economic, environmental, and reliability. The optimization is conducted using P-graph (a powerful graph-theoretic tool) which is capable to determine optimal and near-optimal solutions based on three objective functions: (i) minimizing annual operating cost, (ii) minimizing potential environmental impact, and (iii) maximizing reliability of process. The pool of feasible solutions (optimal and near-optimal) is obtained by satisfying the constraints on both greenhouse gas emissions and its respective reliability along. Thereupon, a further analysis was carried out with the aid of TOPSIS considering three of the assessment aspects to identify the optimal microalgae biorefinery configuration

Keywords: Optimization, Reliability, Microalgae biorefinery, Climate Change, P-graph

1. Introduction

Exponential growth of the worldwide population has led to the urge on exploring sufficient energy sources to suppress the effect of energy droughts that would bring negative impact on the evolution of human civilization. Till-date, the main energy supplies are still dominated by fossil-fuel based energy sources which are depleting at an unaccountable pace. One of the promising solutions on addressing such is by increasing the portion of renewable energy shares in the energy supplies. Among the conventional renewable energy sources, solar and wind energy have been recognized as the most promising alternative energy supplies that could be harvested from the nature. However, one of the critical issues reported with the aforementioned conventional renewable energy sources is the intermittency in providing stable energy as it is highly dependent on the weather condition at the particular location where harvesting facilities are installed. Biofuel, which is another type of renewable energy that has received attention due to its similar calorific value while compared to mineral diesel and is further validated with its compatibility in ignition engine. Common biofuel production is involved with the crops and lignocellulosic biomass in agricultural activities which are categorized as 1st and 2nd generation biofuels, respectively. Yet, both input source of biofuel generation has the known issue of food security (1st generation) and extra processing steps are required for the lignocellulosic biomass (2nd generation).

Microalgae-based biofuel, which is known as the third-generation biofuels, are gaining its popularity especially with its capability in supplying lipids that is essential for producing biofuel *via* microalgae cultivation. A good cultivation condition (i.e., sunlight, nutrient, pH, and salinity) is expected for the microalgae cultivation to maximize the lipid content that is essential in producing biofuel. In norm, the monocultures of microalgae are used in practice where the species with high lipid content is preferable such as the *Chlorella vulgaris* that is commonly used in the industry as it has been reported with 40% to 53% of dry weight lipid content. However, the monocultures of certain microalgae species are often reported with extensive operational cost especially in maintaining the surrounding condition and preventing the cultivation farm from contamination. Therefore, the co-culturing of microalgae is more favourable as it allows the existence of multiple strains at one time by allowing healthy symbiotic relationship among species. Such cultivation strategy has been proven with the capability in enhancing biofuel production as the amount of biomass from cultivation are reported with significant enhancement.

Apart from the microalgae cultivation, a series of biorefinery process is required to upgrade the biomass harvested from the cultivation farm such as pre-treatment, lipid extraction, upgrade, and post-treatment. Due to the intensive energy requirement on producing biofuel, a proper process selection for the microalgae biorefinery is essential to ensure the overall sustainability on producing the biofuel. Herein, an extensive work was proposed to identify the optimal configuration for the biorefinery considering the aspects of economic, environment, and reliability in a single stage optimization framework. An optimization framework is developed to address the aim of this study with P-graph. The graphical aided optimization tool - P-graph is originally developed to solve the problem involving process network synthesis (PNS) alongside on providing a series of near-optimal solutions that is essential in decision making. Till recent, an innovative modification to the algorithm of P-graph was successfully proposed and implemented by Kovacs et al., (2019) which aims to solve the problem of process design with the consideration of its reliability simultaneously. Such reliability incorporated P-graph will be extensively implemented on the process design of microalgae biorefinery considering economic, environment, and reliability.

2. Methodology

A brief superstructure optimization framework targeted on proposing an optimal process configuration for microalgae biorefinery that considers economic, environment, and reliability aspects as shown in Figure 1. The raw material i required for certain process technology j in process stage k along with the final product m are identified accordingly. P-graph tool were originally developed to identify economical feasible solution of the problem declared and further providing a ranking of all feasible pool of solutions. Yet, certain modifications could be made to address the desired assessment criteria on the problem. In such, Lim et al., (2021) has proposed a novel fertilizer selection with the aid of P-graph in consideration of the economic, environmental, and health aspects by aligning certain configuration towards the desired evaluation metrics. Similarly, a configuration was made to assess the economic and environmental aspects of the process configuration proposed alongside with the modification towards the P-graph algorithm by incorporating the reliability assessment which was firstly proposed by Kovacs et al., (2019).

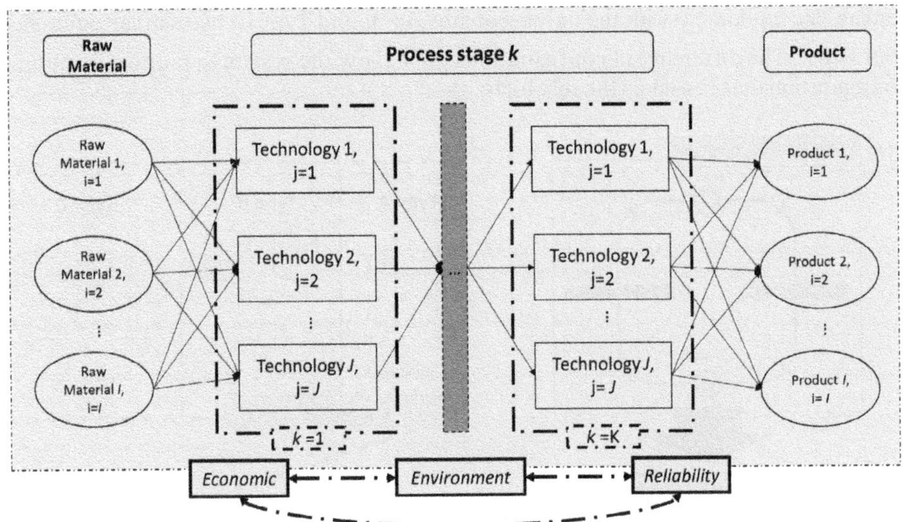

Figure 1. Microalgae process technology selection *via* superstructure optimization considering economic, environmental, and reliability aspects.

The objective function is expressed by minimizing the annual operating cost, *AOC* required for the process (See Eq. (1)) considering the required raw materials (RC_i) and the utility ($U_{n,j,k}$) alongside with its respective cost of materials (RC_i) and utility (UC_n). Whereas the greenhouse gas emissions, *GHG* was assessed similarly based on Eq. (2) in terms of materials and utility used with its respective emission factor of RGF_i, and GFU_n.

$$Min\ TAC = \sum_{i,j,k}(RC_i \times F_{i,j,k}) + \sum_{n,j,k}(UC_n \times U_{n,j,k}) + \sum_{i,j,k}(EC_{i,j,k} \times F_{i,j,k}) \quad (1)$$

$$GHG = \sum_{i,j,k}(RGF_i \times F_{i,j,k}) + \sum_{n,j,k}(GFU_n \times U_{n,j,k}) \quad (2)$$

Reliability analysis of the solutions is incorporated through the P-graph-based method given by Kovacs et al., (2019). The reliability formula, given by Eq (3), determines the $\hat{r}$ reliability from the reliabilities of the operations (p_n), where U represents the operational subnetworks in the solution, and x_n, the state of a unit.

$$\hat{r} = \sum_{(x_1,x_2,\ldots,x_N)\in U}\left(\prod_{n=1}^{N} p_n{}^{x_n}(1-p_n)^{(1-x_n)}\right) \quad (3)$$

3. Development of P-graph model

The configuration of a generic superstructure optimization is demonstrated in Figure 2(a) for selecting feasible processes among two different technology. As previously mentioned, the reliability assessment has been incorporated into the P-graph which a new configuration on such modification is displayed in Figure 2(b). Herein, three different types of process configuration were considered for the specific technology that avail for the selection. Type A: a single equipment with the size x is considered, Type B: three similar size equipment with the halving of size A ($\frac{x}{2}$), and Type C: two similar equipment with size x. The difference in configuration could allow the system to propose an optimal configuration that considers the reliability.

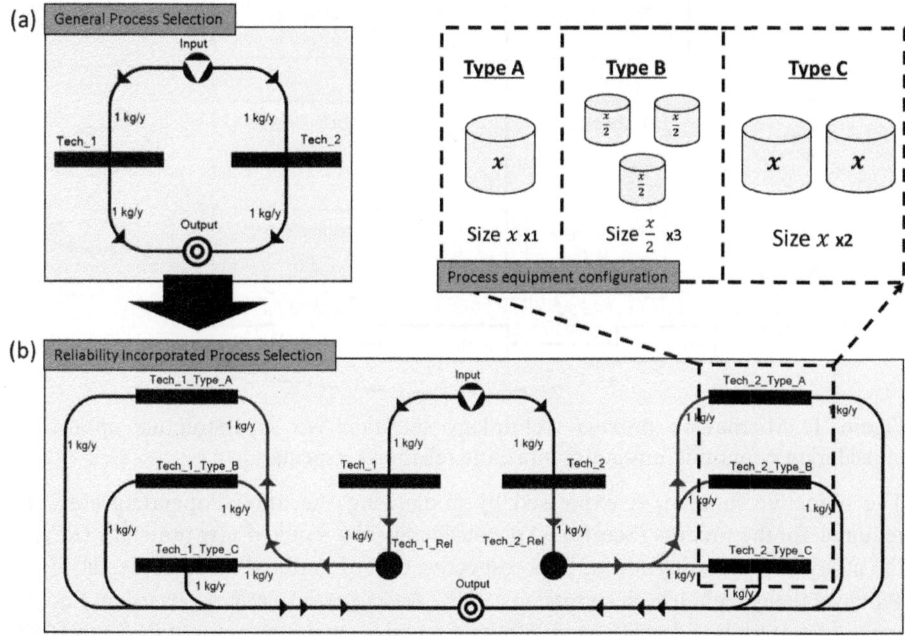

Figure 2. Demonstration of generic process selection superstructure optimization in P-graph: (a) general configuration and (b) configuration after incorporating reliability.

A P-graph model is developed to identify the optimal process in microalgae biorefinery as shown in Figure 3. Such process selection considers the aspects of technical, economic, environment, and reliability which are discussed in Section 2. The P-graph model comprises eight different sections covering: (A) Cultivation, (B) Dewatering and Cell Disruption, (C) Lipids extraction, separation, and recovery, (D) Anaerobic Digestion, (E) Digestate purification, (F) Biogas upgrade, (G) greenhouse gas emissions, and (H) Electricity distribution. Such model developed is solved with the custom solver of combining solution structure generation, linear programming, and reliability analysis. A case study was implemented where an approximation of 6.82 t of dry microalgae are cultivated in an area of 200 ha in Incheon, South Korea. All the process selection parameters considered in this study were based on the one reported by Lim et al., 2020. Due to strategic location of Incheon, various renewable energy sources are avail to be incorporated to fulfil the electricity demand of the microalgae biorefinery.

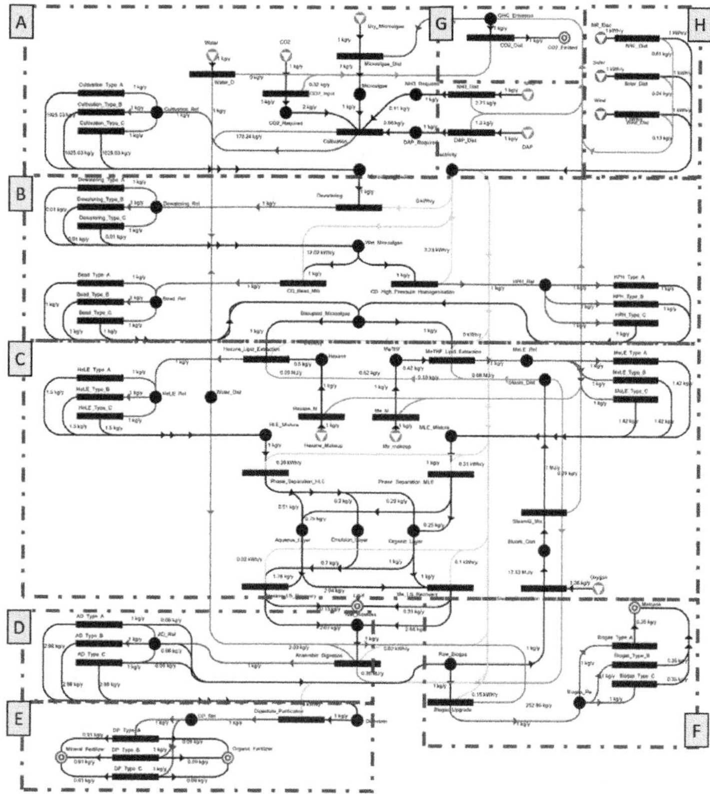

Figure 3. One-stage technical-economical-environmental-reliability P-graph model targeting microalgae biorefinery.

4. Results and discussion

A total of 34,992 solutions were proposed by the P-graph model developed based on the modified solver that incorporated the reliability alongside the calculation (see Figure 4). The total annual cost from the solution pool has reported with the range of 9.04×10^7 to 1.35×10^8 USD/y; whereas the GHG emissions were reported in the range of 1.62×10^5 to 7.24×10^5 kg $CO_{2\text{-eqv}}$/y. As of the incorporated reliability aspects that bounds within 0 (lowest reliability) to 1 (highest reliability), the solution has reported with the reliability range of 0.35 to 0.86. Thereupon, a further analysis was conducted with the aid of *Technique of Preference by Similarity to Ideal Solution* (TOPSIS) that was first proposed by Hwang and Yoon (1981). A detailed calculation steps of TOPSIS can be found similarly in Lim et al., (2021) which a non-bias approach has been implemented where all assessment aspects are considered equally important. Top 100 solutions that are re-ranked according to TOPSIS score are highlighted in Figure 4. The ranked 1 microalgae biorefinery configuration is reported with 9.69×10^7 USD/y, 1.81×10^5 kg $CO_{2\text{-eqv}}$/y, and 0.81 in respect of the total annual cost, GHG emission, and reliability, respectively. The process configuration of the ranked 1 solution is as: cultivation, dewatering, high pressure homogenization, hexane lipid extraction, phase separation, solvent recovery, anaerobic digestion, digestate purification, and biogas upgrade.

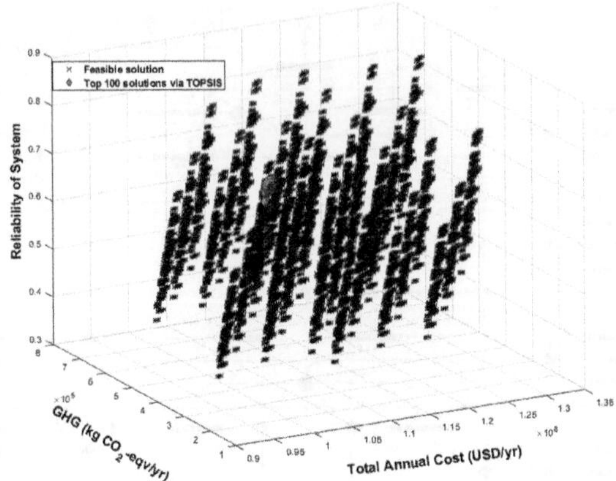

Figure 4. Solution pools generated from P-graph model for the microalgae biorefinery process selection alongside with the top 100 solutions highlighted from TOPSIS.

5. Conclusions

This study has successfully proposed a one stage technical-economical-environmental-reliability P-graph model on the selection of sustainable microalgae biorefinery process configuration. TOPSIS is then implemented to identify the ranked 1 configuration which resulted with 9.69×10^7 USD/y, 1.81×10^5 kg $CO_{2\text{-eqv}}$/y, and 0.81 in respect of the total annual cost, GHG emission, and reliability, respectively.

Acknowledgements

The authors would like to acknowledge financial support from a National Research Foundation of Korea (NRF) grant funded by the Korean government (MSIP) (No. 2021R1A2C2007838), and the Korea Ministry of the Environment (MOE) as a Graduate School specializing in Climate Change. The research presented in this paper was funded by the "National Laboratories 2020 Program – Artificial Intelligence Subprogram – Establishment of the National Artificial Intelligence Laboratory (MILAB) at Széchenyi István University (NKFIH-870-21/2020)" project. Project TKP2020-NKA-10 has been implemented with the support provided from the National Research, Development and Innovation Fund of Hungary, financed under the 2020-4.1.1-TKP2020 Thematic Excellence Programme 2020 - National Challenges sub-program funding scheme.

References

C-L. Hwang, K. Yoon, 1981, Methods for multiple attribute decision making. In: Multiple attribute decision making. Springer, pp 58–191

J.Y. Lim, B.S. How, S.Y. Teng, W.D. Leong, J.P. Tang, H.L. Lam, C.K. Yoo, 2021, Multi-objective lifecycle optimization for oil palm fertilizer formulation: A hybrid P-graph and TOPSIS approach, Resour Conserv Recycl, 166, 105357.

J.Y. Lim, K.J. Nam, C.K. Yoo, 2020, Circular economy assessment towards optimal process configuration of microalgae-based bio-refinery system with consideration of reliability assessment: P-graph approach, PRES'20, Xi'an, China.

K.L. Yeh, J.S. Chang, 2012, Effects of cultivation conditions and media composition on cell growth and lipid productivity of indigenous microalga Chlorella vulgaris ESP-31, Bioresour. Technol. 105, 120–127.

Z. Kovacs, A. Orosz, F. Friedler, 2019, Synthesis algorithms for the reliability analysis of processing systems, Cent Eur J Oper Res, 27, 573–595.

Proceedings of the 14th International Symposium on Process Systems Engineering – PSE 2021+
June 19-23, 2022, Kyoto, Japan
http://dx.doi.org/10.1016/B978-0-323-85159-6.50037-3

Framework for Designing Solid Drug Product Manufacturing Processes Based on Economic and Quality Assessment

Kensaku Matsunami[a*], Sara Badr[a], and Hirokazu Sugiyama[a]

[a]Department of Chemical System Engineering, The University of Tokyo, 7-3-1 Hongo, Bunkyo-ku, Tokyo 113-8656, Japan
kensaku.matsunami@ugent.be

Abstract

This work presents a design framework for solid drug product manufacturing processes based on economic and quality assessment. Process alternatives were generated using a superstructure, which includes novel continuous manufacturing. Each generated alternative can be assessed considering various uncertainties in the design phase. Economic assessment calculates a net present value from the decision stage to the end of commercial production. Product quality assessment predicts dissolution behavior by surrogate models developed from existing mechanistic models. In this work, the use of the tools was presented in the form of an activity model and demonstrated in a case study. The proposed framework and the assessment tools can assist rational and efficient simulation-based design of solid drug product manufacturing processes.

Keywords: Pharmaceuticals, continuous manufacturing, superstructure, economic assessment, quality.

1. Introduction

Solid drug products, e.g., tablets and capsules, are major products in the pharmaceutical industry. Solid drug product manufacturing consists of powder-based unit operations with the active pharmaceutical ingredient (API) as the initial raw material. Examples of unit operations are mixing, granulation, drying, compression, and coating, which have been traditionally performed batch-wise. Recently, continuous manufacturing, where all unit operations are interconnected, has been developed as a novel technology in pharmaceutical manufacturing. Unlike in the chemical industry, continuous solid drug product manufacturing is generally performed within certain running hours, e.g., 12 h. This characteristic increases flexibility in demand change (Lee et al., 2015), but the start-up operation has high impacts on material losses. The number of potential process alternatives has increased with the emergence of continuous manufacturing, which makes process design more complicated.

Numerous studies have been performed toward rational design of solid drug product manufacturing considering continuous manufacturing. Experimental investigations of continuous manufacturing have been reported to identify critical process parameters (e.g., Liu et al., 2019). Economic assessment to compare between batch and continuous manufacturing has been developed focusing on tablet manufacturing using wet granulation (Matsunami et al., 2018). Regarding product quality assessment, mechanistic modeling has been proposed by many researchers. Van Hauwermeiren et al. (2018) established a population balance model for continuous twin-screw wet granulation; Metta et al. (2019) proposed a flowsheet model for continuous wet granulation. However, these studies have focused on specific manufacturing processes and/or drug types. A comprehensive design approach applicable for any drug is still needed.

This study proposes a design framework for solid drug product manufacturing along with assessment models. A superstructure for alternative generation is presented with models for economic and product quality assessment. The use of assessment tools is then presented in the form of an activity model. This work describes the comprehensive design strategy, details of individual tools can be found in the article paper (Matsunami et al., 2020) and the book chapter (Matsunami et al., 2021) by the authors' research group.

2. Developed assessment tools

Tools are developed for process synthesis with alternative generation from a superstructure. The tools also include subsequent economic and quality assessments.

2.1. A superstructure for process synthesis

Process alternatives of solid drug product manufacturing are comprehensively generated using a superstructure created based on the unit, port, conditioning stream (UPCS) representation (Wu et al., 2018), as shown in Figure 1. Characters B and C in general units represent batch and continuous mode in the unit operations. Each process alternative is defined as the combination of streams, ports, and units from source (providing raw materials) to sink (collecting final products) units.

The superstructure in Figure 1, which was created through a literature survey as well as the expert knowledge of the pharmaceutical industry, yields 9,452 process alternatives. Among these alternatives, 1,261 alternatives were identified as "continuous technology," where all unit operations were performed in continuous operation mode. This work uses the granulation step, one of the essential production steps, as a case study for applying the assessment tools. Therefore, a higher-resolution of the available options was used compared to the other steps. In general, there are three options within this step: wet

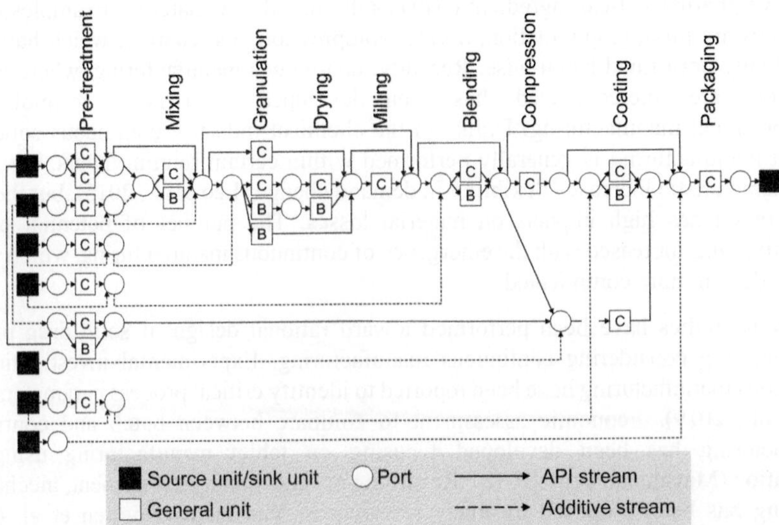

Figure 1. The developed superstructure (Matsunami et al., 2020)

granulation, dry granulation, or direct compression methods. Each option is associated with a range of options for unit operations.

2.2. Economic assessment

The indicator for the economic assessment is the net present value (NPV) to consider the cash flow from a decision stage to the end of the commercial production. Assuming the common decision stage of process alternatives is the beginning of phase II in clinical development, NPV can be defined as shown in Eq.(1):

$$NPV = -\sum_{\tau=0}^{\tau_3} \frac{C_{\mathrm{dev}}(\tau)}{(1+r)^{\tau}} - \sum_{\tau=0}^{\tau_{\mathrm{prod}}} \frac{C_{\mathrm{invest}}(\tau)}{(1+r)^{\tau}} + \sum_{\tau=\tau_{\mathrm{lau}}}^{\tau_{\mathrm{prod}}} \frac{C_{\mathrm{sales}}(\tau) - C_{\mathrm{op}}(\tau)}{(1+r)^{\tau}} \quad (1)$$

where C_{dev} [USD yr^{-1}], C_{invest} [USD yr^{-1}], C_{sales} [USD yr^{-1}], and C_{op} [USD yr^{-1}] represent the development cost, investment cost, sales, and operating cost, respectively. The parameter τ [yr] represents the period from the decision stage to the target phase. The subscripts 3, lau, and prod represent the clinical trials in phase III, the product launch, and the end of the commercial production, respectively. The calculation of NPV can be made by setting the interest rate r. Material losses at the start-up operation are included in C_{op}. Variations in the production scales to accommodate changing demand are reflected in this calculation.

To reflect uncertainty in the decision stage in the economic assessment, the stochastic optimization problem of the expected (E) NPV was determined, as shown in Eq.(2):

$$\begin{aligned} &\max E_{\boldsymbol{\theta}}\big(NPV(l)\big) \\ &\text{s.t.} \\ &E_{\boldsymbol{\theta}}\big(NPV(l)\big) > 0 \\ &\text{(Mass balance constraints)} \\ &\text{(Processing time constraints)} \\ &\text{(Pharma-specific constraints)}\,, \end{aligned} \quad (2)$$

where the design variable and uncertainty parameters are process alternative l and the vector $\boldsymbol{\theta}$, respectively. The developed economic assessment has been implemented as a part of a software tool "SoliDecision" (Matsunami et al., 2020).

2.3. Product quality assessment

As an example of product quality assessment, the dissolution behavior was studied. In this work, dissolution behavior is defined as the profile of mass ratio of API dissolved in water during a dissolution test. It was chosen as an example since it represents a critical quality attribute of solid drug products with a direct impact on drug efficacy. Surrogate modeling was chosen because both applicability to new drugs and calculation speed are important for the assessment in process design. The modeling activities consist of the four steps: (i) flowsheet model development, (ii) input/output data generation, (iii) dissolution behavior fitting, and (iv) random forest regression. Firstly, existing mechanistic models are integrated to create flowsheet models of solid drug product manufacturing. The flowsheet models were then used for the calculation of dissolution behavior by changing the values of input model parameters. After obtaining a set of output data, mass ratio of API dissolved D [%] were fitted by the Weibull model to transfer it into a lower dimension, as shown in Eq.(3):

$$D(t) = 100 \cdot \left(1 - e^{\{-k(t-t_0)^b\}}\right) \tag{3}$$

where the parameters t [min], k [–], t_0 [min], and b [–] represent time from the start of a dissolution test, reciprocal of the scale parameter, time lag, and the shape parameter, respectively. The Weibull model was chosen because it showed the highest fitting accuracy among seven popular dissolution fitting models, e.g., first-order kinetics. Finally, the relationships between the input model parameters and the Weibull model parameters were trained by random forest regression. The hyper-parameters of random forest models were chosen by maximizing coefficients of determination in five-fold cross-validation.

By integrating all the steps, the surrogate model can be expressed as the combination of the Weibull model W and the random forest regression $\boldsymbol{g}$, as shown in Eq.(4):

$$D(t) = W(\boldsymbol{g}(\boldsymbol{P}), t) \tag{4}$$

where $\boldsymbol{P}$ represents the vector of the input model parameters. The developed surrogate model can calculate expected ranges of dissolution behavior under the uncertainty of the input model parameters.

3. Design framework

The application of the assessment tools in the design activities was described as a design framework by using the type zero method of integration definition for function modeling (IDEF0). The top activity of the framework is "evaluate processes for process design," where the viewpoint was set as process designers in the pharmaceutical industry (Matsunami et al., 2021). The four sub-activities of the top activity were defined as shown in Figure 2. The sub-activities are controlled by design cases, which are defined by new drug information as well as the pharma-specific constraints, e.g., regulations and clinical trial results. The developed assessment tools are used as a mechanism of the activities. By executing the activities, promising alternatives are determined, which will be further tested in the subsequent design activities.

The proposed framework was demonstrated by setting a scenario where the beginning of phase II in clinical development was set as the decision stage. The design problem was set as "find a process which maximizes NPV and dissolution rate." In A1, possible process alternatives were chosen based on material properties and design policy. Here, 32 alternatives, including batch/continuous dry granulation and wet granulation methods, were focused on in this demonstration. After defining probability density functions (PDFs) of all input parameters in A2, both economic and product quality assessments were performed. Figure 3 shows violin plots of PDFs of NPV differences between target

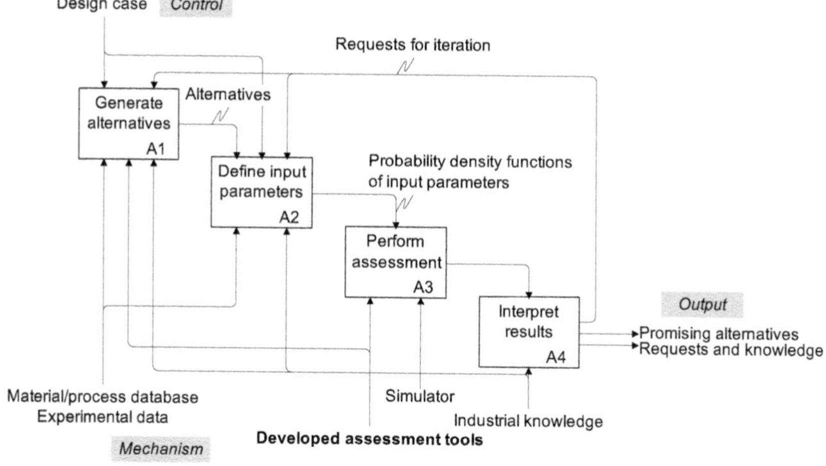

Figure 2. Design framework for solid drug product manufacturing processes

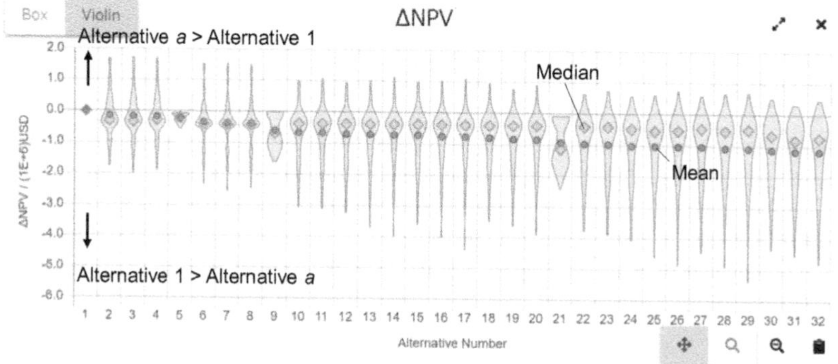

Figure 3. Economic assessment result using SoliDecision.

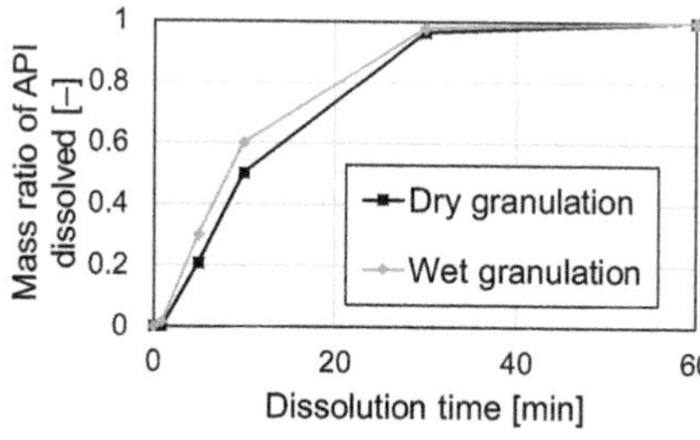

Figure 4. Simulation results of dissolution behavior using average values.

alternatives and the best alternative in terms of $E_{\theta}(NPV(l))$ generated by "SoliDecision". Alternative numbers are defined by the order of $E_{\theta}(NPV(l))$, where an alternative of continuous dry granulation was the best alternative. In product quality assessment, dissolution behavior in continuous dry granulation was compared with that in batch high-shear wet granulation, which is one of the typical production methods. Dissolution behaviors using average values are presented in Figure 4. Batch high-shear wet granulation made dissolution faster than continuous dry granulation. The results of economic and product quality assessments were interpreted in A4. At commercial scale, the expected *NPV* of continuous dry granulation was USD3.37×10^5 higher than that in batch high-shear wet granulation, whereas mass ratio of API dissolved at 10 mins was 9.86% slower. This trade-off between cost and quality should be considered by weighting each indicator to determine the promising alternatives. Continuous dry granulation could be chosen if lowering cost was more important than fast dissolution. Batch wet granulation could be selected if a higher dissolution profile was the most important.

4. Conclusions

A design framework for solid drug product manufacturing processes was presented along with economic and product quality assessment tools as a new mechanism. Process alternatives were comprehensively generated using a superstructure and can be assessed in terms of NPV and dissolution behavior. Both assessments can propagate the uncertainty of the input parameters, which should be high in the design phase, into the results. The application of the tools was described by an activity model and demonstrated in the case study. A part of the tools has been implemented as software, "SoliDecision," which is ready for use in the actual decision-making in the pharmaceutical industry.

Acknowledgment

The authors acknowledge Dr. Hiroshi Nakagawa, Dr. Shuichi Tanabe, and Mr. Keita Yaginuma from Daiichi Sankyo Co., Ltd. for supporting the development of the assessment tools. H. S. is thankful for the financial supports by Grants-in-Aid for Young Scientists (A) [number 17H04964] and Grant-in-Aid for Scientific Research (B) [number 21H01704] from the Japan Society for the Promotion of Science (JSPS). K. M. appreciates the financial support by Research Fellows [number 18 J22793] from JSPS.

References

S. Lee, T. O'Connor, X. Yang, C. Cruz, S. Chatterjee, R. Madurawe, C. Moore, L. Yu, J. Woodcock, 2015. Modernizing pharmaceutical manufacturing: from batch to continuous production, *Int. J. Pharm.*, 10, 191–199.

H. Liu, B. Ricart, C. Stanton, B. Smith-Goettler, L. Verdi, T. O'Connor, S. Lee, S. Yoon, 2019. Design space determination and process optimization in at-scale continuous twin screw wet granulation, *Comput. Chem. Eng.*, 125, 271–286.

K. Matsunami, S. Badr, H. Sugiyama, 2022. Design framework and tools for solid drug product manufacturing processes, *Optimization of Pharmaceutical Processes*, accepted.

K. Matsunami, T. Miyano, H. Arai, H. Nakagawa, M. Hirao, H. Sugiyama, 2018. Decision support method for the choice between batch and continuous technologies in solid drug product manufacturing, *Ind. Eng. Chem. Res.*, 57, 9798–9809.

K. Matsunami, F. Sternal, K. Yaginuma, S. Tanabe, H. Nakagawa, H. Sugiyama, 2020. Superstructure-based process synthesis and economic assessment under uncertainty for solid drug product manufacturing, *BMC Chem. Eng.*, 2, 6.

D. Van Hauwermeiren, M. Verstraeten, P. Doshi, M. am Ende, N. Turnbull, K. Lee, T. De Beer, I. Nopens, 2019. On the modelling of granule size distributions in twin-screw wet granulation: calibration of a novel compartmental population balance model. *Powder Technol.*, 341, 116–125.

Proceedings of the 14th International Symposium on Process Systems Engineering – PSE 2021+
June 19-23, 2022, Kyoto, Japan
http://dx.doi.org/10.1016/B978-0-323-85159-6.50038-5

Marine flue gas desulfurization processes: recent developments, challenges, and perspectives

Gwangsik KIM[a,1], Van Duc Long NGUYEN[a,1], Dongyoung LEE[a,b,1], Yujeong LEE[a], Jonghoon BAEK[a], Wonseok JEONG[a], Myungjin KIM[b], Choongyong KWAG[b], Youngmok LEE[b], Sungwon LEE[b], and Moonyong LEE[a*]

[a]*School of Chemical Engineering, Yeungnam University, Gyeongsan 712-749, South Korea*
[b]*Hanbal Masstech Ltd, holden root complex, Gimhae, South Korea*
shikki47@gmail.com

Abstract

Seawater flue gas desulfurization (SWFGD) is considered to be a viable solution for marine and coastal applications. SWFGD, however, still has a couple of drawbacks that have to be resolved. High pumping costs and poor mass transfer efficiency require large volume and heavy construction. Thus, intensified and advanced process configurations have become necessary in process industries to improve the SWFGD processes performance. This work presents an overview of several advanced SWFGD systems such as swirling gas flow, square-based shapes scrubber, rotating packed bed and addition of a pre-scrubber. This work also presents an overview of industrial uses, challenges, and improved SWFGD processes.

Keywords: seawater flue gas desulfurization (SWFGD); process retrofit; process improvement; Heat integration

1. Introduction

As the energy demand worldwide is overgrowing, many power plant constructions using fossil fuel are increasing [1]. Sulfur oxides (SO_x), mainly consisting of SO_2, are generated and emitted when fossil fuel is combusted, negatively influencing the environment [2]. As a result, many countries have propagated strict SO_x emissions regulations [3].

Furthermore, sea transport, which accounts for more than 90% of international trade [4], emits a considerable amount of SO_x [5]. The International Marine Organization (IMO) recently consented to regulations of sulfur emissions to prevent the negative effect on the environment from its emissions [6].

Many power plants prefer to be built offshore because they require lots of water for cooling. In addition, owing to its high availability and natural alkalinity, seawater has been considered an environmentally and economically reliable candidate for the solvent of flue gas desulfurization (FGD) processes in offshore and maritime applications [7].

However, the seawater FGD (SWFGD) process has a couple of drawbacks that have to be resolved. High pumping costs and poor mass transfer efficiency require large volume and heavy construction [8]. Due to the typical limitations of maritime applications, these drawbacks must be investigated and addressed [6]. Consequently, a lot of research has been performed to improve SWFGD process efficiency and capacity and make this process more compact and lighter due to the constraints of space and weight for maritime applications. This paper focuses on producing a comprehensive review of the improvement of SWFGD, which has been given significant attention recently.

2. SWFGD systems in a coastal area

The flue gas from power plants' combustion of coal contains approximately between 210 to 1540 ppm$_v$ of SO_2 [7], and typical seawater usually has a pH value of 7.6 to 8.4 at a temperature of 5 to 15 °C The reaction procedures of absorption of SO_2 into seawater are tabulated in Table 1 [2,9].

Table 1. SO_2 absorption reactions into seawater

Procedure	Reaction	
Absorption	$SO_2 + H_2O \leftrightarrow HSO_3^- + H^+$	(1)
Oxidation	$HSO_3^- + 1/2O_2 \leftrightarrow SO_4^{2-} + H^+$	(2)
Neutralization	$HCO_3^- + H^+ \leftrightarrow CO_2 + H_2O$	(3)
	$CO_3^{2-} + 2H^+ \leftrightarrow CO_2 + H_2O$	(4)

Figure 1 shows simple configurations of open-loop, closed-loop, and hybrid mode. In the open-loop mode in Figure 1a, raw seawater is fed into the scrubber as a solvent, absorbs SO_2, and neutralizes using its natural carbonate ions (CO_3^{2-}) and bicarbonate ions (HCO_3^-). As shown in Figure 1b, in closed-loop mode, the seawater or freshwater is not discharged into the sea but is recycled inside the scrubber system. Hence, a wash water unit is necessary before releasing the water. Before recycling the wash water, use a heat exchanger to lower its temperature. To remove the moisture in the gas from the scrubber, it goes through a demister or moisture eliminator before entering the stack in both the open and closed loops.

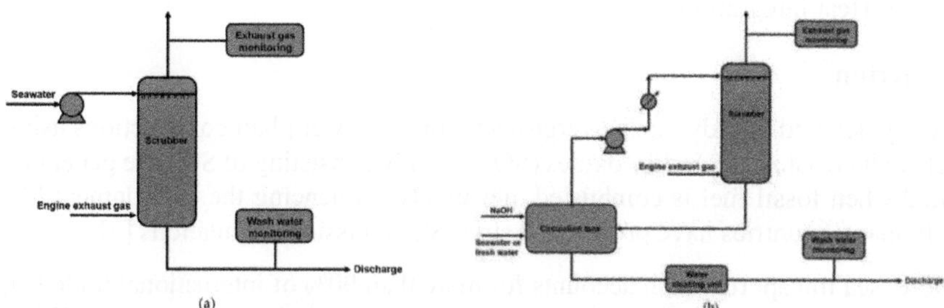

Figure 1. Schematic configurations of the (a) open-loop, (b) closed-loop FGD process mode

3. Maritime SWFGD systems

The fuel gas from the engines of existing ships typically emits SO_2 in concentrations of 80 to 1000 ppm$_v$ [10,11]. Table 1 shows the typical desulfurization process design conditions of the land-based SWFGD system and the SWFGD system used in large ships [9].

Table 2. The typical desulfurization process design conditions of the land-based SWFGD system and the SWFGD system used in large ships

		Land-based	**Large Ships**
Flue gas flow rate	Nm^3/h	600,000 to 4,000,000	23,000 to 540,000

Inlet SO_2 level	ppm_d	100 to 1800	700
Outlet SO_2 level	ppm_d	10 to 220	20
SO_2 removal efficiency	%	75 to 98	97.1 (3.5 %S to 0.1%S): SECAs 85.7 (3.5%S to 0.5%S): global sea areas excluding SECAs
Regulatory items for seawater discharge		pH, dissolved oxygen (DO), temperature, etc	pH, PAH, turbidity, nitrates

For long-distance sea transportation, the SWFGD system with scrubber has many advantages such as simple structure, easy operation, and low initial investment compared to using low-sulfur oil or replacing it with an LNG vessel [12,13]. It usually consists of a spray column using seawater or seawater with NaOH added as a solvent [6], and this column is generally utilized when pressure drop is a critical factor [14] or when high levels of separation are not required [15].

Nevertheless, the scrubber still has some disadvantages that need to be addressed. High pumping costs and poor mass transfer efficiency require large volume and heavy construction [8]. Due to the typical limitations of maritime applications, these drawbacks must be investigated and addressed [6]. So possible developed and integrated process configurations have become necessary in process industries to improve the SWFGD processes performance.

4. Improvement of water and SWFGD systems

If the swirling gas flow concept is used for the flow of gas entering into the spray column, the effect of mass transfer is increased [16]. When this concept is applied, the residence time of the flue gas inside the column becomes longer, resulting in improved mass transfer performance. Figure 2 shows the conceptual diagram of the swirling gas flow of the SOx scrubber [17]. Recently, Schrauwen and Toenes studied the effect of mass transfer after generating a swirling gas flow by injecting flue gas tangentially into the column [18]. The swirling gas flow increases the mass transfer performance, allowing a compact scrubber design and consequently expanding the applicability to marine vessels.

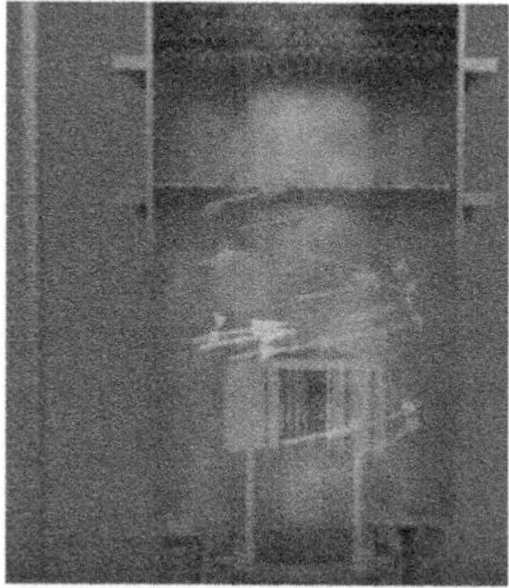

Figure 2. The conceptual diagram of the swirling gas flow of the Sox scrubber.[17]

A square scrubber_[19], which is more efficient in terms of volume than a cylindrical scrubber, is frequently applied to the FGD system [9]. It is because the diameter of the cylindrical scrubber is larger than the side of the square scrubber in the same area. However, the square scrubber has difficulty in evenly distributing the flue gas and can only be used when the operating pressure is low [15,20]. PacificGreem Technologies recently developed a square scrubber that is compact, flexible and does not compromise efficiency [17].

Hansen [8] has developed a method of installing an additional pre-scrubber to effectively remove SO_2 in flue gas from engines of marine vessels. The flue gas temperature is rapidly cooled from about 180-250 °C to 45-60 °C in the pre-scrubber before flowing into the main scrubber. As shown in Figure 3, Alfa Laval installed a jet scrubber that uses water as a coolant to lower the flue gas temperature before the primary scrubber [21]. A venturi scrubber can be used as a pre-scrubber to screen PM [22], but this will increase the pressure drop. The venturi scrubber can be used to cool the hot flue gas (up to 1000 °C) [17].

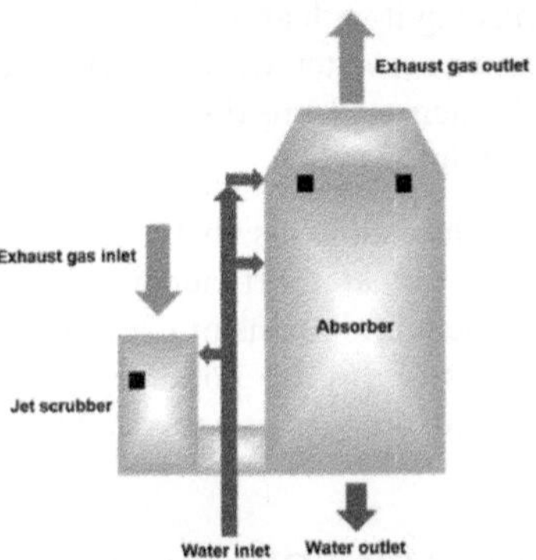

Figure 3. Schematic configuration combining a jet scrubber and an absorber [21].

Rotating packed bed (RPB) generates high acceleration through centrifugal force and forms a thin liquid film and tiny droplets through centrifugal acceleration to improve mass transfer performance [23]. As a result, RPB can improve the removal efficiency of SO_2 [24]. Recently, research has been conducted to enhance the absorption of SO_2 using RPB and ionic liquid [25].

5. Challenges

a. Due to the acidity of the flue gas, the scrubber must consider the effect of corrosion [6]; thus, it is crucial to choose a suitable material that can prevent decay.

b. Since the flue gas pressure from the marine engine is similar to the atmospheric pressure, the pressure drop due to the auxiliary internals such as the demister and gas distributor inside the column should be low [6].

c. Designers must consider essential design factors such as the material of constructions, nozzle droplet size or nozzle type, solvent flow rate, and pressure drop to design an appropriate scrubber. [17].

d. The flue gas from a marine engine contains a complex PM composed of carbon particles [10], especially the soot particles that can cause severe disease [26]. A venturi scrubber, cyclone, dust collector, or electrostatic precipitator can be used to prevent PM from entering the scrubber [27,28].

f. The pH of seawater that absorbs acid gases from marine engines can be reduced to a range of around 2.53 [13]. However, the 2015 IMO guideline regulates the pH of the discharged seawater to be above 6.5. To increase the pH of the discharged seawater, caustic soda can be used as an additive in the SWFGD system [29].

6. Conclusion

Considering the strict IMO environmental regulations worldwide, this paper succeeded in investigating and analyzing SWFGD's current researches and industrial applications. The SWFGD process can be an excellent alternative for marine applications to meet the stringent IMO regulations due to seawater's natural alkalinity and high availability, design simplicity, convenient operation, no chemical solvent requirement, no solid waste, and relatively higher performance of SO_2 removal. Several solutions were assessed, including process modification, integration, and intensification to enhance the SWFGD process effectively. Developed and improved SWFGD systems with compact units, lighter construction, low energy consumption, and reduced seawater flowrate have been commercialized. However, several issues are still to be solved, such as establishing an accurate and broader range of SO_2 solubility, equilibrium data, and developing models describing advanced and improved scrubbers.

7. Acknowledgement

This work was supported by the National Research Foundation of Korea (NRF) grant funded by the Korea government (MSIT) (2021R1A2C1092152) and by the Priority Research Centers Program through the National Research Foundation of Korea (NRF) funded by the Ministry of Education (2014R1A6A1031189).

8. References

[1] H.N. Soud, Z. Wu, East Asia-air pollution control and coal-fired power generation, (1998).

[2] K. Oikawa, C. Yongsiri, K. Takeda, T. Harimoto, Seawater flue gas desulfurization: Its technical implications and performance results, Environ. Prog. 22 (2003) 67–73.

[3] C. Zhang, L. Yang, One-dimensional simulation of synergistic desulfurization and denitrification processes for electrostatic precipitators based on a fluid-chemical reaction hybrid model, Energies. 11 (2018) 3249.

[4] R.F. Nielsen, F. Haglind, U. Larsen, Design and modeling of an advanced marine machinery system including waste heat recovery and removal of sulphur oxides, Energy Convers. Manag. 85 (2014) 687–693.

[5] Z. Wan, M. Zhu, S. Chen, D. Sperling, Pollution: three steps to a green shipping industry, Nat. News. 530 (2016) 275.

[6] D. Flagiello, A. Parisi, A. Lancia, C. Carotenuto, A. Erto, F. Di Natale, Seawater desulphurization scrubbing in spray and packed columns for a 4.35 MW marine diesel engine, Chem. Eng. Res. Des. 148 (2019) 56–67.

[7] D. Flagiello, A. Erto, A. Lancia, F. Di Natale, Experimental and modelling analysis of seawater scrubbers for sulphur dioxide removal from flue-gas, Fuel. 214 (2018) 254–263.

[8] J.P. Hansen, Scrubber System and Method Technical Field, WO. 45272 (2013) A1.

[9] R. Sasaki, T. Nagayasu, T. Shingu, Y. Watanabe, T. Mori, H. Sakurai, Practical design of marine SOx scrubber for mega-container ships, Mitsubishi Heavy Ind. Tech. Rev. 56 (2019) 1–8.

[10] F. Di Natale, C. Carotenuto, Particulate matter in marine diesel engines exhausts: Emissions and control strategies, Transp. Res. Part D Transp. Environ. 40 (2015) 166–191.

[11] EPA, Analysis of commercial marine vessels emissions and fuel consumption data, Tech. Rep. (2000).

[12] J. Rodríguez-Sevilla, M. Álvarez, M.C. Díaz, M.C. Marrero, Absorption equilibria of dilute SO_2 in seawater, J. Chem. Eng. Data. 49 (2004) 1710–1716.

[13] A. Andreasen, S. Mayer, Use of seawater scrubbing for SO_2 removal from marine engine exhaust gas, Energy & Fuels. 21 (2007) 3274–3279.

[14] N.K. Yeh, G.T. Rochelle, Liquid-phase mass transfer in spray contactors, AIChE J. 49 (2003) 2363–2373.

[15] A. Cousins, L. Wardhaugh, A. Cottrell, Absorption-Based Post-Combustio n Capture of Carbon Dioxide, Woodhead Publ. (2016) 649–684.

[16] K.H. Javed, T. Mahmud, E. Purba, Enhancement of mass transfer in a spray tower using swirling gas flow, Chem. Eng. Res. Des. 84 (2006) 465–477.

[17] N.V.D. Long, D.Y. Lee, K.M. Jin, K. Choongyong, L.Y. Mok, L.S. Won, M. Lee, Advanced and intensified seawater flue gas desulfurization processes: Recent developments and improvements, Energies. 13 (2020) 5917.

[18] F.J.M. Schrauwen, D. Thoenes, Selective gas absorption in a cyclone spray scrubber, in: Tenth Int. Symp. Chem. React. Eng., Elsevier, 1988: pp. 2189–2194.

[19] N.V.D. Long, D.Y. Lee, M.J. Kim, C. Kwag, Y.M. Lee, K.J. Kang, S.W. Lee, M. Lee, Desulfurization scrubbing in a squared spray column for a 720 kW marine diesel engine: Design, construction, simulation, and experiment, Chem. Eng. Process. Intensif. 161 (2021) 108317.

[20] P.-E. Just, Advances in the development of CO2 capture solvents, Energy Procedia. 37 (2013) 314–324.

[21] MAN, Emission project guide, MAN Energy Solut. (2017) 111.

[22] Wärtsilä, SOx scrubber technology, (2017) 8.

[23] C. Ramshaw, R.H. Mallinson, Mass transfer process, (1981).

[24] L. Zhang, S. Wu, Y. Gao, B. Sun, Y. Luo, H. Zou, G. Chu, J. Chen, Absorption of SO_2 with calcium-based solution in a rotating packed bed, Sep. Purif. Technol. 214 (2019) 148–155.

[25] Y.-Z. Liu, W. Wu, Y. Liu, B.-B. Li, Y. Luo, G.-W. Chu, H.-K. Zou, J.-F. Chen, Desulfurization intensification by ionic liquid in a rotating packed bed, Chem. Eng. Process. Intensif. 148 (2020) 107793.

[26] D.T. Silverman, C.M. Samanic, J.H. Lubin, A.E. Blair, P.A. Stewart, R. Vermeulen, J.B. Coble, N. Rothman, P.L. Schleiff, W.D. Travis, R.G. Ziegler, S. Wacholder, M.D. Attfield, The diesel exhaust in miners study: A nested case-control study of lung cancer and diesel exhaust, J. Natl. Cancer Inst. 104 (2012) 855–868. https://doi.org/10.1093/jnci/djs034.

[27] H.E. Hesketh, M.P. Cal, Air Pollution Control: traditional and hazardous pollutants, J. Environ. Qual. 26 (1997) 1442.

[28] A. Poullikkas, Review of Design, Operating, and financial considerations in flue gas desulfurization systems, Energy Technol. Policy. 2 (2015) 92–103.

[29] S.-K. Back, A.H.M. Mojammal, H.-H. Jo, J.-H. Kim, M.-J. Jeong, Y.-C. Seo, H.-T. Joung, S.-H. Kim, Increasing seawater alkalinity using fly ash to restore the pH and the effect of temperature on seawater flue gas desulfurization, J. Mater. Cycles Waste Manag. 21 (2019) 962–973.

Proceedings of the 14th International Symposium on Process Systems Engineering – PSE 2021+
June 19-23, 2022, Kyoto, Japan
http://dx.doi.org/10.1016/B978-0-323-85159-6.50039-7

A Novel Process Synthesis of a Dehydrating Unit of Domestic Natural Gas Using TEG Contactor and TEG Regenerator

Renanto Renanto[a*], Sony Ardian Affandy[a], Adhi Kurniawan[a], Juwari Juwari[a] and Rendra Panca Anugraha[a]

[a]*Department of Chemical Engineering, Institut Teknologi Sepuluh Nopember, Surabaya 60111, Indonesia*
renanto@chem-eng.its.ac.id

Abstract

The use of natural gas as a source of energy is widely known. Before it is processed to be a sale gas, the water content in the natural gas should be reduced to 200 ppmv in low pressure level, as water is corrosive in the pipeline. This work was carried out after several configurations in the dehydration unit had been simulated to find the best one in terms of the total annual cost. (Affandy et al, 2020; Affandy et al., 2017). The dehydration unit considered consists of a TEG (triethylene glycol) contactor and TEG regenerator. The contactor is used for dehydrating natural gas, where the water is absorbed using TEG solution while in the regenerator the water is desorbed by using stripping gas to increase the purity of TEG so as to absorb water in the TEG contactor. A new configuration was proposed in this paper. The configuration consists of a packed column in the TEG contactor on one hand, and a coldfinger and the recycled flare gas in the TEG regenerator on the other hand. The results showed that the new configuration had a total annual cost of US\$ 212.829 x 10^3 per year. This indicated that the total annual cost of this configuration was lower than that of the base case where there were no coldfinger and recycled flash gas used. The reduction of total annual cost from the base case was about 33.3 %.

Keywords: Dehydrating Unit; Natural Gas; Process Synthesis; TEG Contactor; TEG Regenerator.

1. Introduction

The use of natural gas as a source of energy source is widely known. It is naturally containing some impurities such as hydrogen sulphide, carbon dioxide, or nitrogen. It is also typically saturated with water moisture at the wellhead. The water moisture may cause problems like hydrate formation and also potentially leads to corrosion in the pipeline. The water moisture needs to be reduced to below certain level, for example to below 200 ppmv before sold as sale gas. There are few methods to reduce the water moisture from the natural gas, i.e. gas condensation using refrigerant, solid adsorption and using liquid absorption (Carrol, 2014).

One of the most widely solvent used in the liquid absorption water dehydration is the Triethylene Glycol (TEG). There are several published works to improve the performance of the TEG dehydration and regeneration system. Kong et al (2018) elaborated several available methods in the TEG regeneration system, covering from conventional regeneration to the use of several stripping agents such as nitrogen, portion of dehydrated gas, as well as liquid volatile hydrocarbon (Drizo process). It also covers the use of water exhauster (Coldfinger) as well as the emerging technologies such as membrane and supersonic separation technologies. The use of water exhauster in the regeneration system has been subject of recent research as well. Rahimpour et al (2013) simulated the dehydration unit using the Coldfinger system in a domestic gas plant. They focused on studying the influence of temperature, pressure and flowrate of the Coldfinger unit to the performance of the dehydration system. They also proposed a new mathematical model to approach the Coldfinger unit. Romero et al (2019) proposed two equilibrium stages operated at different temperatures to model the Coldfinger unit. Affandy et al (2020) investigated the performance improvement through the use of flash gas as a stripping gas source to the regenerator. They revealed that there will be some improvements in the TEG purity (up to 98.8%-wt) and the water moisture in the treated gas. However, it will be limited due to the availability of the flash gas, as well as the water content in the flash gas itself. The Total Annual Cost (TAC) of the proposed configuration showed around 20% reduction of TAC compared to the base case.

This work focuses on the synthesis of the regeneration system involving the Coldfinger concept and reusing the flash gas as the stripping gas source. The performance of the unit should satisfy the water moisture content in the treated gas and should provide lower TAC compared to the base case.

2. Process Description

Process configuration in Figure 1 used as the base case in this work was based on the work developed by Affandy et al (2017). The wet natural gas (stream 3507) was brought into contact with a lean Triethylene Glycol (TEG) solution (stream 4) in a trayed TEG Contactor (C-1). The dehydrated gas (stream 3604) is expected to have water moisture content less than 200 ppmv.

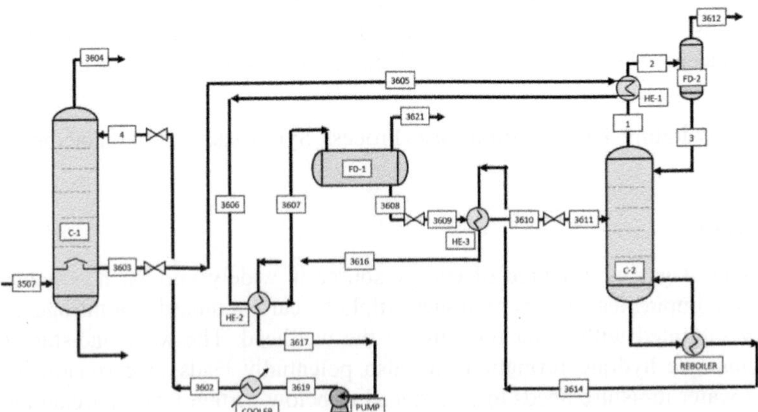

Figure 1 Process configuration of natural gas dehydration unit using TEG: base case

The glycol solution that has absorbed water (i.e. rich glycol solution, stream 3603) was then routed to a regeneration system in which the water content to be reduced to certain level so that it can be used again as lean glycol. The regeneration system consists of a flash drum (FD-1), a series of lean-to-rich heat exchanger (HE-1, HE-2, and HE-3) to conserve the heat, and a regenerator consisting of still column (C-2), condenser and reboiler. The conventional regeneration typically uses a regenerator operating pressure of near atmospheric to maximize the water vaporization. The operating temperature of reboiler typically is limited to 204 °C to minimize TEG glycol degradation. The regenerated lean glycol will have a water content of about 1.5 %-wt. The lean glycol (stream 3614) is then cooled to a temperature of around 45-48 °C (stream 3602) through the lean-to-rich heat exchanger system and further in a glycol cooler, prior to entering the TEG Glycol Contactor.

3. Method

The process simulation model was built in ASPEN Plus V10. The Predictive Redlich-Kwong-Soave (PSRK) was used as the thermodynamic property package used in the simulation model from Affandy et al. (2017). The simulation model was also validated using the actual plant data taken from a domestic gas plant. The base case process configuration was subjected to area optimization of heat exchanger networks as defined in previous work from Affandy et al. (2017).

The proposed process configurations were evaluated to give the lowest Total Annual Cost (TAC). The TAC itself was determined using formulae from Luyben (2011) in which it is the sum of total energy cost and the total capital cost divided by payback period. In this work the payback period was taken as 3 (three) years. The total operating cost consists of steam cost, cooling water, and TEG makeup (Affandy, 2020)

$$TAC = TOC + \frac{TCC}{PB} \tag{1}$$

Where: TAC = Total Annual Cost ($ / year) TCC = Total Capital Cost ($)

TOC = Total Operating Cost ($ / year) PB = Payback period (year)

4. Proposed Configurations

4.1. General

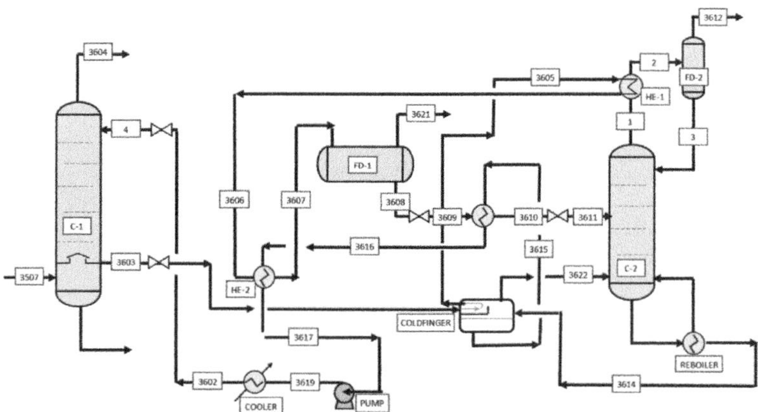

Figure 2 Process configuration of natural gas dehydration unit using TEG: regeneration package using Coldfinger system

The proposed process configurations in this work were based on the additional Coldfinger unit to the regeneration system as depicted in the Figure 2. In this scheme, the lean glycol outlet from reboiler (stream 3614) is routed to the Coldfinger unit that produces a leaner glycol (stream 3615). Furthermore as depicted in the Figure 3, the flash gas (stream 3621) from the Flash Drum was rerouted to the regenerator as the stripping agent (stream 5), following the scheme proposed by Affandy et al (2020).

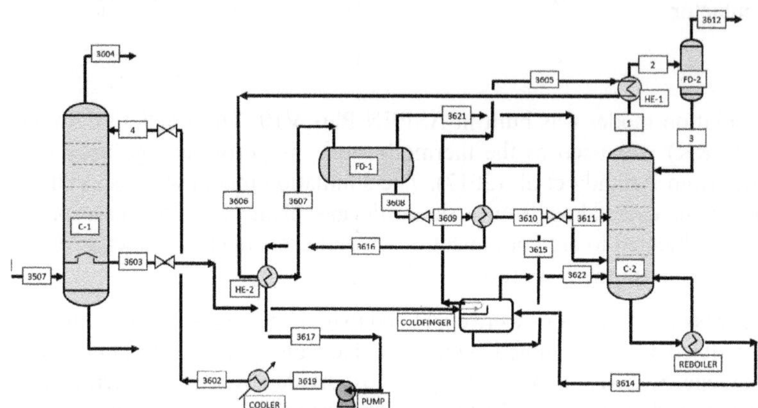

Figure 3 Process configuration of natural gas dehydration unit using TEG: Absorption column using trays column and regeneration package including Coldfinger system and flash gas as stripping gas

4.2. Coldfinger Model

The principle of the Coldfinger process is that the partly regenerated glycol from the distillation column is further concentrated in a two-phase tank with a cold spot (the Coldfinger) and a condensed collector in the gas phase. Figure 4 depicts the model of Coldfinger unit. The condensing of the water results in reduced water pressure in the tank and more water will evaporate from glycol. It shows the coldfinger simulation using two flash units (Affandy, 2020).

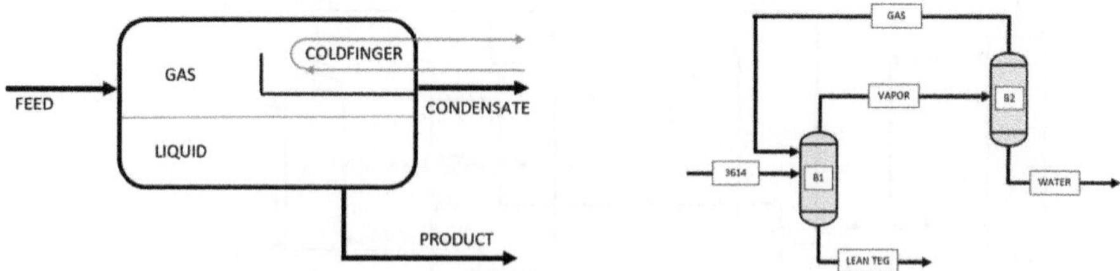

Figure 4 The Coldfinger model

Since the coldfinger unit is difficult to simulate in steady-state simulation program due to the unit is not in equilibrium, the condensing at the cold spot is at a lower temperature than the glycol, therefore coldfinger is simulated using two flash drums similar to the work of Erik and Tyvand (2002). The first flash drum for simulating the equilibrium between the glycol and the vapor above. The vapor is sent to second flash tank simulating the condensing and removal of the water at a lower temperature.

5. Results and Discussion

Among all configurations, the base case simulation has moisture concentration close to maximum limitation (200 ppmv) due to the availability of data validation to plant data. The proposed configurations were set to achieve 180 ppmv moisture content. The purpose of setting the moisture concentration in dry gas stream below the base case result, is to show that the optimized base case and proposed configuration are better than the base case (Affandy, 2020).

Table 1 Performance comparison between the base case and the proposed configurations

Configuration	Lean TEG flowrate (kmole/h)	Lean TEG purity (%-mole)	Dry Gas Moisture (ppmv)	Solvent Loss (kg/h)
Base case	70.0	90.7	198	0.016
+ Coldfinger	16.5	96.1	181	0.013
+ Coldfinger + Flash gas as stripping	17.5	94.9	180	0.037

The proposed configurations using coldfinger system or flash gas as stripping gas have improved the solvent purity. This result will have big relation with the TEG flow rate that needed to obtain the water moisture concentration target in the dry gas stream. Since both proposed configurations gave higher solvent purity, therefore to achieve the moisture target, the system could be run at much lower solvent flowrate as presented in Table 1. The solvent loss based on the TEG make-up needed for every configuration also be studied here. The reason solvent loss occurs in the natural gas dehydration unit using TEG is the solvent carried over in dry gas increase as well as at TEG purification step. The coldfinger system and flash gas as stripping gas in the regeneration column is extremely high compared to another configuration. The combination between coldfinger system and flash gas as stripping gas likely has effect on the solvent loss (Affandy, 2020)

Table 2 Cost comparison between the base case and the proposed configurations

Configuration	TCC ($)	TCC / PB ($/year)	TOC ($/year)	TAC ($/year)
Base case	362,654	120,884	198,144	319,028
+ Coldfinger	366,301	122,100	87,306	209,406
+ Coldfinger + Flash gas as stripping	369,048	123,016	89,803	212,819

Table 2 shows that the addition of coldfinger system in the regeneration package affects to the total capital cost of the configuration that use coldfinger system. The main variables affecting the TOC reduction in the proposed configurations are TEG flow rate and TEG purity. Lower circulation rate has big impact on the total duty in the regeneration process. The proposed configuration to involve flash gas as stripping agent was found to give slightly higher reboiler loads compared to the configuration of regeneration with

Coldfinger only, hence more operating cost required. However, all proposed configurations have lower TAC compared to base case (Affandy, 2020).

6. Conclusions

This article described process synthesis of new configuration for natural gas dehydration using TEG. The configuration consists of a packed column in TEG Contactor and combined Coldfinger and rerouted vent gas as additional stripping gas in the regeneration section. The results showed that the new configuration is capable of providing similar water moisture content in the treated gas stream while minimizing the utilities requirements. This has led to about 33% reduction of the Total Annual Cost of the new configuration compared to the Base Case. It reduced the TAC to US$ 212,819 per year from US$ 319,028 per year.

Acknowledgements

The authors would like to express their gratitude for the financial aid given by the Ministry of Research and Technology/National Research and Innovation Agency Republic of Indonesia and Institut Teknologi Sepuluh Nopember.

References

Affandy, Sony A., Kurniawan, A., Handogo, R., Sutikno, J. P., & Chien, I. (2020). Technical and economic evaluation of triethylene glycol regeneration process using flash gas as stripping gas in a domestic natural gas dehydration unit. *Engineering Reports*, *August 2019*, 1–15.

Affandy, Sony Ardian. (2020). *DESIGN AND OPTIMIZATION OF NATURAL GAS DEHYDRATION UNIT USING TRIETHYLENE GLYCOL (TEG)*. Institut Teknologi Sepuluh Nopember Surabaya.

Affandy, Sony Ardian, Renanto, Juwari, & Chien, I. L. (2017). Simulation and optimization of structured packing replacement in absorption column of natural gas dehydration unit using triethylene glycol (TEG). *2017 6th International Symposium on Advanced Control of Industrial Processes, AdCONIP 2017*, 275–281.

Carrol, J. (2014). Dehydration of natural gas. In *Natural Gas Hydrates A Guide for Engineers* (pp. 175–195). Gulf Professional Publishing. https://doi.org/10.1016/b978-075067569-7/50007-2

Kong, Z. Y., Mahmoud, A., Liu, S., & Sunarso, J. (2018). Revamping existing glycol technologies in natural gas dehydration to improve the purity and absorption efficiency: Available methods and recent developments. *Journal of Natural Gas Science and Engineering*, *56*(June), 486–503. https://doi.org/10.1016/j.jngse.2018.06.008

Lars, Erik Øi, Tyvand, S. (2002). Process simulation of glycol regeneration. *GPA Europe's Meeting*.

Luyben, W. (2011). Economic Basis. In *Principles and Case Studies of Simultaneous Design* (pp. 1–317). John Wiley & Sons.

Rahimpour, M. R., Jokar, S. M., Feyzi, P., & Asghari, R. (2013). Investigating the performance of dehydration unit with Coldfinger technology in gas processing plant. *Journal of Natural Gas Science and Engineering*, *12*, 1–12. https://doi.org/10.1016/j.jngse.2013.01.001

Romero, I. A., Andreasen, A., Nielsen, R. P., & Maschietti, M. (2019). Modeling of the coldfinger water exhauster for advanced TEG regeneration in natural gas dehydration. *Chemical Engineering Transactions*, *74*(June), 661–666.

Proceedings of the 14th International Symposium on Process Systems Engineering – PSE 2021+
June 19-23, 2022, Kyoto, Japan
http://dx.doi.org/10.1016/B978-0-323-85159-6.50040-3

A new trust-region approach for optimization of multi-period heat exchanger networks with detailed shell-and-tube heat exchanger designs

Saif R. Kazi[b], Ishanki A. De Mel[a], and Michael Short[a*]

[a] *Department of Chemical and Process Engineering, University of Surrey, Guildford GU2 7XH, UK*
[b] *Department of Chemical Engineering, Carnegie Mellon University, 5000 Forbes Avenue, Pittsburgh, PA 15232, USA*
m.short@surrey.ac.uk

Abstract

Multi-period Heat Exchanger Networks (HENs) are designed as heat recovery energy efficient systems over a set of operating conditions for process streams. The problem becomes more complex when detailed exchanger designs are accounted for in the network synthesis problem. Typically, in mixed-integer nonlinear programming (MINLP) multi-period HEN optimisation, the maximum area heat exchanger across all periods is considered. However, when considering detailed designs, often this exchanger is unsuitable for operation over all periods. In this study, a trust-region algorithm is proposed to incorporate detailed exchanger designs for multi-period operation. The exchanger design is modelled using surrogate models inside a network-level NLP model which is derived from the multi-period MINLP HENS model solution. The method is applied to a case study and the results show the effectiveness of the proposed algorithm.

Keywords: Process Synthesis, Heat Exchanger Network, Optimization

1. Introduction

HENs are common heat recovery systems in process industries that minimize utility costs. These systems exchange heat between hot process streams required to be cooled and cold process streams which need heat to reach higher desired temperatures. It is increasingly common for industrial plants to be operated over multiple, differing operating conditions, especially in batch processing. This requires HEN designs to be robust and feasible for different possible operating conditions, with this design process called multi-period HEN synthesis. Many studies have addressed this variation of the HEN problem, beginning with Aaltola (2002), which solved a simultaneous MINLP problem over different periods. Verheyen and Zhang (2006) solved the multi-period HEN using the largest exchanger area over the periods in the objective function. While most of these approaches focus on the trade-off between capital costs (exchanger area costs) and operating costs (heating and cooling utilities), the underlying detailed designs of the exchangers are not considered in the optimization. With varying conditions and streams with different thermophysical properties, it becomes more important to include the effect of exchanger design (number of shells, baffles, tubes etc.) in the HEN solution performance (Kang and Liu, 2019).

Mizutani et al. (2003) was the first to use Bell-Delaware based MINLP exchanger design models in HEN synthesis. They used integer variables for discrete decisions such as number of baffles, fluid allocation, tube diameter etc. and nonlinear equations for heat transfer correlations and pressure drop. Due to the nonconvex MINLP nature of the exchanger design model, it is difficult to solve large HEN problems with many exchangers. Short et al. (2016a) developed a two-step hybrid strategy to incorporate the exchanger design based on the Bell-Delaware method, using correction factors in the HEN MINLP model. Short et al. (2016b) used a similar strategy to solve multi-period HEN problems, with feasible detailed exchanger designs over all operational periods, using manual heuristics to design the exchangers at each iteration.

Recently, Goncalves et al. (2019) have used linearization techniques and heuristics to solve the exchanger design model much more efficiently. Kazi et al. (2021a) proposed a discrete differential algebraic equation (DAE) model for detailed exchanger design which requires fewer assumptions than LMTD based methods. They also proposed a trust-region algorithm (Kazi et al., 2021b) to directly incorporate detailed exchanger designs into HEN synthesis, ensuring feasibility and optimality of the solution. In this work, we extend the formulation of Mahmood et al. (2021) to design shell and tube heat exchangers over multiple operating conditions using a discrete first principles model. We formulate a trust-region algorithm which embeds these discrete models inside a network-level HEN NLP model to solve for detailed exchanger designs along with optimal splitting ratios for process streams. To the extent of the authors' knowledge, this is the first study to incorporate multi-period exchanger design directly in HEN synthesis models.

2. Heat Exchanger Model

The heat exchanger design model uses a two-step algorithm, where the first step applies an enumeration-based approach to determine the discrete decision variables (tube diameter, number of baffles etc.). This model is similar to Mahmood et al. (2021) which uses an LMTD-based NLP formulation and smart enumeration to solve multi-period multi-shell heat exchanger designs. We expand this model to reformulate it to include the ability for different heat exchanger shells to have different geometry (tube diameter, tube length and number of baffles), in addition to including multiple tube pass arrangements. This enables the exchanger design to be more robust to varying stream.

The model also has additional degrees of freedom by introducing splitting variables on both tube and shell side for each operational period. This allows the streams to split and mix at the inlet and outlet of each shell respectively. The fraction of splitting provides additional degrees of freedom to find more feasible designs. For simplicity, the number of passes and tube allocation is kept the same across the multiple shells. Splitting and mixing constraints are as follows: For period j and shell k, volumetric flow rate (V_{jk}) is related to total inlet mass flow rate (m_j) using split ratio variable r_{jk}:

$$V_{jk} = (m_j/\rho_j).(1 - r_{jk}) \quad \forall j, 1 \leq k \leq N \tag{1}$$

Similarly, the mixing occurs at the exit of each shell using the following energy balance:

$$T_{jk}{}^{out}(1 - r_{jk}) + T_{jk}{}^{in} r_{jk} = T_{jk+1}{}^{in} \quad \forall j, 1 \leq k \leq N - 1 \tag{2}$$

The duty for the shells, using the tube and shell side temperatures and split ratios, is:

$$Q = m_j.Cp_j.(1 - r_{jk}).(T_{jk}{}^{out} - T_{jk}{}^{in}) \ \forall j, 1 \leq k \leq N \tag{3}$$

LMTD for each shell is approximated using a small positive parameter (ε) as shown:

$$LMTD \approx \Delta T_2 . \sqrt{(((\Delta T_1/\Delta T_2 - 1)^2 + \epsilon)/(log(\Delta T_1/\Delta T_2)^2 + \epsilon))} \quad (4)$$

The other constraints in the model and the design equations are provided in the supplementary section of Kazi et al. (2021a), extended to multi-period.

2.1. *DAE Model*

The heat exchanger design based on the LMTD equation has certain assumptions such as constant physical properties and no phase change. Moreover, the LMTD approximation makes the Bell-Delaware model unsuitable for derivative based solvers. In the second step, a more accurate first principles DAE model which was proposed in Kazi et al. (2021a) is used which does not use the LMTD formula, F_t correction and its assumptions. This is particularly useful in situations where thermophysical fluid properties can change with temperature which is commonplace in batch processing.

The DAE model uses coupled ODEs with algebraic design equations to size the exchanger. The ODEs are discretized using the discrete geometric design variables (number of tube passes and baffles) into finite elements. The heat equation for both tube and shell side is discretized and solved and the size of the discretized elements are used to calculate overall exchanger design variables such as number of tubes, shell diameter etc. In the algorithm, values of the discrete variables are obtained from the solution of the first step using the LMTD method.

Similar to the first step, the multi-period DAE model gives for more flexible design by allowing for streams to split and bypass over exchanger shells. The discretized heat equations inside each element are written as:

$$C^h{}_{jk}\,(T_{jk}{}^{i+1} - T_{jk}{}^{i})/2 + U_{jk}\Delta A_k(T_{jk}{}^{i+1} - t_{jk}{}^{i+1})/3 + U_{jk}\,\Delta A_k(T_{jk}{}^{i} - t_{jk}{}^{i})/6 = 0$$

$$C^c{}_{jk}\,(t_{jk}{}^{i+1} - t_{jk}{}^{i})/2 - U_{jk}\Delta A_k(T_{jk}{}^{i+1} - t_{jk}{}^{i+1})/3 - U_{jk}\,\Delta A_k(T_{jk}{}^{i} - t_{jk}{}^{i})/6 = 0 \quad (5)$$

The complete DAE model is described in Kazi et al. (2021a) with details on discretization and solution strategy.

3. Trust Region Algorithm

The multi-period HEN model has inaccurate and insufficient design equations for each exchanger. To obtain accurate detailed designs for each exchanger, we use a trust-region algorithm, similar to Kazi et al. (2021b), that embeds detailed DAE models as black box functions using surrogate models. The network NLP model can be written as Eq.(6) :

$$\min f(x), s.t.\, g(x) \leq 0, h(x) = 0, y = d(w) \quad (6)$$

where f, g, and h are twice differentiable functions and d is the black box DAE model, whose equations are unknown to the NLP model. y and w are input and output variables to the black box function, and the other variables in the NLP are denoted by z, such that $x^T = [w^T, y^T, z^T]$. The black box function is replaced by reduced model r(w) and a trust-region constraint is added to ensure that the reduced model is a "*good*" approximation of the original model within the trust-region. The trust region subproblem ($TRSP_k$) is then:

$$min\, f(x), s.t.\, g(x) \leq 0, h(x) = 0, y = r_k(w), ||x - x_k|| \leq \Delta_k \quad (7)$$

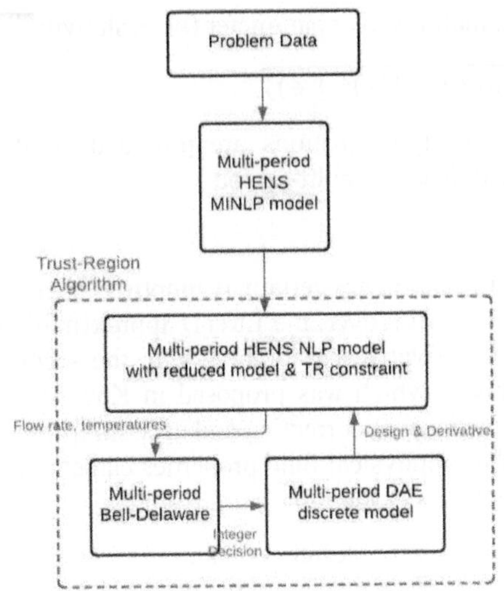

Figure 1: Algorithm illustration

To further simplify and reduce the size of the TRSP NLP problem, the variables can be partitioned into $x^T = [u^T, v^T]$, where u are the degrees of freedom and v are the rest of the variables. The reformulated $TRSP_k$ is written as Eq.(8) follows:

$$\min f(x) + \beta q, s.t. g(x) \leq q \in R^+,$$
$$h(x) = 0, y = r_k(w), \qquad (8)$$
$$||u - u_k|| \leq \Delta_k$$

where β is a penalty parameter and q is a relaxation variable. Eq.(8) ensures that $TRSP_k$ is always feasible and has the same solution as Eq.(7) for sufficiently large value of β.

3.1. *Trust-region filter and update*

The trust-region filter (TRF) compares the infeasibility ($\theta=||d(w)-r(w)||$) and the objective value ($f(x_k)$) to update the trust-region radius (Δ_k) after each iteration of NLP solve. The reduced model (r_k) is also updated using the correction order formula as:

$$r_k(w) = s(w) + (d(w_k) - s(w_k)) + (\nabla d(w_k) - \nabla s(w_k))^T (w - w_k) \qquad (9)$$

where s is a simple surrogate model (in this case s(w) = 0) and $d(w_k), \nabla d(w_k)$ are the solution and sensitivity of the black box function model. The trust-region radius (Δ_k) is updated using the ratio test based on the decrease in infeasibility.

$$\rho = (1 - \theta(w_{k+1})/\theta(w_k), \qquad \Delta_{k+1} = \gamma \Delta_k \; if \; \rho \geq \eta_2, else \; \Delta_{k+1} = \Delta_k/\gamma \qquad (10)$$

4. Case Study

The proposed algorithm is tested with a multi-period HEN case study from Verheyen and Zhang (2006) with 3 hot streams, 4 cold streams, over 3 operational periods. Detailed stream parameters required for detailed design are obtained from Short et al. (2016b).

4.1. *Results*

The optimal network results are shown in Figure 2, with the detailed heat exchanger designs summarised in Table 1. The MINLP finds the optimal network topology to contain 7 heat exchanger matches and 5 utility exchangers, with an overall total annual cost (TAC) of $3,152,295 p.a. When detailed heat exchanger designs are incorporated via the NLP TRF algorithm, a TAC of $3,342,549 p.a. is found, when using the same objective function as used in Short et al. (2016b). This shows that without the consideration of the detailed heat exchanger designs that the costs may be significantly underestimated, particularly when considering multi-pass heat exchangers that may stray far from ideal counter-current flow and requiring more shells. Interestingly, when the tube-side velocities are allowed to be quite low (lower bound of 0.5 m/s), all the optimal detailed heat exchangers can carry out the required duty across all periods of operation. However, if a lower bound of 1 m/s is enforced for the tubeside, there are certain periods that require an additional heat exchanger to perform the heat exchange.

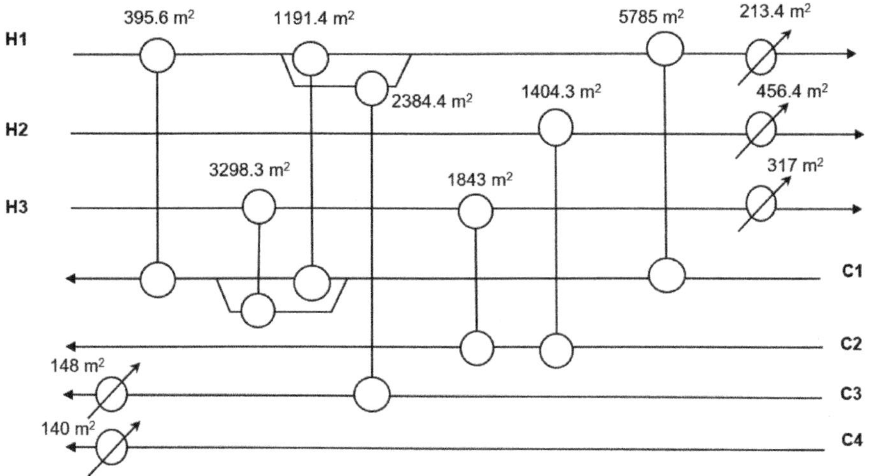

Figure 2: Solution obtained for illustrative Case Study from Verheyen and Zhang (2006)

Table 1: Summarized results for the detailed heat exchanger designs

Exchanger Assignment	Exchanger Area (m^2)	Number of shells	Split-ratio Tubeside (r_p^{tube}) for periods {1, 2, 3}	Split-ratio Shellside (r_p^{shell}) for periods {1, 2, 3}
[H1, C1, 1]	395.6	1	{0.055, 0.147, 0}	{0.263, 0.344, 0.03}
[H1, C1, 2]	1191.4	5	{0.02, 0.038, 0.09}	{0.0154, 0.0267, 0}
[H1, C1, 4]	5785	7	{0.014, 0.0124, 0.01}	{0.051, 0.038, 0.0225}
[H1, C3, 2]	2384.4	4	{0.083, 0.0347, 0}	{0.0334, 0.0203, 0.0083}
[H2, C2, 4]	1404.3	3	{0.023, 0.12, 0.035}	{0, 0, 0.063}
[H3, C1, 2]	3298.3	6	{0.02, 0.132, 0.02}	{0.023, 0.0132, 0.0201}
[H3, C2, 3]	1843.04	4	{0.02, 0.053, 0.073}	{0.003, 0.032, 0.034}

5. Conclusions

In this paper a new approach to the design of multi-period HENs is presented that incorporates detailed heat exchanger designs into the network optimisation via surrogate modelling and a trust-region filter algorithm. This is the first algorithm presented in literature that incorporates detailed shell-and-tube heat exchanger designs in the network synthesis problem for multi-period operation automatically. Detailed shell and tube heat exchangers are designed optimally for the input-output information provided from the NLP network optimisation via a novel hybrid multi-period heat exchanger design algorithm using DAEs to make for a general and rigorous process synthesis framework. The results obtained show that it is important to consider the detailed heat exchanger designs during network synthesis, as the obtained design and optimal solution were shown to be very different, with the MINLP network synthesis using only the maximum area across the operational periods underestimating the overall costs significantly. By including more information regarding numbers of shells, non-counterflow behaviour in the exchangers, and the potential for stream bypassing and splitting, the new algorithm provides more realistic answers within an optimisation framework. The algorithm presented here may help in finding improved networks in dynamic multi-period industrial environments. The DAE formulation also can consider fluids with physical properties that can change within a heat exchanger, as are common in the food and fast-moving consumer goods industries. The current implementation does not allow for multiple network topologies to be systematically assessed, and is computationally costly, and hence future work will focus on improving these aspects.

References

J. Aaltola, 2002, Simultaneous synthesis of flexible heat exchanger networks, Applied Thermal Engineering, 22(8), 907-918.

Goncalves C.O., Costa A.H., Bagajewicz M.J., 2019. Linear method for the design of shell and tube heat exchangers using the Bell-Delaware method. AIChE Journal, 65, e16602.

Kang L., Liu Y., 2019. Synthesis of flexible heat exchanger networks: A review. Chinese Journal of Chemical Engineering, 27 (7), 1485-1497.

Kazi S., Short M., Biegler L., 2021a. Heat exchanger network synthesis with detailed exchanger designs: Part 1. A discretized differential algebraic equation model for shell and tube heat exchanger design. AIChE Journal, 67(1), e17056.

Kazi S., Short M., Biegler L., 2021b. A trust region framework for heat exchanger network synthesis with detailed individual heat exchanger designs. Computers and Chemical Engineering, 153, 107447.

Mahmood Z., De Mel I.A., Kazi, Z., Isafiade, A.J., Short M., 2021. An optimisation algorithm for detailed shell-and-tube heat exchanger designs for multi-period operation. Chemical Engineering Transactions, 88(1), to appear.

Mizutani F.T., Pessoa F.L.P., Queiroz E.M., Hauan S., Grossmann I.E., 2003. Mathematical programming model for heat exchanger network synthesis including detailed heat exchanger designs. 1. Shell and tube heat exchanger design. Industrial & Engineering Chemistry Research, 42, 4009-4018.

Short M., Isafiade A., Fraser D.M., Kravanja Z., 2016a. Two-step hybrid approach for the synthesis of multi-period heat exchanger networks with detailed exchanger design. Applied Thermal Engineering, 105, 807-821.

Short M., Isafiade A., Fraser D.M., Kravanja Z., 2016b. Synthesis of heat exchanger networks using mathematical programming and heuristics in a two-step optimisation procedure with detailed exchanger design. Chemical Engineering Science, 144, 372-385.

Verheyen W., Zhang N., 2006. Design of flexible heat exchanger network for multi-period operation. Chemical Engineering Science, 61(23), 7730-7753.

Proceedings of the 14th International Symposium on Process Systems Engineering – PSE 2021+
June 19-23, 2022, Kyoto, Japan
http://dx.doi.org/10.1016/B978-0-323-85159-6.50041-5

A mathematical technique for utility exchanger network synthesis and total site heat integration

Jui-Yuan Lee[a,b*], Wilasinee Seesongkram[c]

[a] *Department of Chemical Engineering and Biotechnology, National Taipei University of Technology, 1, Sec 3, Zhongxiao E Rd, Taipei 10608, Taiwan, ROC*
[b]*Research Center of Energy Conservation for New Generation of Residential, Commercial, and Industrial Sectors, National Taipei University of Technology, 1, Sec 3, Zhongxiao E Rd, Taipei 10608, Taiwan, ROC*
[c]*Chemical Engineering Practice School, King Mongkut's University of Technology Thonburi, 126 Prachautid Road, Bangmod, Thoongkru, Bangkok 10140, Thailand*
juiyuan@ntut.edu.tw

Abstract

Fossil energy has been increasingly consumed since the second Industrial Revolution, with economic growth and modernisation. This has led to environmental issues such as resource depletion, pollution and climate change. To enhance energy efficiency as a measure to mitigate climate change, heat exchanger networks (HENs) for heat recovery are widely used in various industrial applications. This work develops superstructure-based mathematical models for direct and indirect HEN synthesis for interplant heat integration. The mixed-integer nonlinear programming model minimises the total annualised cost for utility exchanger network synthesis and total site heat integration, and the results are compared with those from the conventional and unified total site targeting methods. An industrial case study is presented to demonstrate the application of the proposed approach.

Keywords: energy efficiency; heat recovery; mathematical programming; stage-wise superstructure.

1. Introduction

Due to population expansion and the Industrial Revolution as well as rapid economic growth, energy consumption in the world has significantly increased. From 2015 to 2040, world energy consumption is expected to increase by about 28% (Rodriguez, 2018). However, energy resources are limited. Therefore, heat exchanger networks (HENs), as an important heat recovery system, plays a significant role in processing plants. Synthesising HENs in chemical processes allows energy efficiency to improve. HEN synthesis has gained a lot of attention in the process industry. There have been numerous studies on HENs (Klemeš and Kravanja, 2013).

HEN research has focused mostly on a single process because of the inability to recover all the waste heat within chemical plants. Hence, considerable amounts of heat and energy are wasted. Subsequently, some researchers were interested in extending the work for a single plant to multi-plant HEN synthesis, which is also known as interplant heat integration. Both the process streams (direct integration) and the intermediate streams (indirect integration) are involved in multi-plant HEN synthesis. The direct method provides more potential for energy saving because heat is transferred directly between process streams. However, this method can entail a higher capital cost than the indirect method. This is due to the large requirement of piping and pumping. Although the indirect method can result in a lower capital cost, the achievable energy saving is reduced because of the use of intermediate fluid. Chang et al. (2019) found that considering both the direct and indirect methods could reduce the energy consumption by 3.2% when compared to using only the direct method. To maximise the benefits from multi-plants HENs synthesis, both the direct and indirect methods should be considered in the optimisation. Tarighaleslami et al. (2018) presented a unified total site integration method for HEN synthesis and utility exchange network (UEN) design. This method only allows utility heat exchangers in series within the same process.

In this work, HEN synthesis is carried out in the multi-plant/process context. Both the direct and indirect methods are used to minimise the total annualised cost (TAC) of the plant(s). A mathematical programming model is developed as an alternative to pinch-based techniques and applied to an industrial case study, where the hot-side and cold-side temperatures of the intermediate fluid (hot water) are treated as optimisation variables. The results obtained are then compared with the results reported in the previous works using pinch analysis.

2. Problem statement

- There are a set of hot process streams $i \in \mathbf{IP}_p$ and a set of cold process streams $j \in \mathbf{JP}_p$ in a set of processes $p \in \mathbf{P}$. The supply and target temperatures of the process streams and their heat capacity flowrates are known parameters.
- A set of hot utilities $hu \in \mathbf{HU}$ and a set of cold utilities $cu \in \mathbf{CU}$ are available for heating and cooling demands that cannot be met by heat recovery. Additionally, intermediate streams (e.g. hot water) that act as both a hot stream ($i \in \mathbf{IM}_p$) and a cold stream ($j \in \mathbf{JM}_p$) are also used in the processes. The supply and target temperatures on both hot and cold sides of the intermediate streams and their heat capacity flowrates are to be determined or optimised.
- The objective is to synthesise an optimal HEN, which consists of a heat recovery network and a UEN, for the minimum total annualised cost (TAC).

In this HEN synthesis problem, direct heat integration of process streams is allowed in individual processes. Inter-process heat integration is carried out indirectly through intermediate streams. It is assumed that intermediate streams are split for the processes that require heating/cooling, and mixed isothermally. Also, the supply temperature of the hot side of an intermediate stream equals its cold-side target temperature, whilst its hot-side target temperature equals its cold-side supply temperature.

3. Model formulation

Figure 1 shows a modified stage-wise superstructure, based on which the mathematical model for multi-process HEN synthesis involving heat recovery and utility exchange is formulated. This superstructure considers heat exchange matches between process and intermediate streams in all stages. However, the match between intermediate streams is excluded because intermediate streams are used for the heating and cooling of process streams. The hot side of an intermediate stream loop may use cold utilities to achieve its target temperature, whilst the cold side achieves its target temperature by heat exchange with hot process streams, without using hot utilities.

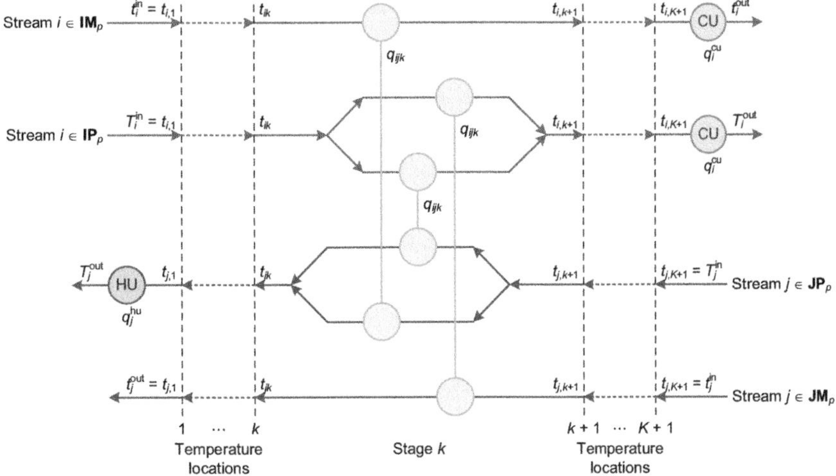

Figure 1. Stage-wise Superstructure for a HEN Involving Utility Exchange

The formulation of the HEN model is as follows. Eqs. (1)-(4) describe the overall heat balances for process and intermediate streams

$$F_i\left(T_i^{\text{in}} - T_i^{\text{out}}\right) = \sum_{j \in \mathbf{J}} \sum_{k \in \mathbf{ST}} q_{ijk} + \sum_{cu \in \mathbf{CU}} q_{i,cu} \quad \forall i \in \mathbf{IP}_p, p \in \mathbf{P} \tag{1}$$

$$F_j\left(T_j^{\text{out}} - T_j^{\text{in}}\right) = \sum_{i \in \mathbf{I}} \sum_{k \in \mathbf{ST}} q_{ijk} + \sum_{hu \in \mathbf{HU}} q_{hu,j} \quad \forall j \in \mathbf{JP}_p, p \in \mathbf{P} \tag{2}$$

$$f_i\left(t_i^{\text{in}} - t_i^{\text{out}}\right) = \sum_{j \in \mathbf{JP}_p} \sum_{k \in \mathbf{ST}} q_{ijk} + \sum_{cu \in \mathbf{CU}} q_{i,cu} \quad \forall i \in \mathbf{IM}_p, p \in \mathbf{P} \tag{3}$$

$$f_j\left(t_j^{\text{out}} - t_j^{\text{in}}\right) = \sum_{i \in \mathbf{IP}_p} \sum_{k \in \mathbf{ST}} q_{ijk} \quad \forall j \in \mathbf{JM}_p, p \in \mathbf{P} \tag{4}$$

Eqs. (5)-(8) describe the heat balances in each stage.

$$F_i\left(t_{ik} - t_{i,k+1}\right) = \sum_{j \in \mathbf{J}} q_{ijk} \quad \forall i \in \mathbf{IP}_p, p \in \mathbf{P}, k \in \mathbf{ST} \tag{5}$$

$$F_j\left(t_{jk} - t_{j,k+1}\right) = \sum_{i \in \mathbf{I}} q_{ijk} \quad \forall j \in \mathbf{JP}_p, p \in \mathbf{P}, k \in \mathbf{ST} \tag{6}$$

$$f_i\left(t_{ik} - t_{i,k+1}\right) = \sum_{j \in \mathbf{JP}_p} \sum_{p \in \mathbf{P}} q_{ijk} \quad \forall i \in \mathbf{IM}_p, p \in \mathbf{P}, k \in \mathbf{ST} \tag{7}$$

$$f_j\left(t_{jk} - t_{j,k+1}\right) = \sum_{i \in \mathbf{IP}_p} \sum_{p \in \mathbf{P}} q_{ijk} \quad \forall j \in \mathbf{JM}_p, p \in \mathbf{P}, k \in \mathbf{ST} \tag{8}$$

Temperature assignments are omitted due to space limitations. Temperature feasibility constraints are given in Eqs. (9)-(12).

$$t_{ik} \geq t_{i,k+1} \geq T_i^{\text{out}} \quad \forall i \in \mathbf{IP}_p, k \in \mathbf{ST} \tag{9}$$

$$T_j^{\mathrm{out}} \geq t_{jk} \geq t_{j,k+1} \quad \forall j \in \mathbf{JP}_p, k \in \mathbf{ST} \tag{10}$$

$$t_{ik} \geq t_{i,k+1} \geq t_i^{\mathrm{out}} \quad \forall i \in \mathbf{IM}_p, k \in \mathbf{ST} \tag{11}$$

$$t_j^{\mathrm{out}} \geq t_{jk} \geq t_{j,k+1} \quad \forall j \in \mathbf{JM}_p, k \in \mathbf{ST} \tag{12}$$

Heat loads for hot and cold utilities are given by Eqs. (13)-(15).

$$F_i(t_{ik} - T_i^{\mathrm{out}}) = \sum_{cu \in \mathbf{CU}} q_{i,cu} \quad \forall i \in \mathbf{IP}_p, p \in \mathbf{P}, k = K+1 \tag{13}$$

$$F_j\left(T_j^{\mathrm{out}} - t_{jk}\right) = \sum_{hu \in \mathbf{HU}} q_{hu,j} \quad \forall j \in \mathbf{JP}_p, p \in \mathbf{P}, k = 1 \tag{14}$$

$$f_i(t_{ik} - T_i^{\mathrm{out}}) = \sum_{cu \in \mathbf{CU}} q_{i,cu} \quad \forall i \in \mathbf{IM}_p, p \in \mathbf{P}, k = K+1 \tag{15}$$

Logical constraints are given in Eqs. (16)-(18).

$$Q_{ij}^{\mathrm{L}} z_{ijk} \leq q_{ijk} \leq Q_{ij}^{\mathrm{U}} z_{ijk} \quad \forall i \in \mathbf{I}, j \in \mathbf{J}, k \in \mathbf{ST} \tag{16}$$

$$Q_i^{\mathrm{L}} z_{i,cu} \leq q_{i,cu} \leq Q_i^{\mathrm{U}} z_{i,cu} \quad \forall i \in \mathbf{I}, cu \in \mathbf{CU} \tag{17}$$

$$Q_j^{\mathrm{L}} z_{hu,j} \leq q_{hu,j} \leq Q_j^{\mathrm{U}} z_{hu,j} \quad \forall j \in \mathbf{JP}_p, hu \in \mathbf{HU} \tag{18}$$

Eq. (19) excludes the matches between intermediate streams. Eq. (20) then excludes the matches between hot and cold streams of different processes.

$$z_{ijk} = 0 \quad \forall i \in \mathbf{IM}_p, j \in \mathbf{JM}_p, p \in \mathbf{P}, k \in \mathbf{ST} \tag{19}$$

$$z_{ijk} = 0 \quad \forall i \in \mathbf{IP}_p \cup \mathbf{IM}_p, p \in \mathbf{P}, j \in \mathbf{JP}_{p'} \cup \mathbf{JM}_{p'}, p' \in \mathbf{P} \wedge p' \neq p, k \in \mathbf{ST} \tag{20}$$

Temperature difference constraints are given in Eqs. (21)-(27).

$$\Delta T^{\min} - \Gamma\left(1 - z_{ijk}\right) \leq t_{ik} - t_{jk} \quad \forall i \in \mathbf{I}, j \in \mathbf{J}, k \in \mathbf{ST} \tag{21}$$

$$\Delta T^{\min} - \Gamma\left(1 - z_{ijk}\right) \leq t_{i,k+1} - t_{j,k+1} \quad \forall i \in \mathbf{I}, j \in \mathbf{J}, k \in \mathbf{ST} \tag{22}$$

$$\Delta T^{\min} - \Gamma\left(1 - z_{i,cu}\right) \leq t_{ik} - T_{cu}^{\mathrm{out}} \quad \forall i \in \mathbf{I}, cu \in \mathbf{CU}, k = K+1 \tag{23}$$

$$\Delta T^{\min} - \Gamma\left(1 - z_{i,cu}\right) \leq T_i^{\mathrm{out}} - T_{cu}^{\mathrm{in}} \quad \forall i \in \mathbf{IP}_p, p \in \mathbf{P}, cu \in \mathbf{CU}, k = K+1 \tag{24}$$

$$\Delta T^{\min} - \Gamma\left(1 - z_{i,cu}\right) \leq t_i^{\mathrm{out}} - T_{cu}^{\mathrm{in}} \quad \forall i \in \mathbf{IM}_p, p \in \mathbf{P}, cu \in \mathbf{CU}, k = K+1 \tag{25}$$

$$\Delta T^{\min} - \Gamma\left(1 - z_{hu,j}\right) \leq T_{hu}^{\mathrm{out}} - t_{jk} \quad \forall j \in \mathbf{JP}_p, p \in \mathbf{P}, hu \in \mathbf{HU}, k = 1 \tag{26}$$

$$\Delta T^{\min} - \Gamma\left(1 - z_{hu,j}\right) \leq T_{hu}^{\mathrm{in}} - T_j^{\mathrm{out}} \quad \forall j \in \mathbf{JP}_p, p \in \mathbf{P}, hu \in \mathbf{HU}, k = 1 \tag{27}$$

The objective function is to minimise the TAC, which consists of the annual operating cost and the annualised capital cost, as given in Eq. (28).

$$\min f_{\mathrm{TAC}} = f_{\mathrm{AOC}} + f_{\mathrm{ACC}} \tag{28}$$

Due to space limitations, detailed operating and capital cost functions are omitted. The complete model is a mixed integer nonlinear programme (MINLP).

In the next section, an industrial case study is presented to demonstrate the proposed HEN model. The MINLP model is solved in GAMS using BARON.

4. Case study

This case study considers a large kraft pulp mill plant, which contains 10 processes and 64 process streams (Bood and Nilsson, 2013). The model for this case study involves more than 10,000 constraints and variables, depending on the number of stages.

In the optimal UEN, high-pressure steam is used for four cold streams in three processes (bleaching, digestion and recovery boiler), with a total requirement of 27,741 kW. This is identical to the target of Tarighaleslami et al. (2018). In addition, low-pressure steam is used for 18 cold streams in nine processes (bleaching, causticizing, digestion, evaporator, district heating, miscellaneous, paper room, stripper and recovery boiler), with a total requirement of 131,128 kW. This is 6.65% less than that of Tarighaleslami et al. (2018). The total cooling water requirement was determined to be 79,309 kW, which is 11.56% more than that of Tarighaleslami et al. (2018).

For indirect inter-process heat integration, low-temperature and high-temperature hot water are used as intermediate streams. The optimised low-temperature hot water loop has a cold temperature of 29.19°C, a hot temperature of 59.96°C and a heat capacity flowrate of 1,051.87 kW/°C, as shown in Figure 2. On the other hand, the optimised high-temperature hot water loop has a cold temperature of 60°C, a hot temperature of 93°C and a heat capacity flowrate of 271 kW/°C, as shown in Figure 3.

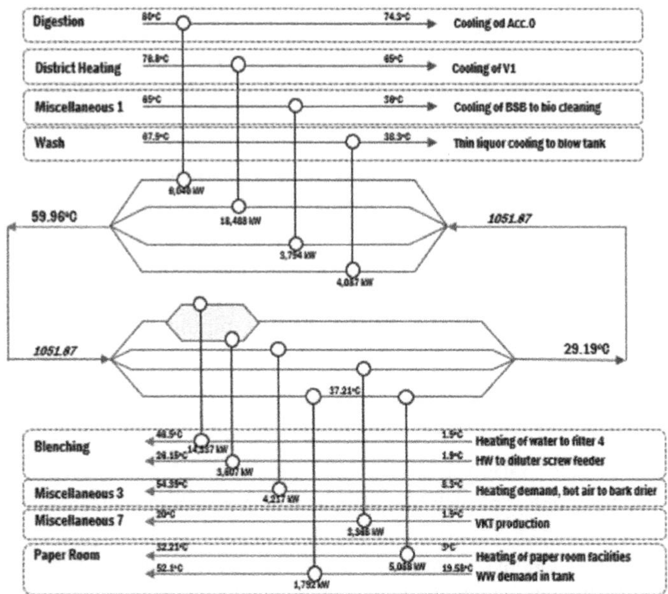

Figure 2. Low-temperature Hot Water Loop in the optimal UEN

Compared to the results of Tarighaleslami et al. (2018), the solution obtained in this work has a lower utility cost (\$42,966,983/y versus \$44,834,691/y) and a higher capital cost (\$2,109,177/y versus \$1,856,486/y). This is due to increased heat recovery in total site integration. Consequently, the TAC is reduced by \$1,615,017 (3.46%). In addition, compared to the sequential unified total site targeting method, the proposed HEN model considers the trade-off between utility and capital costs, and allows better solutions in terms of TAC to be found through a simultaneous optimisation approach.

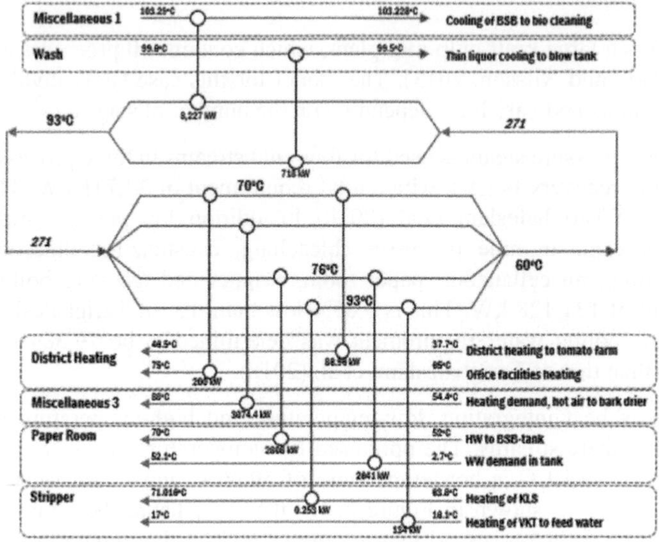

Figure 3. High-temperature Hot Water Loop in the optimal UEN

5. Conclusions

A multi-plant/process heat integration scheme with a HEN model has been presented in this paper. The model comprehensively considers the interactions between utility use, heat recovery and heat transfer area in minimizing the TAC. This model can be used to determine the required heat capacity flowrates of intermediate streams, their supply and target temperatures, and the HEN structure simultaneously. An industrial case study was solved to illustrate the applicability and effectiveness of the proposed model. Compared to sequential targeting approaches, simultaneous optimisation using the proposed model has the capability of finding the minimum-TAC solution. In future work, the objective function will be modified to include further details such as piping requirements for inter-plant/process matches in design.

References

J. Bood, L. Nilsson, 2013, Energy Analysis of Hemicellulose Extraction at a Softwood Kraft Pulp Mill, Case Study of Södra Cell Värö, MSc Thesis, Chalmers University of Technology, Gothenburg, Sweden

C. Chang, Y. Wang, X. Feng, 2019, Optimal Synthesis of Multi-plant Heat Exchanger Networks Considering both Direct and Indirect Methods, Chinese Journal Chemical Engineering, 28, 2, 456-465

J.J. Klemeš, Z. Kravanja, 2013, Forty Years of Heat Integration: Pinch Analysis (PA) and Mathematical Programming (MP). Curr Opin Chem Eng 2, 4, 461-474

J.A. Rodriguez, 2018, EIA Report Projects Fossil and Nuclear Fuels will Provide 83 Percent of Total Global Energy in 2040, Pratt's Energy Law Report, 18, 3, 97-103

A.H. Tarighaleslami, T.G. Walmsley, M.J. Atkins, M.R.W. Walmsley, J.R. Neale, 2018, Utility Exchanger Network Synthesis for Total Site Heat Integration, Energy, 153, 1000-1015

Proceedings of the 14th International Symposium on Process Systems Engineering – PSE 2021+
June 19-23, 2022, Kyoto, Japan
http://dx.doi.org/10.1016/B978-0-323-85159-6.50042-7

Synthesis and Assessment of NOx to Ammonia Conversion Process in Combined Cycle Power Generation Systems

Hideyuki Matsumoto[a*], Kanako Kurahashi[b] , Haruna Tachikawa[a], Takaya Iseki[b]

[a] *Department of Chemical Science Engineering, Tokyo Institute of Technology, Tokyo 152-8550, JAPAN*

[b] *Fundamental Technology Research Institute, Tokyo Gas Co., Ltd., Yokohama 230-0045, JAPAN*

**Corresponding Author's E-mail: matsumoto.h.ae@m.titech.ac.jp*

Abstract

A purpose of the present paper is to demonstrate feasibility of two NOx to ammonia (NTA) processes in the combined cycle power generation systems by using process simulation. In application of NTA process that is single-stage system for conversion of NO to NH_3 available in existence of oxygen, an effect of NTA process operating temperature on power generation efficiency of two class of gas turbines (1300 °C, 1700 °C) was estimated. Possible configurations of the exhaust gas aftertreatment incorporating the NTA system were also proposed and clarified.

Keywords: Process Synthesis; Nitrogen Cycle; Thermal Power Plant; Heat Exchanger Network.

1. Introduction

Exhaust gas, wastewater, and residues generated from industries and living activities contain harmful nitrogen compounds such as NOx, organic nitrogen, ammonia nitrogen [NH_4^+, NH_3, etc.], NO_3^-, etc. It has been reported the amount of reactive nitrogen (NOx) discharged by combustion of fossil fuel and biomass alone accounts for 20% of the total amount discharged from the human systems (Galloway *et al.*, 2008). So far, various selective catalytic reduction (SCR) methods have been reported to remove NOx in combustion exhaust gas. For example, in the urea SCR system, ammonia is utilized as a reductant. Previous study for the SCR system using hydrocarbon (HC-SCR systems) has reported that ammonia formed in the middle of SCR could accelerate the SCR process.

Instead of converting NOx into compound that has no economic value like N_2, possibilities to convert it into valuable product of NH_3 using similar principle as SCR process exists. Recently, development of NOx to ammonia conversion process (NTA process) has been actively promoted, since it is expected that reuse of the produced ammonia as a fuel and a denitration agent will bring about reduction of CO_2 emissions. It is estimated that approximately 250 million ton of ammonia could be produced by using a half of NOx (4%) in exhaust gas from all the thermal power plants located in Japan.

Hence, we consider that the NTA process could achieve both reduction of nitrogen compound emissions and reduction of greenhouse gas emissions, that is, "Cool & Clean

Earth". However, a method of the NTA process incorporation into the plant system and its effect have not been sufficiently investigated. The introduction of the NTA process not only reduces the amount of nitrogen compounds emitted into the environment to zero, but also can be expected to reduce the amount of denitration agent supply, the cost of denitration equipment, and the amount of energy supply to the overall plant system. A purpose of the present paper is to analyse and demonstrate the incorporation of NTA process to combined cycle gas turbine (CCGT) as part of exhaust gas aftertreatment. Process simulation was employed to predict the possible optimum process efficiency, as well as reduction of nitrogen compound emission.

2. Analysis for introducing two-stage NTA process system to CCGT system

A steady-state process simulator for CCGT (Figure 1) was developed by using the free process simulation environment COCO (CAPE-OPEN to CAPE-OPEN: https://www.cocosimulator.org/). The model of the CCGT system consists of a model of a high-pressure steam turbine and a model of a medium-pressure steam turbine. The process simulation of feeding natural gas consisting of CH_4 (about 90%), C_2H_6, C_3H_8, and C_4H_{10} to a gas turbine at about 56 t/h revealed that about 370 MW of energy was recovered in (1) to (4) in Figure 1. The power generation efficiency was estimated to be about 54 %. In this paper, we investigated the introduction methods of the following two types of NTA processes (i) and (ii).

- NTA process (i): Two-stage process system that consists of "adsorption/ concentration of NO" and "conversion of NO to NH_3 that is available in absence of oxygen"
- NTA process (ii): Single-stage process system for conversion of NO to NH_3 that is available in existence of oxygen

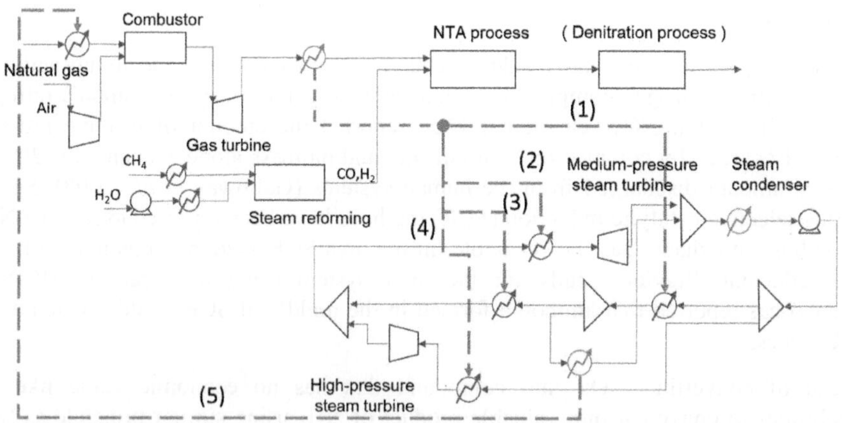

Figure 1 Example of process simulation of combined cycle power generation system.

First, influence of introducing the NTA process (i) in the CCGT system was analysed by the above-mentioned steady-state process simulator. In this simulation, the NTA process model based on the above-mentioned reaction of R1 and R2 was applied.

R1 : $2NO+5CO+3H_2O \rightarrow 2NH_3+5CO_2$

R2 : $2NO+5H_2 \rightarrow 2NH_3+2H_2O$

In reactions R1 and R2, CO and H_2 act as reductant of NO to produce NH_3. Based on the previous literature data (Kobayashi *et al.*, 2019), a correlation equation between the reaction temperature and the NO conversion was estimated (Figure 2), which was applied to the NTA reactor model. In addition, in case of incomplete conversion of NO by the NTA reaction, it was assumed that the generated NH_3 was used for denitration of the remained NO in subsequent conventional SCR process.

The CO and H_2 for these NTA reactions were assumed to be supplied from the process of steam reforming of methane that was utilized from fuel gas to the gas turbine. In this process simulation, the amount of fuel gas used in the CH_4 steam reforming was determined based on the amount of reductant that was stoichiometrically required for conversion of NO in the combustion exhaust gas. In calculation for the steam reforming process, the reaction temperature was 1000 °C, the pressure was 1.4 MPa, and the molar ratio of CH_4 to H_2O was 1.

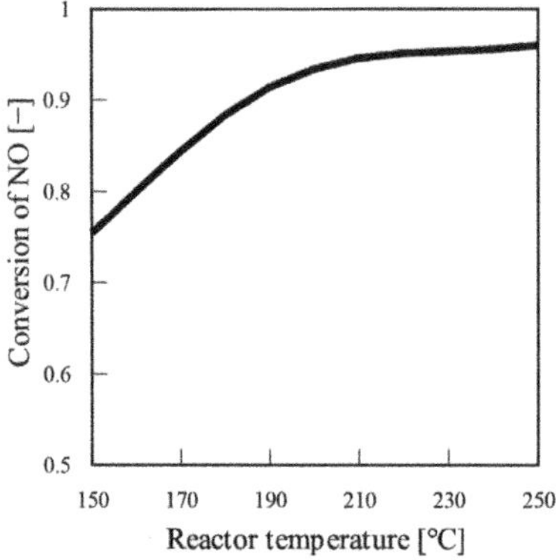

Figure 2 An example of calculation results based on the NTA reactor model.

Simulations for five cases (A—E) were performed as shown in Figure 3 to analyse influence combination of the heat exchanger (1) – (4) (Figure 1) in the heat recovery steam generator (HRSG) and the NTA process. In the cases of A and B, the temperature T_i before the NTA process was too low to commence the NTA reaction. For the case of C, conversion of NO to NH_3 by the NTA reaction was not complete. Subsequently, the SCR post-treatment was required, which consumed a portion of the generated NH_3 and decreased its overall yield. For the cases of D and E, it was seen that the outflow of NO from the NTA process was small. In particular, for case of E, about 1.9 t/h of ammonia, which was the maximum yield, was estimated when the NO concentration in the exhaust gas was about 130 ppm.

In the above simulation analysis, the amount of energy required for the CH_4 steam reforming to produce the reductant (CO, H_2) was estimated to be about 30 MW. Considering that the amount of energy recovered by the high-pressure steam turbine was about 25 MW, it was found that the energy consumption for production of the reductant significantly decreased in the power generation efficiency of the entire CCGT system. In addition, the use of natural gas reforming to produce CO-H_2 reductants offset the benefits of CO_2 reduction from the NTA system. Furthermore, for minimizing the energy consumption of the entire system, it is necessary to optimize position of the installed NTA reactor in the HRSG.

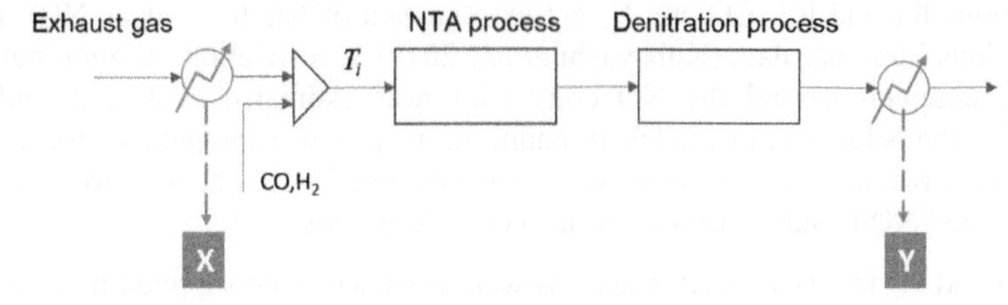

Case	X	Y
A	1,2,3,4	—
B	1,2,3	4
C	1,4	2,3
D	2,4	1,4
E	4	1,2,3

Figure 3 Five cases for combination of heat exchanger and NTA process in heat recovery steam generator (HRSG). Numbers in the table denote the heat exchange combination shown in Figure 1.

3. Design of CCGT system with single-stage NTA process system

We investigated a method for introducing the NTA process (ii) to the CCGT system by using the process simulator. It is considered that the CO_2 emissions derived from power generation can be significantly reduced by raising the combustion temperature of the gas turbine, which was attributed to improvement of the power generation efficiency.

Thus, we analysed influence of combustion temperature for the gas turbine to preferable position of the installed NTA process and the power generation efficiency of the entire CCGT system, by using a simulation system that included the pinch analysis (Figure 4). In the simulation system, the structure of the heat exchanger network in the HSRG that could perform the maximum recovery of heat of steam was derived by pinch analysis. And the amount of power generated by the entire CCGT system was estimated by using process simulation based on the derived heat exchanger network models.

In the present paper, the operating temperature for the NTA reactor was set at 300 °C or higher, by referring to information of the catalyst developed by Prof. Iwamoto research group in Waseda University. Assuming the operating temperature of the conventional ammonia selective catalytic reduction (NH_3-SCR) process in the CCGT system was 350 °C, it was considered that a part of the NH_3-SCR equipment in the HRSG could be replaced by the NTA process. In introduction of the developed NTA process, it is expected that its performance will facilitate revamp of the target CCGT system. Thus, we investigated influence of the operating temperature of the NTA process to energy consumption and power generation efficiency of the entire system. It was also assumed that the outlet temperature of the NTA reactor was different from the operating temperature of NH_3-SCR equipment.

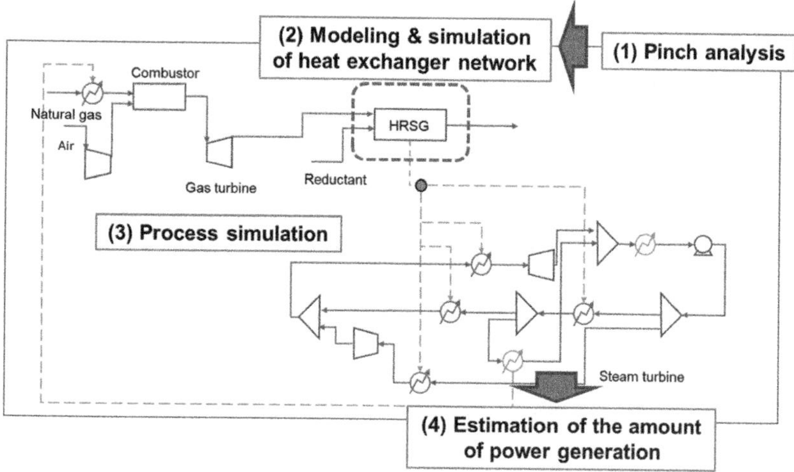

Figure 4 A framework of simulation system for design of CCGT system with one-stage NTA process system.

In a case when the operating temperature of the NTA process was set at 330 °C, which was reported to attain a relatively high NH_3 yield (however, conversion was less than 50%), it was assumed that NH_3-SCR process was placed after the NTA process. Thus, we came up with the two kinds of subprocess (Figure 5) as a means of raising the temperature of outflow from the NTA reactor to 350 °C.

- Subprocess 1: An afterburner is inserted at the midpoint between NTA reactor and NH_3-SCR equipment, and the gas temperature is adjusted to 350 °C.
- Subprocess 2: Part of the exhaust gas is bypassed from the inlet of HRSG to the midpoint between NTA reactor and NH_3-SCR equipment, and the gas temperature is adjusted to 350 ° C.

As mentioned in Section 2, it was found that change of the combustion temperature of the gas turbine from 1300 °C to 1700 °C could increase the NO concentration in the exhaust gas and further reduce CO_2 emissions. Thus, for two case studies with gas turbine combustion temperatures of 1300 °C and 1700 °C, we investigated effects of introducing the above-mentioned two subprocesses on power generation efficiency of the entire system, respectively. In the present simulation analysis, simulation models for two types of gas turbine M701DA, M701JAC (Mitsubishi Heavy Industries, Ltd.) were applied to calculate process data for CCGT system applying 1300 °C class and 1700 °C class, respectively.

Table 1 shows an example of results for optimization of the heat exchanger network in the HSRG based on the pinch analysis for Subprocess 1. For the case study applying a 1700 °C class gas turbine, implementation of the Subprocess 1 increased the amount of power generated by the steam turbine (ST). In contrast, implementation of Subprocess 2 showed decrease in the amount of generated power. As shown in Table 1, positioning of the NTA reactor and the NH_3-SCR equipment differed slightly for Subprocess 1, which depends on the combustion temperature in the gas turbine.

4. Conclusions

For combined cycle power generation systems, we estimated effects of introduction methods for two different types of NTA processes (i) and (ii) on efficiency of the entire system, respectively. In application of NTA process (ii), an effect of the design temperature of the NTA process (around 350 °C) on the decrease in power generation efficiency was estimated, and furthermore the difference of changes in power generation efficiency between two class of gas turbines (1300 °C, 1700 °C) was also clarified. Hence, the optimization of the mass and energy balance and the evaluation of performance of CCGT system from the viewpoint of overall system were demonstrated to be useful for setting target temperature and target performance in the research and development of NTA catalysts.

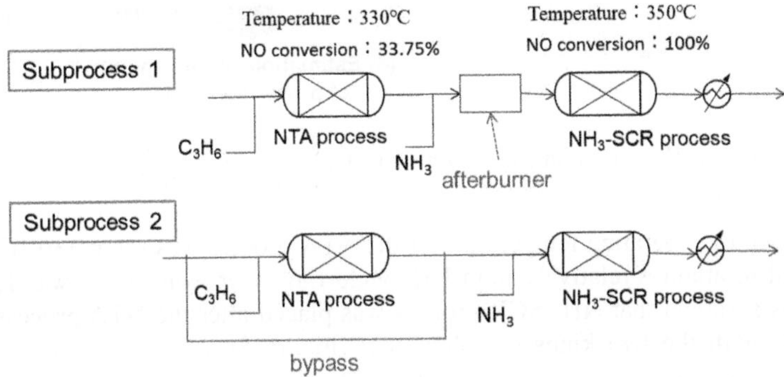

Figure 5 Introduction method of NTA process and NH_3-SCR process.

Table 1 Simulation results for optimization of the heat exchanger network in the HSRG for Subprocess 1.

	1700 °C class gas turbine	1300 °C class gas turbine
Additional fuel	17.81 MW	10.55 MW
Changes in the amount of power generated by ST	+4.6 MW (Increase)	+3.67 MW (Increase)
Changes in power generation efficiency	−0.6 pt (Decrease)	−0.4 pt (Decrease)
Optimum position of NTA & NH_3-SCR processes	In the middle of high-pressure secondary economizer & medium pressure overheating	In the middle of high-pressure steam economizer

Acknowledgement

This paper is based on results obtained from a project, P14004, commissioned by the New Energy and Industrial Technology Development Organization (NEDO).

References

J. N. Galloway *et al.*, 2008, Transformation of the Nitrogen Cycle: Recent Trends, Questions, and Potential Solutions, Science, **320**, 889-892.

K. Kobayashi *et al.*, 2019, Effect of the TiO_2 crystal structure on the activity of TiO_2-supported platinum catalysts for ammonia synthesis via the NO–CO–H_2O reaction, Catal. Sci. Technol., **9**, 2898–2905.

Proceedings of the 14th International Symposium on Process Systems Engineering – PSE 2021+
June 19-23, 2022, Kyoto, Japan
http://dx.doi.org/10.1016/B978-0-323-85159-6.50043-9

Knowledge integrated, deep neural network-based prediction of stress-strain curves of polymer matrix composites for AI-assisted materials design

Nagyeong Lee [a], Jaewook Lee [a] and Dongil Shin [a,b*]

[a] *Department of Chemical Engineering, Myongji University, Yongin, Gyeonggido, 17058, Korea*

[b] *Department of Disaster and Safety, Myongji University, Yongin, Gyeonggido, 17058, Korea*

**dongil@mju.ac.kr*

Abstract

In order to achieve an effective energy transition, development of new materials must be accompanied with the development of new and renewable energy facilities. However, to this day, material design is costly because material development relies on the designer's intuition. Therefore, for the competitiveness of material development, AI-based material design automation must be made through the combination and composition prediction of components. As the first step in the AI-based material reverse engineering system, this study predicts the mechanical properties and behavior of polymer matrix composites (PMC).

The mechanical behavior of a material can be expressed from the strain-stress curve (S-S curve), and the deformation from the elastic section to the plastic section can be judged along with mechanical properties such as tensile strength, elastic modulus, and maximum load. Therefore, this study aims to predict the mechanical behavior of the PMC by learning the minimum tensile test data and information on the components for the two-component PMC based on the deep learning methodology.

Through literature/data analysis, most features that can affect mechanical properties were classified into two predictive models. The first predictive model inputs tensile test data and chemical/mechanical properties, and outputs mechanical properties behavior. And the second prediction model predicts by inputting structural information of each components. Through SMILES of each components, MACCS key was obtained and converted to use functional group information and used as a feature. As a result of comparing the performance of the two predictive models, the second model required less material information than the model that did not learn structural information, and performed better. As a result, it is a model that predicts the behavior of the plastic section beyond the existing prediction model that stayed in the elastic modulus section.

Keywords: Machine learning, Language process model, Polymer matrix composite (PMC), Mechanical property, Chemical language processing

1. Introduction

Stable securing of new materials is one of the important conditions to achieve efficient energy transition. For example, to solve the green mobility issue with low energy efficiency, many companies are paying attention to fuel efficiency improvement through vehicle weight reduction and participating in material development. In particular, a material attracting attention in the face of energy conversion is polymer matrix composites (PMC).

For material development, it is essential to reflect mechanical properties, and there are tensile strength, modulus of elasticity, maximum load, maximum stress, break point, and stress. These can be easily derived from the S-S curve obtained from the tensile test. Mechanical properties and behaviors are expressed differently depending on the components (matrix, filler), the composition of each components, test conditions, process conditions, etc. Because of the various complexity, to this day, designs are made by the designer's intuition. For the competitiveness of material development, we proposed an AI-based reverse engineering system with the mechanical properties required for the application, away from the material design method that relied on experience.

There have been attempts to predict mechanical properties in the past, but in this study, the S-S curve problem over the entire section of the material, which was difficult to predict due to the large plasticity section and complex response, was predicted based on the deep neural network (DNN). The model predicts the entire S-S curve even in the absence of test data by using complex correlations between vast amounts of experimental data. In this paper, tensile test data in various compositions for a two-component combination using amorphous and partially crystalline polymers, which are often used as materials for transportation equipment, as a base material, and ceramic powder, glass fiber, carbon fiber, etc. as reinforcing materials was used to build a data-based prediction model.

2. Background

In this section, 2.1 describes previous studies and challenge for predicting PMC mechanical properties behavior, and 2.2 describes the theoretical background based on the study.

2.1. Challenge

There are two representative mathematical models that predict the S-S curve through numerical models. First, Ramberg-Osgood relationship:

$$\frac{\varepsilon}{\varepsilon_0} = \frac{\sigma}{\sigma_0} + (\frac{\sigma}{\sigma_0})^n \tag{1}$$

$\varepsilon = strain, \quad \varepsilon_0 = \left(\frac{\sigma_0}{E}\right), \; strain, \sigma = stress, \; \sigma_0 = yield\ strength, \; E = elastic\ modulus$. And a second is Hollomon piecewise power law:

$$\frac{\varepsilon}{\varepsilon_0} = \begin{cases} \frac{\sigma}{\sigma_0} & for\, \sigma \geq \sigma_0 \\ (\frac{\sigma}{\sigma_0})^n & for\, \sigma \geq \sigma_0; \;\; 1 < n \leq \infty \end{cases} \tag{2}$$

n=1, it is a complete elastic material, and when n=∞, it is an elastic-complete plastic material.

The two mathematical relational expressions, most of all, are not suitable for functions with high nonlinearity. In the case of Eq.1, the prediction accuracy is lowered for materials with rapid changes in the plasticity section because the calculation is performed without separating the elastic/plastic section (H. C. Hyun et al.). On the other hand, in the case of Equation Eq.2, the prediction rate is higher than the Eq.1 using the section power function method, but it is difficult to apply a new material, due to that it is hard to categorise the carbon/plastic section. The mechanical behavior of PMC has more than one directionality and various parameters, so there is a limit to expressing it in a numerical formula.. Therefore, mechanical properties behavior including the plastic section of PMC is predicted through DNN.

2.2. Theoretical background

(1) Chemical structure information

Chemical structure information was expressed through chemical identifiers. Chemical identifiers are strings designed to encode chemical structures, chemicals, and molecular information. Types of formula identifiers include InCHI, SMILES, and SMARTS. Among them, SMILES advantageous for MACCS keys conversion was selected, and SMILES of matrix, filler were obtained through the database source of PubChem, respectively.

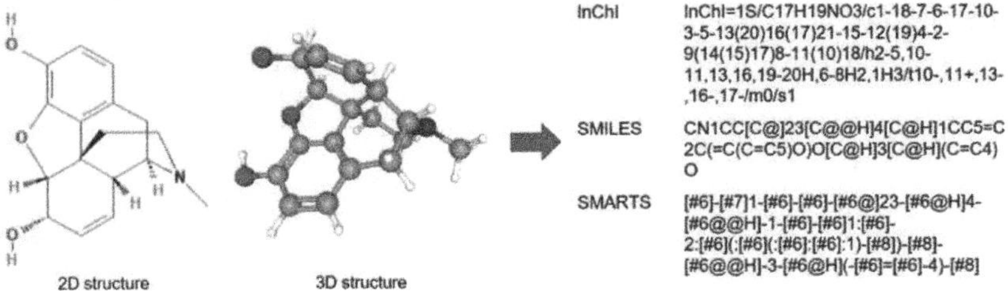

Figure 1. Example of String representation of 2D and 3D chemical structure information

(2) Chemical fingerprints

Fingerprints are the main expression methods that can confirm each molecular information in machine learning, and molecular structures and functional groups can be identified. Recently, predictions using functional groups of Fingerprints have been actively used in the field of drugs and catalysts. However, Binding energy, and Young's Modulus are also highly related to functional groups. When three specific functional groups are placed on Graphene sheets for mechanical properties simulation, the dimension and molecular structure of the functional group affect Binding energy and Young's Modulus. (Qingbin Zheng et al., 2010). In this study, among various methodologies representing Fingerprints of chemical substances, MACCSkeys represented by 0, 1 binary at 166 bits was selected as structural information and used for input. Functional groups represented by MACCS keys are related to the mechanical properties of the material and are used as input features (G. Chen, et al.).

3. Prediction of mechanical behavior based on chemical/mechanical information of components

3.1. Data collection

As for the tensile test data to be used for learning, the tensile test results according to the composition of each type of PMC in provided by the Korea Research Institute of Chemical Technology were used. (Under the same conditions, the test proceeds five times each.) The tensile test results include values such as the type of material, mark distance, and force according to strain. Additionally, the 'Poisson ratio' to reflect the difference in length strain according to the load direction, density for pore reflection, and density and molecular weight for each Matrix/Filler related to mechanical properties were extracted from PubChem's database(https://pubchem.ncbi.nlm.nih.gov/). Through data analysis, it was found that the test conditions were correlated with the S-S curve, so we added the mark distance and type as input features.

3.2. Data preprocessing

First, the experimental error data on the tensile test data is processed. Since the negative value of stress in raw data is physically impossible due to an experimental error, all data of negative values were converted to zero. In addition, values such as molecular weight, density, elastic modulus, Poisson ratio, marker distance, and stress of matrix and filler are pretreated to have a large range of 0.3 to 300. Standardization was performed using the stats module provided by Scipy to improve the performance of the model.

3.3. Model construction and training

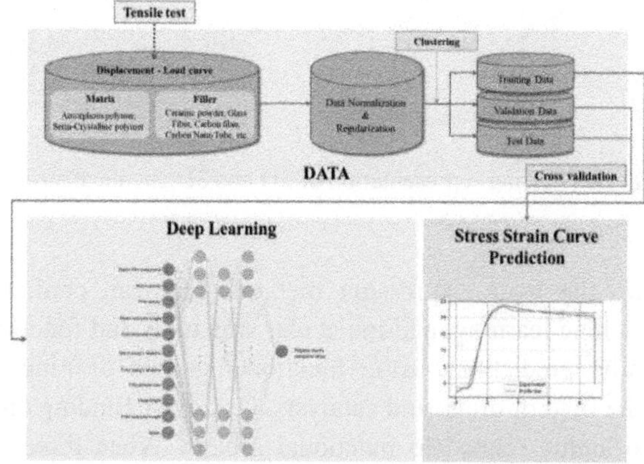

Figure 2. Workflow of mechanical behavior predictive model based on chemical/mechanical information of components. (As input, the density, molecular weight, young's modulus of each components (matrix/filler), matrix composition, filler poisson ratio, tensile test strain data, gauge length are used)

The model learns the remaining composition's data, and predict PMCs mechanical behavior according to the desired composition and test conditions. The learning data set and the test data set are divided into 5:1.The model has a Feed-forward Neural Network (FNN) structure, using TensorFlow Keras, four hidden layers, ReLu as an activation function, Adam as an optimization function, and Mean Square Error (MSE) as a loss function. To further prevent overfitting, Batch Normalization, Regularization, Dropout structure, He-normalization, and L1 Regularization were added to the structure. Bayesian optimization was applied to optimize each hyperparameter, and the accuracy of the model was evaluated as R^2 (N. Lee, et al.).

4. Predicting mechanical behaviour based on structural information of components

4.1. Data collection

SMILES of each component material scraped from PubChem's database is used to reflect structure information in addition to the tensile test data conducted in Section 3.

4.2. Data preprocessing

Section 3 performed the same preprocessing for the same data. MACCS keys compared eight types of MACCS keys functional groups and used only 72 functional groups with differences among 166 functional groups. We compared eight types of component material's functional groups and used only 72 functional groups with differences among 166 functional groups.

4.3. Model construction and training

To check the influence of features, we completed a model with two different types of inputs. Therefore, the same network structure as the model in Chapter 3 was used in the model that reflects the structural information of the components. However, the prediction model was completed by selecting different optimal hyperparameters through the Bayesian optimizer.

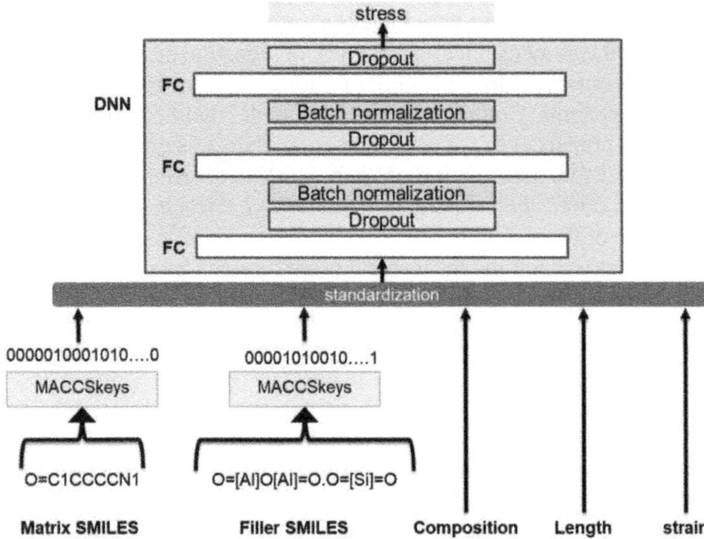

Figure 3. Workflow of mechanical behavior predictive model based on structural information of components.

5. Results

It can be seen that not only different PMC conditions, but also different composition and gauge distance affects the prediction results. Prediction model using the chemical/mechanical properties of the components showed an accuracy of R2≅ 0.45 ~

0.95 depending on the type of polymer composite, and the model using the structural information showed an accuracy of R2≅0.55 ~ 0.93.

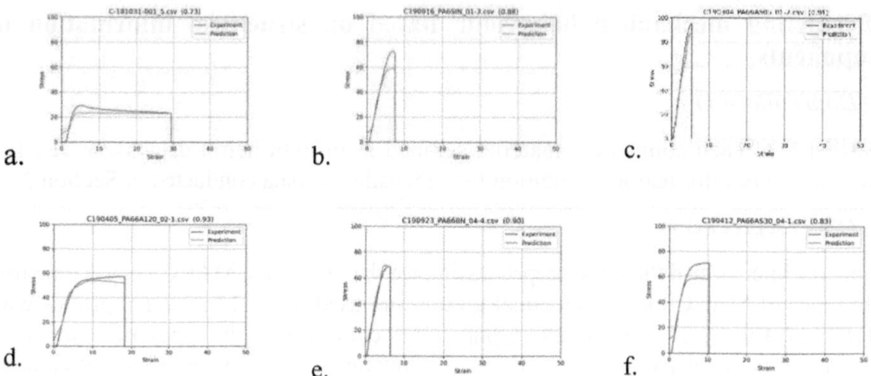

Figure 4. a, b, c above are suggested model based on chemical/mechanical information, and below d,e,f are suggested model based on structural information (a) PP+Al_2O_3, b) PA6+Si_3N_4, c) PA6,6+Al_2O_5Si, d) PA6+Al_2O_3, e),PA6,6+BN, f)PA6,6+Al_2O_5Si) : Orange line is 'prediction', blue line is 'experiment'

6. Conclusion

This study proposes a model for predicting the mechanical properties of a polymer composite resin using deep learning-based material information. Compared with previous studies utilizing chemical/mechanical properties of constituent materials, the model reflecting the component structure has similar performance, but has versatility by using data from fewer components. Compared to the first model that needs to know the seven chemical/mechanical properties of the constituent materials, it is possible to predict using only the SMILES structure information of each constituent material, that is, only two pieces of information about the constituent material. As a result, it was found that the structural information of the molecule had a great influence on the mechanical properties. Accordingly, it is expected that the mechanical properties can be predicted based on the minimum information of the constituent materials. As a follow-up study, the predictive performance of the model will be improved by improving the model structure through Natural Language Processing (NLP).

References

Q. Zheng, Y. Geng, S. Wang, Zh. Li, and J. Kim, 2010, Effects of functional groups on the mechanical and wrinkling properties of graphene sheets, Carbon, vol.48, issue15, 4315-4322

G. Chen, L. Tao, and Y. Li, 2021, Predicting polymers' glass transition temperature by a chemical language processing model, polymers, vol.13, 1898

H. C. Hyun, J.H. Lee and H. Lee, 2008, Mathematical Expressions for Stress-Srain Curve of Metallic Matrerial, Transactions of the KSME A , vol.32, 21-28

N. Lee, Y. Shin, and D.Shin, 2021, Prediction of Mechanical Properties and Behavior of Polymer Matrix Composites Based on Machine Learning. Journal of the Korean Institute of Gas, 25(2), 64-71

PubChem. Retrieved from https://pubchem.ncbi.nlm.nih.gov/

Proceedings of the 14th International Symposium on Process Systems Engineering – PSE 2021+
June 19-23, 2022, Kyoto, Japan
http://dx.doi.org/10.1016/B978-0-323-85159-6.50044-0

EVALUATION OF ECONOMIC PERFORMANCE OF CO_2 SEPARATION PROCESS USING MIXED MATRIX MEMBRANE

Kakeru FUJITA[a], Ryousuke AKIMOTO[a], Yasuhiko SUZUKI[b], Yuki OGASAWARA[b], Masaru NAKAIWA[a] and Keigo MATSUDA[a*]

[a] Department of Chemistry and Chemical Engineering, Graduate School of Science and Engineering, Yamagata University, 4-3-16, Jonan, Yonezawa, Yamagata 992-8510, Japan
[b]Faculty of Chemistry and Chemical Engineering, Yamagata University, 4-3-16, Jonan, Yonezawa, Yamagata 992-8510, Japan

[*]Corresponding Author's E-mail: matsuda@yz.yamagata-u.ac.jp

ABSTRACT: A multi-stage CO_2 capture process using Mixed Matrix Membrane (MMM) could separate molecules with similar molecular diameter such as CO_2 and N_2 by dissolution and diffusion. The required energy and the membrane area were investigated based on the membrane performance such as CO_2 permeance and CO_2/N_2 selectivity. In this multi-stage CO_2 capture process, the feed gas fed into the first and second membranes. The gas permeated through the second membrane was recycled to Feed. The permeate gas from the first membrane was fed to the adsorption column to separate H_2O. The CO_2-rich dry gas was liquefied by using a compressor and a condenser. The residual gas was separated using a membrane, and the permeate gas was recycled to the dry gas. The flue gas assumed from a coal-fired power plant containing 11.6 mol% CO_2. When the CO_2 permeance of 1000 GPU and CO_2/N_2 selectivity of 50 were used for the first and second membranes of the multi-stage CO_2 capture process, the required energy was 139 MW and the membrane area was 3.6×10^6 m^2, respectively. From these results, the operation, construction, and membrane skid costs were calculated. The CO_2 capture cost per ton of CO_2 was found to be \$38/ton-CO_2. In addition, the membrane area of the second was large, and the membrane area could be reduced by using a membrane with high CO_2 permeance and low CO_2/N_2 selectivity. Therefore, a membrane with CO_2 permeance of 1000 GPU and CO_2/N_2 selectivity of 50 was used in the first. A membrane with CO_2 permeance of 3000 GPU and CO_2/N_2 selectivity of 30 was used in the second. As a result, it was clarified that the required energy was 141 MW, and the membrane area was 1.25×10^6 m^2. The CO_2 capture cost was \$29/ton-CO_2.

Keywords: Membrane separation, Carbon dioxide, Process design

1. Introduction

United Nations was accelerating its efforts on the Sustainable Development Goals (SDGs), and the number 13 climate change has been an urgent issue. The main cause of climate change was the increase of greenhouse gases such as CO_2 (T. M. Lenton *et al.*, 2019). IEA has been announced that CO_2 emissions in 2021 would be expected to be about 33 billion tons. Especially, 11 billion tons have been emitted from coal-fired power plant (Ministry of Economy, Trade and Industry, 2019). Recently, to achieve drastic reduction of CO_2 emissions, Carbon dioxide capture and storage (CCS) which is the separation and storage carbon dioxide from large-scale intensive CO_2 emission sources has attracted much attention. Examples of CO_2 separation technologies include chemical absorption and membrane separation. In chemical absorption, gases containing CO_2 have been absorbed in an alkaline aqueous solution in an absorption tower. After that, the absorbed solution has been sent to the stripper where thermal energy is required to strip the CO_2 in the absorbed solution. Although gas absorption could recover CO_2 at a concentration of 99 mol% or higher, it consumes a large amount of thermal energy in the stripper that results in high CO_2 capture cost (D. Leeson *et al.*, 2017). On the other hand, in membrane separation, the driving force has been the difference in partial pressure between the permeate and retentate of the membrane. Therefore, the only energy required for separation was a pressure exchanger such as a compressor or a vacuum pump (A. Stankiewicz *et al.*, 2000). Membranes include inorganic membranes such as zeolite which are permeable by molecular sieves. Polymeric membranes have been separated by dissolution and diffusion. Polymeric membranes are used with close molecular diameter such as CO_2 and N_2 because the effect of molecular sieving is less effective and the separation proceeds by dissolution and diffusion. Among polymer membranes research and development of organic-inorganic hybrid membranes (MMM) which have the advantages of durability of inorganic materials and excellent gas permeability of organic materials has been conducted (M. Tanaka, 2016). However, few studies have been conducted on the required energy and membrane area of processes how parameters such as permeance and selectivity. Therefore, process synthesis and integration based on the process systems engineering approach have been demanded as socioeconomic innovations (B. Ghalei *et al.*, 2017). Process synthesis consists of three methods. 1. Planning of process that examines the selection and combination of process equipment, 2. Functional design of the process that quantitatively assigns functions to this equipment, 3. Evaluation of these process that meet their intended functions. In this study, the multi-stage CO_2 capture process using MMM was developed via process synthesis method and evaluate the economic performances.

2. Modelling

Fig. 1 shows schematic diagrams of multi-stage CO_2 capture process for CCS (T. C. Merkel *et al.*, 2010). Assuming exhaust gas from a coal-fired power plant, this process separated to a recovery ratio of 90% CO_2 against flow rate of CO_2 on Feed. The feed was assumed following conditions; flow rate of 2.2×10^4 mol/s, a pressure of 100 kPa, a temperature 298 K, a composition CO_2:11.6, N_2:73, H_2O:11, O_2:4.4 mol%. The process consists of a pressure exchanger (blower, compressor, vacuum pump), an adsorption column to remove H_2O, a condenser and three membrane modules. The feed gas pressure is elevated to 200 kPa with a blower which fed into the membranes 2 and 3. The permeate is depressed by 20 kPa with vacuum pump. The permeate gas from membrane 3 is recycled to the feed gas. The permeation gas of membrane 2 separated H_2O with adsorption tower of 6. The dry gas is compressed to 2250-3800 kPa with compressor of 7 (253 K). The gas is pumped into the ground at 14,000 kPa by compressor 10. The residual gas in the condenser is separated by the membrane of 9, and the permeate gas is recycled to the dry gas. The membrane module is a cross plug flow module in which the permeate gas exits in the flow direction. The CO_2 permeance and CO_2/N_2 selectivity set to be 1000, 3000, 5000 GPU, CO_2/N_2:10-100, CO_2/H_2O:0.03, N_2/O_2:1, respectively. All of simulation was implemented of the Aspen Plus®V11. The Peng Robinson type equation of state was applied to estimate the vapor-liquid equilibrium for the steady state.

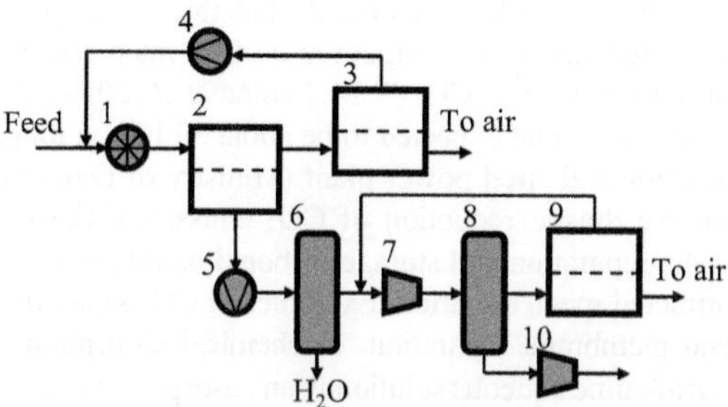

Fig. 1 Schematic diagram of multi-stage membrane CO_2 capture process (CCS)

3. Result and discussion

3.1 Effect of CO_2 Permeance and CO_2/N_2 Selectivity on CO_2 concentration for CCS, required energy, and membrane area

First, the effects of the same CO_2 permeance and CO_2/N_2 selectivity of membranes 2, 3, and 9 on the CO_2 concentration for CCS, the required energy and the membrane area are investigated. In this study, the CO_2 permeance are set to 1000, 3000, and 5000 GPU, and the CO_2/N_2 selectivity is varied in the range of 10-100. Table 1 shows the comparison of CO_2 concentration for CCS, required energy and membrane area. The required energy is the sum of the CO_2 separation process (1-4) and CO_2 storage process (5-10). The membrane area is total of 2, 3 and 9. The CO_2 concentration for CCS increased with high CO_2/N_2 selectivity. The required energy for the storage process decreases with high CO_2/N_2 selectivity due to the higher CO_2 concentration in permeate gas of membrane 2. In addition, the required energy with CO_2/N_2 selectivity 100 decreases by 60% compere to CO_2/N_2 selectivity 10. On the other hand, the CO_2 partial pressure on the permeate is larger for the high CO_2 concentration on the permeate. As a result, the difference between the CO_2 partial pressure on the retentate and that on the permeate is smaller, and the membrane area of the multi-stage CO_2 capture process increases. In addition, the membrane area with CO_2/N_2 selectivity100 increases by 225% compere to CO_2/N_2 selectivity 10. On the other hand, by increasing the CO_2 permeance from 1000 to 5000 GPU, the membrane area is reduced by 80% due to the flow rate of CO_2 on permeates increases.

Table1 Comparison of CO_2 mole fraction, required energy and membrane area

CO_2/N_2 selectivity	-	10	20	30	40	50	60	70	80	90	100
CO_2 concentration	mol%	88.5	93.9	95.6	96.5	97.0	97.3	97.4	97.5	97.7	97.8
Required energy	MW	285	213	170	151	139	133	124	119	117	115
Membrane area (1000 GPU)	$\times 10^6$ m^2	2.40	2.50	2.90	3.20	3.60	4.00	4.30	4.70	5.10	5.40
Membrane area (3000 GPU)	$\times 10^6$ m^2	0.80	0.83	0.97	1.07	1.20	1.33	1.43	1.57	1.70	1.80
Membrane area (5000 GPU)	$\times 10^6$ m^2	0.48	0.50	0.58	0.64	0.72	0.80	0.86	0.94	1.02	1.08

3.2 Evaluate the economic performance for CO_2 capture process for CCS

The cost index is shown in Table 2. The CO_2 capture cost, CC is estimated by Eq. (1)

$$CC = \frac{(P \times T \times E) + (0.2 \times C)}{F_{CO2} \times T} \tag{1}$$

P is the required energy for CO_2 capture process (kW), *T* is the annual operating time (h/year), *E* is the cost of electricity ($/kWh), *C* is the capital cost of the CO_2 capture process ($), F_{CO2} is the mass flow rate of captured CO_2 (T. C. Merkel *et al.*, 2010). Fig. 2 shows CO_2 capture cost for CO_2 permeance and CO_2/N_2 selectivity. The CO_2 capture cost decreases because the reducing the operating cost is larger than the increasing the membrane skid cost with high CO_2/N_2 selectivity. The high CO_2 permeance has a significant effect on the CO_2 capture cost by reducing the membrane area due to increasing flow rate of CO_2 on permeate. It is clarified that the minimum CO_2 capture cost is 18.6 US$/ton-$CO_2$ with the CO_2 performance of 5000 GPU and CO_2/N_2 selectivity of 90 under these conditions.

Table 2 Cost index of CO_2 capture process

Category	Units	Value
Mechanical efficiency	-	0.8
Mechanical cost	\$/kW	500
Membrane skid cost	\$/m^2	50
Cost electricity	\$/kWh	0.04
Annual operating time	h/year	7446

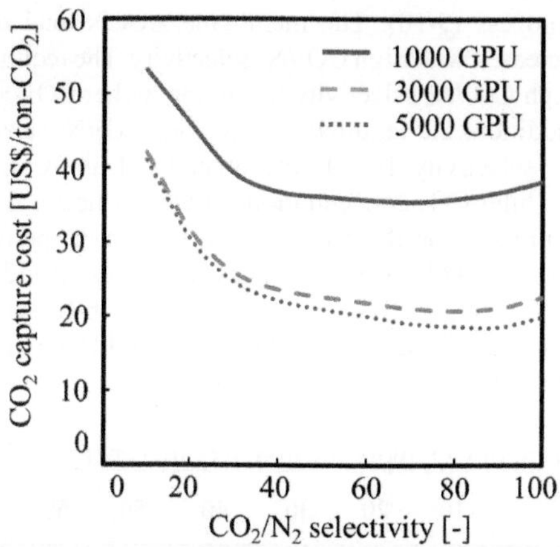

Fig. 2 CO_2 capture cost for CO_2 permeance and CO_2/N_2 selectivity

3.3 Configuring membranes with appropriate separation performance

In this study, the required energy and the membrane area can be reduced with appropriate separation performance in membrane 2 and 3. Table 3 shows the CO_2 permeance and CO_2/N_2 selectivity configured. The membranes used are those with CO_2 permeance of 1000 GPU and CO_2/N_2 selectivity of 50 and those with CO_2 permeance of 3000 GPU and CO_2/N_2 selectivity of 30. In Scenarios 1 and 2, the same CO_2 permeance and CO_2/N_2 selectivity are used for membrane 2 and 3. In Scenarios 3 and 4, membranes with different CO_2 permeance and CO_2/N_2 selectivity are used. Fig. 3 shows the effect of whole scenario on the membrane area. Since the multi-stage CO_2 capture process using MMM requires a larger membrane area for membrane 3 than for membrane 2, membrane 3 with a CO_2 permeance of 1000 GPU and a CO_2/N_2 selectivity of 50 resulted in a larger membrane area due to the pressure difference problem as explained in Section 3.1. In the scenario where the CO_2 permeance and CO_2/N_2 selectivity are changed for each membrane, the membrane area in scenario 3 decreases by 64% compared to scenario 4. Thus, it is found that the membrane area can be reduced by configuring with high CO_2 permeance and low CO_2/N_2 selectivity at membrane 3. Scenario 1 results in the smallest membrane area in whole scenario.

Table 3 Membrane configuration of CO_2 capture process

Category	Unit	Scenario 1	Scenario 2	Scenario 3	Scenario 4
		Membrane 2			
CO_2 permeance	GPU	3000	1000	1000	3000
CO_2/N_2 selectivity	-	30	50	50	30
		Membrane 3			
CO_2 permeance	GPU	3000	1000	3000	1000
CO_2/N_2 selectivity	-	30	50	30	50

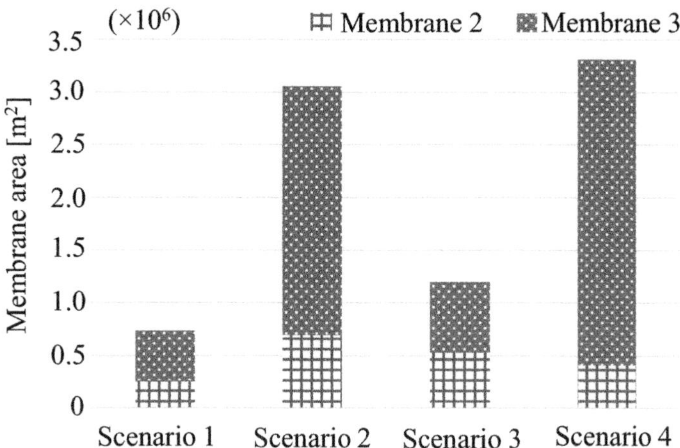

Fig. 3 The effect of membrane area on CO_2 permeance and CO_2/N_2 selectivity

Fig. 4 shows the effect of whole scenario on the required energy. The required energy is the sum of the CO_2 separation process (1-4) and the CO_2 storage process (5-10) as in the study in Section 3.1. The required energy in the CO_2 storage process (5-10) is larger for each scenario in Figure 4. However, required energy for CO_2 storage is reduced in Scenarios 1 and 2. In Scenario 1, the membrane area is the smallest, but the required energy is the largest at 177 MW. In Scenario 3, the required energy is reduced by 33 MW compared to Scenario 1 by setting the CO_2/N_2 selectivity 50 on membrane 2. Furthermore, the required energy in Scenario 3 is reduced by 8 MW compared to Scenario 4 by considering the membrane configuration with appropriate separation performance. In addition, cost evaluation of scenario 3 and scenario 4 is done. The cost of Scenario 3 is \$29/ton-CO_2 and that of Scenario 4 is \$37/ton-CO_2. By considering the appropriate CO_2 permeance and CO_2/N_2 selectivity configuration of the multi-stage CO_2 capture process using MMM as in Scenario 3, the membrane area and required energy are reduced compared to Scenario 4. The CO_2 capture cost is reduced by \$8/ton-CO_2.

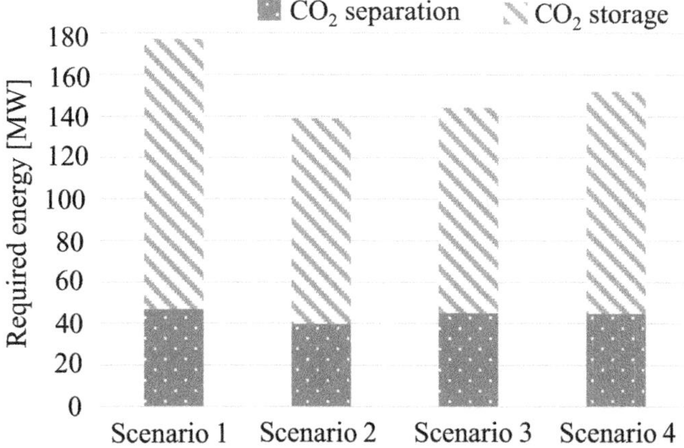

Fig. 4 The effect of membrane area on CO_2 permeance and CO_2/N_2 selectivity

4 Conclusions

The multi-stage CO_2 capture process using MMM were fully developed by Aspen plus V11. The multi-stage CO_2 capture process using MMM was developed via process synthesis method and evaluate the economic performances. The required energy decreased with membranes of high CO_2/N_2 selectivity because of CO_2 concentration on the permeate gas increased. On the other hand, the membrane area increased due to the smaller in the pressure difference as the high CO_2/N_2 selectivity. The CO_2 permeance had a significant effect on the reduction of the membrane area. Regarding the economic evaluation, increasing the CO_2/N_2 selectivity from 30 to 100 reduces the required energy, but because the membrane area increased, the effect of increasing the CO_2/N_2 selectivity above 30 on the cost reduction was small. If a membrane with a CO_2 permeance of 5000 GPU or higher could be developed, the CO_2 capture cost will be less than \$20/ton-CO_2. By configuring membranes with appropriate CO_2 permeance and CO_2/N_2 selectivity in a multi-stage membrane CO_2 capture process, the required energy and membrane area could be reduced.

Acknowledgment

This work was partially supported by JST Mirai project "Development of mixed matrix porous membrane endowed with high performance in CO_2 selectivity and anti-aging".

References

B. Ghalei, K. Sakurai, Y. Kinoshita, K. Wakimoto, A. P. Isfahani, Q. Song, K. Doitomi, S. Furukawa, H. Hirao, H. Kusuda, S. Kitagawa, E. Sivaniah, "Enhanced selectivity in mixed matrix membranes for CO_2 capture through efficient dispersion of amine-functionalized MOF nanoparticles," *NATURE ENERGY,* **2**, 17086 (2017)

D. Leeson, N. M. Dowell, N. Shah, C. Petit, P. S. Fennell, "A Techno-economic analysis and systematic review of carbon capture and storage (CCS) applied to the iron and steel, cement, oil refining and pulp and paper industries, as well as other high purity sources," *Int. J. Greenhouse Gas Control*, **61**, 71–84 (2017)

T. M. Lenton, J. Rockström, O. Gaffney, S. Rahmstorf, K. Richardson, W. Steffen, H. J. Schellnhuber, "Climate tipping points-too risky to bet against," *NATURE ENERGY*, **575**, 592-595(2019)

T. C. Merkel, H. Lin, X. Wei, R. Baker, "Power plant post-combustion carbon dioxide capture: An opportunity for membranes," *J. Membrane Sci*, **359**, 126-139 (2010)

Ministry of Economy, Trade and Industry; White Paper 2019

A. Stankiewicz, J. A. Moulijn, "Process Intensification: Transforming Chemical Engineering," *Chem. Eng. Prog*., **96**, 22-34 (2000)

M. Tanaka, "Gas separation using polymeric membranes," *Chemical and education*, **41**(4), 173-177(2016)

Proceedings of the 14th International Symposium on Process Systems Engineering – PSE 2021+
June 19-23, 2022, Kyoto, Japan
http://dx.doi.org/10.1016/B978-0-323-85159-6.50045-2

Nature vs engineering: Production of methanol from CO_2 capture

Guillermo Galán,[a] Mariano Martín,[a,*] Ignacio E. Grossmann.[b]

[a]Department of Chemical Engineering. University of Salamanca. Plz. 1-5, 37008, Salamanca, Spain
[b]Department of Chemical Engineering. Carnegie Mellon University, 5000 Forbes Ave, 15213, Pittsburgh PA, USA
** mariano.m3@usal.es*

Abstract

This work compares integrated facilities to capture CO_2 from the atmosphere and use it for the production of bulk chemicals, methanol. Two different alternatives have been proposed. On the one hand, the use of direct air capture (DAC) employing either alkaline solutions based in KOH or a bipolar membrane electrodialysis (BPMED). The CO_2 captured is subsequently hydrogenated with electrolytic hydrogen produced using solar and/or wind energy. On the other hand, the use of biomass such as switchgrass, corn stover, miscanthus, wheat straw and forest residues, from spruce and pine, are considered. This biomass is pretreated, gasified, either direct or indirect gasification, the raw syngas followed steam reforming or partial oxidation, it is cleaned and its composition is adjusted for the synthesis of methanol. All units are modelled individually to formulate the superstructure as an MINLP optimization model. The results show that the optimal option consists of the use of spruce bark biomass gasification. The direct air capture has production and investment costs almost 10 times higher due to the large consumption of electricity to power the fans.

Keywords: Process design, CO_2 capture, biomass, renewable methanol

1. Introduction

Since the 18th century with the beginning of the industrial revolution, as well as the development of the use of steam and other energy sources, mainly fossil fuels, human growth and its development was linked to the increasing emission of carbon. Because of this, humanity is in a race to reduce emissions to keep the planet's temperature within 1.5 °C. Some efforts to remove CO_2 from the atmosphere are thus being investigated (Allen et al., 2021). Purified CO_2 can be used in the chemical industry for food production, cosmetics and even for the population of intermediate reagents for the production of acids and aldehydes, among others. This work considers the use of CO_2 to obtain intermediate compounds such as methanol. Two major capture technologies can be used. On the one hand, nature captures CO_2 to grow biomass. This biomass is later gasified to produce methanol. On the other hand, direct air capture (DAC) is an engineered alternative that is emerging in our attempt to remove CO_2 from the atmosphere. By using an air-water contactor, it allows a constant flow of air to circulate through alkaline solutions. CO_2 is absorbed and captured by transforming it into $CaCO_3$. This carbonate is subsequently calcined, thus releasing the captured CO_2 to be purified (Keith et al., 2018). A modification of the DAC process consists of the use of a bipolar electrodialysis membrane (Sabatino et al., 2020). Ion exchange membranes allow the recovery of CO_2 through the use of water and the subsequent regeneration of the H^+ and OH^- species in the respective solutions. The CO_2 is hydrogenated with electrolytic H_2 to produce methanol. This work evaluates, from a techno-economic perspective, both pathways towards the production of methanol comparing the nature and the manmade alternatives. The processes are optimized using a mathematical modelling approach.

2. Process description

The alternative based on biomass requires washing and milling before the gasification. Two technologies are considered: **The Renugas gasifier (R),** direct gasification, operates at medium pressure using oxygen and produces a gas rich in CO_2. It allows large throughput per reactor volume and reduces the need for a downstream pressurization. However, its efficiency is lower (Eggeman, 2005). The low pressure gasifier, **Battelle Columbus (Ferco, F)**, is indirectly heated. The system consists of two chambers, a gasifier and a combustor. Olivine is heated up by burning char to provide the energy for gasification. The syngas shows low CO_2 content but heavier hydrocarbons (Phillips, 2007). Subsequently, the syngas is reformed to remove the hydrocarbons. **Steam reforming (S)** is endothermic but provides a higher concentration of hydrogen in the syngas. **Partial oxidation (O)** is exothermic but its yield to hydrogen is lower. Finally, the raw syngas is cleaned. Two steps are proposed. Cold cleaning by means of a scrubber for low pressure gasification, or a ceramic filter operating at high temperature for high pressure gasification. The second step consists of a multibed PSA system used to remove the last traces of hydrocarbons, H_2S and CO_2 in that order. Once the syngas is purified, we use it for traditional methanol synthesis. The superstructure of alternatives is presented in Figure 1.

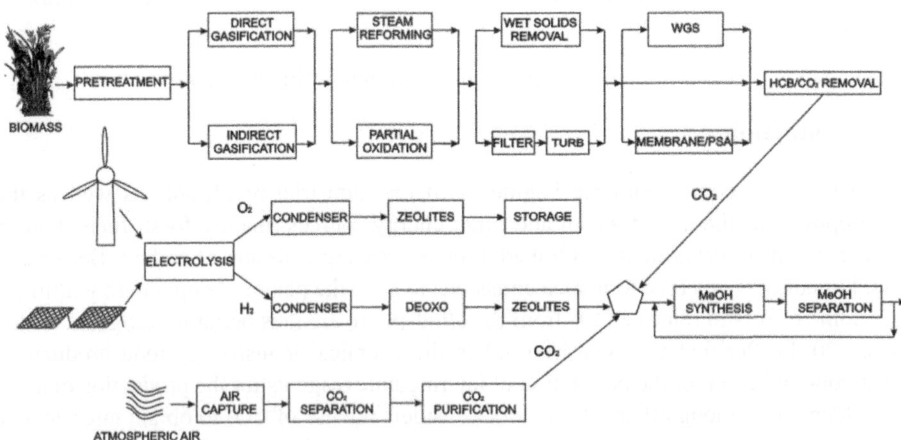

Figure 1.-Superstructure for the production of methanol

The DAC process captures the CO_2 from the air using a counterflow air contactor. The concentration of CO_2 in air is around of 300-400 ppm. This low concentration requires the use of alkaline salts, KOH, to reduce the water flow (Keith et al., 2018). Once the CO_2 has been captured, it can be recovered from the alkaline solution with a pellet-type reactor where CO_2 byproducts react with a stream rich in $Ca(OH)_2$, forming $CaCO_3$ and regenerating the pH of the original solution, releasing OH^-groups. Later the calcination of $CaCO_3$ allows recovering the CO_2 producing CaO, which is sent to a slaker unit where the $Ca(OH)_2$ is regenerated. The high temperatures reached allow to produce medium-low pressure steam, obtaining energy in a turbine. The alternative process employs the bipolar electrodialysis membrane (BPMED), separating a basic solution rich in CO_2 and an acid solution. The control of pH is important to maintain most of the CO_2 dissolved, the recovery yield in the membranes and the regeneration of the H^+ and OH^- species in the respective solutions, avoiding CO_2 bubbles (Sabatino et al., 2020). The stream with CO_2 recovered is sent to the condenser and molecular sieves units to remove the water content and lately hydrogenated with electrolytic hydrogen produced using energy from PV panels or wind turbines is evaluated. The CO_2 is hydrogenated using renewable H_2 for the production of methanol by eq. (1).

$$\begin{aligned} &CO + 2H_2 \leftrightarrow CH_3OH \\ &CO_2 + H_2 \leftrightarrow CO + H_2O \end{aligned} \tag{1}$$

3. Modelling approach

The different units are modelled using first principles, and mass and energy balances based on detailed simulations and/or experimental data. For particular units such as the direct air capture including the bipolar membrane electrodialysis (Sabatino et al., 2020), surrogate models are developed.

The gas composition produced from the gasifiers is defined by experimental correlations. The reforming stage uses conversions from the literature (Eggemann, 2005; Phillips et al., 2007)

The capture of CO_2 from air needs the use of an air contactor where the air and the water streams are placed in contact. The efficiency of capture and the molar flow rate of CO_2 through the membranes are a function of the concentration of bicarbonate and carbonate ions, $[HCO_3]^-$ and $[CO_3]^{2-}$, the concentration of KOH, [KOH], and current density, i. (Sabatino et al., 2020).

$$\begin{aligned} &\eta_{current} = f([\mathrm{HCO_3}]^-,[\mathrm{CO_3}]^{2-},[\mathrm{KOH}],\mathrm{i}) \\ &f_{CO_2} = f([\mathrm{HCO_3}]^-,[\mathrm{CO_3}]^{2-},[\mathrm{KOH}],\mathrm{i}) \end{aligned} \tag{2}$$

The methanol synthesis reactor is modelled based on chemical equilibrium, mass and energy balances (Cherednichenko, 1953).

The superstructure is formulated in terms of total mass flows, component mass flows, component mass fractions, and temperatures of the streams in the network.

4. Optimization procedure

The superstructure is decomposed into three different flowsheet alternatives based on the pretreatments: direct air capture with alkaline solutions, direct air capture with bipolar membrane electrodialysis and the gasification of biomass. An NLP problem is solved for each one where the objective function consists of simplified production costs given by eq. (3)

$$Z = P_{MetOH} m_{MetOH} + P_{O_2} m_{O_2} - P_{Electricity} \sum_i W_{consumed} - \sum_i P_{utilities} \cdot m_{utilities} \tag{3}$$

subject to the models described in section 3. The NLP's consist of around 2000-2500 eqs and 3000 variables and it was solved with GAMS, CONOPT, requiring 30-60 s of CPU-time. After the optimization, a heat exchanger network is designed to reduce energy consumption. Finally, a detailed economic evaluation of the alternatives is performed to compute the production and investment costs of the facility using the cost correlations in Martín and Grossmann (2011) and the procedure described in that work.

5. Results

This section shows the principal operating results, and the economics of the different alternatives. For wind and solar capture, we consider Cadiz, to the south of Spain where high solar irradiance is available, and the wind velocity is fairly high. Different types such as switchgrass, corn stover, miscanthus, wheat straw and pruning residues including pine and spruce bark are evaluated

5.1. Process analysis

The superstructure of alternatives is decomposed by technology to evaluate the yield and performance of each alternative. The biomass path follows indirect gasification followed by steam reforming, since the H_2 to CO ratio required for the production of methanol is around 2, After the gas clean up and the adjustment of the composition, the syngas is fed to the synthesis loop. In the case of DAC processes both alternatives are presented. Tables 1 and 2 show the major results. In general, DAC needs more energy than biomass gasification due to the low concentration of CO_2 in air that forces to move large volumes of air through the fans increasing the requirements of electricity, that is generated using wind turbines or solar panels. The conventional DAC is more efficient than the BPMED resulting in 10% lower energy requirements. However, the cost of PV panels and aerogenerators, together with the requirements of a large surface, increase considerably the investment cost of this technology. Thus, the yield to methanol is higher from those wastes with a composition richer in carbon.

Table 1. Major yields for gasification of biomass

	Gasification					
	Switchgrass	Corn Stover	Wheat Straw	Miscanthus	Pine Bark	Spruce Bark
Product cost(€/kg_{MetOH})	0.192	0.216	0.170	0.224	0.169	0.110
Investment (M€)	181.27	175.09	157.67	172.27	144.16	152.79
kg_{MetOH}/ $kg_{Biomass}$	0.658	0.674	0.620	0.687	0.875	0.816
Productivity (t/ha)	12.00	10.92	7.30	10.00	6.94	4.08
Surface required (ha)	51,840	55,925	90,47	59,552	67,334	122,980

Table 2. Major yields for DAC process paths

		DAC			
		Conventional Process PV panels	**Conventional Process Wind**	**BPMED PV panels**	**BPMED Wind**
Product cost (€/kg_{MetOH})		0.934	1.089	1.059	1.233
Investment (M€)	Plant	959.45	959.45	1,218.75	1,218.75
	PV/Aerogenerators	449.86	685.50	503.83	767.75
Surface required (ha)	PV panels	205.12	-	230.52	-
Number of units	Aerogenerators	-	572	-	643
$kgCO_{2\ air\ captured}$/kW		573.60	573.60	867.03	867.03
$kgCO_{2\ available\ captured}$/kW		968.79	968.79	867.03	867.03

5.2. Process economics

Table 1 presents the investment and the production costs for the six different biomass species. The most economic ones are pine and spruce bark since the higher composition in carbon lead to larger yields to methanol, reducing the production costs. Although spruce bark biomass shows an investment cost above that of pine bark and the largest growing area, the lower cost of biomass, even with a slighter lower yield of kg $_{methanol}$/kg$_{Biomass}$, results in the best option, for a production cost is 0.11 €/kg methanol. The use of biomass is competitive with the production cost of methanol from fossil resources.

Another issue would be to be able to meet the global demand using biomass waste. Although growth of biomass is very efficient to capture CO_2, it is important to indicate that DAC technology is still at an early stage of development and with potential for improvement. Table 2 shows the investment and the production cost of the two DAC alternatives, conventional process and BPMED, both with a renewable power supply from PV panels and/or aerogenerators. These costs could change as a function of the chosen technology and the location. Conventional DAC process has a lower ratio kgCO_2 $_{air\ captured}$/kW than BPMED process due to the use of biogas as fuel in the calciner. The CO_2 from the combustion of this biogas is added to the CO_2 captured from air, decreasing the volume of air and with that the power consumption of the fans, with the corresponding reduction in PV panels and wind turbines.

The location has a direct effect due to the availability of resources. In this case the location was the province of Cádiz (Spain), which shows long sun hours and high wind velocities. The best option corresponds to the use of the conventional DAC power with PV panels. The production and investment costs are the lowest among the DAC alternatives, 0.934 €/kg methanol and 1409.31 M€, which are around 9 and 10 times larger than the values of the best biomass process. Figure 2 shows that the investment cost of the PV panels represents around of 32% of the total, i.e., a third of the investment cost is destined to the energy requirements. The breakdown of the investment in the equipment shows that the fans, the PV panels, and the electrolysis represent around of 90% of the total investment cost, leaving only the remaining 11% destined to capture of CO_2 and synthesis of methanol. The expected improvement in the efficiency of the solar panels would reduce not only the number of panels and the total surface but also the cost.

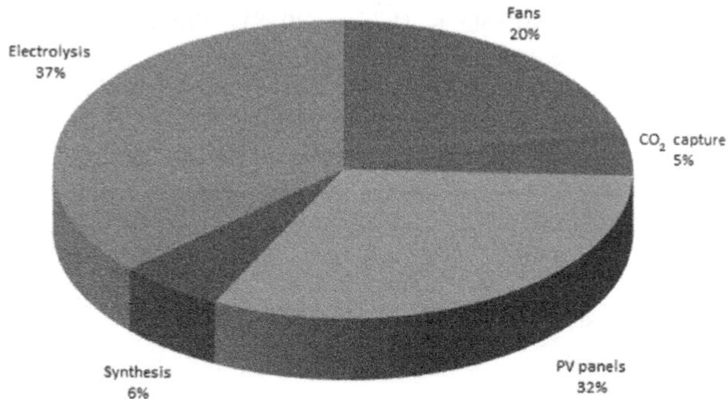

Figure 2.-Distribution of costs in DAC conventional process with PV panels

6. Conclusions

This work systematically compares the capture of CO_2 from atmosphere using a natural, biomass growth, and manmade, direct air capture (DAC), alternatives towards the production of a bulk chemical, methanol, in an attempt to build a sustainable chemicals industry as well. Two different configurations for DAC are optimized, the use of alkaline solutions (Keith et al., 2018) and a membrane (Sabatino et al., 2020), that captures the

CO_2, which is subsequently hydrogenated using electrolytic hydrogen. The facility is powered using wind or solar energy depending on the regional availability. This technology is compared to the Nature's alternative based on biomass, considering switchgrass, corn stover, miscanthus, wheat straw, and forest residues (spruce, pine). The biomass harvested is fed to a gasification-based process, consisting of indirect gasification, steam reforming, syngas clean-up and composition adjustment and methanol synthesis. The most economical alternative to remove CO_2 from the atmospheric air is the gasification of spruce bark biomass due to present a lowest production cost, 0.11 €/kg methanol, a low investment cost, 153M€, and the high yield to methanol, 0.816 kg $_{methanol}$/kg $_{biomass}$. DAC technologies still show 10 higher production and investment costs, that are expected to decrease with the improvements in PV panels, wind turbines and the capture process itself.

Acknowledgment

The authors thank the PSEM3 GIR at USAL and the CAPD at CMU. GG appreciates the FPU PhD fellowship from the Spanish Government.

References

M. Allen, O. P. Dube, W. Solecki, F. Aragón-Durand, W. Cramer, S. Humphreys, M. Kainuma, J. Kala, N. Mahowald, Y. Mulugetta, et al, (2020). Global Warming of 1.5°C; An IPCC Special Report on the Impacts of Global Warming of 1.5°C above Pre-Industrial Levels and Related Global Greenhouse Gas Emission Pathways, in the Context of Strengthening the Global Response to the Threat of Climate Change, Sustainable Development, And Efforts to Eradicate Poverty; IPPC.

V.M. Cherednichenko, V. M., Dissertation, Karpova, Physico Chemical Institute, Moscow, U.S.S.R., 1953.

T. Eggeman, 2005, Updated Correlations for GTI Gasifier – WDYLD8. Technical memorandum for Pam Spath, National Renewable Energy Laboratory, Golden, Colorado. June 27, 2005.

D. W. Keith, G. Holmes, D. St. Angelo, K. Heidel., (2018) A Process for Capturing CO_2 from the Atmosphere. Joule 2, 1573–1594

M. Martin, I.E. Grossmann, (2018). Towards zero CO_2 emissions in the production of Methanol from switchgrass. CO_2 to methanol. Comp. Chem. Eng. 105, 308–316

S. Phillips, A. Aden, J Jechura, D Dayton, T Eggeman, 2007, Thermochemical ethanol via indirect gasification and mixed alcohol synthesis of lignocellulosic biomass. Technical Report, NREL/TP-510–41168, April 2007.

F. Sabatino, M. Mehta, A. Grimm, M. Gazzami, F. Gallucci, G. J. Kramer, M. van Sint Annaland, (2020) Evaluation of a Direct Air Capture Process Combining Wet Scrubbing and Bipolar Membrane Electrodialysis. Ind. Eng. Chem. Res., 59, 7007–7020

Proceedings of the 14th International Symposium on Process Systems Engineering – PSE 2021+
June 19-23, 2022, Kyoto, Japan
http://dx.doi.org/10.1016/B978-0-323-85159-6.50046-4

Superstructure Optimization for the Design of an Algae Biorefinery Producing Added Value Products

Maryam Raeisi[a*], Jiawei Huang[a], Thien An Huynh[a], Meik B. Franke[a], Edwin Zondervan[a]
[a]Sustainable Process Technology, Faculty of Science and Technology, University of Twente, Meander, kamer 216, Postbus 217, 7500 AE Enschede, the Netherlands
m.raeisi@utwente.nl

Abstract

This study presents a superstructure framework to evaluate processing pathways for the production of omega-3 and pigments in an algae biorefinery. Different stages such as cultivation, harvesting, dewatering, drying, cell distribution, and extraction are considered as processing sections in this superstructure. To simplify and speed up modelling, each of these technologies is grouped in blocks.

The superstructure framework is converted to a mixed-integer nonlinear programming (MINLP) model. It has more than 6.000 constraints/variables. The model is implemented in the Advanced Interactive Multidimensional Modelling System (AIMMS) software. The CPLEX and CONOPT are the selected solvers. The most promising pathways for three types of microalgae are proposed. These have differences in the dewatering section. Furthermore, the different pathways are compared in terms of cost and performance. The results show that the Haematococcus Pluvialis biorefinery leads to the highest profits due to pigments products' high amount and price.

Keywords: Superstructure optimization; algae biorefinery; biochemical; MINLP; techno-economic analysis.

1. Introduction

Biomass has been considered a renewable feedstock to overcome the shortage of petroleum-based fuel sources and handle global warming. Microalgal biomass offers incredible possibilities to be used as feedstock for biochemical and bioenergy production compared to other biomass sources. Microalgae is a non-food biomass feedstock that grows very fast in many types of water (such as freshwater, saltwater, wastewater, etc.) (Gebreslassie et al., 2013).

Algae biomass is composed of pigments, lipids, proteins, and carbohydrates that can be converted into various products (de la Noue & de Pauw, 1988). There is a growing industrial interest in using microalgae for an extensive range of applications, including biofuels and bioenergy, biofertilizers, vitamins, and chemical compounds for food production, nutraceutical dietary supplements, cosmetics, and pharmaceutical products, etc. (Torres et al., 2021). Despite the vast potential to use microalgae as a feedstock for various industries, a technical challenge must be addressed to commercially extend the use of biochemicals and biofuels from algal biomass. The optimization of a superstructure is one approach to enhance the application of microalgae on a large scale by finding a cost-effective pathway.

Rizwan et al. (2015) formulated a superstructure as a mixed integer non-linear program (MINLP), optimizing the net present value (NPV) of an algae biorefinery. Although biodiesel, bio-oil, and biogas are produced in this biorefinery, the capital costs are not considered (Rizwan et al., 2015). Galanopoulos et al. (2019) proposed a superstructure for an integrated algae biorefinery to minimize the price of biodiesel. The total biodiesel costs can be decreased with 20 % by producing bioethanol, glycerol, and levulinic acid (Galanopoulos et al., 2019). Their study showed that the price of biodiesel could be decreased by producing added-value products. Still, the profits of this algae biorefinery are not high enough to scale it up to a commercial level. Furthermore, they considered only a Chlorella Vulgaris biorefinery. Including different types of microalgae with different compositions and investigating various bioproducts will increase the prospect of commercializing the algae biorefinery. For this reason, a superstructure that includes three types of microalgae is developed to optimize the production pathway of added value products such as pigments, biodiesel, biogas, glycerol, omega-3, fertilizers.

2. Methodology

2-1 Process description and superstructure development

By using carbon dioxide and wastewater, microalgae can be cultivated. Four technologies (open pond, flat plate photobioreactor, bubble column photobioreactor, turbo column photobioreactor) are available for this cultivation stage. Subsequently, microalgae are separated from water in harvesting (including sedimentation and flotation/filtration), dewatering (flocculation, centrifugation, filter press), and a drying section. Next, the cells are disrupted to extract pigments and various lipids. There are a number of technologies for cell disruption, such as bead beating, high-pressure homogenization, microwaving, sonication, and hydrothermal liquefaction. After cell disruption, the pigments, (which are the most expensive products) are extracted. This stage is commonly done by using organic solvents or supercritical carbon dioxide. The lipids are extracted with appropriate solvents (n-butanol, Hexane, supercritical carbon dioxide) and forwarded to the lipid production stage to produce omega-3, biodiesel, and glycerol. Finally, the remaining parts of the microalgae are transported to the remnant treatment section to produce biogas and biofertilizer. Based on the current technologies, different process pathways can be selected to produce added-value components and bioenergy. All the alternatives are considered in the superstructure, as shown in Figure 1. Each block represents one of the technologies mentioned before.

2-2 Problem statement

Given is a superstructure with all current technologies and pathways. The specifications of products and raw materials are extracted from the literature. Furthermore, the equipment data includes performance (split factors and yields), cost factors (CAPEX/OPEX, Lang factors, and interest rates). The superstructure is optimized under the condition that the mass and energy balance hold and that costs display in economy of scale. The decision to be made is to select one technology at each stage and to determine the mass and energy flows at each stage. Then, the cost-effective pathway and related technologies are decided by optimizing this superstructure to maximize profits and minimize the cost-based as the objective function.

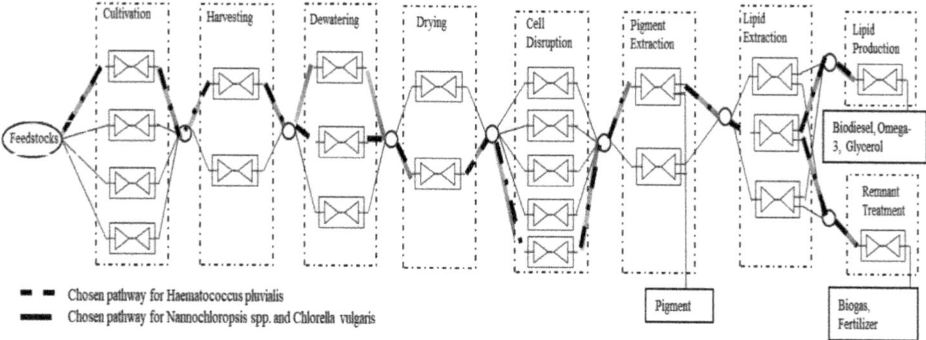

Figure 1: Superstructure of algae biorefinery and cost-effective production pathway for each type of algae

2-3 mathematical model

A mathematical model can be used to optimize the superstructure. This model contains an objective function and various constraints and variables (such as mass and energy balances and equipment limitations). The logical constraints are defined to allow only for the selected one option of each stage. There are nine intervals and 23 options in total (as shown in Figure1).

All flows that can enter/leave each option (j) are shown in figure 2, schematically. In the first part of each block, there is a mixing process to produce input flow (IN). The mass flow of mixing section ($m_{k.j}^{IN}$) for each component (k) is a mixture consisting of two parts, the upstream stream (U) mass flow ($m_{k,j}^{U}$) from the previous stage or feedstock (for four options of cultivation stage) and the reactant stream mass flow ($m_{k,j}^{R}$), which could be used to add solvents or reactants. The concentration factor $x_{k,j}$ is defined for calculating the reactant stream. It is a weight fraction based on the basic component k in the upstream flow. All these flows are added up in the Eq. (1).

$$m_{k,j}^{IN} = m_{k,j}^{U} + m_{k,j}^{R} = m_{k,j}^{U} + x_{k,j} \cdot m_{k,j}^{U} \tag{1}$$

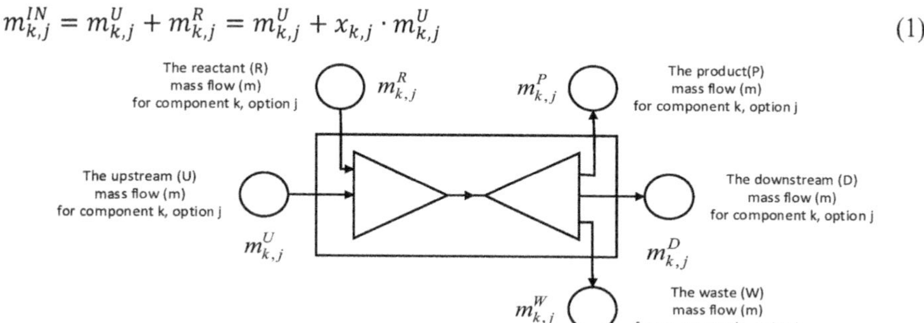

Figure 2. Mass balances in option J

To consider the reaction inside each block, the output (OUT) mass flow ($m_{k,j}^{OUT}$) (Eq. (2)) can be calculated either by a mass stoichiometric coefficient $S_{k,j}$ or by distribution coefficients $D_{k,j}$ in the case of remnant treatment. If no reaction or distribution takes place inside the option, the outlet flow should equal the inlet flow.

$$m_{k,j}^{OUT} = m_{k,j}^{IN} + S_{k,j} \cdot m_{k,j}^{IN} + D_{k,j} \cdot m_{k,j}^{IN} \quad (2)$$

Then the output mass flow ($m_{k,j}^{OUT}$) can be separated into three streams: A downstream (D) mass flow ($m_{k,j}^{D}$) going to the next stage, a waste(w) flow ($m_{k,j}^{W}$), and products(P) flows ($m_{k,j}^{P}$). These streams are calculated by using split factors $SF_{k,j}$as shown in Eq. (3).

$$m_{k,j}^{OUT} = m_{k,j}^{D} + m_{k,j}^{W} + m_{k,j}^{P} = SF_{k,j}^{D} \cdot m_{k,j}^{OUT} + SF_{k,j}^{W} \cdot m_{k,j}^{OUT} + SF_{k,j}^{P} \cdot m_{k,j}^{OUT} \quad (3)$$

For the energy balances, three elements (electricity (U_j^E), heating (U_j^H), and cooling (U_j^C)) are considered. For the utility consumption of each option (U_j), it is assumed that the energy demand is proportional to the total inlet stream mass flow going through the option. (SUC_j) is the specific utility consumption factor (Eq. (4)).

$$U_j = \sum_k m_{k,j}^{IN} \cdot SUC_j \quad (4)$$

The profit margin is defined as the difference of the annualized investment cost (AIC), annualized operating cost (AOC), and the product sales (PS).The AIC are calculated from the total plant installation cost ($TIPC$), the interest rate (IR), and the lifetime (LT), as shown in Eq. (5). The $TIPC$ can be calculated from the equipment cost with an engineering coefficient (K^{ENG}) and the land cost (LC_j) for the cultivation stage, which is shown in Eq. (6). The equipment cost is calculated using the economy-of-scale principle (f_j), with a reference cost(E_j^{ref}), a reference mass flow (m_j^{ref}), a cost index in 2020 (IDX_j^{2020}) and a reference cost index (IDX_j^{ref}). The land cost LC_j is calculated with the land price (P^{Land}) and the productivity for algae cultivation ($Productivity$) by Eq. (7).

$$AIC = TIPC \cdot \frac{IR \cdot (IR+1)^{LT}}{(IR+1)^{LT}-1} \quad (5)$$

$$TIPC = K^{ENG} \cdot \sum_j EC_j^{ref} \cdot \left(\frac{\sum_k m_{j,k}^{IN}}{m_j^{ref}}\right)^{f_j} \cdot \left(\frac{IDX_j^{2020}}{IDX_j^{ref}}\right) + LC_j \quad (6)$$

$$LC_j = P^{Land} \cdot \frac{m_{Algae,1-4}^{OUT}}{Productivity_{Algae,1-4}} \quad (7)$$

The annualized operating cost includes the raw material cost (RMC), the utility cost (UC), the operating and maintenance cost (OMC), and the waste treatment cost (WTC), which are presented in Eq. (8). The RMC and UC are calculated from multiplying the operating hours per year and the material prices and utility price, respectively. The operating and maintenance cost (OMC) are calculated from multiplying the operating and maintenance factor and the AIC. The waste treatment cost (WTC) is linear to the waste stream mass flow with a price for waste treatment.

$$AOC = RMC + UC + OMC + WTC \quad (8)$$

The product sales are calculated using the product prices ($P^{Product}$) , the operating hours per year (H) and the total product mass flow as shown in Eq. (9).

$$PS = H \cdot \sum_p P_p^{Product} \cdot \sum_j \sum_k m_{k,j}^{P} \quad (9)$$

To decrease the number of variables, parameters, and constraints and to relax the model a block integration is generated in this study. With this approach, the whole process of each technology would be considered as one integrated option with one data set. The block integration parameters are calculated in advance based on the parameters for each sub process within the option, ensuring that there is only one series of data for each option.

3. Results

Three types of microalgae (Chlorella Vulgaris (B. Wang et al., 2008), Nannochloropsis spp. (X. Wang et al., 2017), and Haematococcus Pluvialis (Ba et al., 2016)) are considered in this study. These algae grow in influent wastewater in the Netherlands. The required carbon for growing is prepared with pure carbon dioxide gas. Since daylight hours are another factor that influences algae growth, an average of 12hr sunlight per day is assumed in this study.

The Advanced Interactive Multidimensional Modelling (AIMMS) software version 4.82.3.29 64-bit is used to set up a mixed-integer non-linear programming (MINLP) model. It is solved with the Outer Approximation Algorithm (AOA) that consists of the CONOPT 4.1 solver for the non-linear part and the CPLEX 20.1 solver for a mixed-integer part. Furthermore, the model contains 6710 variables, 23 integers variables, and 6161 constraints.

For the Chlorella Vulgaris and the Nannochloropsis spp., the open pond, sedimentation and flotation, flocculation, without a dryer, hydrothermal liquefaction, organic solvent pigment extraction, N-butanol lipid extraction, lipid production, and anaerobic digestion are selected as the most cost-effective pathway (as shown in Figure 1). The optimal process pathway for Haematococcus Pluvialis is different only in the dewatering section. Centrifugation is chosen for this step in the biorefinery. Based on the productivity and cultivation reaction of Haematococcus Pluvialis, the amount of this algae is higher than other types, and it is not economically beneficial to use flocculant for separation water from them.

The Haematococcus Pluvialis biorefinery has the highest profit due to the high amount of pigments. During one year, 1 Mt of influent wastewater and 2 Mt of carbon dioxide are approximately used. 0.7 Kt of pigment and 3 t of Omega-3 can be produced. The daily profit margin of Haematococcus Pluvialis biorefinery is 28 and 34 times higher than Chlorella Vulgaris and Nannochloropsis spp. biorefineries, respectively.

The pigment is one of the expensive bioproducts. Depending on pigment composition, its price is about 2500-7000 ($/t) (Panis & Carreon, 2016). The amount of pigment that can be produced in a Haematococcus Pluvialis biorefinery are 5 and 28 times higher than Chlorella Vulgaris biorefinery and Nannochloropsis spp. biorefinery, respectively. The annual profits Haematococcus Pluvialis biorefinery for this bioproduct is approximately 200M$.

To validate the model, the superstructure is simplified to produce only biodiesel. Furthermore, one common microalgae (Chlorella Vulgaris) with 25 % lipid composition are studied in this comparison. The results are (an estimated biodiesel price of 5.2 $/L) in good agreement with data found in(Davis et al., 2011)who report biodiesel prices of 2.6$/L, as well as data from (Richardson et al., 2021), who found biodiesel prices of 9.2 $/L.

As recycles were not included and an open pond was considered for cultivation, the investment costs are relatively low. To separate large amounts of water, 31 % of total investment costs are attributed to harvesting and dewatering stages. The cell disruption stage is the most expensive part due to disrupting a massive amount of algae (39 % of total investment costs). In addition, the operating costs contribute to approximately 83% of the total costs. Utilities are about 50 % of the total operating costs.

4. Conclusion

A superstructure of an algae biorefinery is developed to produce added-value products from microalgae (Haematococcus Pluvialis, Chlorella Vulgaris, Nannochloropsis spp). These superstructures are optimized in the AIMMS to find cost-effective production pathways. The optimal pathways consist of an open pond, sedimentation and flotation, flocculation/centrifugation, without a dryer, hydrothermal liquefaction, organic solvent pigment extraction, N-butanol lipid extraction, lipid production, and anaerobic digestion. Types of microalgae have an important role in finding the appropriate technology for the dewatering step (flocculation/centrifugation). The profit of Haematococcus Pluvialis biorefinery is more than 28 times higher that of the Chlorella Vulgaris biorefinery and more than 32 times higher than that of Nannochloropsis spp biorefinery. Haematococcus Pluvialis can produce 0.7 Kt of pigment and 3 t of Omega-3 using 1 Mt of influent wastewater and 2 Mt of carbon dioxide.

References

F. Ba, A. V. Ursu, C. Laroche, G. Djelveh, 2016, Haematococcus pluvialis soluble proteins: Extraction, characterization, concentration/fractionation and emulsifying properties. Bioresource Technology, 200, 147–152. https://doi.org/10.1016/j.biortech.2015.10.012

R. Davis, A. Aden, P. T. Pienkos, 2011, Techno-economic analysis of autotrophic microalgae for fuel production. Applied Energy, 88, 3524–3531. https://doi.org/10.1016/j.apenergy.2011.04.018

J. de la Noue, N. de Pauw, 1988 , The potential of microalgal biotechnology: A review of production and uses of microalgae. Biotechnology Advances, 6(4), 725–770. https://doi.org/10.1016/0734-9750(88)91921-0

C. Galanopoulos, P. Kenkel, E. Zondervan, 2019, Superstructure optimization of an integrated algae biorefinery. Computers & Chemical Engineering, 130, 106530. https://doi.org/10.1016/j.compchemeng.2019.106530

G. Panis, J. R. Carreon, 2016, Commercial astaxanthin production derived by green alga Haematococcus pluvialis : A microalgae process model and a techno-economic assessment all through production line. Algal Research, 18, 175–190. https://doi.org/10.1016/j.algal.2016.06.007

M. Rizwan, J. H. Lee, R. Gani, 2015, Optimal design of microalgae-based biorefinery: Economics, opportunities and challenges. Applied Energy, 150, 69–79.https://doi.org/10.1016/j.apenergy.2015.04.018

G. F. Torres, B. P. Elisabeth, J. Pittman, C. Theodoropoulos, 2021 Microalgae strain catalogue: A strain selection guide for microalgae users: cultivation and chemical characteristics for high added-value products. The University of Manchester. https://doi.org/10.5281/zenodo.3780067

B. Wang, Y. Li, N. Wu, C. Q. Lan, 2008, CO2 bio-mitigation using microalgae. Applied Microbiology and Biotechnology, 79(5), 707–718. https://doi.org/10.1007/s00253-008-1518-y

X. Wang, L. Sheng, X. Yang, 2017, Pyrolysis characteristics and pathways of protein, lipid and carbohydrate isolated from microalgae Nannochloropsis sp. Bioresource Technology, 229, 119–125. https://doi.org/10.1016/j.biortech.2017.01.018

Proceedings of the 14th International Symposium on Process Systems Engineering – PSE 2021+
June 19-23, 2022, Kyoto, Japan
http://dx.doi.org/10.1016/B978-0-323-85159-6.50047-6

Process simulation of continuous biodiesel production catalysed by a high stability solid in a reactive distillation

Chatchan Treeyawetchakul[a,*]

[a] *Department of Chemical Engineering, Mahanakorn University of Technology, Bangkok 10530, Thailand*
chatchan@mut.ac.th

Abstract

KF/(Ca/Al) catalyst developed in laboratory robust activity and stable than a conventional CaO catalyst for biodiesel production from refined palm oil. The highest conversion yield of 94.7% wt. obtained by employing KF/(Ca/Al) catalyst (10% wt.) in a 350 ml batch reactor. It was operated at methanol to oil molar ratio of 15:1, reaction temperature of 65°C, and reaction time of 3 hrs, the pseudo-first-order rate law could be used to fit the palm oil transesterification reaction (WongSree et al., 2016). In order to produce biodiesel in industrial scale and intensification, in this work, approximately 1,050 kg hr-1 of biodiesel production rate was considerably basis, and the transesterification reaction was occurred in the reactive distillation (RD) column as shown in Figure 1. The thermophysical parameters of all the components were computed and validated with available experimental data with reasonable accuracy. In addition, the kinetic model obtained from laboratory experiment was also used and modelled in the RD column simulation. The optimal conditions, with a maximum conversion of approximately 90% wt., are a methanol to oil molar ratio of 5:1, a reflux ratio of 0.2, a total number of trays of 15, a reboiler heat duty 20 kW, and the number of reactive trays should not be less than 7.

Keywords: Biodiesel production; KF/(Ca/Al) catalyst; Reactive distillation; Process Simulation.

1. Introduction

Biodiesel from palm oil has been promising and continuously supported by the Thai government since 2010 as an alternative and sustainable energy. Generally, biodiesel is produced from the transesterification of crude palm oil (CPO) or palm stearin with short-chain alcohol (methanol or ethanol) involving homogeneous catalyst (KOH or NaOH) under appropriate conditions and reaction time. However, the use of homogeneous catalysts leads to the continuous catalyst consuming reaction thus reducing the catalytic efficiency over the reaction period. In addition, it is technically difficult to remove unreacted catalyst after the reaction completion and a large amount of wastewater is produced to and it needs to be separated and cleaned the products, which increases the overall cost of the process. Thus, the biodiesel production cost based on homogeneous catalysis, is not yet sufficiently competitive as compared to the cost of diesel production from petroleum (Zhang, 2003).

The development of heterogeneous catalysts is an alternative choice that could eliminate the additional operation costs associated with the aforementioned (separation and purification step). Furthermore, biodiesel production with heterogeneous catalysts does not produce soap as a by-product. Therefore, the study of heterogeneous catalysts has been focused on by several researchers since it leads to a possibility of another pathway for biodiesel production development.

WongSree et al. (2016) developed and studied the effects of KF/(Ca/Al) on biodiesel production from purified palm oil compared with CaO and KF/CaO catalysts on the laboratory scale. They concluded that the highest oil conversion of 94.7% could be achieved by employing the KF/(Ca/Al) catalyst in a batch reactor together with methanol to oil molar ratio 15:1, catalyst loading of 10 wt.%, reaction temperatures of 65 °C, and reaction time 3 hours. They also proposed that the kinetic model of the transesterification could be explained and fitted with the experiments by the pseudo-first order model as shown in Eq. (1)

$$\frac{dc_A}{dt} = \left[5.1\times10^6 \exp\left(\frac{58.47}{RT}\right)\right] c_A \tag{1}$$

Where c_A is concentration of tripalmitin

The aim of this study is in preliminary proposing and applying an RD column simulation of the biodiesel production process via Aspen Plus® as a simulator by using the aforementioned laboratory results as basic parameters for industrial production.

2. Description of RD and methodology

For simulation experiments, based on 1,000 kghr^{-1} biodiesel production rates, the CPO was fed approximately 1,167 kghr^{-1} at 25 °C, 1 atm. The RD column for the biodiesel production process consists of three sections: rectification, reaction, and stripping as shown in Fig. 1. In the reaction stage, the transesterification reaction scheme is:

$$C_{51}H_{98}O_6 + CH_3OH \rightarrow 3C_{17}H_{34}O_2 + C_3H_8O_3 \tag{2}$$

$$C_{57}H_{104}O_6 + CH_3OH \rightarrow 3C_{19}H_{36}O_2 + C_3H_8O_3 \tag{3}$$

In the reaction zone, the pseudo-first order kinetic model as shown in eq.1 was used in the simulation. For this case, methanol excess was released at the top of the RD column while both glycerol and methyl palmitate were separated via decanter.

The Aspen Plus® tool was used for simulation of this process. Regarding the CPO as raw material which is high content of triolein ($C_{57}H_{104}O_6$) and tripalmitin ($C_{51}H_{98}O_6$), then both of them were represented in this simulation. Accordingly, methyl oleate ($C_{19}H_{36}O_2$) and methyl palmitate ($C_{17}H_{34}O_2$) were taken as the FAME products and their properties were available in the library of the Aspen tool. Due to the highly polar components presenting in this process such as methanol and glycerol, the UNIF-DMD and NRTL thermodynamic/activity model were used to estimate the activity coefficients in a liquid phase.

The important parameters such as molar reflux ratio, column pressure, number of the column tray, and so on would be adjusted in order to get highest biodiesel yield and lowest RD column duty.

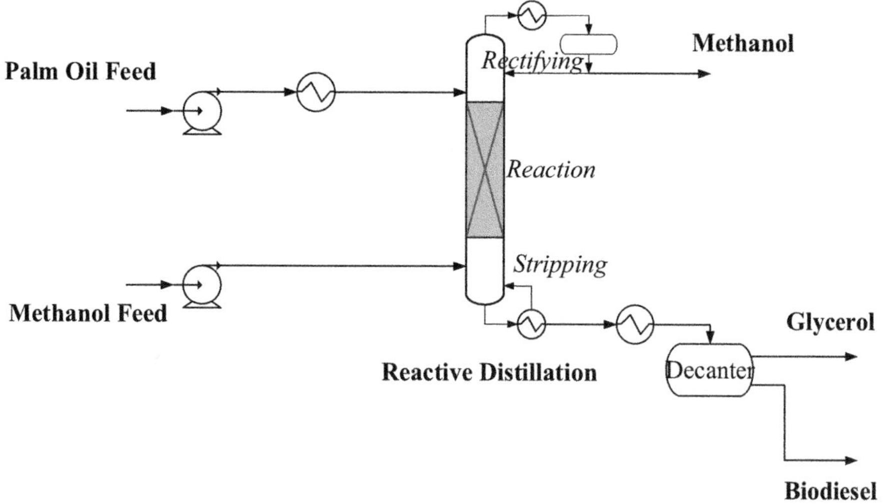

Figure 1. Biodiesel production with RD column

3. Results and Discussion

3.1 Effects of operating pressure and molar reflux ratio

At steady-state simulation, with the 15-theoretical stage of the RD column, the effect of column pressure and molar reflux ratio were shown in Fig. 2 and 3, respectively. Fig. 2 shows that the reboiler duty of the RD column continuously increases with operating pressure increasing and it is the same trend for molar reflux ratio (Fig. 3). It can also be interpreted that the column pressure 0.2 bar and molar reflux ratio 0.5 are optimal operating conditions.

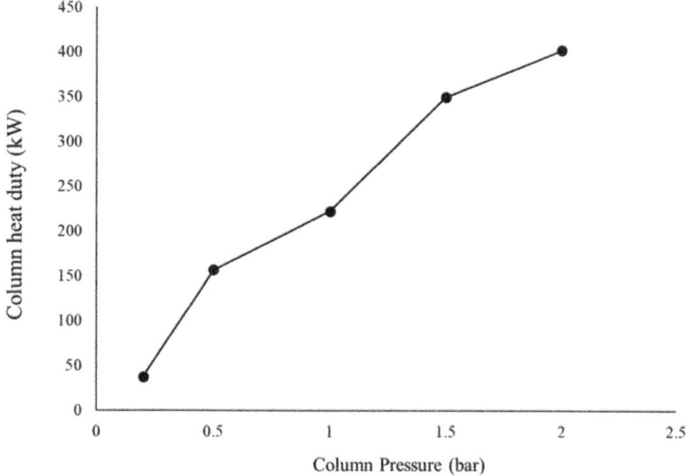

Figure 2. Effect of column pressure on the column duty

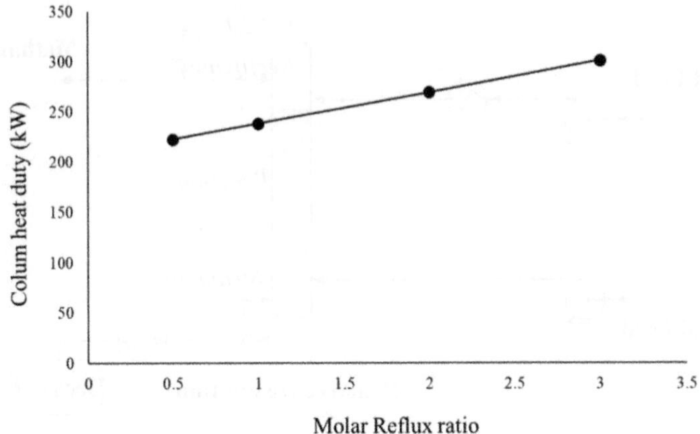

Figure 3. Effect of molar reflux ratio on the column duty

Besides the duty of the column considering, the proper pressure reduction (0.2 bar) was also kept the reboiler temperature lower than 200 °C and condenser temperature higher than 20 °C as shown in Fig. 4. Furthermore, at this pressure, the reaction zone temperature was kept between 60-80 °C which corresponds to the experiments (WongSree et al., 2016). However, the temperature at the 12th tray (methanol feed tray) is rapidly decrease which is different from Karacan and F Karacanb (2014) have reported. This can be explained that this study used methanol fed at the room temperature (25 °C) without preheater.

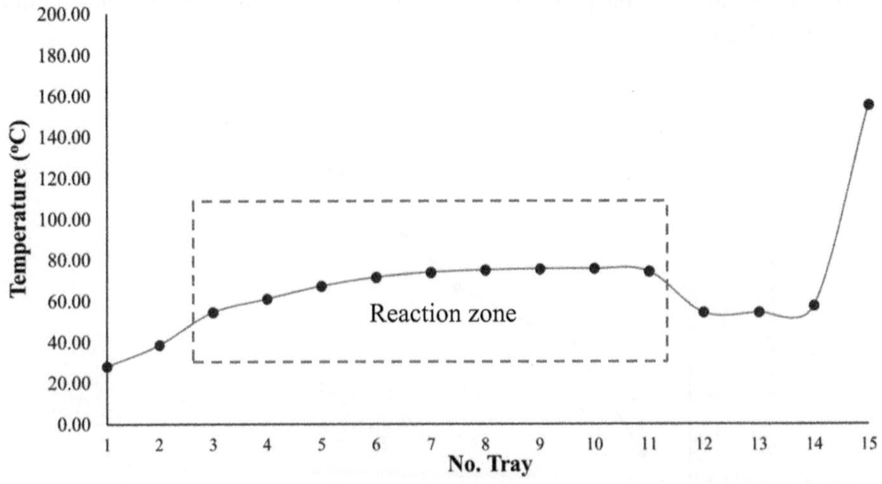

Figure 4. Temperature profiles of the RD column for the operating pressure 0.2 bar

3.2 Effects of methanol to oil molar ratio as feed

At the preliminary optimal conditions of RD column (reflux ratio =3.0, operating pressure 0.2 bar, methanol to oil ratio = 5:1, number of total stages = 15, and number of the reaction stage = 8), the biodiesel product (mixture of methyl oleate and methyl palmitate) was achieved at the flow rate of 1,050 $kghr^{-1}$ with the highest yield at 0.903 as shown in Fig. 5. It can be seen that the yield of biodiesel production from the simulation was closed to the experiments.

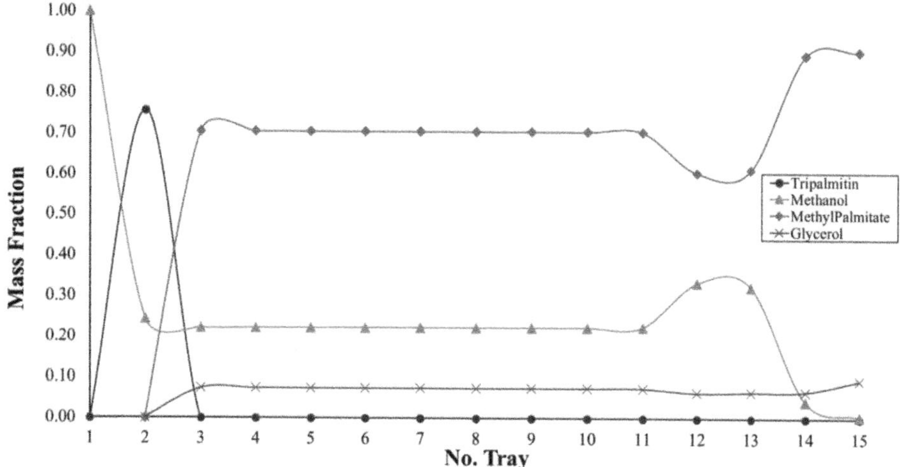

Figure 5. Liquid compositions profiles of the RD column at optimal condition (methanol to oil molar ratio = 5:1)

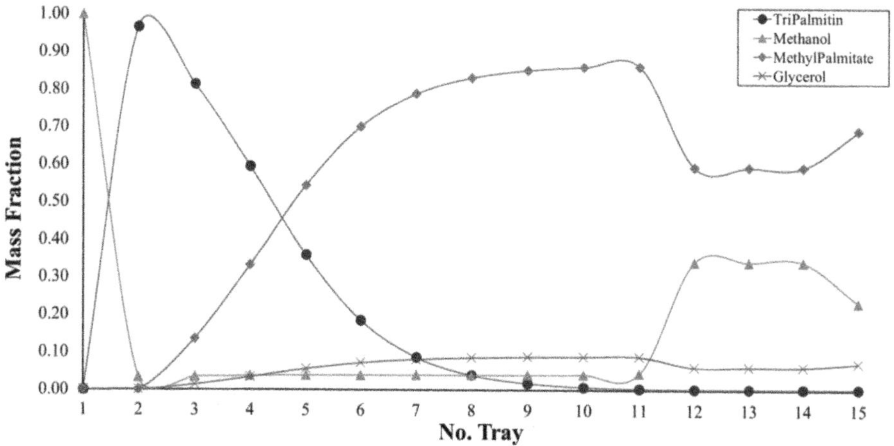

Figure 6. Liquid compositions profiles of the RD column at optimal condition (methanol to oil molar ratio = 15:1)

Fig.5 shows the concentration distribution of all chemicals within RD column. The figure shows that, with the oil feed stage is 2, the rapid reaction rates are occurring on stages 3-4 while the transesterification is occurred continuously between stage 4 and stage 11. Then the biodiesel produced along with glycerol flowed downward to the bottom of the RD column.

However, at the same biodiesel yield, in an experiment, the methanol to oil molar ratio should be 15:1, while this ratio from the simulation is only 5:1. This can be explained that when a large amount of methanol is fed at stage 12, it would be affecting on the bottom temperature to be lower than 150 °C (approximately 80-100 °C). Compared with methanol boiling point temperature (approximately 65 °C), some methanol might not be vaporized to the above stage and poured and mixed with biodiesel product. This phenomenon was proved in Fig. 6.

4. Conclusions

In this paper, the biodiesel production catalysed by KF(Al/CO) was simulated by Aspen Plus with the biodiesel production rate at 1,050 $kghr^{-1}$. The simulation results show that, the biodiesel yields is approximately 90.3% which closed to the experimental result at optimal conditions (molar reflux ratio =3.0, operating pressure 0.2 bar, methanol to oil ratio = 5:1, number of total stages = 15, and number of the reaction stage = 8), and the RD column heat duty is around 50 kW. Then these preliminary results show that this modified process can be interesting to both of energy saving concern.

5. References

N. WongSree, S. Dokmai and T. Prachoomphon, 2016, Continuous production of biodiesel in a reactive distillation catalyzed by a high stability solid catalyst, B.Eng. Thesis, Chemical Engineering Department, Mahanakorn University of Technology, Thailand.

S. Karacan and F Karacanb, 2014, Simulation of Reactive Distillation Column for Biodiesel Production at Optimum Conditions, Chemical Engineering Transactions, 39, 1705-1710

X. Yang, L. Haoyang; X. Guomin, G. Lijing, and P. Xiaomei, 2013, Simulation of the catalytic reactive distillation process for biodiesel production via transesterification, IEEE International Conference on Materials for Renewable Energy and Environment, Chengdu, China. DOI:10.1109/ICMREE.2013.6893646

Y. Zhang, M.A. Dubé, D.D McLean and M.Kates, 2003, Biodiesel production from waste cooking oil: 1. Process design and technological assessment, Bioresource Technology, 89, (1), 1-16

Proceedings of the 14th International Symposium on Process Systems Engineering – PSE 2021+
June 19-23, 2022, Kyoto, Japan
http://dx.doi.org/10.1016/B978-0-323-85159-6.50048-8

Generative Approaches for the Synthesis of Process Structures

Tahar NABIL[a], Jean-Marc COMMENGE[c], and Thibaut NEVEUX[b,c*]

[a] *EDF R&D, Boulevard Gaspard Monge, F-91120 Palaiseau, France*
[b] *EDF R&D, 6 quai Watier, F-78401 Chatou, France*
[c] *Université de Lorraine, CNRS, LRGP, F-54000 Nancy, France*
thibaut.neveux@edf.fr

Abstract

In process synthesis, generative approaches are algorithmic strategies able to produce new structures, which differs from conventional optimization techniques consisting in choosing among a predetermined set of structures (e.g. heuristics and superstructure optimization). The development of these approaches has only intensified recently with the rise of both evolutionary computation and machine learning techniques. This paper aims at introducing some recent experiments, categorized into reward-driven and data-driven algorithms; and discussing key aspects of the generative steps such as: required initial database, process data representation, generative model architecture, reward design, optimization strategy and post-processing for the engineer.

Keywords: Process Synthesis; Machine Learning; Artificial Intelligence; Evolutionary Programming; Optimization

1. Introduction

The essence of process synthesis implies to propose a process structure, i.e. a set of unit operations for the transformation of mass and energy interconnected in a network (process flowsheet), associated with degrees of freedom such as equipment design and operating conditions. Solutions to solve this problem evolved from heuristics and expertise, through iterations with process simulators and experimental works, towards mathematical optimization techniques. A common approach consists in optimizing the process structure among a postulated set of alternative paths, called superstructure, using optimization (Mixed Integer Non-Linear Programming, Generalized Disjunctive Programming, etc.) to select the best structures with respect to given objective(s) and constraints. These approaches are proving to be very complex to implement in real industrial cases and intrinsically introduce an inductive bias due to the restriction to a search space limited by the defined superstructure: if the optimal structure is not in the defined space, the optimizer cannot find it.

Recently, generative approaches have used advanced algorithms to propose process structures directly from a set of available unit operations. These approaches differ from conventional optimization techniques by their capacity to generate new structures, instead of choosing among a predetermined set of structures. This paper aims at introducing some of those recent experiments, discussing the key aspects of the generative steps, and highlighting some remaining challenges.

2. Recent prospective works on "Generative Approaches"

The idea of using algorithmic strategies to generate process structures is not new (Nishida et al., 1981), but its development has only intensified recently with the rise of both evolutionary computation and machine learning techniques (see examples in Figure 1). Yet, most of the works on generative approaches remain prospective with academic proof-of-concept and/or specific case-studies. We provide here a non-exhaustive overview of the various techniques proposed to generate process structures and highlight their key features.

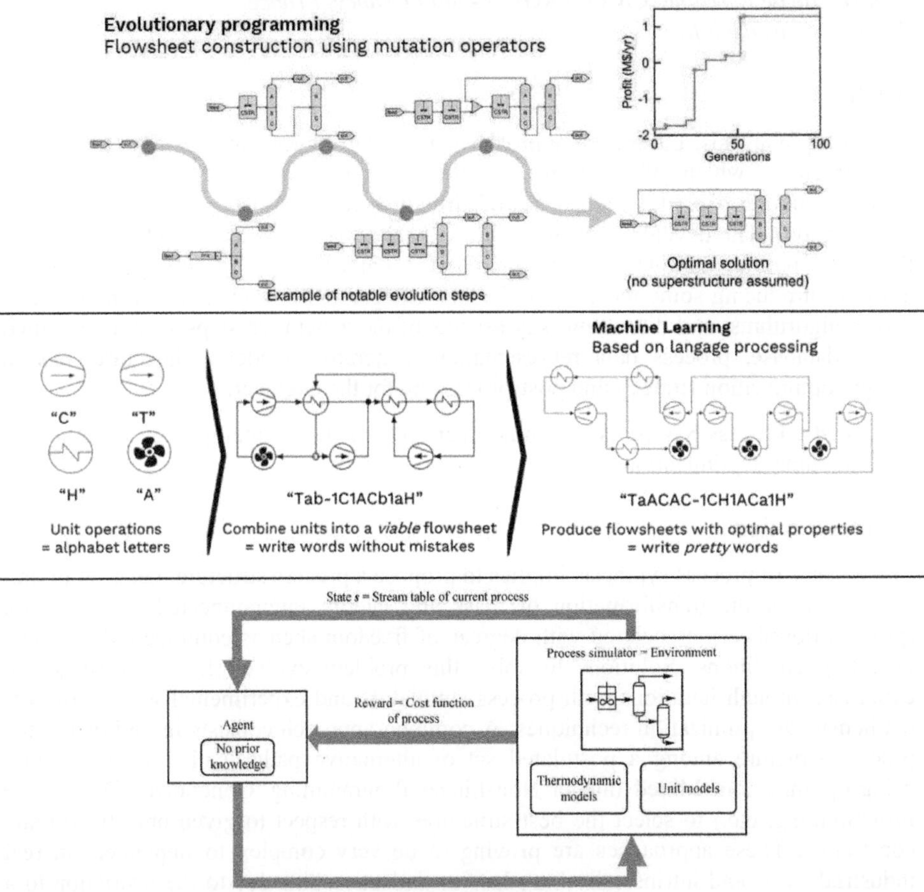

Figure 1. Examples of generative approaches to build flowsheets: evolutionary programming using mutation operators (top), machine learning using language processing (middle), and reinforcement learning using a two-player game (bottom); respectively adapted from Neveux (2018), Nabil *et al.* (2019), and Göttl *et al.* (2022).

Generative approaches usually rely on a two-level decomposition of the process synthesis problem, an upper level for designing the topology (i.e. the process flowsheet) and a lower level for evaluating the flowsheet (i.e. optimizing the degrees of freedom for a given structure). In this paper, we discuss only the topological problem, i.e. the generation of process structures. The more specific task of generating structures with certain desired properties is called targeted process generation; it consists in producing flowsheets which will maximize a given fitness function. Some recent contributions in the field of process synthesis suggest using artificial intelligence algorithms to generate new flowsheets. They could be categorized into:

- Data-driven algorithms, learning from an initial database of known process structures and their performance indicators to generate new structures (see Figure 1, middle). This category is based on Machine Learning and Deep Learning techniques. For instance, Nabil *et al.* (2019) used a string representation of a power cycle and applied Natural Language Processing to generate new structures.
- Reward-driven algorithms, performing a topological optimization driven by a set of objectives and constraints. This category includes Evolutionary algorithms (EA) and Reinforcement Learning (RL) models. For instance, EA could apply mutation operators to modify a population of process structures (Figure 1, top); operators could be elemental such as unit addition, unit removal, stream permutation (Neveux, 2018) or hierarchical with function and technology levels (Wang *et al.*, 2015); while RL techniques (Figure 1, bottom) maximize a reward by sequentially modifying the structure of the process. For instance, Göttl *et al.* (2022) formulated the problem as a turn-based two-player game and applied RL for ethyl tert-butil ether synthesis. Midgley (2020) used RL with deep neural networks to optimize a sequence of reactors and a distillation column train.

Process design could also benefit from initiatives in other research fields with similar data representation and network generation problems. In particular, machine learning generative models have obtained significant successes in the field of molecular design (Elton et al., 2019), and their approaches could be adapted to processes.

3. Discussions on generative aspects

In this section, we formalize the notion of a generative machine learning model and study how to apply it to process synthesis, highlighting some key challenges.

3.1 Generative machine learning models

Consider a set of observed data $\mathcal{D}$. We assume that each element in $\mathcal{D}$ is a sample from an underlying -unknown- data distribution p^*. The goal of a generative machine learning model is to learn a parametric approximation p_θ of p^*, where the model distribution p_θ belongs to a model class $\mathcal{M} = \{p_\theta : \theta \in \Theta\}$, parameterized by a vector θ from the model family Θ. The following optimization problem is thus solved: $\min_{\theta \in \Theta} d(p^*, p_\theta)$, with $d(\cdot)$ a distance between probability distributions. Once it is learned, one may sample from the model distribution to generate new elements: $x_{new} \sim p_\theta(\cdot)$. Hence, one advantage of generative models is that they can produce (infinitely many) new samples, extending $\mathcal{D}$.

3.2 Application to process synthesis: concept and challenges

Applied to process synthesis, e.g. in (Nabil et al., 2019), the generative approach starts by gathering an initial database of flowsheets, determining the set of unit operations to include and their numerical representation. Next, the chosen model architecture is optimized to represent the underlying data distribution and maximize a certain fitness function for targeted generation. The outcome is a large pool of flowsheets with good properties, to be analysed by the design engineer. We call this approach data-driven.

Another complementary approach is also emerging, namely a purely reward-driven optimization including evolutionary programming (Neveux, 2018) and reinforcement learning models (Göttl *et al.*, 2022, Midgley, 2020). In practice, the two approaches can be combined to obtain better performances. For instance, reinforcement learning can accelerate the convergence of the generative model towards good regions of the search space, as in (Olivecrona *et al.*, 2017) for molecules.

In the sequel, we discuss several practical challenges that need to be addressed in order to apply successfully the machine learning approach to process synthesis.

3.2.1 Initial database

The first task is to collect data, i.e. a set $\mathcal{D} = \{x_i, y_i\}_{i=1}^{n}$, where each process structure x_i is associated with a label y_i, e.g. the economic cost, for a large integer n ~ 10^6. Whereas such datasets already exist for molecule synthesis (Elton et al., 2019), it is not the case for processes. We suggest three ways to overcome this issue. Firstly, one can generate processes as random coloured graphs - it was shown by Nabil et al. (2019) that starting with a small-size set of random layouts could yield promising results by iteratively augmenting the training set with the generated data. Secondly, former expert knowledge can be exploited by listing every layout included in a given superstructure. The third option is to re-use artificial samples generated by another method, e.g. reward-driven methods not requiring an initial database (Neveux, 2018).

Besides, each label y_i is not an intrinsic property of the layout x_i but depends instead on certain boundary conditions. y_i is usually found by solving an optimization problem whose complexity depends on the physics of the process. This adds to the computational burden of generative models, since for each new use case with specific boundary conditions, the label y_i should be computed again. Hence, a typical dataset of processes might be sparse (unlabelled x_i's) and noisy or heterogeneous (y_i's obtained from different optimization algorithms). Finally, one last challenge is to create a dataset that is not trivially separable on process structures while covering a large, non-local, fraction of the search space.

3.2.2 Data representation

Generative approaches rely on an abstract representation of a process structure to be processed by a machine learning algorithm, and it remains an open question to determine which format is most suitable for process structures. Two formats stand out particularly, namely a graph-based or a string-based representation. Both formats are bijective and can benefit from advances in artificial intelligence on graphs and Natural Language Processing, respectively. For instance, the underlying representation used by Neveux (2018) or Göttl *et al.* (2022) is a graph, whereas Nabil *et al.* (2019) explicitly created a language with an alphabet and syntactic rules to represent a power cycle. Language encoding could in the future exploit the more generic SFILES (simplified flowsheet-input line-entry system) format (d'Anterroches and Gani, 2005). On the other hand, a graph-based representation, typically a directed graph with node colouring, is closer to the flowsheets known to chemical engineers and removes the need to learn syntactic rules. However, graph generative models have a greater computational cost, since graph isomorphism is not solvable in polynomial time.

It is interesting to note that generative models for molecules were historically based on molecular fingerprints, then strings (so-called SMILES format), and the recent trend is to shift towards graph representations (Elton et al., 2019).

3.2.3 Generative model architecture

Once the observed data $\mathcal{D}$ is available and the data representation chosen, it remains to determine the architecture of the generative model, i.e. to select a class of models $\mathcal{M}$. The deep learning literature is rich of such generative models, which have achieved state-of-the-art performances. The three main classes are the recurrent neural networks (RNNs), the variational autoencoders (VAEs) and the generative adversarial networks (GANs). The field of graph or string generative models is also driven by the application to molecule synthesis, which constitutes thus an excellent first set of architectures to adapt to process synthesis: see e.g. Elton et al. (2019).

3.2.4 Reward design

In targeted process generation, the generative model is biased towards a certain region of the search space by a reward function. The reward should be designed carefully to obtain processes with desirable features such as (i) diversity and novelty (ii) feasibility and respect of the constraints and (iii) high fitness. Diversity and novelty metrics can be found in (Elton et al., 2019). The feasibility and constraints are to be defined on a per use-case basis. In particular, the performances of generative models might decrease whenever the problem is severely constrained, reducing thus the space of valid flowsheets. As an example, if 99% product purity is expected, a process reaching 90% is not valid yet better than 0%; the reward should therefore encode this designer expertise, e.g. by penalizing the objective function (such as an economic cost) by the constraints violation (distance from 99% purity). Hence, softening the constraints by adding adequate penalty terms in the reward function can facilitate the convergence of the model. See also (Göttl *et al.*, 2022) for a discussion on how the reward function might impact the diversity of the generated flowsheets. Finally, the ability to evaluate the fitness of a flowsheet is a nonlinear optimization problem itself. Since generative models are data-intensive and require the evaluation of thousands of flowsheets, efficient evaluation is necessary for the application to real use cases. A promising track to alleviate this computational cost is to develop surrogate meta-models (Gorissen et al., 2010) or train a machine learning regression or classification model on separate data (Nabil et al., 2019).

3.2.5 Optimization strategy

Reward-driven methods are optimization algorithms, as such they are explicitly designed for targeted process generation. Machine learning generative models can also produce focused libraries of processes, although in a less straightforward manner. For instance, transfer learning is used by Nabil et al. (2019) to bias the RNN network towards regions of high efficiency and shaft power output for power cycles while reinforcement learning is combined with generative models by Olivecrona et al. (2017). Whereas the space of process flowsheets is discrete and large, another approach is to take advantage of the latent space built by VAEs or GANs, enabling thus the optimization in a low-dimensional continuous space (Gómez-Bombarelli et al., 2018).

In the future, the ease of the optimization process, for instance the sensibility of the model to hyperparameter tuning, should also be a criterion for discriminating between models, in particular between string-based and graph-based approaches: robust models adaptable to new use cases are preferable for the adoption by the process engineer.

3.2.6 Post-processing for the engineer

The finality of generative models is to produce pools of relevant flowsheets to help the process engineer at the design stage. Beyond the selection of the best topology achieved by the model, it is also beneficial to gain knowledge from the generated data, to extract new heuristic rules. For instance, Zhang et al. (2019) propose a methodology to compare process flowsheets and detect structural similarities between them, by applying text pattern mining algorithms to SFILES.

4. Conclusive remarks

Applying generative approaches for the synthesis of process structures is a new field, with various recent experiments using evolutionary and machine learning techniques. They have been tested on a limited number of use cases, which calls for further investigation to evaluate their most appropriate use and define practical tips for the process engineer. The search space being virtually infinite, the computation effort could become prohibitive. Therefore, there is a need both for results reproducibility and for a comprehensive comparison on identical synthesis problems, to assess the potential and drawbacks of these techniques; whether they could substitute to established techniques (such as heuristics or superstructure optimization) or serve as new search heuristics to better define a restricted search space for conventional synthesis approaches.

References

d'Anterroches, L. and Gani, R. (2005), Group contribution based process flowsheet synthesis, design and modelling. *Fluid Phase Equilibria,* 228:141-146.

Elton, D. C., Boukouvalas, Z., Fuge, M. D. and Chung, P. W. (2019), Deep learning for molecular design—a review of the state of the art. *Mol. Syst. Des. Eng.,* 4:828-849.

Gómez-Bombarelli, R., Wei, J. N., Duvenaud, D., Hernández-Lobato, J. M., Sánchez-Lengeling, B., Sheberla, D., Aguilera-Iparraguirre, J., Hirzel, T. D., Adams, R. P. and Aspuru-Guzik, A. (2018), Automatic Chemical Design Using a Data-Driven Continuous Representation of Molecules. *ACS Cent. Sci.,* 4:268-276.

Gorissen, D., Couckuyt, I., Demeester, P., Dhaene, T. and Crombecq, K. (2010), A surrogate modeling and adaptive sampling toolbox for computer based design. *J. Mach. Learn. Res.*

Göttl, Q., Grimm, D.G. and Burger (2022), J. Automated synthesis of steady-state continuous processes using reinforcement learning. *Front. Chem. Sci. Eng.* 16, 288–302.

Midgley, L. I., (2020), Deep Reinforcement Learning for Process Synthesis, *Preprint arXiv:2009.13265*

Nabil, T. and Le Moullec, Y. and Le Coz, A., (2019), Machine Learning based design of a supercritical CO2 concentrating solar power plant, 3rd European scCO2 Conference, Paris.

Neveux, T., (2018), Ab-initio process synthesis using evolutionary programming, *Chemical Engineering Science,* 185:209–22.

Nishida, N., Stephanopoulos, G. and Westerberg, A.W. (1981), A review of process synthesis. *AIChE Journal,* 27(3):321-351.

Olivecrona, M., Blaschke, T., Engkvist, O. and Chen, H. (2017), Molecular de-novo design through deep reinforcement learning. *J. Cheminform,* 9:48

Wang, L., Voll, P., Lampe, M., Yang, Y. and Bardow, A. (2015), Superstructure-free synthesis and optimization of thermal power plants. *Energy,* 91:700-711.

Zhang, T., Sahinidis, N.V. and Siirola, J.J. (2019), Pattern recognition in chemical process flowsheets. *AIChE Journal,* 65: 592-603.

Proceedings of the 14th International Symposium on Process Systems Engineering – PSE 2021+
June 19-23, 2022, Kyoto, Japan
http://dx.doi.org/10.1016/B978-0-323-85159-6.50049-X

Metal-Organic Framework Targeting for Optimal Pressure Swing Adsorption Processes

Xiang Zhang[a], Teng Zhou[a,b,*], Kai Sundmacher[a,b]

[a]*Process Systems Engineering, Max Planck Institute for Dynamics of Complex Technical Systems, Sandtorstr. 1, D-39106 Magdeburg, Germany*
[b]*Process Systems Engineering, Otto-von-Guericke University Magdeburg, Universitätsplatz 2, D-39106 Magdeburg, Germany*
zhout@mpi-magdeburg.mpg.de

Abstract

Gas separation accounts for a major production cost in chemical industries. So far, pressure swing adsorption (PSA) has been widely used for gas separation applications such as H_2 purification and CO_2 capture. For PSA processes, the adsorption efficiency is greatly affected by the selected adsorbent and process operating conditions. Over the past decade, porous metal-organic frameworks (MOFs) have been recognized as innovative adsorbents featuring tunable properties. For achieving a high separation efficiency, a novel two-step integrated MOF and PSA process design approach has been recently proposed. In the first step, MOF is represented as a set of geometric and chemical descriptors. The MOF descriptors and process operating conditions are simultaneously optimized to maximize the process performance. In this work, the second step, namely MOF targeting, is presented. The objective is to use various computational tools to synthesize hypothetical MOFs and identify potential candidates based on the optimized MOF descriptors. The involved computational tools include Tobacco for computational MOF synthesis, Poreblazer for geometry characterization, and RASPA for rigorous adsorption isotherm simulation.

Keywords: MOF targeting, Hypothetical MOF, Machine learning, Adsorption process design, Gas separation

1. Introduction

Pressure swing adsorption (PSA) has been widely used in chemical and energy industries for gas separation. It exploits different gas affinities on solid adsorbents at different pressures to achieve the separation. Currently, multiple types of porous materials are used as adsorbents such as metal-organic framework (MOF), zeolite, and activated carbon. Among them, MOFs are formed via the self-assembly of various molecular building blocks (i.e., metal nodes and organic linkers) in different topologies. Due to the large variety of building blocks, a near-infinite design space exists for MOFs (Yao et al. 2021). In addition, MOFs have many superior properties such as high porosity, tunable pore geometry, and functional pore surface. Therefore, MOFs have a great potential to enhance process efficiency in adsorption-based gas separation (Wang et al. 2020).

When MOFs are used for adsorption-based gas separation, four alternative mechanisms exist: equilibrium separation, kinetic separation, molecular sieving, and gate-opening separation. Among these, equilibrium separation is the most common method, which is based on the difference in gas equilibrium loadings. So far, numerous MOFs with diverse isotherm characteristics have been synthesized in the laboratory by varying MOF chemistry and structure (e.g., pore geometry and topology). Unfortunately, this experimental trial-and-error approach is time-consuming and inefficient. Importantly, many MOFs cannot lead to good process performance (Burns et al. 2020). It is well-known that adsorbents ultimately serve a specific adsorption process. In this case, the design of a MOF for use in PSA processes is indeed a multiscale design problem that incorporates the inter-linked material, phase, and process levels. Variations of materials and process operating conditions affect the adsorption behavior and thus jointly decide the process performance. With this in mind, a computational approach is desired to expedite the identification of promising MOF adsorbents that can best serve the PSA process.

Recently, focusing on the equilibrium separation, our group has proposed a novel two-step integrated MOF and PSA process design framework to tackle the above challenges (Zhang et al. 2021). As shown in Figure 1, it consists of two steps: descriptor optimization and MOF targeting. Due to the large number of MOF building blocks, it is difficult to build mathematical models to predict adsorption isotherms directly from building blocks. Therefore, in the published first step, a MOF is represented by a set of chemical and geometry descriptors. Several data science techniques are utilized to select proper descriptors, define a valid design space, and build data-driven models for the prediction of adsorption isotherms. This enables an explicit formulation of the integrated MOF and PSA process design problem, where MOF descriptors and process operating conditions are simultaneously optimized to maximize the process performance. In the present work, the second step namely MOF targeting is addressed. We will show how the optimal results obtained in Step 1 can be used to guide the discovery of high-performance MOFs. Same as the first step, this second step is demonstrated on the separation of propene (PE) and propane (PA), which is currently achieved with energy-intensive cryogenic distillation. Clearly, an optimal design of MOF and PSA process is of great importance for energy saving. The paper is organized as follows. First, the specific workflow of the MOF targeting step is introduced, followed by the introduction of MOF decomposition and building block construction. Afterwards, the workflow will be applied to identify the optimal MOFs for the PE/PA separation.

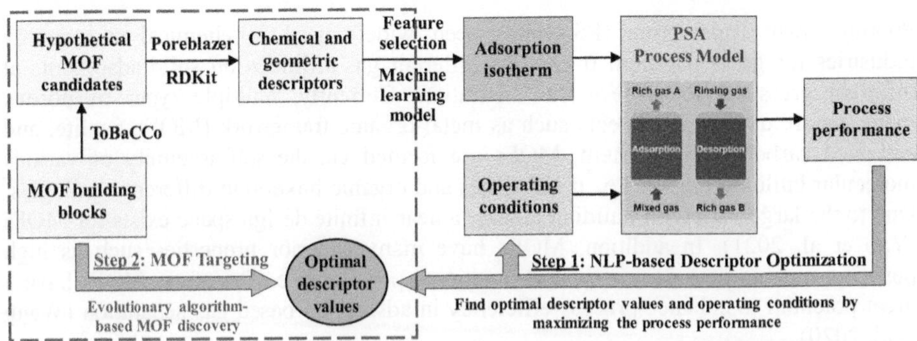

Figure 1. General methodology for integrated MOF and PSA process design

2. Workflow of Descriptor-based MOF Targeting

Figure 2 shows the explicit workflow of the descriptor-based MOF targeting. First, hypothetical MOF candidates are generated by retrieving existing MOF database and computational MOF synthesis via building blocks (BBs). The computational MOF synthesis is performed using genetic algorithm (GA) that continuously generates potential combinations of BBs. The BB combinations are sent to Tobacco that can validate MOF structural feasibility (e.g., connection feasibility, size feasibility, bond feasibility, etc.) based on certain construction rules (Colón et al. 2017). In this case, the computationally feasible MOFs can be obtained. For each MOF candidate generated, its key descriptors (i.e., 9 geometry and 10 chemical descriptors pre-specified in Step 1) are calculated using Poreblazer and RDKit. Afterwards, the feasibility of calculated descriptors are verified, including bound feasibility, design space feasibility, and tailor-made feasibility criteria (see Section 3). For those MOFs whose descriptors are reasonable, rigorous Grand Canonical Monte Carlo (GCMC) simulation is performed to obtain the single-component adsorption isotherms for both PA and PE. Again, these isotherms are verified via the above feasibility criteria. If feasible, the MOFs are used for final PSA process optimization. This can enable the generation of high-performance MOFs and better adsorption process. In the following context, the screening of MOFs from a known database is first demonstrated for defining the benchmark process. Then, the construction of MOF BBs are introduced, followed by the computational synthesis of new advanced MOFs.

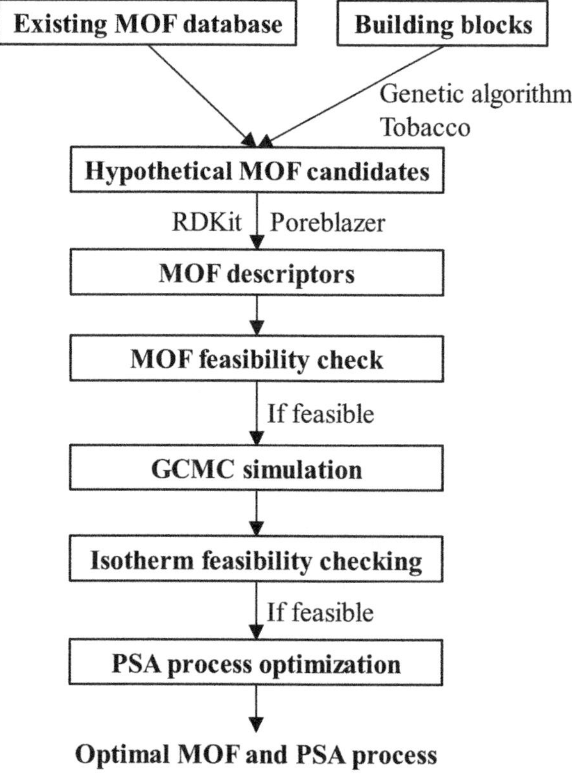

Figure 2. Workflow of descriptor-based MOF targeting

3. Descriptor-based MOF Screening

In Step 1, 471 different MOFs are already selected from the CoRE MOF database where stable and synthesizable MOFs with available atomic coordinates are collected. These 471 MOFs include considerable diversity of chemistry, geometry, and topology. Here, to demonstrate the above workflow, the potential MOFs are first screened out from the 471 MOFs for obtaining a benchmark for subsequent comparison. Before this, two feasibility criteria are established in advance for enhancing screening efficiency. First, based on the optimal isotherm obtained in Step 1, 250 pairs of PA and PE isotherms are sampled using the Latin hypercube sampling approach. The hypothetical isotherms are sent to perform rigorous PSA process optimization. The same as in Step 1, the separation specifications are 99% PE with recovery larger than 30%. The result shows that 116 sets of isotherms can successfully separate PA and PE. Based on the process feasibility data, two criteria can be concluded.

$$PA_2 \leq 2.01 \tag{1}$$

$$PE_{0.01} \leq 6.5879 \times PE_{0.01} - 0.3525 \tag{2}$$

The first criteria is that the adsorption loading of PA at 2 atm should be less than 2.01 mol/kg. The second is that the adsorption loading of PA and PE at 1013 Pa should fulfill a linear constraint. For each of the 471 MOFs, their isotherms have already been estimated using rigorous GCMC simulations and given in our previous publication. Based on those isotherms and the two feasibility criteria, it can be found that only 19 MOFs can be regarded as feasible for PA/PE separation. These 19 MOFs are then sent to PSA process optimization and it can be found that only 9 MOFs can meet the separation specifications. Table 1 lists the top 5 candidates out of the 471 MOFs. Meanwhile, all of the other 452 MOFs are also sent for PSA process optimization. It turns out that none of the 452 MOFs can meet the separation requirements. Thus, from these results, we can conclude that the two criteria (eqs. 1 and 2) can be used as necessary conditions, instead of sufficient conditions, for efficient MOF screening.

Table 1. Feasible and most promising candidates screening from the 471 CoRE MOFs

MOFs	Energy consumption (kWh/kg PE)
SEYDUW	92
QUJFUX	98
XOVVIO	214
VISTUM	251
XEHTUB	257

4. Construction of MOF Building Blocks

In general, MOF can consist of metal vertexes, organic vertexes and organic linkers. The vertexes and linkers are assembled in certain topology. Here, the 471 CoRE MOFs are decomposed into the corresponding building blocks. The decomposition procedures are as follows. First, the topology of each MOF is characterized using Topospro that is a open-source software for topology characterization of periodic structures including MOFs. Then, referring to the introduction of topology templates given in the Reticular Chemistry Structure Resource (RCSR) database, the types of vertexes and the corresponding number of connections are identified. Based on these information, the metal and organic vertexes can be easily identified and the organic linkers between vertexes can be obtained. Following these procedures, Figure 3 shows that 81 metal vertexes, 85 organic vertexes, 133 organic linkers, and 68 regular topologies can be obtained from the 471 CoRE MOFs. The obtained BBs can be subsequently used for computational MOF synthesis. Note that a fraction of MOFs possessing irregular topology that cannot be described by three letters from the RCSR database are simply discarded, since those topologies cannot be used for computational MOF synthesis.

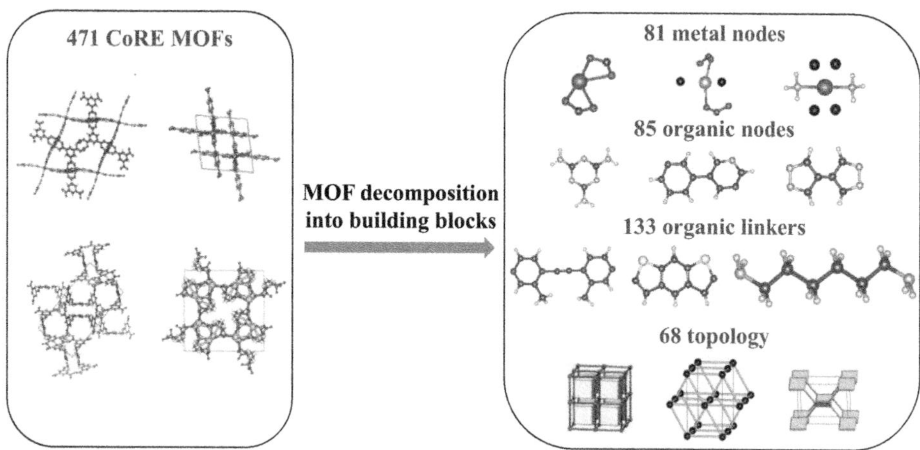

Figure 3. Decomposition of 471 CoRE MOFs into various building blocks

5. Computational MOF Synthesis and MOF Targeting

5.1. GA-based MOF synthesis

For easy implementation, 26 topologies that can usually support the use of only one type of metal vertex are selected out of the 68 topologies. Based on these 26 topologies, GA is adopted to efficiently generate potential combinations of BBs. Each gene consists of 3 integer variables denoting the selection of metal node, organic linker, and topology. The produced BB combinations are directly sent to Tobacco to generate hypothetical MOFs (Colón et al. 2017). In this process, a series of MOF construction feasibility rules will be verified. There are several possible infeasible outcomes such as node connections mismatching with topology, bond infeasibility, etc. Only if a BB combination successfully pass all the feasibility rules, a hypothetical MOF written in the form of crystallographic information framework (.cif) can be obtained. The cif file can be directly used to calculate the corresponding chemistry and geometry descriptors and perform GCMC simulation using the open-source software RASPA (Dubbeldam et al. 2016). Clearly, it is computationally demanding to perform GCMC simulation for each generated hypothetical MOFs. In this case, the synthesized MOFs can go through the screening procedures described above and only the survived MOFs are sent for GCMC simulation as shown in Figure 2.

5.2. Optimal MOF targeting

After over 10 generations of GA operations, a set of potential MOFs that can survive after the feasibility verifications are obtained such as topology *acs* with 6-connection-based two-Zn metal vertex and bromobenzene organic linker and topology *rob* with 6-connection-based two-Ag metal vertex and benzene organic linker.

6. Conclusions

As a continuation, the present work elaborates the second step of our previous proposed integrated MOF and PSA process design framework. The objective is to use computational tools to generate optimal MOFs based on the optimized MOF descriptors obtained from the first step (Zhang et al. 2021). To achieve this, a detailed descriptor-based MOF targeting workflow is invented. First, hypothetical MOF candidates can be either retrieved from known MOF databases or synthesized computationally via building blocks. According to the optimal descriptor values, a set of MOF building blocks are selected and defined in ToBaCCo. From the building blocks, a series of hypothetical MOF candidates with detailed chemical and structural information can be generated. With this information, their descriptors can be computed and used to predict the adsorption isotherms via the machine learning models developed in the first step. Then, the isotherms go through a preliminary screening step where improper isotherms and the corresponding MOFs are discarded. Finally, the remaining candidates can be sent for rigorous GCMC simulation to obtain adsorption isotherms, which are subsequently used in the process evaluation in order to find the real optimal MOFs. As demonstrated by the PA/PE separation example, hypothetical MOFs with a great potential of leading to better process performance can be computationally synthesized. The largest novelty of the present work is the use of multiscale modeling approach to integrate the variations of MOF chemistry and structure into P/VSA process design. This provides a reliable and efficient way for computational adsorbent design to maximize the practical adsorption process performance.

References

D. Dubbeldam, S. Calero, DE. Ellis, RQ. Snurr, 2016, RASPA: molecular simulation software for adsorption and diffusion in flexible nanoporous materials, Molecular Simulation, 42, 81-101

T. Wang, E. Lin, Y-L. Peng, Y. Chen, P. Cheng, Z. Zhang, 2020, Rational design and synthesis of ultramicroporous metal-organic frameworks for gas separation, Coordination Chemistry Reviews, 423, 213484

TD. Burns, KN. Pai, SG. Subraveti, SP. Collins, M. Krykunov, A. Rajendran, TK. Woo, 2020, Prediction of MOF performance in vacuum swing adsorption systems for postcombustion CO_2 capture based on integrated molecular simulations, process optimizations, and machine learning models, Environmental Science & Technology, 54, 4536-4544

X. Zhang, T. Zhou, K. Sundmacher, 2021, Integrated MOF and P/VSA process design: Descriptor optimization, AIChE Journal, doi: 10.1002/aic.17524

YJ. Colón, DA. Gómez-Gualdrón, RQ. Snurr, 2017, Topologically guided, automated construction of metal–organic frameworks and their evaluation for energy-related applications. Crystal Growth & Design, 17, 11, 5801-5810

Z. Yao, B. Sánchez-Lengeling, NS. Bobbitt, BJ. Bucior, SGH. Kumar, SP. Collins, T. Burns, TK. Woo, OK. Farha, RQ. Snurr, A. Aspuru-Guzik, 2021, Inverse design of nanoporous crystalline reticular materials with deep generative models, Nature Machine Intelligence, 3, 1, 76-86

Proceedings of the 14th International Symposium on Process Systems Engineering – PSE 2021+
June 19–23, 2022, Kyoto, Japan
http://dx.doi.org/10.1016/B978-0-323-85159-6.50050-6

Energy integration through retrofitting of heat exchanger network at Equinor Kalundborg Oil Refinery

Niels Normann Sørensen[a], Haoshui Yu[b*], Gürkan Sin[c*].

[a]*Chemical and Biochemical Engineering, Technical University of Denmark, Kgs. Lyngby 2800, Denmark*
[b*]*Department of Chemistry and Bioscience, Aalborg University, Niels Bohrs Vej 8A, Esbjerg 6700, Denmark*
[c*]*Process and Systems Engineering Center (PROSYS), Department of Chemical and Biochemical Engineering, Technical University of Denmark, Kgs. Lyngby 2800, Denmark,*

hayu@bio.aau.dk.,gsi@kt.dtu.dk

Abstract

Heat integration studies are commonly performed in the wider chemical industry to identify current energy utilization and detect potential improvements with respect to energy efficiency. In this regard, there are several established methodologies, such as: Pinch analysis, Mathematical Programming (MP) and Hybrid methods. In pinch analysis, the objective is to remove cross pinch heat transfer and configure appropriate utilities, based on a minimum approach temperature ΔT_{min}. The Minimum Energy Required (MER) for the network can then be calculated. However, a drawback is that the user must specify the changes of the HEN to achieve MER, which may not be the best economical solution. In MP the latter problem can be expressed as an optimization problem. However, due to the complexity of HEN in the industry, pinch analysis is typically the preferred method (Sreepathi and Rangaiah 2014). A similarity for all 3 retrofit solutions, are the challenges regarding data collection and the associated uncertainty. To accommodate for this, we present a methodology that involves an iterative application of a process simulator with plant data (to match the heat flows) and the uncertainty of the pinch point(s).
The pinch analysis was constrained to 1 reforming section and 3 hydrofining sections. Average temperature, pressure, volume flow rate and assay of the heavy feeds and residues were taken over a month. One month was selected, when the refinery had been cleaned and flowrates were in the normal ranges of operation. After balancing mass and energy based on the SRK EOS, enthalpies were segmented and exported into UniSim ExchangerNet. Based on a minimum approach temperature of 20°C, the cold pinch temperature was found to be 127.5°C and the hot pinch temperature was 147.5°C, with a total of 9MW cross pinch. A feasible retrofit solution could not be achieved for the heat exchanger with the highest cross pinch of 2.88 MW. Nonetheless, a retrofit solution was possible for the heat exchanger with the second-highest cross pinch at 1.16MW. However, the payback time exceeded the specified requirement, which made the retrofit economically infeasible. Nevertheless, the uncertainty analysis showed that 2 possible pinch points existed. The uncertainty of the pinch point would change the retrofit considerably and therefore also the economical potential of the retrofit.

Keywords: Pinch analysis, Retrofit, HEN, Process simulation, Oil refinery.

1. Introduction

In 2017 approximately 19% of energy consumed in the EU industrial sector, was by crude oil refining (European Energy Agency 2015, Bourgeois et al. 2012). The potential to increase energy efficiency and decrease CO_2 emissions in the downstream process, is therefore substantial. One way to optimize energy efficiency, is to increase heat recovery in the HEN. Several established methodology exists to achieve MER for an existing HEN, such as: Pinch analysis, mathematical programming (MP) and hybrid methods (Kemp 2006). MP is the ideal solution, as MER is achieved by optimizing capital cost and ΔT_{min}. The drawback is the implementation of MP, due to constraints and complexity in an industrial HEN. Pinch analysis is a proven method to reach MER, in an industrial HEN, due to its simplicity. However, in pinch analysis, the user has to suggest the best option to achieve MER, in contrast to MP.

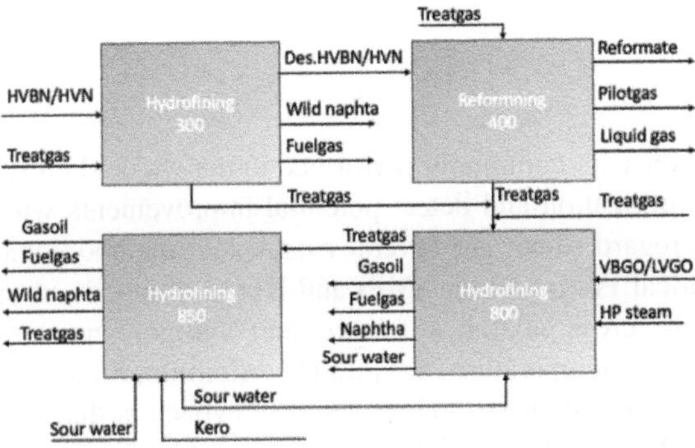

Figure 1: Scope of the retrofit, which includes 3 hydrofining sections and 1 reforming section.

To increase heat recovery and therefore decrease fuel consumption, a retrofit is investigated of a heat exchanger network in Denmark's largest oil refinery, located in Kalundborg. The retrofit will be based on simple pinch analysis, due to the scale of the HEN, which includes 1 reforming section and 3 hydrofining sections (see figure 1).

2. Methodology

The novelty of this study is the clear methodology of using pinch analysis for an industrial retrofit. In studies on industrially HEN retrofits such as: (Alhajri et al. 2021) and (Joe and Rabiu 2013) no emphasis was on: Data extraction, balancing mass, balancing energy and the uncertainty of the pinch point. Real process data has to be balanced by mass and energy due to a combination of sensor calibration errors and taking averages of process data. Process fluctuations have to be accounted for, as it will affect the pinch point and therefore the economical feasibility of the retrofit. Furthermore, in retrofit studies, the estimation of capital cost is usually only based on the HE. However, pipping and instrumentation can be more expensive than the HE, which will increase the payback time considerably.

To accommodate this, we present a systematical approach (see figure 2), to analyze and suggest a retrofit, of the HEN.

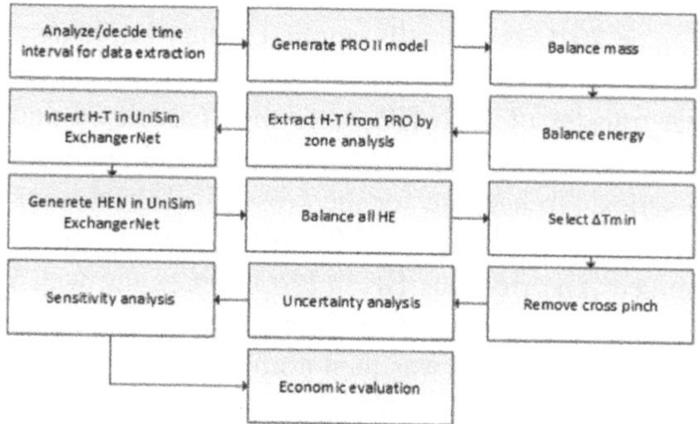

Figure 2: The overall method used for analyzing and suggesting a retrofit, based on pinch analysis.

The first step is to determine, the time interval of data extraction. In general, the time interval for the data extraction, is a trade-off between difficulty in balancing mass/energy and gathering enough data to reflect the uncertainty of the system. To easier balance mass and energy, time interval can be chosen, when key streams are in normal operation. For this HEN, process values were extracted based on 1-month of averages process values, such as: Assay, temperature, pressure, densities and volumetric flow-rate, where major heavy streams were in normal operation. Whereas, data extraction for the uncertainty analysis was based on daily averages values, which meant it was easier to balance mass and energy in contrast to the base case.

In general, for the petroleum industry, it is well known that cubic equations of state can be used as a valid thermodynamic model, as the majority of components are simple hydrocarbons. The Soave-Kwong equation of state (SRK), was therefore the chosen thermodynamic model for all conducted simulations in PRO II.

The properties of the stream in the 4 sections were acquired by modelling all unit operations of the block in PRO II. Where the unit operations included: Distillation's columns, flash drums, heat exchangers, pumps, compressors, and valves.

The composition of the effluent of reactors, for the HF sections, was estimated by using an assay of the remanence. The saturation of olefins could somehow be accounted for, by assuming that most of the product would end up as fuelgas in the stripper. As the volumetric flowrate of fuelgas was known and the molecular weight was expected to be in the range of 25-35g/mol, then the amount and composition of product could be fitted by iterating.

The effluent composition of the reactor in the reforming section was estimated by using GC measurements.

In each section the inlet and outlet massflow, based on averages PV were balanced. Next, all HE was integrated by balancing energy, by using a temperature correction term. When balancing the first HE in the cascade, 4 streams can be corrected. The temperature effluent will then be cascaded to the next HE, which means that the inlet temperature of that HE is fixed. The cascade then continues until all HE's are balanced.

Enthalpy and temperature of cold and heat stream of the respective HE's were then extracted from PRO II, by using zone analysis to account for the nonlinearity. The H-T segments were then inserted into UniSim ExchangerNet. ΔT_{min} of 20°C was then chosen as the minimum approach temperature, as this was the minimum LMTD in the HEN.

Furthermore, a ΔT_{min}= 20°C is typically applied, when implementing a retrofit in the petrochemical industry (March 1998).
The cross pinch heat transfer of each HE, were then calculated and removed based on the methodology of Li and Chang 2010. However, inlet and outlet temperatures were not available for HE in series. To account for the cross-pinch heat transfer for multiple HE in series, rigorous HE was implemented in PRO II by inserting the properties of the shell and tube heat exchanger. The rigorous HE in PRO II uses the well-known design equation, where PRO II can predict the heat transfer coefficient U, correction factor F and the pressure drop. The duty for each HE was then normalized in relative to the total duty, by adjusting the fouling factor.

3. Results

3.1. Removing cross pinch heat transfer

In table 1 one can see that if MER is achieved, one can achieve 9.58MW heat recovery.

Table 1: MER at ΔT=20°C

	Network [MW]	Target [MW]	% Deviation
Q_{hot}	24.61	15.03	163.7
Q_{cold}	27.64	18.07	153
Q_{rec}	59.58	69.16	86

However, one can see in table 2, that the cross-pinch heat transfer is unfortunately distributed on many HE. The highest cross pinch is 2.88MW for E-808D, 1.16MW for E-851 B and 1.11MW for E-411A. A retrofit for E-808D was then investigated.

Table 2: Cross pinch at ΔT_{min}=20°C.

Section	800	850	400	300	800	400	300	300	300	850	800	850	300
HE	E808D	E851B	E411A	E306	E802C	E414	E301F	E301C	E307	E855A	E808B	E856	E302
Cross pinch [MW]	2.88	1.16	1.11	0.95	0.7	-0.387	0.326	0.318	0.237	0.219	0.212	0.114	0.141

First, the required duty to heat the cold stream to the cold pinch. However, the only hot stream below pinch point, that had enough Q, was an air cooler, in the reformate section. If a HE was to be inserted in 0400 then the compressor would compensate for the expected significant pressure drop, which would decrease reformate yield. The option to insert a HE before the air cooler was then discharged.
Another idea was to split the hot streams from several air-coolers. However, the cost of pipping would be too expensive. A feasible hot stream could not be found from a utility stream, so the stream would be needed from another HE. However, due to the relatively high duty required, several splits would be required, which would be expensive, due to the price of pipping. A feasible hot stream could not be found, to heat the cold stream to the cold pinch temperature.
A retrofit solution was not found for E-808D. However, a retrofit was proposed for E-851B, which has the second-highest cross pinch (see table 2). Two options were proposed

to remove the cross pinch. Both options would heat the cold pinch by using air coolers. However, from experience the refinery wanted at least 1.5MW of cross-pinch, due to a specified payback time, for the retrofit to be economically feasible. The ΔT_{min} was then decreased to see if the cross pinch for the 3 mentioned HE would increase, but the increase of cross pinch was not significant. As a result, an economically feasible retrofit solution could not be obtained, due to a combination of cost of pipping and the only HE with a cross pinch of 1.5 MW was E-808D.

3.2. *Uncertainty analysis*

The 2 retrofit solution, analyzed in UniSim ExchangerNet was based on average PV's, taken over a month, which resulted in a pinch temperature of 137.5°C. The composite curves were rather parallel to each other, in which a specific pinch point was not well-defined. Rather, than a pinch point a "pinch region" exists, in a range of 110-220°C. To evaluate the uncertainty of the pinch point, MATLAB was used to see the effect of daily averages mass and temperature fluctuations, considering 614 days. Iterating over 614 days, by using the same methodology as described in figure 1, resulted in figure 3a and figure 3b.

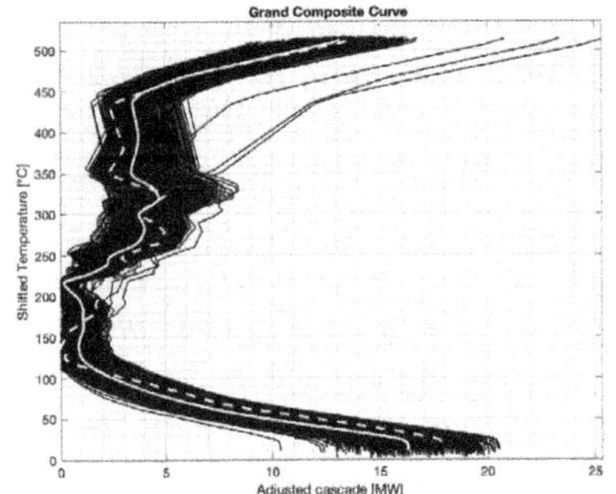

(a) Dashed white lines is the clean HEN, solid white line mean fouled HEN and black solid lines pinch over 614 days.

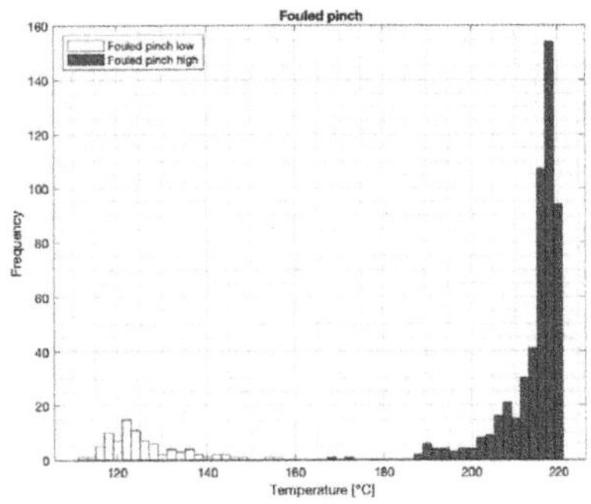

(b) Histogram evlauted over of 614 days.

Figure 3: Uncertainty analysis of pinch point at ΔT_{min}=20°C.

The uncertainty analysis confirms the pinch region as seen in figure 3. However, as seen in 3b it seems that 2-pinch point exists – a high pinch with a mean of 214°C and low pinch temperature with a mean of 126.5 °C. Thermodynamically, it is possible to have multiple pinch points, where the same methodology apply for identifying and removing cross heat transfer. Furthermore, in figure 3b one can see that the higher pinch-point is more frequent and less dispersed than the lower pinch point. In terms of numerical values, the low pinch is in a range of 120-131°C and the high pinch temperature in a range of 213-219°C. The combination of higher frequency and lower uncertainly makes the higher pinch in, relative to the lower-pinch, more significant in terms of calculating the cross-heat transfer. However, even-though all streams were segmented by making polynomial fits, several assumptions were made, in the uncertain analysis. i.e., the pressure and composition were assumed to be the same as the PRO II simulation. However, there will be pressure changes and the composition of: Treatgas, HVN/HVBN, reformate, VBGO and KERO will change over time. These changes will i.e. influence the volatility for the flash, distillation units and the T-H curves. In contrast to a well-defined pinch point, then it is in this HEN, important to decrease the uncertainty of parameter estimation, as the pinch point(s) in this HEN, is very sensitive to the changes in heat flow, as seen in figure 3a. Ideally, the next step is to synchronize the PRO II simulation, with i.e., MATLAB or Python, to reduce the uncertainly/assumption of the input parameters. Furthermore, the cross heat transfer would be calculated again, based the on the 2 pinch point, by using the methodology from Li and Chang 2010.

4. Conclusions

In this study, it has been shown how mass and temperature fluctuation effect the pinch point and therefore the economic feasibility of an industrial retrofit. When considering the base case of averages process values, a pinch temperature of 137.5°C, was found. The base case network hot utility was 24.61MW, which was 163% above target. The network cold utility was found to be 27.64MW, which was 153% above target. To reach MER with a corresponding 59.58MW of heat recovery. The heat recovery would have to be increased with 9.56MW. However, an economically feasible retrofit could not be found, for the HE with the largest cross pinch of 2.88MW. Two retrofit solution could be found for the HE with the second-highest cross pinch of 1.16 MW. However, the relatively low cross pinch meant that the proposed retrofit would exceed the specified payback time. However, when using process values over 614 days, 2 pinch temperatures were found. One temperature with a mean of 126.5 °C and a pinch at a mean of 214°C, which frequency was significant higher than the pinch at 126.5°C. The amount of cross pinch heat transfer would then be different from the base case, in which the same methodology (Li and Chang 2010) can be applied to suggest a retrofit, when dealing with 2 pinch points. Furthermore, to improve the uncertainty analysis, one could combine MATLAB and PRO II to use the properties generated from PRO II and simulate daily averages values and thereby get a better estimation of the "true" pinch point(s) in the HEN.

References

Alhajri, Ibrahim H. et al. (2021). "Retrofit of heat exchanger networks by graphical Pinch Analysis – A case study of a crude oil refinery in Kuwait". In.

Bourgeois, L et al. (2012). "EU refinery energy systems and efficiency". In.

European Energy Agency (2015). "Final energy consumption by sector and fuel". In: *Indicator Assessment — Data and maps*, p. 20.

Joe, John M. and Ademola M. Rabiu (2013). "Retrofit of the Heat Recovery System of a Petroleum Refinery Using Pinch Analysis". In.

Kemp, Ian (2006). *Pinch Analysis and Process Integration*. Elsevier Ltd.

Li, Bao Hong and Chuei Tin Chang (Apr. 2010). "Retrofitting heat exchanger networks based on simple pinch analysis". In: *Industrial and Engineering Chemistry Research.*

March, Linnhoff (1998). *Introduction to Pinch Technology*. Tech. rep.

Sreepathi, Bhargava Krishna and G. P. Rangaiah (July 2014). "Review of Heat Exchanger Network Retrofitting Methodologies and Their Applications". In.

Proceedings of the 14th International Symposium on Process Systems Engineering – PSE 2021+
June 19-23, 2022, Kyoto, Japan
http://dx.doi.org/10.1016/B978-0-323-85159-6.50051-8

Modeling and Optimization of Ionic Liquid Enabled Extractive Distillation of Ternary Azeotrope Mixtures

Alejandro Garciadiego[a], Mozammel Mazumder[a], Bridgette J. Befort[a] and Alexander W. Dowling[a*]

[a] *University of Notre Dame, Notre Dame, IN 46556, USA*
* *adowling@nd.edu*

Abstract

To help slow climate change, international efforts have begun to mandate the phase-out of high global warming potential (GWP) hydrofluorocarbons (HFCs) throughout the next decade. Most HFC refrigerant mixtures form azeotropes, complicating separation into the individual HFC components for reuse and recycling. In this paper, we design and analyze ionic liquid (IL)-enabled extractive distillation processes for ternary HFC separations using AspenPlus. Specifically, we design processes to separate three commercially important HFC refrigerant mixtures (R-404A, R-407C, and R-410A) into high purity HFC streams. We find added value of the separation of R-410A of 0.58 $/kg with current market conditions, specifically laboratory-scale IL manufacturing costs (1000 $/kg of IL) and a low-price differential of 1.00 $/kg between raw materials and separated products. If the IL purchase cost decreases 90 % due to mass production, consistent with prior adoption of ILs for niche separations, the added value increases to 0.76 $/kg. Moreover, under proposed reductions in HFC manufacturing, the price of recovered products may dramatically increase in the future. For example, if the price of R-32 increases by 50 %, the added value would reach 3.08 $/kg. In summary, we find IL-based recycling of HFCs is economically viable based on simple technoeconomic analysis. Moreover, this paper reports capital and operation cost curves and a general analysis framework to analyze evolving market conditions.

Keywords: Extractive Distillation; Azeotrope; Ionic Liquid; Modeling; Economic Analysis.

1. Introduction

Thousands of tons of HFC refrigerant mixtures, commonly used in industrial, commercial, and residential applications, are scheduled for phase-out worldwide under the 2016 Kigali amendment to the Montreal Protocol, the European Union F-Gas regulations (2015), and the American Innovation and Manufacturing (AIM) Act of 2020. The latter directs EPA to phase down production and consumption of HFCs in the US by 85 percent over the next 15 years. Common HFC mixtures such as R-410A (50 % R-32, 50 % R-125), R-404A (44 % R-125, 4 % R-134a, 52 % R-143a), and R-407C (23 % R-32, 25 % R-125, 52 % R-134a) are targeted for phase-out because of their high global warming potential (GWP): R-410A with 2088 GWP, R-404A with 3922 GWP, and R-407C with 2107 GWP, where CO_2 has a GWP of 1 by definition. However, R-32 and other HFCs have a low GWP and could be reused after a global phase-out. R-134a is used in R-450A, offering similar performance but with a lower GWP (547) (Honeywell, 2021). Unfortunately, there is no means to easily separate HFC mixtures due to their azeotropic or near azeotropic nature. Without a new economically viable separation process, the phase-out will require all HFCs to be collected and incinerated.

Extractive distillation, the most common method for separating azeotropic or close-boiling mixtures, is a promising approach to separate HFC mixtures. Moreover, tailored IL solvents can enable extractive distillation of near-azeotropic HFC mixtures. In 2003, Lei et al. first proposed extractive distillation with ILs as entrainers, and Lei et al. (2005) discussed the use of ILs in extractive distillation in detail. ILs have exhibited high capacity as entrainers to separate azeotropic or close-boiling mixtures (Pereiro et al., 2012). ILs can be recycled in separation processes, reducing the material demands and improving the economics (Zhao et al., 2005, Zhao et al., 2017). Shiflett and Yokozeki (2006) proposed extractive distillation to separate fluorinated refrigerant mixtures using ILs.

2. Methods

2.1. HFC Separation Process Development and Modeling

In this work, we design three extractive distillation processes to separate three ternary azeotrope mixtures, R-404A, R-407C, and a mixture of R-410A and R-22 using an IL entrainer. Table 1 summarizes these three case studies (Finberg and Shiflett 2021). We use the Peng-Robison (PENG-ROB) equation of state to calculate thermodynamic properties. We fit the HFC binary interaction parameters similar to Shiflett and Yokozeki (2006, 2007).

Table 1. Compositions of HFCs mixtures separated and IL used.

HFC	R-404A mol/mol	R-407C mol/mol	R-410A mol/mol
R-32	0.00	0.23	0.45
R-125	0.44	0.25	0.45
R-134a	0.04	0.52	0.00
R-143a	0.52	0.00	0.00
R-22	0.00	0.00	0.10
IL used	[emim][Tf_2N]	[bmim][PF_6]	[bmim][PF_6]
IL (kg/h)	2000	400	750

Figure 1 shows the process flow diagram for the R-404A case study. The process flow diagrams for the other case studies are nearly identical and not shown for brevity.

2.2. Sensitivity analysis

We performed single-parameter sensitivity over eight variables. The base case used 20 theoretical stages, a flowrate of IL of 1000 kg/h, the IL is fed in stage 2, the HFC mixture fed at stage 15, the inlet temperature of 25 °C, the pressure of 10 bar, a reboiler temperature of 130 °C, and a reboiler ratio of 2.5. We found that the extractive distillation column's pressure and reflux ratio are most important to minimize energy consumption while obtaining 99.5 mol% purity of all HFC products. Through our sensitivity analysis, we look to obtain the desired purity (99.5 mol%) of R-134a in the distillate of the extractive distillation in the presence of [emim][Tf_2N] with moderate energy consumption. We found that it is impossible to reach the required purity without 25 theoretical stages and a flowrate of IL of 2000 kg/h, even though they significantly influence the capital cost. The IL is fed in stage 2, and the HFC mixture is fed in stage 20 at a temperature of 20 °C. We selected a pressure of 7 bar in the column and a reboiler temperature of 90 °C to ensure the energy consumption was as low as possible while reaching the purity target. Finally, following the same analysis, we selected a reflux ratio of 3. Aspen equipment sizing tools were used to size the equipment.

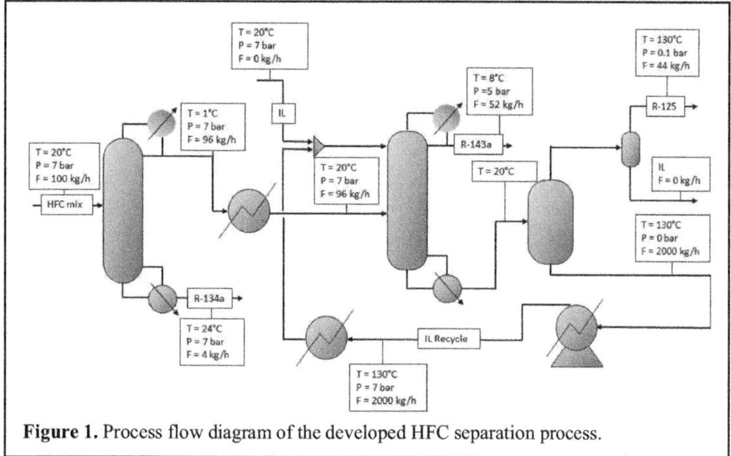

Figure 1. Process flow diagram of the developed HFC separation process.

3. Economic Performance Evaluation

We now analyze the economics of the design HFC separation processes. We evaluate the capital cost, shown in Eq. (1), which includes equipment, installation cost, and the price of the IL as expressed in units of M\$/y.

$$\text{Capital cost}\left(\frac{\text{M\$}}{\text{y}}\right) = \text{Equipment cost}\left(\frac{\text{M\$}}{\text{y}}\right) + \text{Installation cost}\left(\frac{\text{M\$}}{\text{y}}\right) + \text{IL price}\left(\frac{\text{M\$}}{\text{y}}\right) \quad (1)$$

We assume a 20-year (N) plant lifetime and a salvage value of 20 % of the cost of the plant assets (excluding the IL). We assume 24 hours a day workload for 330 days in a year for all calculations. We calculate the annualized capital cost (C_{anm}) using Eq. (2), in which CRF is the capital recovery factor, and C_{NPC} is the net present cost estimated in AspenPlus. We assume a nominal discount rate (i') of 8 % and an expected inflation rate (f) of 3.5 % to calculate the real discount rate (i). With the assumptions above, we calculate a capital recovery factor (CRF) of 0.077 using Eqs. (3) and (4). We estimate 2,000 kg/h of IL, which corresponds to a column fill of 65 %. We estimate operation costs using AspenPlus and the following utility costs: electricity (0.07\$/KW), cooling water (120 \$/MMGAL), and high-pressure steam (8.22 \$/Klb).

$$C_{anm} = (CRF)(C_{NPC}) \quad (2)$$

$$CRF = \frac{i(1+i)^N}{(1+i)^N - 1} \quad (3)$$

$$i = \frac{i' - f}{1+f} \quad (4)$$

As shown in Figure 2, the capital and operating costs ($/kg of HFC feed) of the R-404A, R-407C, and R-410A separation increase as we decrease the mixture feed flow rate. We observe that the significant increase in the capital cost is due to the amount of IL necessary to achieve the 99.5 mol% purity of HFCs desired in the separation. The cost of equipment and installation have minor variations as the size of the equipment is nearly minimum or standard size. As observed in Figure 2, the capital cost may increase to up to 60 % of the total cost. The rise in total capital cost is dependent on the ratio of IL/HFC mixture required for each process. 1 % to 2 % of IL degradation per year corresponds to an increase of the operating cost of 0.03 $/kg to 0.05 $/kg, respectively.

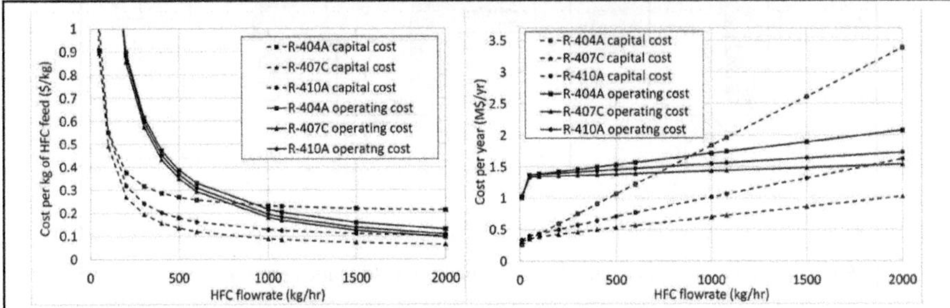

Figure 2. Capital and operating cost of the R-404A, R-407C, and R-410A AspenPlus model. The capital cost of the separation process increases rapidly as we increase the inlet flowrate.

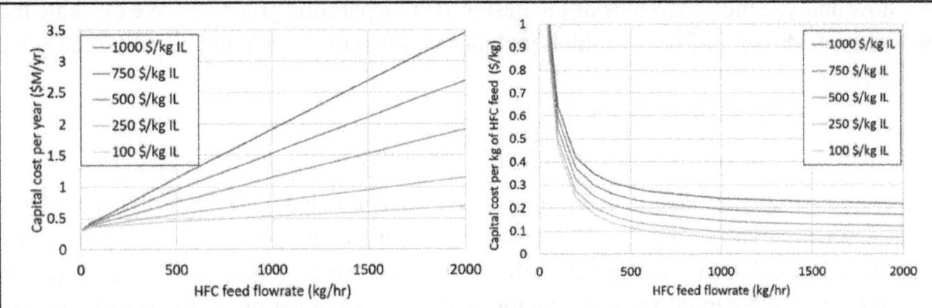

Figure 3. Influence of the ionic liquid price in capital cost for the separation of R-404A.

Currently, most ILs are only available in high purity for laboratory-scale experiments at high prices of $1,000/kg. Historically, after an IL is selected for a commercial application and production increases, the price decreases by 90-92 % (Shiflett et al., 2020). In anticipation of a similar economy of scale, we consider five IL price scenarios: 1,000 $/kg, 750 $/kg, 500 $/kg, 250 $/kg, and 100 $/kg. Figure 3 shows the impact of IL price on capital costs. Specifically, the capital cost (M$/y) increases linearly with the IL flowrate (kg/h) at a given IL price. As expected, changing the IL price changes the slope of this relationship. Moreover, the capital cost is extremely sensitive to the IL price. For example, at 5000 kg/h IL flowrate, decreasing the IL price from 1000 $/kg (laboratory scale specialty chemical) to 100 $/kg (commercial IL) decreases the capital cost from 8

M$/y to 1.5 M$/y. We reiterate that previous commercialization of ILs suggests a 90 % reduction in IL price is reasonable (Shiflett et al., 2020).

$$\text{Added value}\left(\frac{\$}{\text{kg}}\right) = \underbrace{\text{Sell price low GWP components}\left(\frac{\$}{\text{kg}}\right) - \text{Cost of recovery HFC mix.}\left(\frac{\$}{\text{kg}}\right)}_{\text{Price differential}} \underbrace{- \text{Capital Cost}\left(\frac{\$}{\text{kg}}\right) - \text{Operating cost}\left(\frac{\$}{\text{kg}}\right)}_{\text{Costs}} \quad (5)$$

Next, we propose added value, with units \$/kg of HFC feed, as a metric to easily compare different hypothetical scenarios. Eq. (5) calculates added value from the price differential and costs. The selling price of low GWP components is the value of the recycled products, and the cost of recovery HFC mixture corresponds to the value of the used HFC refrigerant mixtures (half of the cost of production and transportation of the HFC mixture used as a base and worst-case scenario). A negative cost of recovery HFC mixture is possible with government subsidies incentivizing HFC recycling (instead of illegal venting). Figure 2 reports the operating and capital costs (\$/kg) as a function of the HFC feed rate. Similarly, Figure 3 shows the dependence of capital cost (\$/kg) on IL price. Because the added value metric represents profit per kilogram of HFC processed, it allows quick evaluation of different market scenarios (e.g., HFC and IL prices).

Using values from these plots, the added value metric can quickly be used to evaluate the benefits of new ILs for the separation process. For example, if a new hypothetical IL required 20 % less mass than the analyzed ILs, the cost in Figure 3 can be proportionally reduced. Likewise, if a new hypothetical IL reduces the separation energy requirement by 50 %, the operating cost value used in Eq. (5) can be reduced by approximately 50 %. This metric gives valuable insights and enables fast "what if" analyses to guide IL and process design.

Under current market conditions, we found that R-410A separation has an added value of 0.55 to 0.72 \$/kg with an IL price of 1000 \$/kg and 100 \$/kg, respectively. Under a futuristic scenario where phase-outs in production doubles the market price for R-32, the added value of the separation of R-410A could be as high as 5.60 \$/kg to 5.78 \$/kg with an IL price of 1000 \$/kg and 100 \$/kg respectively. If the price of R-32 increases by 50 %, the added value would reach 3.08 \$/kg. We found that the price of ILs has the most significant impact on the capital cost, and the price differential between the HFC mixture and the pure HFC impacts the added value and the payback period.

4. Conclusions

In this paper, we show that separating and recycling HFCs with extractive distillation utilizing ILs is economically attractive, especially under anticipated future scenarios. It is important to note that ILs are viscous, and a rate base model is needed for rigorous design and more accurate technoeconomic analyses. This is left as future work.

The presented results are based on currently available ILs [bmim][PF_6] and [emim][Tf_2N]. However, ILs can be tailored for specific purposes due to the vast diversity of anions and cations available. For example, tailored ILs with higher selectivity would reduce the amount of IL required and thus capital costs. Tailoring other properties of the ILs, such as the density, viscosity, and thermal capacity could reduce the operating costs of the process.

There are also unexplored opportunities to optimize the extractive distillation process. While the one and two-dimensional sensitivity analyses presented here show 25 theoretical stages and the amount of IL necessary for the separation, rigorous optimization may find additional opportunities for improvement by exploiting interactions across multiple design decision variables. Moreover, simultaneous process optimization (e.g., flowrates, temperatures) and heat integration may further reduce the energy intensity of the process by systematically balancing reboiler duty and compression costs (e.g., by changing column pressure). This is left as future work.

5. Acknowledgments

We acknowledge support from the National Science Foundation under grant no. CBET-1917474, University of Notre Dame and funding from the Richard and Peggy Notebaert Premier Fellowship. We also thank Ethan Finberg from the University of Kansas for his insights of Aspen Plus modeling.

6. References

Honeywell, Solstice® N13 (R-450A), (DoA: 2021). URL https://www.honeywell-refrigerants.com/europe/wp-content/uploads/2015/03/Solstice-N13-TDS-141027-LR-vF.pdf

Z. Lei, B. Chen, Z. Ding, 2005. Special Distillation Processes, Elsevier Science, Amsterdam, Netherlands

Z. Lei, , C. Li, B. Chen, 2003, Extractive distillation: a review, Separation & Purification Reviews, 32, 121–213.

E. A. Finberg, M. B. Shiflett, Process designs for separating R-410a, R-404a, and R-407c using extractive distillation and ionic liquid entrainers, 2021, Industrial & Engineering Chemistry Research 60, 44.

A. Pereiro, J. Araujo, J. Esperança, I. Marrucho, L. Rebelo, 2012, Ionic liquids in separations of azeotropic systems - a review. J. Chem. Thermodyn. 46, 2–28.

M. B. Shiflett, A. Yokozeki, 2006, Separation of diuoromethane and pentafluoroethane by extractive distillation using ionic liquid, Chimica Oggichemistry, 24, 28-30.

M. B. Shiflett, M. A. Harmer, C. P. Junk, C.P, A. Yokozeki, 2006, Solubility and diffusivity of 1,1,1,2-tetrafluoroethane in room-temperature ionic liquids. Fluid Phase Equilib 242, 220–232.

M. B. Shiflett, A. Yokozeki, 2007, Solubility differences of halocarbon isomers in ionic liquid [emim][Tf_2N]. J. Chem. Eng. Data 52, 2007–2015.

M. B. Shiflett, 2020, Commercial Applications of Ionic Liquids, Springer, Switzerland.

Y. Zhao, R. Gani, R. M. Afzal, X. Zhang, S. Zhang, 2017, Ionic liquids for absorption and separation of gases: An extensive database and a systematic screening method. AIChE Journal, 63, 1353–1367.

H. Zhao, S. Xia, P. Ma, 2005, Use of ionic liquids as 'green' solvents for extractions, Journal of Chemical Technology & Biotechnology. 80, 1089–1096.

Proceedings of the 14th International Symposium on Process Systems Engineering – PSE 2021+
June 19-23, 2022, Kyoto, Japan
http://dx.doi.org/10.1016/B978-0-323-85159-6.50052-X

Optimal Design of Hybrid Distillation/ Pervaporation Processes

Dian Ning Chia and Eva Sorensen*

Department of Chemical Engineering, University College London (UCL), Torrington Place, London WC1E 7JE, united Kingdom

* *Corresponding author: e.sorensen@ucl.a.cuk*

Abstract

Hybrid distillation/pervaporation processes have the potential to reduce the energy consumption and cost of standard distillation for difficult separations such as that of azeotropic systems. Current optimization strategies for such hybrid processes either considers only a simplified membrane system or requires repeated (sequential) optimization for each potential number of membrane stages. This work proposes a superstructure optimization strategy for the optimal design of hybrid distillation/pervaporation processes, and discusses different solution alternatives for how to handle the integer nature of the membrane network, as well as proposes a procedure for systematic initialization, simulation, and optimization of the process. The strategy is illustrated for an azeotropic separation, demonstrating that the optimal design can be obtained in a fraction of the time compared to repeated simulation.

Keywords: Distillation, Hybrid Distillation, Membrane network, Superstructure, Optimization

1. Introduction

The optimization of a hybrid separation process is a challenging task due to the highly integrated and complex design. Current optimization studies typically simplify the membrane system to consider only the membrane area (Singh and Rangaiah, 2019), and/or very limited (typically up to 3) number of membrane stages in series (Koch et al., 2013). A more holistic superstructure optimization of membrane systems was proposed by Marriott and Sorensen (2003), however, the superstructure optimization was solved for *n* superstructure sizes (from one to *n* membrane stages), then compared. This strategy reduces computational burden, but requires some manual effort in reconstructing the superstructure for each stage addition, so the maximum number of membrane stages that can be considered is limited. Moreover, when applying this strategy in a hybrid process, which may potentially involve more than one recycle between units, the number of iterative procedures increases and becomes challenging.

Most studies on the optimization of hybrid processes often reported only their main membrane equations, the flowsheet of the superstructure, and the optimization method used, without clearly describing how to overcome the inevitable numerical/ mathematical issues faced during the initialization/convergence of the optimization.

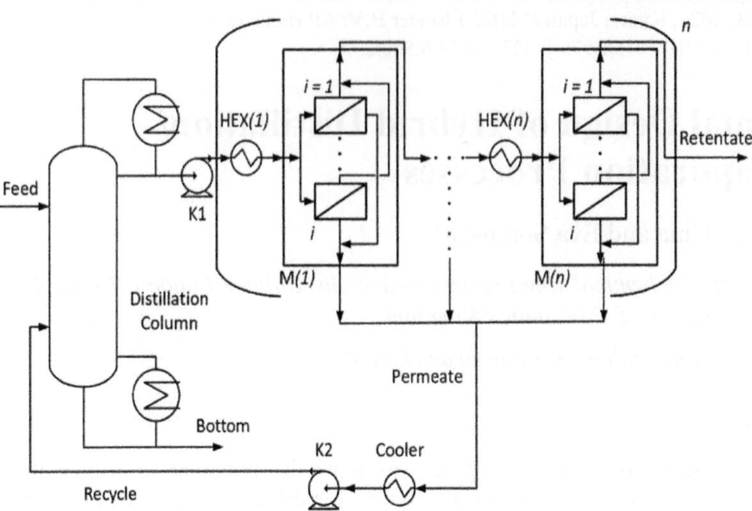

Figure 1: Flowsheet of the hybrid distillation/pervaporation process with a membrane system further purifying the distillate. The membrane system depicts the first and last ($n = n_{max}$) membrane stages connected in series and the i membrane modules connected in parallel within each membrane stage.

This work therefore aims to: (1) propose a membrane superstructure and optimization strategy which improves the convergence and allows the simultaneous optimization of the full membrane system, and (2) apply the full membrane superstructure in a hybrid process with recycle streams.

2. Methodology

2.1. Membrane System Superstructure

A lumped hollow fiber pervaporation membrane model is developed in gPROMS ProcessBuilder (Process Systems Enterprise, 2020) and the model is validated against the work of Tsuyumoto et al. (1997) (not shown). The superstructure of the membrane system extends from the work of Marriott and Sorensen (2003). Due to the small scale plant considered in this work and the fact that the area needed by the heat exchangers are very small for cases with and without recycle streams (outlet streams from a membrane stage recycled back to the previous heater/membrane stage), the capital costs of the heat exchangers are almost constant. Therefore, recycle streams are not considered in this work because a plant with a large recycle flow but with few heaters supplying all the heat would be unrealistic (Marriott and Sorensen, 2003). The membrane stages are connected sequentially in series and in each membrane stage the feed is evenly distributed between the number of membrane modules in parallel (Figure 1), thus greatly reducing the computational burden as only one mathematical model is needed to describe the membrane module (i.e., the membrane stage feed stream is divided by the number of membrane modules in parallel) (Marriott and Sorensen, 2003). A membrane stage feed heater can potentially be added to improve the separation performance. Thus, the optimization task of this membrane system includes the number of membrane stages connected in series (n), the number of membrane modules connected in parallel in a membrane stage (i_n), the existence of the membrane stage feed heater (HEX), and if in existence also the heater temperature, totalling $4n$ optimization variables.

2.2. Membrane System Superstructure Simultaneous Optimization Strategy

The membrane superstructure is a composite model of n_{max} membrane stages, where n_{max} should be set as a parameter which cannot be varied as this might introduce convergence difficulties when optimizing n_{max}. There is a lack of open literature discussing the optimization of a membrane network, thus this work introduces three modelling/optimization strategies which can overcome the computational difficulties.

The first strategy is to eliminate the non-existing membrane stages from the solution. This can be done by setting, for example, the membrane fluxes of each component or membrane length/area in the non-existing membrane stages to zero. This strategy is straight-forward and only requires the related variables to be set to zero (directly or via a binary variable). The simulation results for the outlet of the membrane section can still be collected at the n_{max} stage even if n_{max} is not the optimal number of stages. However, this strategy has difficulties at the initialization stage and often fails to converge into a feasible solution. The membrane model involves differential equations, and a good set of initial values is essential to ensure convergence to a solution. However, it is impossible to provide a different set of initial values for each structure (i.e. for each potential number of membrane stages) in the superstructure, and instead, a single set of initial values is typically provided for the whole superstructure. The existence of zeros for non-existing stages may therefore cause large difference between the initial and final values, and will cause numerical errors such as division by zero.

To avoid using zeros, the non-existing membranes can instead be given a feasible non-zero pseudo-feed. This can be achieved by providing the feed to the non-existing membranes a user-defined pseudo-feed or a copy of the feed from the last-existing membrane. The simulation results can still be taken from the n_{max} membrane stage. This strategy does improve the convergence, but it requires a number of additional "if-else" statements which increases the computational costs and difficulties.

The last strategy is to assume that all membrane stages exist, regardless of the optimization result for the number of membrane stages, but the results are collected at the optimized number of membrane stages. This strategy can avoid using zeros, and has fewer "if-else" statements and smoother simulations. However, although not encountered in this work, theoretically, this strategy may face a situation where the feed streams to the non-existing membrane stages are overly pure if the product purity constraint is high, and may therefore cause mass balance convergence issues. The chance of this issue happening can be minimized by forcing the number of membrane modules in parallel in the non-existing membrane stages to one, thus reducing the separation performance of the non-existing membrane stages (which are after all just theoretical rather than actual). From the authors' experience, this strategy does have the best convergence performance and is therefore recommended and applied in this work.

2.3. Hybrid Process Simulation and Optimization

In this work, the hybrid process shown in Figure 1 is considered following the procedure shown in Figure 2. The membrane system (including heaters) is user-defined using the recommended modelling structure discussed in Section 2.2., whilst the other unit models required are modeled within gPROMS ProcessBuilder.

As the hybrid distillation/pervaporation process is often used for handling separation tasks involving azeotropes, rough mass balance calculations around each unit (without considering the recycle stream) can initially be performed by assuming that the column distillate is at the azeotropic point and all product streams are at the required purity. Then, the initial design of the distillation column can be obtained using a proper shortcut method. The membrane system can initially be set with a large number of membranes stages and membrane modules in parallel, so that the product purities are achieved (some trial-and-errors may be needed). Next, the hybrid process is constructed including the recycle stream from the membrane unit back to the column, then simulated with the simulation results obtained from the individual unit simulations as initial values and providing initial values for the recycle stream. If the simulation failed, the values of the key design variables (e.g., reflux ratio, distillate, and number of membrane stages) should be varied and the simulation rerun. Else, the optimization of the whole process can be carried out. In this work, a user-defined genetic algorithm (GA) coded in MATLAB is used, and the details of the settings and strategies applied can be found in our previous study (Chia et al., 2021). The tool gO:MATLAB (Process Systems Enterprise, 2019) is used for data transfer between gPROMS ProcessBuilder and MATLAB. An improvement is made by using parallel computing (18 workers) in MATLAB to speed up the optimization.

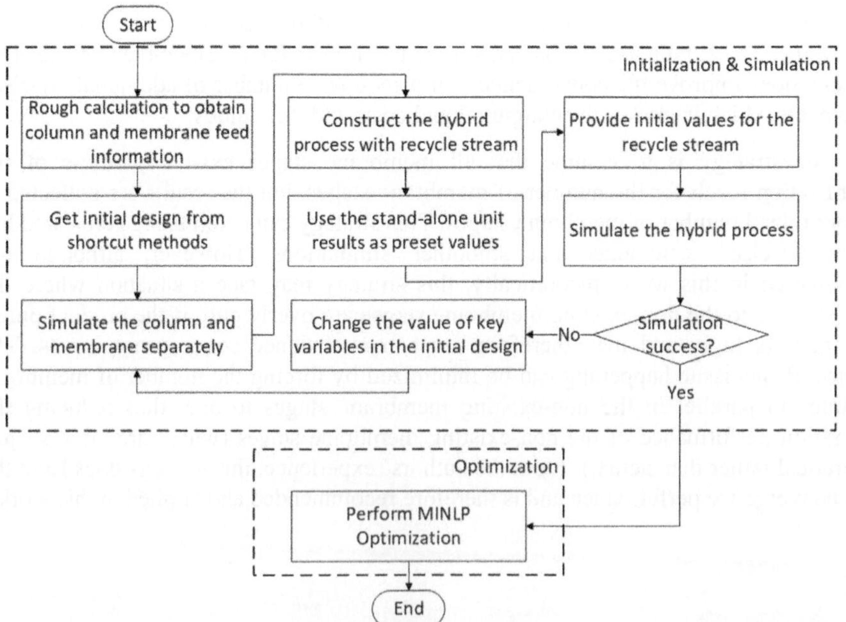

Figure 2: Procedure followed in this work for the initialization, simulation, and optimization of the hybrid process.

Table 1: Main optimization results obtained from repeated optimization and optimization recommended in this work, where *n* is the number of membrane stages. $n = 1,2,3$ are also optimized, but cannot achieve the product specifications, so the results are not shown here. (Purity specifications in all product streams are *99 mol %*.)

Items	**Repeated Optimization**					**This Work**
	$n = 4$	$n = 5$	$n = 6$	$n = 7$	$n = 8$	
Column						
Total stages	23	18	20	20	19	19
Feed stages (Main/Recycle)	19/19	14/17	17/17	15/17	15/17	15/18
Distillate ($kmol\ h^{-1}$)	22.84	23.05	22.72	23.24	23.04	23.23
Molar reflux ratio	1.17	1.21	1.3	1.15	1.23	1.14
Membrane Network *						
No. membrane stages	4	5	6	7	8	6
No. modules in stage 1	13	8	6	8	6	5
No. modules in stage 2	18	12	7	7	2	9
No. modules in stage 3	18	10	11	8	10	9
No. modules in stage 4	19	15	17	17	10	20
No. modules in stage 5	-	18	3	9	12	9
No. modules in stage 6	-	-	17	5	9	12
No. modules in stage 7	-	-	-	10	6	-
No. modules in stage 8	-	-	-	-	8	-
Total no. modules	68	63	61	64	63	64
Total membrane area (m^2)	408	378	366	384	378	384
Fitness and Time						
TAC ($M\$\ y^{-1}$)	0.7669	0.7573	0.7588	0.7609	0.7605	0.7577
CPU time (s) †	802	1193	875	1164	1370	1233
Total CPU time (s)			5404			1233

* The existence of membrane stage feed heater is also optimized but not shown here

† Parallel computing used to speed up optimization, number of workers/cores = 18

3. Case Study

The separation of an azeotropic ethanol-water mixture is used as a case study, with UNIQUAC as the thermodynamic model. The feed is provided at 200 $kmol\ h^{-1}$ with 10 *mol%* ethanol, and is a saturated liquid at 1 *bar*. The optimization task is to minimize the total annualized cost (TAC), where the TAC calculations can be found in Sinnott and Towler (2020) and Seider et al. (2016). To examine the performance and reliability of the proposed optimization strategy, the hybrid process is also optimized using the strategy by Marriott and Sorensen (2003) (where optimization is repeated at each number of membrane stages and the design with minimum TAC is selected as the optimal design) and is termed as "repeated optimization" in this work. For the optimization task, the existence of the heater before each membrane stage is optimized but the temperature is fixed at 343 *K* which is the maximum tested temperature in the experiment (Tsuyumoto et al., 1997).

The main optimization results are shown in Table 1. Due to space limitation, the existence of the heater before each membrane stage is not shown but all the optimization results show that heaters should exist between $n = 2$ to $n = 5$ where possible. The first stage does not require a heater as a subcooled condenser is used in the distillation column to cool the distillate to 343 *K*. From stage six onwards (optimization with n = 6,7,8), the temperature drop across the membrane stages are low, thus the feed heaters are not needed. The best design obtained using the repeated optimization method is when n = 5 with TAC as 0.7573 $M\,\$\,y^{-1}$. The simultaneous optimization strategy recommended in this work gave the optimal structure when n = 6 with a TAC of 0.7577 $M\,\$\,y^{-1}$, with slightly different column and membrane system structures when compared to the repeated optimization, showing that the proposed optimization strategy in this work is reliable and accurate. Moreover, the recommended optimization strategy is more time efficient by considering the total CPU time for the optimization task where the proposed optimization strategy can save 77% time. (This time saving is underestimated as the time taken for the optimization for n = 1,2,3 were also performed but not considered as they could not achieve the product purities.)

4. Conclusions

This work proposes a superstructure optimization strategy for the optimal design of hybrid distillation/pervaporation processes, and discusses different solution alternatives for how to handle the integer nature of the membrane network, as well as proposes a procedure for systematic initialization, simulation, and optimization of the process. The optimization strategy is applied to a case study considering a binary azeotropic separation. The optimization results obtained are compared to solution by repeated optimization (optimize the superstructure at each number of membrane stages). The superstructure optimization strategy is found to be superiority in terms of CPU time (at least 77% time saving) given its ability to simultaneously optimize the distillation column and membrane system superstructures. Theoretically, for membrane systems with recycle streams, the same methodology can be applied but some modifications (e.g., adding stream selectors) may be required which will increase the computational difficulty, and the performance of this methodology will be tested in future work.

References

Chia, D. N., Duanmu, F., and Sorensen, E. (2021). Optimal Design of Distillation Columns Using a Combined Optimisation Approach. In Turkay, M. and Gani, R., editors, *31st European Symposium on Computer Aided Process Engineering*, pages 153–158. Elsevier B.V.

Koch, K., Sudhoff, D., Kreiß, S., Gorak, A., and Kreis, P. (2013). Optimisation-based design method′ for membrane-assisted separation processes. *Chemical Engineering and Processing: Process Intensification*, 67:2–15.

Marriott, J. and Sorensen, E. (2003). The optimal design of membrane systems. *Chemical Engineering Science*, 58(22):4991–5004.

Process Systems Enterprise (2019). gO:MATLAB.

Process Systems Enterprise (2020). gPROMS ProcessBuilder version 1.4.

Seider, W. D., Lewin, D. R., Seader, J. D., Widagdo, S., Gani, R., and Ng, K. M. (2016). *Product and Process Design Principles: Synthesis, Analysis and Evaluation*. Wiley, 4 edition.

Singh, A. and Rangaiah, G. P. (2019). Development and optimization of a novel process of doubleeffect distillation with vapor recompression for bioethanol recovery and vapor permeation for bioethanol dehydration. *Journal of Chemical Technology & Biotechnology*, 94(4):1041–1056.

Sinnott, R. and Towler, G. (2020). *Chemical Engineering Design*. Elsevier, 6 edition.

Tsuyumoto, M., Teramoto, A., and Meares, P. (1997). Dehydration of ethanol on a pilot-plant scale, using a new type of hollow-fiber membrane. *Journal of Membrane Science*, 133(1):83–94.

Proceedings of the 14th International Symposium on Process Systems Engineering – PSE 2021+
June 19-23, 2022, Kyoto, Japan
http://dx.doi.org/10.1016/B978-0-323-85159-6.50053-1

Design and analysis of a single mixed refrigerant natural gas liquefaction process integrated with ethane recovery and carbon removal using cryogenic distillation

Ting He[a,b], Truls Gundersen[a], Wensheng Lin[b*]

[a] *Department of Energy and Process Engineering, Norwegian University of Science and Technology (NTNU), Kolbjoern Hejes v. 1A, NO-7491 Trondheim, Norway*
[b] *Institute of Refrigeration and Cryogenics, Shanghai Jiao Tong University, Shanghai 200240, China*
linwsh@sjtu.edu.cn

Abstract

Currently, the CO_2 purification specification for natural gas liquefaction is fixed as 50 ppm based on the solubility of CO_2 in liquid methane. However, for unconventional natural gas with high ethane content like shale gas and oilfield associated gas, the CO_2 solubility in these cryogenic fluids may increase considerably due to the azeotropic properties of ethane-CO_2 mixture. In this study, a novel integrated process is proposed to simultaneously realize natural gas liquefaction, ethane recovery and CO_2 separation, in which high purity methane and ethane products are obtained through a cryogenic distillation column and an extractive distillation column. The proposed process with refrigeration supplied by a single mixed refrigerant (SMR) cycle is designed, optimized, and comprehensively evaluated through performance indicators such as specific energy consumption, exergy efficiency, CO_2 removal rate as well as ethane recovery rate. Based on a thermodynamic analysis of the CH_4-CO_2-C_2H_6 ternary mixture, the maximum allowable CO_2 content in a feed gas with 2 - 20 mol% ethane is 1.8 - 17 mol%, which is much larger than 50 ppm. In addition, the recovery rate and purity of the ethane product reached 99.5% with a CO_2 removal rate larger than 99.3%. The results show that the specific power consumption and system exergy efficiency corresponding to the maximum allowable CO_2 content are around 0.41 kWh/Nm^3(NG) and 53.1 - 56.4 %, respectively.

Keywords: natural gas liquefaction, ethane recovery, CO_2 removal, cryogenic distillation, extractive distillation

1. Introduction

The world energy system is accelerating the transition to a clean and efficient energy system, and natural gas will play an important role in this transition process before large-scale application of renewable energies. In recent years, unconventional natural gas, has promoted the rapid growth of world natural gas production. In particular, shale gas has successfully transformed the United States from a natural gas importer to an exporter (Shcherba et al., 2019). Unlike conventional natural gas, the ethane content of shale gas in the US is significantly higher (Kort et al., 2016). As an important raw material for ethylene (Yang and You, 2017), the ethane recovery from shale gas can provide additional revenue. The recovery of ethane from natural gas usually requires cryogenic distillation, and this process consumes a large amount of cold energy. If it can be integrated with other parts in the natural gas chain, for example natural gas liquefaction, considerable investment reductions and energy savings can be achieved through integration within the process and the energy system (Ansarinasab and Mehrpooya., 2017). For ethane recovery, the integration of various natural gas liquefaction processes has been considered in our previous studies (He and Lin, 2020), and the results show that when the ethane content in the feed gas is 10-40 mol%, the proposed processes realized desirable separation effects, with both the purity and recovery rate of ethane reaching 99.5%. Besides, much attention has been paid to the integration of natural gas liquefaction and natural gas liquids (NGL) recovery. Vatani et al., (2013) also proposed an integrated process system for NGL-LNG co-production, and when it is applied to a typical feed gas rich in heavy hydrocarbons (75 mol% methane and 23 mol% heavy hydrocarbons), the specific power consumption is 0.414 kWh/kg (LNG).

In general, natural gas contains a certain amount of CO_2 that is causing calorific value reduction, equipment corrosion, even blockage in cryogenic conditions (Park et al., 2021). Thus, strict standards for carbon content are set for commercial natural gas, which lead to the development of carbon removal technologies for natural gas. The widely used methods for carbon removal in natural gas include physical absorption, chemical absorption, adsorption, cryogenic and membrane technologies (Babar et al., 2019). For LNG production, the purification specification of 50 ppm makes most carbon removal methods unsuitable, while chemical absorption and cryogenic methods (Baccioli et al., 2018) stand out. Although cryogenic carbon removal is considered to be environmentally friendly, it has not been widely used due to high energy consumption. More importantly, the freeze-out problem of CO_2 during cryogenic processes brings another challenge. However, the disadvantage in energy consumption can be overcome if it can be combined with the natural gas liquefaction process (Lin et al., 2018). In addition, because of the azeotropic properties of ethane and CO_2 (Gugnoni et al., 1974), the problem of blockage inside the distillation column due to CO_2 freeze-out may also be solved. However, there are few reports on the natural gas liquefaction process integrated with cryogenic carbon removal, especially by distillation. Focused on natural gas with high ethane content, this study proposes a novel single mixed refrigerant (SMR) liquefaction process integrated with ethane recovery and carbon removal. The separation of CO_2 and ethane is realized through cryogenic distillation and extractive distillation.

2. Process simulation and optimization

2.1. Process description

The flow diagram of the entire process is described in Figure 1. Focusing on the liquefaction and CO_2 removal process, the upstream natural gas processing, such as water removal, are excluded in this study and the feed gas (101) is simplified as a mixture of methane, ethane and CO_2.

The feed gas (101) first passes through a multi-stage compression unit (C-101, C-102) equipped with interstage coolers, and then passes through heat exchangers HEX-101, H-101, and HEX-102 to be partially condensed. Next, it enters the cryogenic distillation column (D-101) to obtain the enriched methane flow (109). After further pressure increase by the cryogenic compressor (C-103), it is completely condensed in HEX-102 and subcooled in HEX-103. Finally, it enters the storage tank (T-101) after throttling. The liquid flow from D-101, a mixture of CO_2 and C_2H_6, is first throttled by valve V-201, and then provides cooling capacity in heat exchangers H-203 and H-205. Finally, it enters the extractive distillation column (D-102), where C_2H_6 is produced in liquid form by the extractant isobutane, and CO_2 gas is obtained at the top of the column. The mixture of ethane and isobutane (205) enters the distillation column D-103 to obtain high-purity ethane, and the separated isobutane (301) enters D-102 for recycling. High-purity ethane (207) is also subject to further condensation, subcooling, throttling and finally storage as a liquid product with a pressure slightly above atmospheric. The refrigeration needed in heat exchangers and condensers in this process is provided by a standard SMR cycle (the black lines in Figure 1).

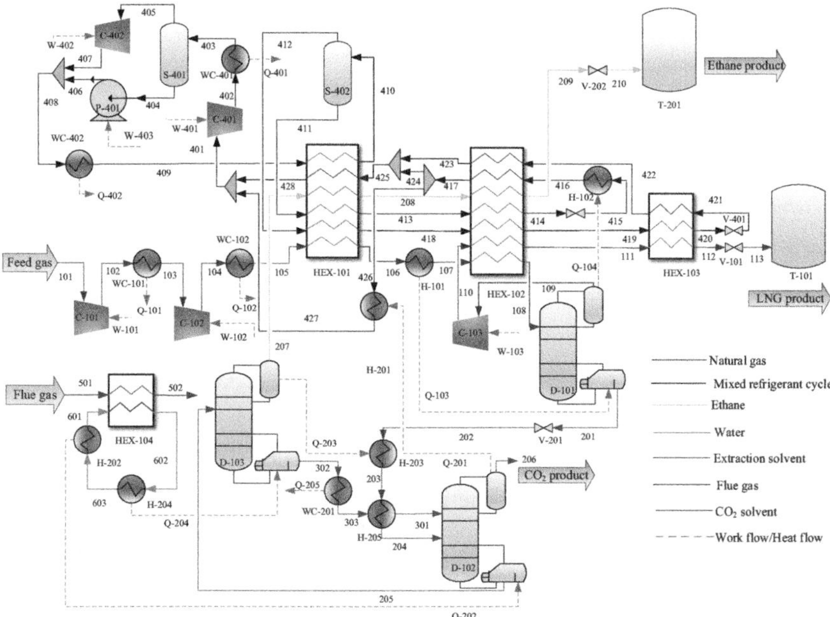

Figure. 1. Diagram of the SMR natural gas liquefaction process integrated with ethane recovery and carbon removal by cryogenic distillation. The process units are classified as follows: C: compressor, D: distillation column, H: heat exchanger, HEX: multi-stream heat exchanger, P: pump, Q: heat flow, S: separator, T: tank, V: valve, W: work; WC: water cooler

In addition to the cooling demand, the reboilers of D-102 and D-103 in this process require heat load with a temperature up to 112°C. Waste heat in the flue gas from the combustion-driven compressor unit is integrated in HEX-104 with circulating hot water that provides the required heat to the reboilers.

2.2. Initial settings and assumptions

The proposed process is modeled in Aspen HYSYS V11 by utilizing the Peng–Robinson equation of state to calculate thermodynamic properties of the feed gas and the mixed refrigerant. To simply the simulation, some parameters need to be set or assumed as presented in Table 1 according to initial conditions, product requirements or industry standard.

Table 1 Initial parameter settings and assumptions (Δp: Pressure drop)

Initial parameter settings	Value	Assumptions	Value
t_{101} /°C	40	Δp in water coolers /kPa	0

p_{101} /kPa	120	Δp in heat exchangers /kPa	0
n_{101} /kmol/h	1000	Δp in separator/mixer /kPa	0
Products storage pressure /kPa	120	Adiabatic efficiency of compressors	85 %
CO_2 in LNG	< 50 ppm	Adiabatic efficiency of pump	75 %
Ethane purity	> 99.5 mol%	Temperature after water cooling / °C	40

2.3. Process evaluation and optimization

In this study, the system evaluation involves the calculation of energy efficiency, carbon removal effect, ethane recovery rate, etc. The definition of each performance indicator used is shown in Table 2.

Table 2 Definition of evaluation indexes

Evaluation index	Definition	Annotation
ideal minimum work (W_{min})	$W_{min} = W_l + W_s$	W_l: minimum theoretical liquefaction work, kW;
total power consumption (W)	$W = \sum W_P + W_C$	W_S: minimum theoretical separation work, kW;
specific power consumption (w)	$w = \frac{\sum W_P + W_C}{N_{NG} V_M}$	W_P: power consumption of pump, kW;
exergy efficiency (η)	$\eta = \frac{W_{min}}{W} = \frac{W_l + W_s}{W}$	W_C: total power consumption of compressors, kW;
methane loss rate (α)	$\alpha = \left(1 - \frac{N_{109} C_{109, C1}}{N_{101} C_{101, C1}}\right) \times 100\%$	V_M: nominal molar volume, Nm^3/kmol;
CO_2 removal rate (β)	$\beta = \frac{N_{206} C_{206, CO2}}{N_{101} C_{101, CO2}} \times 100\%$	N: molar flow, kmol/h;
ethane recovery rate (γ)	$\gamma = \frac{N_{207} C_{207, C2}}{N_{101} C_{101, C2}} \times 100\%$	C: mole fraction

In this study, sequential search and a genetic algorithm (GA) are combined to find the optimal solution for the parameters that have an influence on the energy consumption of the proposed process. The objective function is minimum specific power consumption.

3. Results and discussion

3.1. Calculation of the maximum allowable CO_2 content

First, this study analyzes the maximum allowable CO_2 content under different ethane fractions by comparing the CO_2 freeze-out temperature in both gas and liquid phases with tray temperature under given operating conditions. To be specific, for a certain ethane content, the CO_2 fraction in the feed gas is gradually increased, and then the freeze-out temperature of CO_2 is calculated based on a thermodynamic analysis of the CH_4-CO_2-C_2H_6 ternary mixture. By determining whether the CO_2 freeze-out temperature is lower than the tray temperatures of the distillation column, the corresponding maximum allowable CO_2 content without blockage due to freeze-out can be found in Table 3.

Table 3 Maximum allowable CO_2 content under different ethane contents

Ethane content	0.02	0.05	0.1	0.15	0.2
Maximum allowable CO_2 content	0.018	0.07	0.11	0.14	0.17

3.2. Process optimization results

After obtaining the maximum allowable CO_2 content, the process is optimized, and the results for a typical feed gas (15 mol% C_2H_6, 14 mol% CO_2) are presented in Table 4.

Table 4 Optimization results

Stream	t (°C)	p (Pa)	N (kmol/h)	Stream	t (°C)	p (kPa)	N (kmol/h)

101	40.0	120	1000	302	112.4	2500	247
105	40.0	3600	1000	303	40.0	2500	247
108	-72.0	3600	1000	401	34.8	183	2679
109	-92.0	3550	710	403	40.0	1000	2679
110	-75.7	4600	710	409	40.0	2688	2679
111	-95.0	4600	710	410	26.0	2688	2679
112	-161.3	4600	710	414	-96.0	2688	1485
113	-159.7	120	710	415	-96.1	183	1485
201	-2.1	3600	290	420	-160.0	2688	1194
202	-16.2	2500	290	421	-164.6	183	1194
203	-14.8	2500	290	426	-45.9	183	290
204	30.0	2500	290	427	22.0	183	290
205	54.1	2500	397	428	36.9	183	2389
206	-12.8	2400	140	501	500.0	120	1505
207	-0.2	2400	150	502	283.9	120	1505
209	-89.0	2400	150	601	120.2	200	1150
210	-88.1	120	150	602	122.0	200	1150
301	20.0	2500	247	603	120.2	200	1150

3.3. Process performance

Table 5 shows the performance indicators of the proposed process under different feed gas conditions (the CO_2 content is the maximum allowable). It can be seen that the proposed process can remove more than 99.3% of the CO_2 and recover 99.5% of high-purity ethane with very little methane loss, which indicates that this carbon removal method has obvious advantages over other methods like membrane separation. In addition, with increased contents of ethane and CO_2, the minimum theoretical work gradually decreases, while the actual work consumed by the system rises slightly, which leads to a slight decline in the exergy efficiency.

Table 5 System performance indexes of the optimal state

Ethan content	0.02	0.05	0.10	0.15	0.20
W_{min} (kW)	5137	5117	5059	4983	4883
W (kW)	9116	9120	9260	9250	9189
η	0.5635	0.5611	0.5463	0.5387	0.5314
w (kWh/Nm³(NG))	0.4070	0.4071	0.4134	0.4129	0.4102
α (%)	0.28	0.11	0.41	0.48	0.45
β (%)	99.31	99.60	99.52	99.44	99.40
γ (%)	99.50	99.51	99.50	99.50	99.51

According to previous research results that only consider natural gas liquefaction and ethane recovery, the liquefaction power consumption is 0.38 - 0.42 kWh/Nm^3(NG) (He and Lin, 2020). Therefore, from the energy perspective, the CO_2 removal process proposed in this study increase the energy consumption of the liquefaction system only marginally through reasonable system integration. When adopting the most widely used chemical absorption method, although the additional power consumption is not very large, an additional heat load of 2.2 - 2.5 MJ/kg CO_2 for solvent regeneration is needed (Baccioli et al., 2018). As for equipment required, chemical absorption processes require at least two columns, one for the CO_2 absorption and the other for the absorbent regeneration. If ethane recovery is considered, one more cryogenic distillation column is also required. So, the required main equipment for the two methods are similar. Besides, the solvent required in this study is hydrocarbons, which can be directly obtained from natural gas, while the chemical absorption method requires a large amount of absorbent, thereby increasing its cost.

4. Conclusion

In this study, a novel integrated Single Mixed Refrigerant (SMR) natural gas liquefaction process is proposed, which combines cryogenic distillation and extractive distillation to realize ethane recovery and CO_2 removal. The proposed process is designed and optimized using Aspen HYSYS and Matlab. The results show that the process can handle a maximum allowable CO_2 content of 1.8 - 17 mol% when the ethane fraction is 2 - 20 mol %. More than 99.3% of the CO_2 can be removed with very little methane loss and over 99.5% of the ethane can be recovered as a high-purity product. The specific power consumption corresponding to the maximum allowable CO_2 content is about 0.41 kWh/Nm^3(NG), and the system exergy efficiency is in the range 53.1 - 56.4 %.

Acknowledgement

This publication has been funded by HighEFF - Centre for an Energy-Efficient and Competitive Industry for the Future. The authors gratefully acknowledge the financial support from the Research Council of Norway and user partners of HighEFF, an 8-years Research Centre under the FME-scheme (Centre for Environment-friendly Energy Research, 257632).

The authors gratefully acknowledge the financial support from China Scholarship Council (CSC) during Ting He's visit to Norwegian University of Science and Technology.

References

H. Ansarinasab, M. Mehrpooya. 2017. Evaluation of novel process configurations for coproduction of LNG and NGL using advanced exergoeconomic analysis, Applied Thermal Engineering, 115, 885-898.

M. Babar, M. A. Bustam, A. Ali, A. Shah Maulud, U. Shafiq, A. Mukhtar, S. N. Shah, K. Maqsood, N. Mellon, A. M. Shariff. 2019. Thermodynamic data for cryogenic carbon dioxide capture from natural gas: A review, Cryogenics, 102, 85-104.

A. Baccioli, M. Antonelli, S. Frigo, U. Desideri, G. Pasini. 2018. Small scale bio-LNG plant: Comparison of different biogas upgrading techniques, Applied Energy, 217, 328-335.

R. J. Gugnoni, J. W. Eldridge, V. C. Okay, T. J. Lee. 1974. Carbon dioxide-ethane phase equilibrium, AlChE Journal, 20, 357-362.

T. He, W. S. Lin. 2020. A novel propane pre-cooled mixed refrigerant process for coproduction of LNG and high purity ethane, Energy, 202, 117784.

E. A. Kort, M. L. Smith, L. T. Murray, A. Gvakharia, A. R. Brandt, J. Peischl, T. B. Ryerson, C. Sweeney, K. Travis. 2016. Fugitive emissions from the Bakken shale illustrate role of shale production in global ethane shift, Geophysical Research Letters, 43, 9, 4617-4623.

W. S. Lin, X. J. Xiong, A. Z. Gu. 2018. Optimization and thermodynamic analysis of a cascade PLNG (pressurized liquefied natural gas) process with CO_2 cryogenic removal, Energy, 161, 870-877.

J. Park, S. Yoon, S.Y. Oh, Y. Kim, J.K. Kim. 2021. Improving energy efficiency for a low-temperature CO_2 separation process in natural gas processing, Energy, 214, 118844.

V. A. Shcherba, A. P. Butolin, A. Zieliński. 2019. Current state and prospects of shale gas production, IOP Conference Series: Earth and Environmental Science, 272, 032020.

A. Vatani, M. Mehrpooya, B. Tirandazi. 2013. A novel process configuration for co-production of NGL and LNG with low energy requirement, Chemical Engineering and Processing: Process Intensification, 63, 16-24.

M. Yang, F. You. 2017. Process Modeling and analysis of manufacturing pathways for producing ethylene and propylene from wet shale gas and naphtha, Computer Aided Chemical Engineering, 40, 361-366.

Proceedings of the 14th International Symposium on Process Systems Engineering – PSE 2021+
June 19-23, 2022, Kyoto, Japan
http://dx.doi.org/10.1016/B978-0-323-85159-6.50054-3

A new decomposition approach for synthesis of heat exchanger network with detailed heat exchanger sizing

Zekun Yang[a], Nan Zhang[a*] and Robin Smith[a]

[a]Centre for Process Integration, Department of Chemical Engineering and Analytical Science, The University of Manchester, Manchester, M13 9PL, UK
nan.zhang@manchester.ac.uk

Abstract

Due to the complexities arisen from the non-convexities in the mathematical models for the HEN synthesis incorporating detailed exchanger design, constant heat transfer coefficients and short-cut model for the calculation of exchanger capital cost are used for a majority of approaches to obtain a synthetic network topology, which causes inaccurate heat transfer areas and trade-offs between energy usage and capital investment. This paper presents an enhanced iterative-based decomposition algorithm to achieve realistic HEN synthesis with detailed heat exchanger sizing, which targets to overcome the drawbacks associated with the use of short-cut heat exchanger model in configuration synthesis, and further presents how these exchanger details can be employed to lead the HEN synthesis towards generating more cost effective solutions. Fouled individual stream heat transfer coefficients and corrected total process cost are updated iteratively between heat exchanger design (HED) and HEN superstructure (HENS) to guide HEN topology optimization. Global optimization for heat exchanger sizing is achieved in each iteration using a global solver BARON/GAMS.34 to overcome instability in the iteration process caused by local optimum issues. A case study shows that it can provide a better solution than the results in the literature with a lower total annual cost and computational time.

Keywords: Heat exchanger network synthesis, Detailed heat exchanger sizing, Mathematical programming, Optimization, Process synthesis

1. Introduction

The increased pressure of reducing carbon emissions in the worldwide chemical industries leads to rising awareness for incorporating cost-effective ways of saving energy. Heat exchanger networks (HEN) are essential in the process industries, since they can improve energy efficiency and reduce "greenhouse" gas emissions by heat integration of process heat sources and sinks to reduce utility consumptions. The approaches used in HEN synthesis can be categorized into sequential and simultaneous methods. Pinch Technology has been developed based on the sequential thermodynamic analysis, but it requires experienced designers and may lead to missing promising solutions.

Mathematical programming has been developed by many researchers for simultaneous HEN synthesis. The synthesis problem is commonly formulated as a superstructure, in which the HEN topologies, stage temperatures, utilities and heat duties can be optimized simultaneously. A widely used stage-wise superstructure (SWS) was proposed by Yee and Grossmann (1990). By using SWS, the HEN synthesis is formulated as an MINLP problem, targeting the minimum total annual cost. In addition, several other approaches have been reported to solve the HEN synthesis problem by using different algorithms, such as stochastic algorithm (Rathjens and Fieg, 2020) and a deterministic approach (Yang et al., 2021).

Understandably, to achieve industrial applications, practical considerations related to heat exchanger details are significant for HEN synthesis, as short-cut heat exchanger calculations can lead to impractical design. More recently, simultaneous and iterative-based decomposition approaches have been developed to enhance the HEN synthesis towards realistic design by bringing heat exchanger details in the HEN optimization. Xiao et al. (2019) adopted a simultaneous approach based on a hybrid GA/SA algorithm. But their implementation coupled with stochastic algorithms inclines to generate a local HEN solution as requiring a relatively high utility usage.

Alternative to the simultaneous optimization, iterative-based decomposition strategies deal with detailed heat exchanger design as an individual block to avoid the massive nonlinearities in the MINLP HEN superstructure, which can helps to reduce the combinational difficulties for a large-scale MINLP problem. Ravagnani and Caballero (2007) presented a heuristic decomposition method to update stream heat transfer coefficients from heat exchanger design to HEN superstructure. Short et al. (2016) and Kazi et al. (2021) proposed a two-step optimization procedure, in which several correction factors were introduced to the iterative procedures to correct investments of heat exchangers in HENS. But their method brings two certain problems, including (1) tricky convergence of the proposed algorithm with many preliminary iterations; (2) difficulty to solve large-scale problems. This work addresses the existing problems identified from the literature, and proposes a novel iterative-based decomposition algorithm that integrates a heat exchanger network superstructure (HENS) (Yang et al., 2021) and heat exchanger design (Yang et al., 2020).

2. Mythologies

2.1. Global optimization for detailed heat exchanger sizing

In this work, we focus on Shell and Tube Heat Exchangers (STHEs) with plain tubes and single segmental baffles. The mathematical optimization model has been proposed in previous work (Yang et al., 2021). The geometrical variables include tube pinch Pt, tube number N_t, tube length L, tube inside and outside diameters D_i, D_O , shell inner diameter D_{SI}, tube outside bundle diameter D_{SB}, baffle spacing B_S, baffle cut B_c, baffle number N_b, the number of tube passes N_{TP}, the number of shell passes N_S. Some discrete decisions are formulated by generalized disjunction programming, including the selection of tube passes, tube sizes, tube angle arrangement. These geometries are optimized for their impacts on heat transfer coefficients, pressure drops and heat transfer area, which is guided by the constraints associated with Tubular Exchanger Manufactures Association (TEMA) standards. The objective function is to minimize the total exchanger cost.

Notably, global optimization plays an important role in the iterative method. Local optimum for individual heat exchanger design could mislead HEN synthesis solutions and cause convergence issues in the iterative algorithm. A case study (Yang et al., 2020) is tested in this work to investigate the need of global optimization. Fig.1 shows the result comparison of using the MINLP local solver DICOPT and global solver BARON, by GAMS, with 38.5 % of total exchanger cost savings from the global optimization and acceptable CPU time of 292 s. Consequently, the application of global optimization in

HED can lead to the cost of exchanger always being minimized and promoting the iterative process to reach convergence rapidly because of consistent corrections.

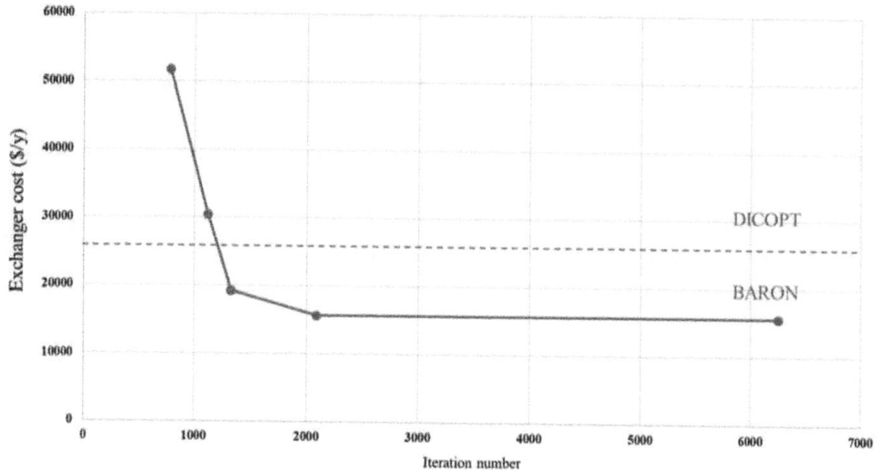

Figure 1. Comparison of problem-solving process between DICOPT and BARON

2.2. HEN superstructure optimization

The mathematical model for HEN topology optimization is based on the well-known stage-wise superstructure (SWS) proposed by Yee and Grossmann (1990), and stages are introduced, in which all possible matches between hot streams and cold streams are optimized simultaneously. By adopting the enhanced deterministic-based approach proposed in the earlier work (Yang et al., 2021), a cost effective solution can be targeted with low computational time. The iso-thermal mixing assumed in the original SWS method is removed, and additional constraints are employed to model non-isothermal mixing. This proposed model is formulated as a non-convex MINLP problem that is solved by the global solver BARON/GAMS.

2.3. Iterative algorithm

The proposed algorithm adopts a modification of the heuristic-based decomposition approach proposed by Ravagnani and Caballero (2007), which integrates heat exchanger design model (Section 2.1) for detailed exchanger geometries, heat transfer coefficients, pressure drops and cost details, and the HEN superstructure approach (Section 2.2) for optimal HEN configurations, heat duty for each exchanger, inlet and outlet temperatures of each exchanger and split ratios for mass flow rate calculation.

In this work, a correction factor for total process cost (F_{TPC}) is introduced to correct the deviation of total process cost derived by multiple shell passes, LMTD correction factor (F_T), geometries, tube and shell side pressure drops. Furthermore, convergence criteria are introduced to select optimal results, including the percentage differences of stream fouled stream heat transfer coefficient (Re_{HTC}) and total process cost (Re_{TPC}) between that are used in HENS and obtained by HED at an individual iteration. Re_{HTC} and Re_{TPC} are employed to reflect the stability of the iteration process. They are able to indicate how the corrections work in the iterative procedures and guide to generate realistic solutions, which is more accurate to represent the level of convergence. The tolerances of both Re_{HTC} and Re_{TPC} can be specified, for which 5% for each individual iteration seems to be reasonable in our test cases. Fig.2 shows the scheme of this approach, including seven steps, as described:

Step-1: Define process parameters and constant heat transfer coefficients in HENS. The constant heat transfer coefficients can be supplied by the program or generally assumed at a range from 0.5 kW/m^2°C to 1 kW/m^2°C. Next, generate an initial HEN configuration considering stream splitting.

Step-2: According to heat duty allocations and temperatures from the initial HEN configuration, optimize each heat exchanger design by solving the MINLP HED model.

Step-3: By using HED, calculate the fouled HTC of each stream, using an average value of fouled tube side (shell side) HTC h_{TF} (h_{SF}) from exchangers that are installed for an individual stream. Meanwhile, calculate the correction factor for total annual process cost by $F_{TPC} = TPC_{HE}/TPC_{HEN}$.

Step-4: Update these calculated fouled HTC and F_{TPC} in HENS. Solve the HENS to generate optimal HEN configuration. In this step, the maximum acceptable computational time could be specified in HENS.

Step-5: Use MINLP HED mode to optimize each heat exchanger and calculate relatively errors Re_{HTC} and Re_{TPC}. Meanwhile, calculate the total annual cost TAC_{HE} of the HEN with detailed heat exchanger design.

Step-6: Check if the relatively error Re_{HTC}, Re_{TPC} are lower than the tolerance. If yes, go to Step-7. Otherwise, go to Step-3.

Step-7: Check if the TAC_{HE} is higher than the current one. If yes, stop and output the current HEN as the optimal result. Otherwise, replace the previous HEN result and return to Step 3.

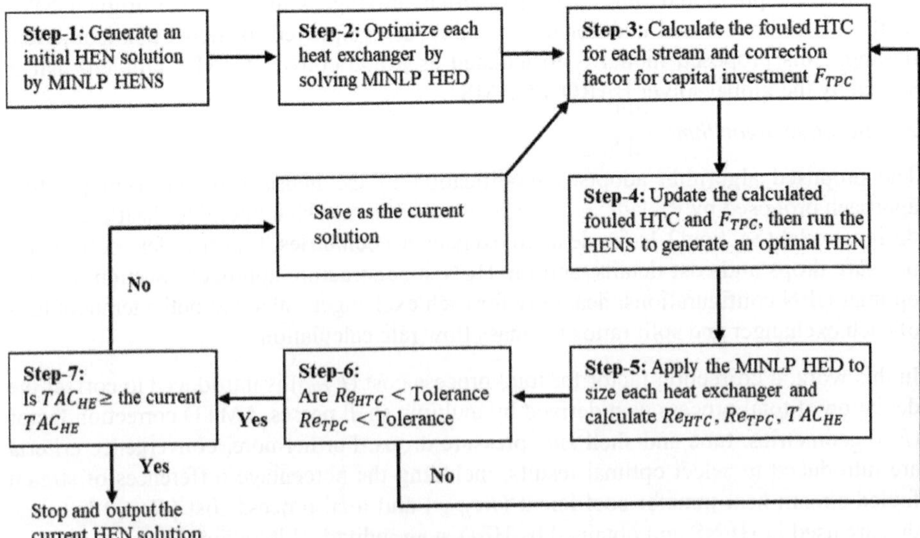

Figure 2. Iterative decomposition algorithm

3. Case study

This case study is taken from the literature (Ravagnani and Caballero, 2007; Xiao et al., 2019; Short et al., 2016; Kazi et al., 2021). It was solved on a computer resource Intel ® Core™, I7-8700 CPU, 3.20 GHz with 16 GB RAM, 6 cores, 12 processors. Global solver BARON in GAMS.34 was applied. Constant heat transfer coefficients of 0.888 kW/m^2°C are assumed for the initial synthesis.

At the initial design, the practical consideration of multiple shells and pump operating cost associated with detailed HED model leads to the total process cost (TPC) to be much higher than that from the HENS design with constant heat transfer coefficients. Large stream Re_{HTC} mean that the assumed heat transfer coefficients need to be corrected. Iteratively, Re_{HTC} reduces gradually from iteration-1 to iteration-4, when it is less than the specified tolerance of 5 %. F_{TPC} is first calculated at the iteration-1, as 2.829, then updated from iteration-2. From that point, the deviation of TPC between HED and HENS is decreased promptly under an allowed Re_{TPC} (within 5 %). The final optimal TPC-HED is 2.985 times the initial TPC-HENS with assumed coefficients. Using the proposed approach, the best solution was found at iteration-4 with 5760 s CPU time, which brings 77% of computational time saving compared with that demanded by Kazi et al. (2021).

Fig.3 illustrates the optimal HEN configuration of the case study. The comparison of results is presented in Table 1. Compared with the best solution so far (Kazi et al., 2021), the proposed approach led a lower TAC with 3,620,095 \$/y. The TAC saving is not significant, because the cost is dominated by energy cost (Total operating cost/TAC > 0.95). But for the total process cost, 26.5 % of TPC is achieved, because considering the trade-off between area cost and pumps cost in heat exchanger optimization, the better utilization efficiency of exchanger geometries that are guided by the proposed global optimization, generates 58.4 % of total process pump cost saving even using the similar total process area.

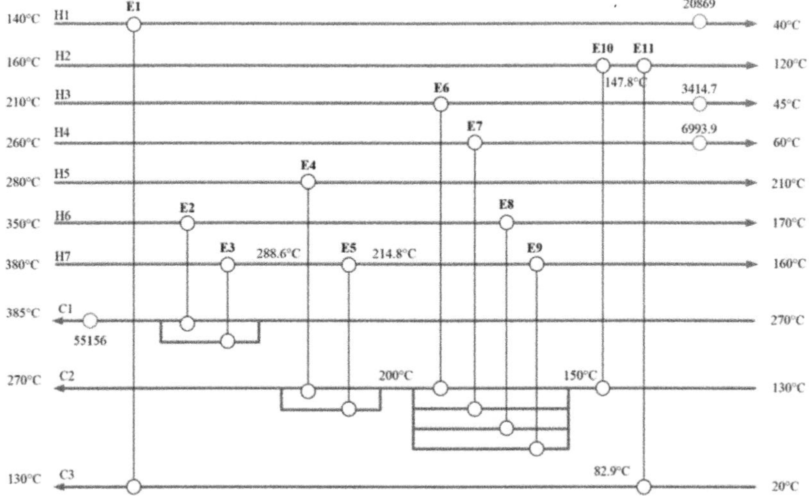

Figure 3. Optimal HEN solution of Example

Table 1: Results comparison

	Short et al.	Xiao et al.	Kazi et al.	This work
Hot utility usage (kW)	64,187	61,063	55,156	55,156
Cold utility usage (kW)	40,299	37,175	31,267	31,267
Total utility cost ($/y)	4,091,975	3,886,803	3,496,972	3,496,972
Total process area (m^2)	5451	10754	12,151	12,187
The number of exchangers	22	18	38	35
Process capital cost ($/y)	44,998	45,747	99,705	94,993
Process pump cost ($/y)	46,099	6907	67,692	28,129
Total process cost ($/y)	91,097	52,654	167,397	123,123
Total annual cost ($/y)	4,183,072	3,939,457	3,664,369	3,620,095

4. Conclusions

This work proposed an iterative approach for the heat exchanger network synthesis with detailed heat exchanger sizing. Corrected stream heat transfer coefficients and process investment were determined by global optimization of STHE-HED through an iterative procedure. The proposed method shows better performance than the existing approaches, with 1.2 % savings of total annual cost (TAC), 58.4 % savings of pump cost and 26.5 % savings of total process cost. This methodology offered a time-efficient way towards a cost effective and practical HEN design with quick convergence, further improving the feasibility for solving industrial-scale problems.

References

M.A.S.S. Ravagnani, J.A. Caballero, Optimal heat exchanger network synthesis with the detailed heat transfer equipment design, Computers & Chemical Engineering 31 (2007) 1432-1448.

M. Rathjens, G. Fieg, A novel hybrid strategy for cost-optimal heat exchanger network synthesis suited for large-scale problems, Applied Thermal Engineering 167 (2020) 114771.

M. Short, A.J. Isafiade, D.M. Fraser, Z. Kravanja, Synthesis of heat exchanger networks using mathematical programming and heuristics in a two-step optimisation procedure with detailed exchanger design, Chemical Engineering Science 144 (2016) 372-385.

S.R. Kazi, M. Short, A.J. Isafiade, L.T. Biegler, Heat exchanger network synthesis with detailed exchanger designs—2. Hybrid optimization strategy for synthesis of heat exchanger networks, AIChE Journal 67 (2021) e17057.

T.F. Yee, I.E. Grossmann, Simultaneous optimization models for heat integration—II. Heat exchanger network synthesis, Computers & Chemical Engineering 14 (1990) 1165-1184.

W. Xiao, K. Wang, X. Jiang, X. Li, X. Wu, Z. Hao, G. He, Simultaneous optimization strategies for heat exchanger network synthesis and detailed shell-and-tube heat-exchanger design involving phase changes using GA/SA, Energy 183 (2019) 1166-1177.

Z. Yang, Y. Ma, N. Zhang, R. Smith, Design optimization of shell and tube heat exchangers sizing with heat transfer enhancement, Computers & Chemical Engineering 137 (2020) 106821.

Z. Yang, N. Zhang, R. Smith, Enhanced deterministic approach for heat exchanger network synthesis, Computer Aided Chemical Engineering, (2021), vol. 50, pp. 833-838. Elsevier.

Proceedings of the 14th International Symposium on Process Systems Engineering – PSE 2021+
June 19-23, 2022, Kyoto, Japan
http://dx.doi.org/10.1016/B978-0-323-85159-6.50055-5

A mathematical approach for the synthesis of a wastewater treatment plant using the concept of circular economy

Jo Yee Ho[a], Wai Teng Tee[a], Yoke Kin Wan[a*]

[a] *Department of Chemical and Environmental Engineering, University of Nottingham Malaysia, Broga Road, 43500 Semenyih, Selangor, Malaysia.*

yokekin.wan@nottingham.edu.my

Abstract

Huge generation of waste from industrial manufacturing processes has become a concern to many countries especially in the world with finite resources. Among these wastes, wastewater generation is one of the biggest issues faced by most industrial processes as the treatment of these wastewaters requires different treatment stages. Consequently, improper treatment and direct discharge of wastewater often occurs which had contaminated the world's waterways. Therefore, stricter environmental discharge regulations had been enforced by local government authorities. This becomes a challenge for new manufacturing plants in designing their wastewater treatment process to comply with the government regulations set while reducing environmental impacts. This paper presents the preliminary evaluation of a model-based decision making on wastewater treatment technologies selection based on the concept of circular economy. To prolong the natural water cycle, treated wastewater were recycled back to the manufacturing process which reduces freshwater consumption. A case study on semiconductor manufacturing process and its wastewater treatment plant is solved in this work. Based on the results, the synthesis of the wastewater treatment plant incorporating circular economy has obtained 55.83% circular economy efficiency of water being recycled back to the semiconductor manufacturing process.

Keywords: Wastewater treatment process, Circular Economy, Mathematical model.

1. Introduction

Circular economy (CE) is a well-established concept in encouraging sustainable development initiatives. The CE mainly focuses on a perfectly balanced operation by promoting and utilizing renewable energy resources such as biomass, water, and solar. It replaces the 'end-of-life' concept by restoration and turns the goods and services into alternative resources with minimum waste leakage and toxic chemicals. A circular economy-orientated business model prioritizes reusing, refurbishing, remanufacturing, recycling, and repairing the waste creation after the consumption stage instead of discarding them into landfills (Pires and Martinho, 2019). As a result, these materials and products can be productively used repeatedly, thereby increasing and retaining the value of the products. In this respect, this research aims to develop a preliminary decision-making tool integrating with the concept of circular economy to prolong and sustain the natural water cycle. Unlike linear manufacturing process, a transition towards a circular economy model will maximise the circularity of water in the system which reduces the discharge of wastewater while minimising the use of natural resources. The circularity metrics can be categorised into circularity measurement indices and circularity assessment tools. In this work, circularity measurement indices will be applied to directly determine the circularity of water for a new manufacturing plant. This way, the selection of wastewater treatment technologies will ensure maximise recovery of treated wastewater back to the manufacturing process. This work is expected to benefit industry sectors, policy makers and local government authorities on future sustainable development of new manufacturing sectors.

2. Problem statement

Figure 1 illustrates the problem statement of a wastewater treatment process for new manufacturing plants. Wastewater feed $i \in I$ from manufacturing process enters a series of wastewater treatment process beginning from pre-treatment stage $a \in A$, chemical treatment $b \in B$, biological treatment $c \in C$ and tertiary treatment $d \in D$ to ensure the treated wastewater produced complies with local discharge regulation. In light of this, recycle streams are designed in these four treatment stages to maximise water reuse in the manufacturing company. Removal of contaminants will generate sludge water during the chemical treatment and biological treatment. Eventually, these sludge water will enter sludge treatment $e \in E$ for wastewater removal before disposal of sludgecake.

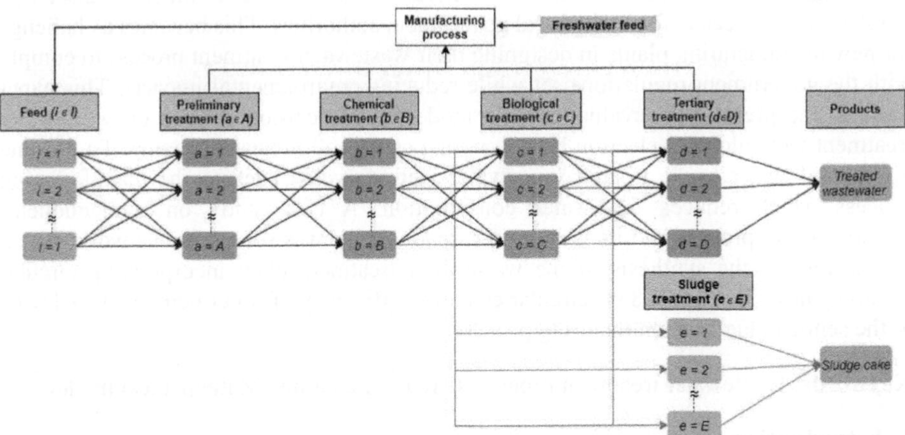

Figure 1: Generic superstructure of wastewater treatment process in a new manufacturing plant

3. Circular economy optimization model

The mathematical model developed in this model consist of flowrate balance, contaminant component balance and circular economy index formulations. By applying law of conservation of mass, the wastewater treatment flowrate balance and contaminant component balance are repetitive in each treatment stage as shown in Figure 1. Hence, Eq. (1) to Eq. (6) depicts a more generic set of equations to represent these formulations. The generic formulation appoints index t to represent preceding treatment stage, index u as current treatment stage, and index v as succeeding treatment stage respectively. For example, to formulate the equations for chemical stage b, the current index u will be chemical stage b ($u = b$), the previous index t will be preliminary treatment stage a ($t = a$) and subsequent index v will be biological treatment stage c ($v = c$). The same formulation method is repeated for other stages. In this model, all the parameters and variables are represented as non-Italic and Italic, respectively.

3.1. Flowrate of wastewater treatment process

The flowrate balance of treatment stage *u* is summarised in Eq. (1) to Eq. (3).

$$F_u^{in} = \sum_{t=1}^{T} F_{t,u} \qquad \forall u \qquad (1)$$

$$F_u^{in} = F_u^{out} \qquad \forall u \qquad (2)$$

$$F_u^{out} = \sum_{v=1}^{V} F_{u,v} + F_u^{ww,recycle} \qquad \forall u \qquad (3)$$

Where, F_u^{in} (m^3/day) and F_u^{out} (m^3/day) represents the inlet and outlet flowrate of wastewater at treatment stage *u*; $F_{t,u}$ (m^3/day) and $F_{u,v}$ (m^3/day) represents the flowrate transferred between the treatment stages; $F_u^{ww,recycle}$ represents the treated wastewater from treatment stage *u* that can be recycled back to the manufacturing process.

3.2. Contaminant component balance

The formulation of generic component balance for contaminant *g* at treatment stage *u* were summarized as shown in Eqs.(4) to (7). Contaminant *g* refers to any wastewater contaminant characteristics. As shown, the mass of contaminant *g* entering technology *u* $M_{g,u}^{in}$ (kg/day) depends on the concentration of contaminant *g* present in the inlet stream of technology *u*, $C_{g,u}^{in}$ (kg/m^3). At every stage of the wastewater treatment process, a certain mass of contaminant *g* will be removed from technology *u*, $M_{g,u}^{removed}$ (kg/day) based on the removal efficiency of technology *u*, $\mathrm{R}_{g,u}$ (kg contaminant/m^3 WWT). The mass of contaminant *g* discharging from technology *u*, $M_{g,u}^{out}$ (kg/day) can then be calculated. The constraint equation is shown in Eq. (8) where M_g^{std} is referring to the discharge limit set by government.

$$M_{g,u}^{in} = C_{g,u}^{in} F_u^{in} \qquad \forall g \forall u \qquad (4)$$

$$M_{g,u}^{\mathrm{removed}} = M_{g,u}^{\mathrm{in}} \mathrm{R}_{g,u} \qquad \forall g \forall u \qquad (5)$$

$$M_{g,u}^{in} = M_{g,u}^{removed} + \sum_{v=1}^{V} M_{g,u,v} \qquad \forall g \forall u \qquad (6)$$

$$M_{g,u}^{out} = M_{g,u}^{in} - M_{g,u}^{removed} \qquad \forall g \forall u \qquad (7)$$

$$M_{g,u}^{out} < \mathrm{M}_g^{std} \qquad \forall g \forall u \qquad (8)$$

3.3. Circular economy efficiency index

In this research, the concept of circular economy efficiency by Molina-Moreno et al. (2017) is adapted to recover treated wastewater back into the manufacturing process. The total recycled wastewater, $F^{total,recycle}$ (m^3/day) comes from treated wastewater from pretreatment a, chemical treatment b, biological treatment c and tertiary treatment d as shown in Eq. (9). Water consumption required by the manufacturing process, $F^{watercomsumption}$ (m^3/day) can be obtained from the total recycled treated wastewater and freshwater feed as illustrated in Eq. (10). To reduce freshwater consumption, circular economy index, I^{ww} will be maximised as shown in Eqs. (11) and (12).

$$F^{total,recycle} = \sum_{a=1}^{A} F_a^{ww,recycle} + \sum_{b=1}^{B} F_b^{ww,recycle} + \sum_{c=1}^{C} F_c^{ww,recycle} + \sum_{d=1}^{D} F_d^{ww,recycle} \quad (9)$$

$$F^{watercomsumption} = F^{total,recycle} + F^{freshwater} \quad (10)$$

$$I^{ww} = \frac{F^{total,recycle}}{F^{waterconsumption}} \times 100\% \quad (11)$$

$$\text{Max } I^{ww} \quad (12)$$

4. Case study

Due to the increasing demand of electronic product and solar energy, the semiconductor industry has been expanding and increasing rapidly over the years. The manufacturing process of semiconductors involves large quantity of water which causes huge volume of wastewater being generated during the process (Huang et al., 2011). Thus, the proposed approach is illustrated in this research by using a local semiconductor manufacturing plant in Penang, Malaysia to synthesize a WWTP to maximize the recovery of treated wastewater from each treatment stage back to the manufacturing process. The wastewater discharged from the manufacturing process typically has a higher chemical oxygen demand (COD) (Lin and Kiang, 2003). Therefore, Figure 2 illustrates the case study superstructure of a wastewater treatment process in a semiconductor manufacturing plant consisting of high COD removal treatment technologies.

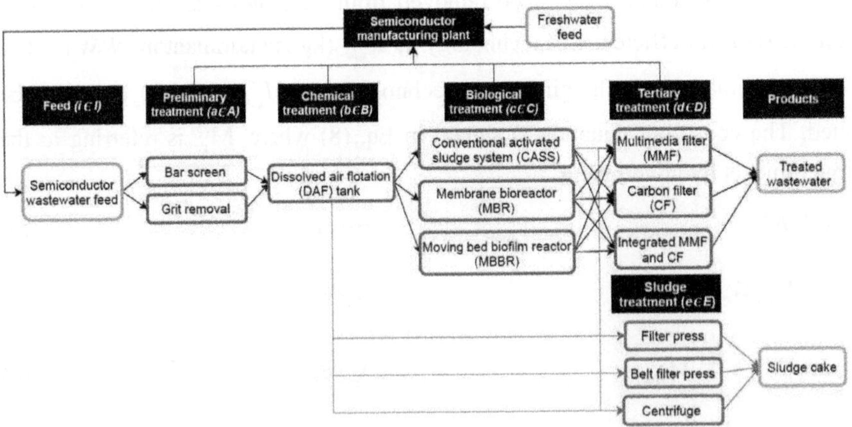

Figure 2: Case study superstructure of wastewater treatment process in a semiconductor manufacturing plant

Based on technologies selected in Figure 2, case study parameters were obtained. The average wastewater flowrate generated from the semiconductor manufacturing plant is 1,012 m^3/d. Table 1 summarise the case study wastewater characteristics from the partnered semiconductor manufacturing plant along with the local discharge regulation Standard A (Department of Environment Malaysia, 2010). Meanwhile, Table 2 and Table

3 summarises the COD removal efficiency for the case study wastewater treatment technologies.

Table 1: Case study wastewater contaminants characteristic and discharged regulations by Department of Environment (2013).

Concentration (ppm)	COD
Semiconductor wastewater	2,285
Discharge regulations (Standard A)	80

Table 2: COD removal efficiency of wastewater treatment technologies (Ho et al., 2019)

	Technologies	COD removal efficiency (%)
Preliminary treatment	Bar Screen	0
	Grit Removal	0
Chemical treatment	Dissolved air flotation (DAF)	65
Biological treatment	Conventional aerated filter (CAF)	85
	Moving bed biofilm reactor (MBBR)	90
	Membrane bioreactor (MBR)	90
Tertiary treatment	Multimedia filter (MMF)	0
	Carbon filter (CF)	50
	Integrated multimedia filter and carbon filter (MMF + CF)	65

Table 3: Dryness of sludge cake produced by each sludge treatment technology (Faure Equipments, 2018).

Technologies	Dryness (kg SS/m^3)
Filter press	25
Belt filter press	29.9
Centrifuge press	28.5

The case study is solved using the mathematical formulation developed in this research from Eqs. (1) to (12). These formulations and case study parameters from Table 1 to Table 3 were coded into a commercial optimization software, LINGO version 19 and solved using the global solver in 5 seconds. The specifications of computer used for this case study were Intel ® Core ™ i7-6500U with 8 GB RAM and x64-based processor. The developed mathematical model is a MINLP model, consisting of 194 variables, 198 constraints and 11 integers.

The global optimized results consist of bar screen, DAF, MBBR, integrated multimedia filter and carbon filter as well as belt press as shown in Figure 3. These technologies were selected due to their high COD removal efficiency to maximize the recovery of treated wastewater. Due to the compliance to wastewater discharge regulation Standard A (COD level < 80ppm), wastewater that can be recovered back to the manufacturing system must pass through all treatment stages to achieve a justifiable COD level (28 ppm). The results have clearly shown that the total flowrate of treated wastewater recycled back is more than half of the freshwater input needed for the semiconductor manufacturing process. Therefore, this has proven that a circular economy oriented WWTP can achieve 55.58% of circular economy efficiency of treated wastewater recycled by minimizing the wastewater generation to the environment and reduce the demand of freshwater resources as well as lower the cost of freshwater input.

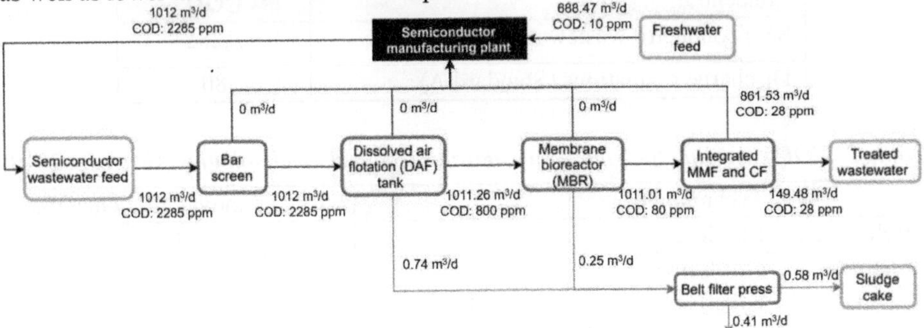

Figure 3: Synthesised WWTP for case study

5. Conclusions

Water scarcity is an important issue to be solved due to the rising number of water pollution around the world. Due to this reason, this research has incorporated the concept of circular economy in synthesizing a WWTP for industrial manufacturing process. This prominently reduces the discharge of untreated wastewater to the environment and decreases consumption of freshwater using the concept of circular economy. A case study on a local semiconductor manufacturing process is solved. By maximizing the circularity index of treated wastewater recycling, the results from the case study indicates an approximate of 45% reduction of freshwater consumption. As future work, other contaminant components such as BOD and TSS levels can be included to further enhance WWTP optimization.

References

Department of Environment Malaysia, 2010. Environmental Requirements : A guide for investors.

Equipments, F., n.d. Filter Presses Leading mechanical dewatering system.

Ho, J.Y., Wan, Y.K., Andiappan, V., Ng, D.K.S., 2019. Material Flow Cost Account-based Approach for Synthesis and Optimisation of Wastewater Treatment Plant. Chem. Eng. Trans. 76, 529–534.

Huang, C.J., Yang, B.M., Chen, K.S., Chang, C.C., Kao, C.M., 2011. Application of membrane technology on semiconductor wastewater reclamation: A pilot-scale study. Desalination 278, 203–210.

Lin, S.H., Kiang, C.D., 2003. Combined physical, chemical and biological treatments of wastewater containing organics from a semiconductor plant. J. Hazard. Mater. 97, 159–171.

Molina-Moreno, V., Carlos Leyva-Díaz, J., Llorens-Montes, F.J., Cortés-García, F.J., 2017. Design of Indicators of Circular Economy as Instruments for the Evaluation of Sustainability and Efficiency in Wastewater from Pig Farming Industry. Water 9, 1–13.

Pires, A., Martinho, G., 2019. Waste hierarchy index for circular economy in waste management. Waste Manag. 95, 298–305.

Proceedings of the 14th International Symposium on Process Systems Engineering – PSE 2021+
June 19-23, 2022, Kyoto, Japan
http://dx.doi.org/10.1016/B978-0-323-85159-6.50056-7

Convex Q-learning: Reinforcement learning through convex programming

Sophie Sitter[a], Damien van de Berg[a], Max Mowbray[b], Antonio del Rio Chanona[a], Panagiotis Petsagkourakis[a*]

[a]*Sargent Center for Process Systems Engineering, Imperial College London, South Kensington Campus, SW72AZ, London, United Kingdom*
[b]*Centre for Process Integration, The Mill, University of Manchester, M1 3AL, United Kingdom*
p.petsagkourakis@ic.ac.uk

Abstract

Over the last decade, Reinforcement Learning (RL) has received significant attention as it promises novel and efficient solutions to complex control problems. This work builds on model-free RL, namely Q-learning, to determine optimal control policies for nonlinear, complex biochemical processes. We propose convex functions instead of deep neural networks as state-action value function approximators to reduce computational complexity. A convex Q-function surrogate is trained using semidefinite programming. The surrogate is then minimized to determine the optimal control action. This results in 75.3% lower computational time compared with deep Q-networks. By alleviating the computational burden of traditional RL approximation functions, this work addresses one of the major obstacles for the successful implementation of RL to real-world engineering applications.
Keywords: machine learning; convex Q-learning; semi-definite programming; data-driven batch optimization; dynamic process control;

1. Introduction

Biochemical production generally has a higher cost than its fossil fuel counterpart (del Rio-Chanona et al. 2015), for this to be sustainable, production costs must be lowered. An important aspect of this, is to lower cost by leveraging dynamic optimization with robust and effective control schemes. Yet, the dynamic optimization of highly nonlinear, complex real-world biochemical processes is often hindered by plant-model mismatch and computational intractability (del Rio-Chanona et al. 2016). Model-free Reinforcement Learning methods do not require an explicit model of the environment. They `learn' environment dynamics through data generated by environment interaction. Model-free RL is categorized into value-based, policy-based, and actor-critic optimization methods. Value-based methods seek to maximize the sum of future rewards for reaching a certain state or for taking a certain action given a state. Policy-based methods directly optimize the policy in accordance with the sampled reward values (Dong et al. 2020). The combination of the two, actor-critic, learns approximations to value functions and policy, overcoming the challenges associated with either method. Chemical processes generally provide little data. Since RL algorithms are usually regarded as "data-hungry", these applications call for the most data-efficient algorithms, namely value-based methods.

Pan et al. (2020) as well as Singh and Kodamana (2020) investigate the application of state-action value functions within Q-learning (a model-free RL method) to the dynamic optimization of batch processes. Pan et al. (2020) illustrate the superior performance of Q-learning in navigating process uncertainties through its closed-loop feedback; they address the challenge of safe reinforcement learning by proposing a chance-constrained Q-Learning algorithm based on deep Q-networks (DQN), extending the work of Mowbray et al. (2021a), and Petsagkourakis et al. (2020a). This approach mitigates the shortcomings of previously proposed ways of handling operational and safety constraints, which reintroduce model dependencies (safety filter or barrier function methods), or achieve constraint satisfaction only in expectation (penalty-adjusted rewared functions, constrained Markov Decision Processes, policy projection to safety layer) (S. Huh, I, Yang, 2020 & J. Cho et al. 2020).

However, DQNs are time-intensive to train, which severely hinders algorithm efficiency. Our work tackles this obstacle by substituting the DQNs with tractable convex functions. Finding safe Q-functions that are accurate and tractable is a considerable step towards the successful implementation of RL to real-world chemical engineering systems, and this work adds to this effort.

2. Methodology

At each iteration, data is generated which maps states x∈R^(n_x), controls u∈R^(n_u) and the respective time step t to their respective state-action value (Q-value). Q(·) denotes the empirical, cumulative cost required after enacting control u in state x, and is given by Eq. (1):

$$Q(\boldsymbol{x},\boldsymbol{u}) = \sum\nolimits_{t}^{T_f} R_t \tag{1}$$

where R_t denotes the cost incurred at time step t. Next, a convex approximation $Q_{convex}(\boldsymbol{u},\boldsymbol{x};\ \boldsymbol{\theta})$ of $Q(\boldsymbol{x},\boldsymbol{u})$ is built using a combination of convex basis functions, such as those in Table 1.

To find the parameters $\boldsymbol{\theta}$ including weigh coefficients of the basis functions a nonlinear least squares optimization problem is formulated. Its objective function (Eq. 2) minimizes the error between the estimated and empirical Q-values:

$$\min_{\theta\in\Theta} \sum_{j} \left(Q_{convex}(\boldsymbol{u}_j,\boldsymbol{x}_j;\boldsymbol{\theta}) - Q_{data\,j}\right)^2 \tag{2}$$

where j is the iteration counter over all historic data points; and Q_{data} is an empirical estimate of the state-action value for the pair $(\boldsymbol{x}_j,\boldsymbol{u}_j)$ obtained in training via Monte Carlo simulation of the policy (discussed subsequently) under the process model. Taking advantage of the structure of the problem, to ensure positive definiteness of the norm matrices, and to maximize solution efficiency, a semidefinite program (SDP) is formulated (Vandenberghe and Boyd 1996) and solved using the Python-embedded modelling language CVXPY (S. Diamond and S. Boyd, 2016). This procedure produces the convex approximation $Q_{convex}(\boldsymbol{u},\boldsymbol{x};\boldsymbol{\theta})$ of $Q(\boldsymbol{x},\boldsymbol{u})$.

To find the optimal control action at every step, the convex Q-function approximation is optimized:

$$\pi_*(\cdot) = \begin{cases} \underset{\boldsymbol{u}_t}{\operatorname{argmin}} \ Q_{convex}(\boldsymbol{u}_t, \boldsymbol{x}_t;\ \boldsymbol{\theta}) \\ \qquad \boldsymbol{u}_t \in \mathbb{U} \subseteq \mathbb{R}^{n_u} \end{cases} \tag{3}$$

where subscript t denotes the current timestep, $\boldsymbol{x}$ and $\boldsymbol{u}$ are state and control action at t and $\mathbb{U} \subseteq \mathbb{R}^{n_u}$ defines the constraints on controls.

Table 1. Convex basis functions

Function type	Expression	Domain
Affine	$f_1(\boldsymbol{x}) = \boldsymbol{a}^T\boldsymbol{x} + b$	$\boldsymbol{x} \in \mathbb{R}^{n_x},\ \boldsymbol{a} \in \mathbb{R}^{n_x}, b \in \mathbb{R}$
Exponential	$f_2(\boldsymbol{x}) = e^{\boldsymbol{a}^T\boldsymbol{x}+b}$	$\boldsymbol{x} \in \mathbb{R}^{n_x},\ \boldsymbol{a} \in \mathbb{R}^{n_x}, b \in \mathbb{R}$
Powers	$f_3(x_i) = x_i^{\alpha_i}$	$\alpha_i \geq 1,\ x_i \in \mathbb{R}_+, \quad i = 1, \dots, n_x$
Negative entropy	$f_4(x_i) = x_i \log x_i$	$x_i \in \mathbb{R}_+, \quad i = 1, \dots, n_x$
Negative logarithms	$f_5(x_i) = -\log x_i$	$x_i \in \mathbb{R}_+, \quad i = 1, \dots, n_x$
P-norm	$f_6(\boldsymbol{x}) = \lVert\boldsymbol{x}\rVert_p$	$\boldsymbol{x} \in \mathbb{R}^{n_x}$
Quadratic over linear	$f_7(x_i, y_i) = \dfrac{x_i^2}{y_i}$	$x_i, y_i \in \mathbb{R}_+, \quad i = 1, \dots, n_x$

Notes on implementation

The algorithm implementation can be found in Algorithm 1. We distinguish between pre-training (steps 1-3) and main training (steps 4-11). In pre-training, the Q-function approximation is fitted off-line using numerical simulations. This pre-fitted Q-function can then be leveraged on-line during main training to improve data collection. Our

---

Algorithm 1: Q-Learning through convex programming

Input: Environment simulation and reward function, number of pre-training iterations M, number of epochs N, Number of time steps per epoch n_T,Final time T_f, Batch size s_B, Initial conditions for optimal control $\mathbf{x}_{init}$

Initialise: Replay buffer $\mathcal{B}$ of size s_B

Pre-training:

1 Generate explorative samples using randomized control trajectories

2 Record generated states $\mathbf{x}_t$, controls $\mathbf{u}_t$, and Q-values in $\mathcal{B}$ as $\mathcal{B} = [X, \mathbf{y}]$ where: $X = [[\mathbf{x}_0, \mathbf{u}_0]_0, \dots, [\mathbf{x}_{T_f}, \mathbf{u}_{T_f}]_0, \dots, [\mathbf{x}_0, \mathbf{u}_0]_N, \dots, [\mathbf{x}_{T_f}, \mathbf{u}_{T_f}]_N]$ and $\mathbf{y} = [Q_{0,0}, \dots, Q_{t_f,0}, \dots, Q_{0,N}, \dots, Q_{t_f,N}]$

3 Find parameters θ that minimize $Q_{convex}(\cdot)$ in Eq. 5 using all entries j of X and y

Main training:

4 **for** *training iteration* $i = 1, \dots, M$ **do**

5   Initialise: $\mathbf{x} = \mathbf{x}_{init}$

6   **for** $j = 1, \dots, n_T$ **do**

7   Find $\mathbf{u}_{t_{j-1}}$ by minimising $Q_{convex}(\mathbf{u}; \mathbf{x}_{j-1}, \theta)$ using Eq. (3)

8   Sample the next state $\mathbf{x}_{t_j}$ by implementing control $\mathbf{u}_{t_{j-1}}$ in $\mathbf{x}_{t_{j-1}}$

9   Add $X_{new} = [[\mathbf{x}_{t_0}, \mathbf{u}_{t_0}], \dots, [\mathbf{x}_{n_T}, \mathbf{u}_{n_T}]]$ to X, and all associated Q-values in $\mathbf{y}_{new} = [Q_{t_0}, \dots, Q_{t_{n_T}}]$ to Y

10   Update $\mathcal{B}$ as $\mathcal{B} = [X, \mathbf{y}]$

11   Update optimal parameters θ by repeating step 3

---

approach essentially follows the typical RL pipeline, but rather than using DQNs for the Q-function approximation, we use convex surrogates that can be trained efficiently on fixed points using semidefinite programming, meaning that the controls identified are globally optimal given the learning approximation.

3. Results and Discussion

The selected case study in this paper simulates the photo-production of phycocyanin synthesised by *Arthrosporic platensis* which is a highly sought-after bioproduct. The dynamic system is assumed to take place in a semi-batch fixed volume fed-batch reactor and is set up in accordance with E.A. del Rio-Chanona et al. (2015). The two dependant states C_x and C_N represent *Arthrosporic platensis*'s biomass concentration in g.L^{-1} and nitrate concentration within the batch in mg.L^{-1}. In order to control the process, light intensity I in µmol.m^{-2}.s^{-1} and nitrate inflow rate F_N in mg.L^{-1}.h^{-1} can be manipulated within their hard path constraints described by the continuous intervals $I \in [0, 300]$ and $F_N \in [0,7]$. To best reflect the process' economic viability, the objective function maximizes the biomass product while minimizing waste product nitrate concentration. It also considers initial conditions and the overall cost in form of controls expended:

$$R_{t_f} = -100 * \left(C_{X_{t_f}} - C_{X0}\right) + \left(C_{N_{t_f}} - C_{N0}\right) + \sum_{t=0}^{T_f} ||\boldsymbol{u}_t||_{U_{max}}^2 \quad (4)$$

$$with\ \boldsymbol{u}_t = [I_t, F_{N_t}]^T and\ U_{max} = \begin{bmatrix} F_{N_{max}}{}^{-2} & 0 \\ 0 & I_{max}{}^{-2} \end{bmatrix}$$

It is found that the most accurate predictions are given by the convex Q-function approximation as presented in Eq. (5).

$$\begin{aligned} Q_{convex}(\boldsymbol{u}_t, \boldsymbol{x}_t, \boldsymbol{\theta}) \\ = \boldsymbol{x}_t{}^T P \boldsymbol{x}_t + \boldsymbol{u}_t{}^T \mathrm{W} \boldsymbol{u}_t + \boldsymbol{x}_t{}^T R \boldsymbol{u}_t - \boldsymbol{x}_t{}^T S \log(\boldsymbol{u}_t + 1) \\ - \boldsymbol{u}_t{}^T T \log(\boldsymbol{x}_t + 1) + \boldsymbol{q} \boldsymbol{x}_t + \boldsymbol{s}\, \boldsymbol{u}_t - r \end{aligned} \quad (5)$$

where $\boldsymbol{x}_t \in \mathbb{R}^{3x1}, \mathbf{u_t} \in \mathbb{R}^{2x1}$, $\mathrm{P} \in \mathbb{R}^{3x3}$, $\mathrm{W} \in \mathbb{R}^{2x2}$, $\mathrm{R} \in \mathbb{R}^{3x2}$, $\mathrm{S} \in \mathbb{R}^{3x2}$, $\mathrm{T} \in \mathbb{R}^{2x3}$, $\mathrm{q} \in \mathbb{R}^{1x3}$, $\mathrm{r} \in \mathbb{R}$, $\mathrm{s} \in \mathbb{R}^{1x2}$, $\boldsymbol{\theta} = [P, Q, R, S, T, \boldsymbol{q}, \boldsymbol{s}, r]$.

The established Q-function approximation is next optimized to determine the optimal control profile resulting in maximum cumulative reward. The progress of convex optimization is tracked and can be seen converging after 80 iterations to a stable maximum of -173.6 with a standard deviation of 14.8 upon convergence as depicted in Figure 1a. The cumulative reward generated by the last training iteration is benchmarked against gPROMS' and Pyomo's optimization of the same case study, which, in both cases, yields -175.17. The slight difference of 0.91 % in cumulative cost (Figure 1a) might be attributable to differences in numerical solvers or rounding errors.

Lastly, the decrease in computational time by substituting the DQN utilized by Pan et al. (2020) with a convex Q-function is evaluated. Figure 1b tracks the computational time required to train the Q-function approximator versus the number of iterations. It must be noted that the DQN-based algorithm's computational time is cleared of the additional time that its explorative steps necessitate to ease plotting and comparing results. Consequently, Figure 1b depicts an underestimation of the DQN-based Q-learning's computational time. Still, it can be observed that our proposed algorithm consistently outperforms the DQN-based algorithm by a factor of around 3.6 with respect to time. When considering explorative behaviour, total computational time of the DQN-based Q-learning takes 1680 seconds over the course of conducting 100 training iterations. In comparison, convex Q-learning only requires 415.53 seconds for the same amount of training, reducing computational time by 75.3%.

Our results suggest that convex function approximations can estimate Q-functions of highly nonlinear bioprocesses over continuous action spaces at similar solution quality to conventional dynamic optimization while requiring less computing power than DQN-based Q-learning.

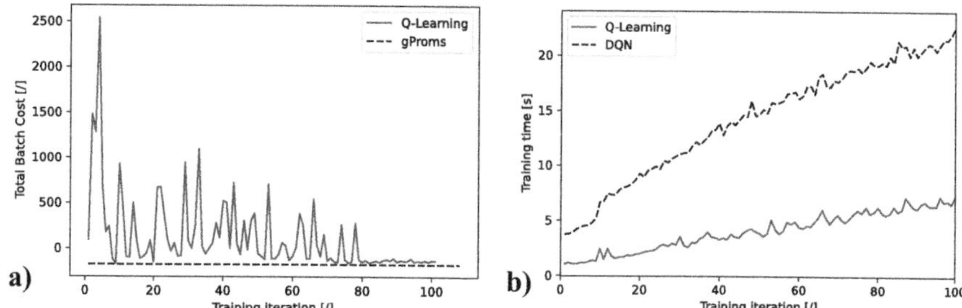

Figure 1. a) Training plot. Convergence to optimum of cumulative cost over training iterations. b) Training time. Computational time of convex Q-learning vs. DQN based Q-learning over training iteration

4. Conclusion and Future Work

In this work, an algorithm that utilizes convex function approximation for the Q-function in Q-learning is designed. Its generated results when applied to the photo-production of phycocyanin demonstrate high performance in precisely and efficiently approximating the Q-function as well as finding an optimal control policy even in a highly nonlinear environment with a continuous action space. Special focus is put on the algorithm's overall efficiency as it is benchmarked against a Q-learning algorithm using deep Q-networks optimized by evolutionary algorithms. This efficiency stems from utilizing convex functions as Q-function approximators which can be fitted efficiently on the whole replay buffer by using semidefinite programming.

In future work, the algorithm could be further improved by automating the finding of the convex Q-function approximation. Secondly, state constraints could be added to the model to better ensure process safety and demonstrate Q-learning's ability to learn uncertain systems as demonstrated by Pan et al. (2020). Thirdly, this algorithm could be implemented to conduct bi-level optimization to couple design and control problems or to couple scheduling and control problems as demonstrated by Sachio et al. (2021).

References

E. A. del Rio-Chanona, P. Dechatiwongse, D. Zhang, G. C. Maitland, K. Hellgardt, H. Arellano-Garcia, and V. S. Vassiliadis, 2015, Optimal Operation Strategy for Biohydrogen Production, Industrial & Engineering Chemistry Research, 52, 24, 6334-6343.

E.A. del Rio-Chanona, D. Zhang, V. S. Vassiliadis, 2016, Model-based real-time optimisation of a fed-batch cyanobacterial hydrogen production process using economic model predictive control strategy, Chemical Engineering Science, 142, 289-298, https://doi.org/10.1016/j.ces.2015.11.043

E.A. del Rio-Chanona, P. Dechatiwongse, D. Zhang, G. C. Maitland, K. Hellgardt, H. Arellano-Garcia, V. S. Vassiliadis, 2015, Optimal Operation Strategy for Biohydrogen Production, Industrial&Engineering Chemistry Research, 6334

H. Dong, Z. Ding, S. Zhang, 2020, Deep reinforcement learning : fundamentals, research and applications, Springer Singapore.

M. Mowbray, T. Savage, C. Wu, Z. Song, B. Anye Cho, E. A. Del Rio-Chanona, D. Zhang, 2021, Machine learning for biochemical engineering: A review, Biochemical Engineering Journal, 172, 108054.

E. Pan, P. Petsagkourakis, M. Mowbray, D. Zhang, E. A. del Rio-Chanona, 2020, Constrained Model-Free Reinforcement Learning for Process Optimization, Computers & Chemical Engineering, 154, 107462.

P. Petsagkourakis, I.O. Sandoval, E. Bradford, D. Zhang, E.A. del Rio-Chanona, 2020, Reinforcement learning for batch bioprocess optimization, Computers & Chemical Engineering, 133, 106649.

P. Petsagkourakis, I.O. Sandoval, E. Bradford, D. Zhang, E.A. del Rio-Chanona, 2020a, Constrained Reinforcement Learning for Dynamic Optimization under Uncertainty, IFAC-PapersOnLine 53 (2), 11264–11270.

S. Huh, I, Yang, 2020, Safe reinforcement learning for probabilistic reachability and safety specifications: A Lyapunov-based approach, arXiv preprint arXiv:2002.10126

J. Choi, F. Castañeda, C. J. Tomlin, K. Sreenath, 2020, Reinforcement Learning for Safety-Critical Control under Model Uncertainty, using Control Lyapunov Functions and Control Barrier Functions, arXiv preprint arXiv: 2004.07584

S. Diamond and S. Boyd, 2016, A python-embedded modeling language for convex optimization, Journal of Machine Learning Research, 17 (83)

S. Sachio, M. Mowbray, M. Papathanasiou, E. A. del Rio-Chanona, P. Petsagkourakis, 2021, Integrating process design and control using reinforcement learning, Submitted to Elsevier and available online at https://arxiv.org/pdf/2108.05242.pdf (accessed 9/26/2021).

V. Singh, H. Kodamana, 2020, Reinforcement learning based control of batch polymerisation processes, IFAC-PapersOnLine, 53, 1, 667-672.

L. Vandenberghe, S. Boyd, 1996, Semidefinite Programming, SIAM Review, 38(1), 49-95

J. Zhang, J. Kim, B. O'Donoghue, S. Boyd, 2020, Sample efficient reinforcement learning with REINFORCE. arXiv preprint arXiv:2010.11364.

Proceedings of the 14th International Symposium on Process Systems Engineering – PSE 2021+
June 19–23, 2022, Kyoto, Japan
http://dx.doi.org/10.1016/B978-0-323-85159-6.50057-9

Differential Dynamic Programming Approach for Parameter Dependent System Control

Hyein JUNG[a], Jong Woo KIM[b], Jong Min LEE[a*]

[a]*School of Chemical and Biological Engineering, Seoul National University, 1, Gwanak-ro, Gwanak-gu, Seoul 08826, Republic of Korea.*
[b]*Technische Universität Berlin, Chair of Bioprocess Engineering, Straße des 17. Juni 135, 10623 Berlin, Germany*

[*]*jongmin@snu.ac.kr*

Abstract

This paper gives a differential dynamic programming (DDP) method for parameter-dependent system control. Parameter dependent system appears in the chemical and biological process engineering field, due to variable feed conditions, plant deterioration, etc. Model predictive control (MPC) has been applied to it in various forms, but its high online computation requirement makes practical application unrealistic. In contrast, DDP approach offers a simple state feedback control policy by approximating the value function based on the assumption of quadratic system dynamics and objectives. To handle parameter-dependent system without online re-calculation of the value function and control policy, parameter-dependent DDP (PDDP) method is proposed. PDDP method utilizes hyper-state, state and parameter augmented vector, and least square (LS) parameter estimator. Hyper-state enables PDDP method to retain the benefits of DDP method while incorporating parameter sensitivity information within its dynamics. The method was applied to a simple discrete-time linear system and outperformed its DDP counterpart.

Keywords: Process dynamic control, Adaptive control, Optimal control, Differential dynamic programming

1. Introduction

There has been great interest and challenge to control the systems with unknown parameters in chemical and biological process engineering. Common sources of parameter change include inaccurate estimates of model parameters and unknown aspect of the model itself - for example, variable feed condition or plant deterioration. Both data-driven models and first principle models require corrections using online data to resolve model plant mismatch. The problem of model plant mismatch becomes severe if a model structure is used more explicitly. This raised a need for an adaptive control method by [Anderson, 1985].

As a remedy, many researchers proposed model predictive control (MPC) approaches, as well-reviewed by [Heirung et al., 2018]. With MPC, parameter estimates can be easily applied after exploration, due to its recursive optimization structure. However, this suffers from a high online computation load when parameter uncertainty is taken into account.

Another approach is approximate dynamic programming (ADP). Its root is in dynamic programming (DP) which is an optimization methodology based on Bellman's principle of optimality. It solves a multi-step decision-making problem by breaking it down into a one-step problem and encoding the information in a "reward-to-go" function, as known as value function. The resulting optimal control action is in state-feedback format, which is easy and fast to implement online. However, its offline computation burden suffers from "the curse of dimensionality," because of its backward sweep process.

ADP solves the bottleneck with value function approximation. Within a limited range of the state space, the original optimal control problem is approximated with a known function structure. However, in contrast to the MPC approach, the pre-computed optimal policy of ADP is useless when parameter changes. Accordingly, the offline computation should be implemented whenever there is a parameter change. Therefore, it is an important issue that how to implement the newly changed parameter value in the model when it comes to the ADP approach.

One solution is k-nearest neighbor (kNN) approximator [Lee and Lee, 2009]. This approach has proven its performance when applied to a batch bio-reactor [Byun et al., 2020]. The kNN approximation requires the Monte-Carlo search to approximate the value function. It can cover a wide range of parameter space, compensating its offline computation cost of the Monte-Carlo search.

One solution is using quadratic programming (QP), referred to as differential dynamic programming (DDP) method [Kobilarov et al., 2015]. DDP uses first and second-order derivative information of system dynamics and objective function to construct an approximate problem based on the Taylor expansion. This unconstrained QP problem has an analytical closed-form solution, which is state feedback. In this extension, the parameter-dependent differential dynamic programming (PDDP) method adopted hyper-state which is an augmented state of system state and parameter.

This concept has been proposed for robotic system control, where the unknown parameters are assumed to follow the Gaussian process [Kobilarov et al., 2015]. It provides the optimal control concerning the estimated parameter without online re-computation. This paper expands the application of PDDP to the step-change in parameter values with an online estimation of the least-squares (LS) method. Numerical simulation of the method is implemented in a parameter-dependent system of 2 by 2 linear system.

2. Background

2.1. Problem Formulation

The optimal control problem concerning parameter-dependency is formulated as below:

$$\begin{aligned} \min_{u_{[0:N-1]}} \quad & J = \sum_{k=0}^{N-1} (\|x_k - x_{ref,k}\|_Q^2 + \|u_k\|_R^2) + \|x_N - x_{ref,N}\|_{Q_f}^2 \\ \text{s.t.} \quad & x_{k+1} = f(x_k, u_k, p), \; y_k = h(x_k, p) + v_k, \; v_k \sim \Sigma_v \end{aligned} \tag{1}$$

Throughout this paper, x_k and u_k denote state and input respectively at time step k. A parameter, p, is also a variable, but it is assumed as an unknown constant for a finite time horizon, because its dynamical behavior is much slower than that of the state. The operator $\|\cdot\|_X^2$ stands for the square of the ℓ_2-norm with a weight matrix X, i.e. $\|a\|_X^2 = a^T Xa$. In PDDP method, a parameter variable is incorporated into a hyper-state, augmented with a state variable, z.

2.2. *Differential Dynamic Programming*

The DDP approximates nonlinear dynamics into a quadratic equation based on the Taylor expansion to utilize a quadratic programming structure. As the method only requires the local relationship between state, control input, and parameter, the second-order Hessian terms can be neglected in practice.

$$\delta x_{k+1} = f_{x,k}\delta x_k + f_{u,k}\delta u_k, \quad \delta y_k \quad = h_{x,k}\delta x_k \tag{2}$$

In the above equation, $f_{x,k}, f_{u,k}$, and $h_{x,k}$ refer to Jacobian matrices of the function $f(x_k, u_k, p_k)$ and $h(x_k, p_k)$ with regard to the subscript variables at their nominal values, $\bar{x}_k$ and $\bar{u}_k$, respectively, and $\delta x_k = x_k - \bar{x}_k$.

The control cost function, J, to be minimized is separated into two terms as a stage-wise cost, $l(x_k, u_k)$, and a terminal cost, $l_f(x_N)$. Based on this control cost function, a value function is defined as an expected sum of cost values beginning from the present time step given the state information:

$$V_k(x_k) = \min_{u_k, \ldots u_{N-1}} \sum_{i=k}^{N-1} l(x_i, u_i) + l_f(x_N). \tag{3}$$

Eq. (3) can be obtained recursively based on the Bellman optimality relation.

$$V_k(x_k) = \min_{u_k}[l(x_k, u_k) + V_{k+1}(f(x_k, u_k))] \tag{4}$$

To use deviation variables, let's set the deviation of Eq.(4) as $Q(\delta x, \delta u)$:

$$Q(\delta x, \delta u) = l(\bar{x} + \delta x, \bar{u} + \delta u) + V'(f(\bar{x} + \delta x, \bar{u} + \delta u)) - l(\bar{x}, \bar{u}) - V'(f(\bar{x}, \bar{u})), \tag{5}$$

where a subscript k is dropped to simplify a notation and $V' = V_{k+1}$. This notation applies to the equations appearing from now on. As the cost function can be exactly formulated as a quadratic form, the value function and Q function are also quadratic.

$$Q(\delta x, \delta u) = \frac{1}{2} \begin{pmatrix} 1 \\ \delta x \\ \delta u \end{pmatrix}^T \begin{bmatrix} \bar{Q} & Q_x^T & Q_u^T \\ Q_x & Q_{xx} & Q_{xu} \\ Q_u & Q_{ux} & Q_{uu} \end{bmatrix} \begin{pmatrix} 1 \\ \delta x \\ \delta u \end{pmatrix} \tag{6}$$

Now, the coefficients in Eq. (6) is recursively obtained through Eq. (5).

$$\begin{aligned} Q_x &= l_x + f_x^T V'_x, & Q_u &= l_u + f_u^T V'_x, & Q_{ux} &= l_{ux} + f_u^T V'_{xx} f_x \\ Q_{xx} &= l_{xx} + f_x^T V'_{xx} f_x, & Q_{uu} &= l_u + f_u^T V'_{xx} f_u \end{aligned} \tag{7}$$

As a result, the optimal control input is analytically given as a minimizer of Q-function and can be expressed as below.

$$u^* = \bar{u} - Q_{uu}^{-1}(Q_u + Q_{ux}\delta x) \tag{8}$$

3. Methodology

3.1. Least Squares Parameter Estimation

Before implementing parameter-dependent control, a parameter estimation is required. In this paper, parameter estimation is formulated as a LS parameter estimation [Englezos and Kalogerakis, 2000].

$$\begin{aligned}\min_{\hat{p}} J &= \sum_{i=0}^{k} \|v_i\|_{Q_v}^2 + \|\hat{p} - p_0\|_{Q_p}^2 \\ \text{s.t. } \hat{x}_{i+1} &= f(\hat{x}_i, u, \hat{p}), \quad i = 1, ..., k \\ \hat{y}_i &= h(\hat{x}_i, \hat{p}) + v_i, \quad i = 0, ..., k\end{aligned} \tag{9}$$

where the sequence of y_i and u_i is an accumulated data from the initial time ($i = 0$) to the current time ($i = k$). The variables $\hat{x}_i, \hat{y}_i$ and $\hat{p}$ are the estimated variables, when initial value of state, x_0, and parameter, p_0, is given. A weighting parameter $Q_v = \Sigma_v^{-1}$, where Σ_v is given from the system of interest. The second term in the objective function, a parameter arrival cost, gives a smoothing effect for parameter estimation.

3.2. Parameter Dependent Differential Dynamic Programming

PDDP is formulated upon the hyper-state, z, instead of the state, x, extending the DDP method.

$$\delta z_{k+1} = F_{z,k}\delta z_k + F_{u,k}\delta u_k, \quad \delta y_k = H_{z,k}\delta z_k \tag{10}$$

Here, $F_{z,k}$, $F_{u,k}$, and $H_{z,k}$ refer to Jacobian matrices of the function $F(z_k, u_k)$ and $H(z_k)$ with regard to $\bar{z}_k$ and $\bar{u}_k$, respectively. Since there is no assumption for parameter dynamics or its uncertainty, it is assumed that the parameter value stays the same as the previous value. Hence, it can be said:

$$F_{z,k} = \begin{bmatrix} f_{x,k} & f_{p,k} \\ 0 & I_p \end{bmatrix}, F_{u,k} = \begin{bmatrix} f_{u,k} \\ 0 \end{bmatrix}, \tag{11}$$

where I_p stands for an identity matrix with the dimension of parameter vectors.

Then the cost function, J, from Eq. (1) is separated into two terms, stage-wise cost, $L(z_k)$ and the terminal cost, $L_f(z_N)$.

$$L(z_k) = \|x_k - x_{ref,k}\|_Q^2 + \|u_k\|_R^2, \quad L_f(z_N) = \|x_N - x_{ref,N}\|_{Q_f}^2 \tag{12}$$

The Q function is acquired equivalently as in the DDP method, and the optimal control is given as:

$$u^* = \bar{u} - Q_{uu}^{-1}(Q_u + Q_{uz}\delta\hat{z}). \tag{13}$$

where $\hat{z}$ is an estimated hyper-state from the estimator. This optimal state feedback control policy should be iteratively trained beforehand, saving Jacobian matrices and state-feedback gains $K_{u,k} = Q_{uu}^{-1}Q_u$ and $K_{z,k} = Q_{uu}^{-1}Q_{uz}$ at nominal states according to a model. For linear time-invariant systems, however, the optimal solution can be found directly from the given dynamics.

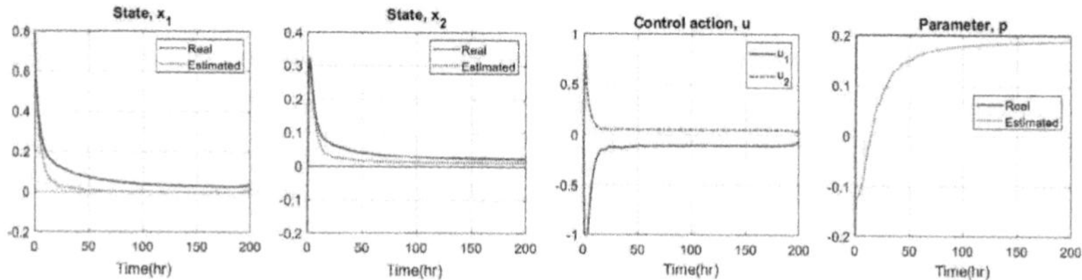

Figure 1: Linear system simulation result for PDDP with LS estimation

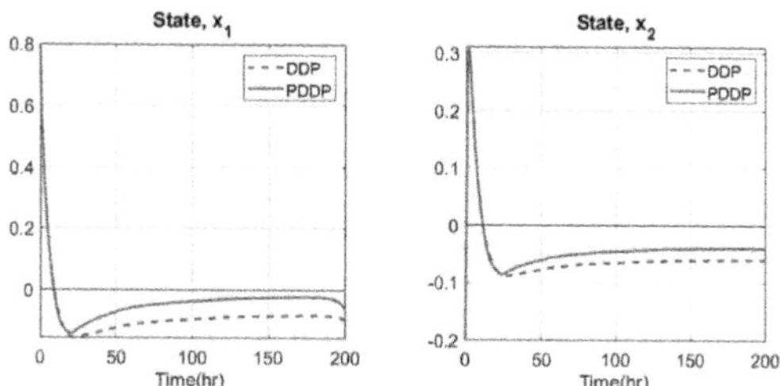

Figure 2: PDDP and DDP simulation result compared

4. Simulation Results

In this section, the efficacy of the proposed PDDP algorithm is shown with a following simple discrete time linear system:

$$\begin{aligned} x_{k+1} &= \begin{bmatrix} 0.9146 & 0.1665 \\ 0.2665 & 0.3353 \end{bmatrix} x_k + \begin{bmatrix} 0.0544 & -0.0757 \\ 0.0053 & 0.1477 \end{bmatrix} u_k + \begin{bmatrix} 0.0405 \\ 0.0058 \end{bmatrix} p_k \\ y_k &= x_k + v_k, \quad v_k \sim \begin{bmatrix} 0.01 & 0 \\ 0 & 0.01 \end{bmatrix}, \end{aligned} \tag{14}$$

where v_k is uncorrelated measurement noise. This kind of parameter deviation may occur, for example, when process inlet condition (flow rate, composition, or temperature) changes.

With the change of parameter, PDDP with LS parameter estimation was able to successfully control the system as shown in Fig. 1. Also, it was compared with its DDP counterpart which uses the same hyper-state LS estimator in Fig. 2. As a result, PDDP was able to draw the states near the desired origin, while DDP was not.

5. Conclusions

In this paper, the solution of parameter-dependent system control was considered using an adaptive dynamic programming approach. With the use of hyper-state, PDDP is derived from the common DDP approach. For its application with unknown parameters, LS parameter estimation is combined. The test on a simple linear system showed that PDDP can utilize the estimated parameter information through a state feedback format with nearly zero computation burden online. The works presented in this paper can be extended to nonlinear process by linearizing the process dynamics. Also, application combined with any other popular estimation methods such as Kalman filter is left as future work, which will guarantee the control performance even with unknown or unmeasurable disturbances.

ACKNOWLEDGEMENT

This paper was supported by Korea Institute for Advancement of Technology(KIAT) grant funded by the Korea Government (MOTIE) (P0008475, The Competency Development Program for Industry Specialist).

References

[Anderson, 1985] Anderson, B. D. (1985). Adaptive systems, lack of persistency of excitation and bursting phenomena. *Automatica*, 21(3):247–258.

[Byun et al., 2020] Byun, H.-E., Kim, B., and Lee, J. H. (2020). Robust adaptive control with active learning for fed-batch process based on approximate dynamic programming. *IFAC-PapersOnLine*, 53(2):5201–5206.

[Englezos and Kalogerakis, 2000] Englezos, P. and Kalogerakis, N. (2000). *Applied parameter estimation for chemical engineers*. CRC Press.

[Heirung et al., 2018] Heirung, T. A. N., Paulson, J. A., Lee, S., and Mesbah, A. (2018). Model predictive control with active learning under model uncertainty: Why, when, and how. *AIChE Journal*, 64(8):3071–3081.

[Kobilarov et al., 2015] Kobilarov, M., Ta, D.-N., and Dellaert, F. (2015). Differential dynamic programming for optimal estimation. In *2015 IEEE International Conference on Robotics and Automation (ICRA)*, pages 863–869. IEEE.

[Lee and Lee, 2009] Lee, J. M. and Lee, J. H. (2009). An approximate dynamic programming based approach to dual adaptive control. *Journal of process control*, 19(5):859–864.

Proceedings of the 14th International Symposium on Process Systems Engineering – PSE 2021+
June 19-23, 2022, Kyoto, Japan
http://dx.doi.org/10.1016/B978-0-323-85159-6.50058-0

Optimization of an air-cooler operation in an industrial distillation column

Masaharu Daiguji[a,b*] and Yoshiyuki Yamashita[b]

[a]*ENEOS Corporation, Otemachi 1-1-2, Chiyoda-ku, Tokyo 100-8162, Japan*
[b]*Department of Chemical Engineering, Tokyo University of Agriculture and Technology, Naka-cho 2-24-16, Koganei, Tokyo 184-8588, Japan*
daiguji.masaharu@eneos.com

Abstract

In the process industry, air coolers are some of the main cooling equipment. The air cooler of the atmospheric distillation column has fixed and variable fans, and the cooling duty is controlled. When the controller output exceeds the operating limits, the number of fixed fans in operation is changed to return it within the limits. However, the power consumption of the air cooler is not minimized. Daiguji and Yamashita (2022) proposed a method for optimizing the number of fixed fans in operation to minimize the power consumption, while reducing the frequency of fixed-fan starts and stops. Unfortunately, when this optimization method is applied to an air cooler with several variable fans, multiple fixed fans start and stop simultaneously, excessively disturbing the process. This paper proposes a modified optimization method in which the fixed fans start or stop one at a time. The modified optimization method was applied to industrial process, and the results showed that the power consumption was reduced, compared to the actual operation.

Keywords: Mixed-integer non-linear optimization, air cooler, optimal operation.

1. Introduction

Refineries and petrochemical plants have many facilities for cooling process streams. However, these cooling systems typically cannot be operated at the lowest cost. Recently, several studies have been conducted on minimizing the operating cost of water-cooling systems (Rubio-Castro et al., 2013; Muller and Craig, 2015; Viljoen et al., 2018; Viljoen et al., 2020). These studies also attempted to minimize the operating costs of air coolers and showed good results with hybrid nonlinear model-predictive control (HNMPC). Zhang et al. developed a dynamic model of the cold side of the cooling system of a power-generation boiler and proposed a model-predictive control with the model-based feed-forward compensation (Zhang et al., 2019). It has been shown that the back pressure of the unit can be controlled to the desired setpoint, while suppressing the disturbance of the air temperature, by properly manipulating the rotation speed.

The atmospheric-distillation columns are equipped with air coolers to cool the column-overhead gas and pump-around liquids. Tower overhead air coolers are often configured with a combination of multiple fixed and variable-pitch fans, because the cooling duty must be changed, according to the annual change in air temperature, while suppressing the equipment cost. Some air coolers have variable-speed fans instead of variable-pitch fans. The air coolers are not only disturbed by air temperature changes, but also by process-side disturbances. To suppress these disturbances, variable-pitch fans usually control the process outlet temperature or column-top pressure. When the controller output exceeds the variable-pitch operating range, it is necessary to start or stop the fixed fan to return to the operating range. This causes problems.

One problem is that the power consumption of the fans is not minimized. Conventionally, a fixed fan is started or stopped, only when the controller output exceeds the operating range. At that time, the fact that it is designed to return to the operating range means that there is a choice in the number of fixed fans in operation required to obtain any given cooling duty. Therefore, it is possible to change the number of operating fixed fans to minimize the power consumption. However, frequently starting and stopping a fixed fan should be avoided because it causes the cooling duty to fluctuate and loads the process. Minimizing the power consumption of the fans, while considering the frequent starts and stops, is a challenge.

Daiguji and Yamashita (2022) attempted to stabilize the control and minimize the power consumption of an existing air cooler of a distillation column, without process changes. To optimize the number of fixed fans in operation, the paper proposed a method for minimizing power consumption while reducing the number of fixed-fan operation changes, and described the results of applying the proposed method to simulation data.

However, when the above optimization method is applied to an air cooler with several variable fans, which is often seen in industrial processes, another problem was found, where multiple fixed fans started or stopped simultaneously. In this paper, we propose a modified optimization method in which the fixed fans start or stop one at a time (Section 2). Then, the modified optimization method is applied to industrial data, and the results are compared with actual operation and other methods (Section 3). Finally, the conclusions are presented in Section 4.

2. Method for optimizing the number of fixed fans in operation

Daiguji and Yamashita (2022) described the results of a basic study on optimizing the number of fixed fans in operation to minimize the power consumption, while changing the number of fans less frequently under equal air-flow rates. Their study investigated a method for an air cooler with two fixed fans and two variable fans; however, this paper describes a method that can be applied to an air cooler with more variable fans.

2.1. Fans power consumption

According to the proportional law of basic fan characteristics, the relationship between the fan speed ω and power consumption W is as follows:

$$\frac{W_2}{W_1} = \left(\frac{\omega_2}{\omega_1}\right)^3. \tag{1}$$

Therefore, the power consumption W of the air cooler is given by

$$W = L_1 N \omega^3 + L_2 m, \tag{2}$$

where N is the number of variable-speed fans, m is the number of operating fixed fans, ω is the speed of a variable-speed fan, L_1 is the power-consumption coefficient of the variable-speed fan, and L_2 is the power consumption of the fixed fan. The above study is based on the assumption of a variable-speed fan; however, even in the case of a variable-pitch fan, the power consumption increases at an accelerating rate when the air-flow rate is increased (Johnson, 1988). Therefore, the same explanation can apply.

2.2. Optimizing the number of fixed fans in operation

As described in Section 1, variable fans are typically used to control the process outlet temperature or the column-top pressure. If this control consists of a conventional single-loop PID controller, it fluctuates significantly when the fixed fan starts or stops. In addition, Sen (2012) states that induction motors draw three to eight times their rated value during startup. This means that starting a fixed fan increases the power consumption. Therefore, it is necessary to consider a method to reduce the frequency of changing the number of fixed fans. The following penalty function is defined, using the elapsed time t_a after the change in the number of fans as a variable:

$$\mathrm{f}(t_a) = \begin{cases} 1/t_a & \text{if changing the number of fixed fans.} \\ 0 & \text{if not changing the number of fixed fans.} \end{cases} \tag{3}$$

By multiplying this penalty function by the weight λ and adding it to Eq. (2), the following evaluation equation J is obtained:

$$J = L_1 N \omega^3 + L_2 m + \lambda \cdot \mathrm{f}(t_a). \tag{4}$$

Minimizing the value of this evaluation equation J minimizes the power consumption. Moreover, if the number of fixed fans is repeatedly changed in a short period of time, the penalty function becomes large, which reduces the frequency of the changes. Even if the number of fixed fans changes, the cooling duty must remain constant. Assuming that the independent variables, other than the number of fans (e.g., air-inlet temperature), do not change, the cooling duty can be considered to be constant when the air-flow rate Q is constant. Therefore, the following constraint conditions are obtained:

$$Q = K_1 N \omega + K_2 m = \text{const.}, \tag{5}$$

where K_1 is the air-flow coefficient of the variable fan and K_2 is the air-flow rate of the fixed fan. Another constraint is that the speed of the variable fan ω must be within the allowable upper and lower limits, which is expressed by the following equation:

$$\omega_{\min} \leq \frac{1}{K_1 N}(Q - K_2 m) \leq \omega_{\max}. \tag{6}$$

Furthermore, in the case of air coolers with several variable fans, which are often used in industrial processes, the number of fixed fans with minimum power consumption easily changes for disturbances of the same magnitude. Therefore, it is necessary to add the following constraint condition so that the fixed fans start and stop one by one:

$$\max(0, m_{old} - 1) \leq m \leq \min(M, m_{old} + 1), \tag{7}$$

where m_{old} is the number of fixed fans in operation before optimization, and M is the number of fixed-fan facilities. Under the constraints in Eqs. (5), (6), and (7), a modified optimization method is proposed to find the number of fixed fans in operation that minimizes the result of Eq. (4).

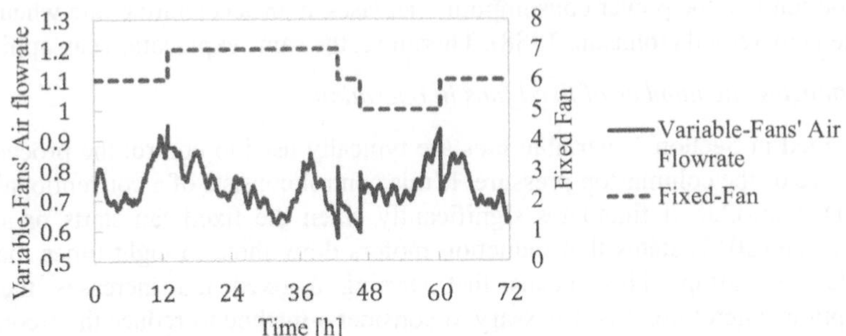

Fig.1 Time-series data of the air-flow rate of the variable fans and the number of fixed fans in operation, collected from an industrial plant.

3. Application example using operation data from the process industry

In this section, we describe the results of applying the proposed method to industrial process data, and confirm its effectiveness by comparing it with actual operations.

3.1. Identification of air-flow rate and power-consumption equations

The example air cooler has eight fixed fans and eight variable-pitch fans. The fans' equipment specifications state that the column-top pressure is controlled in the range of 57.4–95.2% of the variable-fan air-flow capacity. The following equation for the air-flow rate Q of the air cooler and the air-flow ratio q of the variable fan was obtained:

$$Q \propto 8q + m, 0.574 \leq q \leq 0.952, m \in \mathbb{Z}, 0 \leq m \leq 8. \quad (8)$$

Next, the following equation for the relationship between the power consumption W and the air-flow capacity ratio q of the variable fan was obtained:

$$W \propto 8(8.15q^3 + 18.3q) + 26.45m. \quad (9)$$

3.2. Industrial-data collection

Five-second cycle operation data were collected for three days from the output of the column-top pressure controller and the ON/OFF status of each fan. Based on these historical data and the number of fixed fans in operation, Eq. (8) was used to obtain the air-flow rate data of the variable fans (Fig. 1).

3.3. Application of conventional method

Figure 2(a) shows the results of applying the conventional method to industrial data. In the conventional method, when the air-flow rate of the variable fans reaches the lower or upper limit, the number of fixed fans is changed, such that it returns within the range. The results showed that the number of fixed fans changed four times in three days, which is the same as the actual operation. Regarding the average power consumption, the difference from the actual operation was less than 0.01%.

3.4. Application of proposed method

The optimization method proposed in Section 2 was coded in the MATLAB® environment using the genetic-algorithm function of the Global Optimization Toolbox

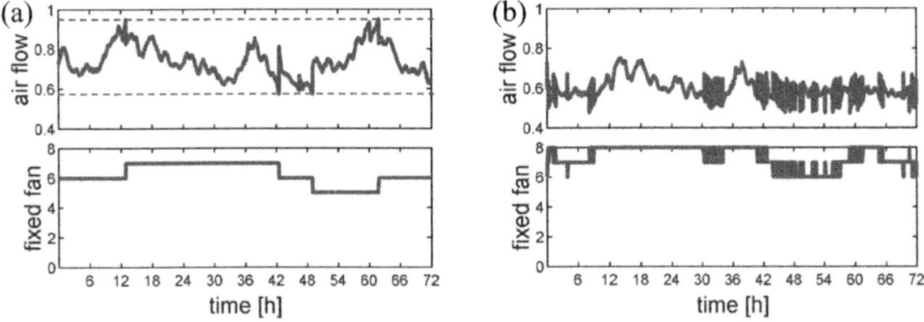

Fig.2 (a) Control response for the minimizing the frequency of changing the number of fixed fans (conventional method). (b) Control response of the optimization without the penalty (power-consumption minimization).

(Deep et al., 2009). Figure 2(b) shows the results of applying the proposed method, without a penalty, to industrial data. Optimization without penalty results in the minimum power-consumption solution. The results showed that the air-flow rate of the variable fans operated to stay in the range of 47–75%, and the power consumption was reduced by 1.3%, on average, compared to the conventional method. However, the number of fixed fans changed 166 times in three days.

Figure 3(a) shows the results of applying the proposed method with a penalty to the industrial data. By considering the elapsed time after starting or stopping a fixed fan, it was found that the air-flow rate of the variable fan was extended over a range of 38–81% and the reduction in power consumption was 1.1%. In contrast, the change in the number of fixed fans was reduced to 4, and the fixed fans no longer started and stopped continuously within a short period of time. However, it was found that two fixed fans started and stopped simultaneously, causing excessive disturbances to the process.

Figure 3(b) shows the results of applying the modified proposed method—which limits the number of simultaneous fixed-fan starts and stops to one—to industrial data. By considering the number of simultaneous starts and stops, the air-flow rate of the variable fan was further extended to the range of 38–88%, and the reduction in power consumption was 0.9%. On the other hand, the change in the number of fixed fans was maintained at four times, with one fan per change.

4. Conclusions

In this paper, a modified method for minimizing the power consumption of controlled

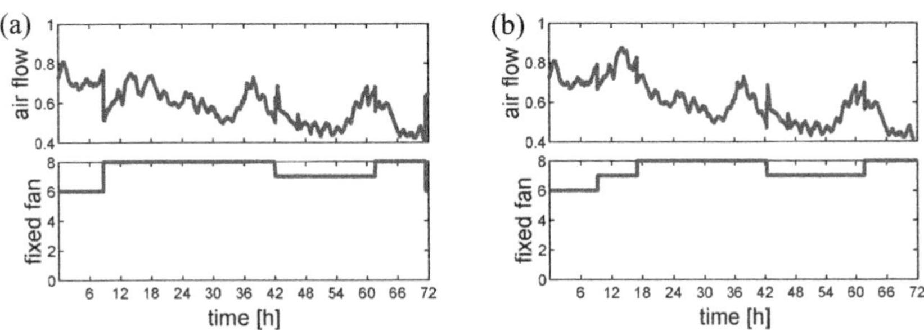

Fig.3 Control response of the optimization with a penalty, (a) Original method. (b) Limiting the number of simultaneous fixed-fan starts and stops to one (proposed method).

Table 1. Comparison of controller performances

	Max. number of simultaneous fixed-fan starts or stops	Power-consumption reduction ratio [%]	Number of fixed-fan starts or stops
Actual data	1	-	4
Conventional method	1	0.0	4
Proposed method (modified)	1	0.9	4
Proposed method (original)	2	1.1	4
Power-consumption minimization	1	1.3	166

air coolers was proposed. When the using the method to minimize power consumption, while reducing the frequency of changing the number of fixed fans, it is possible to start and stop multiple fixed fans simultaneously. Therefore, a modified method was proposed that limited the number of simultaneous fixed-fans changes to one.

Next, the proposed method was applied to industrial data, and the actual operation was compared with the method that minimized the frequency of changing the number of fans (conventional method), the power-consumption minimization method, and the proposed method (Table 1). The results showed that the proposed method reduced the power consumption by approximately 1%, compared to the actual operation, although it was slightly inferior to the power-consumption minimization method. However, the number of fixed-fan starts or stops was approximately 40 times greater in the power-consumption minimization method than in the actual operation. It was the same in the proposed method as in the actual operation, with a minimum of four times. Furthermore, the fixed fans started or stopped one at a time using the modified proposed method.

References

C. J. Muller and I. K. Craig, 2015, Modelling of a dual circuit induced draft cooling water system for control and optimization purposes, Journal of Process Control, 25, 105-114

C. M. Johnson, 1988, Comparison of variable pitch fans and variable speed fans in a variable air volume system, *Building Serv. Eng. Res. Technol*, 9, 89-98

E. Rubio-Castro and J. M. Ponce-Ortega, 2013, Synthesis of cooling water systems with multiple cooling towers, *Applied Thermal Engineering*, 50, 957-974

J. H. Viljoen, C. J. Muller and I. K. Craig, 2018, Dynamic modelling of induced draft cooling towers with parallel heat exchangers, pumps and cooling water network, Journal of Process Control, 68, 34-51

J. H. Vilijoen, C. J. Muller and I. K. Craig, 2020, Hybrid nonlinear model predictive control of a cooling water network, *Control Engineering Practice*, 97 104319

K. Deep, K. P. Singh, M. L. Kansal and C. Mohan, 2009, A real coded genetic algorithm for solving integer and mixed integer optimization problems, *Applied Mathematics and Computation*, 212, 505-518

M. Daiguji and Y. Yamashita, 2022, Optimization of multiple-fan air-cooler control in a distillation column, *Kagaku Kogaku Ronbunshu*, accepted

P. C. Sen, 2012, 2012, Chapter 9 Transients and Dynamics, *Principles of Electric Machines and Power Electronics*, John Wiley and Sons, Inc., USA

Y. Zhang, F. Zhang and J. Shen, 2019, On the dynamic modeling and control of the cold-end system in a direct air-cooling generation unit, *Applied Thermal Engineering*, 151, 373-384

Proceedings of the 14th International Symposium on Process Systems Engineering – PSE 2021+
June 19-23, 2022, Kyoto, Japan
http://dx.doi.org/10.1016/B978-0-323-85159-6.50059-2

Dynamic Operability Analysis for the Calculation of Transient Output Constraints of Linear Time-Invariant Systems

San Dinh[a], Fernando V. Lima[a*]

[a]*West Virginia University, Morgantown, West Virginia, 26506, U.S.A*
**Fernando.Lima@mail.wvu.edu*

Abstract

In this work, a dynamic operability mapping is developed to find an operable funnel for a linear time-invariant dynamic system. The existing operability mapping method to find this funnel is computationally expensive, which makes it unsuitable for online control applications. A novel two-step calculation procedure is proposed, which includes an offline computation of the nominal funnel by constructing a convex hull of the manipulated variable projections, followed by an online update that adjusts the funnel to an operable region based on the current state information. As a result, a dynamic funnel that contains all achievable outputs regardless of the process disturbances and measurement noises is obtained in the form of transient output constraints for model predictive control implementation.

Keywords: Dynamic Operability, Linear Control, Output Constraints

1. Introduction

Process operability is defined as the design and control ability to achieve desired performance from the given available inputs regardless of the realization of the disturbances (Gazzaneo et al., 2020). If the operability analysis is able to be carried out along with the operation of a process, not only the achievable portions of the desired outputs are known, but also the feasible output constraints can be provided for model predictive control to guarantee feasibility (Lima and Georgakis, 2009). However, the currently available operability analysis involves an exhaustive generation of the input combinations, and thus this approach may quickly become intractable.

In this paper, the achievable output sets at all values of the disturbances are formulated as a set of time-dependent polyhedra, which is referred to as the dynamic operable funnel. To avoid confusion between control theory and process operability concepts, external output constraints are defined here as the constraints on the output variables that are given by the physical nature of a process, such as thermodynamic and equipment's safety limits. In the application to online model predictive control, the dynamic funnel provides the transient output constraints to keep the process from moving toward an inoperable region, and the online calculation must be done efficiently to assure a sufficient time for the controller to solve for an optimal path.

In particular, the dynamic operable funnel of a linear time-invariant dynamic process is proven to be defined as a polyhedron. Also, the ability of the current process to move toward its stable operating region is quickly verified following Phase I of the simplex algorithm for linear programming, and the operable region in the presence of external output constraints can be obtained via the convex hull of suitable geometric duals with respect to a feasible solution (Muller and Preparata, 1978). Therefore, the remaining challenge is constructing the dynamic operable funnel in a tractable manner. In the proposed framework, the funnel calculation is divided into two steps: the first step is computing the funnel offline before the full state information arrives; and the second step is updating the funnel online according to the full state information that becomes available. The preliminaries and concepts necessary to define the proposed approach are detailed next.

2. Dynamic Operability Problem Background

2.1. Preliminaries

Consider the following discrete-time linear time-invariant dynamic system:

$$x(k+1) = Ax(k) + Bu(k) + Gw(k);\ x(0) = x_0 \tag{1}$$

$$y(k) = Cx(k) + Du(k) + v(k) \tag{2}$$

in which $x(k) \in \mathbb{R}^{n_x}, u(k) \in \mathbb{R}^{n_u}$ *and* $y(k) \in \mathbb{R}^{n_y}$ are the vectors of state variables, input/manipulated variables and output/controlled variables, respectively; $w(k) \in \mathbb{R}^{n_w}$ and $v(k) \in \mathbb{R}^{n_v}$ are the zero-mean multivariate Gaussian distributed vectors with the respective positive definite covariance matrices, $\Sigma_w \in \mathbb{R}^{n_w \times n_w}$ and $\Sigma_v \in \mathbb{R}^{n_v \times n_v}$. The initial time $k = 0$ is defined to be the current time instead of the time in which the process begins, and the initial state variables, x_0, are assumed to be given by a state observer.

Since $w(k)$ and $v(k)$ are assumed to be zero-mean with Gaussian distributions, the states and the outputs are also multivariate Gaussian random variables with the respective means $\bar{x}(k)$ and $\bar{y}(k)$. The sequences of covariance matrices for the states, $\Sigma_x(k)$, and the outputs, $\Sigma_y(k)$, are:

$$\Sigma_x(k+1) = A\Sigma_x(k)A^T + G\Sigma_w G^T; \Sigma_x(0) = 0_{n_x \times n_x} \tag{3}$$

$$\Sigma_y(k) = C\Sigma_x(k)C^T + \Sigma_v \tag{4}$$

When a random vector $p \in \mathbb{R}^{n_p}$ is a Gaussian random vector with a mean $\bar{p}$ and a covariance matrix Σ_p, its 95% highest density region, $HDR(p)$, is the following ellipsoid with the scale l_p^2 equals to the inverse cumulative distribution function of the chi-squared distribution with n_p degrees of freedom:

$$HDR(p) = \{p | (p - \bar{p})^T \Sigma_p^{-1} (p - \bar{p}) \leq l_p^2; l_p^2 = Inv_{\chi^2}(95\%; n_p)\} \tag{5}$$

2.2. Dynamic operability sets

The Available Input Set at the discretized time k (AIS_k) is defined as the set of all feasible sequences of manipulated variables from the initial time 0 to time k.

$$AIS_k = \{u_k = [u(0)^T, u(1)^T, \dots, u(k-1)^T]^T | u_{k,min} \leq u_k \leq u_{k,max}\} \tag{6}$$

The Expected Disturbance Set (EDS_k^d) is the set of all realizations of the disturbances, d, at the time k. The two sources of disturbances assumed here are the $w(k)$ and $v(k)$, which can take any real values due to their Gaussian distributions. Their values are constrained to their respective 95% highest density regions as follows:

$$EDS_k^d = \left\{ d(k) = [w(k)\ v(k)]^T \middle| \begin{matrix} d(k)^T diag(\Sigma_w^{-1}, \Sigma_v^{-1}) d(k) \leq l_d^2 \\ l_d^2 = Inv_{\chi^2}(95\%; n_w + n_v) \end{matrix} \right\} \quad (7)$$

The Achievable Output Set at a fixed disturbance d ($AOS(d)$) is the set of all possible outputs at the discretized time k given the linear system (1), (2) and the range of manipulated variables. A necessary condition for a process to be operable is that the set of achievable outputs regardless of the realizations of the process disturbances, AOS_k, has to be nonempty. The AOS_k is defined as the intersection of all achievable output sets at fixed realizations of the disturbance:

$$AOS_k = \bigcap_{d \in EDS_k^d} AOS_k^d(d) = \left\{ y(k) \middle| \begin{matrix} (1), (2)\ are\ satisfied; \\ u_k \in AIS_k; d(k) \in EDS_k^d; \end{matrix} \right\} \quad (8)$$

3. Calculation of Transient Output Constraints

3.1. Offline computation of transient state funnel at nominal-valued disturbances

The following assumptions are considered for the offline calculation of the dynamic funnel that can be later addressed in the online update: $x_0 = 0_{n_x}$; $C = I_{n_x \times n_x}$; $D = 0_{n_x \times n_u}$; $w(i) = 0_{n_w}$; $v(i) = 0_{n_x}$ $\forall\ i \leq k$. The considered outputs are the predicted state variables before $w(k)$ and $v(k)$ are accounted for, and the AOS_k has the form:

$$AOS_k = \{x(k) | x(k) = \bar{B}_k u_k; u_k \in AIS_k\} \quad (9)$$

where $\bar{B}_k = [A^{k-1}B\ A^{k-2}B \ldots AB\ B]$. From the definition (6), the AIS_k is a bounded convex polyhedron. From the formulation of (9), $\bar{B}_k: \mathbb{R}^{k \times n_{nu}} \rightarrow \mathbb{R}^{n_x}$ is a linear transformation of the AIS_k into the AOS_k, so that the AOS_k is exactly the smallest convex hull that contains all the projections of the available input sequences on the state vector space. Additionally, for an achievable state $x(k)$ to be a vertex of the AOS_k, its preimage, u_k, must be a vertex of the AIS_k. Then the AOS_k can be computed by taking the convex hull of the $2^{k \times n_u}$ vertices of the AIS_k, which is the vector of the input sequence in which each element is either taken from the value of the lower bound $u_{k,min}$ or the upper bound $u_{k,max}$:

$$AOS_k = convexhull\left(\bar{B}u_k | u_k^T e_i \in \{u_{k,min}^T e_i, u_{k,max}^T e_i\}, \forall i \leq k \times n_u\right) \quad (10)$$

where $e_i = [0,0,\ldots,0,1,0,\ldots,0]^T \in \mathbb{R}^{k \times n_u}$ is a standard basis for which only the ith location has the value of 1. An efficient approach to find the convex hull in high-dimensional spaces is the Quickhull Algorithm (Barber et al., 1996). According to the Minkowski-Weyl's Theorem, every polyhedron is identically described by its vertex representation and its hyperplane representation, and thus the formulation of AOS_k in (10) can be equivalently converted to a set of linear constraints using the Double Description Method (Fukuda and Prodon, 1996):

$$AOS_k = \{x(k) | \bar{H}_k x(k) \leq \bar{l}_k\} \quad (11)$$

In the simplest case of the online calculation, if the process disturbances and the measurement noises are not considered, the online update of the dynamic funnel can be established by the substitution of (11) into the state-space model (1), and the dynamic funnel at the current state x_0 is simply:

$$AOS_k = \{x(k) | \bar{H}_k x(k) \leq \bar{\bar{l}}_k; \bar{\bar{l}}_k = \bar{l}_k + \bar{H}_k A^k x_0\} \quad (12)$$

3.2. Transient state funnel with process disturbances

In this subsection, the interested outputs are the state variables, and the following assumptions are considered: $C = I_{n_x \times n_x}$; $D = 0_{n_x \times n_u}$; $v(i) = 0_{n_x}, \forall\, i \leq k$. The process disturbance sequence can be redefined as the deviation, $w_x(k)$, from the mean value of the state vector, and the EDS is chosen as the HDR with respect to $x(k)$:

$$EDS_k^x = \{w_x(k) | w_x(k)^T \Sigma_x^{-1}(k) w_x(k) \leq l_x^2; l_x^2 = Inv_{\chi^2}(95\%; n_x)\} \quad (13)$$

The formulation of AOS_k in this subsection is

$$AOS_k = \bigcap_{w_x(k) \in EDS_k^x} AOS_k^w(w_x(k)) = \left\{ x(k) \middle| \begin{matrix} x(k) = A^k x_0 + \bar{B}_k u_k + w_x(k) \\ u_k \in AIS_k; w_x(k) \in EDS_k^x; \end{matrix} \right\} \quad (14)$$

Let $\Sigma_x(k) = V_x(k) S_x(k) V_x^{-1}(k)$ be the eigenvalue decomposition of the covariance matrix $\Sigma_x(k)$. Since a basic property of any covariance matrix is positive definiteness, $V_x^{-1}(k) = V_x^T(k)$ is an orthogonal matrix, and $S_x(k)$ is a diagonal matrix with positive elements. Denoting $S_x^{-0.5}(k)$ to be an inverse of the square root of $S_x(k)$, a bijective mapping $L = S_x^{-0.5}(k) V_x^T$ that transforms the state vector $\hat{x}(k) = Lx(k)$ is introduced. The covariance matrix of the transformed vector $\hat{x}(k)$ is:

$$\Sigma_{\hat{x}}(k) = L \Sigma_x(k) L^T = S_x^{-0.5}(k) V_x^T V_x(k) S_x(k) V_x^T(k) V_x(k) S_x^{-0.5}(k) = I_{n_x \times n_x} \quad (15)$$

Because the covariance $\Sigma_{\hat{x}}$ is an identity matrix, the proposed linear mapping L corresponds to a change of coordinates to transform the state vector into a standard Gaussian random vector, and the ellipsoid EDS_k^x is transformed into an n-sphere $EDS_k^{\hat{x}}$ with radius l_x. This provides an advantage when finding the intersection AOS_k of all achievable output sets for the disturbance realizations based on the following theorem:

Theorem 1: Let $[H]_i$ denote the ith row of a matrix $H: \mathbb{R}^{n_1} \rightarrow \mathbb{R}^{n_2}$. Given a bounded polyhedron in the form of $P_x = \{x \in \mathbb{R}^{n_x} | Hx \leq l\}$ and its image under a bounded translation according to an n-sphere $P_x(d) = \{\hat{x} | \hat{x} = x + d; Hx \leq l; d^T d \leq l_d^2\}$, the intersection of all $P_x(d)$ is given by:

$$P = \bigcap_{d^T d \leq l_d^2} P_x(d) = \left\{ x \middle| Hx \leq \hat{l}; [\hat{l}]_i = [l]_i - l_d \sqrt{[H]_i^T [H]_i}\ \forall\, i \leq n_2 \right\} \quad (16)$$

Proof: For each hyperplane $[H]_i x \leq [l]_i$, the hyperplane $[H]_i x \leq [l]_i - l_d \sqrt{[H]_i^T [H]_i}$ is the parallel hyperplane shifted toward the feasible half-space by a distance of l_d. Thus, a translation of all feasible points in $[H]_i x \leq [l]_i$ by a distance d can only violate $[H]_i x \leq [\hat{l}]_i$ if $d > l_d$. Therefore, $Hx \leq \hat{l}$ is the intersection of all hyperplanes $[H]_i x \leq [l]_i$ when the translation distance is less than or equal to l_d.

Note that the disturbance effects on the state vector are the same as translating the achievable output set in (12) by a translation vector in EDS_k^x, and the linear mapping L puts the AOS_k^w in the form that is applicable for Theorem 1. Finally, since L is a bijective mapping, the final form of the transient state funnel with process disturbances in the original state vector $x(k)$ is given by:

$$AOS_k = \left\{ x(k) \middle| \bar{H}_k x(k) \leq \hat{l}_k; [\hat{l}_k]_i = [\bar{l}_k + \bar{H}_k A^k x_0]_i - l_x \sqrt{[\bar{H}_k L^{-1}]_i^T [\bar{H}_k L^{-1}]_i} \right\} \quad (17)$$

3.3. Transient output funnel with process disturbances and measurement noises

The output vector can be interpreted as a projection of the state variables and the manipulated variables at the same time step. Similarly to the previous subsection, using the Double Description Method, all the vertices of AOS_k in the state vector space can be found. Following the same procedure from (10) to (12), one can arrive at the achievable output set with process disturbances before considering the measurement noises:

$$AOS_k(v(k) = 0) = \{y(k) | H_k y \leq \bar{b}_k\} \quad (18)$$

Since the effects of the measurement noises on the outputs are the same as the disturbances on the state variables, a similar procedure from (13) to (17) can be followed with the linear mapping $L_y = S_y^{-0.5}(k) V_y^T(k)$ defined according to the eigenvalue decomposition of $\Sigma_y(k) = V_y(k) S_y(k) V_y^{-1}(k)$. The final form of the achievable output set is:

$$AOS_k = \left\{ y(k) \middle| H_k y \leq b_k; [b_k]_i = [\bar{b}_k]_i - l_y \sqrt{[H_k L_y^{-1}]_i^T [H_k L_y^{-1}]_i} \right\} \quad (19)$$

4. Numerical Example

Consider the system given in (1), (2) with the following matrices:

$$A = \begin{bmatrix} 0.59 & -0.43 \\ -0.06 & 0.39 \end{bmatrix}; B = \begin{bmatrix} 0.42 & 1.82 \\ 2.48 & -0.71 \end{bmatrix}; G = \begin{bmatrix} 0.52 & -0.47 \\ 1.22 & 0.47 \end{bmatrix};$$
$$C = \begin{bmatrix} 0 & 1 \\ 1 & 1 \end{bmatrix}; D = 0_{2\times 2}; \Sigma_w = \begin{bmatrix} 0.04 & 0 \\ 0 & 0.02 \end{bmatrix}; \Sigma_v = 10^{-5} \begin{bmatrix} 5 & 0 \\ 0 & 1 \end{bmatrix}; x_0 = \begin{bmatrix} 20 \\ -30 \end{bmatrix} \quad (20)$$

The prediction horizon is chosen to be 6 for illustrative purposes, and the objective is constructing the six achievable output sets AOS_k for $k = 1, \ldots, 6$. The input ranges of the considered AIS_k are $-1 \leq u_1(k) \leq 1$ and $-2 \leq u_2(k) \leq 2$. In the offline computation, the vertices of the AIS_k, which are all combinations of $u(k) \in \{[-1\ -2]^T, [-1\ 2]^T, [1\ -2]^T, [1\ 2]^T\}$ for all $0 \leq k \leq 5$, are applied to the linear state-space model to calculate the associated basis state vectors. The set of convex hulls of these basis state vectors at each time k is the nominal AOS_k, and the funnel of nominal state vectors obtained for this case is shown in Figure 1(a).

In the online update of the dynamic funnel, at each value of k, the AOS_k is adjusted according to (12), and the new dynamic funnel at $w(k) = 0$ and $v(k) = 0$ is shown in Figure 1(b). To find the intersection of all AOS_k at different values of $w(k)$ in the 95% highest density region, (17) is applied, and the new AOS_k that takes into account process disturbances, $w(k)$, is shown as the dashed-edge empty polytopes in Figures 1(c) and (d). In the next step, AOS_k of state vectors are projected into the space of the output vectors, and the convex hulls of the images at every time k is the AOS_k of output vectors, which is represented as the dashed-edge empty polytopes in Figures 1(e) and (f). Finally, to address the measurement noise, the hyperplanes of every AOS_k are shifted inward according to (19). The result is a funnel of output vectors that can always be achieved regardless of the realization of the process disturbances and the measurement noises by varying the constrained manipulated variables. This funnel is plotted with dotted-edge grey-filled polytopes in Figures 1(e) and (f).

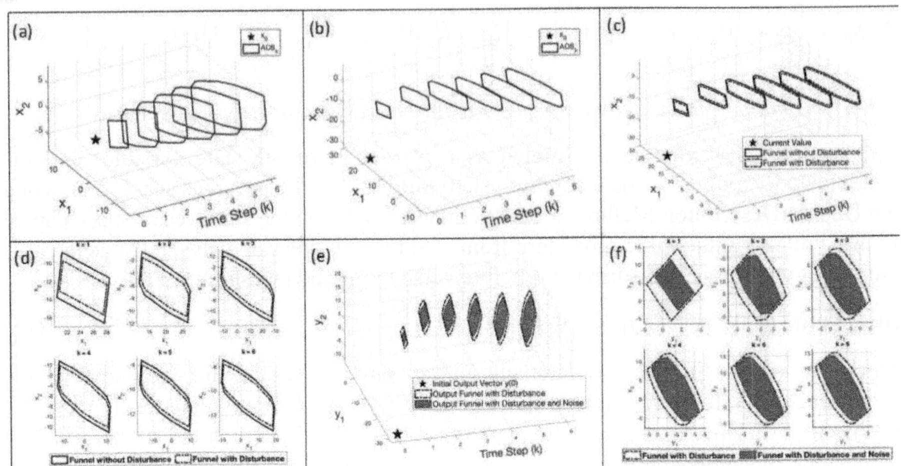

Figure 1: Dynamic operable funnels. (a): Funnel of state vector considering nominal initial state; (b): Funnel of state vector considering actual initial state without disturbances; (c), (d): Adjustment of funnel of state vectors with process disturbances; (e), (f): Funnels of output vectors with and without measurement noises.

5. Conclusions

Dynamic operability corresponds to an output controllability measure that can be used to assist with the formulation of online constrained control problems (Gazzaneo et al., 2020). However, in dynamic operability mapping, exhaustive input discretization methods in the reported literature quickly become intractable with the increase in predictive horizon length. In this work, a novel dynamic operability mapping was proposed in a two-step framework that allows the majority of the computational effort being performed offline. The achievable output sets at different predictive times were formulated as set of inequality constraints that are updated online according to the current full state information and uncertainty propagation. Even though the current framework is limited to a linear time-invariant dynamic process, the proposed theory is a valid basis for future work on linear time-varying and nonlinear dynamic processes.

References

Barber, C.B., Dobkin, D.P., Huhdanpaa, H., 1996. The Quickhull Algorithm for Convex Hulls. ACM Transactions on Mathematical Software (TOMS) 22, 469–483.

Fukuda, K., Prodon, A., 1996. Double Description Method Revisited, in: Deza, M., Euler, R., Manoussakis, I. (Eds.), Combinatorics and Computer Science, Lecture Notes in Computer Science. Springer Berlin Heidelberg, Berlin, Heidelberg, pp. 91–111.

Gazzaneo, V., Carrasco, J.C., Vinson, D.R., Lima, F.V., 2020. Process Operability Algorithms: Past, Present, and Future Developments. Ind. Eng. Chem. Res. 59(6), 2457–2470.

Lima, F.V., Georgakis, C., 2009. Dynamic Operability for the Calculation of Transient Output Constraints for Non-Square Linear Model Predictive Controllers. IFAC Proceedings Volumes 42(11), 231–236.

Muller, D.E., Preparata, F.P., 1978. Finding the Intersection of Two Convex Polyhedra. Theoretical Computer Science 7, 217–236.

Proceedings of the 14th International Symposium on Process Systems Engineering – PSE 2021+
June 19-23, 2022, Kyoto, Japan
http://dx.doi.org/10.1016/B978-0-323-85159-6.50060-9

Effective Re-identification of a Multivariate Process under Model Predictive Control Using Information from Plant-Model Mismatch Detection

Masanori Oshima[a], Sanghong Kim[b*], Yuri A. W. Shardt[c], Ken-Ichiro Sotowa[a]

[a]Department of Chemical Engineering, Kyoto University, Nishikyo-ku, Kyoto 615-8510, Japan
[b]Department of Applied Physics and Chemical Engineering, Tokyo University of Agriculture and Technology, Naka-cho, Koganei-city, Tokyo 184-8588, Japan
[c]Department of Automation Engineering, Technical University of Ilmenau, P.O. Box 10 05 65, Ilmenau D-98684, Germany
sanghong@go.tuat.ac.jp

Abstract

A process under model predictive control is required to be re-identified when plant-model mismatch (PMM) occurs. During data acquisition for re-identification, the process is excited to enable accurate re-identification. However, the excitation of the process worsens control performance. This research proposes a new method for re-identification that can deal with the problem. In the proposed method, only the inputs of the transfer functions that have significant PMM are excited, and, at the same time, the other inputs are manipulated to suppress the variations of the controlled variables. The usefulness of the proposed method was confirmed through a simulation case study of a 3-input, 3-output process. As a result, it was shown that the proposed method can reduce the mean absolute control error during data acquisition to 87% of that of an existing method without compromising model accuracy after re-identification.

Keywords: Dual control; Model predictive control; Multivariate process; Plant-model mismatch; Re-identification

1. Introduction

Due to the spread of the Internet and the concept of mass customization, external demands on industrial processes are changing more rapidly than they were previously. Also, the characteristics of industrial processes change over time due to various factors such as degradation of catalysts or fouling of pipes. Therefore, to improve process productivity, a control system that adapts to the internal and external changes of the process and achieves optimal operation is required. One possible solution is the use of model predictive control (MPC). MPC can adaptively achieve optimal operation for various processes including nonlinear processes, time-varying processes, and processes with constraints. Since MPC is a model-based control method, the control performance depends on the prediction accuracy of the model. Therefore, it is important to maintain the high prediction accuracy of the model used for MPC.

In order to prevent degradation of the prediction accuracy due to plant-model mismatch (PMM), re-identification of the process is required when significant PMM occurs. During re-identification, data containing useful information can be obtained by applying persistent excitation signals to the process. However, at this time, the variations of the controlled variables usually increase, and thus, the control performance will decrease. Therefore, there is a trade-off between the excitation level of the process and the control performance during data acquisition.

In previous studies, various dual control methods using MPC have been proposed to find the optimal operating condition, considering this trade-off (Shouche et al., 1998; Aggeligiannaki and Sarimveis, 2006; Sotomayor et al., 2009; Zacekova et al., 2013; Gonzalez et al., 2014; Marafioti et al., 2014; Patwardhan et al., 2014; Larsson et al., 2015; Zheng et al.; 2018; Thangavel et al., 2018). These approaches modify the optimization problem of the MPC so that the excitation of the process can be achieved without considerable loss of control performance. Yet, these approaches still have room for improvement. In the modified optimization problem, all the inputs of the process are excited even though only a few elements of the transfer function matrix of the process have large PMM. The excitation of the inputs of transfer functions with small PMM will lead to excessive loss of control performance. Therefore, more efficient re-identification can be realized by exciting only the inputs of the transfer functions with large PMM. As far as the authors know, such a re-identification method has not yet been proposed.

In this research, the re-identification method for multivariate processes using PMM information is proposed. In the proposed method, the excitation signals are applied only to the inputs of the transfer functions with large PMM, to avoid excessive excitation of the process. Furthermore, the other input variables are used to suppress the variations of the controlled variables. The transfer functions with large PMM can be detected using existing methods, such as those proposed by Badwe et al. (2009) and Kano et al. (2010). This allows us to obtain informative data for re-identification while high control performance is maintained. The validity of the proposed method is examined by a simulation case study of a 3-input, 3-output process.

2. Problem setting

In this paper, the multivariate process of interest is given as

$$\boldsymbol{y}(s) = \boldsymbol{G}(s)\boldsymbol{u}(s) + \boldsymbol{v}(s), \tag{1}$$

where $\boldsymbol{y}(s) = [y_1(s), \cdots, y_N(s)]^\top$, $\boldsymbol{u}(s) = [u_1(s), \cdots, u_M(s)]^\top$ and $\boldsymbol{v}(s) = [v_1(s), \cdots, v_N(s)]^\top$ are respectively the output, input, and noise vectors; N and M are respectively the numbers of output variables and input variables; and $\boldsymbol{G}(s)$ is the transfer function matrix of the true process given as

$$\boldsymbol{G}(s) = \begin{bmatrix} G_{1,1}(s) & \cdots & G_{1,M}(s) \\ \vdots & & \vdots \\ G_{N,1}(s) & \cdots & G_{N,M}(s) \end{bmatrix}, \tag{2}$$

where $G_{n,m}(s)$ is a transfer function from the m-th input u_m to the n-th output y_n. The model of the process is

$$\hat{\boldsymbol{y}}(s) = \hat{\boldsymbol{G}}(s)\boldsymbol{u}(s). \tag{3}$$

The process is controlled by MPC using Eq. (3) as the prediction model. The objective function in the optimization problem solved at each time step in the MPC is

$$J = \sum_{t=t_0+1}^{t_0+N_P} \|\boldsymbol{y}_{\mathrm{ref}}(t) - \hat{\boldsymbol{y}}(t)\|_{\boldsymbol{W}_y}^2 + \sum_{t=t_0}^{t_0+N_C-1} \|\boldsymbol{u}(t) - \boldsymbol{u}(t-1)\|_{\boldsymbol{W}_u}^2, \tag{4}$$

where t_0 is the current time, $N_P \in \mathbb{N}$ is the length of the prediction horizon, $N_C \in \mathbb{N}$ is the length of the control horizon, $\|\boldsymbol{x}\|_{\boldsymbol{W}}^2 = \boldsymbol{x}^{\mathrm{T}}\boldsymbol{W}\boldsymbol{x}$, $\boldsymbol{W}_y$ and $\boldsymbol{W}_u$ are the weighting matrices, and $\boldsymbol{y}_{\mathrm{ref}}$ is the reference trajectory vector defined as:

$$\boldsymbol{y}_{\mathrm{ref}}(t) = \gamma^{t-t_0}\boldsymbol{y}(t_0) + (1-\gamma^{t-t_0})\boldsymbol{y}_{\mathrm{set}}, \tag{5}$$

where $\boldsymbol{y}_{\mathrm{set}} = \left[y_{\mathrm{set},1}, \cdots, y_{\mathrm{set},N}\right]^{\mathrm{T}}$ is a setpoint vector, and $\gamma \in [0,1]$ is a parameter.

In this paper, it is assumed that at least one of the transfer functions has significant PMM. As well, the locations of the elements with large PMM in the transfer function matrix are known before data acquisition for re-identification. The following sets are used to define the location of the PMM:

$$\mathbb{I}_{1:M} = \{1,2,\cdots,M\}, \tag{6}$$

$$\mathbb{M}_n = \left\{m \mid \exists\omega > 0 \text{ s.t. } \left|G_{n,m}(j\omega) - \hat{G}_{n,m}(j\omega)\right| > \epsilon\right\}, \tag{7}$$

$$\overline{\mathbb{M}}_n = \mathbb{I}_{1:M} \setminus \mathbb{M}_n, \tag{8}$$

$$\mathbb{N}_{\mathrm{PMM}} = \{n \mid \mathbb{M}_n \neq \phi\}, \tag{9}$$

where $G_{n,m}(j\omega)$ and $\hat{G}_{n,m}(j\omega)$ are the frequency transfer functions of respectively the process and the model, ϵ is a tolerance, and ϕ is the empty set.

3. Proposed Method

In the proposed method, the data acquisition and re-identification of the process are performed as follows:

1. Set $\mathbb{N}_{\mathrm{MPM}}^* = \mathbb{N}_{\mathrm{MPM}}$.
2. Set $n^* = \min \mathbb{N}_{\mathrm{MPM}}^*$ and remove n^* from $\mathbb{N}_{\mathrm{MPM}}^*$.
3. Operate the target process using MPC which solves the optimization problem defined by Eqs. (10) to (13) at each time step, to obtain the input-output data $\mathbb{D}_{n^*} = \{u_m(t), y_{n^*}(t) \mid m \in \mathbb{M}_{n^*}, t = 1, \cdots, T\}$, where T is sample size, that is,

$$\min_{\boldsymbol{u}(t_0),\cdots,\boldsymbol{u}(t_0+N_C-1)} J \tag{10}$$

subject to

$$\hat{\boldsymbol{y}}(s) = \hat{\boldsymbol{G}}(s)\boldsymbol{u}(s), \tag{11}$$

$$u_m(t) = \tilde{u}_m(t), \qquad m \in \mathbb{M}_{n^*}, t_0 \le t \le t_0 + N_C - 1, \tag{12}$$

$$\boldsymbol{u}(t) = \boldsymbol{u}(t_0 + N_C - 1), \qquad t_0 + N_C \le t \le t_0 + N_P - 1, \tag{13}$$

where $\tilde{u}_m$ is an excitation signal applied to u_m.

4. Using $\mathbb{D}_{n^*}$, calculate the estimate $\hat{s}_{\mathbb{M}_{n^*}}$ of the sum of the outputs from the transfer functions with significant PMM in the n^*-th row using

$$\hat{s}_{\mathbb{M}_{n^*}}(t) = y_{n^*}(t) - \sum_{m \in \bar{\mathbb{M}}_{n^*}} \hat{y}_{n^*,m}(t), \qquad y_{n^*}(t) \in \mathbb{D}_{n^*}, \tag{14}$$

where $\hat{y}_{n^*,m}$ is the estimate of the output from $G_{n^*,m}$ and is calculated as follows:

$$\hat{y}_{n^*,m}(s) = \hat{G}_{n^*,m}(s) u_m(s), \qquad u_m(t) \in \mathbb{D}_{n^*}, \tag{15}$$

where $\hat{G}_{n^*,m}$ is a transfer function model from the m-th input u_m to the n^*-th output y_{n^*}.

5. Using the data $\mathbb{D}'_{n^*} = \left\{u_m(t) \in \mathbb{D}_{n^*}, \hat{s}_{\mathbb{M}_{n^*}}(t) \mid m \in \mathbb{M}_{n^*}, t = 1, \cdots, T\right\}$ as input-output data, re-identify the transfer functions $\left\{G_{n^*,m} \mid m \in \mathbb{M}_{n^*}\right\}$.
6. If $\mathbb{N}^*_{\mathrm{PMM}} = \phi$, then stop the procedure; otherwise, go back to step 2.

The data acquisition for re-identification is performed in Step 3. Here, the inputs to the transfer functions with significant PMM are excited by the constraint in Eq. (12), while the remaining other inputs are optimized to improve control performance. Note that the degree of improvement in the control performance will be limited when the number of input variables is much smaller than that of the output variables. Steps 4 and 5 are the re-identification steps. Note that, in Step 4, the sum of the outputs from the transfer functions with large PMM in the n^*-th row is estimated without using the models with large PMM.

4. Case study

4.1. Settings

The target process in this paper is a 3-input, 3-output process with first-order transfer functions given as

$$\boldsymbol{G}(s) = \begin{bmatrix} \frac{4.7}{55s+1} & \frac{4.5}{49s+1} & \frac{5.0}{52s+1} \\ \frac{5.2}{48s+1} & \frac{4.6}{52s+1} & \frac{5.5}{50s+1} \\ \frac{4.5}{47s+1} & \frac{5.2}{46s+1} & \frac{4.7}{53s+1} \end{bmatrix}. \tag{16}$$

In this case study, the transfer function model given by Eq. (16) is used as the true process, and the sampling period is set to 1 s. Only the (3, 2)-entry of the transfer function matrix has significant PMM with a steady-state gain 50% larger in the prediction model than in the true process. The output noise vector is defined as

$$\boldsymbol{v}(t) = \left[\frac{1-0.1551q^{-1}}{1+0.8648q^{-1}} w_1(t) \quad \frac{1+0.0464q^{-1}}{1+0.6807q^{-1}} w_2(t) \quad \frac{1+0.9650q^{-1}}{1+0.5256q^{-1}} w_3(t)\right]^{\mathrm{T}}, \tag{17}$$

where $w_n(t) \sim \mathcal{N}(0, 0.1)$ $(n = 1,2,3)$, and q^{-1} is the backward shift operator.

4.2. Procedure

In this case study, the proposed method and the existing method by Shouche et al. (1998) were used for excitation of the process. For each excitation method, the following procedure was conducted 100 times with different seed values for generating w_n. Note that the M-series signals with the clock period of 5 s and amplitudes of 0.2, 0.3, 0.4, and 0.5 were used as $\tilde{u}_2$ in the proposed method; 9 patterns of the parameters, which affect excitation level during data acquisition, were used in the existing method.

Table 1: Parameters of the MPC

Parameters	N_{P}	N_{C}	γ	$\boldsymbol{W}_y$	$\boldsymbol{W}_u$
Values	20 s	5 s	0.8	diag(1,1,1)	diag(1,1,1)

I. Five-hundred data samples were acquired during operation using MPC with either the proposed method or the existing method. Here, the MPC parameters were set as in Table 1, and the setpoint vector was set to $[0,0,0]^{\top}$. The control performance in this step was validated using MAE, which is defined as

$$\mathrm{MAE} = \sum_{n=1}^{N}\left(\frac{1}{T}\sum_{t=1}^{T}\left|y_n(t) - y_{\mathrm{set},n}\right|\right). \tag{18}$$

II. Using the data acquired in Step I, re-identification of the transfer function with a considerable PMM was performed using Steps 4 and 5 of the proposed method. Here, the prediction error method was used as the system identification method.

III. Five-hundred steps of the control simulation were performed to assess the performance of the MPC system after re-identification. Here, the setpoint vector was changed from $[0,0,0]^{\top}$ to $[2,2,2]^{\top}$ at $t = 1$ s, and MAE was used as the performance index.

4.3. Results

Fig. 1 shows the relationship between the mean MAE in step I (MAE_1) and step III (MAE_2). MAE_1 is smaller when the control performance during data acquisition is high, and MAE_2 is smaller when the model accuracy after re-identification is high. Therefore, we can achieve both higher control performance during data acquisition and higher model accuracy after re-identification as we move in Fig. 1 to the lower left corner. In the existing method, MAE_2 tends to increase steeply as MAE_1 decreases because the sufficiently information-rich data cannot be obtained at the smaller MAE_1 due to the significant reduction of the excitation level. Therefore, the plots for the existing method in Fig. 1 cannot approach the lower left corner. In the proposed method, on the other hand, MAE_2 tends to increase more gently as MAE_1 decreases than in the existing method, and the data points of the proposed method are more closely located to the lower left corner of the figure than those of the existing method. Specifically, MAE_1 of the proposed method can be reduced to 87% of the minimum MAE_1 of the existing method, while keeping MAE_2 smaller than the minimum MAE_2 of the existing method. Thus, the proposed method can realize both higher control performance during data acquisition and higher model accuracy after re-identification than the existing method.

5. Conclusions

In this paper, a new re-identification method for multivariate processes using MPC was proposed. In the proposed method, only the inputs of the transfer functions with large PMMs are excited, and the other inputs are used for suppressing the variations of the controlled variables. The usefulness of the proposed method was validated using a simulation case study of a 3-input, 3-output process with first-order transfer functions. As a result and compared with the existing method, the proposed method improves the control performance during data acquisition by 13% while maintaining a high model accuracy after re-identification. As well, it is expected that the proposed method will be useful when it is applied to more complicated processes, such as unstable processes and non-minimum-phase processes. This will be confirmed in future work.

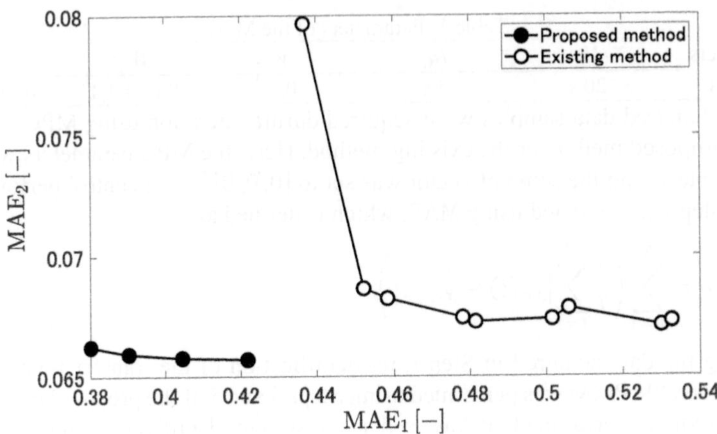

Fig. 1: The relationship between MAE_1 and MAE_2.

References

E. Aggelogiannaki, H. Sarimveis, 2006, Multiobjective constrained MPC with simultaneous closed-loop identification, International Journal of Adaptive Control and Signal Processing, 20, 4, pp. 145-173.

A. S. Badwe, R. D. Gudi, R. S. Patwardhan, S. L. Shah, S. C. Patwardhan, 2009, Detection of model-plant mismatch in MPC applications, Journal of Process Control, 19, 8, pp. 1305-1313.

A. H. González, A. Ferramosca, G. A. Bustos, J.L. Marchetti, M. Fiacchini, D. Odloak, 2014, Model predictive control suitable for closed-loop re-identification, Systems and Control Letters, 69, 1, pp. 23-33.

M. Kano, Y. Shigi, S. Hasebe, S. Ooyama, 2010, Detection of significant model-plant mismatch from routine operation data of model predictive control system, IFAC Proceedings Volumes (IFAC-PapersOnline), 43, 5, pp. 685-690.

C. A. Larsson, C. R. Rojas, X. Bombois, H. Hjalmarsson, 2015, Experimental evaluation of model predictive control with excitation (MPC-X) on an industrial depropanizer, Journal of Process Control, 31, pp. 1-16.

G. Marafioti, R. R. Bitmead, M. Hovd, 2014, Persistently exciting model predictive control, International Journal of Adaptive Control and Signal Processing, 28, 6, pp. 536-552.

R. S. Patwardhan, R. B. Goapluni, 2014, A moving horizon approach to input design for closed loop identification, Journal of Process Control, 24, 3, pp. 188-202.

M. Shouche, H. Genceli, P. Vuthandam, and M. Nikolaou., 1998, Simultaneous constrained model predictive control and identification of DARX processes. Automatica, 34, 12, pp. 1521-1530.

O. A. Z. Sotomayor, D. Odloak, L. F. L. Moro, 2009, Closed-loop model re-identification of processes under MPC with zone control, Control Engineering Practice, 17, 5, pp. 551-563.

S. Thangavel, S. Lucia, R. Paulen, S. Engell, 2018, Dual robust nonlinear model predictive control: A multi-stage approach, Journal of Process Control, 72, pp. 39-51.

E. Žáčeková, S. Prívara, M. Pčolka, 2013, Persistent excitation condition within the dual control framework, Journal of Process Control, 23, 9, pp. 1270-1280.

H. Zheng, T. Zou, J. Hu, H. Yu, 2018, A framework for adaptive predictive control system based on zone control, IEEE Access, 6, pp. 49513-49522.

Proceedings of the 14th International Symposium on Process Systems Engineering – PSE 2021+
June 19-23, 2022, Kyoto, Japan
http://dx.doi.org/10.1016/B978-0-323-85159-6.50061-0

Model Predictive Control of Grade Transition with Attention Base Sequence-to-Sequence Model

Zhen-Feng Jiang[a], Xi-Zhan Wei[a], David Shan-Hill Wong[a*], Yuan Yao[a*], Jia-Lin Kang[b*], Yao-Chen Chuang[c], Shi-Shang Jang[a], John Di-Yi Ou[d]

[a]*Department of Chemical Engineering, National Tsing Hua University, Hsinchu 30043, Taiwan*
[b]*Department of Chemical and Materials Engineering, National Yunlin University of Science and Technology, Yunlin 64002, Taiwan*
[c]*Tsing Hua Intelligent Chemical Engineering Ltd. Co., Hsinchu 30043, Taiwan*
[d]*Center for Energy and Environmental Research, National Tsing Hua University, Hsinchu 30043, Taiwan*
**jlkang@yuntech.edu.tw, dshwong@che.nthu.edu.tw, yyao@mx.nthu.edu.tw*

Abstract

In industry, process input-output data exhibit complex nonlinear dynamics. Such behavior must be modeled by nonlinear time series for use in model-based control, optimization, and monitoring. In this work, a sequence-to-sequence (StS) model was developed for the ASPEN Polymer Plus simulator of an industrial high-density polyethylene (HDPE) slurry reactor. Inclusion of attention mechanism and elastic net (EN) training was found to substantially improve the gain consistency and time dynamics of the model. The resulting model was utilized as a non-linear model predictive control (NLMPC) to control the hydrogen to ethylene ratio (HER) and pressure. The NLMPC can navigate the grade transition of the reactor as well as maintaining the steady state.
Keywords: Sequence-to-Sequence; Attention mechanism; HDPE reactor; Grade transition.

1. Sequence-to-Sequence Model

Chemical processes or unit operations can be described by nonlinear state-space models with x and d being the unknown state and disturbance variables, and y being the observed output variables and u being the observed input variables

$$\frac{dx}{dt} = f(x,u,d), y = g(x) \tag{1}$$

In order to utilize the above model for model predictive control, the unknown x and d must be identified using past observation of u and y in a past window known functions of f and g. For a complex chemical process such as a polymerization reactor, both the identification procedure and the development of physics-based models f and g are nontrivial tasks.

It is desirable that the model development and variable identification procedure can be done in a purely data-driven approach. In such an approach it is necessary to ensure that predictions $\tilde{y}$ of action response in a future horizon, is consistent with the actual process. Previously, Chou et al. (2019) employed a sequence-to-sequence (StS) model developed for natural language processing to establish a data-driven dynamic model for a distillation column. An StS (as shown in Figure 1) consists of an encoder-observer of gated recurrent units (GRU) with input $\hat{u}_{t-i}, \hat{y}_{t-i}, \hat{h}_{t-i-1}$, and a hidden state output $\hat{h}_{t-i}$, for $i = 1 \cdots W$; and a decoder-predictor GRUs with input $\tilde{u}_{t+i}, \tilde{h}_{t+i-1}$, and output $\tilde{y}_{t+i}, \tilde{h}_{t+i}$, for $i = 1 \cdots H$.

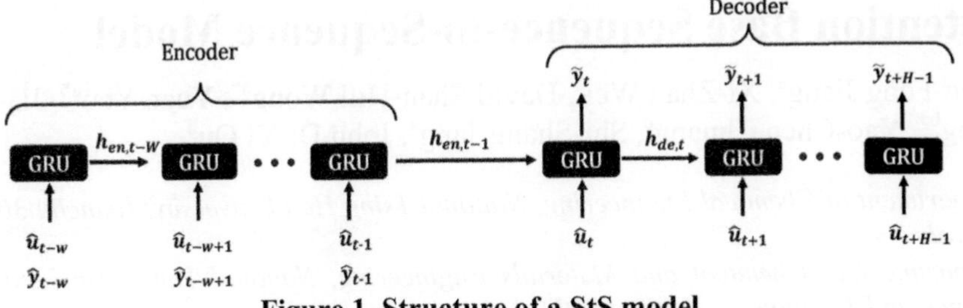

Figure 1. Structure of a StS model

Various forms of similar models have been used for soft sensors (Yuan et al., 2019) and key variable identification (Zhou et al., 2021) to identify latent variables for a time series.

2. Attention Mechanism

The StS structure is shown in Figure 1 leveraged information of the current hidden state identified at the current time t. In a physical state-space model, the knowledge of the current unobserved variables x and d is sufficient for prediction of the future. However, in a data-driven model, there is no guarantee that the observed hidden state h has successfully captured such information, Hence the attention mechanism (Figure 2, Bahdanau et al., 2014) can be included to improve the prediction.

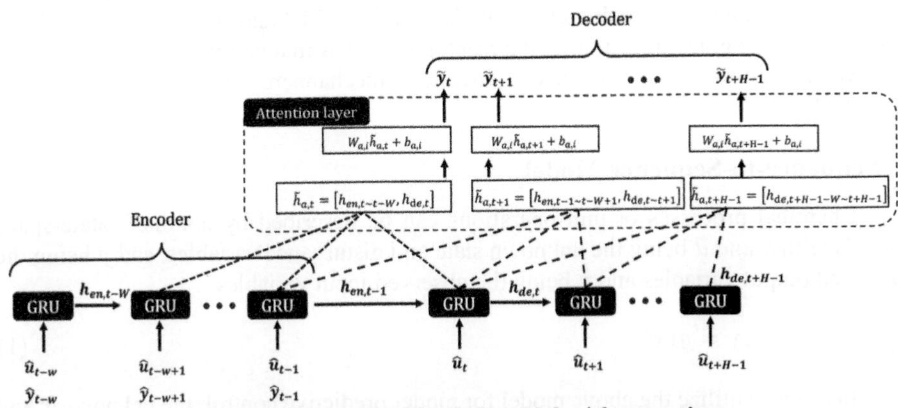

Figure 2. Structure of a StS model with attention

3. Elastic Net and Systematic Model Improvement

Normally the prediction loss for the training model can be given by mean absolute error:

$$\mathcal{L}^{pred} = \frac{\sum_{D \in \mathcal{Tr}} \sum_{p=1}^{M} \sum_{t=1}^{H} \|\hat{y}_{p,t,D} - \tilde{y}_{p,t,D}\|}{M \times H} \quad (2)$$

where $\hat{y}_{p,t,D}$ and $\tilde{y}_{p,t,D}$ are observed and predicted values of output respectively, H is the length of decoder, M is the number of sensor variables and the data set D is the training set $\mathcal{Tr}$.

To avoid overfitting, elastic net (EN, Zhou and Hastie, 2005) included the l_1 (Lasso) and l_2 (ridge regression) norms of the network weights in the loss function with weight parameters of λ_1 and λ_2

$$\mathcal{L}^{total} = \mathcal{L}^{pred} + \lambda_1 \sum_i |w_i| + \lambda_2 \sum_i w_i^2 \tag{3}$$

The training of such a model is done by minimizing the loss function via adjusting parameters λ_1 and λ_2 of weight w_i. The performance of the trained model is rated by the following combined objective function:

$$\mathcal{J} = R_{\mathcal{V}}^2 + \mathcal{G}_{\mathcal{V}} \tag{4}$$

where $R_{\mathcal{V}}^2$ is the coefficient of determination of the validation set $\mathcal{V}$ and $\bar{y}$ is the average of observed value $\hat{y}_D$.

$$R_{\mathcal{V}}^2 = 1 - \frac{\sum_{D\in\mathcal{V}} \sum_{p=1}^{M} \sum_{t=1}^{H} \|\hat{y}_{p,t,D} - \tilde{y}_{p,t,D}\|^2}{\sum_{D\in\mathcal{V}} \sum_{p=1}^{M} \sum_{t=1}^{H} \|\hat{y}_{p,t,D} - \bar{y}_D\|^2} \tag{5}$$

and the gain consistency $\mathcal{G}_{\mathcal{V}}$ of the validation set $\mathcal{V}$.

$$\mathcal{G}_{\mathcal{V}} = \frac{\sum_{i\in\mathcal{C}, j\in\mathcal{M}} \left(\sum_{D\in\mathcal{V}} \sum_{t=1}^{T} Con_{t,ij,D} \right)}{T_{\mathcal{V}}} \tag{6}$$

where $\mathcal{C}$ is the set of all controlled variables (CV) and $\mathcal{M}$ is the set of all manipulated variables (MV). A dynamic gain $K_{t,ij}$ is obtained by changing a manipulated variable $u_j, j \in \mathcal{M}$ with a value $\Delta u_{t,j}$ at time instant t and finding the change in the predicted output $\Delta\tilde{y}_{t,j}$ in the future horizon of the controlled variable $\tilde{y}_i, i \in \mathcal{C}$.

$$K_{t,ij} = \frac{\Delta\tilde{y}_{t,i}}{\Delta u_{t,j}} \tag{7}$$

The consistency $Con_{t,ij}$, a binary variable is given by

$$Con_{t,ij} = Heaviside\left(K_{t,ij} \langle K^{ss}{}_{ij} \rangle\right) \tag{8}$$

where $K^{ss}{}_{ij}$ is the expected steady-state gain provided by physics-based simulation or experience of the operator. The $Heavside$ function indicated that we are only concerned with the sign of the gain rather than the absolute value. This is because the sign of the gain is usually known based on understanding the physics of the process while predicting the absolute value required a lot of modeling efforts.

Since both $R_{\mathcal{V}}^2$ and $\mathcal{G}_{\mathcal{TUV}}$ are between 0 and 1, they can be summed and optimized without any weighting factors. The following optimization problem can be solved by any global optimization procedure such as the differential evolution algorithm (DEA, Qin et al., 2008) to find the best solution $\max_{\lambda_1,\lambda_2} \mathcal{J}$ in terms of prediction accuracy and gain consistency.

Such a model should serve as an adequate model to navigate and control a process. In our previous work (Chou et al., 2019), we found that $R_{\mathcal{V}}^2$ and $\mathcal{G}_{\mathcal{TUV}}$ are not correlated when a simple deep neural network. The good values of $R_{\mathcal{V}}^2$ and $\mathcal{G}_{\mathcal{TUV}}$ can be obtained by using an StS model. In this work, the aforementioned procedure of using EN and optimization with respect to parameters of EN constitutes a systematic improvement of our process model.

4. A High-Density Polyethylene Reactor

An ASPEN Polymer Plus dynamic model of an HDPE reactor was developed using the kinetic model provided by Khare et al. (2002). Sensors and controllers data of daily steady-state and grade transition operations were generated based on the operation of a local plant with varying catalyst activities. MV and CV in the HDPE polymerization process as shown in Table 1. The operator employed catalysts flow and hydrogen flow as daily MV to control the HER and pressure, The directionality of MV/CV pairs utilized for determining gain consistency is shown in Table 2.

Table 1. List of variables

Type	Tag
MV	Flow rate of ethylene
MV	Flow rate of hydrogen
MV	Flow rate of 1-butene
MV	Flow rate of catalyst
MV	Flow rate of cocatalyst
MV	Flow rate of hexane
MV	Temperature of reactor
CV	Pressure of reactor
CV	HER of purge gas

Table 2. Directionality of gain

	HER	Pressure
Flow rate of catalyst	+	−
Flow rate of hydrogen	+	+

5. Dynamic Modelling

The generated data were sampled at 10 minutes intervals. The window length of encoder and decoder horizon consists of 24, and 18 samples, or 240 and 180 minutes respectively; to ensure that the model can consider time delay and slow dynamic of the system. The data of transition between different grades are distributed to the training, validation, and testing data set according to the ratio of 6:2:2. There are six kinds of grade transition in total, five of which are assigned to the training, validation data set. The other is assigned to the testing data set and utilized as the indicator of grade transition navigation.

Comparison of prediction accuracy and gain consistency results of the StS model and StS with attention mechanism (StS-ATT) model for the testing data is given in Table 3. Substantial improvement can be achieved by including the attention mechanism.

Table 3. The prediction RMSE and R^2 result of StS and StS-ATT model in the testing dataset.

Model	Pressure		HER		$\mathcal{G}_{Te}$
	$RMSE_{Te}$	R^2_{Te}	$RMSE_{Te}$	R^2_{Te}	
StS	0.596	0.898	0.064	0.957	0.988
StS-ATT	0.138	0.995	0.047	0.977	0.999

Figure 3 (a) shows the HER contribution plot of the hidden states at various time points in the past window. The contribution peaks at around 80 minutes in the past showing a long time characteristic time and possible time delay of the system. Figure 3 (b) demonstrated substantial improvement in gain consistency during the optimization of EN parameters due to the fact that gain consistency was not included in the neural network parameter training.

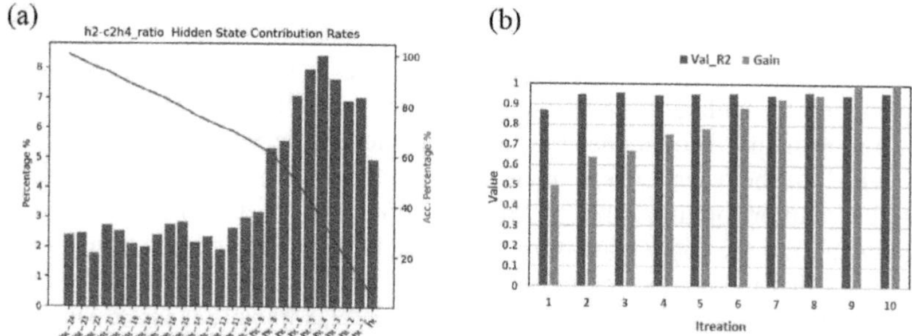

Figure 3. (a)HER contribution plot of attention state in the past (b)The result of gain consistency and R squared at various iteration points.

6. Grade Transition Navigation

To demonstrate the usefulness of the dynamic input-output model developed, it is applied to operation navigation of grade transition of the HDPE reactor. An artificial intelligence model predictive control (AIMPC) algorithm was developed based on our StS-ATT model using the following bounded optimization:

$$\min_{u_{j,t+k,k=1\cdots H,j\in\mathcal{M}}} \sum_{k=1}^{H}\left\{\sum_{i\in\mathcal{C}}\left|\tilde{y}_{i.t+k}-y_i^{sp}\right|^2+\alpha\sum_{j\in\mathcal{M}}\left|u_{j.t+k}-u_{j.t+k-1}\right|^2\right\}$$
$$s.t. \tag{9}$$
$$u_{j.lb}\leq u_{j.t+k}\leq u_{j.ub}$$

The DEA calculates the minimized change of manipulated variable $u_{j.t+k}-u_{j.t+k-1}$ at each point of time to make the prediction $\tilde{y}_i$ closer to setpoint y_i^{sp}. Simultaneously, the manipulated variable $u_{j.t+k}$ at each point of time will be within the operating upper and lower limits, $u_{j.ub}$ and $u_{j.lb}$. Again the DEA is used to solve optimization and the solution is implemented on the ASPEN Polymer Plus dynamic model to simulate the grade transition. The operation changes in HER, pressure, catalyst flow, and hydrogen flow are shown in Figure 4(a) to (d) respectively. The blue line is the result of AIMPC and the red line is a manual control procedure suggested by the operator. It is found that the pressure is more stable than the manual control as shown in Figure 4 (b), and the operation navigation adjusts more quickly and amplitude is relatively stable than the manual control to make the HER achieve and stay on the setpoint 1 as shown in Figure 4(a).

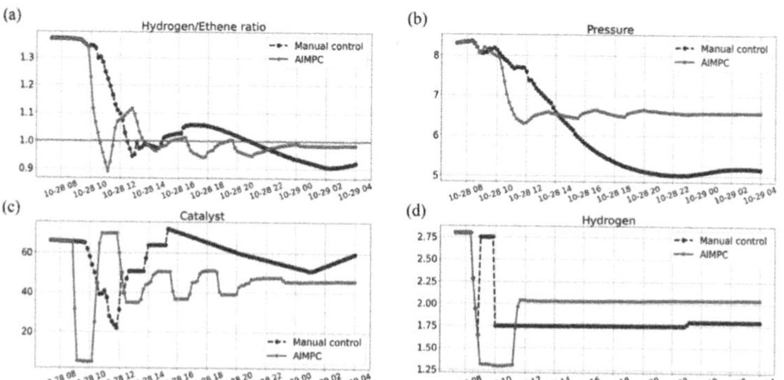

Figure 4. AIMPC with the StS-ATT (a) the H_2/C_2H_4 ratio (b) pressure of reactor (c) the flow rate of catalyst (d) the flow rate of hydrogen.

7. Conclusion

In this work, the StS-ATT model is used to model the dynamics of a high-density polyethylene reactor without the knowledge of catalyst activity, polymerization kinetics, or other first principle knowledge. Furthermore, the physical consistency of the gain relation, which is between critical manipulated variables and sensor variables, and differential evolution optimization of weight parameters of L1 and L2 norm. Such improvement allows the application of model predictive control of grade transitions. The results showed that the model predictive control of grade transition using the dynamic model is more efficient and stable compared to manual transition based on operator advice. The optimized operation guidelines can be found that a much quicker transition can be achieved by using the model predictive control of our data-driven model.

Acknowledgment

This work was supported by the Ministry of Science and Technology, ROC (Grant number: MOST 110-2221-E-007 -014 -).

References

Bahdanau, D., Cho, K., & Bengio, Y. (2014). Neural machine translation by jointly learning to align and translate. arXiv preprint arXiv:1409.0473.

Chou, C. H., Wu, H., Kang, J. L., Wong, D. S. H., Yao, Y., Chuang, Y. C., ... & Ou, J. D. Y. (2019). Physically consistent soft-sensor development using sequence-to-sequence neural networks. IEEE Transactions on Industrial Informatics, 16(4), 2829-2838.

Khare, N. P., Seavey, K. C., Liu, Y. A., Ramanathan, S., Lingard, S., & Chen, C. C. (2002). Steady-state and dynamic modeling of commercial slurry high-density polyethylene (HDPE) processes. *Industrial & engineering chemistry research*, *41*(23), 5601-5618.

Qin, A. K., Huang, V. L., & Suganthan, P. N. (2008). Differential evolution algorithm with strategy adaptation for global numerical optimization. IEEE transactions on Evolutionary Computation, 13(2), 398-417.

Yuan, X., Gu, Y., Wang, Y., Yang, C., & Gui, W. (2019). A deep supervised learning framework for data-driven soft sensor modeling of industrial processes. IEEE transactions on neural networks and learning systems, 31(11), 4737-4746.

Zou, H., & Hastie, T. (2005). Regularization and variable selection via the elastic net. Journal of the royal statistical society: series B (statistical methodology), 67(2), 301-320.

Zhou, J., Wang, X., Yang, C., & Xiong, W. (2021). A novel soft sensor modeling approach based on Difference-LSTM for complex industrial process. IEEE Transactions on Industrial Informatics.

Proceedings of the 14th International Symposium on Process Systems Engineering – PSE 2021+
June 19-23, 2022, Kyoto, Japan
http://dx.doi.org/10.1016/B978-0-323-85159-6.50062-2

Real Time Optimization of series of fixed bed catalytic reactors

Naganjaneyulu Suruvu [a*] , Kazuya Ijichi [a], Satoru Hashizume [a]

[a]Sumitomo Chemical Co., Ltd , 5-1, Anesakkaigan, Ichihara 299-0195, Japan
suruvun@sc.sumitomo-chem.co.jp

Abstract

Real time optimization has become an increasingly important subject in the chemical industry due to high competition. The combination of process modelling and computer simulation provides clear understanding to know about the improvement potential of the plant.

This paper introduces the real time optimization, and its online implementation in series of fixed-bed catalytic reactors process. In general, catalyst deactivation occurs in most of the fixed bed reactors, and optimal operation of reactor systems undergoing catalyst deactivation is an important economic issue. In the process of controlling the chemical reaction, it is necessary to change the operating conditions according to the catalyst activity. A system is developed to deal with the depreciating catalyst activity by using the concept of mathematical optimization methods that allow to calculate the optimal operating conditions of multiple variables simultaneously. The system consists of 3 modules, (i) Analyser: This module consists of steady state one-dimensional plug flow reactor model, which automatically receives the plant historian data as well as lab analysis data such as flow rate, temperature, concentration etc. to estimate the catalyst activity. (ii) Predictor: This module develops the empirical equation using the activity data from the analyser with the help of Recursive Least Square method. This empirical model estimates the real time catalyst activity where no process data is available. In general the catalyst activity is assumed to decrease at a constant rate with respect to the age as given by the vendor information. (iii)Optimizer: In this module the objective function and its constraints are defined. Minimization of objective function is carried out using appropriate algorithm while ensuring the product quality constraints.

Online implementation is carried out by connecting this system with plant historian data and displaying the calculated optimum conditions on the dashboard. The operators adjust the process conditions based on the dashboard. As a result it is determined that the production cost has significant reduction.

Keywords: Control; Optimization; Operation; Digital Twin.

1. Introduction

Catalytic fixed bed reactors are widely used in the chemical industries, from refinery to the fine chemicals. In a general chemical plant life cycle, once the plant has designed, constructed and started operations, the duty of the process engineer is to optimise the operating conditions in order to realize the maximum production with minimum production cost and high profits. In order to minimize the cost, it is necessary to decrease the by-products formation rate and improve the yield of desired product. The performance of the reactor system is adversely affected by the catalyst decay. As the catalyst deactivates, the performance of the reactor decreases which means conversion rate of raw materials decreases. A common operation strategy to increase the conversion is to adjust the operating condition such as temperature of the reactor to compensate the decrease in activity. Change in the temperature leads to change in conversion rate as well as the by-products formation rate. In order to optimize the process with minimum by-products and maximum conversion, a real time optimization model is necessary to simulate, understand the potential and to achieve the better economic efficiency of the plant. A number of variables are involved in the optimization of the fixed bed reactors, such as feed composition, catalyst activity, flowrates, bed temperature etc. Feed composition, flowrates and temperature are online measurable variables and catalyst activity is difficult to measure online. There has been a lot of works (Biscarri et al., 2012 & Fuada et al., 2012) carried out on optimization of fixed bed reactors undergoing catalyst deactivation. But in most of the cases the catalyst activity is assumed to decrease at a constant rate with respect to the age as given by the vendor information. The vendor information is based on the ideal conditions, where as in real case, overall catalyst bed activity depends so many factors like porosity, historical operation conditions in catalyst life such as feed flow rate, temperatures etc.

In this article, a Digital Twin technology is proposed to deal with the optimization problem. A Digital Twin is a simulator that reflects the real system behaviour with maximum possible precession. The proposed Digital Twin estimates the overall catalyst bed activity in real time and based on that activity the system calculates the optimum conditions. This Digital Twin consist of a steady state plug flow reactor model to simulate the series of fixed bed catalytic reactors. The catalyst activity is estimated using lab analysis data such as inlet and outlet concentrations of the reactant and process historian data such as temperature, flowrate etc. Along with the reactor model a regression equation is developed to estimate the catalyst activity in the absence of lab data.

2. Digital Twin Development

In this section, detailed procedure of Digital Twin development is described. Before going into the Digital Twin development, brief description about the process is presented here. The raw materials (A & B in below equations) are passed through the series of fixed bed reactors and the reactants convert into the products over the catalyst. Along with the desired products C, undesired products (D, E, and F) are also formed from the reaction. Products and unreacted fluids absorbs the heat generated from the reaction and carry on to the next process. As shown in Figure 1, the inlet temperature of the reactor is controlled by manipulating the utility of heat exchanger.

$$A + B \rightarrow C \text{ (desired product)} + \Delta H \text{ (heat)} \quad \text{(i)}$$

$$A + B \rightarrow D \text{ (undesired product)} + \Delta H1 \text{ (heat)} \quad \text{(ii)}$$

$$C + B \rightarrow E \text{ (undesired product)} + \Delta H2 \text{ (heat)} \quad \text{(iii)}$$

$$D + B \rightarrow F \text{ (undesired product)} + \Delta H3 \text{ (heat)} \quad \text{(iv)}$$

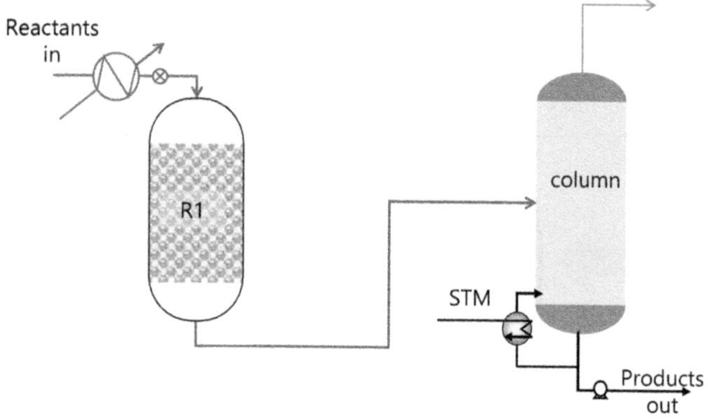

Figure 1. Simplified process flow

This system is configured with following 3 modules. All these modules are developed using python. The detailed explanation of each module are as follows.

I. Analyser

This module consists of steady state one-dimensional plug flow reactor model, which automatically receives the plant historian data as well as lab analysis data like concentration etc. to estimate the catalyst activity. Algorithm for the analyser is shown in the Figure 2.

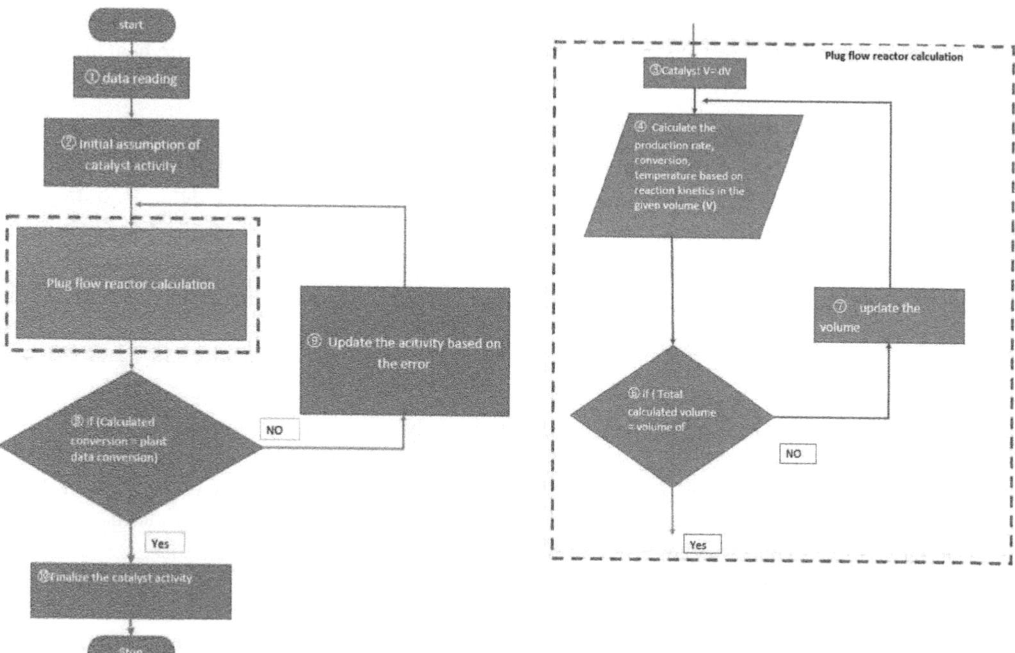

Figure 2. Calculation flow chart for the Analyser

In step 1, Analyser reads the data from the Plant historian, and does all the pre-processing like data cleaning, etc.

In step 2, initial value for the catalyst activity is assumed in order to carry out the plug flow reactor calculations.

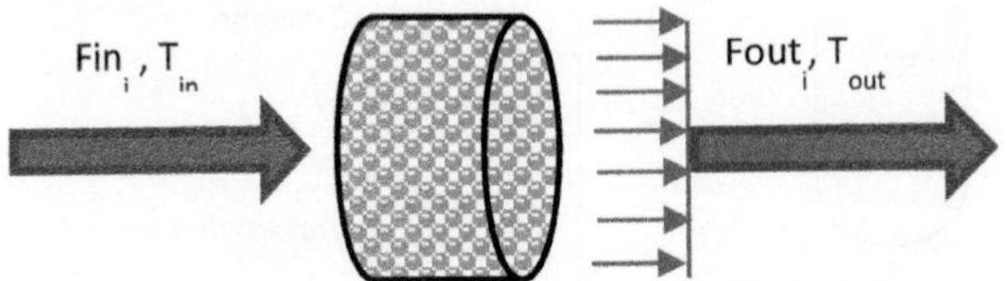

Figure.3 Mass and Energy balance around tiny part of reactor

In step 3 to step 7, plug flow reactor calculation is carried out by dividing the reactor into small parts and in each part the material & energy balance equation (v) to (vii) reported below are used to calculate the temperature and concentration of each component.

$$Fin_i - Fout_i = r_i \cdot \Delta V \tag{v}$$

$$r_i = K_i \cdot e^{-\left(\frac{Ea_i}{RT}\right)} \tag{vi}$$

$$\rho \cdot C_P(T_{in} - T_{out}) = Q_{rxn} \tag{vii}$$

Where i refers to component and K_i is pre-exponential factor which is directly proportional to the catalyst activity and the relation is derived from the experimental data for each component. Q_{rxn}, ρ, C_P, T are the reaction heat, density, specific heat and temperature respectively.

In step 8, once the entire plug flow reactor calculation is done, the overall reactor conversion rate is calculated using concentration result obtained. This conversion rate is compared with conversion rate calculated from the lab analysis data. If both conversion rates are not equal then catalyst activity is updated based on the error and the entire calculation procedure from step 3 is repeated. If both the conversion rates are equal then catalyst activity is finalized and updated into the plant historian from the module.

II. Predictor

In this module, the catalyst activity data and catalyst run time is obtained from the plant historian. Using this data, regression equation is developed to predict the catalyst activity in real time when there is no lab analysis data. Coefficients of regression equations are estimated using recursive least square method. This coefficients are updated to the plant historian.

III. Optimizer

In this module, the objective function as well as its constraints are defined. Minimization of objective function is carried out using appropriate algorithm while ensuring the product quality constraints.

The objective function is the value of loss in production cost which includes raw material loss due to undesired products and utility loss. The price of raw material and utility are included in the function. Process constraints such as concentration of by-product (F) which effects quality of products are also included in the function.

Optimization problem can be represented in the following equations

Minimization of Objective function f = (cost of Material loss + cost of utility loss) (1)

Subject to (impurities quantity) $x_F < z$ (2)

Decision variable are temperature and flowrate for the reactor.

Where, x_F is the concentration of component F, z is the product specification (Target value of impurities)

By-products formation rate is calculated from the process data such as catalyst activity, flowrates, temperature etc. and plug flow reactor model. Raw material loss is calculated from the by-product formation rate. Utility loss is calculated based on the reactor temperature. With help of both heat and material loss optimum operating conditions are derived using the optimization algorithm.

When coming to multivariable optimization problem, searching for global optimization is crucial. However, popular methods like Gradient, Newton etc. does not guarantee the global optima, in most of the times these methods struck in the local optima. And the same time it is difficult to do deterministically as it is non-linear problem. Recently meta-heuristic algorithms have become a topic of interest in multivariable optimization. In this system, PSO (Particle Swarm Optimization) (Deng et al., 2013), one of the meta-heuristic algorithms is used to calculate the optimum operation conditions.

3. Online Implementation

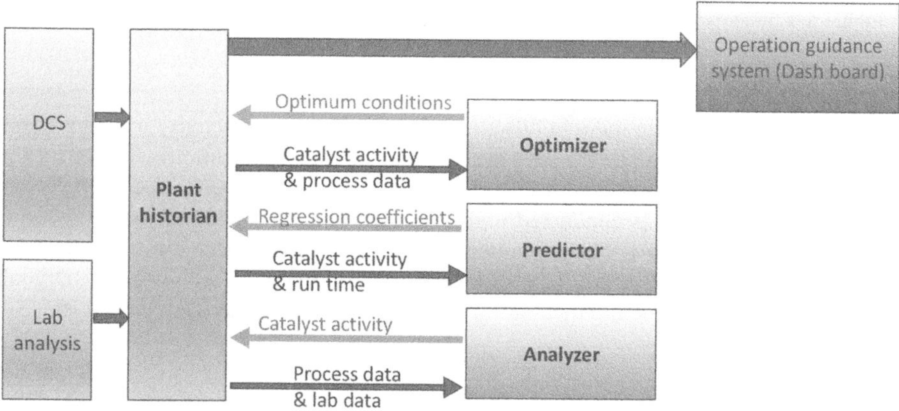

Figure 4. Online implementation Framework

As shown in the Figure 4, all the modules are connected to the plant historian to receive the plant process data as well as lab analysis data. Each module perform their task as per the schedule and write back the result to the plant historian. With help of commercial package, dashboard (operation guidance system) is developed and the plant optimum operating conditions are displayed on operation guidance system. The plant operator adjusts the operating conditions according to the display.

4. Results

In this section, optimum operating condition are compared with the conventional operation. In conventional operation, temperature of the reactors are determined by monitoring the raw materials in the exit of reactor from the lab analysis. When the raw material is detected in the exit of the reactor, the temperature of the reactor is increased. This increase in temperature leads to increase in conversion rate but at the same time it might decrease the selectivity. So, it is necessary to calculate the optimum temperature to balance conversion rate & selectivity.

In order to quantify the changes in the production cost with respect to catalyst activity, comparison of conventional operation and optimum operation is carried out. Figure 5 shows the difference between optimum operation and conventional operation. As shown in the figure, in the first half of catalyst life, the production cost is same (assuming 100% for fresh catalyst) in both the conditions. But coming to the later half of the catalyst life, production cost is less in optimum operating conditions. Based on the results, optimum operating conditions have good impact on the economic point. This system also considers the real time market changes of utility and material cost.

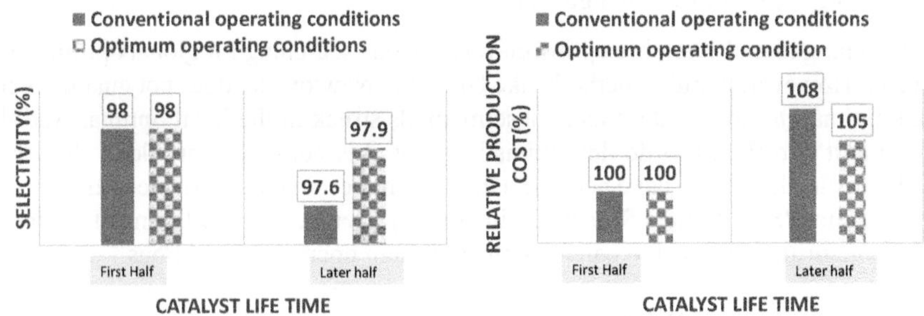

Figure 5. Comparison of conventional operating conditions and optimum operating conditions

5. Conclusions

Developed Digital Twin model allows to estimate the current activity of the catalyst and from that activity it also estimates the optimum operating conditions while ensuring the product quality constraints. A comparison study between conventional operation and optimum operation is conducted under relevant reaction conditions such as same catalyst volume and same inlet flowrates and concentrations. Decrease in production cost and increase in selectivity has achieved using this Digital Twin. These Digital Twins are one of the effective method for the processes with deactivating catalyst.

References

F.Biscarri, I.Monedero, C.León, J.I.Guerrero, R.González, L.Lombard, 2012, A Decision Support System for consumption optimization in a naphtha reforming plant, Computers and Chemical Engineering, 44, 1-10

M.Fuada, M.Hussaina, A.Zakaria, 2012, Optimization strategy for long-term catalyst deactivation in a fixed-bed reactor for methanol synthesis process, Computers and Chemical Engineering, 44, 104– 126

Y.Deng, Q.Jiang, Z.Cao, 2013, Online Optimization of Industrial FCC Unit Based on PSO Algorithm nad RBF Neural Network、(AASRI-WIET 2013)

Proceedings of the 14th International Symposium on Process Systems Engineering – PSE 2021+
June 19-23, 2022, Kyoto, Japan
http://dx.doi.org/10.1016/B978-0-323-85159-6.50063-4

Self-triggered MPC for Perturbed Continuous-time Non-linear Systems

Yueyang Luo[a], Xinmin Zhang[a]*, Zhihuan Song[a]

[a]*State Key Laboratory of Industrial Control Technology, College of Control Science and Engineering, Zhejiang University, Hangzhou 310027, China*
xinminzhang@zju.edu.cn

Abstract

Recently model predictive control has made great progress both in theory and in practical. To further reduce the computational load, this paper introduces a self-triggered mechanism in model prediction control with a decreasing prediction horizon for continuous-time non-linear systems subject to bounded disturbances and certain constraints. Under this strategy, the next updating point of the optimal control sequence is determined according to the current system behaviours instead of the fixed sampling period. Besides, a dual-mode scheme is implemented based on the terminal region. Both the feasibility of the algorithm and the convergence of the controlled system are proved. The application results on a numerical example and a practical system demonstrated the superiority of the proposed strategy.

Keywords: model predictive control, self-triggered mechanism, continuous-time nonlinear systems, dual-mode scheme

1. Introduction

Model predictive control (MPC), also known as receding horizon control (Morari, 1999), mainly consists of prediction model, rolling optimization, and feedback correction (Ding, 2010). Prediction model aims to show the dynamic behaviour of the controlled system in the future. Previous information of the system and the upcoming inputs can be used to obtain the prediction of the nominal system, which therefore provides the prior messages for the optimal algorithm. Since it is hard for the model-based prediction to match the actual controlled process precisely, rolling optimization is adopted.

So far, MPC has also been extensively studied and developed in theory (Mayne, 2000) (Mayne, 2014). Some scholars proposed a self-triggering control strategy that adaptively selects the sampling interval for input affine nonlinear systems (Hashimoto, 2016). Different from the normal pattern of MPC, the next update instant can be pre-calculated based on the current information under the self-triggered mechanism (Sun, 2019). Therefore, the computational burden of carrying out self-triggered MPC is decreased both on frequency and one-shot complexity of solving the OCP with the adaptive prediction horizon.

A predictive control strategy based on self-triggered mechanism is proposed for nonlinear continuous-time systems subject to external additive disturbance and constraints of states and inputs. In the framework of dual-mode model predictive control (Michalska, 1993), sufficient conditions are derived to guarantee the recursive feasibility in MPC control mode, the convergence to the terminal region within finite time, and the stability of the system after entering the terminal region. Furthermore, a simulation example is presented to verify the feasibility and effectiveness of the proposed strategy.

The remainder of this paper is organized as follows. Section 2 gives the description of system model and preliminary. In Section 3, the main problems to be solved are introduced, and the associated strategy in MPC control mode is described. In Section 4, simulation results are provided. Section 5 draws the conclusions.

2. Preliminary

2.1. System Model

The perturbed continuous-time nonlinear system and its nominal form are considered as:

$$\dot{x}(t) = f\big(x(t), u(t)\big) + w(t), \quad x(0) = x_0 \tag{1}$$

$$\dot{\hat{x}}(t) = f\big(\hat{x}(t), \hat{u}(t)\big), \quad \hat{x}(0) = x_0 \tag{2}$$

where $x(t) \in R^n$, $u(t) \in R^m$, and $w(t) \in R^n$ are the state, control input, and bounded disturbance, respectively. Required constraints are presumed as follows:

$$x(t) \in \mathcal{X}, \quad u(t) \in \mathcal{U}, \quad w(t) \in \mathcal{W} \tag{3}$$

Specifically, both $\mathcal{X} \subseteq \mathcal{R}^n$ and $\mathcal{U} \subseteq \mathcal{R}^m$ are compact sets containing the origin as an interior point. $\mathcal{W} \triangleq \{w \in \mathcal{R}^n : \|w\| \leq \rho\}$ represents the boundary of the disturbance. The system function $f(x,u)$ is a twice continuously differentiable nonlinear function satisfying $f(0,0) = 0$, and is stabilizable in linearization form (Dunbar, 2007). Besides, it is assumed that $f(x,u)$ is Lipschitz continuous respect to $x \in \mathcal{X}$ with Lipschitz constant L_f, i.e.,

$$\|f(x_1,u) - f(x_2,u))\|_P \leq L_f \|x_1 - x_2\|_P \tag{4}$$

2.2. Lemma 1

The Gronwall-Bellman inequality in continuous-time form is introduced. If function $\beta(\cdot): \mathcal{R} \to \mathcal{R}_{>0}$ satisfies the following inequality (Rawlings, 2017):

$$\mu(t) \leq \alpha(t) + \int_a^t \beta(s)\mu(s)ds \, , t \in [a,b]$$

Then, for $t \in [a,b]$, we have:

$$\mu(t) \leq \alpha(t) + \int_a^t \alpha(s)\beta(s) \exp\left(\int_s^t \beta(r)dr\right) ds \, , t \in [a,b]$$

Moreover, if $\alpha(\cdot): \mathcal{R} \to \mathcal{R}$ is a nondecreasing function, then a more explicit conclusion can be drawn:

$$\mu(t) \leq \alpha(t) \exp\left(\int_a^t \beta(s)ds\right), t \in [a,b] \tag{5}$$

2.3. Lemma 2

For the system (2)(1), within the scope that $X_r = \{\hat{x}: \|\hat{x}\|_P^2 \leq r^2\}$, there exists a state feedback $Kx \in U$ such that:

$$\frac{d(\|\hat{x}(t)\|_P^2)}{dt} \leq -\|\hat{x}(t)\|_\Phi^2 \tag{6}$$

Suppose A and B are the linearization matrices. Given a $Q > 0$, $R > 0$ and K satisfying that $\lambda(A + BK) < 0$, there is a Lyapunov equation to comply with:

$$P(A + BK + \kappa I) + (A + BK + \kappa I)^T P = -\Phi$$

where $\Phi = Q + K^T RK$.The value of κ is selected to ensure $\lambda(A + BK + \kappa I) < 0$.

3. Description for OCP and Triggering Mechanism

3.1. OCP

At the triggering instant, the optimal control trajectory can be obtained by solving an optimal control problem as follows:

$$\begin{aligned} \hat{u}^*(s; t_k) &= \arg \min_{\hat{u}(s;t_k)} J_N(\hat{x}(s; t_k), \hat{u}(s; t_k), T_k) \\ &= \arg \min_{\hat{u}(s;t_k)} \int_{t_k}^{t_k+T_k} \|\hat{x}(s; t_k)\|_Q^2 + \|\hat{u}(s; t_k)\|_R^2 \, ds \\ &\qquad + \|\hat{x}(t_k + T_k; t_k)\|_P^2 \end{aligned}$$

$$\begin{aligned} s.t.\ &\dot{\hat{x}}(s; t_k) = f(\hat{x}(s; t_k), \hat{u}(s; t_k)), \quad \hat{x}(t_k; t_k) = x(t_k) \\ &\hat{u}(s; t_k) \in \mathcal{U} \\ &\hat{x}(s; t_k) \in \mathcal{X}_{s-t_k} \triangleq \mathcal{X} \ominus \mathcal{T}_{s-t_k} \\ &\hat{x}(t_k + T_k; t_k) \in \mathcal{X}_\varepsilon \triangleq \{x: \|x\|_P^2 \leq \varepsilon^2\} \end{aligned} \tag{7}$$

$\mathcal{X}_{s-t_k}$ represents the contracted constraints at the s instant from t_k. Moreover, $\mathcal{T}_{s-t_k}$ denotes the deviation between the predictive state from the actual state at s. The detailed definition of $\mathcal{X}_{s-t_k}$ and $\mathcal{T}_{s-t_k}$ will be discussed below.

3.2. Self-triggered Strategy

At the current time t_k, the interval between t_k and t_{k+1} and the reduction of prediction horizon are defined as follows:

$$m_{t_k} \triangleq t_{k+1} - t_k$$

$$n_{t_k} = T_k - T_{k+1}$$

$$m_{t_k} = min\{\widehat{m}_{t_k}, \breve{m}_{t_k}, T_k\} \tag{8}$$

$$\widehat{m}_{t_k} = sup\{m_{t_k} > 0: \bar{\lambda}(\sqrt{P}) \cdot \rho \cdot m_{t_k} \cdot e^{L_f T_k} \leq r - \varepsilon\} \tag{9}$$

$$\begin{aligned} \breve{m}_{t_k} = sup\{m_{t_k} > 0: &\bar{\lambda}(\sqrt{P}) \cdot \rho \cdot m_{t_k} \cdot e^{L_f T_k} \cdot (r + \varepsilon) \\ &+ \int_{t_{k+1}}^{t_k+T_k} \Big[\big(\bar{\lambda}(Q) \cdot \rho \cdot m_{t_k} \cdot e^{L_f(s-t_k)}\big)^2 \\ &2\bar{\lambda}(Q)\rho m_{t_k} e^{L_f(s-t_k)} + \|\hat{x}^*(s; t_k)\|_Q^2\Big] ds \\ &\leq \sigma \int_{t_k}^{t_{k+1}} \left(\|\hat{x}^*(s; t_k)\|_Q^2 + \|\hat{u}^*(s; t_k)\|_R^2\right) ds\} \end{aligned} \tag{10}$$

$$T_{k+1} = min\{ m_{t_k}, \widetilde{T_k}\} \tag{11}$$

where $\sigma \in (0,1)$, and $\widetilde{T_k}$ is defined as:

$$\widetilde{T_k} = inf\{0 \le h < T_k : \hat{x}^*(t_k + h; t_k) \in \mathcal{X}_\varepsilon\} \tag{12}$$

Algorithm 1 Dual-mode Self-triggered MPC

while at time t_k **do**
  if $x(t_k) \in \mathrm{X}_\varepsilon$ **then**
    Switch to $\kappa(x)$ to stabilize the system;
  else
    Update the initial state of OCP by $\hat{x}(t_k) = x(t_k)$;
    Solve the OCP in (7) to obtain the optimal predicted control sequence $\hat{u}^*(t_k)$ as well as the state trajectory $\hat{x}^*(t_k)$;
    Calculate the next triggering instant t_{k+1} by (8) and the next prediction horizon T_{k+1} by (11);
    Apply the first m_{t_k} control input in $\hat{x}^*(t_k)$ to (1);
  end if
  Assign $t_k = t_{k+1}$;
end while

4. Simulation

In this section, a cart-damper-spring system are given to verify the effectiveness of the proposed control scheme. The application results are compared with the conventional time-triggered MPC. The specific application of a cart-damper-spring system is presented by the following dynamics (Li, 2014):

$$\begin{cases} \dot{x}_1(\mathrm{t}) = x_2(t) \\ \dot{x}_2(\mathrm{t}) = -\dfrac{\zeta}{M_c} e^{-x_1(t)} x_1(t) - \dfrac{h_d}{M_c} x_2(t) + \dfrac{u(t)}{M_c} + \dfrac{v(t)}{M_c} \end{cases} \tag{13}$$

where $x_1(t)$ and $x_2(t)$ denote the location and velocity of the cart, respectively. $\omega(t)$ is the external disturbance bounded by $\|v(t)\| \le 0.0025$. The weight of the cart is $M_c = 1.25kg$, and the stiffness of the spring is $\zeta = 0.9N/m$. The damper factor is $h_d = 0.42N/m$. The input $u(t)$ is constrained as $-0.9 \le u(t) \le 0.9$. The state constraint set is given by $\mathcal{X} = x{:}\ \|x_1\| \le 0.35, \|x_2\| \le 1$. The stage weighting matrix Q is $Q = \begin{pmatrix} 0.06 & 0 \\ 0 & 0.06 \end{pmatrix}$, the input weighting matrix R is 0.001, and then the terminal weighting matrix can be calculated as $P = \begin{pmatrix} 0.1248 & 0.0260 \\ 0.0260 & 0.0358 \end{pmatrix}$. The Lipschitz constant of the system in (13) is $L_f = 0.1703$, and the feedback matrix K is $K = (-1.6000 \quad -2.3300)$. The terminal parameters are presented as $\varepsilon = 0.072$ and $r = 0.076$. The compromising factor σ is 0.12, and the initial state is $x_0 = (0.3 \quad -1)^T$. Fig.1 presents the state and input trajectory. Fig.2 denotes the triggered instants and prediction horizons at each sampling instant t_k. Similar to the former numerical case, the validity of the strategy has been shown from a drastic descension in triggering interval and a moderate falling in prediction horizon.

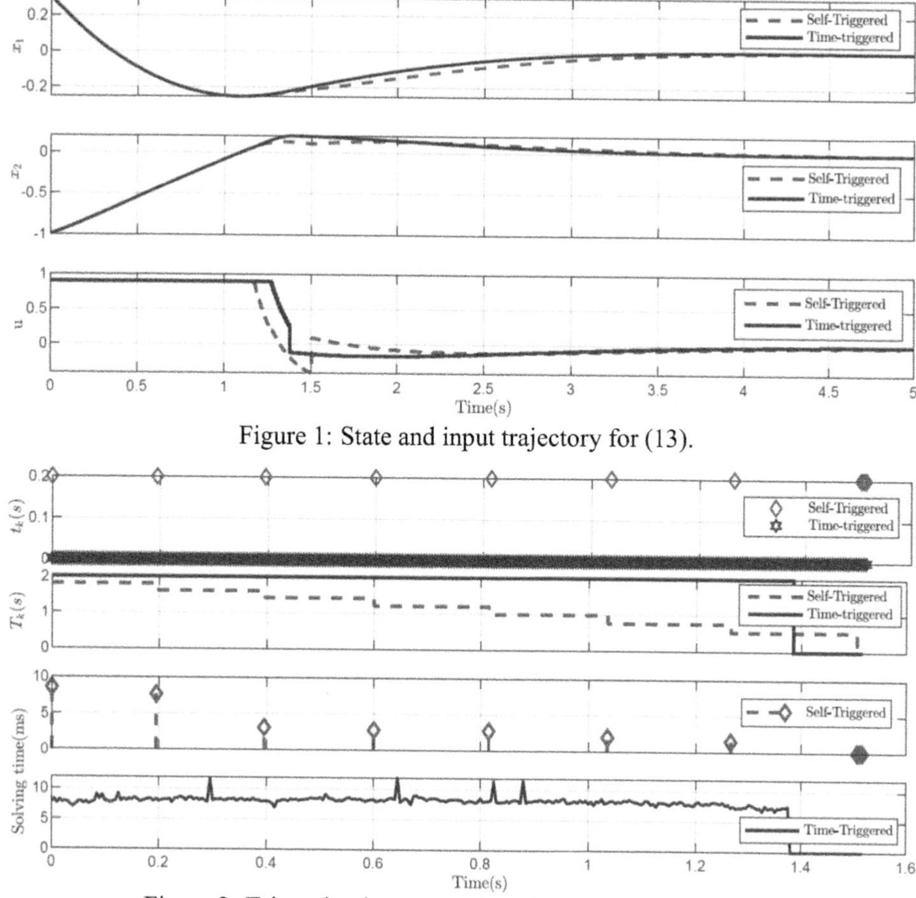

Figure 1: State and input trajectory for (13).

Figure 2: Triggering instants and prediction horizons for (13).

5. Conclusions

In this paper, we proposed a dual-mode MPC with a self-triggered strategy and declining prediction horizons. First, a self-triggered algorithm was proposed. Second, the feasibility and stability in and out of the terminal region were analysed. In addition, within the terminal region, the ultimate boundary of the system states related to perturbs was estimated. Moreover, a sufficient condition is proposed to prevent Zeno behavior. Finally, simulation results were presented to show the effectiveness of the proposed algorithm.

References

Baocang Ding, 2017, Theory and Method of Predictive Control, Machinery Industry Press.

William B Dunbar, 2007, Distributed receding horizon control of dynamically coupled nonlinear systems, IEEE Transactions on Automatic Control, 52, 7, 1249-1263.

Kazumune Hashimoto, Shuichi Adachi, and Dimos V Dimarogonas, 2016, Self-triggered model predictive control for nonlinear input-affine dynamical systems via adaptivecontrol samples selection, IEEE Transactions on Automatic Control, 62, 1, 177- 189.

Huiping Li and Yang Shi, 2014, Event-triggered robust model predictive control of continuous-time nonlinear systems, Automatica, 50, 5, 1507-1513.

David Q Mayne, 2014, Model predictive control: Recent developments and future promise, Automatica, 50, 12, 2967–2986.

David Q Mayne, James B Rawlings, Christopher V Rao, and Pierre OM Scokaert, 2000, Constrained model predictive control: Stability and optimality, Automatica, 36, 6, 789–814.

Hanna Michalska and David Q Mayne, 1993, Robust receding horizon control of con- strained nonlinear systems, IEEE transactions on automatic control, 38, 11, 1623–1633.

Manfred Morari and Jay H Lee, 1999, Model predictive control: past, present and future, Computers & Chemical Engineering, 23, 4-5, 667–682

James Blake Rawlings, David Q Mayne, and Moritz Diehl, 2017, Model predictive control: theory, computation, and design, WI: Nob Hill Publishing.

Zhongqi Sun, Li Dai, Kun Liu, Dimos V Dimarogonas, and Yuanqing Xia,2019, Robustself-triggered mpc with adaptive prediction horizon for perturbed nonlinear sys- tems, IEEE Transactions on Automatic Control, 64, 11, 4780–4787.

Proceedings of the 14th International Symposium on Process Systems Engineering – PSE 2021+
June 19-23, 2022, Kyoto, Japan
http://dx.doi.org/10.1016/B978-0-323-85159-6.50064-6

A comparative study between MPC and selector-based PID control for an industrial heat exchanger

Anikesh Kumar[a], S. Lakshminarayanan[a*], I. A. Karimi[a], Rajagopalan Srinivasan[b]

[a]*Department of Chemical & Biomolecular Engineering, National University of Singapore, Singapore 117585, Singapore*

[b]*Department of Chemical Engineering, Indian Institute of Technology Madras, Chennai 600036, India*

laksh@nus.edu.sg

Abstract

This study compares the performance of two widely used control strategies for industrial systems with constraints, namely MPC and selector-based PID control. The simulation studies are carried out using models built from historical data provided to us for an industrial heat exchanger employed at a South-East Asian processing facility. The comparative studies specifically address the deterioration of performance for the two aforementioned strategies in the presence of varying degrees of valve stiction. Aspects of performance recovery via addition of derivative action and retuning of PI parameters for selector-based control are also discussed. The studies suggest that in addition to being a more formal and robust method to handle constraints, MPC is also able to retain its performance to a larger degree in the presence of stiction as compared to selector-based control.

Keywords: Selector-based PID control; Heat exchanger control; Model predictive control; Valve stiction.

1. Introduction

Heat exchangers are an indispensable part of process industries owing to their major role in the energy efficient operation of plants. Since processes operate in the vicinity of an operating point (or a few such points), a heat exchanger control loop is primarily designed for the regulatory control of the temperatures of relevant exit streams. Proportional-Integral-Derivative (PID) controllers are the most widely deployed controllers in the process industry because of their simplicity and an abundance of pre-existing tuning rules. However, tuning PID controllers for a heat exchanger control loop is not a trivial task when heat exchangers display non-linearity and time changing behavior. Additionally, some processes have inherent economic and safety constraints which impose bounds on the controlled and manipulated variables (CVs and MVs). For instance, direct manipulation of the hot/cold stream may be sufficient for control if it is an utility, however if there are constraints on both streams, bypassing is widely used in the industry (Luyben, 2011). Despite the popularity of PID controllers, one major drawback in their implementation is their inability to innately accommodate the aforementioned constraints. In order to circumvent this problem, many industrial practitioners resort to the usage of ad-hoc measures like selector-based PID control. In a selector-based control framework, a single MV is linked with multiple CVs through different PID controllers. At a given instant, all these controller outputs are fed to a selector block and the value of the MV is chosen based on a safety logic. Although, selector-based control is widely prevalent, tuning the multiple controllers acting on the same MV is not straighforward and is usually carried out based on the empirical knowledge of plant operators. Furthermore, this approach becomes very cumbersome as the number of variables increase and an attractive alternate is the use of multivariable controllers such as Model Predictive Control (MPC) (Krishnamoorthy & Skogestad, 2020). MPC formally encapsulates the objectives and constraints of a system irrespective of its size (Camacho & Bordons, 2007) and has served as an effective control tool across numerous disciplines over the last few decades (Lee, 2011). Given the contrasting natures of the two aforementioned control strategies, it is interesting to assess their performance on industrial systems with constraints. Additionally, to the best of our knowledge, such a comparative assessment is scarce in the literature. To this end, we have conducted simulation studies comparing the performance and robustness of the two methods on an industrial heat exchanger in our forthcoming work (Kumar et al., 2021). However, it does not consider the effect of control valve faults on the two methodologies. Since, valve stiction is one of the most commonly occurring valve faults (Choudhury et al., 2008), comparative studies specifically addressing the deterioration of performance for the two aforementioned strategies in the presence of varying degrees of valve stiction is considered in this work.

The rest of this paper is organized as follows. Section 2 contains the description of the industrial heat exchanger considered in this study. Section 3 comprises the simulation studies for selector-based control and MPC in the presence of stiction for two different modes of operation of the exchanger. Finally, conclusions and prospective future works are discussed in the last section.

2. Heat exchanger system

The heat exchanger system considered in this study (see Figure 1) is currently employed at a South-East Asian processing facility. The exchanger cools a gas stream to a pre-specified temperature by exchanging heat with a liquid stream. Under nominal operating conditions, the gas outlet temperature can be readily controlled via the manipulation of the valve at the liquid outlet. However, because of the nature of process operation, there is a substantial variation in the gas flow rate throughout the day. This variability leads to the possibility of two-phase flow on the outlets of both streams. At low gas flows, the gas outlet may reach its due point; whereas for high gas flows, the liquid outlet might reach its bubble point. As the system is not designed for two-phase flow, the employed control architecture needs to take these constraints into account. To this end, there is a provision to bypass the gas so as to avoid two-phase flow on either side. Hence, in the bypass mode, the system has three CVs: Gas outlet temperature (CV_1), Liquid outlet temperature (CV_2), and Combined gas outlet temperature (CV_3); two MVs: Liquid valve (MV_1) and Gas main valve[1] (MV_2); and three disturbance variables (DVs): Gas flow rate (DV_1), Gas inlet temperature (DV_2) and Liquid inlet temperature (DV_3).

In order to handle the constraints on the outlet stream temperatures, the currently employed control architecture uses four controllers (TICs 1-4) in unison with two selectors. TIC-1 controls CV_1 through MV_1 under nominal conditions, whereas under the

[1] The main and bypass valves for the gas side are manipulated simultaneously by the same magnitude in opposite directions. Hence, they are together considered as one MV in the current control architecture.

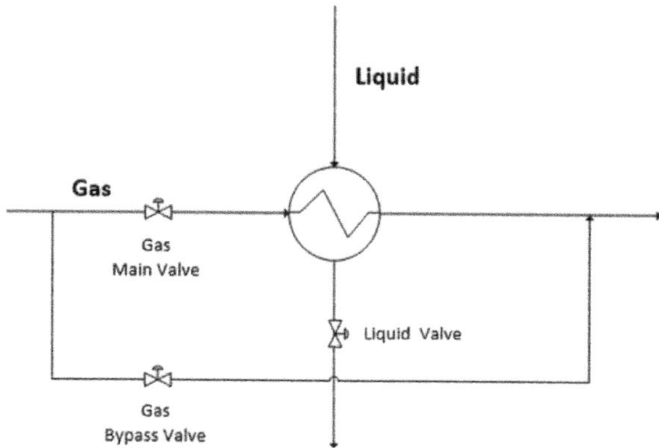

Figure 1: Schematic of the heat exchanger under study

bypass mode, TIC-4 controls CV_3 through MV_2. TIC-2 and TIC-3 both control CV_2 with set-points 10 degrees apart through MV_1 and MV_2 respectively. This accounts for large abrupt changes in gas flow, where bypassing may not be sufficient to prevent liquid overheating and hence MV_1 needs to be adjusted proactively. A max selector on the output of TICs 1 and 2 controls MV_1, whereas a min selector on TICs 3 and 4, controls MV_2. All the aforementioned information is captured in the Simulink model shown in Figure 2.

3. Simulation studies

The simulations conducted in this section are carried out using models identified, PID controller tuning, and MPC parameters used in Kumar et al. (2021). The models used are discrete state-space models (see Eqs. (1-2)) identified using an in-house developed multivariable identification algorithm (Schaper et al., 1994) on the historical plant data available to us[2].

$$X_{t+1} = \Phi X_t + Gu_t + w_t \tag{1}$$

$$y_t = HX_t + Au_t + Bw_t + v_t \tag{2}$$

For the purpose of this work, we have considered stiction only in the liquid valve (MV_1) as it is the primary manipulated variable and is subject to more wear and tear as opposed to the gas valve (MV_2). Additionally, to quantify stiction, a single parameter stiction model as proposed by Srinivasan et al. (2005) has been used.

$$x(t) = \begin{cases} x(t-1) & if\ |x(t-1) - u(t)| \leq d \\ u(t) & otherwise \end{cases} \tag{3}$$

where $x(t)$ and $x(t-1)$ are the present and past MV movements, $u(t)$ is the present controller output (OP), and d is the stiction band which is usually represented as a fraction/percentage of the controller output (OP) range. A non-zero d value suggests the presence of stiction and its severity is directly proportional to the value of d.

[2] Please contact the authors for detailed information on the models used in the simulations.

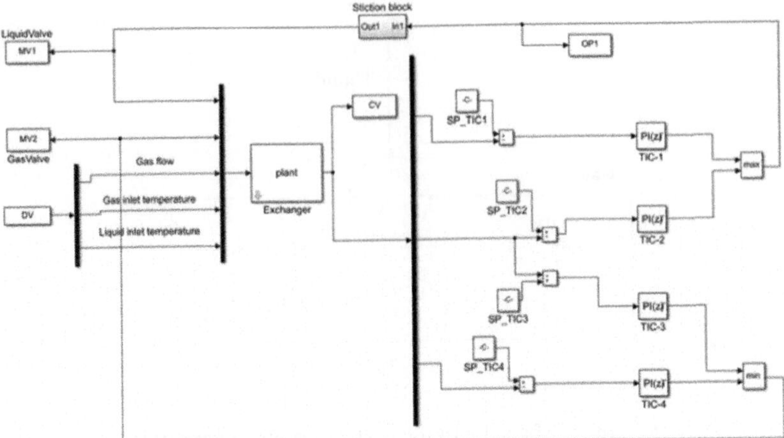

Figure 2: Exchanger model with selector-based control and stiction in liquid valve

3.1. *Simulation results for nominal mode*

We first consider the nominal mode of operation wherein only MV_1 is active. For disturbance trends observed during a day of operation, we simulate the closed-loop performance of the two control strategies under the presence of 1 and 2 percent stiction. Additionally, since the current controllers in the selector-based strategy are PI and judicious addition of derivative action is recommended as one of the methods of stiction compensation (Patwardhan, 2014), simulation studies with PID control are also included. Figures 3 and 4 show the closed-loop responses[3] for all the control strategies for $d = 1\%$ and $d = 2\%$ respectively. For all the strategies, both the outlet temperatures are at a safe margin from the two-phase regimes, despite the presence of stiction. The integral of squared errors (ISE) for CV_1 using PI, PID, and MPC for $d = 1\%$ and $d = 2\%$ are $[432.62\ \ 339.02\ \ 158.07]$ and $[1116.65\ \ 1082.08\ \ 699.05]$ respectively. It can be seen that MPC provides the best performance whereas addition of derivative action does lead to improvement in the performance of the selector-based methodology. However, since there is only one MV at the disposal of MPC, the performance gap with respect to selector-based control in the presence of stiction is not as stark as the stiction free case.

3.2. *Simulation results for bypass model*

Similar to the nominal mode, simulation studies were carried out for the bypass mode for two different levels of stiction in the liquid valve. MPC is able to keep CV_3 close to the set-point with ISE values of 35.18 and 39.43 for $d = 1\%$ and $d = 2\%$ respectively, while satisfying the safety constraints on other variables (see Figure 5). It is also able to keep the secondary variable (MV_2) at the desired opening of 100%. Selector-based control provides inferior performance in terms of squared error and shows a significant deviation from the set-point for CV_3 as opposed to MPC with an ISE value of 240.67 for $d = 1\%$ as evident from Figure 5. For $d = 2\%$, MV_1 saturates leading to two-phase flow on the gas side, and the responses have been omitted for the sake of brevity. It is apparent from the

[3] The numerical values of the controller set-points and stream temperatures have been omitted in all simulation studies for proprietary reasons.

simulation results that MPC can handle stiction without retuning any of the parameters whereas the selector-based methodology can be severely limited in its presence.

4. Conclusions and future work

In this work, we carry out comparative studies between selector-based control and MPC for an industrial heat exchanger with a sticky valve. Simulation studies show that judicious inclusion of derivative action can improve the performance of selector-based control in the presence of stiction; however, MPC is able to preserve its performance better, and one can expect its higher performance to hold, especially for more complex systems. Future work includes inclusion of stiction in the gas valve, exploration of strategies for retuning of PID controllers for multivariable systems using selectors, and optimization of MPC parameters for different levels of stiction.

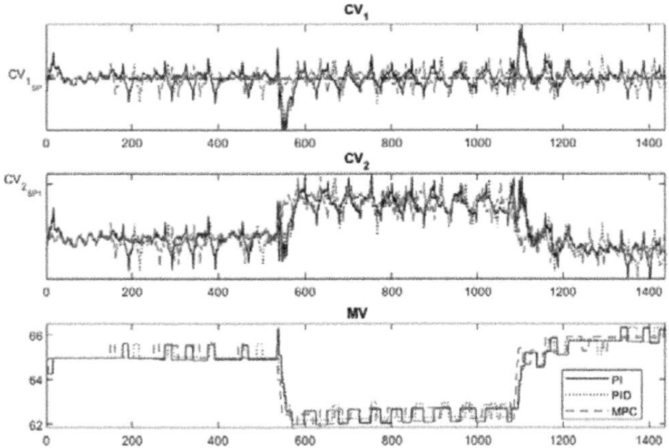

Figure 3: Performance Comparison for Nominal Mode with d=1% for Liquid Valve

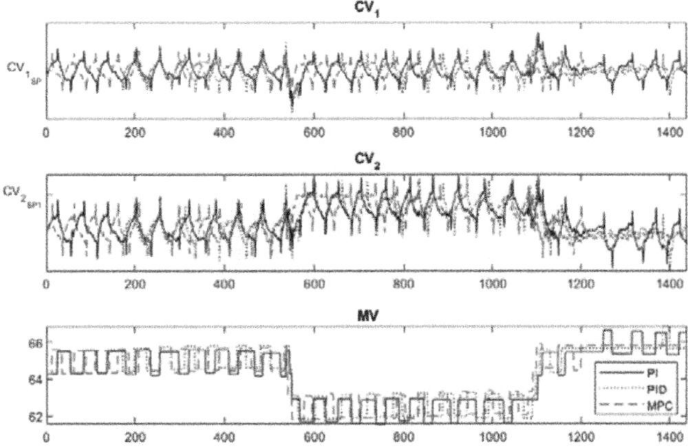

Figure 4: Performance Comparison for Nominal Mode with d=2% for Liquid Valve

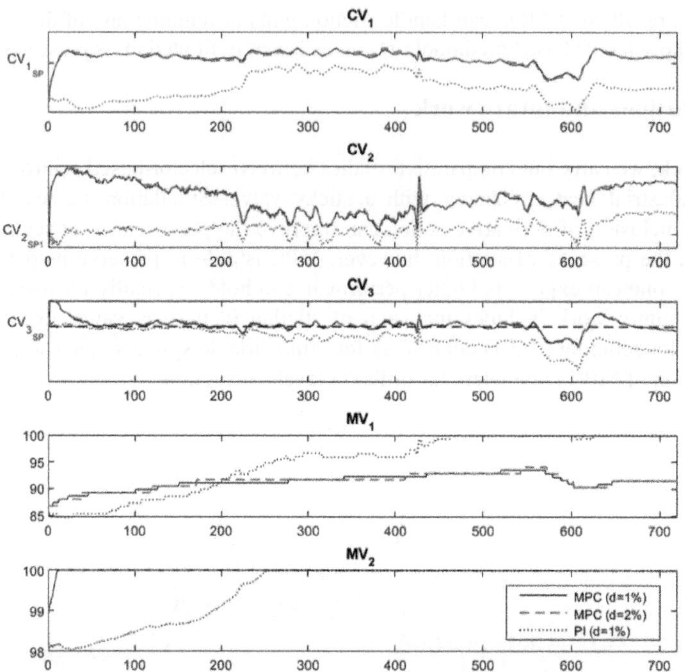

Figure 5: Closed-loop responses for bypass Mode with Sticky Liquid Valve

References

Camacho, E. F., & Bordons, C. (2007). Model predictive control (2nd ed.). London;New York;: Springer.

Choudhury, S. M. A. A., Shah, S. L., & Thornhill, N. F. (2008). Stiction: Definition and Discussions. In S. M. A. A. Choudhury, S. L. Shah & N. F. Thornhill (Eds.), Diagnosis of Process Nonlinearities and Valve Stiction: Data Driven Approaches (pp. 143-151). Berlin, Heidelberg: Springer Berlin Heidelberg.

Krishnamoorthy, D., & Skogestad, S. (2020). Systematic design of active constraint switching using selectors. Computers & chemical engineering, 143.

Kumar, A., Lakshminarayanan, S., Karimi, I. A., & Srinivasan, R. (2021). Critical assessment of control strategies for industrial systems with input-output constraints. Industrial and Engineering Chemistry Research (under review).

Lee, J. H. (2011). Model predictive control: Review of the three decades of development. International Journal of Control, Automation and Systems, 9, 415.

Luyben, W. L. (2011). Heat-Exchanger Bypass Control. Industrial & Engineering Chemistry Research, 50, 965-973.

Patwardhan, R. (2014). Managing the performance of control loops with valve stiction: An Industrial Perspective.

Schaper, C. D., Larimore, W. E., Seborg, D. E., & Mellichamp, D. A. (1994). Identification of chemical processes using canonical variate analysis. Computers & chemical engineering, 18, 55-69.

Srinivasan, R., Rengaswamy, R., Narasimhan, S., & Miller, R. (2005). Control Loop Performance Assessment. 2. Hammerstein Model Approach for Stiction Diagnosis. Industrial & Engineering Chemistry Research, 44, 6719-6728.

Proceedings of the 14th International Symposium on Process Systems Engineering – PSE 2021+
June 19-23, 2022, Kyoto, Japan
http://dx.doi.org/10.1016/B978-0-323-85159-6.50065-8

MILP Formulation for Dynamic Demand Response of Electrolyzers

Florian Joseph Baader[a,b], André Bardow[a,c], Manuel Dahmen[a]*

[a]Institute of Energy and Climate Research - Energy Systems Engineering (IEK-10), Forschungszentrum Jülich GmbH, 52425 Jülich, Germany
[b]RWTH Aachen University, Aachen 52062, Germany
[c]Energy & Process Systems Engineering - Department of Mechanical and Process Engineering, ETH Zurich, 8092 Zürich, Switzerland
**m.dahmen@fz-juelich.de*

Abstract

Electrolyzers can reduce their electricity costs through demand response (DR) by adapting their production rate to time-varying market prices. Although the production rate can often be adapted rapidly, exploiting the full DR potential of an electrolyzer requires to consider slow temperature dynamics, leading to challenging mixed-integer dynamic optimization problems. In this contribution, we propose a dynamic ramping reformulation for real-time scheduling optimization of electrolyzers considering these slow temperature dynamics. Starting from a nonlinear dynamic model, the limits of the temperature gradient are derived to guarantee that the optimization result is feasible on the original model. The limits are then approximated conservatively by piece-wise affine functions leading to a mixed-integer linear program (MILP). Varying the number of piece-wise affine segments allows to explicitly balance model conservativeness against computational burden. We apply our reformulation to a validated alkaline electrolyzer model from literature. Our dynamic temperature ramping approach reduces production costs by 15.9 % compared to nominal operation. A quasi-steady-state optimization, which is restricted to production rates with steady-state temperatures in the allowed range, only leads to 12.8 % improvement. The proposed formulation achieves optimization runtimes below one minute, which is sufficiently fast for real-time scheduling.

Keywords: Electrolysis, Demand response, Mixed-integer linear programming

1. Introduction

Demand response (DR) allows consumers to reduce their electricity costs by adapting production rate to time-varying market-prices and ideally also stabilizes the electricity grid (Zhang and Grossmann, 2016). Particularly suitable for DR are electrochemical production processes such as chlor-alkali or water electrolysis because they can often adapt their production rate rapidly (Burre et al., 2020). More specifically, the time scale of electrochemical reactions is significantly faster than the hourly time scale typical for electricity prices (Simkoff and Baldea, 2020). Therefore, step changes of the production rate can often be assumed in electrolyzer scheduling optimization. Scheduling usually considers a time horizon in the order of one day. However, electrolyzers feature slow temperature dynamics in the order of hours (Gabrielli et al., 2016). Neglecting these slow temperature dynamics during scheduling, reduces the flexibility of the electrolyzer to steady-state-feasible production points that are limited by the minimum and maximum allowed temperature (Simkoff and Baldea, 2020). From a technical point of view, production rates outside of the steady-state-feasible range can be applied in transient operation for a limited amount of time (Flamm et al., 2021). For example, the energy park Mainz (Germany) has a PEM electrolyzer with 4 MW nominal power that can operate at a peak power of 6 MW for 15 minutes if load is reduced afterwards to allow cooling (Kopp et al., 2017). Simkoff and Baldea (2020) consider temperature effects of a chlor-alkali electrolyzer using dynamic optimization but replace the original nonlinear model with a data-driven surrogate model. On top of dynamic effects, electrolyzers have a minimum allowed current (Ulleberg, 1998). Consequently, the possibility to turn off the electrolyzer can only be considered in scheduling if discrete decisions are included, leading to computationally challenging mixed-integer dynamic optimization (MIDO) problems.

In this contribution, we propose a mixed-integer linear programming (MILP) formulation for electrolyzer scheduling optimization. To this end, we consider temperature dynamics using a dynamic ramping approach (Baader et al., 2021). Accordingly, the limits of the temperature gradient are functions of the electrolyzer state. In contrast to data-driven surrogate models, our reformulation guarantees results that are feasible on the original nonlinear model. The dynamic temperature ramping reformulation is introduced in Section 2. In Section 3, we apply the reformulation to an alkaline electrolyzer model (Ulleberg, 1998) and present results in Section 4. Section 5 concludes the work.

2. MILP Formulation for Electrolyzer Scheduling

2.1. Assumptions

Our reformulation is not restricted to one specific electrolyzer model. The reformulation only relies on a few assumptions that are typically satisfied. The main assumption is that the temperature T is the only differential state. Accordingly, all other states can be considered in (quasi-)steady-state on the scheduling-relevant hourly timescale, which is often valid as electrochemical reactions typically occur on a much faster time scale. Further, we assume that there are two degrees of freedom in electrolyzer operation: the current I and an input u_{cool} acting on the cooling power. For instance, u_{cool} can be the temperature of raw material (Simkoff and Baldea, 2020) or the flow rate of a cooling fluid (Ulleberg, 1998). Thus, the scheduling-relevant variables product flow rate n_{prod}, electric power P_{elec}, and temperature gradient $\frac{dT}{dt}$ can be calculated as nonlinear functions of I, u_{cool}, and T (Figure 1, left). For instance, in a simple model, the voltage U is modeled as an empiric function of I and T (Ulleberg, 1998). The voltage U is needed to calculate both electric power and temperature gradient. In more physically motivated models, the voltage also depends on partial pressures, which are determined by the mass balances (Gabrielli et al., 2016). As these mass balances can be assumed to be in steady state on the hourly time scale, the balances give a nonlinear system of algebraic equations that can be solved for given I, u_{cool}, and T. Thus, our assumption is still valid. Moreover, we assume that the nonlinear functions can be inverted for a given temperature T. More specifically, the input I can be calculated as a function $I = \phi_I(T, n_{prod})$ of temperature T and output n_{prod}, and the input u_{cool} can be calculated as a function $u_{cool} = \phi_{u_{cool}}(T, n_{prod}, \frac{dT}{dt})$, which additionally to T and n_{prod} depends on the output $\frac{dT}{dt}$.

Finally, the variables n_{prod}, u_{cool}, T are bounded by minimum and maximum values. We assume that step changes can be applied on the scheduling time scale to the current I (Flamm et al., 2021). Thus, ramping constraints on the current I are neglected, but can be added in a straightforward way if necessary.

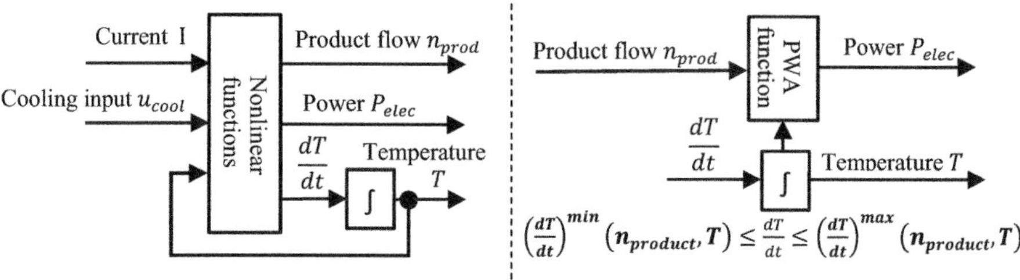

Figure 1: Original nonlinear model (left) and reformulation with piece-wise affine (PWA) function and dynamic ramping constraint in bold font (right).

2.2. Reformulation

In our reformulation, we directly use the scheduling-relevant variables product flow n_{prod}, and temperature gradient $\frac{dT}{dt}$ as degrees of freedom and do not model I and u_{cool} explicitly, which is possible as they can be calculated from n_{prod} and $\frac{dT}{dt}$. The bounds of the temperature gradient depend on both temperature T and product flow rate n_{prod} (Figure 1, right). To choose these bounds, we sample the two-dimensional space given by the bounds of n_{prod} and T. For every pair (n_{prod}, T), we first calculate the current I from the function $\phi_I(T, n_{prod})$ introduced above. Second, we calculate the true nonlinear ramping limits $\left(\frac{dT}{dt}\right)^{min}$, $\left(\frac{dT}{dt}\right)^{max}$ by inserting u_{cool}^{min}, u_{cool}^{max} into the right-hand side function of $\frac{dT}{dt}$. Subsequently, we approximate the nonlinear ramping limits conservatively by piece-wise affine (PWA) functions. Because of this conservativeness, the resulting temperature profile is guaranteed to be feasible on the original nonlinear model. In principle, choosing the conservative limits can be done by bivariate regression (Adeniran and El Ferik, 2017). However, in our case study, we observe that the true nonlinear limits have an almost linear dependence on the electrolyzer temperature T. This observation is likely transferable to other cases because the ramping limits are mainly temperature dependent due to the heat loss to the ambient. This heat loss is essentially proportional to the temperature difference between electrolyzer temperature T and ambient temperature. However, the ramping limits are nonlinear in the production rate n_{prod}. Thus, we set up piece-wise affine functions by dividing the range of n_{prod} into segments. In every segment, the affine functions are parametrized through an optimization that minimizes the distance to the nonlinear bounds. By including more PWA segments, the ramping limits come closer to the true nonlinear limits. However, also the number of binary variables increases.

Finally, we follow the established approach to approximate the electric power P_{elec} as affine function of n_{prod} and T using linear regression (Flamm et al., 2021). Here, small approximation errors are acceptable as they can be compensated by adapting grid electricity consumption. An MILP formulation is achieved by discretizing the temperature evolution using orthogonal collocation on finite elements (Biegler, 2010).

3. Case Study

As case study, we apply our reformulation to a validated alkaline electrolyzer model (Ulleberg, 1998). This model uses empirical functions for the voltage and hydrogen production depending on current I and temperature T. The input u_{cool} is the cooling flow rate, and the temperature gradient $\frac{dT}{dt}$ can be computed as function of I, T, and u_{cool}. Thus, the model satisfies our assumptions (compare to Subsection 2.1 and left part of Figure 1).

The operating range is given by minimum and maximum current density $i^{min} = 40\ \frac{\text{mA}}{\text{cm}^2}$ and $i^{max} = 300\ \frac{\text{mA}}{\text{cm}^2}$ as well as minimum and maximum temperature $T^{min} = 50$ °C and $T^{max} = 80$ °C (Ulleberg, 2003).

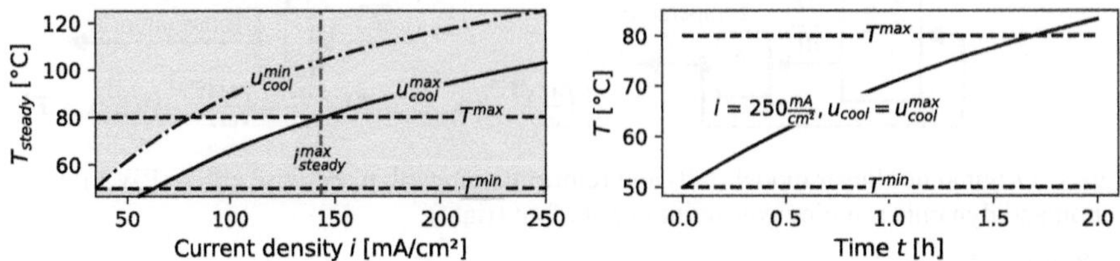

Figure 2: Left: Minimum and maximum temperature, T^{min}, and T^{max}, maximum steady-state-feasible current i_{steady}^{max}, and steady-state temperature T_{steady} for minimum and maximum cooling fluid rate u_{cool}^{min}, and u_{cool}^{max}. Right: Evolution of temperature T for fixed current density i and u_{cool}^{max}.

The steady-state-feasible operating region is given by $i^{min} = 40\ \frac{\text{mA}}{\text{cm}^2}$ and the maximum steady-state-feasible current density $i_{steady}^{max} = 144\ \frac{mA}{cm^2}$ (Figure 2, left). However, significantly higher currents are possible for a scheduling-relevant time. Exemplarily, if the temperature starts from $T^{min} = 50$ °C, a current density of $250\ \frac{\text{mA}}{\text{cm}^2}$ can be applied for more than 1.5 hours until the maximum temperature is reached (Figure 2, right).
In order to describe the temperature dynamics by PWA temperature ramping limits $\left(\frac{dT}{dt}\right)^{min}$, $\left(\frac{dT}{dt}\right)^{max}$, we divide the range of the production rate n_{prod} into equidistant segments, as described in Section 2. We observe that the nonlinearities with respect to n_{prod} are so strong that for less than three affine segments the minimum and maximum ramping limits overlap. We vary the number of affine segments n_{seg} between 3 and 10 and choose 5 segments, which give a reasonable approximation (Figure 3).

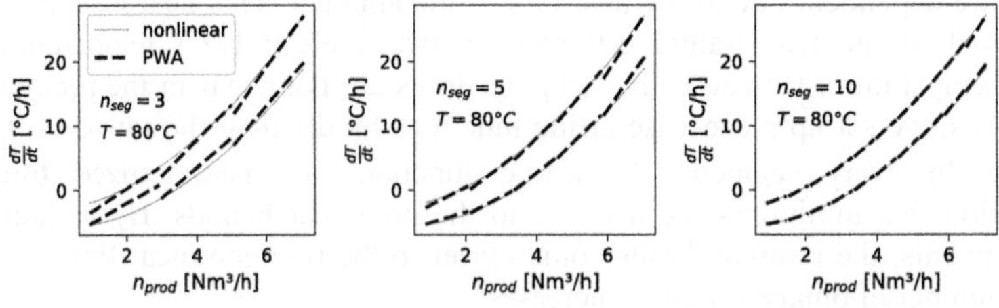

Figure 3: Nonlinear and piece-wise affine (PWA) limits of temperature gradient $\frac{dT}{dt}$ as function of product flow n_{prod} for temperature $T = 80$ °C and different numbers of segments n_{seg}.

In our numerical study, we choose a nominal production rate of $n_{prod}^{nom} = 2.69\ \frac{\text{Nm}^3}{\text{h}}$, which equals 80 % of the production rate achieved with the maximum steady-state feasible current density i_{steady}^{max}. Furthermore, we assume that the nominal production rate must be met on average over the one-day time horizon and use a recent German day-ahead market electricity price profile from April 2nd, 2021. We study the economic performance of our scheduling optimization in a simulation with the original nonlinear process model. This strategy allows us to check the suitability of the chosen time discretization and to verify that the cooling flow rate u_{cool} and the temperature T always stay within the respective bounds. We benchmark our dynamic temperature ramping approach against (i) a nominal operation with constant production rate n_{prod}^{nom} and (ii) a quasi-steady-state (QSS) optimization that does not consider temperature dynamics and thus can only operate within the steady-state-feasible range. For this QSS optimization, we calculate the efficiency curve assuming that the electrolyzer is at the maximum steady-state-feasible temperature for every current (compare to Figure 2) because the efficiency increases with temperature. To this end, we set the cooling input u_{cool} to zero in the simulation when the temperature is below the maximum allowable temperature and otherwise select u_{cool} such that the temperature stays constant. All optimization problems are solved using gurobi 8.1.0 on an Intel Core i5-8250U processor with an optimality gap of 1 %. Only for the QSS benchmark, zero optimality gap is used such that our dynamic ramping approach is benchmarked against the optimal QSS schedule.

4. Results

Compared to nominal operation at constant production rate n_{prod}^{nom}, QSS optimization based on the steady-state-feasible region reduces electricity costs by 12.8 %. In contrast, our dynamic temperature ramping approach with 5 piece-wise affine segments achieves 15.9 % cost reduction. The optimization runtime is 32 seconds. Using 3 and 10 PWA segments, we achieve 13.6 % in 16 s and 16.5 % in 165 s, respectively. Consequently, dynamic optimization increases savings by up to 29 % compared to QSS.

Figure 4 shows the resulting operation for QSS optimization and for the dynamic temperature ramping with 5 segments. The dynamic temperature ramping approach exploits the fact that the electrolyzer can be cooled down, while it operates at low powers. Afterwards, production rates and electric powers can increase above the steady-state feasible point (see hours 2, 13, 14, and 22 in Figure 4). Interestingly, QSS optimization turns off the electrolyzer for 4 hours of high prices, while our dynamic ramping approach keeps the electrolyzer active for the complete 24 hours. The reason is that for the studied electrolyzer the heat transfer coefficient of the internal heat exchanger increases with the current I (Ulleberg, 1998). Consequently, when the electrolyzer is active it can be cooled down faster and thus deeper, which allows to operate at higher powers later in hours 13 and 14. Even if the lowest electricity price occurs at hour 15, the hours 13 and 14 show the highest input powers. The intuitive decision to schedule the highest power in hour 15 is not optimal as the efficiency decreases at lower temperatures. Thus, waiting with the temperature ramp-up until hour 15 would lead to one more hour of operating at low efficiency. These complex temperature dynamics explain why our dynamic approach outperforms the quasi-steady-state benchmark.

5. Conclusion

Electrolyzers are promising demand response (DR) candidates; however, realizing their full DR potential requires challenging mixed-integer dynamic optimization. We propose dynamic temperature ramping which allows to reformulate the nonlinear dynamic model into a mixed-integer linear model. By conservatively approximating the limits of the temperature gradient, the resulting trajectory is guaranteed to be feasible on the original nonlinear model. Our case study considers a validated alkaline electrolyzer model and shows that dynamic temperature ramping reduces costs by 15.9 % compared to nominal operation. A steady-state optimization, which is limited to operate within the steady-state feasible region, only achieves 12.8 % cost reduction. Moreover, our approach allows to explicitly balance computational complexity against solution quality and thereby reaches optimization runtimes below one minute. We expect our approach to be transferable to many other applications because our main assumption that the temperature evolution is the only dynamic relevant on an hourly timescale is typically true for electrolyzers.

Acknowledgements

The present contribution is supported by the Helmholtz Association under the Joint Initiative 'Energy Systems Integration'.

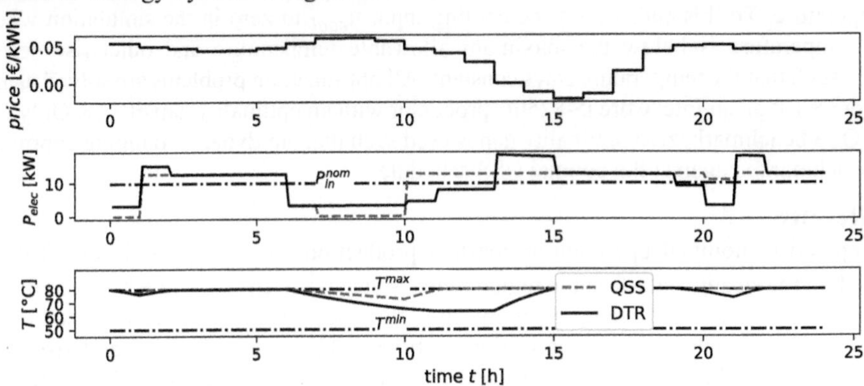

Figure 4: Electricity price (top), simulated electric power P_{elec} (middle), and simulated temperature T (bottom) for quasi-steady-state (QSS) and dynamic temperature ramping (DTR) with $n_{seg} = 5$ segments. The nominal input power P_{in}^{nom} is shown for comparison.

References

A. A. Adeniran, S. El Ferik, 2017, Modeling and identification of nonlinear systems: A review of the multimodel approach—Part 1, IEEE Transactions on Systems, Man, and Cybernetics: Systems, 47 (7), 1149–1159

F. J. Baader, P. Althaus, A. Bardow, M. Dahmen, 2021, Dynamic ramping for demand response of processes and energy systems based on exact linearization, arXiv:2110.08137v1

L. T. Biegler, 2010, Nonlinear programming, SIAM, Philadelphia

J. Burre, D. Bongartz, L. Brée, K. Roh, A. Mitsos, 2020, Power-to-X: Between electricity storage, e-production, and demand side management, Chemie Ingenieur Technik, 92, 74–84

B. Flamm, C. Peter, F. N. Büchi, J. Lygeros, 2021, Electrolyzer modeling and real-time control for optimized production of hydrogen gas, Applied Energy, 281, 116031

P. Gabrielli, B. Flamm, A. Eichler, M. Gazzani, J. Lygeros, M. Mazzotti, 2016, Modeling for optimal operation of PEM fuel cells and electrolyzers, 2016 IEEE 16th International Conference on Environment and Electrical Engineering, 1–7

M. Kopp, D. Coleman, C. Stiller, K. Scheffer, J. Aichinger, B. Scheppat, 2017, Energiepark Mainz: Technical and economic analysis of the worldwide largest power-to-gas plant with PEM electrolysis, International Journal of Hydrogen Energy, 42 (19), 13311–13320

J. M. Simkoff, M. Baldea, 2020, Stochastic scheduling and control using data-driven nonlinear dynamic models: Application to demand response operation of a chlor-alkali plant, Industrial & Engineering Chemistry Research, 21, 10031-10042

Ø. Ulleberg, 1998, Stand-alone power systems for the future: Optimal design, operation and control of solar-hydrogen energy systems, PhD-thesis, Trondheim

Ø. Ulleberg, 2003, Modeling of advanced alkaline electrolyzers: A system simulation approach, International Journal of Hydrogen Energy, 1, 21-33

Q. Zhang, I.E. Grossmann, 2016, Planning and scheduling for industrial demand side management: Advances and challenges, Alternative Energy Sources and Technologies, Ed. M. Mariano, Springer International Publishing, 383-414

Proceedings of the 14th International Symposium on Process Systems Engineering – PSE 2021+
June 19-23, 2022, Kyoto, Japan
http://dx.doi.org/10.1016/B978-0-323-85159-6.50066-X

Real-Time Optimal Operation of a Chlor-Alkali Electrolysis Process under Demand Response

Erik Esche[a*], Joris Weigert[a], Christian Hoffmann[a], Jens-Uwe Repke[a]

[a]Process Dynamics and Operations Group, Technische Universität Berlin, D-10623 Berlin, Germany
erik.esche@tu-berlin.de

Abstract

Real-time implementation of nonlinear model-predictive control (NMPC) for systems under demand response remains a challenge. Deep recurrent neural networks may serve as approximators for online application. Using hyperparameter tuning through Bayesian and Bandit optimization, deep neural networks are trained to high accuracy regarding testing data. An NMPC applied on an industrial chlor-alkali electrolysis example with a reactive distillation section is replaced by deep neural nets. The resulting approximation shows a perfect match to the offline NMPC using a Jordan RNN with 1 or 2 hidden layers, which surpasses the performance of LSTMs.

Keywords: demand response, optimal process operation, chlor-alkali electrolysis, neural network.

1. Introduction & Motivation

Given the surge in renewable energy into electricity markets, heavy fluctuations of electricity prices can be observed leading to both spikes as well as infrequent negative prices. To balance fluctuating production and demand, demand response has become an important tool and opened a market worth billions of euros worldwide, for example, in Germany. Within the European Union, demand response involves load shedding or increases within seconds (FCR), minutes (aFRR), or up to quarter hours (mFRR). Chemical plants with direct electricity input, e.g., air separation units or electrochemical processes, can profit from this market. More recently, investigation of the practical realization of demand response in operations has started. Recurring issues are the sizable and fast load drops or increases with no forewarning: For FCR and aFRR, load changes are directly implemented by the grid operator. Given that these load changes might involve complete shutdown or restart of an entire plant, this is a challenge for standard control solutions. It is unlikely that a nonlinear model predictive controller (NMPC) with a full mechanistic model can be solved in real-time. For speed-up, Vaupel et al. (2020) proposed two different approaches to train artificial neural networks (NN) to (1) serve as initial guess for NMPC or (2) as basis for a control update by quadratic programming. On the other hand, Karg and Lucia (2019) employed deep learning to learn entire robust NMPCs by deep NN.

For learning nonlinear dynamic relationships, a wide range of recurrent neural networks (RNN) exist. RNN feature internal feedback, i.e., outputs are passed as inputs for the next iteration / time step. They exist in various forms, from "fully connected" to leaner types, such as Elman RNN and Jordan RNN (Jordan, 1997). Long short-term memory (LSTM) units (Hochreiter and Schmidhuber, 1997) were developed to learn long-term effects. However, a recent contribution by Gonzalez and Wen (2018) noted that for some basic

nonlinear systems LSTM-based RNNs do not work well and combination with more basic RNN types are necessary for satisfactory results. At this point, RNNs are applied on chemical engineering examples without specific adjustment. It is unclear, which types of RNN are sufficient for which types of systems in chemical engineering.
The present contribution will evaluate deep NNs as approximators for nonlinear model predictive control applied on continuously operated chemical processes under demand response. To this end, Section 2 describes the methodology that we pursue to obtain a representative RNN approximator of the NMPC, before Section 3 discusses the chloralkali electrolysis process and a subsequent reactive distillation as case study.

2. Methodology

For our methodology, we will assume that a suitable dynamic process model exists, which mimics the process behavior throughout the demand response scope. Also, a sampling is available with realistic scenarios given the process dynamics and the energy market. This entails, e.g., scheduling based on fluctuations in the electricity price.

2.1. Optimal Process Control

With such scheduling results and a dynamic process model, optimal control actions may be obtained. We assume a basic discrete-time implementation of an NMPC with a finite prediction horizon N focusing on tracking control, which is solved at sample time l:

$$\min_{u_k \, \forall k=l\ldots l+N} \Phi(x_{k\ldots k+N}, u_{k\ldots k+N}) \tag{1}$$

$$x_{k+1} := g(x_k, u_k, d_k) \quad \forall k = l \ldots l+N-1, \tag{2}$$

$$0 \leq h(x_{k+1}, u_k, d_k) \quad \forall k = l \ldots l+N-1, \tag{3}$$

$$u^L \leq u_k \leq u^U \quad \forall k = l \ldots l+N-1, \tag{4}$$

with states x_k, control inputs u_k, disturbances d_k, dynamic process model g, and inequality constraints h as well as bounds for the control inputs u^L, u^U. Based on the scenarios of step 2, the NMPC formulation may be solved offline, which yields optimal control input u^* for current process state x and disturbances d, which contain the load changes required by the electricity market.

2.2. Approximate Control Law

Using these optimal control inputs u^*, a neural net may be trained as a direct approximator for the nonlinear optimal controller:

$$u^*_{k+} \approx \tilde{u}_{k+} = f(x_{k-}, u_{k-}, d_{k-}), \tag{5}$$

wherein f is a neural network mapping from current state estimate to approximate optimal control input. $k+$ denotes time points in the future, while k- is current and possibly past information. We assume that a good estimate of the current process is always available. A variety of structural choices are at hand for f. Here, we shall limit ourselves to RNNs of type Jordan and LSTM. For these, the number of neurons per layer, the number of hidden layers overall, and regularization parameters need to be selected. Further options concern the number of additional input variables, e.g., the number of past control inputs u to be considered and for Jordan RNNs the number of past states held internally. The former goes well beyond a standard NMPC application and might allow to also include the state estimation step as part of the controller. Choosing these hyperparameters to obtain a suitable NN is not trivial for general nonlinear systems. This issue can be resolved by hyperparameter optimization: Continuous decisions may be made by Bayesian optimization (Frazier, 2018) and discrete decisions based on Bandit optimization (Dimmery et al., 2019). Both are employed through the python framework Ax (https://ax.dev). During the hyperparameter optimization, all decisions mentioned above are made – apart from the selection of RNN type and number of hidden layers (1 up to 4), which are varied manually. The hyperparameter optimization uses the mean squared error (MSE) regarding the testing data as objective and runs for 50 iterations. Ranges for the hyperparameters are based on prior experience to values set in Table 1. The Jordan-type RNN is constructed in scikit-learn (Pedregosa, 2011), while Keras' LSTM is used as is (https://keras.io). The time series obtained from step 2 is split into training (80 %) and testing (20 %) data set. For scaling of inputs StandardScaler of scikit-learn and MinMaxScaler for outputs is used. The results of the NMPC are rearranged into tuples of input-output pairs with varying size depending on the hyperparameters:

$$\text{Input: } \left(x_{j-l} \dots x_j, d_{j-l} \dots d_j, u_{j-m} \dots u_{j-1}\right), \text{Output: } \left(\tilde{u}_j \dots \tilde{u}_{j+N}\right), \tag{6}$$

with m number of past controls, l number of past states, for current time point j.
To train the neural net f, the MSE of the training data between u^* and predicted $\hat{u}$ is minimized. This is amended with a weighted bias penalty term (L2 norm) for regularization. Adam (Kingma and Ba, 2014) is used as solver for training with a fixed batch size of 200 and early stopping with a tolerance of 1.0e-6 and patience of 10.

Table 1. Ranges for hyperparameters chosen during the hyperparameter optimization.

Hyperparameter	Lower Bound	Upper Bound
Number of past controls m	1	50
Number of past states (Jordan) l	10	50
Number of neurons per hidden layer	10	300
Type of activation function	ReLU or tanh	
Regularization parameter (L2)	1.0e-5	10.0

3. Case Study

The operation under demand response of a chlor-alkali electrolysis (CAE) and a subsequent synthesis of 1,2-dichloroethane (DCE) from chlorine and ethene is investigated here (see Figure 1). While storage of chlorine is limited due to safety restrictions, DCE can easily be stored in large quantities. The application of demand response on the CAE causes a fluctuation in both the electrolysis as well as the reactive distillation section producing DCE.

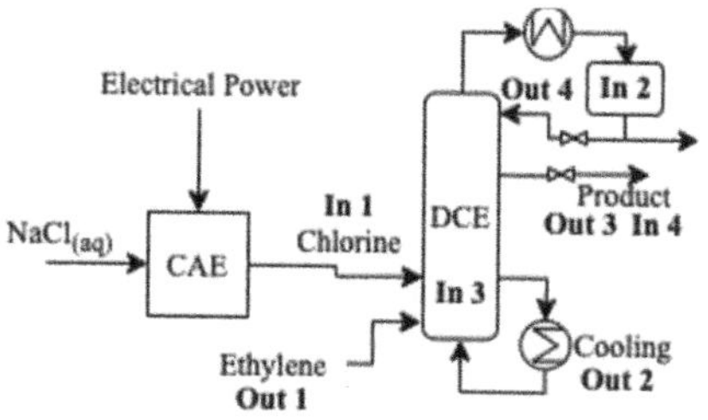

Figure 1. Simplified flowsheet of case study.

Particularly, operation of the DCE under heavy fluctuations of the chlorine stream from the CAE is a challenge. The combined reaction and distillation section of the DCE is modeled with a typical tray-based formulation with a special focus on dynamic load changes (Hoffmann et al., 2020).

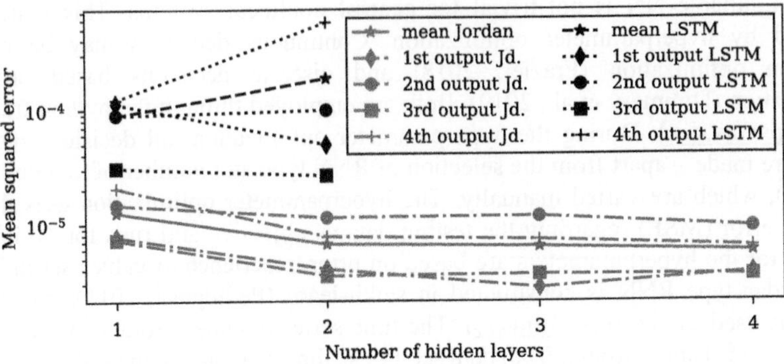

Figure 2. Mean squared error (MSE) of the testing data per output and overall, for Jordan RNN (Jd.) and LSTM with 1 up to 4 hidden layers.

Hoffmann et al. (2021) developed a framework to obtain realistic load profiles for the CAE-DCE process under demand response. A 200-hour profile computed with their framework will serve as a basis for the subsequent case study here. The profile contains load changes of up to 30 % due to either aFRR or mFRR.

3.1. Optimal Process Control

The NMPC formulation described by Eq. (1)-(4) contains an objective ensuring the adherence to the required DCE purity in the outlet of the reactive distillation section. The model consists of the complete dynamic reactive distillation as described in (Hoffmann et al., 2020). As inequality constraints strict ramp restrictions on the changes of the control variables are implemented to ensure technical feasibility. A more detailed discussion may be found in (Hoffmann, 2021). The prediction horizon N is set to 45 minutes as the slow mFRR contains ramps lasting 15 minutes. By solving the NMPC problem with the electricity market profile as disturbance d, optimal control inputs u^* are obtained.

3.2. Approximate Control Law

With the NMPC results, a set of neural nets is trained with 1 to 4 hidden layers of type Jordan and LSTM. Here, we focus on the main inputs of interest for the control of the DCE: The chlorine stream stemming from the CAE represents the market signal and is regarded as an external disturbance (In 1). The state of the DCE is overall captured by the current level in the reflux drum (In 2), the liquid level in the column bottom (In 3), and the concentration of DCE in the product stream (In 4).

Table 2. Training results of the neural nets with two hidden layers of type Jordan and LSTM.

Hyper-parameters	Jordan RNN (2 hidden layers)				LSTM (2 hidden layers)			
	Out 1	Out 2	Out 3	Out 4	Out 1	Out 2	Out 3	Out 4
m	46	47	39	43	46	43	49	37
l (Jordan)	27	7	10	44	-	-	-	-
Neurons	53/115	26/126	128/102	23/257	30/115	86/64	147/88	18/193
Activation	ReLU	tanh	ReLU	ReLU	ReLU	tanh	ReLU	ReLU
Reg. (L2)	5.3e-3	2.5e-3	1.1e-2	2.0e-3	3.7e-5	5.8e-5	3.7e-5	2.1e-4

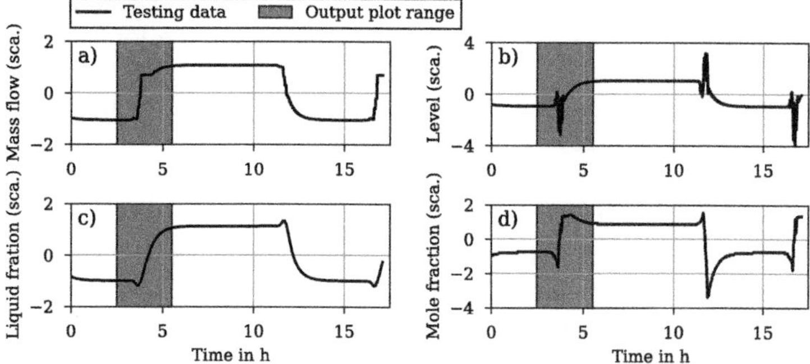

Figure 3. Scaled profiles of the four input variables in the testing data.

The most important control actions on the process are the ethylene dosing (Out 1), the auxiliary column cooling (Out 2) to remove some of the heat of reaction at the bottom, the product flow (Out 3), and the reflux from the reflux drum (Out 4). Results of hyperparameter optimization and training are shown in Figure 2, which states the MSE regarding the testing data per output. For the Jordan RNN with a single layer, the error per output is small and an order of magnitude smaller than for the LSTM. With 2 or more hidden layers, the error decreases further, although the improvements become negligible. Given the increase of the MSE for 2 hidden layers, the further results for LSTM are omitted here. In Table 2, further details are given on Jordan RNN and LSTM with two hidden layers: All hyperparameters are chosen within the specified ranges. Strong variations can be observed with respect to the specific regularization for the various outlets here. Similarly, the choice in activation function appears to lean towards ReLU, although output 2 favors tanh. The number of neurons here is high, but common compared with available publications.

3.3. Quality of the Approximation

To evaluate the quality of the prediction, the testing data will be further examined. Figure 3 shows the testing data for the four input variables named above. Observe that the plots show an interval of 17 hours and the profiles in the minute range are smooth. Figure 4 focusses at a two-hour interval marked in Figure 3 and shows the results for Jordan RNN and LSTM with one and two hidden layers respectively. All four trained models can follow the trajectory computed by the NMPC.

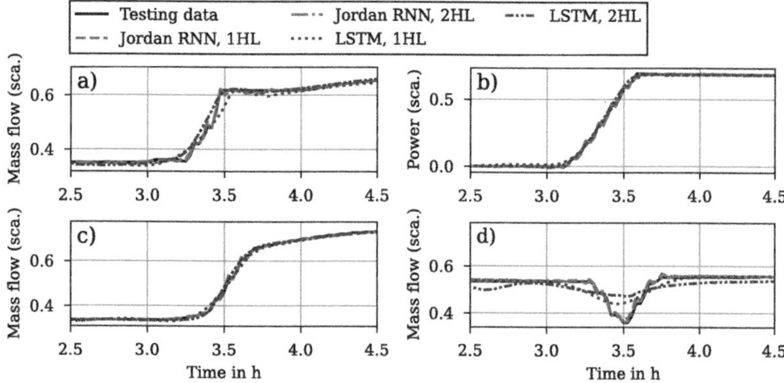

Figure 4. Scaled profiles of the four output variables. Close-up of a two hour interval of the testing data with the results of Jordan RNN and LSTM with one and two hidden layers (HL).

However, the Jordan RNNs manage to follow the slightest control actions of the NMPC, so much so that the testing data disappears behind the plot of the Jordan RNN with two hidden layers. Overall, using the Jordan RNN instead of the original NMPC would here lead to almost no approximation error and the suboptimality is nearly unquantifiable with respect to the solution accuracy of the NMPC itself.

4. Conclusions & Outlook

Direct application of NMPC particularly on fast and highly nonlinear systems remains a challenge. Using offline computation based on realistic demand response scenarios, optimal control trajectories can be computed offline and learned to high accuracy by neural nets. Particularly, Jordan RNNs with two or more hidden layers show a great adaptability in this regard. Using hyperparameter optimization during training greatly eases the effort to obtain suitable NNs. It appears that the learned approximate control law may be applied in real-time to replace slow NMPCs.

Several issues remain to be solved in future work, ensuring the reliability of neural nets beyond the operation window they were originally trained on is always a point of contention. More advanced techniques beyond more extensive sampling are needed, which ensure feasibility of the approximated NMPC results throughout.

5. Acknowledgements

The authors acknowledge the financial support by the Federal Ministry of Economic Affairs and Energy of Germany in the project ChemEFlex (project number 0350013A).

References

D. Dimmery, E. Bakshy, J. Sekhon, 2019, Shrinkage Estimators in Online Experiments, arXiv: 1904.12918v1

P.I. Frazier, 2018, A Tutorial on Bayesian Optimization, arXiv: 1807.02811v1

J. Gonzalez, Y. Wen, 2018, Non-linear System Modeling Using LSTM Neural Networks, IFAC-PaperOnLine, 51, 13, 485-489

S. Hochreiter, J. Schmidhuber, 1997, Long Short-term Memory, Neural Computation, 9, 8, 1735-1780

C. Hoffmann, J. Weigert, E. Esche, J.-U. Repke, 2020, Towards demand-side management of the chlor-alkali electrolysis: dynamic, pressure-driven modeling and model validation of the 1,2-dichloroethane synthesis. Chemical Engineering Science, 214, 115358.

M. Hofmann, R. Müller, A. Christides, P. Fischer, F. Klaucke, S. Vomberg, G. Tsatsaronis, 2021, Flexible and economical operation of chlor-alkali process with subsequent polyvinyl chloride production, AiChE Journal, DOI: https://doi.org/10.1002/aic.17480

M.I. Jordan, 1997, Serial Order: A Parallel Distributed Processing Approach, Neural-Network Models of Cognition, 121, 471-495

B. Karg and S. Lucia, 2019, Learning-based approximation of robust nonlinear predictive control with state estimation applied to a towing kite, 18th European Control Conference (ECC), 16-22, doi: 10.23919/ECC.2019.8796201

D.P. Kingma, J. Ba, 2014, Adam: A Method for Stochastic Optimization, arXiv: 1412.6980v9

F. Pedregoas, G. Varoquaux, A. Gramfor, V. Michel, B. Thirion, O. Grisel, M. Blondel, P. Prettenhofer, R. Weiss, V. Dubourg, J. Vanderplas, A. Passos, D. Cournapeau, M. Brucher, M. Perrot, E. Duchesnay, 2011, Scikit-learn: Machine Learning in Python, Journal of Machine Learning, 12, 85, 2825-2830

Y. Vaupel, N.C. Hamacher, A. Caspari, A. Mhamdi, I.G. Kevrekidis, A. Mitsos, 2020, Accelerating nonlinear model predictive control through machine learning, Journal of Process Control, 92, 261-270

Proceedings of the 14th International Symposium on Process Systems Engineering – PSE 2021+
June 19-23, 2022, Kyoto, Japan
http://dx.doi.org/10.1016/B978-0-323-85159-6.50067-1

Explicit Multi-Objective and Hierarchical Model Predictive Control

Styliani Avraamidou[a*], Iosif Pappas[b,c], Efstratios N. Pistikopoulos[b,c]

[a]*Department of Chemical and Biological Engineering, University of Wisconsin-Madison, Engineering Drive, Madison, WI 53703, United States*
[b]*Texas A&M Energy Institute, Texas A&M University, Address, College Station, TX 77800, United States*
[b]*Artie Mc Ferin Department of Chemical Engineering, Texas A&M University, Address, College Station, TX 77800, United States*
avraaamidou@wisc.edu

Abstract

Model predictive control (MPC) problems can involve multiple, often conflicting objectives, including economic performance, tracking accuracy, disturbance rejection, safety, or environmental criteria. Each of these objectives can be used to design different MPCs that will have different input trajectories and consequently different operational behaviours in closed-loop operation. Various approaches have been proposed in the open literature for the development of multi-objective model predictive controllers in an effort to combine some of the objectives. Multiple objectives can also be ranked in a hierarchy, where every control level in the hierarchy is controlling a subset of the overall control variables, by manipulating a subset of the overall control variables, resulting in hierarchical model predictive controllers. This work utilizes multi-parametric programming to generate both multi-objective and hierarchical explicit model predictive controllers. A case study on a combined stirred tank reactor with two competing objectives, an economic and a tracking objective, is used to illustrate the developed control strategies. The results of this study clearly indicate the effect of the different control strategies on the operation of the reactor.

Keywords: Model Predictive Control; Multi-Parametric Programming; Multi-level Optimization; Multi-Objective Optimization; Explicit Control.

1. Main Text

The optimal operation of a system can involve multiple, often conflicting objectives, due to the complexity of the problems that are studied. These objectives that need to be optimized include economic performance, safety, or environmental criteria. In the context of operational optimization through process control, various approaches have been proposed in the open literature in an attempt to incorporate these objectives simultaneously in the development of optimal control policies. One approach is multi-objective model predictive control (MOMPC), where in two of these strategies the different objectives can be added and combined into a single objective, known as the

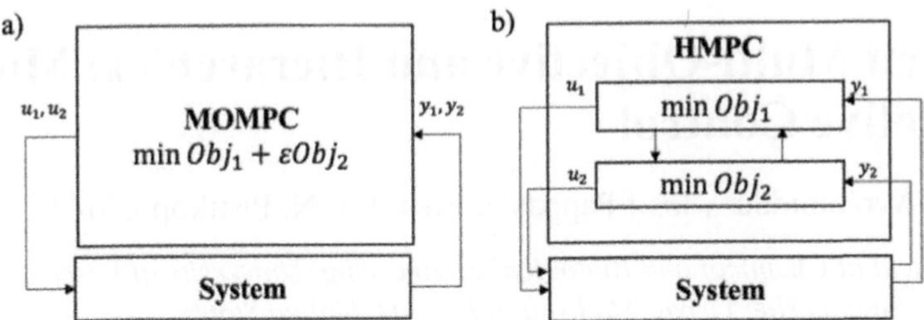

Figure 1 Optimal Controller structures for the incorporation of two objectives for the control of a process system: a) Mutli-objective optimization approach (weighted sum) - MOMPC, b) Hierarchical Optimization Approach – HMPC.

weighted sum method (Fairweather et al. 2012), or objectives can be part of the constraint set, known as the ε-constraint approach (Zavala, 2005; Bemporad et al. 2009).

Another approach that can be used for the consideration of multiple objectives in a control scheme is to rank the objectives in a hierarchy, where every control level in the hierarchy is controlling a subset of the overall control variables, by manipulating a subset of the overall control variables (Avraamidou and Pistikopoulos, 2017; Katebi and Johnson, 1997). Figure 1 illustrates both aforementioned approaches for the consideration of multiple objectives in discrete-time optimal control problems, where u_1 and u_2 are the set of manipulated variables, and y_1 and y_2 are the set of control variables.

MPC strategies require the solution of the optimization problem at every control time step, making the use of most multi-objective or hierarchical solution methods challenging. To this end, this work proposes the use of multi-parametric programming to generate both multi-objective and hierarchical explicit MPCs. More specifically, assuming that there exist two or more control objectives described by linear or convex quadratic functions, we develop multi-parametric based approaches for the derivation of i) the explicit Pareto front of MOMPC, and ii) the explicit solution of HMPC. The MOMPC problem is reformulated into a multiparametric programming problem (Pappas et al. 2021a), which can then be exactly solved using state-of-the-art algorithms (Pappas et al. 2021b), while the HMPC problem is reformulated into a multiparametric multi-level programming problem, which can be exactly solved using the algorithms proposed in (Avraamidou and Pistikopoulos, 2019a).

The following section focuses on the formulation and solution method for the MOMPC, while section 2 focuses on the formulation and solution method of the HMPC. In section 3, a case study on a reactor with two competing objectives, an economic and a tracking objective, is used to illustrate the two developed control strategies. The results of this study indicate the effect of the two strategies and their applicability for the optimal operation of the stirred tank reactor.

2. Multi-Objective Model Predictive Control Structure

2.1. Problem Formulation

Consider problem (1) where q objectives need to be simultaneously minimized by manipulating the inputs, u_i, to calculate the states, x_i, and outputs y_i, at time step i. The process model is a discrete linear state-space model described by the matrices A, B and C and a prediction horizon of N steps along with a terminal set X are assumed.

$$
\begin{aligned}
\min_{u_i} \quad & \sum_{j=1}^{q} f_j(x,u) \\
\text{s.t.} \quad & x_{i+1} = Ax_i + Bu_i \\
& y_i = Cx_i \\
& x_i^L \le x_i \le x_i^U \\
& u_i^L \le u_i \le u_i^U \\
& x_N \in X
\end{aligned} \tag{1}
$$

2.2. Solution Strategy

The first step in the proposed solution approach is to reformulate the multi-objective MPC problem in to an ε-constraint problem, following the approach presented by Pappas et al. 2021a, where the reformulated problem is solved using multi-parametric programing while treating the initial states of the system and the ε variables as parameters.

3. Hierarchical Model Predictive Control Structure

3.1. Problem Formulation

$$
\begin{aligned}
\min_{u_1} \quad & f_1(x,u) \\
\text{s.t.} \quad & \min_{u_2} \; f_2(x,u) \\
& \vdots \\
& \quad \text{s.t.} \quad \min_{u_q} \; f_q(x,u) \\
& \quad \quad \text{s.t.} \quad x_{i+1} = Ax_i + Bu_i \\
& \quad \quad \quad y_i = Cx_i \\
& \quad \quad \quad x_i^L \le x_i \le x_i^U \\
& \quad \quad \quad u_i^L \le u_i \le u_i^U \\
& \quad \quad \quad x_N \in X
\end{aligned} \tag{3}
$$

3.2. Solution Strategy

To solve this multi-level optimization problem, the algorithm proposed by Avraamidou and Pistikopoulos 2019a and 2019b is utilised. The proposed algorithm transforms the multi-level optimization problem into a series of single-level optimization problems by solving the lower level problems multi-parametrically while treating the states and upper level variables as parameters.

4. Case-study: Continuous Stirred Tank Reactor

4.1. System Definition

Consider a non-isothermal continuously stirred tank reactor (CSTR), adopted from (Kazantzis and Kravaris, 2000), where the following reaction occurs

$$2Na_2S_2O_3 + 4H_2O_2 \rightarrow Na_2SO_3O_6 + Na_2SO_4 + 4H_2O \tag{4}$$

The reactants and the products of the above components are represented by A and B and C, D and E respectively. It is assumed that stoichiometry is preserved in the reactor at all times and hence the reactants are fed to the reactor through a feedstock stream at concentration $C_{A,in}$ and $C_{B,in}$, for A and B respectively, at a ratio $C_{B,in}$:2 $C_{A,in}$, flowrate F, and temperature T_{in}. The CSTR is assumed to have a constant liquid hold-up. A jacket provides energy to or from the reactor.

It is desired that the outlet concentration and temperature of the controlled variables of the CSTR. The inlet concentrations and temperature are varying between 0.9 and 1.2 mol/L, and 275 to 295 K respectively, and can be considered as measured disturbances. The inlet dilution rate $\left(\frac{F}{V}\right)$ and the coolant temperature T_j can be manipulated by the control system and are therefore considered as manipulated variables. The inlet concentration and temperature are treated as measured disturbances.

4.2. Controller Development – PAROC Framework

To develop the control system for the CSTR defined above, the PAROC framework (Pistikopoulos et al. 2015) was followed.

4.2.1. High-fidelity Model

As a first step a high-fidelity model (5-6) was developed by applying first principles and standard modelling assumptions (constant density and heat capacity, Arrhenius rate, etc.). The details of the model can be found in (Kazantzis and Kravaris, 2000).

$$\frac{dC_A}{dt} = \frac{F}{V}\left(C_{A,in} - C_A\right) - 2k(T)C_A^2 \tag{5}$$

$$\frac{dT}{dt} = \frac{F}{V}(T_{in} - T) + 2\frac{(-\Delta H)_R}{\rho C_p}k(T)C_A^2 - \frac{UA}{V\rho C_p}(T - T_j) \tag{6}$$

where $k = 2k_0 \exp\left(-\frac{E}{RT}\right)$.

4.2.2. Model Approximation

Due to the dynamic nature of the system and its nonlinear components, the original model is linearized around the steady-state of $\begin{bmatrix} C_{A,s} \\ T_s \end{bmatrix} = \begin{bmatrix} 0.076 \\ 376.270 \end{bmatrix}$. Subsequently the linear system ordinary differential equation is discretized using a discretization step of 1 second assuming zero order hold. Consequently, the model is a now a discrete time-invariant state-space model. Here we are also using the variables in deviation form for the inputs and the outputs (e.g. $\hat{C}_A = C_A - C_{A,s}$).

4.2.3. Controller Formulation

Four different control strategies were implemented. The first controller is a classic explicit MPC controller with the tracking objective formulated in (7).

Tracking Objective:

$$\min_{\frac{F}{V},\hat{T}_j} \begin{bmatrix} \hat{C}_{A_N} & \hat{T}_N \end{bmatrix} P \begin{bmatrix} \hat{C}_{A_N} & \hat{T}_N \end{bmatrix}^T + \sum_{i=1}^{i=N-1} \begin{bmatrix} \hat{C}_{A_i} & \hat{T}_i \end{bmatrix} Q \begin{bmatrix} \hat{C}_{A_i} & \hat{T}_i \end{bmatrix}^T + \begin{bmatrix} \widehat{\frac{F}{V_i}} & \hat{T}_{j,i} \end{bmatrix} R \begin{bmatrix} \widehat{\frac{F}{V_i}} & \hat{T}_{j,i} \end{bmatrix}^T \tag{7}$$

The second controller is an explicit economic MPC with the same constraints as the first controller but with objective (8).

Economic Objective:

$$\min_{\bar{F},\bar{V}} \sum_{i=1}^{i=N-1} \begin{bmatrix}\bar{F}\\ \bar{V}_i\end{bmatrix} v \begin{bmatrix}\bar{F}\\ \bar{V}_i\end{bmatrix}^T \qquad (8)$$

The third controller is a multi-objective economic and tracking controller (MOMPC) with both objectives (7) and (8) in its objective function., while the last controller is a bi-level controller (HMPC) with the economic objective (8) on the upper level optimization problem and the tracking objective (7) on the lower level optimization problem. The constraint set for both the MOMPC and HMPC controllers is identical to the two single objective controllers.

The two single level explicit controllers were solved through POP toolbox, whereas the MOMPC and HMPC were solved as described in sections 2 and 3 respectively. The parameters for all optimization problems consist of the states, the measured disturbances, the previous control action and the output set-point. The prediction horizon was set to 2. The pareto front resulting from the MOMPC controller is presented in Figure 2.

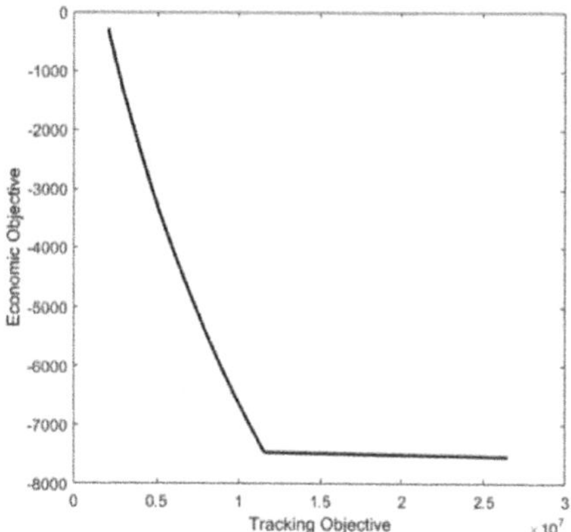

Figure 2 Pareto front of the MOMPC

4.3. Closed-loop Validation

The last step is the closed-loop validation to evaluate the performance of the designed controllers. The inputs and results of this step are presented in Figures 3 and 4.

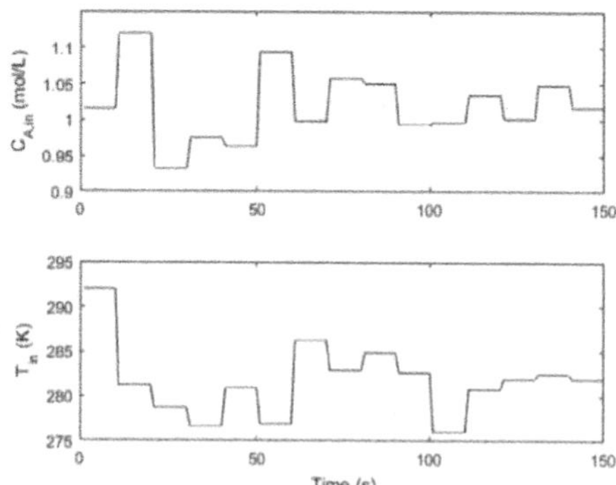

Figure 3 Process Disturbances

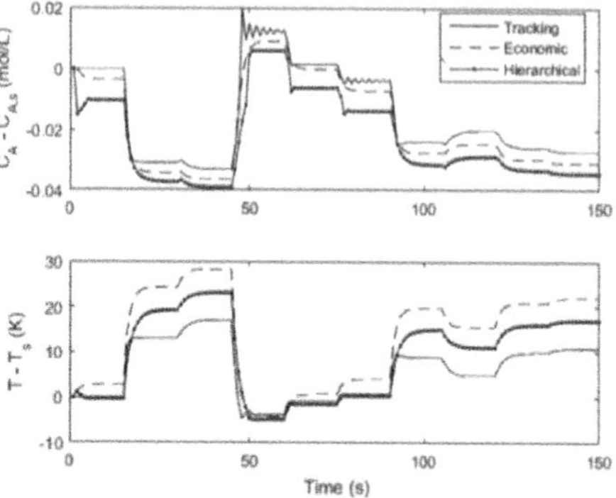

Figure 4 Process Output

5. Conclusion

We presented two multi-parametric based approaches for the incorporation of multiple objectives in model predictive control. A simple CSTR system, with both economic and set-point tracking objectives was used to illustrate the effectiveness of the proposed approaches. The resulting explicit controllers were able to effectively reject disturbances and maintain the system at the given set-points according to their objectives.

Acknowledgements

This work is supported by the DOE-CESMII Energy Efficient Operation of Air Separation Processes Project (DE-EE0007613) and the Rapid Advancement in Process Intensification Deployment (DE-EE0007888-09-04). The authors are also grateful for financial support from UW-Madison, and Texas A&M Energy Institute.

References

M. Fairweather, M. Vallerio, F. Logist, J. F. Impe, 2012, Towards enhanced weight selection for (N)MPC via multi-objective optimization, Proceedings of the 22nd European Symposium on Computer Aided Process Engineering

V. M. Zavala, 2015, A multiobjective optimization perspective on the stability of economic MPC, IFAC-PapersOnLine 48, 8, 974-980

A. Bemporad, D. Munoz de la Pena, 2009, Multiobjective model predictive control, Automatica, 45, 2823-2830

S. Avraamidou, E. N. Pistikopoulos, 2017, A multi-parametric bi-level optimization strategy for hierarchical model predictive control. 27th European Symposium on Computer-Aided Process Engineering (ESCAPE-27); Elsevier, 1591-1596

M. Katebi, M. Johnson, 1997, Predictive control design for large-scale systems, Automatica, 33 (3), 421–425

I. Pappas, D. Kenefake, B. Burnak, S. Avraamidou, H. Ganesh, J. Katz, N. A. Diangelakis, E. N. Pistikopoulos, 2021a, Multiparametric Programming in Process Systems Engineering: Recent Developments and Path Forward, Frontiers in Chemical Engineering, 2, 32

I. Pappas, S. Avraamidou, J. Katz, B. Burnak, B. Beykal, M. Türkay, E. N. Pistikopoulos, 2021b, Multiobjective Optimization of Mixed-Integer Linear Programming Problems: A Multiparametric Optimization Approach. Industrial & Engineering Chemistry Research, 60, 23, 8493-8503

S. Avraamidou, E. N. Pistikopoulos, 2019a, A Multi-Parametric optimization approach for bilevel mixed-integer linear and quadratic programming problems, 125, 98-113

S. Avraamidou, E. N. Pistikopoulos, 2019b, B-POP: Bi-level parametric optimization toolbox. Computers & Chemical Engineering, 122, 193-202

E. N. Pistikopoulos, N. A. Diangelakis, R. Oberdieck, M. M. Papathanasiou, I. Nascu, M. Sun, 2015, PAROC-An integrated framework and software platform for the optimisation and advanced model-based control of process systems, Chemical Engineering Science, 136, 115-138

N. Kazantzis, C. Kravaris, 2000, Synthesis of state feedback regulators for nonlinear processes. Chemical Engineering Science, 55, 17, 3437-3449

Proceedings of the 14th International Symposium on Process Systems Engineering – PSE 2021+
June 19-23, 2022, Kyoto, Japan
http://dx.doi.org/10.1016/B978-0-323-85159-6.50068-3

A Robust Optimization Strategy for Explicit Model Predictive Control

Iosif Pappas[a,b], Nikolaos A. Diangelakis[a,b], Richard Oberdieck[c],
Efstratios N. Pistikopoulos[a,b,*]

[a]*Artie McFerrin Department of Chemical Engineering, Texas A&M University, College Station, TX 77843, U.S.A.*
[b]*Texas A&M Energy Institute, Texas A&M University, College Station, TX 77843, U.S.A.*
[c]*Gurobi Optimization, Beaverton, OR 97008, U.S.A.*
stratos@tamu.edu

Abstract

Explicit model predictive control is an established strategy to calculate the model-based optimal control decisions for a process system, while alleviating the computational cost of repetitively solving an optimization problem online. Since models are not ideal representations of the original processes and due to a potentially necessary approximation of the original model for computational efficiency reasons, the optimal solution of the explicit model predictive control problem is based on an imperfect model. Hence, the aforementioned model discrepancy and the presence of unmeasured disturbances facilitate uncertainty that can result to undesirable process behaviour or infeasibility. In this work, a strategy that derives the explicit solution of a robust model predictive control problem with a single multiparametric formulation is exhibited. The proposed approach is founded on the successive robustification of the constraint set of the problem, eliminating the risk of constraint violation, and hence guaranteeing feasibility of closed-loop operation. The benefits of the presented methodology are demonstrated through a linear quadratic regulator problem of an uncertain system.

Keywords: Model Predictive Control; Robust Optimization; Multiparametric Programming

1. Introduction

Model predictive control (MPC) is the established paradigm for the advanced control of multivariable systems, extensively studied and applied by both the academic and industrial communities (Mayne, 2014). In its most encountered form, an MPC problem is a convex quadratic mathematical optimization problem, whose solution is the optimal vector of inputs to regulate the operation of a system. Assuming a finite prediction horizon and a discrete time-invariant linear model, a performance index is minimized to calculate the optimal behavior of the underlying model. Subsequently, only the first control input is applied to the system and the horizon is shifted forward by one step. This procedure is repeated for each sampling time, when new measurements (or estimates of theirs) are made available, facilitating an implicit feedback policy. Explicit MPC refers to the approach of deriving exactly the same optimal vector of inputs, but in an explicit manner. Instead of repetitively solving an optimization problem, the optimal decisions are expressed analytically (explicitly) by treating the MPC problem as a multiparametric optimization problem. By solving multiparametric optimization problems, the optimal solution of the studied problem is provided as a function of the vector of its uncertain parameters, based on its location at the uncertainty space (critical regions). In the case of MPC, the states are part of the uncertainty vector. The benefits of the explicit solution are, i) the online computational cost of calculating the solution of the problem is substantially reduced by substituting solving an optimization problem with a function evaluation, ii) a complete analysis of the uncertainty (state) space is available a priori, as well as its impact on the solution of the control problem, and iii) the explicit nature of the solution allows for the solution of nested optimization problems. These properties are of particular importance for control applications which are not equipped with the computational power to solve optimization problems online (Pappas et al., 2021).

Robustness is a fundamental element in process control and refers to the ability of the controller to handle uncertainty, and especially unmeasured uncertainty. Since MPC is a model-based control strategy, the quality of the solution is based on the considered model. Nevertheless, process models are not ideal representations of the real system which is to be regulated. In addition, an approximation of the original model is typically required, since the latter is comprised — in many cases — by a large-scale system of differential and algebraic equations that is computationally challenging to be solved online. Finally, the operation of processes includes unmeasured disturbances which affect real-time operations. All of the above sources of uncertainty lead to the undesirable or even infeasible behavior of the plant in closed-loop. For this reason, robust MPC strategies have been proposed to deal with this issue (Kouvaritakis and Cannon, 2016).

Robust explicit MPC aims to derive the explicit solution of the MPC problem by additionally guaranteeing that all sources of uncertainty are taken into account, and at least feasibility is satisfied. In this respect, multiple research efforts have been contributed that tackle the case where the uncertainty source is added to the future prediction (additive uncertainty) and the case where the future prediction is multiplicatively affected by it (multiplicative uncertainty). Sakizlis et al. (2004) included constraints in the design phase of the controller that guarantee that for the worst case of the additive uncertainty, the system is feasible. Bemporad et al. (2003) proposed a min-max approach where the solution is found for problems with a linear objective function and linear constraints for multiplicative uncertainty. Kouramas et al. (2013) tackled the case of explicit MPC problems with a quadratic objective function, linear constraints, and multiplicative uncertainty by employing dynamic programming and robust optimization. More recently, Oberdieck (2016) demonstrated that dynamic programming can be avoided and extended it to hybrid systems by performing projections of the feasible space into the future. This projection operation was achieved my solving a multiparametric linear programming problem. An open question in the robust explicit MPC field is how can the robust solution of an explicit MPC problem with a quadratic cost, linear constraints, and multiplicative uncertainty be developed, by using a single multiparametric optimization formulation.

In this contribution, an algorithm that solves the aforementioned challenge is presented. We formulate a suitable robust control invariant set, successively robustify the constraints, and incorporate linear manipulations to formulate a single multiparametric problem. We solve the optimization program, and as a result, the implementation of the robust policy hedges against the presence of uncertainty and manages to regulate the system. The remainder of this paper is organized as follows: Section 2 describes the problem formulation, while in Section 3 we present the proposed approach. In Section 4 we demonstrate the benefits of the strategy while in Section 5, we conclude.

2. Problem Formulation

Consider a linear discrete time dynamic model of the following form:

$$x_{k+1} = Ax_k + Bu_k \tag{1}$$

where $x_k \in \mathbb{R}^m$ and $u_k \in \mathbb{R}^n$ are the state and control input vectors respectively at time instant k, and are multiplied by the matrices $A \in \mathbb{R}^{mxm}$ and $B \in \mathbb{R}^{mxn}$. Instead of considering that the system matrices are constant, in this study we assume that the model is uncertain and described by box uncertainty. Specifically:

$$A = A_0 + \Delta A \tag{2}$$

$$B = B_0 + \Delta B \tag{3}$$

$$\Delta A \in \mathbb{A} = \{\Delta A \in \mathbb{R}^{mxm} | -\epsilon_\alpha |A_0| \leq \Delta A \leq \epsilon_\alpha |A_0|\} \tag{4}$$

$$\Delta B \in \mathbb{B} = \{\Delta B \in \mathbb{R}^{mxn} | -\epsilon_\beta |B_0| \leq \Delta B \leq \epsilon_\beta |B_0|\} \tag{5}$$

A_0 and B_0 are the nominal matrices of the model, while ΔA and ΔB is their uncertain component. This element-wise deviation from the nominal matrix value is prescribed by the matrices ϵ_α and ϵ_β which are of equivalent dimensions to A_0 and B_0. The consideration of box uncertainty allows for its description through halfspace representation, and hence avoids the performance of vertex enumeration which would have been the case if a general polytopic uncertainty set was considered (Oberdieck, 2016). Assuming a prediction horizon N, the following robust explicit linear quadratic regulator problem (LQR) problem can be formulated:

$$\begin{aligned} \min_{u_0,\ldots,u_{N-1}} \quad & x_N^T P x_N + \sum_{k=0}^{N-1} x_k^T Q_R x_k + u_k^T R u_k \\ s.t. \quad & x_{k+1} = Ax_k + Bu_k \\ & x_k \in X \\ & u_k \in U \\ & x_N \in T \end{aligned} \tag{6}$$

whose objective is to find the explicit control inputs, $u(x)$, that will drive the system to the origin in the presence of the uncertainty. The weights on the states and inputs are $Q_R \in \mathbb{R}^{mxm}$ and $R \in \mathbb{R}^{nxn}$ respectively, while $P \in \mathbb{R}^{mxm}$ is the terminal cost matrix derived from the solution of the discrete-time algebraic Riccati equation. The states at the end of the prediction are required to belong to the terminal set T (Blanchini, 1999).

3. Methodology

The methodology presented in this section has the goal of ensuring feasibility of the uncertain system. Specifically, the first step of our approach is to derive the robust counterpart of problem (6), which requires the successive robustification of the state constraints of the formulation. Assume that the state constraints for the first timestep are expressed as:

$$Gx_1 \leq g \tag{7}$$

$$G(Ax_0 + Bu_0) \leq g \tag{8}$$

The robust counterpart of the above constraint is:

$$GA_0x_0 + \epsilon_\alpha|G||A_0||x_0| + GB_0u_0 + \epsilon_\beta|G||B_0||u_0| \leq g \tag{9}$$

The nonlinearity introduced from the absolutes values is addressed by introducing the artificial variables z_0 and v_0, along with their corresponding box constraints:

$$\begin{aligned} &GA_0x_0 + \epsilon_{\alpha|}|G||A_0|z_0 + GB_0u_0 + \epsilon_\beta|G||B_0|v_0 \leq g \\ &-z_0 \leq x_0 \leq z_0 \\ &-v_0 \leq u_0 \leq v_0 \end{aligned} \tag{10}$$

By following the proposed robustification scheme, all constraints are successively robustified for the length of the prediction horizon. That enforces state constraint satisfaction until – and including – the Nth step of the horizon. Moreover, the system states are required to enter the invariant set at the Nth horizon step, hence the system feasibility thereafter is also ensured. In summary, at each robustification step, an artificial variable for each state and control input is introduced. This challenge is addressed by eliminating the state artificial variables through the Fourier-Motzkin (FM) elimination, which allows for removal of the artificial variables. As an example, assume that $a_{i,j}$ are scalar coefficients and that $a_{1,2} \geq 0$ and that $a_{2,1} \leq 0$:

$$a_{1,1}x_0 + a_{1,2}z_0 + a_{1,3}u_0 + a_{1,4}v_0 \leq g_1 \tag{11}$$

$$a_{2,1}x_0 + a_{2,1}z_0 + a_{2,3}u_0 + a_{2,4}v_0 \leq g_2 \tag{12}$$

That can be rewritten as

$$z_0 \leq \frac{1}{a_{1,2}}(g_1 - a_{1,1}x_0 - a_{1,3}u_0 - a_{1,4}v_0) \tag{13}$$

$$z_0 \geq \frac{1}{a_{2,1}}(g_2 - a_{2,1}x_0 - a_{2,3}u_0 - a_{2,4}v_0) \tag{14}$$

Consequently, the variable z_0 can be eliminated by combining the two expressions:

$$\frac{1}{a_{2,1}}(g_2 - a_{2,1}x_0 - a_{2,3}u_0 - a_{2,4}v_0) \leq \frac{1}{a_{1,2}}(g_1 - a_{1,1}x_0 - a_{1,3}u_0 - a_{1,4}v_0) \tag{15}$$

However, the drawback of the FM elimination is the introduction of additional inequality constraints in the problem. Hence, after applying the FM algorithm, we eliminate the unnecessary inequality constraints by solving a linear programming problem to check redundancy. As a result, a robustified version of problem (6) is derived and is solved with state-of-the-art multiparametric optimization algorithms. We note that the proposed approach is applicable to mixed-integer linear models too have recently shown to play an important role in model building for explicit MPC applications (Katz et al., 2020).

4. Results

Consider an uncertain system of form (1), adopted from (Kouramas et al., 2013). The nominal matrices of the system are $A_0 = \begin{bmatrix} 1 & 1 \\ 0 & 1 \end{bmatrix}$ and $B_0 = \begin{bmatrix} 0 \\ 1 \end{bmatrix}$. It is assumed that these nominal matrices can deviate from their nominal value by 20% (i.e. $\varepsilon_\alpha = \varepsilon_\beta = 0.2$). The horizon of the problem is $N = 2$, while the cost matrices are $Q_R = \begin{bmatrix} 1 & 1 \\ 0 & 1 \end{bmatrix}$, $R = 0.01$ and $P = \begin{bmatrix} 2.62 & 1.63 \\ 1.63 & 2.64 \end{bmatrix}$. The formulation is solved using the approach presented previously. The problem has eighty two critical regions and is simulated in closed-loop for a constant and random value of the model. The controller can stir the system to the origin.

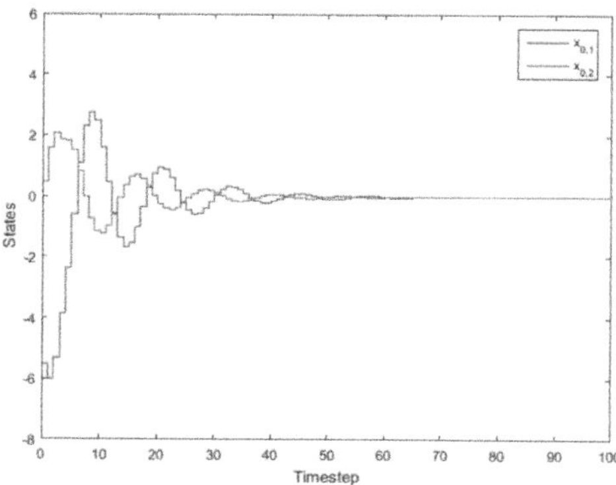

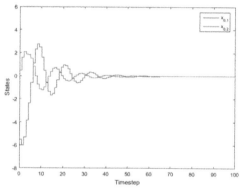

Figure 1: Closed-loop simulation of the system for a random but constant value of the system matrices.

As a next step we generate multiple scenarios of the matrices which are randomly altered at each time step of the closed-loop simulation. The system is regulated for all of them, achieving the control objective of driving the system to the origin.

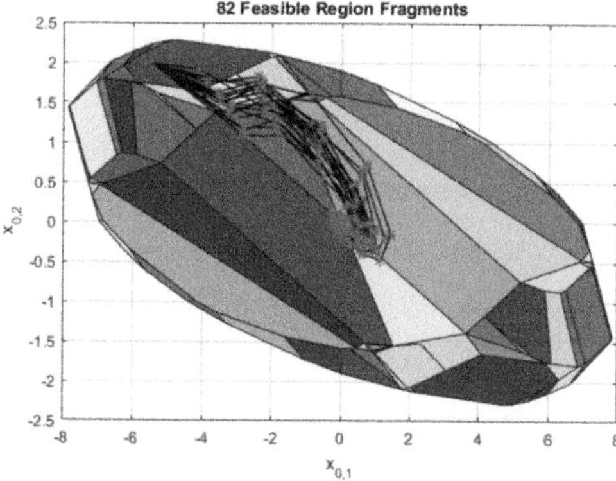

Figure 2: The map of optimal solutions along with closed-loop simulations of the system for multiple scenarios where the values of the matrices are randomly altered.

As expected, the robustification of the constraints forces the system to remain feasible for all different scenarios, while having the benefit of the explicit form of the solution.

5. Conclusions

In this work, we presented an algorithm to solve robust explicit MPC problems. Our approach is based on the successive robustification of the constraints of the problem which along with the terminal set guarantee the feasibility of the system in closed-loop. Additionally, we eliminated the complexity introduced by using the FM elimination algorithm and redundancy checks to remove variables and constraints respectively from the problem formulation. We demonstrated our findings on a numerical MPC case study where we exhibited that the system can be driven to the original for any arbitrary bounded value of the uncertainty. Our next steps include the analysis of the conservativeness of the solution stemming from the robustification.

6. Acknowledgements

The financial support from the Texas A&M Energy Institute, and CESMII (DE-EE0007613, 4550 G WA324) and RAPID (DE-EE0007888-09-04) Institutes are gratefully acknowledged.

7. References

A. Bemporad, F. Borelli, M. Morari, 2003, Min-max control of constrained uncertain discrete time linear systems. IEEE Transactions on automatic control, 48(9), 1600-1606.

B. Kouvaritakis, M. Cannon, 2016, Model Predictive Control, Switzerland: Springer International Publishing, 38.

D. Q. Mayne, 2014, Model predictive control: Recent developments and future promise, Automatica, 50, 12, 2967-2986.

F. Blanchini, 1999, Set invariance in control. Automatica, 35, 11, 1747-1767.

I. Pappas, D. Kenefake, B. Burnak, S. Avraamidou, S. H. Ganesh, J. Katz, N. A. Diangelakis, E. N. Pistikopoulos, 2021, Multiparametric Programming in Process Systems Engineering: Recent Developments and Path Forward. Frontiers in Chemical Engineering, 2.

J. Katz, I. Pappas, S. Avraamidou, E. N. Pistikopoulos, 2020, Integrating Deep Learning Models and Multiparametric Programming. Computers & Chemical Engineering, 138, 106801.

K. Kouramas, C. Panos, N. P. Faísca, E. N. Pistikopoulos, 2013, An algorithm for robust explicit/multi-parametric model predictive control. Automatica, 49, 2, 381-389.

R. H. Oberdieck, 2016, Theoretical and algorithmic advances in multi-parametric optimization and control, Ph.D. Thesis, Imperial College London, London, U.K.

V. Sakizlis, N. M. Kakalis, V. Dua, J. D. Perkins, E. N. Pistikopoulos, 2004, Design of robust model-based controllers via parametric programming. Automatica, 40, 2, 189-201.

Proceedings of the 14th International Symposium on Process Systems Engineering – PSE 2021+
June 19–23, 2022, Kyoto, Japan
http://dx.doi.org/10.1016/B978-0-323-85159-6.50069-5

Data-driven Design of a Feed-forward Controller for Rejecting Measurable Disturbance

Yoichiro Ashida[a*], Masanobu Obika[b]

[a]*Department of Electrical Engineering and Computer Science, National Institute of Technology, Matsue College, 14-4 Nishiikuma-cho, Matsue, 690-8518, JAPAN*
[b]*ADAPTEX Co., Ltd., 3-13-36 Kagamiyama, Higashi-Hiroshima 739-0046, JAPAN*

yashida@matsue-ct.jp

Abstract

Many large-scale multi-input multi-output systems are treated as a combination of single-input single-output systems in reality. At such times, interference from input signals not focused on work as disturbances. For observable disturbances, feed-forward controllers are effective to reject the influence. On the other hand, many data-driven controller tuning schemes are proposed for feed-back controllers. The schemes require not any mathematical models of controlled systems but only operating-data like input and output. This paper proposes a data-driven tuning scheme of feed-forward controllers. Existing data-driven scheme tunes feed-back controller at the same time as the feed-forward controller. In contrast, the proposing scheme only designs the feed-forward controller. By this feature, it is easy to guarantee stability of the control system. Effectiveness of the proposing scheme is verified by a simulation example.

Keywords: process control, disturbance rejection, feed-forward controller

1. Introduction

Most large-scale processes are multi-input multi-output (MIMO) systems. However, the processes are often treated as a group of single-input single-output (SISO) systems because it is difficult to design suitable controllers for a MIMO system. By focusing each SISO system, interference from other SISO systems can be regarded as disturbances. Therefore, disturbance rejection is very important in large-scale process control.

Feed-back controller like PID controller is often employed to realize set-point tracking, and some parameters tuning methods are proposed. Among them, data-driven tuning methods are actively researched. Typical methods are iterative feed-back tuning (IFT) which uses repeated experiment proposed by Hjalmarsson et al. (1998), fictitious reference iterative tuning (FRIT) which uses only off-line optimizations proposed by Soma et al. (2004). The methods can tune controller without any system parameters. Effectiveness of the schemes are verified for experiments. For example, Nakamoto (2003) and Kano et al., (2011) apply IFT and extended-FRIT methods to processes respectively.

Feed-back controllers can improve performance not only set-point tracking but also disturbance rejection. However, it is impossible to reject influence of disturbance perfectly when controlled process has time-delay shown in Alagoz et al. (2015). In addition, the longer the time-delay are, the larger influence of disturbance are. To solve this problem, feed-forward controllers are often employed like Elso et al. (2013). When disturbance can be observable, the feed-forward controller can reject influence of disturbance completely.

The objective of this paper is to propose a data-driven design method of the disturbance rejection feed-forward controller. In the proposing method, not both feed-back and feed-forward controllers but only feed-forward controller is tuned. Sometimes, control-loop becomes unstable by tuning feed-back controller. Therefore, designing only feed-forward controller is safer than designing both controllers. In addition, FRIT method is employed to determine controller parameters. In the FRIT method, an evaluation function to be minimized is derived directly from tracking error signal. Thus, the evaluation function of FRIT and tracking error have close connection. Effectiveness of the proposing design method is checked by a numerical example.

2. Design Scheme of Disturbance Rejection Controller

2.1. Feed-forward Controller

This research assumes a control system as shown in Figure 1. $r(t), u(t), y(t)$, and $\nu(t)$ denote reference, input, output, and unknown noise signals respectively. Additionally, $d(t)$ denotes trigger signal of disturbance.

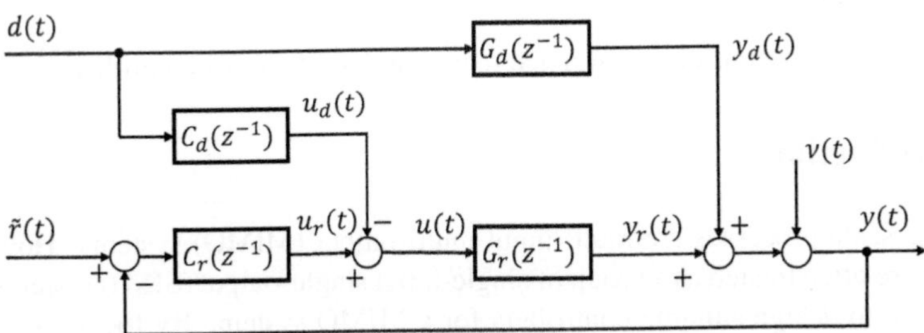

Figure 1: Block diagram of the proposing control system.

Aim of this research is to design disturbance rejection controller $C_d(z^{-1})$. Feed-back controller $C_r(z^{-1})$ is assumed to exist, and proposing design method does not touch the controller. This is because it is easy to ensure stability of control system and to employ the method to industries. Controlled system $G_r(z^{-1})$ and disturbance system $G_d(z^{-1})$ are

$$G_r(z^{-1}) = \frac{B_r(z^{-1})}{A_r(z^{-1})} z^{-k_r}, \tag{1}$$

$$G_d(z^{-1}) = \frac{B_d(z^{-1})}{A_d(z^{-1})} z^{-k_d}, \tag{2}$$

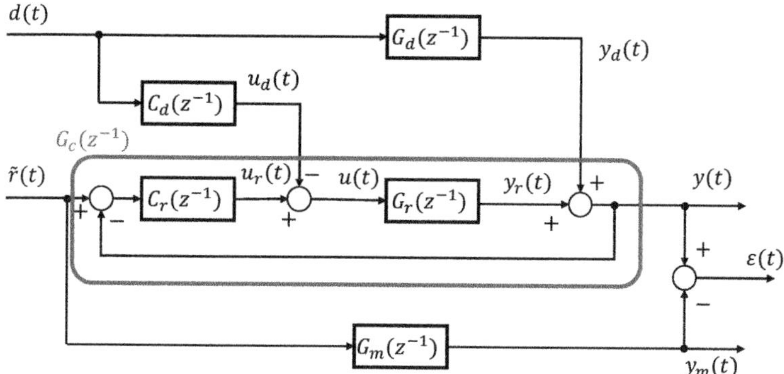

Figure 2: Conceptual diagram of the proposing FRIT method.

where $A_r(z^{-1}), B_r(z^{-1}), A_d(z^{-1})$, and $B_d(z^{-1})$ are

$$A_r(z^{-1}) = 1 + a_{r1}z^{-1} + \cdots + a_{rna}z^{-rna}, \tag{3}$$

$$B_r(z^{-1}) = 1 + b_{r1}z^{-1} + \cdots + b_{rnb}z^{-rnb}, \tag{4}$$

$$A_d(z^{-1}) = 1 + a_{d1}z^{-1} + \cdots + a_{dna}z^{-dna}, \tag{5}$$

$$B_d(z^{-1}) = 1 + b_{d1}z^{-1} + \cdots + b_{dnb}z^{-dnb}. \tag{6}$$

When $C_d(z^{-1})$ is designed as

$$C_d(z^{-1}) = G_d(z^{-1})G_r(z^{-1})^{-1}, \tag{7}$$

influence of $d(t)$ is rejected from $y(t)$. To realize the controller, $k_d \geq k_r$ must be hold.

2.2. *Data-driven controller tuning*

Soma et al.(2004) proposes data-driven controller tuning named fictitious reference iterative tuning (FRIT) to tune feed-back controllers for set-point tracking. This paper extends FRIT method for designing disturbance rejection feed-forward controller $C_d(z^{-1})$. Conceptual diagram of proposing FRIT is shown in Figure 2.

$\varepsilon(t)$ denotes error as $\varepsilon(t) = y(t) - G_m(z^{-1})\tilde{r}(t)$, thus minimizing $\varepsilon(t)$ means minimizing control error between reference trajectory and control output directly.

Assuming that one-set of operating-data $u(t), y(t)$ and $d(t)$ has been obtained, and closed-loop transfer functions with $d(t) = 0$ is set as $G_c(z^{-1})$. When Eq.(7) holds, influence of $d(t)$ is neglected from $y(t)$, and $y(t)$ can be expressed as $y(t) = G_c(z^{-1})\tilde{r}(t)$. Therefore, $\varepsilon(t)$ becomes zero when $G_m(z^{-1})$ and $G_c(z^{-1})$ are identical. By using these relations, proposing FRIT determines $C_d(z^{-1})$.

In Figure 2, $u(t)$ is calculated as

$$u(t) = C_r(z^{-1})r(t) - C_r(z^{-1})y(t) - C_d(z^{-1})d(t). \tag{8}$$

Based on Eq.(8), fictitious reference signal $\tilde{r}(t)$ is defined as

$$\tilde{r}(t) := y(t) + C_r(z^{-1})^{-1}\left\{u(t) + C_d(z^{-1})d(t)\right\}. \tag{9}$$

Therefore, $\varepsilon(t)$ is expressed as

$$\varepsilon(t) = y(t) - G_m(z^{-1})\left[y(t) + C_r(z^{-1})^{-1}\left\{u(t) + C_d(z^{-1})d(t)\right\}\right]. \tag{10}$$

From the previous discussion, suitable $C_d(z^{-1})$ can be obtained by minimizing the following cost function J:

$$J := \sum_{i=1}^{N} \varepsilon(i)^2, \tag{11}$$

where N denotes size of operating-data.

The following two sets of optimization variables can be considered in Eq.(10).

1. $C_d(z^{-1})$ and $G_m(z^{-1})$,
2. $G_r(z^{-1})$ and $G_d(z^{-1})$.

The first approach directly determines controller $C_d(z^{-1})$ and closed-loop model $G_m(z^{-1})$. Although ideal $C_d(z^{-1})$ of Eq.(7) and closed-loop $G_c(z^{-1})$ both include $G_r(z^{-1})$, first approach determines both of them independently. In contrast, the second approach determines controlled system and disturbance transfer function. From controlled system $G_r(z^{-1})$ and known $C_r(z^{-1})$, $G_m(z^{-1})$ is easily calculated, and $C_d(z^{-1})$ is also calculated using $G_r(z^{-1})$ and $G_d(z^{-1})$ by Eq.(7). Although it looks system identification, this is still data-driven tuning because minimized error is not modeling error but control error $\varepsilon(t)$. This paper employs the second approach.

3. Numerical examples

Simulations of this section was executed as Figure 1. $G_r(z^{-1})$, $G_d(z^{-1})$, and $C_r(z^{-1})$ were set as

$$G_r(z^{-1}) = \frac{0.0004821z^{-1} + 0.0004648z^{-2}}{1 - 1.895z^{-1} + 0.8958z^{-2}} z^{-30}, \tag{12}$$

$$G_d(z^{-1}) = \frac{0.002415z^{-1} + 0.002332z^{-2}}{1 - 1.9000z^{-1} + 0.9003z^{-2}} z^{-50}, \tag{13}$$

$$C_r(z^{-1}) = \frac{0.02 - 0.01z^{-1}}{\Delta}. \tag{14}$$

In addition, unknown noise was introduced as

$$v(t) = \frac{0.004988z^{-1}}{1 - 0.995z^{-1}} \xi(t), \tag{15}$$

where $\xi(t)$ is a Gaussian white noise with zero mean and 3.0^2 variance.

Initial operating-data which was obtained with $C_d(z^{-1}) = 0$ is shown as Figure 3. It is clear that controlled output is affected by disturbance.

Next, the following $G_r(z^{-1})$ and $G_d(z^{-1})$ were obtained by the proposing method. For minimization of J, fminunc function of MATLAB R2021a software was employed. The

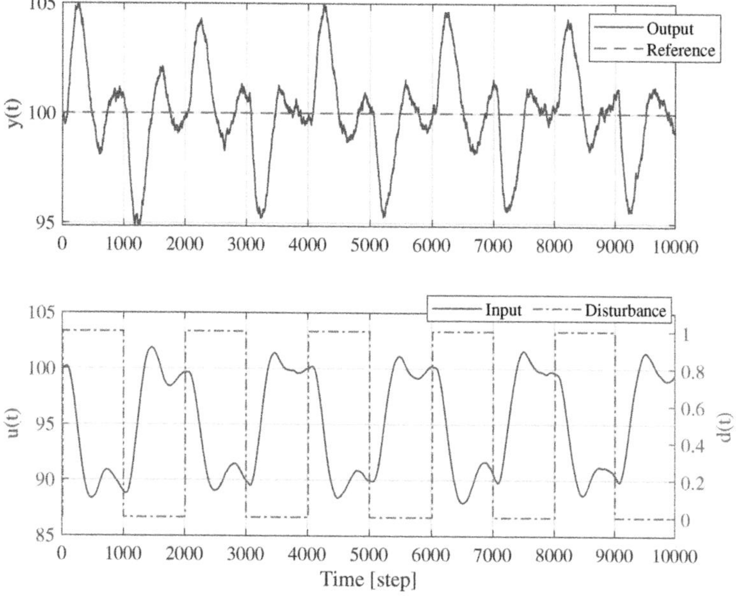

Figure 3: Initial operating-data with $C_d(z^{-1}) = 0$.

function uses quasi-Newton method with bfgs algorithm for optimization. Time-delays were given as known parameters.

$$G_r(z^{-1}) = \frac{0.0086z^{-1}}{1 - 0.9923z^{-1}} z^{-30}, \tag{16}$$

$$G_d(z^{-1}) = \frac{0.0448z^{-1}}{1 - 0.9962z^{-1}} z^{-50}. \tag{17}$$

Even though $G_r(z^{-1})$ and $G_d(z^{-1})$ are both second order systems, they are modeled as first order systems in this simulation.

Figure 4 shows the result using $C_d(z^{-1})$ calculated by the proposing method. Upper figure shows that proposing method mostly rejected influence of disturbance. Shown as lower figure, input signal quickly changed after varying disturbance signal. As a result, influence of disturbance was canceled before appearing to the output. $G_r(z^{-1})$ and $G_d(z^{-1})$ are second order systems, and unknown noise is added. Therefore, the proposing scheme is considered effective for some uncertain elements.

4. Conclusions

This paper has proposed a design method of feed-forward disturbance rejection controller. FRIT method has been employed to tune the controller. A feature is to tune not feed-forward and feed-back controllers but only feed-forward controller. Effectiveness of proposing scheme has been verified by a numerical example. It is considered that proposing scheme is effective for system with some uncertain elements.

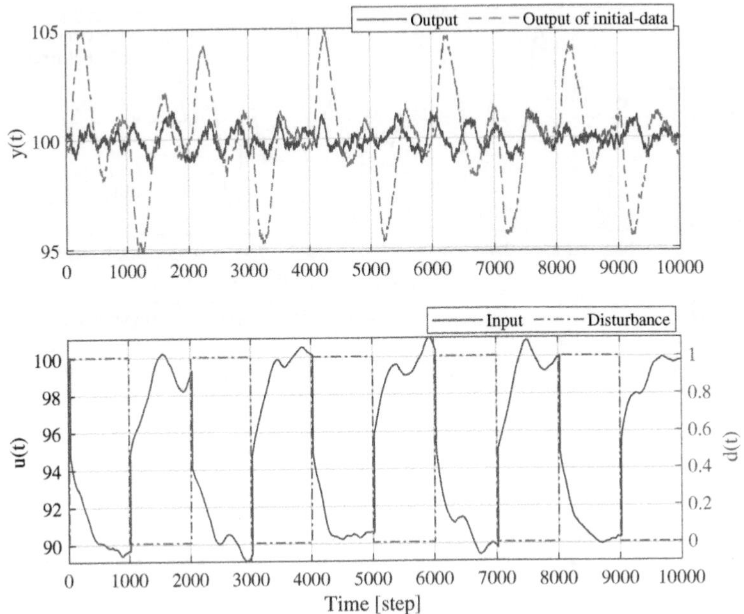

Figure 4: Control result with $C_d(z^{-1})$ calculated by the proposing method.

References

Hjalmarsson, H., Gevers, M., Gunnarsson, S., and Lequin, O., 1998, Iterative Feedback Tuning: Theory and Applications, IEEE Control Systems Magazine, 18, 8, 26-41

Soma, S., Kaneko, O., and Fujii, T., 2004, A New Method of Controller Parameter Tuning based on Input-Output Data – Fictitious Reference Iterative Tuning (FRIT) –, IFAC Proceedings Volumes, 37, 12, 789–794

Nakamoto, M., 2003, An Application of Iterative Feedback Tuning for a Process Control, Trans. of the Society of Instrument and Control Engineers, 39, 10, 924-932

Kano, M., Tasaka, K., Ogawa, M., Takinami, A., Takahashi, S., and Yoshii, S., 2011, Extended Fictitious Reference Iterative Tuning and Its Application to Chemical Processes, Proc. of 2011 International Symposium on Advanced Control of Industrial Processes

Elso, J., Gil-Martínez, M., García-Sanz, M., 2013, Quantitative feedback–feedforward control for model matching and disturbance rejection, IET Control Theory & Applications, 7, 6, 894-900

Alagoz, B.B., Deniz, F.N., Keles, C., Tan, N., 2015, Disturbance rejection performance analyses of closed loop control systems by reference to disturbance ratio, ISA Transactions, 55, 63-71

Proceedings of the 14th International Symposium on Process Systems Engineering – PSE 2021+
June 19–23, 2022, Kyoto, Japan
http://dx.doi.org/10.1016/B978-0-323-85159-6.50070-1

Optimal Operation of Heat Exchanger Networks with Changing Active Constraint Regions

Lucas Ferreira Bernardino[a*], Dinesh Krishnamoorthy[a], Sigurd Skogestad[a]

[a]*Department of Chemical Engineering, Norwegian University of Science and Technology, Trondheim, Norway*

lucas.f.bernardino@ntnu.no

Abstract

In this paper, we study the optimal operation of heat exchanger networks with stream splits. In particular, we extend previous approaches on the unconstrained optimization of the system to the constrained case, with temperature constraints on each flow branch, and with changing disturbances so that the set of optimally active constraints changes during operation. The simplest way to achieve optimal operation when some of the constraints are active, is to control the constraints to their limiting value, known as active constraint control. For the remaining unconstrained degrees of freedom, we propose to control linear combinations of the gradient as self-optimizing controlled variables. To automatically switch between the different active constraint regions, we use classical advanced control elements such as selectors, thereby achieving optimal operation using only the temperature measurements as feedback in different active constraint regions. The performance of the proposed feedback optimizing control structure for the heat exchange network is compared with the traditional model-based real-time optimization using simulations. In the presence of structural plant-model mistmach, we show that our proposed approach performs optimally for all disturbances, while traditional real-time optimization fails to converge for some cases, as the optimization problem becomes infeasible depending on the estimated disturbances.

Keywords: process control, optimal operation, self-optimizing control, applications

1. Introduction

In the context of optimal operation of process systems, the choice of controlled variables plays a vital role, as it will dictate how efficiently a process can operate without interference of higher layers (Skogestad, 2000). The ideal design of a supervisory control layer would result in a structure that is able to operate optimally under constant setpoints. This concept is known as self-optimizing control, and recent developments aim for systematic choice of control objectives (Krishnamoorthy and Skogestad, 2019). A known challenge in supervisory layer design is the change in optimally active constraints during operation, which can be caused by changes in disturbances that affect process objectives. When that happens, reconfiguration of the controlled structure is usually desired to minimize the operational losses. If that does not happen, interactions with the higher optimization layer become stronger, as the sensitivity of the optimal setpoint values with relation to the changing disturbances is high when there are no changes in the control structure. Krishnamoorthy and Skogestad (2019) discusses the handling of changes in active constraints through feedback control, without the solution of online optimization problems, by selector-based control structures. This approach is to be evaluated in this work, compared to the solution of real-time optimization (RTO) problems, which can be problematic in the presence of model-plant mismatch.

2. Case study modeling

The case study considered in this work consists of three heat exchangers in parallel, see Figure 1. Each exchanger has its own source of hot fluid, such that the cold fluid is split and sent to the exchangers, and the operational goal is to maximize the outlet temperature of the cold fluid, subject to constraints related to the maximum temperature in the individual exchangers.

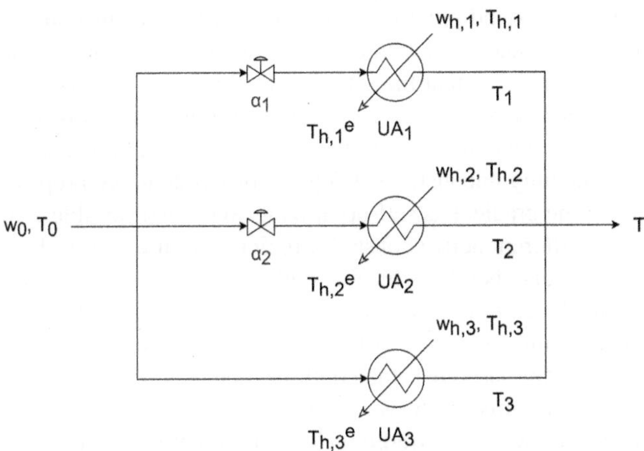

Figure 1: Heat exchanger network scheme

In addition to the mass and energy balances, an additional relation is necessary for calculating the total exchanged heat in each equipment, Q_i. The analytic solution, assuming constant heat capacities and countercurrent flow, is given by Eq.(1).

$$Q_i = UA_i \, \Delta T_{LM,i} \tag{1}$$

In this equation, $\Delta T_{LM,i}$ represents the logarithmic mean of temperature differences inside the heat exchanger. Although exact, this model presents some numerical challenges, especially when the heat capacities are too close, or when the temperature differences assume opposite signs during iteration. A simplified linear version of this model makes use of the arithmetic mean of temperature differences, $\Delta T_{AM,i}$, and for this model, simple analytic expressions for the gradient can be derived (Jäschke and Skogestad, 2014).

The steady-state optimization problem considered for the optimal operation of this system can therefore be written as:

$$\begin{aligned} \min_{\alpha} \quad & J = -T \\ \text{s.t.} \quad & g_i = T_i - T_{max} \leq 0, \quad i = 1, 2, 3 \end{aligned} \tag{2}$$

3. Proposed control structure

The optimal operation of heat exchanger networks has been extensively studied by Jäschke and Skogestad (2014) for the unconstrained case. In this case, the gradient J_u to be driven to zero can be approximately written in terms of the Jäschke temperatures. For the constrained case, however, the set of controlled variables need to change so that optimal operation is achieved. Given that the active constraints g_A are effectively controlled, there are still unconstrained degrees of freedom that need to be used for optimal operation. As proven by Krishnamoorthy and Skogestad (2019), we can find the additional controlled variables as a linear combination of the gradient such that the necessary conditions of optimality are satisfied. These correspond to $c = N^T J_u$, where N is the nullspace of the gradient of the active constraints with relation to the inputs, $\nabla_u g_A$, at the optimal point. This procedure results in a set of controlled variables per region, defined by the respective set of active constraints.

For this case study, there are 7 feasible operating regions, one of which is fully unconstrained, 3 being partially constrained (one active constraint per region), and the remaining being fully constrained (two active constraints per region). The case with all 3 constraints being active is infeasible with the available degrees of freedom, and will therefore not be considered. The fully unconstrained region can be optimally operated by controlling the plant gradient to zero, and the fully constrained regions are optimally operated through active constraint control. For the optimal operation in the partially constrained regions, the combinations of the gradient to be controlled in addition to the active constraints are given in Table 1.

Active constraint	N^T
g_1	$\begin{bmatrix} 0 & 1 \end{bmatrix}$
g_2	$\begin{bmatrix} 1 & 0 \end{bmatrix}$
g_3	$\begin{bmatrix} -\frac{1}{\sqrt{2}} & \frac{1}{\sqrt{2}} \end{bmatrix}$

Table 1: Linear combinations of gradient per active constraint

The next step for the design of a simple control structure is defining the pairing between manipulated and controlled variables, and the switching between active controllers. In the current case study, there are 2 manipulated variables and 3 constraints, which means that the constraints cannot be assigned to one specific input if optimal operation over all regions is desired. Therefore, at least one of the constraints needs to be controlled by multiple inputs.

Based on this reasoning, this work proposes an adaptive control structure to deal with all possible active constraint regions. The full control structure, showing the logic blocks and controllers, is presented in Figure 2. and the pairing between manipulated and controlled variables is summarized in Table 2. All presented controllers have integral action, so that steady-state offset is eliminated.

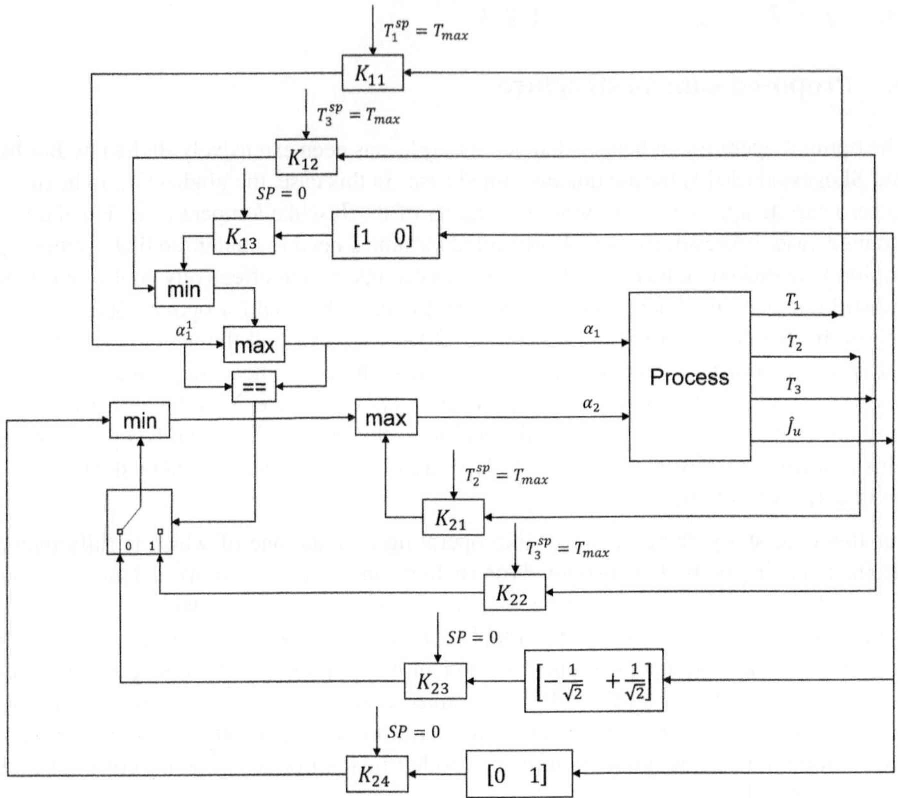

Figure 2: Proposed adaptive control structure

α_1	α_2 (T_1 inactive)	α_2 (T_1 active)
T_1	T_2	T_2
$\begin{bmatrix}1 & 0\end{bmatrix} J_u$	$\begin{bmatrix}0 & 1\end{bmatrix} J_u$	$\begin{bmatrix}0 & 1\end{bmatrix} J_u$
T_3	$\begin{bmatrix}-\frac{1}{\sqrt{2}} & \frac{1}{\sqrt{2}}\end{bmatrix} J_u$	T_3

Table 2: Proposed adaptive pairing for all operating regions

4. Simulation results and discussion

The control structure previously presented is now evaluated in closed-loop simulation face to changing disturbances. Figure 3 shows the simulation results, where all 7 possible regions are explored. As the process itself is considered to be at steady state at all times, the dynamics of the system is fully attributed to the tuning of the controllers. Operation in the fully constrained regions is optimal at steady state, whereas there is some deviation from the optimal conditions in the partially constrained and unconstrained regions. This is due to the estimation of gradients by Jäschke temperatures, which does not fully represent the plant model, but gives a reasonable estimate for control, so that low operational loss is achieved.

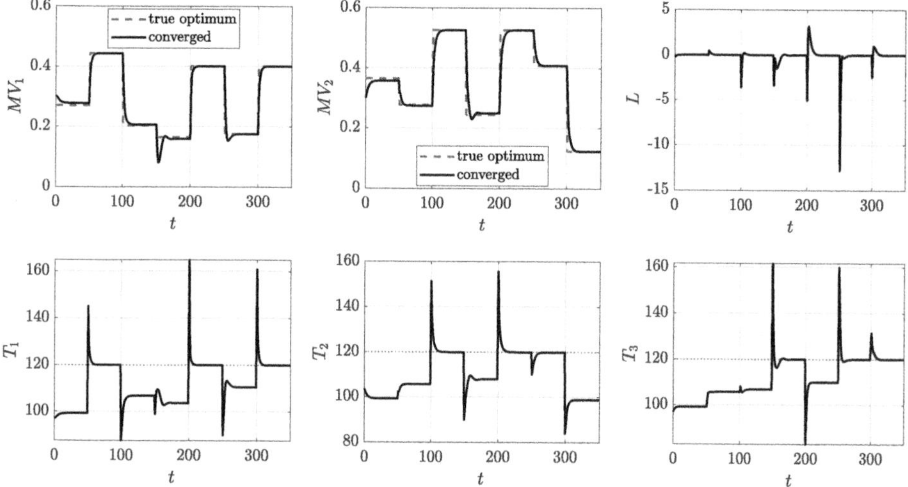

Figure 3: Simulation of region-based control structure using Jäschke temperatures

These results are compared with a traditional RTO implementation, see Figure 4. This implementation consists of a two-step approach, with disturbance estimation followed by model-based constrained optimization. The system converges in few iterations, with similar steady-state behavior to the region-based control structure. The unconstrained and partially constrained regions suffer from deviations from the true optima, due to model-plant mismatch, and the converged state is quite similar to that of the region-based control structure. This is to be expected, as Jäschke temperatures represent the gradient information extracted from the model used in the RTO framework.

In the RTO simulation, a curious undesired behavior is observed. From $t = 40$, in the fifth simulated region, the system converges to an infeasible point. This happens because the disturbance estimation step returns parameter values that make the optimization problem infeasible, meaning that there are no inputs that satisfy all constraints on the model with the given parameters, even if the estimation step returns parameters that agree with the plant measurements. Some workarounds are therefore deemed necessary for the effective implementation of the RTO strategy, such as the adaptation of the optimization problem itself, based on the estimation of gradients from the true plant (Marchetti et al., 2009).

5. Conclusion

In this work, we extended previous work on the optimal operation of heat exchanger networks to the constrained case, where the ideal self-optimizing variables known as Jäschke

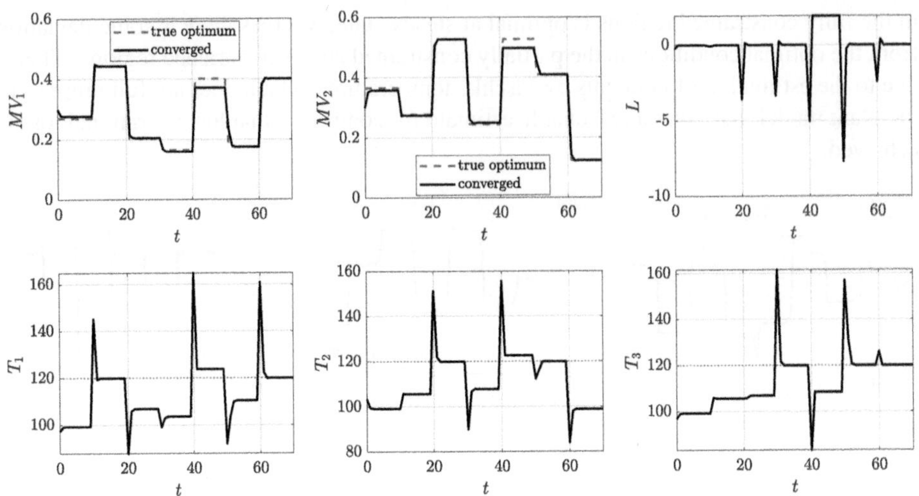

Figure 4: Simulation of steady-state RTO with model-plant mismatch

temperatures cannot be applied to every operating condition. Instead, control of the active constraints becomes necessary for optimal operation, and the challenge lies in deciding automatically what are the best controlled variables during operation. This has been achieved with the use of selectors, with steady-state performance comparable to a traditional model-based RTO implementation. With the proposed control implementation, one avoids the solution of online optimization problems, which can be problematic, as highlighted by the presented results. However, the simultaneous use of the presented tools is encouraged, so that near-optimal operation is achieved in the faster timescales, and optimization tools can correct for mismatches under more careful evaluation of the results.

References

Jäschke, J., Skogestad, S., 2014. Optimal operation of heat exchanger networks with stream split: Only temperature measurements are required. Computers & chemical engineering 70, 35–49.

Krishnamoorthy, D., Skogestad, S., 2019. Online process optimization with active constraint set changes using simple control structures. Industrial & Engineering Chemistry Research 58, 13555–13567.

Marchetti, A., Chachuat, B., Bonvin, D., 2009. Modifier-adaptation methodology for real-time optimization. Industrial & engineering chemistry research 48, 6022–6033.

Skogestad, S., 2000. Plantwide control: The search for the self-optimizing control structure. Journal of process control 10, 487–507.

Proceedings of the 14th International Symposium on Process Systems Engineering – PSE 2021+
June 19–23, 2022, Kyoto, Japan
http://dx.doi.org/10.1016/B978-0-323-85159-6.50071-3

Iterative Feedback Tuning for Regulatory Control Systems Using Estimate of Sensitivity Function

Shiro Masuda[a*]

[a]*Dept. of Systems Design, Tokyo Metropolitan University, 6-6 Asahigaoka, Hino, 191-0065, Japan*

smasuda@tmu.ac.jp

Abstract

The paper provides a method for Iterative Feedback Tuning (IFT) for regulatory control systems. The IFT estimates the gradient of a prescribed cost criterion using collected data. However, the original approaches require special experiments for gradient estimate. The proposed method makes it possible to estimate the sensitivity function that leads to the gradient estimate from regulatory control data. The proposed approach uses two sets of regulatory control data. The first one is used for rough estimate of the sensitivity function. Then, the second data are used for the correction of the estimation error of the sensitivity function. A numerical example shows that the proposed method can optimize the cost criterion even in the case where the identifiability condition does not hold.

Keywords: Iterative feedback tuning, Regulatory control systems, Sensitivity function

1. Introduction

The Iterative Feedback Tuning (IFT), which was originally initiated by Hjalmarsson (1998), is a data-driven controller parameter tuning method that achieves optimal control parameters by way of parameter updating laws using gradient estimates for a prescribed cost criterion. While the original IFT requires a special experiment for gradient estimate, the present work concerns a gradient estimation method using regulatory control data. However, the methods discussed in Kammer (2000) required a certain plant test for estimating sensitivity functions. The method in Masuda (2019) sometimes brings numerical problems in the derivation of gradient estimates. Therefore, the paper provides an estimating method for sensitivity functions leading to the gradient estimate. The proposed approach uses two sets of regulatory control data. The first one is used for the estimation of plant and disturbance model. Then, after calculating a sensitivity function using the estimated plant model, the estimation error is compensated by using the second regulatory control data. The effectiveness of the proposed approach is shown through a numerical example.

2. IFT for regulatory control

2.1. Process description and regulatory control Systems

Consider the following process model described by

$$y(t) = G(q)u(t) + H(q)w(t), \tag{1}$$

where q is a shift operator, i.e. $q^k y(t) = y(t+k)$. $u(t)$ and $y(t)$ are process input and output signals at discrete time instant t. $w(t)$ is zero mean white noise with the variance σ_w^2. The process model $G(q)$ and the disturbance model $H(q)$ are expressed as

$$G(q) = \frac{B(q^{-1})}{F(q^{-1})}, \quad H(q) = \frac{C(q^{-1})}{D(q^{-1})}, \tag{2}$$

$$B(q^{-1}) = b_0 + b_1 q^{-1} + \cdots + b_{n_b} q^{-n_b}, \tag{3}$$

$$F(q^{-1}) = 1 + f_1 q^{-1} + \cdots + f_{n_f} q^{-n_f}, \tag{4}$$

$$C(q^{-1}) = 1 + c_1 q^{-1} + \cdots + c_{n_c} q^{-n_c}, \tag{5}$$

$$D(q^{-1}) = 1 + d_1 q^{-1} + \cdots + d_{n_d} q^{-n_d}, \tag{6}$$

where $n_b,\ n_f,\ n_c,$ and n_d are the orders of $B(q^{-1}),\ F(q^{-1}),\ C(q^{-1}),$ and $D(q^{-1})$, respectively. It can be supposed that the disturbance model $H(q^{-1})$ is a stable, minimum phase, and bi-proper rational function without loss of generality, so both the zeros of $C(q^{-1})$ and $D(q^{-1})$ lie in a unit circle in the complex plane.

The present work deals with the regulatory control system with the the following feedback controller $K(q)$

$$K(q) = \frac{X(q^{-1})}{Y(q^{-1})} \tag{7}$$

$$X(q^{-1}) = x_0 + x_1 q^{-1} + \cdots + x_{n_x} q^{-n_x}, \tag{8}$$

$$Y(q^{-1}) = y_0 + y_1 q^{-1} + \cdots + y_{n_y} q^{-n_y}, \tag{9}$$

where n_x and n_y are the orders of $X(q^{-1})$ and $Y(q^{-1})$, respectively. The process input signal is calculated as $u(t) = -K(q)y(t)$. As for the controller $K(q)$, the paper considers the case where the parameters of the numerator are tuning parameters for control performance improvement. Hence, the paper represents the controller $K(q)$ in the following parametrization.

$$K(q, \boldsymbol{\rho}) = \boldsymbol{\varphi}(q)^{\mathrm{T}} \boldsymbol{\rho}, \tag{10}$$

$$\boldsymbol{\rho} = \begin{bmatrix} x_0 & x_1 & \cdots & x_{n_x} \end{bmatrix}^{\mathrm{T}}, \ \boldsymbol{\varphi}(q) = \begin{bmatrix} \frac{1}{Y(q^{-1})} & \frac{q^{-1}}{Y(q^{-1})} & \cdots & \frac{q^{-n_x}}{Y(q^{-1})} \end{bmatrix}^{\mathrm{T}}, \tag{11}$$

where $\boldsymbol{\varphi}(q)$ is a basis vector that specifies controller structures and $\boldsymbol{\rho}$ is a controller parameter vector, which will be tuned for control performance improvement.

The assumptions of the present work are as follows.

(A1) The parameters of the process $G(q)$ and the disturbance model $H(q)$ are unknown, but the order of the numerators and the denominators, $n_b,\ n_f,\ n_c,$ and n_d are known.

(A2) The controller structure is predetermined. Namely, $\boldsymbol{\varphi}(q)$ and the dimension of parameter vector n_x is assumed to be given beforehand.

(A3) Two different controller parameters that stabilize the closed-loop system for the prescribed controller structure are attainable, and the closed-loop output implemented by the stabilized controller parameters can be collected for a certain interval.

2.2. Control objective

The control objective of the present work is the disturbance attenuation for the regulatory control systems. To this end, the present work will reduce the problem into the optimization problem minimizing the cost criterion.

$$J = J_y + \lambda J_u,\ \lambda > 0, \quad J_y = \mathrm{E}\left[\frac{1}{T}\sum_{t=1}^{T} y(t)^2\right],\ J_u = \mathrm{E}\left[\frac{1}{T}\sum_{t=1}^{T} u(t)^2\right], \tag{12}$$

where $\mathrm{E}[\cdot]$ represents the expectation operator. However, the present work employs the IFT approach for controller parameter tuning, which tunes the controller parameters every T steps by using collected process output signals at the corresponding interval. Hence, the paper updates the controller parameters in order to decrease the following cost criterion at every interval instead of the minimization of Eq.(12).

$$J^{(i)} = J_y^{(i)} + \lambda J_u^{(i)},\ \lambda > 0, \quad J_y^{(i)} = \frac{1}{T}\sum_{t=iT+1}^{(i+1)T} \left(y^{(i)}(t)\right)^2,\ J_u^{(i)} = \frac{1}{T}\sum_{t=iT+1}^{(i+1)T} \left(u^{(i)}(t)\right)^2, \tag{13}$$

where $i = 0, 1, 2, \cdots$ is trial numbers, and $y^{(i)}(t)$ and $u^{(i)}(t)$ are the process output and input signals when the controller parameters $\boldsymbol{\rho}^{(i)}$ is implemented. The objective of the paper is to provide a way how the controller parameters $\boldsymbol{\rho}^{(i)}$ are tuned so that the cost criterion Eq.(13) is decreased at every interval $iT + 1 \leq t \leq (i+1)T,\ i = 0, 1, 2\cdots$ under the assumption (A1), (A2), and (A3).

3. Controller parameter tuning via IFT

3.1. Gradient estimate

In order to achieve the control objective, the present work estimates the gradient of the cost criterion Eq.(13) from the collected data. The following is the gradient of the cost criterion at the i-th trial.

$$\frac{\partial J^{(i)}}{\partial \boldsymbol{\rho}^{(i)}} = \frac{\partial J_y^{(i)}}{\partial \boldsymbol{\rho}^{(i)}} + \lambda \frac{\partial J_u^{(i)}}{\partial \boldsymbol{\rho}^{(i)}}, \tag{14}$$

$$\frac{\partial J_y^{(i)}}{\partial \boldsymbol{\rho}^{(i)}} = \frac{2}{T}\sum_{t=1}^{T} y^{(i)}(t)\frac{\partial y^{(i)}(t)}{\partial \boldsymbol{\rho}^{(i)}}, \quad \frac{\partial J_u^{(i)}}{\partial \boldsymbol{\rho}^{(i)}} = \frac{2}{T}\sum_{t=1}^{T} u^{(i)}(t)\frac{\partial u^{(i)}(t)}{\partial \boldsymbol{\rho}^{(i)}} \tag{15}$$

In Eq.(15), $\frac{\partial y^{(i)}}{\partial \boldsymbol{\rho}^{(i)}}$ and $\frac{\partial u^{(i)}}{\partial \boldsymbol{\rho}^{(i)}}$ are calculated as

$$\frac{\partial y^{(i)}}{\partial \boldsymbol{\rho}^{(i)}} = -\frac{\boldsymbol{\varphi}(q)^{\mathrm{T}}}{K(q, \boldsymbol{\rho}^{(i)})} T_f(\boldsymbol{\rho}^{(i)}) y^{(i)}(t), \quad \frac{\partial u^{(i)}}{\partial \boldsymbol{\rho}^{(i)}} = -\boldsymbol{\varphi}(q)^{\mathrm{T}} S_f(\boldsymbol{\rho}^{(i)}) y^{(i)}(t), \tag{16}$$

where $S_f(\boldsymbol{\rho}^{(i)})$ is the sensitivity function, and $T_f(\boldsymbol{\rho}^{(i)})$ is the complementary sensitivity function represented as

$$S_f(\boldsymbol{\rho}^{(i)}) = \frac{1}{1 + G(q)K(q, \boldsymbol{\rho}^{(i)})}, \quad T_f(\boldsymbol{\rho}^{(i)}) = 1 - S_f(\boldsymbol{\rho}^{(i)}) \tag{17}$$

From Eq.(14), Eq.(15), and Eq.(16), it follows that if the sensitivity function $S_f(\boldsymbol{\rho}^{(i)})$ is estimated from the collected data $y^{(i)}(t), iT+1 \leq t \leq (i+1)T$, the gradient $\frac{\partial J^{(i)}}{\partial \boldsymbol{\rho}^{(i)}}$ could be estimated. Therefore, the next section shows how the sensitivity function $S_f(\boldsymbol{\rho}^{(i)})$ could be estimated.

4. Estimate of sensitivity function

As shown in the assumption (A3), it is assumed that two different controller parameters stabilize the closed-loop, and each closed-output are collected. The subsection considers the case where one set of controller parameters are the i-th trial controller parameters $\boldsymbol{\rho}^{(i)}$, and another set of controller parameters are the controller parameters $\boldsymbol{\rho}^c$ for the correction of the estimate of the sensitivity function. The proposed estimation method firstly estimates the sensitivity function using the collected data $y^{(i)}(t), iT+1 \leq t \leq (i+1)T$ implemented by the controller parameters $\boldsymbol{\rho}^{(i)}$. Then, the estimate of the sensitivity function is corrected by using the collected data $y^c(t), t_c+1 \leq t \leq t_c+T$ implemented by the controller parameters $\boldsymbol{\rho}^c$. t_c is a certain starting time instant for the data collection of $y^c(t)$. The detail procedure is as follows.

4.1. *Rough estimate of sensitivity function*

This stage roughly estimates the sensitivity function and the disturbance model in the case of the controller parameters $\boldsymbol{\rho}^{(i)}$. Let $\hat{\boldsymbol{\theta}}$ denote the estimated plant and disturbance model parameter vector, and let $\tilde{H}(q, \hat{\boldsymbol{\theta}})$ and $\tilde{S}_f(\hat{\boldsymbol{\theta}}, \boldsymbol{\rho}^{(i)})$ denote the estimated disturbance model and the estimated sensitivity function, respectively. The proposed method does not require the preciseness of each estimate of the sensitivity function and the disturbance model. Meanwhile, suppose that the proposed method successfully estimates the product of sensitivity function and disturbance model. The request will hold because time series analysis of the collected data $y^{(i)}(t)$ would lead to the estimates of $\tilde{H}(q, \hat{\boldsymbol{\theta}})\tilde{S}_f(\hat{\boldsymbol{\theta}}, \boldsymbol{\rho}^{(i)})$.

Additionally, Gevers (2009) proves that the prediction error method makes the request hold even in the case where the identifiability condition does not hold. Hence the estimated disturbance model and the sensitivity function can be parametrized by a bi-proper, minimum phase, stable rational function $\Delta^{(i)}(q)$.

$$H(q, \boldsymbol{\theta}^*) = \tilde{H}(q, \hat{\boldsymbol{\theta}})\Delta^{(i)}(q), \quad S_f(\boldsymbol{\theta}^*, \boldsymbol{\rho}^{(i)}) = \tilde{S}_f(\hat{\boldsymbol{\theta}}, \boldsymbol{\rho}^{(i)})\Delta^{(i)}(q)^{-1}, \tag{18}$$

where the $\boldsymbol{\theta}^*$ is the true parameters of the disturbance model. The next step determines the $\Delta^{(i)}(q)$ so that the roughly estimated sensitivity function becomes close to the true sensitivity function $S_f(\boldsymbol{\theta}^*, \boldsymbol{\rho}^{(i)})$.

4.2. *Correction of the roughly estimated sensitivity function*

The step uses the the collected data $y^c(t)$ implemented by the controller parameters $\boldsymbol{\rho}^c$. Let the controller and the sensitivity function using $\boldsymbol{\rho}^c$ be defined as $K(\boldsymbol{\rho}^c)$ and $S_f(\boldsymbol{\theta}^*, \boldsymbol{\rho}^c)$, respectively. By cancellation of the process model $G(q)$ between the $S_f(\boldsymbol{\theta}^*, \boldsymbol{\rho}^c)$ and $S_f(\boldsymbol{\theta}^*, \boldsymbol{\rho}^{(i)})$, the following equation can be derived.

$$S_f(\boldsymbol{\theta}^*, \boldsymbol{\rho}^c)^{-1} = 1 + \left(S_f(\boldsymbol{\theta}^*, \boldsymbol{\rho}^{(i)})^{-1} - 1\right) \frac{K(\boldsymbol{\rho}^c)}{K(\boldsymbol{\rho}^{(i)})} \tag{19}$$

Now, note that the prediction error for the collected data $y^c(t)$ can be represented as

$$\varepsilon^c(t,\boldsymbol{\theta}) = H(q,\boldsymbol{\theta}^*)^{-1}S_f(\boldsymbol{\theta}^*,\boldsymbol{\rho}^c)^{-1}y^c(t). \tag{20}$$

Hence, using Eq.(18), the prediction error Eq.(20) can be expressed as

$$\varepsilon^c(t,\hat{\boldsymbol{\theta}}) = \tilde{H}(q,\hat{\boldsymbol{\theta}})\Delta^{(i)}(q)\left(1+\left(\tilde{S}_f(\hat{\boldsymbol{\theta}})^{-1}\Delta^{(i)}(q)-1\right)\frac{K(\boldsymbol{\rho}^c)}{K(\boldsymbol{\rho}^{(i)})}\right)y^c(t). \tag{21}$$

The ideal $\Delta^{(i)}(q)$ that leads to the true sensitivity function minimizes the prediction error Eq.(21). Thus, the optimal $\hat{\Delta}^{(i)}(q)$ is obtained so that the mean square error of the prediction error Eq.(21) is minimized. Namely, $\hat{\Delta}^{(i)}(q)$ can be described as

$$\hat{\Delta}^{(i)}(q) = \arg\min_{\Delta^{(i)}(q)} \frac{1}{T}\sum_{t=1}^{T}\varepsilon^c(t,\boldsymbol{\theta})^2 \tag{22}$$

Finally, the corrected sensitivity function can be obtained as

$$\hat{S}_f(\boldsymbol{\theta}^*,\boldsymbol{\rho}^{(i)}) = \tilde{S}_f(\hat{\boldsymbol{\theta}},\boldsymbol{\rho}^{(i)})\hat{\Delta}^{(i)}(q)^{-1} \tag{23}$$

5. Numerical Example

Consider the following process model and disturbance model.

$$G(q) = \frac{0.3q^{-1}}{1-0.45q^{-1}},\ H(q) = \frac{1-0.75q^{-1}}{1-1.2q^{-1}+0.36q^{-2}} \tag{24}$$

The proposed method was applied to the numerical example. We set the time interval $T = 5000$, the variance of white noise is $\sigma_w^2 = 1$. The controller structure is $n_x = 1$ and $\varphi(q) = \frac{1}{1-0.8q^{-1}}$. Hence, the controller is parametrized as $K(q,\rho) = \varphi(q)\rho$. Note that the orders of the process model, the disturbance model, and the controller are $n_b = 1, n_f = 1, n_c = 1, n_d = 2, n_x = 0, n_y = 1$, and the identifiability condition does not hold. i.e. $\max(n_x - n_f, n_y - n_b) = 0 < 2 = n_d$. Hence, the prediction error method does not estimate the true model. In the numerical example, the first controller parameter $\rho^{(0)} = 1.8$ was used. On the other hand, as the controller parameter for the correction of the sensitivity estimates $\rho^c = 1.5$ was used. The rough estimate of the sensitivity function was calculated using the estimated process and disturbance model parameters. Since the identifiability condition does not hold, the estimated parameter remains bias error. Hence, the rough estimate also remains bias error. Fig.1 shows the comparison results. From the figure, we can see that the proposed method successfully corrects the estimate of the sensitivity function. Fig.2 and Fig.3 show how the cost criterion and controller parameter varies by applying the gradient of corrected estimate and rough estimate. From the figures, it follows that the proposed method works effectively.

6. Conclusions

The paper proposed IFT for regulatory control systems by way of estimating sensitivity functions. The numerical example showed that the proposed method can optimize the cost criterion even in the case where the identifiability condition does not hold. The further theoretical analysis remains open problems.

This work was partly supported by JSPS KAKENHI Grant Number 19K04456.

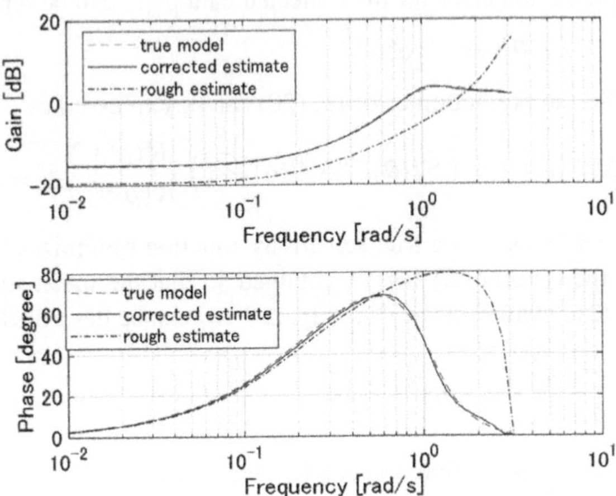

Figure 1: Sensitivity function oftrue model, corrected estimate, and rough estimate

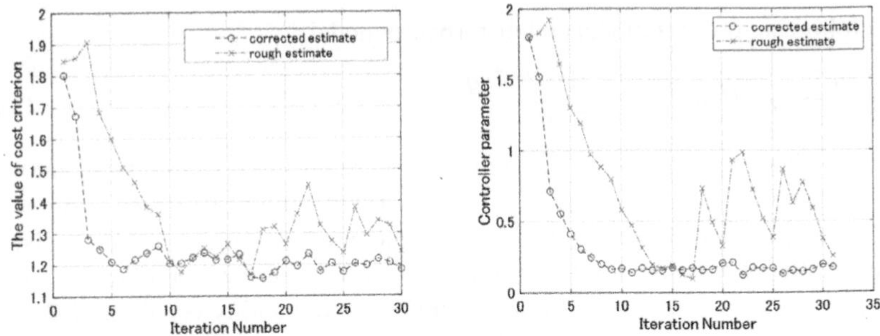

Figure 2: Cost criterion in case of corrected estimate and rough estimate

Figure 3: Controller parameter in case of corrected estimate and rough estimate

References

M. Gevers, A. S. Bazanella, X. Bombois, and L. Mišković, 2009. Identification and the Information Matrix: How to Get Just Sufficiently Rich. IEEE Transaction Automatic Control, Vol. 54, No. 12, pp.2828-2840.

H. Hjalmarsson, M. Gevers, S. Gunnarsson, and L. Lequin, 1998. Iterative feedback tuning: Theory and applications. IEEE Control System Magazine, Vol. 18, No. 4, pp.26-41.

L. C. Kammer, R. R. Bitmead, P. L. Bartlett, 2000. Direct iterative tuning via spectral analysis. Automatica, Vol. 36, pp.1301-1307.

S. Masuda, 2019. Iterative Controller Parameters Tuning Using Gradient Estimate of Variance Evaluation. In Proc. of 2019 International Conference on Advanced Mechatronic Systems (ICAMechS).

Proceedings of the 14th International Symposium on Process Systems Engineering – PSE 2021+
June 19-23, 2022, Kyoto, Japan
http://dx.doi.org/10.1016/B978-0-323-85159-6.50072-5

D-RTO as Enabler for Green Chemical Processes – Systematic Application and Challenges in Reactive Liquid Multiphase Systems

Markus Illner[a*], Volodymyr Kozachynskyi[a], Erik Esche[a], Jens-Uwe Repke[a]

[a] *Process Dynamics and Operations Group, Technische Universität Berlin, Straße des 17. Juni 135, Berlin, D-10623, GERMANY*
markus.illner@tu-berlin.de

Abstract

To date the realization of processes following the principles of Green Chemistry is still challenging due to their novelty, unknown properties of applied feedstocks and solvents, or unidentified system phenomena. Process operation and control is impeded by high system dynamics and unknown behavior. To enable early-stage realization of such "green" processes, optimal process control and especially dynamic real-time optimization (D-RTO) is advised. However, for implementation on real processes key requirements on model adequacy, measurement sufficiency, and robustness must be fulfilled. This is investigated for a reactive liquid multiphase system. Based on identified critical challenges, a tailored D-RTO framework is developed and tested using mini-plant operations. Results indicate greatly improved process operation and reaction performance.

Keywords: Microemulsions, Real-Time Optimization, Multi-Rate State Estimation, Catalysis, Mini-Plant Operation.

1. Introduction and Motivation

With an increasing need for sustainability, Green Chemistry processes considering, e.g., new synthesis paths for renewable feedstocks and the application of reactants, solvents, or additives with low environmental impact are strived for. However, large-scale industrial application of (continuous) production processes are still impeded by the complexity of novel component systems, unknown thermodynamics, and challenging process control (Ivanković, 2017). Developed methods in process systems engineering (PSE) are considered as enabler and assist process development (Mitsos et al., 2018) and operation (Müller et al., 2017; Rafiei and Ricardez-Sandoval, 2020). Their application depends on the specific challenges arising from the process and requirements for a robust implementation of suitable PSE methods, which need to be tailored based on a systematic approach. Such a procedure is outlined within this contribution for the realization of a novel "green" process concept for the hydroformylation of long-chained oily substrates in microemulsion systems and demonstrated for continuous mini-plant operations. Surfactant-based microemulsions offer beneficial properties in providing large interfacial areas for contacting aqueous catalyst solutions with oily substrates in a reactor and a thermomorphic phase separation behavior allowing for product separation and recycling of catalyst and surfactant using simple gravity settlers. However, process operation of such systems using standard automation usually fails due to the complex phase separation behavior and immeasurable states (Illner et al., 2016). Hence, a systematic analysis is conducted to identify critical operation challenges and collect sufficient information on the system behavior. This enables the tailored development of a D-RTO framework based on multi-rate state estimation and dynamic optimization, while systematically considering key requirements such as suitable process models, measurability of plant states, and communication structures. With regard to process industry, a real-life application of D-RTO was tested using long-term mini-plant runs of up to 200 h, aiming for stable and continuous operation of the crucial phase separation and optimal reaction performance.

2. System Information and Technical Application

As example system the long-chained 1-dodecene, the surfactant Marlipal® 24/70, and an aqueous catalyst solution from the rhodium precursor (CAS: 14874-82-9) and Sulfo-XantPhos are used to form a microemulsion. The hydroformylation reaction network with the product tridecanal and possible by-products is found in (Pogrzeba et al., 2019).

2.1. Separation Behavior of the Microemulsion System

Microemulsions are mixtures of oil, water, and an amphiphile, which are characterized by complex rheology and phase separation behavior. Several phase states (1, $\underline{2}$, $\overline{2}$, 3) are possible (Figure 1), developing surfactant-rich emulsion phases and highly pure excess phases (oil or water). The separation dynamics show a distinct minimum of the separation time for the three-phase region, making it the sole feasible operation region.

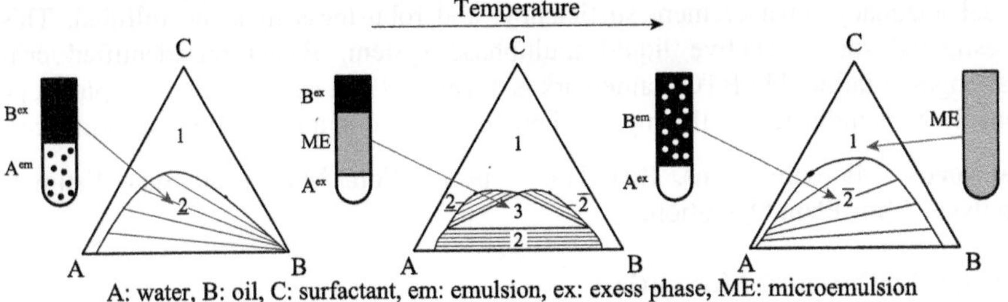

Figure 1: Schematic isothermal Gibbs triangles for microemulsion system. Phases are labeled according to the continuous liquid. Figure adapted from (Sottmann and Stubenrauch, 2009).

2.2. Mini-Plant Configuration

For testing microemulsions as green and superior reaction media, a mini-plant is operated by our group at Technische Universität Berlin. Following Figure 2, a CSTR is used for emulsification of catalyst solution, surfactant, and substrate. With addition of syngas, the reaction is conducted at 15bar and 90°C. Phase separation into up to three liquid phases is then carried out in a gravity settler holding a flow sight glass and three phase drains.

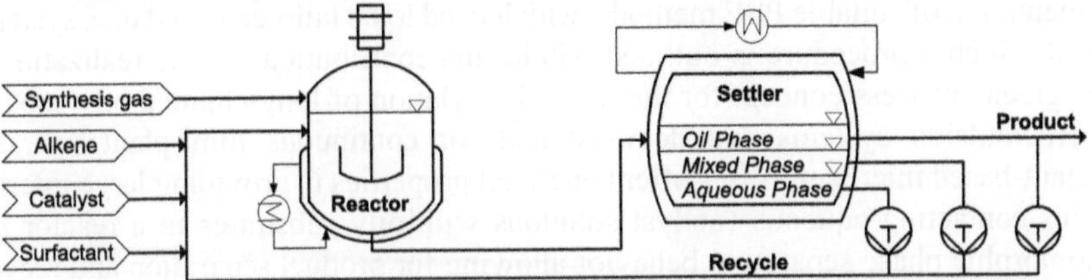

Figure 2: Simplified sketch of the mini-plant at TU Berlin consisting of reactor, settler, and recycles.

The reaction product is syphoned off from the top-most liquid phase, while the rest is recycled into the reactor. Plant automation is realized with Siemens PCS7 using an OPC server-client structure for data communication (OPC Foundation, 2021), while reaction tracking is done via offline gas chromatography (GC). Additional information on safety measures, automation layers, and analytics can be found in (Illner, 2020).

2.3. Operational Challenges and Requirements for D-RTO Application

Successful plant operation depends on efficient control of the phase separation, which is complicated by the complex phase behavior of microemulsions. A systematic analysis of relevant influences regarding sensitivity on phase separation operation, measurability, and controllability is deployed (Illner, 2020). This reveals small and dynamically shifting operation regions (due to concentration shifts by recycling and reaction) and an unmeasurability of relevant concentrations (surfactant). To support plant start-up and to enable continuous operation with an optimal reaction performance, D-RTO is considered based on a review of existing methods and initial case studies. Here, state estimation is deployed to adapt the state of a process model to current plant measurements before calculating control trajectories by dynamic optimization. However, real-life application of D-RTO faces several theoretical and practical requirements, which have to be fulfilled for the given process (Biegler and Zavala, 2009; Bonvin and Srinivasan, 2013):
R1: A suitable model describing influences of relevant disturbances, feasible operation regions (plant optimum), and (active) process constraints is required. It needs to be twice continuously differentiable and of fast and reliable convergence behavior.
R2: State and optimality of the plant need to be quantifiable, which requires availability of specific measurements and sensitivity of the objective function regarding model states.
R3: By consequence, it needs to be verified that the problem formulation of D-RTO for the plant is robust with respect to model or measurement uncertainty.
R4: Weights in objective functions of estimators and optimizers demand tuning.
R5: A suitable communication structure between state estimation, optimization, distributed control systems (DCS), and additional analytics is required for data handling.
R6: State estimation needs to treat different sampling rates, as valuable but rare concentration measurements (gas chromatography) are mandatory to be incorporated.
R7: The D-RTO framework should allow for re-initialization after operator interactions, as unexpected events can occur, which might be out of the model's scope.

3. Model Development and D-RTO Framework

Cornerstone for the application of D-RTO on the mini-plant for the hydroformylation of 1-dodecene in microemulsions systems is a suitable dynamic process model, describing all relevant phenomena in the system (R1-R3). Key element is a model-based description of the three-phasic separation of the microemulsion, possible phase changes (constrain feasible operation region) and the derivation of a soft-sensor for otherwise inaccessible concentration information. Based thereon, a D-RTO framework is built to track and optimize plant operation using DCS, offline GC, and soft-sensor information.

3.1. Dynamic Mini-Plant Model

A dynamic model of the full mini-plant system, including relevant tanks, actuators, and available measurements is set up based on first principles and aiming for representing plant states from *fully empty* to *continuous operation*. Of special interest are the reactor and the settler model. The former considers a mechanistic reaction network for the hydroformylation reaction, which is systematically adapted to incorporate influences of the microemulsion on the reaction (Pogrzeba et al., 2019). A power-law formulation for reaction enhancement by the surfactant concentration and a twice continuously differentiable selectivity switch (sigmoidal function) have been implemented (Illner, 2020). Regarding the settler unit, one suffers from the lack of profound thermodynamic descriptions of microemulsions (VLLLE model). For plant operation, it is however mandatory to track and describe the desired three-phase state, constrain it from shifting into undesired states, and obtain concentration information on all present phases (feedback on reaction via recycle). To achieve this, a polynomial surrogate model is derived from lab experiments, connecting experimental inputs (integral concentration x_i and temperature T) with composition x_i^{Phase} and volume fraction ϕ^{Phase} of each existing phase. This enables the formulation of a soft-sensor working on ϕ^{Phase} and T to predict the otherwise inaccessible concentrations of surfactant and water (Illner, 2020):

$$x_i^{Phase}, x_i = g(T, \phi^{Phase}) \tag{1}$$

The soft-sensor is a vital element for enabling D-RTO since it enables observation of the plant state using state-estimation, while also optimality conditions become tractable (R2). The separation model is then implemented into a settler unit model holding multiple liquid hold-ups and three fixed phase drains. Twice continuously differentiable sigmoidal functions are deployed to enable switching of the outlet flow composition according to the present phase at the respective outlet. The whole process model is available as DAE system or fully discretized via MOSAICmodeling (Esche et al., 2017).

3.2. D-RTO Framework

The structure of the developed D-RTO scheme is given in Figure 3. As a first step, moving horizon (state-)estimation (MHE) is chosen due to its superior features in handling nonlinearities and constraints (Weigert et al., 2018). As a special feature, multiple sampling rates are considered (R6). The MHE continuously provides estimates based on fast measurements (temperature, flow, level), which are updated on a second layer, whenever slow but valuable concentration measurements are available (2 to 4 h). Deployed objective functions for both layers are structured as in Eq. (2) and contain matrices P, Q, and R to weight arrival cost of estimates z, measurements y, and process noise ξ.

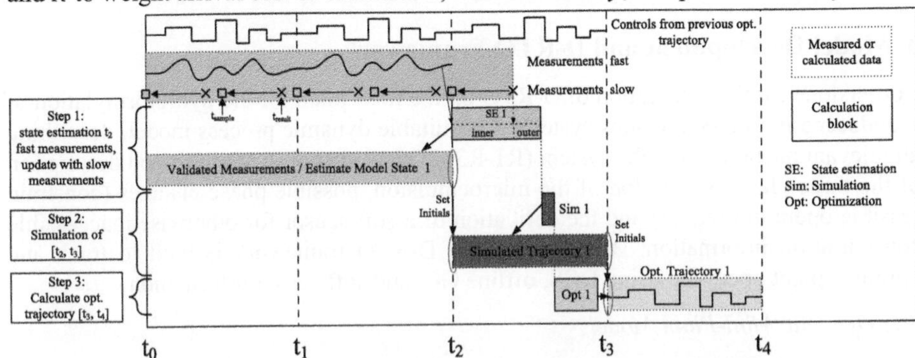

Figure 3: Graphical representation of interaction between state estimator, optimizer, and plant.

Convergence of the MHE is found to be sensitive to the choice of respective weights and online tuning is advised, if largely differing operation modes are considered (R4). Given a state estimate at t_2, a future plant state t_3 is simulated based on the available control trajectory applied on the plant. This way, feasible initials for optimization are obtained.

The dynamic optimization considers feed and recycle flows, reactor and settler temperature, and product flow as manipulables and yields trajectories of controller setpoints for a horizon of 4 h based on an economic objective function considering the product stream and penalties for catalyst loss. In parallel, MHE continuously captures the plant's state and re-optimization is triggered on larger estimated deviations. The efficient interaction of MHE, optimizer, analytics, and the plant is realized by an OPC UA-based server client structure, allowing each tool to directly communicate with the DCS.

$$\min_{z,\xi} \sum \Delta z^T P^{-1} \Delta z + \Delta y^T R^{-1} \Delta y + \Delta \xi^T Q^{-1} \Delta \xi \qquad (2)$$

4. Case Study

D-RTO application was tested for long-term mini-plant runs of more than 200 h each. Pre-calculated (gPROMS) optimal trajectories ensured a stable operation throughout the critical start-up phase and provided suitable initials for the D-RTO framework. The latter was used to successfully stabilize continuous operation, as shown in Figure 4. For the shown horizons, conversion, product yield, and selectivity are stabilized on high levels, while the optimizer takes action on adaption of reaction conditions in the reactor. This resulted in further increase of the product selectivity (track optimality, R2) and successful phase separation operation in the desired three-phase state (purity of 99.5 % of oily compounds in oil phase obtained). Hence, an overall (optimal) reaction performance with a yield of 38 % and a product selectivity of 92 % was obtained. Both values are in perfect agreement with reference lab-scale experiments. Furthermore, online applicability of the D-RTO scheme is proven. For the given horizon of 4 h, feasible solutions were obtained within 72 min (e.g., horizon 1: state estimation - 735 CPU seconds; optimization - 3535 CPU seconds) given a maximum of 120 min for calculations and result implementation. However, convergence behavior significantly depends on the choice of the solver and its parameters. Here, CONOPT is preferred due to superior handling of high nonlinearities.

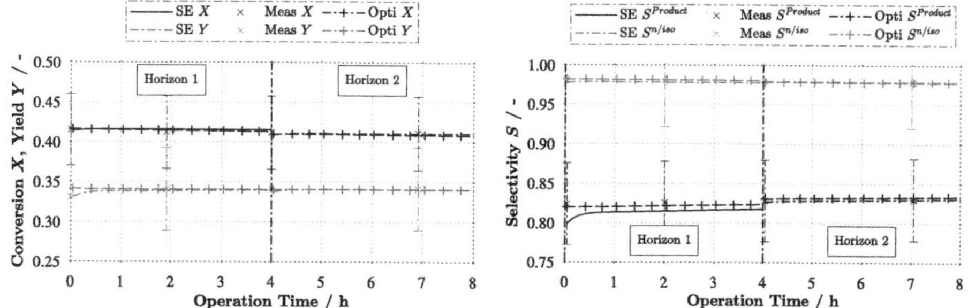

Figure 4: D-RTO application on the mini-plant. Left: Reaction conversion X and product yield Y. Right: Product selectivity $S^{Product}$ and regio-selectivity $S^{n/iso}$. Two application horizons with trajectories from state estimation (SE) and optimization (Opti) compared to measurement data (Meas).

5. Conclusion and Outlook

D-RTO is ideally suited to assist the realization of complex liquid multiphase systems as reaction media. However, key challenges for application are identified in providing suitable model structures, measurement availability and accuracy. This is demonstrated for a complex reactive multiphase system and handled with a first-time implementation of a phase separation model for microemulsions, as well as a soft-sensor for unmeasurable model states. Based on this, a tailored D-RTO framework is successfully tested using mini-plant operation runs over 200 h each. However, future work is required on the task: how to systematically derive adequate models including phenomena relevant for the desired process, online tuning procedures for weights of state-estimator and optimizer formulations, as well as the incorporation of uncertainty.

Acknowledgements

Gefördert durch die Deutsche Forschungsgemeinschaft (DFG) - TRR 63 "Integrierte chemische Prozesse in flüssigen Mehrphasensystemen" (Teilprojekt D2, D4) - 56091768.

References

L. T. Biegler, V. M. Zavala, 2009, Large-scale nonlinear programming using IPOPT: An integrating framework for enterprise-wide dynamic optimization, Computers & Chemical Engineering, 33, 575–582.

D. Bonvin, B. Srinivasan, 2013, On the role of the necessary conditions of optimality in structuring dynamic real-time optimization schemes, Computers & Chemical Engineering, 51, 172–180.

E. Esche, C. Hoffmann, M. Illner, D. Müller, S. Fillinger, G. Tolksdorf, H. Bonart, G. Wozny, J.-U. Repke, 2017, MOSAIC - Enabling Large-Scale Equation-Based Flow Sheet Optimization, Chemie Ingenieur Technik, 89, 620–635.

M. Illner, 2020, Rigorous analysis of reactive microemulsion systems for process design and operation, PhD Thesis, Technische Universität Berlin.

M. Illner, T. Pogrzeba, M. Schmidt, D. Müller, E. Esche, R. Schomäcker, J.-U. Repke, G. Wozny, 2016, Hydroformylation of 1-dodecene in Microemulsions: Operation and Validation of Lab Results in a Miniplant, In: Technical Transactions, 1-M (1).

A. Ivanković, 2017, Review of 12 Principles of Green Chemistry in Practice, International Journal of Sustainable and Green Energy, 6, 39.

A. Mitsos, N. Asprion, C. A. Floudas, M. Bortz, M. Baldea, D. Bonvin, A. Caspari, P. Schäfer, 2018, Challenges in process optimization for new feedstocks and energy sources, Computers & Chemical Engineering, 113, 209–221.

D. Müller, M. Illner, E. Esche, T. Pogrzeba, M. Schmidt, R. Schomäcker, L. T. Biegler, G. Wozny, J.-U. Repke, 2017, Dynamic real-time optimization under uncertainty of a hydroformylation mini-plant, Computers & Chemical Engineering, 106, 836–848.

OPC Foundation, 2021. https://opcfoundation.org (accessed October 18, 2021).

T. Pogrzeba, M. Illner, M. Schmidt, N. Milojevic, E. Esche, J.-U. Repke, R. Schomäcker, 2019, Kinetics of Hydroformylation of 1-Dodecene in Microemulsion Systems Using a Rhodium Sulfoxantphos Catalyst, Industrial & Engineering Chemistry Research, 58, 4443–4453.

M. Rafiei, L. A. Ricardez-Sandoval, 2020, New frontiers, challenges, and opportunities in integration of design and control for enterprise-wide sustainability, Computers & Chemical Engineering, 132, 106610.

T. Sottmann, C. Stubenrauch, 2009, Phase Behaviour, Interfacial Tension and Microstructure of Microemulsions, In: Microemulsions, 1–47.

J. Weigert, M. Illner, E. Esche, J.-U. Repke, Development of a State Estimation Environment for the Optimal Control of a Mini-plant for the Hydroformylation in Microemulsions. Chemical Engineering Transactions, 2018, 973–978.

Proceedings of the 14th International Symposium on Process Systems Engineering – PSE 2021+
June 19-23, 2022, Kyoto, Japan
http://dx.doi.org/10.1016/B978-0-323-85159-6.50073-7

Design of PID controllers using semi-infinite programming

Evren Mert Turan[a], Rohit Kannan[b], Johannes Jäschke[a*]

[a]Department of Chemical Engineering, Norwegian University of Science and Technology (NTNU), Trondheim, 7491, Norway
[b]Center for Nonlinear Studies and Theoretical Division (T-5), Los Alamos National Laboratory, Los Alamos, NM 87545 USA
johannes.jaschke@ntnu.no

Abstract

The PID controller is widely used, and several methods have been proposed for choosing the controller parameters to achieve good performance. The controller tuning problem is set up as a semi-infinite program (SIP), with the integrated squared error (ISE) or the H_∞ norm of the frequency domain error function ($|E(s)|_\infty$) as the objective function, and H_∞ constraints for robustness and noise attenuation. Previous authors considered discrete points to enforce the H_∞ constraints, however this is an outer approximation that does not guarantee a feasible point. When a feasible point can be found, it may require multiple iterations with a finer and finer discretisation. Here, the SIP is solved using a global optimisation algorithm. Several numerical experiments show that the proposed formulation converges quickly (<10 seconds) and gives sensible controller tuning values without the need to apply expert knowledge to the tuning problem. These results suggest that this is an attractive method for automated controller tuning.

Keywords: Controller tuning; Global Optimisation; Process Dynamics and Control; Semi-infinite Programming

1. Introduction

The PID controller has found widespread use in industry and there are many methods in the literature to tune PID parameters. Typically, tuning involves a trade-off between rejecting disturbances and robustness to uncertainty (Åström and Hägglund, 2006). Finding parameters by trial and error is time-intensive, which has led to the formulation of tuning rules, e.g. the Ziegler-Nichols tuning rule and SIMC, see Åström and Hägglund (2006) for an overview. An alternative to tuning rules, is to find controller parameters by solving an optimisation problem. Optimisation-based tuning is a powerful tool, especially when system complexity, non-standard parameterisations, or requirements on performance and robustness mean that tuning rules are ill-suited (Grimholt and Skogestad, 2018; Åström and Hägglund, 2006).

Balchen (1958) presented the first "modern" formulation of the PID optimisation problem, that explicitly included a performance and robustness trade off. Since then, various authors have proposed different formulations, see e.g. Soltesz et al. (2017). Here, we place constraints on the H_∞ norm of transfer functions, i.e. the constraints should be satisfied for all considered frequencies ($w \in \Omega \subset \mathbb{R}_+$), which means there are an infinite number of constraints (Grimholt, and Skogestad, 2018; Soltesz et al. 2017).

Previous authors (Grimholt, and Skogestad, 2018; Soltesz et al. 2017) discretised the frequencies to form a finite problem, e.g., Grimholt, and Skogestad (2018) used 10 000 points. This is an outer approximation that does not guarantee a feasible point. It also raises the problem of how to select the discretisation frequencies. If we consider the PID tuning problem as one in which the constraints must be satisfied, then this means that multiple iterations with a finer discretisation or the use of expert knowledge to choose a good prior discretisation may be necessary.

In this work we use the global optimisation algorithm proposed by Djelassi and Mitsos (2017) to solve the semi-infinite PID tuning problem. This algorithm iteratively solves discretised subproblems, where at each iteration a new discretisation point is added at the frequency that results in the largest constraint violation at the incumbent solution. To facilitate the global optimisation algorithm, we use an objective function in the frequency domain. Initial results show that the proposed formulation converges in reasonably quick computation times (<10 seconds) and gives sensible controller tuning values without the need to apply expert knowledge to the tuning problem.

1.1. System

We consider the closed loop linear system in Figure 1, with disturbances at the plant input and output (d_u and d_y), and noise (n) entering the system at the measurement output. The system is represented by the following transfer functions (Åström and Hägglund, 2006):

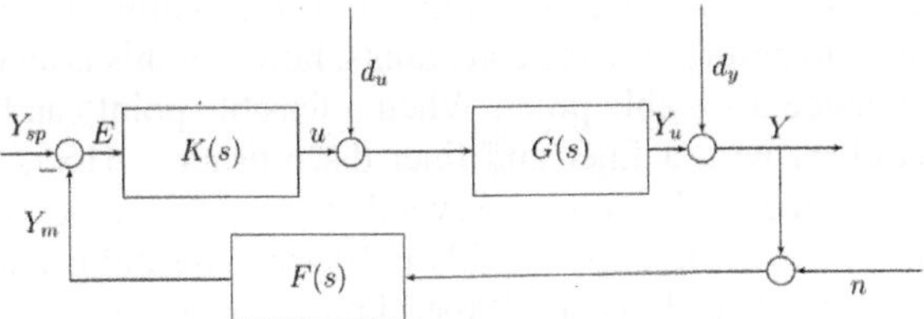

Figure 1. Block diagram of closed loop system. K(s) is the controller, G(s) is the process and F(s) is the filter.

$$S(s) = \frac{1}{1 + G(s)K(s)}, \qquad T(s) = 1 - S(s), \qquad TF(s) = T(s)F(s),$$

$$GS(s) = G(s)S(s), \qquad KS(s) = K(s)S(s), \qquad KFS(s) = K(s)F(s)S(s),$$

where s is the complex frequency ($s = iw$), and $S(s)$ and $T(s)$ are the sensitivity and complementary sensitivity functions, respectively. Here, we consider the case of pure error feedback ($F = 1$). The controller error, E, is the difference between the measured output (y) and setpoint (y_s):

$$-E(s) = y - y_s = S(s)d_y + GS(s)d_u - T(s)n. \tag{1}$$

In this work we consider PID controllers that are parameterised in the linear form:

$$K(s) = k_p + \frac{k_i}{s} + k_d s, \tag{2}$$

where k_p, k_i, and k_d are the tuning parameters. In this form the optimiser can selected a PID subtype, e.g. setting k_d to zero yields a PI controller.

1.2. Objective

We wish to pick control parameters that minimise the error after some disturbance. Various performance indices have been proposed, with the most widely used measure being the integral absolute error (IAE):

$$IAE = \int_0^\infty |e(t)|\, dt. \tag{3}$$

This formulation requires the error function in the time domain ($e(t)$). Finding the time domain error function generally involves explicit simulation or taking the inverse Laplace transform. Balchen (1958) proposed the use of a performance index in the frequency domain that approximates the IAE. The rationale behind the approximation is that $|e(t)| = e(t)\frac{|e(t)|}{e(t)}$, where if $e(t)$ is oscillatory then the fraction defines a square wave. The IAE can then be approximated by introducing a sine wave with free parameters w and a, that are chosen to maximise the integral, i.e. reduce the approximation error. This allows one to write the objective in the frequency domain:

$$IAE = \int_0^\infty |e(t)|\, dt \approx \max_{a,w} \int_0^\infty e(t)\sin(wt + a)\, dt \tag{4}$$

$$= \max_{w} |E(iw)| = |E(s)|_\infty = HIE,$$

where $|\cdot|_\infty$ is the H_∞ norm. For convenience, we shall refer to this as the H-infinity error (HIE). The HIE is bounded by the integral error (IE) and IAE: $IE \leq HIE \leq IAE$. If the system is well-dampened, then $IE \approx HIE \approx IAE$. Using Parseval's theorem, the integral squared error can be (exactly) represented in the frequency domain:

$$ISE = \int_0^\infty e(t)^2\, dt = \frac{1}{\pi}\int_0^\infty |E(iw)|^2 dw. \tag{5}$$

1.3. Robustness

We enforce robustness by constraining the maximums in the sensitivity and complementary sensitivity functions M_S and M_T, where

$$M_S = |S(iw)|_\infty, \qquad M_T = |T(iw)|_\infty.$$

The magnitude of M_S and M_T, describe the sensitivity of the system to process uncertainty or change, e.g., M_S gives the worst-case amplification of a disturbance and, on a Nyquist plot, is the distance from the loop transfer function to the point (-1,0).

Constraining the magnitude of M_S and M_T defines circles on the Nyquist plot that the loop transfer function must lie out of. A combined sensitivity constraint can be defined that covers both excluded regions. For $M = M_S = M_T$, this constraint is a circle on the Nyquist plot with centre (C, 0) and radius R given by (Åström and Hägglund, 2006):

$$C = -\frac{2M^2 - 2M + 1}{2M^2 - 2M}, \qquad R = -\frac{2M - 1}{2M^2 - 2M}.$$

1.4. Noise attenuation

It is also desirable to limit control usage due to noise. This can be performed by bounding the noise amplification ratio, $\frac{\sigma_u^2}{\sigma_n^2}$, where σ_u^2 and σ_n^2 are the variances of the control and noise respectively. Let $\phi_n(w)$ be the unknown spectral density of the (unclassified) noise, and Q be the transfer function from noise to the control signal ($Q = -KFS$, see Figure 1). The following inequality holds (Soltesz, et al. 2017):

$$\sigma_u^2 \leq |Q|_\infty^2 \sigma_n^2. \tag{6}$$

Thus, the constraint $|Q|_\infty \leq M_Q$ conservatively constrains the noise amplification ratio. This inequality can be written in the form:

$$|KF(iw)| - M_Q|1 + L(iw)| \leq 0, \qquad \forall w \in \Omega \subset \mathbb{R}_+, \tag{7}$$

where Ω defines the range of frequencies considered.

1.5. Optimisation problem

Semi-infinite programs are optimisation programs with a finite number of variables, and an infinite number of constraints. In the PID problem we have an infinite number of constraints as the constraint must hold for all considered frequencies ($w \in \Omega \subset \mathbb{R}_+$). The optimisation problem for some performance index (P_I) in the frequency domain is:

$$\min_{k_p, k_i, k_d} \eta \tag{8.a}$$

$$P_I(iw) - \eta \leq 0, \qquad \forall w \in \Omega \subset \mathbb{R}_+, \tag{8.b}$$

$$R^2 - |C - L(iw)| \leq 0, \qquad \forall w \in \Omega \subset \mathbb{R}_+, \tag{8.c}$$

$$|KF(iw)| - M_Q|1 + L(iw)| \leq 0, \qquad \forall w \in \Omega \subset \mathbb{R}_+, \tag{8.d}$$

where the constraints are explicitly parameterised by the frequency.

2. Numerical examples

This work is coded in Julia and with the use of the global optimisation package EAGO.jl (Wilhelm and Stuber, 2020), GLPK (Makhorin, 2008), IPOPT (Wächter and Biegler, 2006), and the JuMP modelling language (Dunning, et al. 2017).

2.1. First order process with time delay

Consider the system from Grimholt and Skogestad (2018) with transfer functions:

$$G(s) = \frac{\exp(-s)}{s+1} \qquad F(s) = \frac{1}{0.001s + 1}$$

To compare with the published results, we use the same weighted cost of the error from a step disturbance in u and y: $\eta = \frac{1}{1.56} HIE_{dy} + \frac{1}{1.42} HIE_{du}$. We enforce constraints on the sensitivity and complementary sensitivity with $M_S = M_T = 1.3$ and only consider frequencies w in the interval $[0.01\ 100]$. No constraint is used for the input usage.

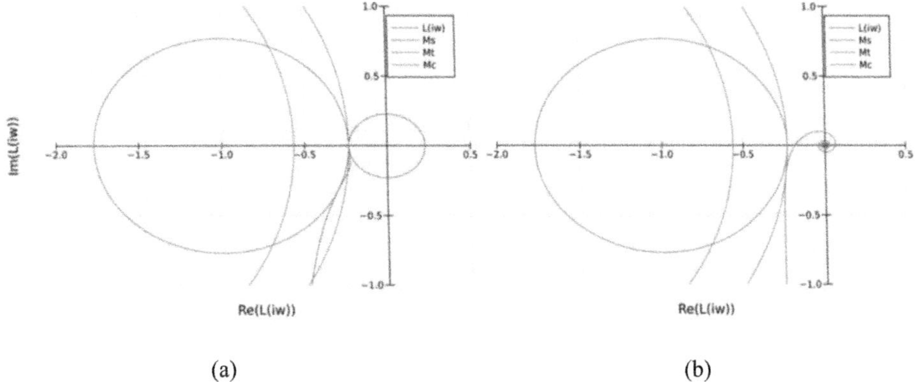

Figure 2: Nyquist plots of first order process with time delay. Left plot has constraints on maximum sensitivity and complementary sensitivity. Right plot has constraints on combined sensitivity and noise attenuation.

The optimiser finds the parameters $[0.51, 0.54, 0.23]$ in 2.6 seconds, with the Nyquist plot shown in Figure 2a. This closely matches the reported solution of $[0.52, 0.53, 0.22]$, despite the use of HIE instead of the IAE (Grimholt, and Skogestad, 2018).

For comparison, introducing a constraint on input usage ($M_Q = 1.0$) and using the combined circle constraint gives the control parameters [0.32 0.28 and 0.01], with the Nyquist plot shown in Figure 2b.

2.2. *Third order process with inverse response*

Consider the system process transfer functions:

$$G(s) = \frac{1 - 0.2s}{(s + 1)^3}, \qquad F(s) = 1.$$

We consider a constraint on the maximum combined sensitivity (≤ 1.3) and error function $E(s) = GS(s)d_u$. We consider frequencies in the interval [0.01 100], and bounds on controller parameters of 0.0 and 2.0.

The optimisation is performed with HIE and ISE as the objective, giving parameters of [1.58, 1.00, 1.73] and [1.54, 1.05, 1.87] respectively, in less than 5 seconds each. The system response using the HIE parameters is shown in Figure 3.

2.3. *Discussion*

Despite the potential for HIE to go to zero, this did not occur in the above examples. Numerical experiments have shown that this generally occurs with oscillatory systems or large upper bounds on the control parameters and no constraint on input usage. Providing good bounds on the control parameters (e.g. by using a tuning rule) can improve the speed of optimisation. If the bounds could ensure that the control system is well-dampened, then $HIE \approx IAE$. The proposed SIP formulation can be readily extended to other linear fixed-order controllers.

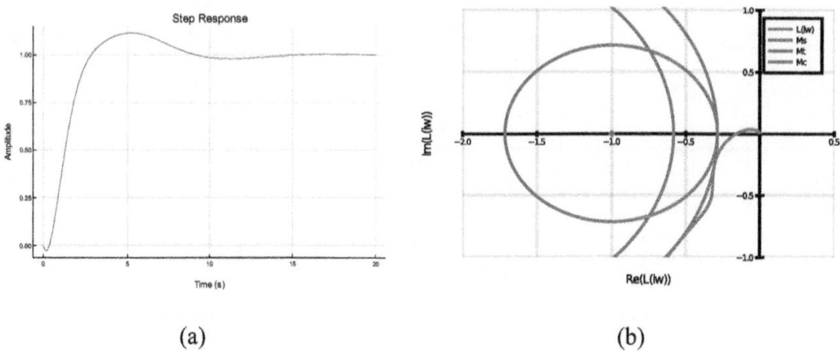

(a) (b)

Figure 3: Step response and Nyquist plot for third order process with inverse response. HIE is used as the objective with no constraint on input usage.

3. Conclusions

We demonstrate that the robust PID tuning problem can be formulated and solved as a semi-infinite program, entirely in the frequency domain, using the HIE or ISE as objective functions. Robustness is enforced via H_∞ constraints on the sensitivity and complementary sensitivity functions, or an H_∞ constraint on the combined sensitivity. Control usage is restricted via an H_∞ constraint on the noise amplification ratio. On a range of systems, sensible controller parameters were found, typically in less than 10 seconds. Potential further work could include an extension to multiple output systems, or other controllers.

4. Acknowledgments

J.J. and E.M.T. acknowledge the support of the Norwegian Research Council through the AutoPRO project. R.K. acknowledges the support of the U.S. Department of Energy through the LANL/LDRD Program and the Center for Nonlinear Studies.

References

K.J. Åström, and T. Hägglund, 2006, Advanced PID control, Vol. 461, Research Triangle Park, NC: ISA-The Instrumentation, Systems, and Automation Society.

J. G. Balchen, 1958, A performance index for feedback control systems based on the Fourier transform of the control deviation, Norges tekniske vitenskapsakademi.

H. Djelassi, and A. Mitsos, 2017, A hybrid discretization algorithm with guaranteed feasibility for the global solution of semi-infinite programs, Journal of Global Optimization, 68(2), 227-253.

I. Dunning, J. Huchette and M. Lubin, 2017, JuMP: A modeling langauge for mathematical optimization, SIAM Reivew, 59, 2, 295-320.

C. Grimholt, and S. Skogestad, 2018, Optimization of fixed-order controllers using exact gradients. Journal of Process Control, 71, 130-138.

A. Makhorin, 2008, GNU linear programming kit, http://www.gnu.org/s/glpk/glpk.html

K. Soltesz, C. Grimholt, & S. Skogestad, 2017, Simultaneous design of proportional–integral–derivative controller and measurement filter by optimisation, IET Control Theory & Applications, 11(3), 341-348.

A. Wächter and L.T. Biegler, 2006, On the implementation of an interior-point filter line-search algorithm for large-scale nonlinear programming, Mathematical Programming, 106.1, 25-57.

M.E. Wilhelm and M.D. Stuber, 2020, EAGO.jl: easy advanced global optimization in Julia, Optimisation Methods and Software, 1-26.

Proceedings of the 14th International Symposium on Process Systems Engineering – PSE 2021+
June 19-23, 2022, Kyoto, Japan
http://dx.doi.org/10.1016/B978-0-323-85159-6.50074-9

Safe Chance Constrained Reinforcement Learning for Batch Process Optimization and Control

Max Mowbray[a], Panogiotis Petsagkourakis[b], Antonio Del Rio Chanona[b], and Dongda Zhang[a,*]

[a] *Centre for Process Integration, School of Chemical Engineering and Analytical Science, The University of Manchester, Manchester, M13 9PL, United Kingdom*
[b] *Centre for Process Systems Engineering (CPSE), Department of Chemical Engineering, Imperial College London, London, SW7 2AZ, United Kingdom*
dongda.zhang@manchester.ac.uk

Abstract

Reinforcement Learning (RL) has generated excitement within the process industries within the context of decision making under uncertainty. The primary benefit of RL is that it provides a flexible and general approach to handling systems subject to both exogenous and endogenous uncertainties. Despite this there has been little reported uptake of RL in the process industries. This is partly due to the inability to provide optimality guarantees under the model used for learning, but more importantly due to safety concerns. This has led to the development of RL algorithms in the context of 'Safe RL'. In this work, we present an algorithm that leverages the variance prediction of Gaussian process state space models to a) handle operational constraints and b) account for mismatch between the offline process model and the real online process. The algorithm is then benchmarked on an uncertain Lutein photo-production process against nonlinear model predictive control (NMPC) and several state-of-the-art Safe RL algorithms. Through the definition of key performance indicators, we quantitatively demonstrate the efficacy of the method with respect to objective performance and probabilistic constraint satisfaction.

Keywords: Safe Reinforcement Learning; Optimal Control; Dynamic Optimization; Bioprocess Operation; Machine Learning

1. Introduction

There are two main drivers for the development of (nonlinear) model based controllers within the context of the process industries. The first of those is how best to account for the expression of model uncertainties and account for the various scenarios in decision making. The second of the drivers is inspired by the conceptualisation behind the 4th Industrial Revolution and pertains to the best use of data from the ongoing process to inform control decisions. The primary approaches to these drivers within the academic community exist in the form of stochastic (as well as scenario and robust) variants of (nonlinear) model predictive control (sNMPC), learning model predictive control (L-MPC) and Reinforcement Learning (RL) (and various hybrids). In this work, we further investigate the application of RL for online optimization of (bio)chemical processes.

RL has gained traction within the community for its ability to identify an approximately optimal control policy for a Markov decision process (MDP) independently of explicit assumption regarding the underlying process dynamics or the way in which process uncertainty is propagated. This is because RL instead *learns* a control policy (or a functionalisation of it) via trial and error of various control strategies. This process of interaction, and general policy iteration, ultimately enables the learning of an approximately optimal policy. The major benefit of RL over the other avenues discussed is that the other avenues are dependent upon identification of a closed form, finite dimensional description of the underlying system and the associated uncertainties. This is not the case in RL, and enables the flexible expression of a wide range of process uncertainties even when the model structure is nonlinear or nonsmooth. RL also has the ability to address the desire to account for process data from the real process. Conceivably, policies could either be updated online or from batch to batch using conceptually similar algorithms to those used in offline policy learning.

Despite the apparent potential of RL, there has been few reported incidents of deployment to the process industries. This is primarily because of the inability of RL to naturally handle constraints within the MDP framework and the potential for errors introduced from process-model mismatch to propagate through the control function when it is deployed to provide control on the real process. Use of a model is however absolutely required for initial policy learning due to the expense and potential safety issues arising from conducting the RL process online *from scratch.* The framework for identifying RL policies is elucidated by Figure 1.

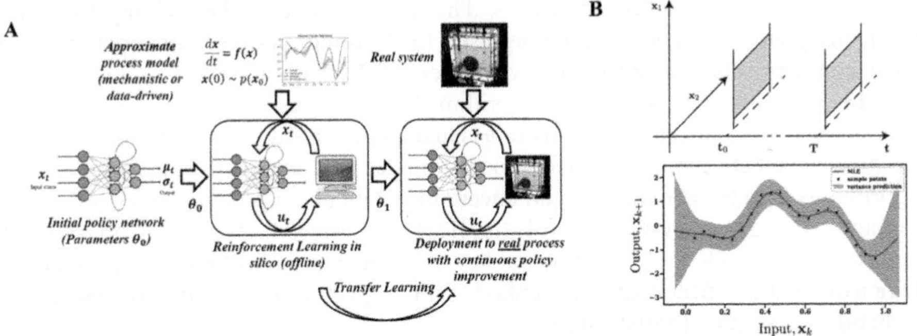

Figure 1: Demonstration of the A) Framework for RL policy training and deployment, B) Considerations for satisfaction of constraint sets and accounting for process model mismatch.

Recent works have addressed the handling of constraints via translation of the concept of constraint tightening as founded in the domain of SMPC (Pan *et al.*, 2021). Other works, based in the domain of offline or batch RL, have considered the development of algorithmic mechanisms to account for learning from a finite and stationary dataset or an approximate process model. A dominant idea in this domain is that of pessimism, which in practice is a mechanism to bias the policy away from regions of the model or data manifold characterised by high epistemic uncertainty (i.e. areas of the domain where there is little information) (Yu *et al.,* 2020). However, few works have considered the development of algorithms that consider both factors (Brunke *et al.,* 2021). In this work, we present an algorithm that considers precisely this joint problem of constraint satisfaction and mismatch (known as Safe RL), through the integration of a Gaussian process state space models as the offline process model, as well as the concepts of constraint tightening and pessimism to handle joint chance constraints and mismatch, respectively. The method is demonstrated on a fed-batch Lutein photo-production process, which is both highly nonlinear and uncertain. The benchmarks consist of state-of-the-art safe RL algorithms and NMPC (which represents the best case deterministic method).

2. Methodology

In this work we assume that the system concerned is Markovian and expresses uncertain process dynamics, such that discrete time process evolution may be described as follows:

$$\boldsymbol{x}_{t+1} = f(\boldsymbol{x}_t, \boldsymbol{u}_t, \boldsymbol{s}_t) \tag{1}$$

where $\boldsymbol{x} \in \mathbb{X} \subseteq \mathbb{R}^{n_x}$ are states; $\boldsymbol{u} \in \mathbb{U} \subseteq \mathbb{R}^{n_u}$ are control inputs from a given control set; $\boldsymbol{s} \in \mathbb{S} \subseteq \mathbb{R}^{n_s}$ are realisations of process uncertainty termed generally to describe various sources of uncertainty; and, $t \in \{0, \dots, T\}$ is a discrete time index within a discrete time, finite horizon. We would like to solve the following chance constrained problem:

$$P(\pi_c) = \begin{cases} \max\limits_{\pi_c} \mathbb{E}_{\pi_c}\left[\sum_{t=0}^{T-1} R_{t+1}\right] \\ \boldsymbol{x}_0 \sim p(\boldsymbol{x}_0) \\ \boldsymbol{x}_{t+1} = f(\boldsymbol{x}_t, \boldsymbol{u}_t, \boldsymbol{s}_t) \\ \boldsymbol{u}_t \sim \pi_c(\boldsymbol{u}_t|\boldsymbol{x}_t) \\ \boldsymbol{u}_t \in \mathbb{U}_t \\ P\left(\bigcap_{t=0}^{T} \boldsymbol{x}_t \in \overline{\mathbb{X}}_t\right) \geq 1-\alpha \\ \forall\, t \in \{0, \dots, T\} \end{cases} \tag{2}$$

where $\pi_c(\boldsymbol{u}_t|\boldsymbol{x}_t)$ defines a conditional probability density function, that provides a distribution over controls given observation of state; $\overline{\mathbb{X}}_t = \left\{\boldsymbol{x}_t \in \mathbb{R}^{n_x} : A_j^T \boldsymbol{x}_t - b_j \leq 0, \forall\, j \in \{1, \dots, n_g\}\right\}$ is the set of states that satisfy a given affine ($A_j \in \mathbb{R}^{n_x}$ and $b_j \in \mathbb{R}$) constraint set at a given time index; $\alpha = (0,1]$ is the probability allowed for violation of the constraint set for all time indices; $p(\boldsymbol{x}_0)$ defines the initial state distribution; and, $R_{t+1} \in \mathbb{R}$ defines a scalar cost, provided by a function, $R: \mathbb{X} \times \mathbb{U} \times \mathbb{X} \rightarrow \mathbb{R}$, that ranks process evolution with respect to control objectives.

Conventional RL algorithms identify a policy, $\pi^* = argmax_\pi \mathbb{E}_\pi[\sum_{t=0}^{T-1} R_{t+1}]$ and do not naturally handle constraints. In this work, we are concerned with identifying a policy, π_c, that also satisfies a joint constraint set, with a given probability $1-\alpha$, that may be defined by the implementation.

To handle this, we propose to translate the concept of constraint tightening (Valdez-Navarro and Ricardez-Sandoval, 2019) to tighten the constraint set, such that we can reformulate our probabilistic expressions into deterministic surrogates. The tightened constraint set is expressed as $\widehat{\mathbb{X}}_t = \{\boldsymbol{x}_t \in \mathbb{R}^{n_x} : A_j \overline{\boldsymbol{x}}_t + \varepsilon_{j,t} - b_j \leq 0,\ \forall\, j = \{1, \dots, n_g\}$, where $\varepsilon_{j,t} \in \mathbb{R}$ is a constraint tightening mechanism (known as a *backoff*) specific to both time index and constraint, and $\overline{\boldsymbol{x}} \in \mathbb{R}^{n_x}$ is the nominal process state. The idea of the backoff is to essentially back the nominal state away from the constraint boundary to allow for process variation. Explicit, closed form expressions for the backoffs may be derived from the Cantelli-Chebyshev inequality. Together, with Boole's inequality, this enables us to decompose the probability of constraint satisfaction across the various constraints, and identify the backoffs required by the following:

$$\varepsilon_{j,t} = \sqrt{\frac{1-\iota_j}{\iota_j}}\sqrt{A_j^T\Sigma[\boldsymbol{x}_t]A_j} \tag{3}$$

where $\Sigma[\boldsymbol{x}_t]$ is the finite variance of the system state at time index t and $\iota_j = \alpha/n_g$ is the probability with which one may allow for violation of constraint j. This enables formalisation of the tightened constraint set. Solving for this enables the satisfaction of the joint chance constraints with desired probability. In this work, we parameterise both $\overline{\boldsymbol{x}}$ and $\Sigma[\boldsymbol{x}]$ of the state by a Gaussian process state space model. Expressions for both may then be obtained in closed form, providing deterministic expressions of the constraint set that can be incorporated into a penalty function. Additionally, we incorporate $\Sigma[\boldsymbol{x}]$ to penalise exploitation of the regions of the state space characterised by high epistemic uncertainty (this is the mechanism for pessimism). In short, what we propose here is to identify an optimal constrained policy that maximises a penalty function in expectation:

$$\pi_c^{\,*} = argmax_\pi \mathbb{E}_\pi\left[\sum_{t=0}^{T-1} R_{t+1} - tr(\zeta\Sigma[\boldsymbol{x}_{t+1}]) - \kappa\|[A^T\overline{\boldsymbol{x}}_{t+1} + \boldsymbol{\epsilon}_{t+1} - \boldsymbol{b}]^-\|_2\right] \tag{4}$$

where $\zeta \in \mathbb{R}^{n_x \times n_x}$ is a diagonal matrix; $\kappa \in \mathbb{R}$ is a large real value; $A = \left[A_1, \dots, A_{n_g}\right]$; $\boldsymbol{b} = \left[b_1, \dots, b_{n_g}\right]^T$ and $\boldsymbol{\epsilon}_t = \left[\varepsilon_{1,t}, \dots, \varepsilon_{n_g,t}\right]^T$. In practice, the Cantelli-Chebyshev backoffs identified are typically conservative, so we propose to tune them by a set of multipliers $\boldsymbol{\xi} \in \mathbb{R}^{n_g}$. This problem is an expensive black box optimization and so we deploy use of Bayesian optimization (BO) to identify the multipliers. At a given iterate i of optimization the backoffs are defined, $\Xi^i = \{\boldsymbol{\xi}^i\boldsymbol{\epsilon}_t\}_{t=1:T}$. The objective for BO, J_{BO}, is formalised:

$$\boldsymbol{\xi}^* = argmax_\xi J_{BO} = \left(G_{\pi_c^*} - \beta\sigma_{\pi_c^*}\right)\exp(-cU) \tag{5}$$

where $c \in \mathbb{R}$, $\beta \in \mathbb{R}$ are constants; $U = \left(F_{LB} - (1-\alpha)\right)^2$, where F_{LB} is a robust statistic evaluating the probability of joint chance constraint satisfaction; $\sigma_{\pi_c^*} = \Sigma_{\pi_c^*}\left[\sum_{t=0}^{T-1} R_{t+1}\right]$ is the variance of the returns with respect to the process objective; $G_{\pi_c^*} = \mathbb{E}_{\pi_c^*}\left[\sum_{t=0}^{T-1} R_{t+1}\right]$ is the expected returns with respect to the process objective. The statistic, F_{LB}, is a statistically robust sample approximation of probabilistic constraint satisfaction.

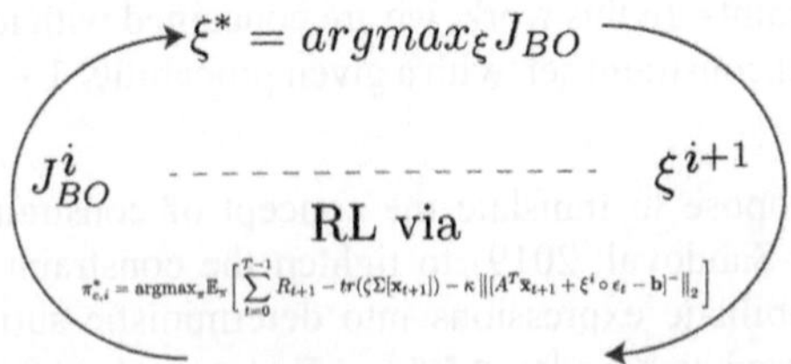

Figure 2: Figurative description of the algorithm proposed. In practice, we propose the use of Gaussian process based Bayesian Optimization.

3. Case Study

3.1. A Fed-batch Lutein Photo-production process

To demonstrate the methodology, we propose the use of a computational study involving a fed-batch Lutein photo-production process, which was first detailed in Del Rio-Chanona *et al.* (2017) and described by a set of nonlinear ordinary differential equations (ODEs). We direct the interested reader to that paper for more information on the underlying system and parameter values.

3.2. Case Study Design and Benchmarks

Additional to the parameter values detailed by the original work, we assume the presence of 5% parametric uncertainty on the point estimates provided. We then leverage the availability of the uncertain, mechanistic model (that is equivalent to Eq. 1) and conceptualise that it represents the *real* system. Description of the case study follows: a) generate a dataset (that in practice could be available from e.g. design of experiments) by sampling the uncertain mechanistic model with space filling control trajectories, b) deploy the methodology described by building a GP state space model with the dataset and identify a policy through the framework detailed by Figure 1, c) deploy the policy identified to optimize the *real* uncertain process (model) and d) benchmark the performance against NMPC, first order constrained optimisation in policy space (FOCOPS) (Zhang *et al.*,2021), the model-based offline policy optimization (MOPO) algorithm (Yu *et al.*, 2020), and the conservative offline model based policy optimization (COMBO) algorithm (Yu *et al.*, 2021). The first two benchmarks represent the best case deterministic method, and a state-of-the-art constrained RL method, respectively. The latter two represent state-of-the-art offline (batch) RL methods that are designed to account for mismatch. In all RL benchmarks, constraints were handled by incorporating deterministic expressions for the original constraint sets into a penalty function (i.e. they were treated as hard constraints) within the GP state space model.

3.3. Process Constraints, Objective and Key Performance Indicators

The objective of process operation is productivity maximisation. The control inputs, $\boldsymbol{u} = [I_0, F_{in}]$, are the incident light intensity to the reactor, and the nitrate inflow rate and they are bounded. The path constraint set is defined by Eq. 6. The set defined represents constraints on the maximum concentration of biomass c_x (g/L), the minimum nitrate concentration and the ratio between biomass and Lutein concentration. The desired probability of constraint violation, $\alpha = 0.01$. The process objective is provided by Eq. 7.

$$A = \begin{bmatrix} 1 & 0 & -1.67 \\ 0 & -1 \times 10^{-3} & 0 \\ 0 & 0 & 1 \end{bmatrix}, \quad b = \begin{bmatrix} 2.6 \\ 0.15 \\ 0 \end{bmatrix} \tag{6}$$

$$R_{t+1} = \begin{cases} \boldsymbol{d}^T \boldsymbol{x}_{t+1} - \Delta \boldsymbol{u}_t^T \boldsymbol{C} \Delta \boldsymbol{u}_t & if\ t = T - 1 \\ -\Delta \boldsymbol{u}_t^T \boldsymbol{C} \Delta \boldsymbol{u}_t & else \end{cases} \tag{7}$$

where $T = 6$, $\boldsymbol{d} = [0, -0.001, 4]^T$, $\Delta \boldsymbol{u}_t = \boldsymbol{u}_t - \boldsymbol{u}_{t-1}$, $\boldsymbol{x} = [c_x, c_N, c_L]^T$ and $C = diag([0.16, 8.1 \times 10^{-5}])$. Key performance indicators include F_{LB}, F_{SA} and $G_{\pi_c^*}$.

4. Results and Discussion

The results from validation of the control policies identified by each respective method over 500 Monte Carlo simulations on the *real* uncertain process model are outlined by Table 1.

Table 1: Results from benchmarks and method proposed (SCCPO) in online optimization of the real uncertain process

Method	Sample approx. of probability of constraint satisfaction, F_{SA}	Robust approx. of probability of constraint satisfaction, F_{LB}	Fulfilment of process operational objective, $G_{\pi_c^*}$.
NMPC	0.12	0.148	11.58 +/- 4.07
MOPO	1.0	1.0	10.98 +/- 0.072
COMBO	1.0	1.0	10.69 +/- 0.070
FOCOPS	1.0	1.0	13.11 +/- 0.090
SCCPO	1.0	1.0	**14.17 +/- 0.095**

The results demonstrate the ability of the method proposed to handle both constraints and mismatch. This is especially reinforced by the relative performance to NMPC, where the model is exactly the same as the uncertain real process and the only difference that exists is the presence of parametric uncertainty in the real process. All RL benchmark methods (MOPO, COMBO, FOCOPS) handle constraints with the desired probability. It is thought that this arises due to the implementation of a backoff as introduced through a) the pessimism term, $tr(\zeta\Sigma[x_{t+1}])$, present in MOPO and FOCOPS, and b) the nature of the conservative mechanisms as present in COMBO. However, it should be noted that the action of these mechanisms is not specific to any given constraint, which may go some way to explaining the conservative control performance.

5. Conclusions

In this work, we have presented an algorithm that handles both operational constraints and process model-mismatch for the deployment of RL policies for the online optimization of uncertain, nonlinear fed-batch process systems. The algorithm has been benchmarked against best case deterministic methods in the form of NMPC and state-of-the-art safe and offline RL methods. The performance was demonstrated to be competitive if not advantageous relative to the benchmarks proposed.

References

L. Brunke, M. Greeff, A.W. Hall, Z. Yuan, S. Zhou, J. Panerati, A.P. Schoellig, Safe Learning in Robotics: From Learning-Based Control to Safe Reinforcement Learning, arXiv:2108.06266 (2021)

E. Pan, P. Petsagkourakis, M. Mowbray, D. Zhang, E. A. del Rio-Chanona, Constrained Model-Free Reinforcement Learning for Process Optimization, arXiv preprint arXiv: 2011.07925 (2021)

Y. I. Valdez-Navarro, L. A. Ricardez-Sandoval, A novel back-off algorithm for integration of scheduling and control of batch processes under uncertainty, Industrial & Engineering Chemistry Research 58 (48) (2019)

T. Yu, G. Thomas, L. Yu, S. Ermon, J. Zou, S. Levine, C. Finn, T. Ma, Mopo: Model-based offline policy optimization, . arXiv:2005.13239 (2020)

E.A. Del Rio-Chanona, N. Ahmed, D. Zhang, Y. Lu, K. Jing, Kinetic modeling and process analysis for Desmodesmus sp. lutein photo-production,

Y. Zhang, Q. Vuong, K. W. Ross, First Order Constrained Optimization in Policy Space, arXiv preprint arXiv: 2002.06506 (2020)

T. Yu, A. Kumar, R. Rafailov, A. Rajeswaran, S. Levine, C. Finn, COMBO: Conservative Offline Model-Based Policy Optimization, arXiv:2102.08363 (2021)

Proceedings of the 14th International Symposium on Process Systems Engineering – PSE 2021+
June 19-23, 2022, Kyoto, Japan
http://dx.doi.org/10.1016/B978-0-323-85159-6.50075-0

Combining Machine Learning with Mixed Integer Linear Programming in Solving Complex Scheduling Problems

Iiro Harjunkoski[a,b*], and Teemu Ikonen[a]

[a]*Department of Chemical and Metallurgical Engineering, Aalto University, 00076 Finland*
[b]*Hitachi Energy Research, 68309 Mannheim, Germany*
iiro.harjunkoski@aalto.fi / iiro.harjunkoski@hitachienergy.com

Abstract

With the increasing digitalization of industrial production processes and the quest for maximizing the synergies through more integrated operations, there is an increasing need also to automatize the decision making. In terms of scheduling, problems are becoming larger and need to consider more aspects making both the modeling and the solution of the resulting problems cumbersome. Suitable methods to deal with these problems include, e.g., simplifying the problem as necessary to speed up the optimization (i.e., balancing the optimality and solution speed where possible), using heuristics to support faster solution, deploying simulation tools to predict the values of most complex variables, using decomposition methods to divide the problem into smaller subproblems, and a rich mixture of all of the above. This paper discusses various approaches to support optimization by using machine learning and related challenges in implementing them.

Keywords: scheduling, machine learning, hybrid models, efficiency

1. Introduction

The topic of combining machine learning (ML) with optimization, foremost the combinatorially complex mixed integer linear programming (MILP) problems, has many facets and has recently received increasing attention in the literature. In its simplest form, the focus can lie either on modeling or on the solution procedure. In modeling, the main target is to reduce the workload of a modeler – or the large, often experimental, efforts in parameter tuning that is coupled with complex analysis. In solving complex problem related to scheduling, the main target is either to reduce the size of the search space or provide more guidance (similar to strong branching) while traveling through the search tree. An inspiring and insightful view into artificial intelligence (AI) and chemical engineering is provided by Venkatasubramanian (2019), who also highlights the challenges of reasoning and explainability of ML-based decisions.

Production scheduling problems are often modeled and solved as MILP problems, at least partially, as this provides a framework to systematically embed problem-specific constraints and facilitates solving the models by state-of-the-art solvers. Theoretically, scheduling problems are NP-complete (Garey et al., 1979) for generic approaches in finding the shortest-length (makespan) schedule, as well as minimizing the mean-flow time. When focusing on MILP approaches (Méndez et al., 2006), the main complexities are related to the combinatorial space arising from the large number of binary decision variables that stem both from the assignment (yes/no) and sequencing (before/after) decisions involved in scheduling. Often, the sequencing decisions are more complex especially in continuous-time approaches due to the typically deployed big-M constraints that in general show poor relaxation characteristics.

As scheduling problems typically lie in between the control (local) and business (enterprise) layers, they need to adopt some characteristics from both worlds. Lower-level decisions need to ensure the feasibility of operations by taking into account sometimes complex equipment-related choices – or even such a simple task to avoid simultaneous overlaps of multiple jobs in a producing equipment. Business decisions may also be complex to model in practice due to the multitude of conditions that may impact the scheduling. One example can be found in scheduling of power generation units, where both the dispatching of electricity and providing electricity reserves to account for sudden losses of generation must be procured with different pricing schemes. In other scheduling problems, complex modeling tasks may apply when estimating highly non-linear processes, equipment degradation, taxation, or inventory policies. Thus, there are potential challenges both in the modeling and solution of scheduling problems that may be improved by using ML-based methods.

Figure 1 shows a rough overview of the procedure where the original problem data is first transformed into a scheduling model using both domain knowledge (here we assume also including the standard well-known model structures), as well as process data and ML to create data-driven model components. Second, the resulting model is passed onto the solution procedure, which typically deploys mathematical programming (e.g., Branch & Bound or Branch & Cut) or evolutionary methods (e.g., genetic algorithms). The solution procedure can be supported either by heuristics to speed up the solution process, leading to a local optimum or a good starting point, or ML-based decision support. In this paper, we focus on the latter. In the following, we discuss both the modeling (Section 2) and solving aspects (Section 3) of using ML to enhance scheduling.

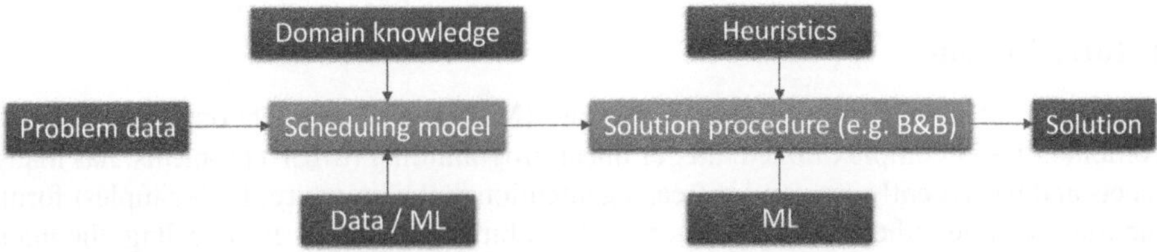

Figure 1. Main options for using ML in formulating and solving large MILP problems

2. Modeling

For the efficient modeling of complex constraints based on e.g., experimental or simulated data, machine learning based tools have been proposed, such as ALAMO (Wilson and Sahinidis, 2017) to derive automatically generated constraints, where the accuracy between the observed points and the resulting model equations is optimally balanced with the resulting numerical complexity. As opposed to typical parameter estimation schemes, the ALAMO approach also selects the structural constraint components. This approach can be very efficient when the order of the resulting equations is low. However, good linear representations, necessary for MILP models, may be difficult to identify. Other aspects to consider are whether there is enough data available for a reliable result or whether the existing equations can directly be mathematically re-formulated or approximated through piece-wise linear functions or over/under-estimators. Also, if the domain is well-defined and scope relatively narrow, alternative self-written codes may well support the modeling by benefiting from the existing ML toolkits. The main idea of ML-supported modeling is to reduce the sometimes significant and error-prone engineering efforts that can occupy highly-trained personnel on routine tasks, which could be better handled if automated. The challenge, on the other hand, is to identify the use cases where domain expertise can be reliably generated by a system that mainly builds on already existing data – leaving very little room for creative approaches, should a new and unexpected operational situation take place. One option could be whether the ML tool would be able to identify its own capability limitations and notify an operator/planner about a situation that is out of its designed scope.

Already before the increased attention on ML, the concept of surrogate models has been utilized also for scheduling (Bhosekar and Ierapetritou, 2018) and recently also methodologies have been used to effectively utilize the data available for more accurate modeling (Shi and You, 2018). The number of related activities is increasing, indicating that there are still significant opportunities ahead on this research avenue.

3. Solution efficiency

Apart from the modeling step, probably even more efforts have been made in expediting the solution procedures of large and complex problems. Such approaches comprise methods to reduce the combinatorial complexity; in scheduling applications this typically leads to reducing the number of binary variables through pre-fixing the values of some of these or adding constraints that relate the values of different variables to each other (falling into the category of tightening constraints). When using rigorous MILP models for scheduling, this can also be achieved through analyzing the LP-relaxation, based on which one can derive e.g. variable lower bounds for the remaining MILP problem (Castro et al., 2020). This method can be performed per instance and can provide a significant reduction in solution time, as efficient cuts are added to the original MILP model. Other decomposition approaches have been suggested e.g. in Terrazas-Moreno and Grossmann (2011). If, on the other hand, there are sufficiently large data sets available, one can also use AI (Venkatasubramanian, 2019), or more specifically, ML to efficiently single out some decision options that either should be always selected (i.e., fixing related binary variables to one) or systematically excluded (i.e., fixing binary variables to zero).

Here we cannot dive into individual case studies but some related results are reported in Harjunkoski et al. (2020), where several options to speed up the solution of large-scale MILP problems are discussed. If sufficient data is available, e.g. in the paper industry case described by Mostafaei et al. (2020), one can use machine learning to dynamically generate more accurate (up-to-date) scheduling parameters such as change-over times for a grade-change in papermaking using machine learning over a large set of production data. Having access to multiple years of operational data also poses the challenge of how to balance between the recent and past data instances (often referred to as the *forgetting factor*), in order to ensure that the estimates remain accurate and are responsive for possible changes in the process. Apart from the scheduling parameters, one can also use the above data to eliminate product sequences that do not appear in the process history – these might be either unpractical or costly and have therefore not been selected by skilled operators. The approach results in a fraction of possible sequences, making intractable problems solvable. In short, instead of selecting from all possible sequences, the optimization focuses only on those that have been applied in the past.

In the presence of equipment degradation, it may be complex to decide whether a unit needs to be maintained or replaced – decisions that are often represented by binary variables. Having good statistical data at hand, it may be possible to either enforce, as well as exclude possible maintenance actions for components that with a very high certainty can be expected to fail or not to fail before the next planned maintenance stop (Ikonen et al., 2020a). Thus, instead of using a single instance as a basis of knowledge, as is done in the case of analyzing the problem through its LP-relaxation or specific decomposition schemes, the use of advanced AI/ML-techniques for creating more generic decision-making patterns can be a very efficient way of reducing the combinatorial complexity of the problem.

The above approach results in models where the variable bounds are tightened or fixed before the solution of the problem. There are many other avenues reported in the literature. One of the very interesting approaches focuses on trying to deploy several approaches to collect more understanding of the problem and the structure of its search tree in order to reduce the complexity and in a way learn to solve a problem in a better way (Xavier et al., 2019). This is especially promising for problems that are solved over-and-over-again with little variations and also involves implementing machine learning into the Branch & Bound (or Branch & Cut) tree search. There exists already a platform ECOLE (Provoust et al., 2020) for supporting the research in doing this. Commercial solver providers are already exploring and equipped with similar capabilities, e.g. the optimization provider Gurobi has done quite a bit of investigations on this and implemented some ideas (see reference on https://www.gurobi.com). Also, IBM CPLEX uses ML to automatically decide whether to use some algorithmic choices in solving quadratic optimization problems (reference https://developer.ibm.com). It is certain that this research challenge is going to be addressed by many researchers in the next years.

Recently, some research groups have investigated how to enhance process scheduling by reinforcement learning (Sutton and Barto, 2018). Hubbs et al. (2020a) examines the use of deep reinforcement learning in process scheduling. Another option is to deploy reinforcement learning at a higher level. Ikonen et al. (2020b) propose a framework where a reinforcement learning (RL) agent is trained to decide the timing of rescheduling procedures, select the scheduling algorithms to be used (e.g., MIP or heuristic) and estimate the time budget needed for the optimization. The Python-based library OR-GYM (Hubbs et al., 2020b) provides test environments for developing reinforcement learning algorithms to address operations research problems.

4. Main Challenges

As the problem space is very broad, the challenges are manifold so here we highlight only a few:

1. **Data.** Using machine learning in supporting optimization requires the presence of sufficient and high-quality data. In any of the above approaches a successful application must get hold on sufficient – often business critical – data, which often limits the work to company-internal exercises, hindering experts from the outside to get involved. Because of this, there are unfortunately almost no open data-sets available from the process industries. Possible tampering with the data may be difficult to detect and without dedicated domain experts, the interpretation of data may be close to impossible.

2. **Automated modeling.** Even if there exist well-documented model alternatives the modeling of scheduling problems is often almost an "art", while combining physical/business/operational requirements in a way that meets the company policies. It should be well considered which part of this can be automated without compromising any of the company objectives.
3. **Algorithmic complexity.** As mathematical modeling alone is often complex, adding another layer of ML makes it even more difficult to manage without good support. Today, there are limited number of experts that can master both disciplines and targeted training efforts are needed to ensure sufficient in-house knowledge.
4. **Deployability.** So far, purely ML-based approaches are able to handle mainly "routine tasks", where a human operator would need to react fast and perform a limited number of actions. How to widen the scope of ML is still open but a balanced mixture of e.g. ML and MILP could be one way to increase this capability.
5. **Balancing multiple objectives.** The strength of mathematical optimization is to be able to mix various objective components and balance them through given weights also in highly varying conditions. As ML alone may not be able to do this, the combination with optimization technologies can be very useful.

A relatively recent approach of Physics-informed neural networks (PINNs) reported e.g. in Raissi et al. (2019) provides an interesting approach of combining the use of data for learning with existing models of physical and biological systems and allows to benefit from the vast amount of existing prior knowledge that are not utilized in most common ML-methods. Encoding such structured information into a learning algorithm results in amplifying the information content of the data that the algorithm sees, enabling it to quickly steer itself towards the right solution and generalize well even when only a few training examples are available.

5. Conclusions

The topic of combining machine learning to support or complement mixed integer linear programming in solving scheduling problems is extremely interesting and has many possible avenues for successful applications. It is, however, important to have realistic expectations and start by working on tangible problems, where the benefits can be observed and quantified. Simultaneously, it would be important to create sufficiently large, shared datasets for development and comparison of different approaches. Through continued research, new discoveries can without doubt be made and some form of collaborative approaches will likely very soon become the future standard for the efficient and successful solutions of complex scheduling problems, once the major challenges have been overcome.

References

Bhosekar, A., and Ierapetritou, M. (2018). Advances in surrogate based modeling, feasibility analysis, and optimization: A review. Computers and Chemical Engineering, 108, 250-267

Castro, P. M., Dalle Ave, G., Engell, S., Grossmann, I. E., and Harjunkoski, I. (2020). Industrial demand side management of a steel plant considering alternative power modes and electrode replacement. Industrial and Engineering Chemistry Research, 59(30), 13642-13656

Harjunkoski, I., Ikonen, T., Mostafaei, H., Deneke, T., and Heljanko, K. (2020). Synergistic and intelligent process optimization: First results and open challenges. Industrial and Engineering Chemistry Research, 59(38), 16684-16694

https://developer.ibm.com/docloud/blog/2019/11/28/using-machine-learning-in-cplex-12-10/

https://www.gurobi.com/resource/integrating-machine-learning-with-mathematical-optimization-resource-matching/

Hubbs, C. D., Li, C., Sahinidis, N. V., Grossmann, I. E., & Wassick, J. M. (2020a). A deep reinforcement learning approach for chemical production scheduling. Computers & Chemical Engineering, 141, 106982

Hubbs, C.D., Perez, H.D., Sarwar, O., Sahinidis, N.V., Grossmann, I.E., & Wassick, J.M. (2020b). OR-Gym: A Reinforcement Learning Library for Operations Research Problem. ArXiv, abs/2008.06319.

Ikonen, T. J., Mostafaei, H., Ye, Y., Bernal, D. E., Grossmann, I. E., & Harjunkoski, I. (2020a). Large-scale selective maintenance optimization using bathtub-shaped failure rates. Computers and Chemical Engineering, 139, 106876

Ikonen, T. J., Heljanko, K., and Harjunkoski, I. (2020b). Reinforcement learning of adaptive online rescheduling timing and computing time allocation. Computers and Chemical Engineering, 141, 106994

Garey, M. R., Johnson, D. S., & Sethi, R. (1976). Complexity of Flowshop and Jobshop Scheduling. Mathematics of Operations Research, 1(2), 117-129

Méndez, C. A., Cerdá, J., Grossmann, I. E., Harjunkoski, I., & Fahl, M. (2006). State-of-the-art review of optimization methods for short-term scheduling of batch processes. Computers and Chemical Engineering, 30(6-7), 913-946

Mostafaei, H., Ikonen, T., Kramb, J., Deneke, T., Heljanko, K., and Harjunkoski, I. (2020). Data-driven approach to grade change scheduling optimization in a paper machine. Industrial and Engineering Chemistry Research, 59(17), 8281-8294

Prouvost, Antoine et al. "Ecole: A Gym-like Library for Machine Learning in Combinatorial Optimization Solvers." ArXiv abs/2011.06069 (2020)

Raissi, M., Perdikaris, P., and Karniadakis, G. E. (2019). Physics-informed neural networks: A deep learning framework for solving forward and inverse problems involving nonlinear partial differential equations. Journal of Computational Physics, 378, 686-707

Shi, H., and You, F. (2015). A novel adaptive surrogate modeling-based algorithm for simultaneous optimization of sequential batch process scheduling and dynamic operations. AIChE Journal, 61(12), 4191-4209

Sutton, R. S., & Barto, A. G. (2018). Reinforcement learning: An introduction. MIT press.

Terrazas-Moreno, S., and Grossmann, I. E. (2011). A multiscale decomposition method for the optimal planning and scheduling of multi-site continuous multiproduct plants. Chemical Engineering Science, 66(19), 4307-4318

Venkatasubramanian, V. (2019). The promise of artificial intelligence in chemical engineering: Is it here, finally? AIChE Journal, 65(2), 466-478

Wilson, Z. T., and Sahinidis, N. V. (2017). The ALAMO approach to machine learning. Computers and Chemical Engineering, 106, 785-795

Xavier, A.S., Qiu, F., and Ahmed, S. (2019). Learning to Solve Large-Scale Security-Constrained Unit Commitment Problems, arXiv:1902.01697 [math.OC]

Proceedings of the 14th International Symposium on Process Systems Engineering – PSE 2021+
June 19-23, 2022, Kyoto, Japan
http://dx.doi.org/10.1016/B978-0-323-85159-6.50076-2

Knowledge-guided Hybrid Approach for Scheduling Multipurpose Batch Plants

Dan Li[a], Dongda Zhang[a], Nan Zhang[a], Liping Zhang[b], and Jie Li[a]*

[a] *Centre for Process Integration, Department of Chemical Engineering, The University of Manchester, Manchester M13 9PL, UK*
[b] *Department of Industrial Engineering, Wuhan University of Science and Technology, Wuhan, Hubei, 430081 P. R. China*
jie.li-2@machester.ac.uk

Abstract

In this work, a novel hybrid algorithm integrating knowledge-guided GA and sequence-based mixed-integer linear programming (MILP) model is proposed for scheduling of industrial multipurpose batch plants. The computational results demonstrate that the proposed hybrid algorithm can generate the optimal solutions within 5 minutes for all tested industrial-scale examples. It can generate the same or better solutions using less computational effort than the existing methods.

Keywords: Scheduling; Multipurpose batch plants; Hybrid algorithm; Genetic algorithm

1. Introduction

Multipurpose batch plants have shared facilities and product-specific processing steps, whose flexibility provides industrial application prospect but poses challenges on scheduling. A plethora of mixed-integer linear programming (MILP) models have been proposed, including time-grid-based and sequence-based formulations (Harjunkoski et al., 2014). Their capabilities for small-size problems are well established. However, they may fail to solve industrial-scale problems because appropriate number of time points is unknown a priori and feasible solutions are hard to yield in short time frames. Although various decomposition approaches (Nishi et al., 2010) have been attempted, large computational efforts are still inevitable to obtain near optimal or optimal solutions.

Genetic algorithm (GA) is widely embraced to address industrial-scale problems (Woolway and Majozi, 2018) because it can generate good-quality solutions quickly with strong global search capability and inherent parallelism. However, GA is at disadvantage in solution optimality. Han and Gu (2021) showed that worse solutions were obtained for some large examples than MILP models, although computational effort could be significantly reduced. The hybrid algorithm combining advantages of GA on fast convergency and mathematical programming on solution optimality may eliminate limitations of a single algorithm and solve challenging large-scale problems.

In this work, we propose a hybrid algorithm integrating GA and the sequence-based MILP model to generate near-optimal or optimal solutions for industrial-scale scheduling problems. The computational results show that the proposed algorithm can solve large-size problems to optimality within 5 minutes and yield the same or better solutions within shorter computational time compared to the existing MILP methods. Also, the hybrid framework has better performance on both computational effort and optimality than GA and the sequence-based MILP model.

2. Sequence-based MILP formulation

We define three binary variables including $X_{imi'm'}$, $XS_{imi'm's}$, and z_{im}. Specifically, $X_{imi'm'}$ equals 1 if batch m of task i is performed before batch m' of task i' on one unit. $XS_{imi'm's}$ equals 1 when batch m of task i is transferred earlier or simultaneously than batch m' of task i' for storage vessel of state s. z_{im} is 1 if batch m of task i is performed. A task having multiple processing units is split into different tasks. Batches of a task should be processed in sequence, as Eq.(1).

$$z_{im} \leq z_{i(m-1)} \qquad \forall i, m > 1 \tag{1}$$

$$X_{imi'(m'+1)} \geq X_{imi'm'} \qquad \forall j, i \in \mathbf{I}_j, i' \in \mathbf{I}_j, i \neq i', m, m' < M \tag{2}$$

$$X_{i(m-1)i'm'} \geq X_{imi'm'} \qquad \forall j, i \in \mathbf{I}_j, i' \in \mathbf{I}_j, i \neq i', m > 1, m' \tag{3}$$

$$X_{imi'm'} + X_{i'm'im} \geq z_{im} + z_{i'm} - 1 \qquad \forall j, i \in \mathbf{I}_j, i' \in \mathbf{I}_j, i < i', m, m' \tag{4}$$

Eq.(2) ensures that if batch m of task i is processed before the batch m' of a task i' on a unit j, then this batch m must also be processed before the batch $(m'+1)$ of task i'. If batch m' of task i' is processed after the batch m of task i on a unit j, then this batch m' must be processed after the batch $(m-1)$ of task i, as Eq.(3). Eq.(4) tells the sequential relation between any two batches of two tasks in the same unit. Batch size b_{im} is bounded by the maximum B_i^{max} and minimum B_i^{min} capacity, as indicated in Eq.(5).

$$B_i^{min} \cdot z_{im} \leq b_{im} \leq B_i^{max} \cdot z_{im} \qquad \forall i, m \tag{5}$$

The duration of a batch is ensured by Eq.(6), where a_i and β_i are fixed and variable terms in the processing time, respectively. If a state s is subject to zero-wait ($s \in \mathbf{S}^{ZW}$), the duration is exactly equal to the processing time in Eq.(7). Sequencing constraints for the same task and different tasks in a unit are given in Eq.(8) and Eq.(9).

$$T_{im}^{\mathrm{f}} \geq T_{im}^{\mathrm{b}} + a_i \cdot z_{im} + \beta_i \cdot b_{im} \qquad \forall s \in \mathbf{S} \backslash \mathbf{S}^{ZW}, i \in \mathbf{I}_s^P, m \tag{6}$$

$$T_{im}^{\mathrm{f}} = T_{im}^{\mathrm{b}} + a_i \cdot z_{im} + \beta_i \cdot b_{im} \qquad \forall s \in \mathbf{S}^{ZW}, i \in \mathbf{I}_s^P, m \tag{7}$$

$$T_{i(m+1)}^{\mathrm{b}} \geq T_{im}^{\mathrm{f}} \qquad \forall i, m < M \tag{8}$$

$$T_{i'm'}^{\mathrm{b}} \geq T_{im}^{\mathrm{f}} - H \cdot (1 - X_{imi'm'}) \qquad \forall j, i \in \mathbf{I}_j, i' \in \mathbf{I}_j, i \neq i', m, m' \tag{9}$$

T_{ims}^{s} is defined as the transfer time of batch m of task $i \in \mathbf{I}_s$ into or out from the storage vessel of state s. Eq.(10) enforces the transfer time of batch m of task $i \in \mathbf{I}_s^P$ producing state s into storage equals its finish time T_{im}^{f}. The start time (T_{im}^{b}) of batch m of task i consuming state s is equal to the transfer time out from the storage. Sequence constraints on storage for batches of the same tasks and different tasks are given by Eqs.(12-13). Sets $\mathbf{S}^P, \mathbf{S}^R$ and $\mathbf{S}^{in}$ indicate product, raw material and intermediate state, respectively.

$$T_{ims}^{\mathrm{s}} = T_{im}^{\mathrm{f}} \qquad \forall s \in \mathbf{S}^{in}, i \in \mathbf{I}_s^P, m \tag{10}$$

$$T_{ims}^{\mathrm{s}} = T_{im}^{\mathrm{b}} \qquad \forall s \in \mathbf{S}^{in}, i \in \mathbf{I}_s^C, m \tag{11}$$

$$T_{i(m+1)s}^{\mathrm{s}} \geq T_{ims}^{\mathrm{s}} \qquad \forall s \in \mathbf{S}^{in}, i \in \mathbf{I}_s, m < M \tag{12}$$

$$T_{i'm's}^{\mathrm{s}} \geq T_{ims}^{\mathrm{s}} - H \cdot (1 - XS_{imi'm's}) \qquad \forall s \in \mathbf{S}^{in}, i \in \mathbf{I}_s, i' \in \mathbf{I}_s, m, m', i \neq i' \tag{13}$$

Eqs.(14-16) are formulated to enforce precedence of batches in different tasks on storage, which are similar to Eqs.(2-4). When two tasks can be processed in the same unit and related to the same state s, sequence relations for their batches keep consistent on unit and storage, as formulated in Eq.(17).

$$XS_{imi'(m'+1)s} \geq XS_{imi'm's} \qquad \forall s \in \boldsymbol{S}^{in}, i \in \mathbf{I}_s, i' \in \mathbf{I}_s, i \neq i', m, m' < M \quad (14)$$

$$XS_{i(m-1)i'm's} \geq XS_{imi'm's} \qquad \forall s \in \boldsymbol{S}^{in}, i \in \mathbf{I}_s, i' \in \mathbf{I}_s, i \neq i', m > 1, m' \quad (15)$$

$$XS_{imi'm's} + XS_{i'm'ims} \geq z_{im} + z_{i'm'} - 1 \quad \forall s \in \boldsymbol{S}^{in}, i \in \mathbf{I}_s, i' \in \mathbf{I}_s, m, m', i < i' \quad (16)$$

$$XS_{imi'm's} = X_{imi'm'} \qquad \forall j, s \in \boldsymbol{S}^{in}, i, i' \in \mathbf{I}_s \cap \mathbf{I}_j, m, m', i \neq i' \quad (17)$$

$CB_{imi'm's}$ is introduced to monitor batches m' transferred before batch m of different tasks in Eqs.(18-20) or the same tasks by Eq.(21). It equals to $b_{i'm'}$ if batch m' of task i' is transferred before or at the same time as batch m of task i. Otherwise, it equals to 0. Parameter $\rho_{i,s}$ is the fraction for task i to produce ($\rho_{i,s}$>0) or consume ($\rho_{i,s}$<0) state s. The inventory level in storage is calculated by Eq.(22), being positive and smaller than the maximum storage capacity ST_s^{max} after any transfer. Eq.(23) enforces total amount transferred for batches must satisfy storage limitation, where $\mathrm{In0}_s$ is the initial inventory.

$$CB_{imi'm's} \leq B_{i'}^{max} \cdot XS_{i'm'ims} \qquad \forall s \in \boldsymbol{S}^{in}, i, i' \in \mathbf{I}_s, m, m', i \neq i' \quad (18)$$

$$CB_{imi'm's} \geq b_{i'm'} - B_{i'}^{max} \cdot (1 - XS_{i'm'ims}) \quad \forall s \in \boldsymbol{S}^{in}, i, i' \in \mathbf{I}_s, m, m', i \neq i \quad (19)$$

$$CB_{imi'm's} \leq b_{i'm'} \qquad \forall s \in \boldsymbol{S}^{in}, i, i' \in \mathbf{I}_s, m, m', i \neq i' \quad (20)$$

$$CB_{imi'm's} = b_{i'm'} \qquad \forall s \in \boldsymbol{S}^{in}, i \in \mathbf{I}_s, m, m' < m \quad (21)$$

$$0 \leq \sum_{i' \in \mathbf{I}_s} \sum_{m'} \rho_{i's} CB_{imi'm's} + \rho_{i,s} b_{im} + \mathrm{In0}_s \leq ST_s^{max} \; \forall s \in \boldsymbol{S}^{in}, i \in \mathbf{I}_s, m \quad (22a,b)$$

$$0 \leq \sum_{i \in \mathbf{I}_s} \sum_m \rho_{is} \cdot b_{im} + \mathrm{In0}_s \leq ST_s^{max} \qquad \forall s \in \boldsymbol{S}^{in} \quad (23)$$

For the objective of minimizing makespan (*MS*), demand constraints are given in Eq.(24). Makespan must exceed the finish and transfer time of all batches.

$$\sum_{i \in \mathbf{I}_s^P} \rho_{is} \cdot \sum_m b_{im} \geq D_s \qquad \forall s \in \boldsymbol{S}^P \quad (24)$$

$$MS \geq T_{im}^{\mathrm{f}} \qquad \forall i, m \quad (25)$$

$$MS \geq T_{ims}^{\mathrm{s}} \qquad \forall s \in \boldsymbol{S}^{in}, i \in \mathbf{I}_s, m \quad (26)$$

We fix some variables for two batches of the same task by Eq.(27) because these two batches must be performed in sequence. The variables in Eq. (28) control the state inventory being positive and lower than storage capacity. As there are always abundant raw materials and infinite storage for products, the related variables are fixed as zero.

$$X_{imim'} = 1; X_{im'im} = 0; XS_{imim's} = 1; XS_{im'ims} = 0; CB_{imim's} = 0 \; \forall s, i, m' > m \quad (27)$$

$$XS_{imim's} = 0, CB_{imim's} = 0, T_{ims}^{\mathrm{s}} = 0 \qquad \forall s \in (\mathbf{S}^P \cup \mathbf{S}^R), i, m, i', m' \quad (28)$$

3. Genetic algorithm

A knowledge-guided GA is designed to generate good-quality solutions in short time frames. A three-part chromosome $c = (c^P, c^U, c^R)$ is constructed to represent a solution for a given problem. Elements $c_n^P \in [1, P]$ are ordinal numbers of products, thus the sequence in c^P indicates production sequence of products. c^U covers assigned units for batches of tasks that have multiple feasible units. Here, one position of c^U corresponds to one batch of a task and the element $c_n^U \in [1, \mathbf{J}_n]$ decides the assigned unit j. $c_n^R \in [0,1]$ is used to determine if the latest processed task is repeated. c^R is introduced to influence the sequence of tasks that are processed to produce different batches of products.

Fig. 1 An example of the designed chromosome

The fitness value of the chromosome is evaluated based on Makespan for the schedule, which is synthesized by decoding. The decoding algorithm works as follows. It steps iteratively through c^P to produce products until demand requirements are met. While producing a product for one batch, any involved task would be performed if its produced material is insufficient. Assigned unit for batch of task is determined by c^U, and latest performed task would be repeated when its corresponding element in c^R is 1. A heuristic rule 'earliest starting strategy' is adopted to start tasks as early as possible. As states are subject to finite or no intermediate storage, inventory level of storage must be monitored and checked at the start and finish times while processing tasks. In GA, the roulette wheel method is adopted to select parents who would be subjected to two-point crossover and two-point mutation. A knowledge-based search (Zheng and Wang, 2018) is incorporated to adjust sequence and assignment of child chromosome based on experiential possibility.

4. Hybrid algorithm

The proposed hybrid algorithm is illustrated in Figure 2. The number of feasible solutions transmitted from GA to MILP is $P_{size} \cdot 0.01$, where P_{size} is the population size of GA.

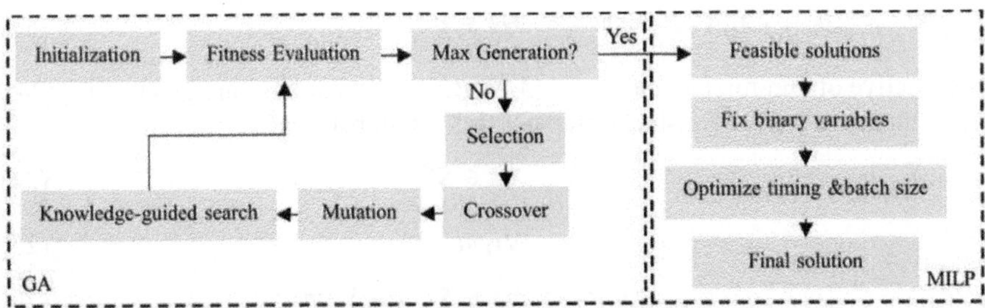

Fig. 2 The proposed hybrid solution algorithm

The strategies used to fix binary variables in the MILP model are described as follows. First, the batches of a task that can be processed in only one unit are fixed to be 1. That is $z_{im} = 1$. Second, tasks i and i' denote one task processing in different units ($j \in \mathbf{J}_i, j' \in \mathbf{J}_{i'}$), and batch m of task i is performed at T_{im}^{b} on unit j. If unit j' from time T_{im}^{b} to $(T_{im}^{\text{b}} + a_i + \beta_i \cdot B_i^{max})$ is idle, batch m is potential to be divided into multiple batches performed on different units, implying z_{im} and $z_{i'm'}$, where batch m' of task i' is not performed in the solution of GA, would be optimized in MILP. Otherwise, $z_{im} = 1$. Third, the precedence between batches of tasks, whose batch information is fixed in the first two steps, on a processing unit in the solution of GA are used to fix $X_{imi'm'}$. $XS_{imi'm's}$ is partially fixed by enforcing batch m' of task $i' \in \mathbf{I}_s^C$ starts after batch m of task $i \in \mathbf{I}_s^P$ providing required state for batch m' (i.e., $XS_{imi'm's} = 1$). Also, batch m' of task i' finishes before batch m of task i whose produced state is consumed by batch m' to ensure inventory level of state s lower than maximum storage capacity (i.e., $XS_{i'm'ims} = 1$).

5. Computational Results

Seven examples from the literature are solved to illustrate the capability of the proposed hybrid algorithm. While Examples 1-3 are from He and Hui (2010), Examples 4-7 refer to the Kallrath example I9, I11, I14, and I15 from Vooradi and Shaik (2012). Examples 1, 2, and 3-7 are small-, medium- and industrial- scale examples, respectively. GA is implemented in MATLAB 2020 and the MILP model is solved using GAMS 33.2 on an AMD Ryzen™ 9 3900X 3.8 GHz, 48 GB RAM, running Windows 10. All examples are also solved using the MILP models of Vooradi and Shaik (2012) and Velez et al. (2015), denoted as VS2012 and VM2015.

The computational results are provided in Table 1, where N is the number of event point required, Gap is the relative gap, and H denotes the time horizon. A competitively efficient algorithm is perceived to find smaller Makespan (MS) or take shorter computational time (CPU). From Table 1, it can be seen that the proposed hybrid algorithm can obtain smaller MS using less CPU time for most examples, compared to VS2012. This can be attributed to the strong global search capacity of the first-stage GA in our model, finding good-quality solutions quickly for industrial-scale problems with a large number of binary variables. The proposed algorithm leads to generate the same global optimum for all examples, as those obtained by VM2015. In our work, sufficient population size and reproduction at the first stage and solutions transmitted to the second stage are required even for simple problems to explore global searching space and reach optimal areas. The CPU time thus is longer than that from VM2015 for small-scale Examples 1-2, but it is still accepted for industrial application. For industrial-scale examples 3-7, much less computational effort is required. The CPU time is reduced by an order of magnitude for Examples 3 and 5.

Table 1. Computational results from the proposed hybrid algorithm and the existing methods

	VS2012				VM2015			Hybrid algorithm	
Ex	N	MS	Gap	CPU (s)	H	MS	CPU (s)	MS	CPU (s)
1	22	37	-	45.2	60	37	0.8	37	3.1
2	65	109	1.4%	>3600	110	108	11.0	108	61.0
3	131	229	5.6%	>3600	219	217	3298.0	217	250.3
4	11	33	3.1%	>3600	60	32	13.2	32	12.1
5	12	40	-	1856.3	60	39	103.9	39	18.7
6	10	36	-	56.3	60	36	50.6	36	9.6
7	23	58	17.3%	>3600	60	52	93.9	52	58.2

The computational results from the hybrid algorithm with GA and the sequence-based MILP model are compared in Table 2. The average MS (denoted as Avg) and the standard deviation (denoted as SD) of MS in 50 runtimes are calculated. Although the hybrid algorithm and GA can find identical optima using similar computational time, the hybrid algorithm outperforms GA due to smaller average MS and more stability (i.e., smaller SD), implying the generation of the global optimum with higher probability. This can be attributed to the integration of the MILP model to further improve quality of feasible solutions from GA. The sequence-based MILP model obtains near-optimal solutions for Examples 4-5 and 7. However, it cannot find any feasible solution (denoted as NA) for

Examples 2-3 in 1 hour, whilst the hybrid algorithm can find the optimal solution within 5 minutes because the majority binary variables at the second stage have been fixed.

Table 2. Comparative results for hybrid algorithm and single algorithms

	GA				Sequence-based MILP			Hybrid algorithm			
Ex	MS	Avg	SD	CPU(s)	MS	Gap	CPU(s)	MS	Avg	SD	CPU(s)
1	37	37.1	0.2	2.6	37	0	1845	37	37.0	0	3.1
2	108	108.2	0.4	51.6	NA	-	>3600	108	108	0	61.0
3	217	217.3	0.5	169.1	NA	-	>3600	217	217.2	0.4	250.3
4	32	32.2	0.5	25.1	34	35.3%	>3600	32	32.1	0.3	12.1
5	39	39.2	0.4	53.5	40	30.0%	>3600	39	39.1	0.2	18.7
6	36	36.1	0.3	16.4	36	26.7%	>3600	36	36.0	0	9.6
7	52	52.4	0.7	87.3	60	33.3%	>3600	52	52.1	0.4	58.2

6. Conclusions

In this work, a hybrid algorithm combining GA and the sequence-based MILP formulation is proposed for scheduling multipurpose batch process. The computational results have demonstrated the capability of the proposed algorithm to solve large-size problems, showing that the same or better optimal solutions can be obtained with dramatically decreased computational time compared to the existing methods. In addition, the hybrid algorithm is superior to the sequence-based MILP model and GA.

Acknowledges

Dan Li appreciates financial support from UOM/CSC Joint Scholarship (201908130170). Jie Li would like to appreciate the financial support from EPSRC (EP/T03145X/1).

References

Y. Han, X. Gu, 2021, Improved multipopulation discrete differential evolution algorithm for the scheduling of multipurpose batch plants, Ind. Eng. Chem. Res., 60, 5530-5547.

I. Harjunkoski, C.T. Maravelias, P. Bongers, P.M. Castro, S. Engell, I.E. Grossmann, J. Hooker, C. Mendez, G. Sand, J. Wassick, 2014, Scope for industrial applications of production scheduling models and solution methods, Comput Chem Eng, 62,161-193.

Y. He, C.W. Hui, 2010, A binary coding genetic algorithm for multi-purpose process scheduling: A case study, Chem. Eng. Sci., 65(16), 4816-4828.

T. Nishi, Y. Hiranaka, M. Inuiguchi, 2010, Lagrangian relaxation with cut generation for hybrid flowshop scheduling problems to minimize the total weighted tardiness, Comput. Oper. Res., 37, 189-198

S. Velez, A.F. Merchan, C.T. Maravelias, 2015, On the solution of large-scale mixed integer programming scheduling models, Chem. Eng. Sci., 136(2), 139-157.

R. Vooradi, M.A. Shaik, 2012, Improved three-index unit-specific event-based model for short-term scheduling of batch plants, Comput Chem Eng., 43, 148-172.

M. Woolway, T. Majozi, 2018, A novel metaheuristic framework for the scheduling of multipurpose batch plants, Chem. Eng. Sci., 192, 678-687.

X. Zheng, L. Wang, 2016, A knowledge-guided fruit fly optimization algorithm for dual resource constrained flexible job-shop scheduling problem, Int. J. Prod. Res.54, 5554-5566.

Proceedings of the 14th International Symposium on Process Systems Engineering – PSE 2021+
June 19-23, 2022, Kyoto, Japan
http://dx.doi.org/10.1016/B978-0-323-85159-6.50077-4

Scheduling of Electrical Power Systems under Uncertainty using Deep Reinforcement Learning

Akshay Ajagekar[a*], Fengqi You[a]

[a]*Cornell University, Ithaca, New York, 14853, USA*
asa273@cornell.edu

Abstract

In this work, a deep reinforcement learning-based solution approach for the unit commitment of power generation resources in energy systems with intermittent renewable energy resources and uncertain loads is presented. Real-world unit commitment problems are plagued with uncertain parameters introduced by the possibility of forecast errors or equipment failure that may negatively impact the power supply. It is imperative to develop a robust and computationally tractable framework to provide cost-effective commitment decisions. In the proposed solution technique, temporal and spatial correlational structures of uncertainties present in the system are captured with a neural network function approximator. The proposed solution technique is able to capture the temporal and spatial correlational structure of uncertainties present in the system. A causal policy is obtained which relies only on previously observed wind power and demand forecasts along with forecast errors. We conduct computational experiments on the IEEE 39-bus test case to demonstrate the effectiveness of the proposed solution strategy and improvement over existing unit commitment solution techniques. The proposed deep reinforcement learning-based solution strategy demonstrates effective computational performance and a reduction in operating costs over deterministic and stochastic approaches.

Keywords: Unit Commitment, Deep Reinforcement Learning, Machine Learning

1. Introduction

Unit commitment (UC) is one of the widely used optimization models in the power industry for scheduling and dispatch of electric power generation resources (Padhy, 2004). The UC problem is NP-hard and is challenging to solve as its size increases (Tseng, 1996). Real-world UC problems are plagued with uncertain parameters caused by the possibility of forecast errors or equipment failure (Håberg, 2019). Forecast uncertainty can affect solution quality and causes service interruptions (Ning et al., 2019, 2022). A more price-responsive demand and high penetration of wind power pose new challenges to the UC problem (Qiu et al., 2021), thus stressing the need for an effective methodology that produces robust UC decisions in the presence of real-time uncertainty (Shang et al., 2019). Several formulations of the UC problem have been previously proposed in terms of different uncertainty representations and solution techniques (Abujarad et al., 2017). Stochastic optimization techniques suffer from high computational costs while robust approaches may yield solutions that are too conservative (Zheng et al., 2014). Therefore, it is imperative to develop a more robust and computationally tractable framework as compared to other stochastic optimization approaches that provide more cost-effective commitment decisions.

Machine learning offers a powerful alternative to solving this scheduling optimization problem (Ning and You, 2019), especially on handling uncertainty. UC problems can also be formulated under a dynamic programming framework for decision-making in multiple stages (Pang & Chen, 1976). There have been attempts to solve stochastic UC problems with reinforcement learning (RL) techniques, including the use of deep neural networks as function approximators (Jasmin et al., 2016). In this paper, we propose a deep reinforcement learning (DRL) based technique for the effective solution of the UC problem under demand and wind power uncertainty. The proposed scheduling technique is capable of capturing the causal nature of uncertainties present in the system with deep neural networks. To demonstrate the applicability and efficiency of the proposed DRL-based solution approach, we conduct computational experiments with the IEEE 39-bus test case. The obtained solutions are also compared with UC solutions obtained using deterministic approaches that use point forecasts for demand load and wind power generation along with other stochastic approaches.

2. MDP Formulation and Safety

We formulate the UC problem as a Markov decision process (MDP). At any time step *t* on any given day, the day-ahead point forecast predictions for demand load and wind power are available. The net load, defined as the difference between total electrical load and total wind generation power, is denoted by $n_t = \sum_b d_{bt} - \sum_b w_{bt}$ and is considered for energy balance. The resulting net load forecasts are obtained accordingly. The uncertainty associated with net load is captured by ζ_t defined as the ratio of forecast error to net load forecast. Along with historical net load forecasts $n^f_{<t}$, historical uncertainty realizations $\zeta_{<t}$, and current forecast n^f_t, the commitment, startup, and shutdown decisions at the previous stage also constitute the system state. To decouple the state variables from multiple stages, additional state variables are introduced at each stage *t*, and are denoted by $u^\tau_{it-1}, \tau = 1,...,UT_i - 1$ and $v^\tau_{it-1}, \tau = 1,...,DT_i - 1$. These state variables store the historical account of startup and shutdown decisions for a duration of minimum up and down-times, respectively. The system's state for all generators $i \in G$ is then fully described by the tuple $s_t = \left(n^f_{<t}, \zeta_{<t}, n^f_t, z_{it-1}, u_{it-1}, v_{it-1}, u^\tau_{it-1}, v^\tau_{it-1}\right)$ The action space for the MDP includes the commitment decisions z_{it} accompanied by the startup and shutdown decisions, u_{it} and v_{it}, respectively. Prediction for the net load forecast error uncertainty denoted by $\hat{\zeta}_t$ is also considered as an action variable. The estimated net load can then be calculated as $n^f_t\left(1+\hat{\zeta}_t\right)$. The safe exploration of UC decisions is performed by solving the optimization problem denoted by $UC\left(\hat{\zeta}_t\right)$ in (1)-(7) which guarantees operational constraint satisfaction in UC. Minimum up and down-time constraints are reformulated to use the additional state variables u^τ_{it-1} and v^τ_{it-1}, and are given by Eq. (4) and (5).

$$\min \sum_{i \in G} \left[C_i(p_{it}) + C^{NL}_i z_{it} + C^{SU}_i u_{it} + C^{SD}_i v_{it} \right] \tag{1}$$

$$s.t. \quad z_{it} P^{\min}_i \le p_{it} \le z_{it} P^{\max}_i \quad \forall i \in G \tag{2}$$

$$\sum_{i \in G} p_{it} = n^f_t \left(1 + \hat{\zeta}_t\right) \tag{3}$$

$$u_{it} + v_{it-1} + \sum_{\tau=1}^{DT_i-1} v_{it-1}^{\tau} \le 1 - z_{it-1} \quad \forall i \in G \tag{4}$$

$$v_{it} + u_{it-1} + \sum_{\tau=1}^{UT_i-1} u_{it-1}^{\tau} \le z_{it-1} \quad \forall i \in G \tag{5}$$

$$z_{it} - z_{it-1} = u_{it} - v_{it} \quad \forall i \in G \tag{6}$$

$$z_{it}, u_{it}, v_{it} \in \{0,1\},\ p_{it} \ge 0,\ \forall i \in G \tag{7}$$

Selection of control actions is followed by the realization of forecast error ratio uncertainty ζ_t. Based on the observed net load, the commitment decisions can be updated to minimize incurred costs, which is consistent with UC as a multistage decision-making problem. To meet actual net load requirements, fast-start generators can be potentially turned ON or OFF, leading to additional startup or shutdown costs. The objective is to minimize such costs by selecting the control actions. To achieve this, we seek to maximize the reward in (8) with C_u defined in Eq. (9). The maximum achievable reward at any timestep t is zero. The optimal control actions required to meet actual net load requirements also constitute the next state s_{t+1}. The additional state variables are updated using transition dynamics shown in Eqs. (10) and (11).

$$r_t = -\left| C_u(\zeta_t) - C_u(\hat{\zeta}_t) \right| \tag{8}$$

$$\begin{aligned} C_u(\zeta) &= \sum_{i \in G} C_i^{NL} z_{it} + C_i^{SU} u_{it} + C_i^{SD} v_{it} \\ s.t.\ &(z_{it}, u_{it}, v_{it}) \in \arg\min UC(\zeta) \end{aligned} \tag{9}$$

$$u_{it}^{\tau} = u_{it-1}^{\tau-1},\ \forall i \in G, \tau = 2,\ldots,UT_i - 1 \tag{10}$$

$$v_{it}^{\tau} = v_{it-1}^{\tau-1},\ \forall i \in G, \tau = 2,\ldots,DT_i - 1 \tag{11}$$

3. Actor-Critic Method for Policy Learning

A deterministic policy that estimates net load forecast error ratio is considered here, which also serves to obtain control actions through safely exploring the constrained decision space. The forecast errors are independent of the system states like power dispatch and commitment decisions. So, the policy is considered to be a function of system states consisting of net load forecasts, current forecast, and previous uncertainty realizations, as shown in Eq. (12).

$$\hat{\zeta}_t = \pi\left(n_{<t}^f, n_t^f, \zeta_{<t}\right) \tag{12}$$

The DRL agent is trained using an off-policy actor-critic algorithm. Due to the deterministic nature of the policy and the continuous action space spanned by it, an actor-critic algorithm based on DDPG is used (Lillicrap et al., 2015). Both actor and critic are implemented using deep neural networks and can be parameterized by the networks' weights and biases. The architectures of the parameterized actor and critic can be denoted as $\pi_\theta\left(n_{<t}^f, n_t^f, \zeta_{<t}\right)$ and $Q_\phi(s_t, a_t)$, respectively. π_θ is a feed-forward deep neural network with two fully connected layers with 32 and 16 hidden units with a rectified linear unit (ReLu) activation. A linear activation is used for this final layer since the errors may have negative values. Similarly, the critic Q_ϕ uses the historical

UC decisions $\{u_{it-1}^{\tau}, v_{it-1}^{\tau}\}$, previous commitment decisions z_{it-1}, as input, along with the predicted forecast errors $\hat{\zeta}_t$ and time-state T_r. All the above state and action variables are concatenated and fed to a feed-forward deep neural network. The deep neural network consists of three fully connected layers with 32, 32, and 16 units, each following a ReLu activation. A single output is then obtained by adding a layer with a single neuron with linear activation that corresponds to the Q-value.

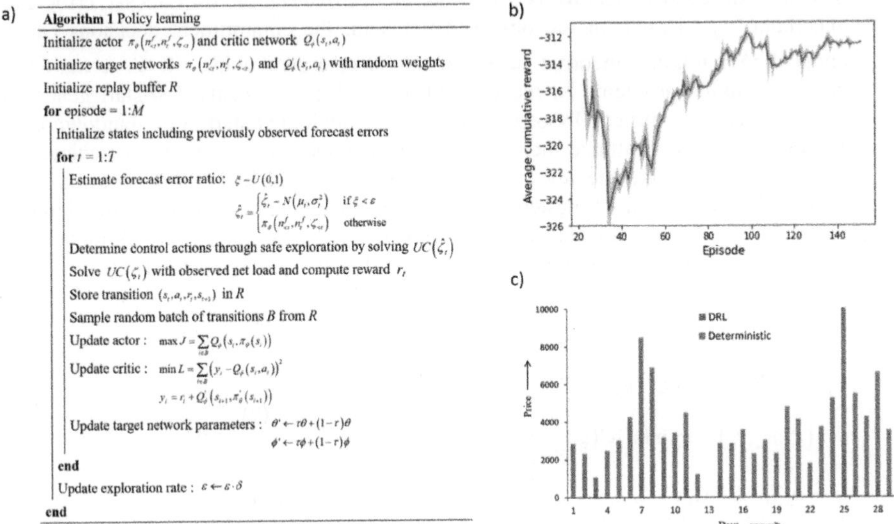

Fig 1. a) Actor-critic based algorithm for policy learning with conservative policy iteration to predict forecast errors, b) average cumulative returns obtained at each episode during policy learning and c) costs incurred by the system operator for starting additional generating units due to insufficient dispatch by the committed units

In order to perform soft updates in conservative policy iteration, we also initialize copies of actor and critic as targets denoted as $\pi_\theta'(n_{<t}^f, n_t^f, \zeta_{<t})$ and $Q_\phi'(s_t, a_t)$. Typically, exploration in DDPG is performed by generating noise by sampling from a correlated normal distribution. Parameters of this normal distribution must be carefully chosen for effective performance. To bypass this restriction, an alternate approach based on the epsilon-greedy strategy is employed. In epsilon-greedy, forecast error ratio estimates are selected randomly with a probability of ε, also termed as exploration rate. $\hat{\zeta}_t$ is randomly sampled from a normal distribution $N(\mu_t, \sigma_t^2)$ where the parameters μ_t and σ_t are obtained by fitting historical values of forecast error ratios at t^{th} hour of the day to a normal distribution. The commitment and startup/shutdown control decisions are obtained through safely exploring the decision space without violating any constraint imposed by the estimated net load. This is followed by solving $UC(\zeta_t)$ with the observed net load. The transitions are stored in a replay buffer R of a fixed size. To train the actor and critic networks, we randomly sample a batch of transitions B from the replay buffer. The pseudo-code of the algorithm is provided in Fig. 1a.

4. Case Study: IEEE 39-Bus System

We consider an IEEE test system to demonstrate the applicability of the proposed DRL-based approach. We use historical demand data from NYISO for both learning and evaluation purposes. Both hour-ahead load forecasts and actual loads in various zones in New York are extracted from the historical data. The Eastern Wind Integration dataset provided by National Renewable Energy Laboratory (NREL) consists of hour-ahead wind power forecasts for simulated wind farms. A real-time dispatch process is simulated to validate the viability of the proposed DRL-based solution approach. The training process for the DRL agent is conducted in an episodic manner with episodes of length 24 hourly timesteps and converges in approximately 150 episodes. The length of the horizon for historical values that constitute the state is set to 12. The reward curves can be visualized in Fig. 1b, where the average cumulative returns over the length of the horizon are plotted. We conduct UC and economic dispatch simulations for each day of five consecutive months. The daily average costs are reported in Table 1 for each solution technique. The daily costs reported for the deterministic approach and DRL-based approach are the actual incurred real-time costs. Costs incurred with the DRL-based approach are considerably lower than the upper bounds provided by the SDDiP algorithm. SDDiP is a sampling-based variant of Bender's decomposition typically used for scenario decomposition techniques to solve the stochastic UC problem. Optimal costs of operation obtained with perfect uncertainty information can be used to compute the gap between the lower bound and the obtained solution. An average optimality gap of 6.65% is observed with the DRL-based solution for UC.

Table 1. Daily average costs obtained by different approaches for the IEEE 39-bus system

	Perfect knowledge ($)	*Deterministic approach ($)*	*SDDiP ($)*	*DRL ($)*
September	380,966	404,326	426,592	403,792
October	402,485	432,194	442,540	430,969
November	396,632	424,512	440,353	423,378
December	401,738	430,380	445,365	429,449
January	397,962	425,625	439,851	424,593

Since the goal of the DRL agent is to minimize excess penalty costs, the DRL approach is expected to produce minimum penalties by committing appropriate units capable of satisfying the observed load requirements. A representation of the penalties and their frequency for the month of January is shown in Fig. 1c. The costs incurred by the system operator for starting additional units to meet net load requirements are significantly higher than excess costs incurred by the DRL approach. Low penalties are eventually responsible for lower total operating costs with the DRL approach as compared to the deterministic approach. From the penalty costs, their frequency, and observed commitment status of generators, it can be inferred that the trained DRL agent is able to anticipate appropriate forecast error uncertainties and yields UC decisions that can satisfy net load requirements without starting additional units.

5. Conclusion

In this paper, we proposed a DRL-based scheduling approach for the UC problem under demand and wind power uncertainty. This involved formulating the UC problem as an MDP and maximizing cumulative rewards by the actor-critic algorithm. A trained actor that predicts the net load forecast error ratios was obtained by training the DRL agent. Here, both actor and critic networks were parameterized by deep neural networks. Zero violation of any operational constraint in the UC problem is also guaranteed by our proposed approach. The efficiency of the proposed approach was evaluated on the IEEE 39-bus test system. Evaluation of the trained policy on the real-world load and wind power forecast data resulted in a reduction of penalty costs of commitment of additional units as well as a substantial overall cost saving with the proposed DRL-based scheduling approach.

References

S. Y. Abujarad, M. W. Mustafa, J. J. Jamian, 2017, Recent approaches of unit commitment in the presence of intermittent renewable resources: A review. Renewable and Sustainable Energy Reviews, 70, 215-223.

A. Ajagekar, F. You, 2021, Quantum computing based hybrid deep learning for fault diagnosis in electrical power systems. Applied Energy, 303, 117628.

M. Håberg, 2019, Fundamentals and recent developments in stochastic unit commitment. International Journal of Electrical Power & Energy Systems, 109, 38-48.

E. Jasmin, T. I. Ahamed, T. Remani, 2016, A function approximation approach to Reinforcement Learning for solving unit commitment problem with Photo voltaic sources. IEEE International Conference on Power Electronics, Drives and Energy Systems (PEDES).

T. P. Lillicrap, J. J. Hunt, A. Pritzel, N. Heess, T. Erez, Y. Tassa, D. Silver, D. Wierstra, 2015, Continuous control with deep reinforcement learning. arXiv preprint arXiv:1509.02971.

C. Ning, F. You, 2018, Data-driven stochastic robust optimization: General computational framework and algorithm leveraging machine learning for optimization under uncertainty in the big data era. Computers & Chemical Engineering, 111, 115-133.

C. Ning, F. You, 2019, Optimization under uncertainty in the era of big data and deep learning: When machine learning meets mathematical programming. Computers & Chemical Engineering, 125, 434-448.

C. Ning, F. You, 2019, Data-Driven Adaptive Robust Unit Commitment Under Wind Power Uncertainty: A Bayesian Nonparametric Approach. IEEE Transactions on Power Systems, 34, 2409-2418.

C. Ning, F. You, 2022, Deep Learning Based Distributionally Robust Joint Chance Constrained Economic Dispatch Under Wind Power Uncertainty. IEEE Transactions on Power Systems, 37, 191-203.

N.P. Padhy, 2004, Unit commitment-a bibliographical survey. IEEE Transactions on Power Systems, 19, 1196-1205.

C. Pang, H. Chen, 1976, Optimal short-term thermal unit commitment. IEEE Transactions on Power Apparatus and Systems, 95(4), 1336-1346.

H. Qiu, W. Gu, F. You, 2021, Bilayer Distributed Optimization for Robust Microgrid Dispatch With Coupled Individual-Collective Profits. IEEE Transactions on Sustainable Energy, 12, 1525-1538.

H. Qiu, F. You, 2020, Decentralized-distributed robust electric power scheduling for multi-microgrid systems. Applied Energy, 269, 115146.

C. Shang, F. You, 2019, Data Analytics and Machine Learning for Smart Process Manufacturing: Recent Advances and Perspectives in the Big Data Era. Engineering, 5, 1010-1016.

C. L. Tseng, 1996, On power system generation unit commitment problems. University of California, Berkeley.

A. J. Wood, B. F. Wollenberg, G. B. Sheblé, 2013, Power generation, operation, and control. John Wiley & Sons.

Q. P. Zheng, J. Wang, A. L. Liu, 2014, Stochastic optimization for unit commitment—A review. IEEE Transactions on Power Systems, 30(4), 1913-1924.

Proceedings of the 14th International Symposium on Process Systems Engineering – PSE 2021+
June 19-23, 2022, Kyoto, Japan
http://dx.doi.org/10.1016/B978-0-323-85159-6.50078-6

A Reinforcement Learning Approach to Online Scheduling of Single-Stage Batch Chemical Production Processes

Max Mowbray[a], Dongda Zhang[a], and Antonio Del Rio Chanona[b,*]

[a] *Centre for Process Integration, School of Chemical Engineering and Analytical Science, The University of Manchester, Manchester, M13 9PL, United Kingdom*
[b] *Centre for Process Systems Engineering (CPSE), Department of Chemical Engineering, Imperial College London, London, SW7 2AZ, United Kingdom*
a.del-rio-chanona@imperial.ac.uk

Abstract

The field of Reinforcement Learning (RL) has received a lot of attention for decision-making under uncertainty. Lately, much of this focus has been on the application of RL for combinatorial optimisation. Recent work has showcased the use of RL on a single-stage continuous chemical production scheduling problem. This work highlighted the potential of RL for optimal decision-making under uncertainty in the paradigm of (bio)chemical production scheduling. However, this novel approach is yet to be tested in the context of parallel unit operations and batch processing systems. In this work, we outline a framework for the use of RL to handle single-stage parallel, batch production. In particular, we incorporate elements such as uncertainties in the model data, limited batch size, sequencing constraints, and uncertainties in processing times and product demand, which make for a substantially harder problem. To handle the presence of precedence or succession constraints, by taking inspiration from approaches such as generalised disjunctive programming, we propose a novel methodology that identifies transformations of the control set available to the RL at each control interaction. Given that production typically operates under standard operating procedures, such transformations can be identified by logic. The efficacy of policy synthesis via evolutionary RL methods is benchmarked against mixed integer programming. The results of this study provide further support for the use of RL in online scheduling.

Keywords: Reinforcement Learning; Combinatorial Optimization; Production Scheduling; Machine Learning.

1. Introduction

The production scheduling of (bio)chemical processes is a major field of process systems engineering research. The foundational developments in the area from the 1980s – 2010s focused on the development of efficient, rigorous, finite dimensional mathematical models for use in optimization. The contributions made by Kondili *et al.* (1993) and Pantelides (1994), formed basis for the general description of production scheduling problems via discrete time and continuous time mixed integer programming (MIP) formulations on the basis of various network models of the scheduling problem. Additionally, due to the practical difficulties in solving mixed integer nonlinear models, typical MIP models that are developed are linear or are dependent upon linearizations of nonlinearities. Further drivers of the field include the development of robust optimization models and innovative frameworks in the context of reactive (online) scheduling that aim to update the process schedule as uncertainties are realised. Despite the developments made to date in the field, in practice many production schedules are generated (in real plants) by teams of schedulers who rely upon their working knowledge and available heuristic rules, with relatively little reliance upon the rigorous mathematical models proposed by academia (Harjunkoski *et al.*, 2014) . This is due to a) the complexities of obtaining finite dimensional models robust to the underlying uncertainties that are computationally tractable online, and b) difficulties in accurately estimating suitable uncertain parameters (i.e. sets or probability distributions descriptive of them).

In an attempt to handle the challenges mentioned, recent works have investigated the use of Reinforcement Learning (RL) in the context of (bio)chemical production scheduling (Hubbs *et al.,* 2020a). RL promises to remedy the challenges previously discussed by a) providing reactive, uncertainty aware scheduling decisions via inference (i.e. prediction of scheduling decisions from a function) and shifting the computational load offline, and b) providing basis for the use of a greater range of models and descriptions of the underlying uncertainty. However, the application of RL to (bio)chemical production scheduling has been relatively limited. In the novel study provided by Hubbs *et al.* (2020a), the authors consider the sequencing of tasks on a single unit, in a single-stage continuous chemical production problem. The work demonstrates results that are competitive with stochastic and deterministic reactive MILP approaches.

Despite the promise of RL, it is yet to be demonstrated on case study with the type of complexity in decision-making seen in a real plant (globally). In this work, we consider the development of a methodology for the use of RL in a parallel, single-stage batch (bio)chemical production scheduling study with multiple units and various sources of uncertainty. We present a methodology based on a discrete time transcription of the production scheduling problem, although it is possible to use a continuous time (event-based) approach. Due to the presence of sequencing constraints derived from standard operational procedures (SOPs), the problem is complex. To mitigate the demands of learning a feasible policy through the reward function, we propose to aid the control selection by identifying nonlinear transformations of the prediction based on the SOPs stated in case study. This reduces the demands of learning through a reward signal alone. Such an approach has been previously studied, where transformations have instead been learned (Bamford and Ovalle, 2021). A similar idea is exploited in generalised disjunctive programming (GDP).

2. Methodology

In this work, we assume that there is a Markov decision process (MDP) that well represents the problem of scheduling single-stage batch operations in parallel in a (bio)chemical production plant. Specifically, we assume that there is: a set of states, $\boldsymbol{x} \in \mathbb{X} \subseteq \mathbb{R}^{n_x}$, that make the problem fully observable; a set of available control inputs $\boldsymbol{u} \in \mathbb{U} \subseteq \mathbb{Z}^{n_u}$ that may be selected; a reward function, $R: \mathbb{X} \times \mathbb{U} \times \mathbb{X} \rightarrow R_{t+1} \in \mathbb{R}$, that ranks process evolution with respect to control objectives; and, a probabilistic description of process evolution, such that:

$$\boldsymbol{x}_{t+1} = f(\boldsymbol{x}_t, \boldsymbol{u}_t, \boldsymbol{s}_t) \tag{1}$$

where $t \in \{0, \dots, T\}$ is a discrete time index and the process is considered to evolve over discrete time horizon; and, $\boldsymbol{s} \in \mathbb{S} \subseteq \mathbb{R}^{n_s}$ is a realization of (general) process uncertainties.

Operationally, there is a constraint set, $\hat{\mathbb{U}}_t \subset \mathbb{Z}^{n_u}$, that defines the available tasks or jobs, that may be scheduled in a given unit, $L \in \{1, \ldots, n_u\}$, at any given time index. This can be derived from standard operating procedures (SOPs) that define the viable sequencing of operations in units, requirements for unit cleaning and maintenance periods, requirements for orders to be processed in campaigns (i.e. multiple batches consecutively if the order size is greater than maximum batch size of a unit) and that these batches must finish before another job or task is assigned to a given unit. Given the scheduling problem that we consider in this work adheres to a discrete time transcription, in essence, we are solving the following discrete time, finite horizon stochastic optimal control problem:

$$P(\pi_c) = \begin{cases} \max_{\pi_c} \mathbb{E}_{\pi_c}\left[\sum_{t=0}^{T-1} R_{t+1}\right] \\ X_0 \sim p(\boldsymbol{x}_0) \\ \boldsymbol{x}_{t+1} = f(\boldsymbol{x}_t, \hat{\boldsymbol{u}}_t, \boldsymbol{s}_t) \\ \boldsymbol{u}_t = \pi_c(\boldsymbol{u}_t|\boldsymbol{x}_t) \\ \boldsymbol{u}_t \in \hat{\mathbb{U}}_t \subseteq \mathbb{Z}^{n_u} \\ \forall\, t \in \{0, \ldots, T\} \end{cases} \tag{2}$$

where $X_0 \in \mathbb{X}$ is a random variables described by the initial state distribution, $p(\boldsymbol{x}_0)$; and, $\pi_c(\boldsymbol{u}_t|\boldsymbol{x}_t)$ is a conditional probability mass function over controls, given the current state. In RL practice, the aim is to learn a functionalization of the policy, $\pi_c(\boldsymbol{u}_t|\boldsymbol{x}_t;\theta)$, where $\theta \in \mathbb{R}^{n_\theta}$. Conventionally, the functionalization is chosen to be nonlinear and suited to *end-to-end* learning, such that neural networks are often favoured. Selection of control inputs to the system (conditional to the state) are then provided by inference and learning of the optimal policy parameters, $\theta^* \in \mathbb{R}^{n_\theta}$, are learned through the reward function, R, and general policy iteration algorithms. Two points are worth noting here that provide basis for the methodology subsequently presented: a) the MDP framework does not naturally handle the hard constraints imposed by $\boldsymbol{u}_t \in \hat{\mathbb{U}}_t$, and b) Eq. 2 formulates control inputs (decisions) as integer values that identify the allocation of a given task or job in a unit at a given time index. We explore how best to handle these two issues in the following.

Handling the constraints imposed on control selection in classical problems such as dynamic optimization of fed-batch processes with continuous control spaces (with upper and lower bounds) is often implicit (i.e. use of an activation function over the ANN output layer naturally places upper and lower bounds on control selection). In this class of problem the structure of the constraints on the control space is different and arises from SOPs. Given SOPs are typically defined logically (as in sequencing constraints), one can identify an additional transformation of the set of available controls, $\mathbb{U}$, at each control interaction, t, based on the current state of the plant and the SOPs themselves. This functional transformation is denoted, $f_{SOP}: \mathbb{U} \times \mathbb{X} \rightarrow \hat{\mathbb{U}}$ and is assumed non-differentiable.

The conventional approach to select discrete control decisions from a function is either to a) predict the conditional probability density of each control explicitly in the output of the policy functionalisation, or b) predict the state-action value of each control in the output of the policy functionalization (this then enables the generation of a conditional probability mass function according to e.g. ϵ – greedy policies). However, these approaches scale poorly with the number of orders and units common to scheduling problems. A more intelligent approach is instead to predict a real value in a continuous latent space, $w \in \mathbb{W}$, and then transform that prediction to a corresponding discrete control decision, $\boldsymbol{u}_t$. This is a common approach in recommender systems. The transformation could either be guided by the state-action value of the k nearest integer controls, or could be a deterministic rounding policy (i.e. the nearest integer function), denoted $f_r: \mathbb{W} \to \mathbb{U}$, as demonstrated (implicitly) in Hubbs *et al.* (2020b). Both transformations are non-differentiable.

Assuming the constraint set, $\hat{\mathbb{U}}$, at each control interaction can be identified, the rounding policy can be defined in this work as $f_r: \mathbb{W} \to \hat{\mathbb{U}}$, which enables selection of controls that explicitly satisfy the constraint set. In the case one is unable to identify $\hat{\mathbb{U}}$ absolutely via f_{SOP}, one can penalise violation of those constraints not handled innately by incorporating a deterministic expression for the constraint violation into a penalty function, $\varphi: \mathbb{X} \times \mathbb{U} \times \mathbb{X} \to \mathbb{R}$, (this is trivial if the constraint is neither subject to uncertain parameters, $\boldsymbol{s} \in \mathbb{S}$, nor soft). A figurative description of the algorithm proposed is provided by Figure 1.

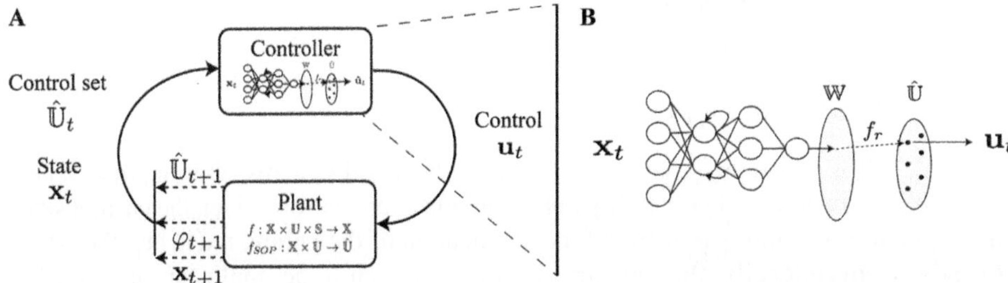

Figure 1: Figurative description of A) the handling of constraints on the control inputs via logical expression, as well as method of control selection, B) shows control selection in more detail.

Due to the problem posed, and the structure of the control space, this work uses evolutionary RL. Here, the exploration-exploitation paradigm is moved directly to the parameter space - removing reliance on first order gradients indicative of directions for policy improvement and mitigates the potential for policies to get stuck in local optima as well as instability in training. This is particularly likely using conventional policy optimization, given a) directions to improve policy parameters are estimated from the state distribution induced under the policy and b) in this work small changes in the policy parameters have potential to drastically alter the state distribution induced.

3. Case Study

To demonstrate the ideas presented in the methodology we work from the case study presented in Cerdá *et al.* (1997). In this work, the authors present a continuous time MILP model for the optimization of a single stage, parallel batch production environment (based on the state-task network representation). The problem definition is provided in Cerdá *et al.* (1997) and we refer the reader there for more details, however uncertain modifications are detailed by Table 1. It is of note that the methodology applies when uncertainty is derived from set based descriptions too. The problem is transcribed from a continuous time to a discrete time formulation (for RL) and to ensure the two are comparable, all processing times and cleaning times, are modified so that their greatest common factor is equivalent to the discrete time interval, Δt, used to define the time grid. In this work, $\Delta t =$ 0.5 days and the modified case study data is provided by Table 2. Here we demonstrate the methodology with $J = 8$ orders and $T = 200$ (corresponding to 100 days). Due to the nature of the scheduling problem and the simulation-based methodology proposed, the underlying simulation model used to generate the following results is both non-smooth and dependent on logic.

Table 1: Definition of the uncertain process parameters

Description	Descriptive distribution
A due date, τ_i for each customer order is uncertain, but has been estimated via a nominal value of $\bar{\tau}_i$ days from the start of the horizon. The variable τ_i is realized two days before delivery	$\tau_i \sim Pois(\bar{\tau}_i)$
The processing time, p_{il}, of task i in a unit l is subject to uncertainty but has a nominal value in days, $\bar{p}_{il}$	$p_{il} \sim U(p_{il}^{LB}, p_{il}^{UB})$ $p_{il}^{LB} = \max(0.5, \bar{p}_{il} - 0.5)$ $p_{il}^{UB} = \bar{p}_{il} + 0.5$

Table 2: Detail of the modified parameters from the original case study to enable comparison between the two time transcriptions. All other parameters are the same as the original study.

	Cleaning Time (days) between preceding task, i, and successor task, j								Nominal Processing Time (days) of task i			
	Task, j								Unit			
Task i	1	2	3	4	5	6	7	8	1	2	3	4
1	-	-	-	-	-	0.5	-	-	2.0	-	-	-
2	-	-	1.0	-	-	-	-	-	-	-	1.0	-
3	1.0	0.5	-	-	-	-	0.5	-	1.0	-	1.0	-
4	-	-	-	-	0.5	-	-	-	-	1.5	-	-
5	-	-	-	0.5	-	0.5	1.0	0.5	-	1.5	-	1.0
6	1.5	-	0.5	0.5	-	-	-	-	2.5	2.0	-	-
7	-	2.0	-	-	1.0	-	-	0.5	-	-	1.0	1.5
8	-	-	-	-	-	-	1.5	-	-	-	-	2.0

In practice, we are unable to explicitly identify $\hat{\mathbb{U}}_t$ explicitly. Instead, we are only able to identify $\bar{\mathbb{U}}_t$, where $\hat{\mathbb{U}}_t \subset \bar{\mathbb{U}}_t$. The constraint not handled innately through f_r is that a given task cannot be processed in more than one unit at the same time. Given, the objective of the scheduling function is to minimise tardiness in orders and makespan, we can declare the following penalty function (reward) and propose to use particle swarm optimization (PSO) to maximise it:

$$\varphi_{t+1} = \sum_{i=1}^{I} r_{t+1,i} + m - \kappa \|C\|_2 \tag{3}$$

where $C = [[c_1]^-, \ldots, [c_I]^-] \in \mathbb{Z}^{n_u}$; $c_i = \sum_{l \in L} W_{ilt} - 1$, where $W_{ilt} \in \mathbb{Z}_2$ is a binary variable indicating whether task i is scheduled in unit l at time t; $[v]^- = \max(0, v)$; $\kappa = 250 \in \mathbb{R}^{++}$ is a penalty weight; $r_i = -1 \in \mathbb{R}^-$ is a penalty for the tardiness of an order (i.e. where $\tau_i < t_f^i$); and, $m = -1 \in \mathbb{R}^-$ is a penalty per discrete time step. Key performance indicators are $G_{\pi_c} = \mathbb{E}_{\pi_c}[\sum_{t=1}^{T} \varphi_t]$ and $\sigma_{\pi_c} = \Sigma[\sum_{t=1}^{T} \varphi_t]^{0.5}$.

4. Results and Discussion

To first benchmark the performance of the RL approach, we analyse the optimality of the solution policy found under a nominal model, which essentially corresponds to the generation of a schedule offline (i.e. for a deterministic reality). We find that the RL is able to obtain the same score under the objective function as the original MILP model for the case when there is no finite release time and when there is (i.e. $\varphi_{NoRT} = -62$ and $\varphi_{RT} = -65$). Now, we turn our attention to benchmarking the method when uncertainties are present. The results are detailed by Table 3. We conduct 8 experiments investigating the potential of RL to handle process uncertainty and benchmark to a shrinking horizon MILP approach, which uses the nominal data (corresponding to $\bar{p}_{ij}$ and $\bar{\tau}_{ij}$).

Table 3: Results of online optimization of the production schedule for RL and MILP approaches. The more positive G_{π_c} the better (as the RL problem is posed as a maximization).

Exp No.	Due Date uncertainty	Processing time uncertainty	Release Times	RL (G_{π_c}+/- σ_{π_c})	MILP (online) (G_{π_c}+/- σ_{π_c})
1	False	True	False	**-61.9** +/- 4.4	-63.3 +/- 4.4
2	False	True	True	**-66.0** +/- 4.9	-66.3 +/- 4.9
3	True	False	False	**-66.8** +/- 8.7	-70.1 +/- 9.6
4	True	False	True	-73.8 +/- 10.7	**-73.6** +/- 10.3
5	True	True	False	**-67.4** +/- 10.9	-71.6 +/- 11.3
6	True	True	True	-75.3 +/- 11.5	**-75.1** +/- 11.7

From Table 3, it is clear that the RL approach proposed is competitive with the MILP benchmark proposed in Cerdá *et al.* (1997). In fact, the RL outperforms the MILP approach in 4 out of the 6 experiments. It is thought the benefits arise from the ability of RL to explicitly consider uncertainty. Furthermore, in this study the RL approach is 150 times computationally cheaper to identify a reactive scheduling decision online.

5. Conclusions

In alignment with the drivers for production to become more distributed, flexible and reactive to realisations of real world uncertainty, we have demonstrated the application of RL for the online optimization of single-stage, parallel batch (bio)chemical production scheduling. We show that the approach is competitive with online MILP approaches, but has the benefit of significant computational savings online. Future work will consider: the application to a larger plant; transcription to a continuous time model; application to multi-stage processes with resource constraints; and, integration into a framework that provides certainty for operators.

References

C.C. Pantelides, Unified frameworks for optimal process planning and scheduling, Proc. Second Conf. on Foundations of Computer Aided Operations, 253-274, (1994)

E. Kondili, C.C. Pantelides, R.W.H. Sargent, A general algorithm for short-term scheduling of batch operations – I. MILP formulation,, Comput. Chem. Eng. 17, (1993)

I. Harkunkoski, C.T. Maravelias, P.Bongers, P.M. Castro, S. Engell, I.E. Grossmann, J. Hooker, C. Mendez, G. Sand, J. Wassick, Scope for industrial applications of production scheduling models and solution methods, Comput. Chem. Eng. 62, (2014)

C. D. Hubbs, C. Li, N.V. Sahinidis, I.E. Grossmann, J.M. Wassick, A deep reinforcement learning approach for chemical production scheduling, Comput. Chem. Eng., 141 (2020a)

C. Bamford, A. Ovalle, Generalising Discrete Action Spaces with Conditional Action Trees, arXiv preprint arXiv:2104.07294v1 (2021)

C.D. Hubbs, H.D. Perez, O.Sarwar, N.V. Sahinidis, I.E. Grossmann, J.M. Wassick, OR-Gym: A Reinforcement Learning Library for Operations Research Problems, arxiv:2008.06319 (2020b)

J. Cerdá, G. P. Henning, I.E. Grossmann, A Mixed-Integer Linear Programming Model for Short-Term Scheduling of Single-Stage Multiproduct Batch Plants with Parallel Lines, Ind. Eng. Chem. Res. 36, 5, (1997)

Proceedings of the 14th International Symposium on Process Systems Engineering – PSE 2021+
June 19-23, 2022, Kyoto, Japan
http://dx.doi.org/10.1016/B978-0-323-85159-6.50079-8

An adaptive multi-cut decomposition based algorithm for integrated closed loop scheduling and control

Ilias Mitrai[a], Prodromos Daoutidis[a,*]

[a]*Department of Chemical Engineering and Materials Science, University of Minnesota, Minneapolis, 55455, USA*
daout001@umn.edu

Abstract

The integration of scheduling and control leads to large scale optimization problems whose monolithic solution is challenging. In this paper we propose an adaptive muti-cut algorithm to solve the integrated optimization problem to global optimality in reduced time. The reduction of the CPU time is achieved via the addition of multiple cuts and the adaptive addition/removal of cuts based on the executed schedule. We apply the proposed approach to a continuous system and analyze its computational performance.

Keywords: Control; Optimization; Operation

1. Main Text

Fast changing economic environments render the traditional sequential decision-making strategy suboptimal. The integration of scheduling and control is considered a promising avenue to improve the economic performance of process systems by considering simultaneously decisions at both time scales [Daoutidis et al., 2018]. Closed loop scheduling, i.e. modification of the schedule in response to production changes or disturbances is also essential to guarantee its feasibility and optimality during real time operation [Zhuge and Ierapetritou, 2012, Risbeck et al., 2019]. The implementation of such a closed loop approach is limited by the computational complexity of the problem. The key difficulty arises due to the nonlinear behavior of process systems, which leads to nonconvex, large scale optimization problems whose real time solution is challenging. Different approaches have been proposed to address this issue. In one approach, surrogate models have been used to approximate the dynamic behavior of the system [Pattison et al., 2017] and the cost associated with the execution of processing tasks [Charitopoulos et al., 2019, Chu and You, 2013]. The solution time can also be improved by exploiting the structure of the problem using decomposition based solution algorithms [Chu and You, 2015]. However, these methods cannot always guarantee global optimality due to the nonconvexity of the problem. In this work we propose an adaptive multi-cut decomposition based algorithm for integrated closed loop scheduling and control for multiproduct continuous systems. The proposed algorithm is based on a hybrid multi-cut Generalized Benders Decomposition (GBD) algorithm proposed by Mitrai and Daoutidis (2021). In this approach the integrated problem considers simultaneously all the transitions between the products for all the slots and the cost associated with the dynamic transitions between the products is approximated using cuts. The solution of this problem provides the production sequence and the state and manipulated variable profiles to be implemented. The integrated problem is resolved to compensate for updated process information (the values of the state variables of the system, the time horizon, the inventory level, product demand and price, etc.). In order to accelerate the solution of the integrated problem at different time points, we propose the adaptive addition/removal of cuts. Specifically, the cuts added at previous time points are incorporated directly in the solution of the problem, only for the transitions that can possible occur. This adaptive approach leads to a reduction in computational time and thus enables fast rescheduling as necessary. We apply this approach to a continuous stirred tank reactor and analyze the ability of the proposed approach to handle disturbances at both the scheduling and control level.

2. Problem formulation and decomposition

2.1. Scheduling problem

We will assume that N_p products must be produced over a time horizon H which is discretized into N_s slots. We define variable $W_{ik} \in \{0,1\}$ which is equal to 1 if product i is produced in slot k and zero otherwise, and variable $Z_{ijk} \in \{0,1\}$ which is equal to 1 if a transition occurs between products i and j in slot k and 0 otherwise. The logic constraints are:

$$\sum_i W_{ik} = 1 \; \forall \, k \tag{1}$$

$$Z_{ijk} \geq W_{ik} + W_{j,k+1} - 1 \; \forall \, i, j, k \neq N_s \tag{2}$$

The starting and ending time in slot k are T_k^s ($T_1^s = T_0$) and T_k^e ($T_{N_s}^e = H$) respectively. The production time of product i in slot k is Θ_{ik}, the transition time in slot k is θ_k^t. The timing constraints are the following:

$$T_k^e = T_k^s + \sum_i \Theta_{ik} + \theta_k^t \;\; \forall k \neq N_s \tag{3}$$

$$T_{k+1}^s = T_k^e \;\; \forall k \neq N_s \tag{4}$$

$$\Theta_{ik} \leq W_{ik} H \; \forall i, k \tag{5}$$

The amount of product i manufactured and stored in slot k is q_{ik} and S_{ik} respectively. The demand of product i is d_i, the production rate is r_i and the amount of product i sold in slot k is S_{ik}. The production constraints are

$$\begin{aligned} I_{ik} &= I_{ik-1} + \mathrm{r_i}\, \Theta_{\mathrm{ik}} - S_{ik} \;\; \forall i, k, k > 1 \\ S_{iN_s} &\geq d_i \; \forall \, i. \end{aligned} \tag{6}$$

2.2. Dynamic model

The dynamic behaviour of the system is described by a set of ordinary differential equations $\dot{x} = F(x, u)$, where x are the state variables, u are the manipulated variables and F are vector functions. These equations are discretized using the method of orthogonal collocation on finite elements. We consider simultaneously all the transitions and define x_{ijfck}^n and u_{ijfck}^m as the value of state n and manipulated variable m for a transition from product i to product j in slot k, finite element f and collocation point c. Finally, we define θ_{ijk} as the transition time for a transition from product i to j in slot k, and the discretized equations are

$$x_{ijfck} = F_d(\dot{x}_{ijfck}, u_{ijfck}, x0_{ijfk}, \theta_{ijk}) \;\forall\, n, i, j, f, c, k$$
$$x0_{ij1k} = x_i^{ss},\; x_{ijN_{fe}N_{cp}k} = x_i^{ss} \;\forall\, i, j, k \tag{7}$$
$$u_{ij11k} = u_i^{ss},\; u_{ijN_fN_ck} = u_j^{ss} \;\forall\, i, j, k$$

where x_i^{ss}, u_i^{ss} are the steady state values of the state and manipulated variables for product i and F_d denote the discretized equations.

2.3. Integrated problem

The objective function of the integrated optimization problem is $\Phi_1 - \Phi_2$, where

$$\Phi_1 = \sum_{ik}\left(P_{ik}S_{ik} - C_{ik}^{op}q_{ik} - C^{inv}I_{ik}\right) - \sum_{ijk} C_{ij}^{tr} Z_{ijk}$$

$$\Phi_2 = \sum_{ijk} Z_{ijk} a_u \left(\sum_{fc} N_{fe}^{-1} t_{ijfck}^d \Lambda_{cN_c}\left(u_{ijfck} - u_j^{ss}\right)^2\right) = \sum_{ijk} Z_{ijk} a_u f_{ijk}^{dyn}.$$

P_i, C_i^{op} are the price and operating cost of product i, C^{inv} is the inventory cost, C_{ij}^{tr} is the transition cost from product i to j and a_u is a weight coefficient. Finally, the transition time for each slot and period depends on the transitions that occur and we define θ_{ijk} as the transition time from product i to j in slot k (the lower bound is the minimum transition time $\theta_{ij}^{\min}$) and the following equations are added:

$$\theta_k^t = \sum_{i,j} \theta_{ijk} Z_{ijk} \;\;\forall\, i, j, k \neq N_s \tag{8}$$

The goal of the optimization problem is to maximize $\Phi_1 - \Phi_2$ subject to Eq. 1-8.

3. Decomposition based solution algorithm

In this section we present the hybrid multi-cut GBD algorithm [Mitrai and Daoutidis, 2021]. Analysis of the structure of the problem via Stochastic Blockmodeling [Mitrai et al., 2021] reveals a hybrid core-community structure. The scheduling constraints/ variables form the core and the variables/constraints associated with the dynamic optimization problems are assigned in communities. The core and the communities are connected via the transition times θ_{ijk}. Given the structure of the problem, we define ϕ_{ijk} as the value function of a transition from product i to j in slot k, and the dynamic optimization problem for this transition can be written as:

$$\phi_{ijk}(\theta_{ijk}) = \text{minimize}\, f_{ijk}^{dyn} \text{ subject to } g_{ijk}^{dyn} \leq 0\; (Eq.\ 7),\; \hat{\theta}_{ijk} = \theta_{ijk} : \lambda_{ijk} \tag{9}$$

where λ_{ijk} is the Lagrange multiplier and is equal to the negative of the subgradient of ϕ_{ijk} for $\theta_{ijk} = \bar{\theta}_{ijk}$. The optimization problem can be written as [Geoffrion, 1970]

$$\begin{aligned}&\text{maximize } \Phi_1 - \sum_{ijk} Z_{ijk}\eta_{ijk}\\ &\text{subject to } Eq.\ 1-6,\ 8,\ \eta_{ijk} \geq \phi_{ijk}^v - \lambda_{ijk}^v\left(\theta_{ijk} - \bar{\theta}_{ijk}^v\right)\ \forall i,j,k,v \in \mathcal{V}\ \text{(Eq. 11)}\end{aligned} \tag{10}$$

We will follow a hybrid multicut GBD approach to solve this problem. The master problem is a Mixed Integer Nonlinear Program solved with Gurobi [Gurobi, 2021] and the subproblems, which are nonlinear programs solved with IPOPT [Wachter and Biegler, 2006], are the dynamic optimization problems only for the transitions that occur. Since η_{ijk} approximates the transition from product i to j in slot k, this approximation will also be valid for other slots. Hence in each iteration, Eq. 11 for a given i, j is added for all slots. We refer the reader to [Mitrai and Daoutidis, 2021] for a detailed explanation of the algorithm.

4. Adaptive multicut algorithm

The solution of the above problem will provide the production sequence, production times and dynamic transition profiles of the states and manipulated variables. We will assume that at some time t a disturbance affects the system and the value of the state variable is $\bar{x}$ (the predicted value from the initial schedule is x), the demand is d and the inventory of product i is I_i^0. At this point a modified integrated problem must be solved. Specifically, the time horizon is $H - t$ since the system was following the initial schedule during the first t hours. Also, at time t different amounts of each product have been produced, hence the initial inventory if product i, I_i^0, can be nonzero. Finally, in the first slot two transitions can occur. The first is a transition from $\bar{x}$ to the steady state of the new product i (x_i^{ss}) that will be manufactured in the first slot. Once $x = x_i^{ss}$, product i will be produced and then a transition will occur between product i produced in slot 1 and product j produced in slot 2. In order to model this problem, we will define a binary variable $\hat{Z}_i$ which is equal to 1 if a transition occurs from the intermediate state $\bar{x}$ to product i and 0 otherwise. We also define $\hat{\theta}_i$ as the transition time for the aforementioned transition. In order to model the transition in this slot we add the following constraint:

$$\hat{Z}_i = W_{i1} \; \forall i \tag{12}$$

Based on the above constraint a transition from the intermediate state to the steady state of product i is performed only if product i is manufactured in the first slot. We also define $\hat{\eta}_i$ as the approximation of the value function $\hat{\phi}_i$ for the transition from the intermediate state to the steady state of product i. Given these variables, the transition time in the first slot is given by the following constraint:

$$\theta_1^t = \sum_i \hat{Z}_i \, \hat{\theta}_i + \sum_{ij} Z_{ij1} \theta_{ij1} \tag{13}$$

Overall the optimization problem is:

$$\text{maximize } \Phi_1 - \sum_{ijk} Z_{ijk} \eta_{ijk} - \sum_i \hat{Z}_i \, \hat{\eta}_i \tag{14}$$

$$\text{subject to } Eq. 1-6, 8, 12, 13, \; \hat{\eta}_i \geq \hat{\phi}_i^v - \hat{\lambda}_i^l \left(\hat{\theta}_i^l - \bar{\hat{\theta}}_i^l\right) \; \forall l \in \mathcal{L}$$

where $\hat{\lambda}_i^l$ is the optimal Lagrangean multiplier for the equality constraint $\hat{\theta}_i = \bar{\hat{\theta}}_i$ and l denotes the iteration number. The hybrid multicut GBD can be used to solve the above problem once a disturbance affects the system. In order to reduce the CPU time further we propose an adaptive solution approach, where for the solution of the integrated problem at time t we add all the cuts evaluated in the previous iterations for the transitions that can occur. This strategy leads to a reduction in the CPU time, since fewer iterations are necessary. However, we must note that the cost associated with the transition from the intermediate state must be approximated every time the integrated problem is solved.

5. Case study

We will assume that the system is an isothermal CSTR where an irreversible reaction occurs $3A \rightarrow B$, and the dynamic behaviour is described by the following equation $\frac{dc}{dt} = \frac{Q}{V}\left(c_{feed} - c(t)\right) - k\,c(t)^3$, where $c\ (mol/L)$ is the concentration, $Q\ (L/hr)$ is the inlet flowrate (manipulated variable) and V, c_{feed}, k are the reactor volume, inlet concentration and reaction constant respectively. First we solve the integrated problem (Eq. 10) to obtain the initial schedule. The optimality gap tolerance is set to 1%. The hybrid multi-cut GBD algorithm solves the problem in 13 CPU seconds and the production sequence is $2 \rightarrow 1 \rightarrow 3 \rightarrow 4 \rightarrow 5$, the value of the objective function is 7.5 10^5 and the production results are presented in Fig. 2.

Table 1 Operating conditions and economic data, scheduling horizon $H = 24$

Product	c^{ss}	Q^{ss}	Prod. rate	Demand	Price	C^{op}	$C^{tr}/10$				
							1	2	3	4	5
1	0.24	200	150	600	200	13	0	10	6	12	15
2	0.2	100	80	550	160	22	15	0	5	8	10
3	0.3	400	278	600	130	35	20	15	0	10	15
4	0.39	1000	607	1200	110	29	90	10	12	0	10
5	0.5	2500	1250	2500	140	25	15	10	15	14	0

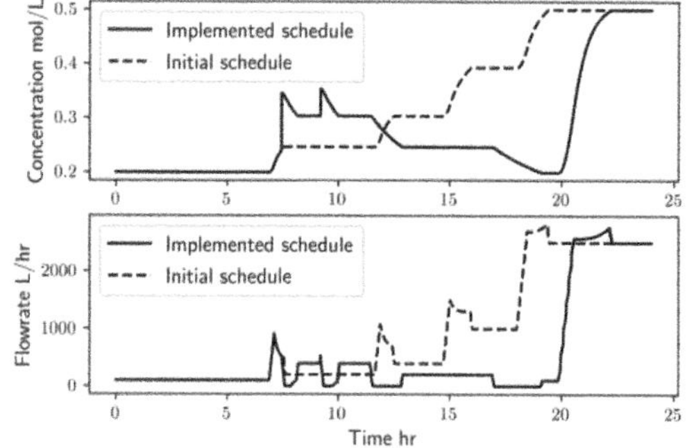

Figure 1 Concentration and inlet flowrate profiles for the nominal and implemented schedule

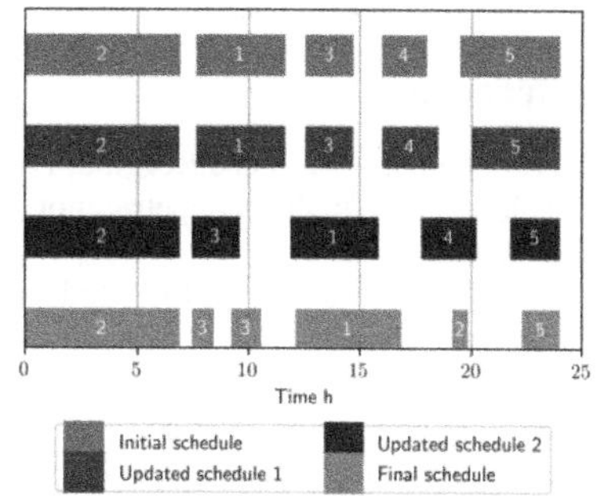

Figure 2 Gantt chart for the initial and updated schedules

First we will consider a case where after 4 hours of operation, the demand of product 4 changes from 1200 to 1500. At this point, 320 mol of product 2 have been produced and the length of the time horizon is 20 hours. Using the adaptive algorithm the integrated problem (Eq. 14) is solved in 1.8 CPU seconds, the value of the objective function is 7.1 10^5 and the updated schedule is presented in Fig. 2 (Update 1). In this case, the value of the objective function is lower, compared to the initial schedule, since more time is dedicated to the production of product 4. Solving the problem hybrid multi-cut GBD algorithm requires 20 CPU seconds. In this case the adaptive algorithm reduces the CPU time by 91 %.

Next, we will assume that after 7.4 hours, a disturbance in the inlet concentration causes the concentration in the reactor to be equal to 0.33 mol/l. At this point, the demand of product 2 is satisfied and the associated cuts are not considered. The integrated problem is solved in 17 CPU seconds using the adaptive algorithm, the optimal sequence is 3 → 1 → 4 → 5 (Fig. 2 Update 2) and the value of the objective function is 4.2 10^5. In this case the CPU time is higher than the previous case since the transition from the intermediate state to the different products must be approximated. Also, the value of the objective function is reduced since more time is spent in transitions. Solving the problem with the hybrid GBD multi-cut algorithm requires 33 CPU seconds. Finally, after 9.1 hours of operation the concentration in the reactor is 0.35 (the nominal value is 0.3), the order of product 4 is cancelled, the demand of product 3 changes to 650 and additional 50 mol of product 2 are ordered. The adaptive algorithm solves the problem in 9.6 CPU seconds and the production sequence is 3 → 1 → 2 → 5 (Fig. 2 Final schedule). The hybrid GBD algorithm requires 20 CPU seconds. The profiles of the concentration and inlet flowrate for the initial and final schedule are presented in Fig. 1.

6. Conclusions

The real time solution of integrated optimization problems is computationally challenging. In this paper, we propose an adaptive multi-cut algorithm which can solve the integrated optimization problem in reduced computational time via the adaptive addition/removal of cuts, which approximate the cost associated with dynamic transitions between products. We consider disturbances in both the control and scheduling and we show that the proposed approach can update the schedule in order to guarantee optimality and feasibility. In the future we intend to apply this algorithm to more complicated continuous systems and batch systems.

References

Charitopoulos, V.M., Papageorgiou, L.G. and Dua, V., 2019, Closed-loop integration of planning, scheduling and multi-parametric nonlinear control. Computers & Chemical Engineering, 122, pp.172-192

Chu, Y. and You, F., 2015, Model-based integration of control and operations: Overview, challenges, advances, and opportunities. Computers & Chemical Engineering, 83, pp.2-20

Daoutidis, P., Lee, J.H., Harjunkoski, I., Skogestad, S., Baldea, M. and Georgakis, C., 2018, Integrating operations and control: A perspective and roadmap for future research. Computers & Chemical Engineering, 115, pp.179-184

Geoffrion, A.M., 1970. Elements of large-scale mathematical programming Part I: Concepts. Management Science, 16(11), pp.652-675.

Risbeck, M.J., Maravelias, C.T. and Rawlings, J.B., 2019. Unification of closed-loop scheduling and control: State-space formulations, terminal constraints, and nominal theoretical properties. Computers & Chemical Engineering, 129, p.106496.

Gurobi Optimization, 2021, Gurobi optimizer reference manual. URLhttp://www.gurobi.com

Mitrai, I., and Daoutidis, P., 2021, A multicut Generalized Benders Decomposition approach for the integration of process operations and dynamic optimization for continuous systems, under review

Mitrai, I., Tang, W. and Daoutidis, P., 2021. Stochastic blockmodeling for learning the structure of optimization problems. AIChE Journal, p.e17415.

Pattison, R.C., Touretzky, C.R., Harjunkoski, I. and Baldea, M., 2017, Moving horizon closed-loop production scheduling using dynamic process models. AIChE Journal, 63(2), pp.639-651

Wächter, A., & Biegler, L. T., 2006, On the implementation of an interior-point filter line-search algorithm for large-scale nonlinear programming. Mathematical programming, 106(1), 25-57

Zhuge, J. and Ierapetritou, M.G., 2012, Integration of scheduling and control with closed loop implementation. Industrial & Engineering Chemistry Research, 51(25), pp.8550-8565

Proceedings of the 14th International Symposium on Process Systems Engineering – PSE 2021+
June 19-23, 2022, Kyoto, Japan
http://dx.doi.org/10.1016/B978-0-323-85159-6.50080-4

Uncertainty Evaluation of Biorefinery Supply Chain's Economic and Environmental Performance Using Stochastic Programming

Yuqing Luo[a], Marianthi Ierapetritou[a*]

[a]*Department of Chemical and Biomolecular Engineering, University of Delaware, 150 Academy Street, Newark, Delaware, 19716, USA*

mgi@udel.edu

Abstract

Life cycle assessment (LCA) and technoeconomic analysis (TEA) are essential tools for evaluating biorefinery performance and designing cost-effective and environmentally friendly supply chains. However, biorefinery operations often suffer from significant temporal and spatial uncertainties, including raw material supply and product demands. This work uses stochastic programming and multi-period planning to design a cost-efficient modular biorefinery supply chain under uncertain demand and material supply. Next, the proposed model is used to design and evaluate modular biorefinery performance in the Baltimore-Wilmington-Philadelphia region. Moreover, the optimization result illustrates the seasonal variability of biomass-based product emission due to demand/supply uncertainty, which cannot be captured by the conventional LCA uncertainty analysis.

Keywords: Biorefinery, modular production, supply chain optimization, stochastic programming, life cycle assessment

1. Introduction

The use of cheap and abundant biomass feedstocks in chemical production is established as a promising alternative to cut greenhouse gas emissions of the chemical industry [Ulonska *et al.*, 2018]. However, biomass feedstocks are often complex mixtures with a considerable amount of lignin, cellulose, and hemicellulose. Thus, the biomass conversion facilities often adopt the so-called biorefinery strategy to use a combination of different reaction units and generate multiple products from each feedstock component. A superstructure optimization framework is commonly used to select the appropriate feedstocks, operating conditions, conversion technologies, and facility locations from the numerous alternatives [You and Wang, 2011].

Nevertheless, parameters used in the biorefinery design often come with considerable uncertainties, such as availability of feedstocks, volatile prices, and experimental yields with intrinsic variations [Baral *et al.*, 2019]. Ignoring such uncertainties often leads to suboptimal or infeasible design [Li *et al.*, 2011]. On the other hand, uncertainty analysis also plays an essential role in LCA. However, most of the LCA uncertainty analyses are limited to sensitivity analysis or the semi-quantitative Pedigree method. The LCA Pedigree approach starts with rating the data reliability, completeness, temporal correlation, geometric correlation, and further technological correlation using indicator scores from 1 to 5. These scores are then transformed to uncertainty factors between 1 to

2 before being assigned as the geometric standard deviation for uncertain parameters, such as the raw material usage [Ciroth *et al.*, 2016]. Although the Pedigree method is a good indicator of data quality, encoding qualitative assessment descriptions into probability distributions inevitably suffers from subjectivity [Henriksson *et al.*, 2015]. Recently, technology choices under parameter uncertainties have been modeled in consequential LCA with optimization tools when multiple technologies exist for manufacturing the same product [Kätelhön *et al.*, 2016]. Nevertheless, this model uses the arithmetic mean of each linear programming problem's solution for LCA calculation, which is less effective than the stochastic programming with recourse actions in capturing the actual supply chain behavior and corrective actions when facing uncertainties [Sahinidis, 2004].

As a promising strategy for biomass supply chain design, modular manufacturing has demonstrated excellent cost reduction potential and extra supply chain flexibility under uncertainties of biomass feedstock availability [Allman *et al.*, 2021]. It has also been shown to benefit from the economy of numbers that reduce capital investment [Bhosekar *et al.*, 2021].

This work utilizes the two-stage stochastic programming and rolling horizon formulation to design a distributed biorefinery supply chain under demand and supply uncertainties. To enhance the process's flexibility, the expansion and movement of modular biomass conversion units are permitted after the initial installation at each production site [Allman *et al.*, 2021]. In addition to the optimal design, the proposed stochastic programming model also provides quantitative insights into the uncertainties of economic and environmental performance using only historical data, which has the potential to replace the Pedigree methods for LCA uncertainty evaluation.

2. Modular Biorefinery Supply Chain Model

2.1. Stochastic programming formulation of distributed biorefinery supply chain

The expansion and module's movement at each site are modelled by the following conservation equation (1):

$$\boldsymbol{n_{j,m,t} = n_{j,m,t-1} + z_{j,m,t} + \sum_{j' \in J'} (v_{j',j,m,t-1} - v_{j,j',m,t-1})} \tag{1}$$

where m is the module types for process units; $n_{j,m,t}$ is the number of unit m at production site j during time period t; $z_{j,m,t}$ is the newly purchased m units at time t at the same site; $v_{j,j',m,t-1}$ is the number of modules moved from site j to j' at time t-1. The material flow in and out of the process site follows the mass balance equation (2).

$$\boldsymbol{\sum_{w \in W} Q_{j,w,p,t} = \sum_{s \in S} \sum_{f \in F} conv_{f,p} \cdot Q_{s,j,f,t}} \tag{2}$$

where $Q_{s,j,f,t}$ is the flowrate of feedstock f from supplier s to site j during time t; $conv_{j,p}$ is the conversion of product p using feedstock f; $Q_{j,w,p,t}$ the flowrates of product p from site j to warehouse w. The production activity cannot exceed the total installed capacity at site j, which is shown in equation (3).

$$\boldsymbol{\sum_{s \in S} \sum_{j \in J} Q_{s,j,f,t} \le \sum_{j \in J} \sum_{m \in J} c_m \cdot n_{j,m,t}} \tag{3}$$

where c_m is the maximum capacity of unit m. The inventory balance is equation (4).

$$I_{w,p,t} = I_{w,p,t-1} + \sum_{j\in J} Q_{j,w,p,t} - \sum_{r\in R} Q_{w,r,p,t} \tag{4}$$

where $I_{w,p,t}$ is the inventory of product p at warehouse w during time t; $Q_{w,r,p,t}$ is the flowrates of products from warehouse w to market r during time period t, respectively. The objective function is the total expected costs in equation (5):

$$\zeta = \sum_{j\in J}\sum_{m\in M} q_m \cdot n_{j,m,0} + \mathbb{E}[\sum_{t\in T}\sum_{m\in M}\sum_{j\in J}(\sum_{j'\in J'} r_{j,j',m} \cdot v_{j,j',m,t} + o_m \cdot x_{j,m,t} + q_m \cdot z_{j,m,t}) + \sum_{t\in T}\sum_{f\in F}\sum_{s\in S}\sum_{j\in J} h_{j,s} \cdot Q_{s,j,f,t} + \sum_{t\in T}\sum_{p\in P}\sum_{r\in R} b_{r,p} \cdot B_{r,p,t} + \sum_{t\in T}\sum_{p\in P}\sum_{w\in W}(\sum_{j\in J} h_{j,w} \cdot Q_{j,w,p,t} + \sum_{r\in R} h_{w,r} \cdot Q_{w,r,p,t} + g_{w,p} \cdot I_{w,p,t})] \tag{5}$$

where q_m is the capital cost and o_m is the operating cost of module m; $r_{j,j',m}$ is the cost of moving unit m from site j to j'; $h_{j,s}$, $h_{j,w}$, and $h_{w,r}$ are the transportation costs of feedstocks from supply s to site j, product from site j to warehouse w and to market r; $g_{w,p}$ is the inventory holding cost of product p at warehouse w and $b_{r,p}$ is the backorder cost for product p at market r; $B_{r,p,t}$ is the unmet demand for product p at market r during time t, which is calculated by equation (6).

$$B_{r,p,t} = \delta_{r,p,t} - \sum_{w\in W} Q_{w,r,p,t} \tag{6}$$

where $\delta_{r,p,t}$ is the uncertain demand of product p at market r during t.

2.2. Life cycle assessment for each scenario of the stochastic programming

Using a cradle-to-gate LCA system boundary, carbon sequestration during plant growth, the emission of production activity, transportation, and upstream emission of backorder are included. Since multiple products are often generated in the biorefinery, the "avoided burden" approach is adopted to account for the credits of by-products by calculating the emissions of their production in standalone processes and deducting them from the initial emission [Anastasopoulou *et al.*, 2020]. The total emission of the biorefinery supply chain is given by equation (7).

$$\textbf{emission} = \sum_{t\in T}\sum_{m\in M}\sum_{j\in J}(\sum_{j'\in J'} \alpha_{j,j',m} \cdot v_{j,j',m,t} + \beta_m \cdot x_{j,m,t}) + \sum_{t\in T}\sum_{f\in F}\sum_{s\in S}\sum_{j\in J} \theta_{s,j} \cdot Q_{s,j,f,t} + \sum_{t\in T}\sum_{p\in P}\sum_{r\in R} \eta_{r,p} \cdot B_{r,p,t} + \sum_{t\in T}\sum_{p\in P}\sum_{w\in W}(\sum_{j\in J} \theta_{j,w} \cdot Q_{j,w,p,t} + \sum_{r\in R} \theta_{w,r} \cdot Q_{w,r,p,t}) - \sum_{t\in T}\sum_{p'\in P'}\sum_{r\in R} \eta_{r,p'} \cdot \delta_{r,p',t} \tag{7}$$

where $\alpha_{j,j',m}$ is the emission of moving module m from j to j'; β_m is the gate-to-gate emission of modular m occurring at production stage; $\theta_{s,j}$, $\theta_{j,w}$, $\theta_{w,r}$ are the emissions when transporting feedstocks f or product p from supplier s to site j, from site j to warehouse w, and from warehouse w to market r; $\eta_{r,p'}$ is the cradle-to-gate emission of the by-product p' bought from market r to satisfy the unmet demand.

2.3. Case study of distributed modular biorefinery operation

The aforementioned model is then applied to a case study of designing distributed biorefinery supply chain in the Baltimore-Wilmington-Philadelphia area, which covers 6 counties in Pennsylvania, 4 counties in Maryland and the New Castle County in Delaware. Figure 1 listed the structure and location of the supply chain containing 7 supply regions, 7 processing sites, 3 warehouses, and 3 market locations.

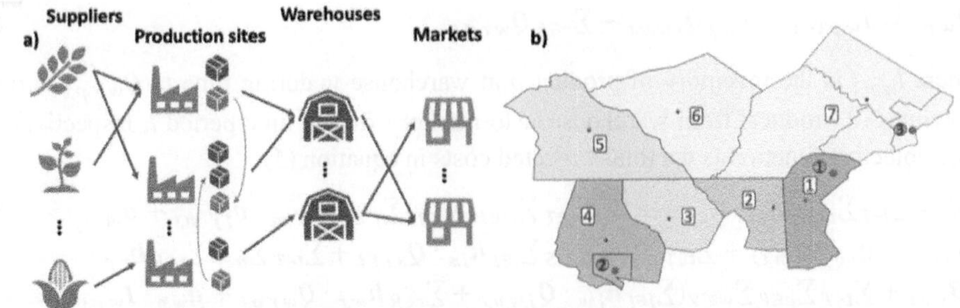

Figure 1. a) structure of modular biorefinery supply chain. b) suppliers, production sites (blue), warehouses, and markets (red) for the case study.

The supply of corn stover, poplar and willow are based on the regional biomass supply data [Langholtz *et al.*, 2016]. The temporal variation in biomass supply is also considered as corn is harvested only from August to November in these three states, while poplar and willow are more stable sources of feedstocks throughout the year. As for the biomass conversion systems, three scales of process units (1.2 kt/y, 2.4 kt/y, and 6 kt/y) for two biomass conversion technologies are available. The molten salt hydrate (MSH) units convert biomass feedstocks to furfural, 5-hydroxymethylfurfural (HMF), and lignin, while the reductive catalytic fractionation (RCF) units further utilize lignin to produce pressure-sensitive adhesives (PSA). The yields of the above technologies are extracted from the Aspen Plus simulation (Aspen Tech, Burlington, MA).

The functional unit of LCA is chosen as 1 kg of PSA supplied to the market. Then, background data of transportation and upstream emissions come from the Ecoinvent v3.3 database and literature results [Athaley *et al.*, 2019, Wernet *et al.*, 2016]. The capital and operating costs are based on the Aspen Plus simulation and technoeconomic analysis for MSH and RCF technologies [Athaley *et al.*, 2019, Bhosekar *et al.*, 2021]. The optimization model is implemented in GAMS 33.1 and cplex 12.10 solver on a computer with Intel Xeon E-2274G CPU @ 4.00GHz 32 GB RAM.

3. Results and discussion

When the weights of conversion units are high, the number of modules at each site increases monotonically over time through capacity expansion (left of Figure 2). This increase is more pronounced after September when the demand for chemicals rises and the supply of corn stover emerges. However, the movement of process unit between processing sites is not observed since the moving cost of heavy modules is relatively high s. On the other hand, when the weights of MSH units are low (right of Figure 2), they are moved around frequently, which accounts for the decrease of Cecil County's MSH units in May and October.

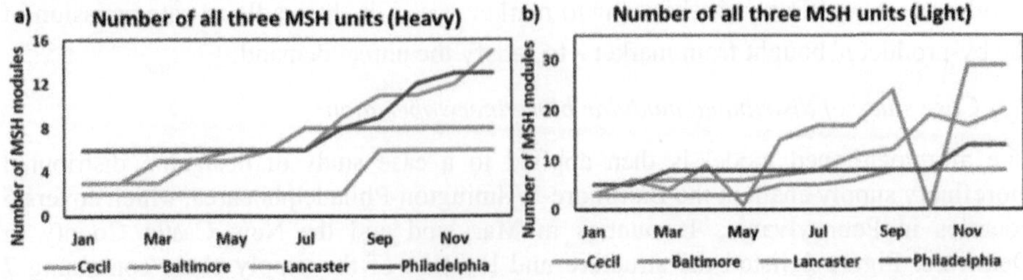

Figure 2. Number of all MSH units in four sites [a) heavy units, b) light units].

The rolling horizon approach implements the first-stage decisions (module moving, expansion, production, transportation, and inventory management) to minimize the expected supply chain cost of all generated future scenarios [Bhosekar *et al.*, 2021]. The predicted costs and GWPs of these possible scenarios in the next period (the shaded area in Figure 3) are compared to the actual cost and GWP of the implemented action (solid lines in Figure 3). The rolling horizon approach underestimated the unmet demand in the next stage, especially before September, when the supply of biomass feedstocks is tight. Thus, the actual realization of the cost and GWP of purchasing PSA from the market (solid lines in Figure 3) is higher than the center of the predicted uncertainty ranges.

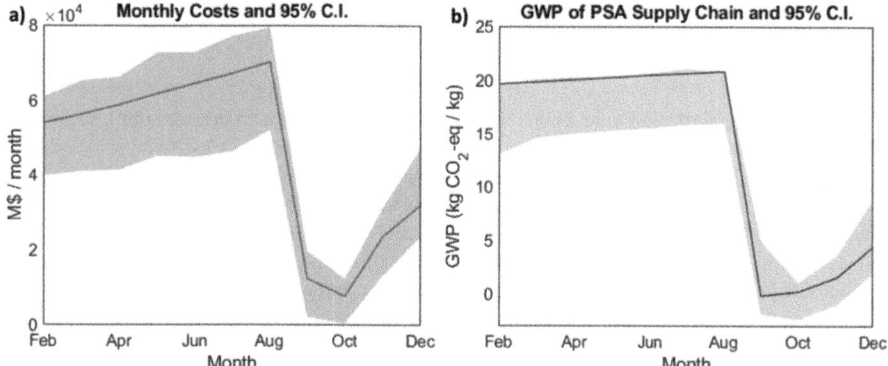

Figure 3. a) predicted 95% confidence interval of uncertain scenarios' cost (orange) and actual cost after uncertainty realization (red line); b) predicted 95% confidence interval of GWP (green) and actual GWP after uncertainty realization (black line).

In September, a large quantity of corn stover supply appears as the corn stover is harvested. More units are added and moved to the sites near the corn stover supply so that as much demand is met as possible. Since buying PSA from conventional oil-based chemical plants for the unmet demand is both expensive (backorder cost) and has high greenhouse gas emission, there is a sudden drop of costs and GWPs when most of the demand is fulfilled with increased production capacities in September. This result demonstrates the flexibility of the distributed modular biorefinery to address the uncertain and shifting supply through gradual expansion and reallocation, rather than overdesigning the capacity in the first place.

Moreover, the traditional Pedigree method applied to LCA is not capable of translating the demand and supply uncertainties into probability distributions because they only indirectly affect the material flows. Therefore, it cannot illustrate the GWP changes throughout the year due to differences in biomass supply. Nevertheless, the proposed stochastic programming method naturally chooses the appropriate supply chain decisions under each scenario, accurately reflecting GWP's response to supply and demand's seasonal variation. Consequently, the empirical distribution of bio-based PSA production emission could then be used as the uncertain input for other LCA studies.

4. Conclusions

In this work, a two-stage stochastic programming model is used to design a distributed biorefinery supply chain that produces value-added chemicals from poplar, willow, and corn stover. Historical supply data are utilized to build the multiperiod scenarios in a case study that contains 3 biomass feedstocks, 7 supply regions, and 3 markets. Next, rolling horizon approach is utilized to design the supply chain with minimal expected cost. Not only is this model able to design and evaluate the economic and environmental performance of the modular biorefinery supply chain, but also the emission in each scenario of the stochastic programming provides valuable LCA uncertainty information. The LCA uncertainty evaluated in this manner uses actual historical data and represents the rational selection of suppliers and technologies, providing the empirical foundation of uncertainty that the traditional Pedigree method is weak in [Ciroth *et al.*, 2016].

Acknowledgements: The authors are grateful for financial support from the National Science Foundation (NSF GCR CMMI 1934887) and U.S. Department of Energy's RAPID Manufacturing Institute for Process Intensification (DE-EE000788-7.6).

References

Allman, A., Lee, C., Martín, M. and Zhang, Q., (2021) Biomass waste-to-energy supply chain optimization with mobile production modules, *Comput. Chem. Eng.,* **150,** 107326

Anastasopoulou, A., Keijzer, R., Patil, B., Lang, J., van Rooij, G. and Hessel, V., (2020) Environmental impact assessment of plasma-assisted and conventional ammonia synthesis routes, *Journal of Industrial Ecology,* **24,** 1171– 1185

Athaley, A., Annam, P., Saha, B. and Ierapetritou, M., (2019) Techno-economic and life cycle analysis of different types of hydrolysis process for the production of p-Xylene, *Comput. Chem. Eng.,* **121,** 685-695

Baral, N. R., Davis, R. and Bradley, T. H., (2019) Supply and value chain analysis of mixed biomass feedstock supply system for lignocellulosic sugar production, *Biofuels, Bioprod. Bioref.,* **13,** 3, 635-659

Bhosekar, A., Athaley, A. and Ierapetritou, M., (2021) Multiobjective Modular Biorefinery Configuration under Uncertainty, *Ind. Eng. Chem. Res.,* **60,** 35, 12956-12969

Bhosekar, A., Badejo, O. and Ierapetritou, M., (2021) Modular supply chain optimization considering demand uncertainty to manage risk, *AIChE Journal,* **n/a,** n/a, e17367

Ciroth, A., Muller, S., Weidema, B. and Lesage, P., (2016) Empirically based uncertainty factors for the pedigree matrix in ecoinvent, *Int. J. Life Cycle Assess.,* **21,** 9, 1338-1348

Henriksson, P. J. G., Heijungs, R., Dao, H. M., Phan, L. T., de Snoo, G. R. and Guinée, J. B., (2015) Product Carbon Footprints and Their Uncertainties in Comparative Decision Contexts, *PLoS One,* **10,** 3, e0121221

Kätelhön, A., Bardow, A. and Suh, S., (2016) Stochastic Technology Choice Model for Consequential Life Cycle Assessment, *Environ. Sci. Technol.,* **50,** 23, 12575-12583

Langholtz, M. H., Stokes, B. J. and Eaton, L. M., (2016) 2016 Billion-ton report: Advancing domestic resources for a thriving bioeconomy, Volume 1: Economic availability of feedstock, *Oak Ridge National Laboratory, Oak Ridge, Tennessee, managed by UT-Battelle, LLC for the US Department of Energy,* **2016,** 1-411

Li, Z., Ding, R. and Floudas, C. A., (2011) A Comparative Theoretical and Computational Study on Robust Counterpart Optimization: I. Robust Linear Optimization and Robust Mixed Integer Linear Optimization, *Ind. Eng. Chem. Res.,* **50,** 18, 10567-10603

Sahinidis, N. V., (2004) Optimization under uncertainty: state-of-the-art and opportunities, *Comput. Chem. Eng.,* **28,** 6, 971-983

Ulonska, K., König, A., Klatt, M., Mitsos, A. and Viell, J., (2018) Optimization of Multiproduct Biorefinery Processes under Consideration of Biomass Supply Chain Management and Market Developments, *Ind. Eng. Chem. Res.,* **57,** 20, 6980-6991

Wernet, G., Bauer, C., Steubing, B., Reinhard, J., Moreno-Ruiz, E. and Weidema, B., (2016) The ecoinvent database version 3 (part I): overview and methodology, *Int. J. Life Cycle Assess.,* **21,** 9, 1218-1230

You, F. and Wang, B., (2011) Life Cycle Optimization of Biomass-to-Liquid Supply Chains with Distributed–Centralized Processing Networks, *Ind. Eng. Chem. Res.,* **50,** 17, 10102-10127

Proceedings of the 14th International Symposium on Process Systems Engineering – PSE 2021+
June 19–23, 2022, Kyoto, Japan
http://dx.doi.org/10.1016/B978-0-323-85159-6.50081-6

An Improved Optimization Model for Scheduling of an Industrial Formulation Plant based on Integer Linear Programming

Vassilios Yfantis[a*], Alexander Babskiy[a], Christian Klanke[b], Martin Ruskowksi[a], Sebastian Engell[b]

[a]*Chair of Machine Tools and Control Systems, Technische Universität Kaiserslautern, Gottlieb-Daimler-Str. 42, 67663 Kaiserslautern, Germany*
[b]*Process Dynamics and Operations Group, TU Dortmund University, Emil-Figge-Str. 70, 44227 Dortmund, Germany*

vassilios.yfantis@mv.uni-kl.de

Abstract

This contribution deals with the development of an integer linear programming (ILP) model and a solution strategy for a two-stage industrial formulation plant with parallel production units for crop protection chemicals. Optimal scheduling of this plant is difficult, due to the number of units and operations that must be scheduled while at the same time a high degree of coupling between the operations is present. The problem is further complicated by the presence of optional intermediate storage that leads to alternative branches in the processing sequence of the products. The presented approach is compared to previous ones, namely a mixed-integer linear programming- and a constraint programming-based one. The ILP-based approach exhibits vastly superior computational performance, while still achieving the same solution quality.

Keywords: Batch Process Scheduling, Integer Linear Programming, Decomposition

1. Introduction

The increasing competition on the global market in addition to varying customer demands necessitates an increase in the efficiency and flexibility of production processes. Batch processes offer this kind of flexibility in the case of demand-driven production. A key component to the efficiency of such batch processes is optimal scheduling, i.e., the allocation of limited resources to manufacture several products over a given time horizon. Schedules should be generated in a fast and reliable manner to adapt to varying customer demands. Furthermore, schedules should try to optimize some criterion, e.g., minimizing production time or maximizing profit. These requirements for scheduling can be addressed by optimization methods, like integer and mixed-integer programming. Optimization models can include various constraints that describe the production process while simultaneously optimizing a scheduling objective. The main bottleneck of most optimization models in production scheduling is the computation time. This issue can be handled by applying decomposition techniques, where the scheduling problem is solved in an iterative manner (Elkamel et al., 1997). A straightforward decomposition approach is the iterative scheduling of batches or orders. The realization of the decomposition then mainly depends on the

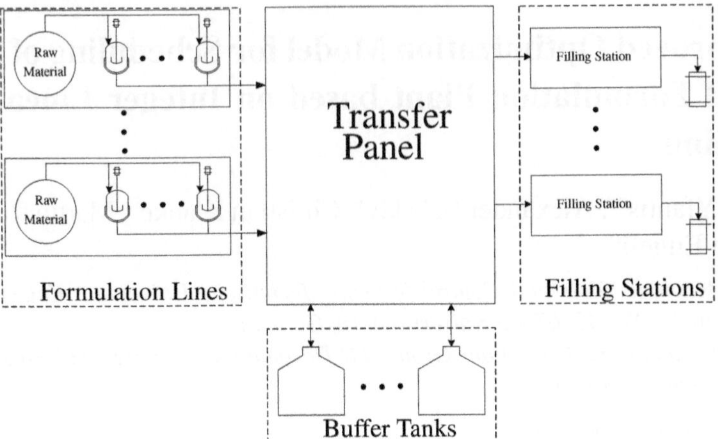

Figure 1: Schematic representation of the industrial formlation plant (Yfantis et al., 2019).

model structure, e.g., whether the model represents time through a time grid (Yfantis et al., 2019) or through precedence relations (Elekidis et al., 2019). In this contribution an efficient integer linear programming model for an industrial formulation plant is presented. A decomposition approach is employed, where orders are scheduled in an iterative fashion, while considering decisions from previous iterations. The solution approach is evaluated on an industrial-scale case study.

2. Indutrial Formulation Plant

The industrial formulation plant is schematically depicted in Figure 1. It can be divided into three parts, the formulation lines, the filling stations, and the buffer tanks. The plant operates in a sequential manner. Intermediate products are produced in the formulation lines and then filled into their final containers by the filling stations. The buffer tanks serve to decouple the two production stages. All sections of the plant are connected by a transfer panel. Each formulation line consists of a raw material pre-processing line, in which the preparation of active ingredients and solvents takes place, and several identical standardization tanks. After the pre-processing, a batch mixing operation takes place in one of the standardization tanks. The standardization tanks are always utilized to their full capacity, i.e., overproduction can occur. As a single pre-processing line feeds multiple standardization tanks, only one batch can start processing in each formulation line at each time point. Furthermore, each order can only be processed on a subset of available formulation lines. After a minimum standardization time, the intermediate product can be filled by a filling station. However, intermediate storage in the standardization tank or in an available buffer tank is also possible. The filling stations operate in a continuous manner, i.e., without an internal storage. A connected standardization or buffer tank is continuously drained by the filling station with an order and station dependent flowrate. Each filling station can only process a subset of available orders. After an operation finishes in any piece of equipment, a sequence dependent changeover time must elapse before the start of the next operation. The filling stations constitute a bottleneck of the process, as they cannot operate during the night shift, unlike the formulation lines, which operate continuously during the entire time horizon. The scheduling task consists of allocating the batches of the different orders to the standardization tanks and the subsequent filling operations to the filling stations while minimizing the total production time of the schedule. The buffer tanks can be used to decouple the two production stages, while accounting for constraints on the maximum capacity of the tanks. The case study has been investigated by Yfantis et al. (2019) and Klanke et al. (2021b). In the former work, mixed-integer linear programming (MILP) was employed together with a decomposition strategy, and a problem instance identical to the one examined in this paper was solved for a scheduling horizon of one week. In Klanke et al. (2021b) the same problem instance was solved by combining constraint programming (CP) and a moving-horizon strategy, outperforming the previous MILP formulation. Furthermore, different case studies for the same formulation plant were solved in Klanke et al. (2021a) using a heuristics-assisted genetic algorithm.

3. Solution Approach

3.1. Integer Linear Programming Model

In this section, the proposed integer linear programming model is presented. Since the model is very complex, this sections only focuses on some key constraints and variables, as well as on the objective function. The goal is to schedule the set of orders $\mathcal{I}$ on the available machines J. The machines are divided into the standardization tanks of the formulation lines $\mathcal{J}^{\text{FL}}$ and the filling stations $\mathcal{J}^{\text{FS}}$. The machines that can process order i are denoted by $\mathcal{J}_i$. The available buffer tanks are modeled by the set $\mathcal{B}$. The time horizon is discretized into equidistant time points $\mathcal{T}$. Some of the key constraints are shown in Eq. (1) - (6). The binary variable R_{ijt} indicates that a batch of order i is released from standardization tank j at time t. Eq. (1) guarantees the satisfaction of demand D_i, where cap_j is the batch size in tank j. The binary variable is set to one once the tank has been emptied. This is modeled by Eq. (2), where $E^{\text{fill}}_{ijj't}$ is a binary variable indicating the end of filling of a batch of order i from standardization tank j by filling station j' at time t and $Ref_{ijbj't}$ is a binary variable indicating a refilling of this batch into buffer tank b, in order to later be filled by filling station j'. A batch can be stored inside a standardization tank prior to its release. Intermediate storage of a batch of order i in standardization tank j at time t is indicated by the binary variable L_{ijt}. This variable is updated by Eq. (3), where E_{ijt} is a binary variable representing the end of a standardization operation, $S^{\text{fill}}_{ijj't}$ models the start of a filling operation from standardization tank j by filling station j'. When a standardization tank j is processing a batch of order i at time t the binary variable X_{ijt} is active. It is updated through the starting (S_{ijt}) and ending (E_{ijt}) binary variables in Eq. (4). Processing in the filling station is modeled by similar constraints. An important aspect of the scheduling problem is the modeling of the buffer balances. Instead of modeling stored quantities in the buffer tanks, Eq. (5) models the time intervals necessary to empty buffer tank b, containing order i by filling station j, if filling starts at time t through the integer variable I_{ibjt}. This variable is updated at every time step, using the parameter $p_{ijj'}$, which is equal to the number of time points needed to fill a batch of order i from standardization tank j' by filling station j and the binary variable Y_{ibjt}, indicating that an order i is filled from buffer b by filling station j at time t. Eq.

(6) ensures that the buffer level does not exceed its maximum capacity by considering an upper bound on the required filling time. Further constraints include the changeovers in the different machines, modeled in a similar fashion to Eq. (4), also using binary variables for their start, end, and processing. The processing times are modeled by linking the binary variables for the start and end of an operation through their time indices. The objective of the optimization problem is modeled by Eq. (7). In the first term the starting and end times of the filling operations are minimized. The remaining terms serve to minimize idle times, which occur in a makespan minimization due to multiple symmetric solutions. The second term penalizes the use of the buffer tanks. The scaling parameter w_{ij} is equal to the mean filling time of batches of order i by filling station j. The third term discourages intermediate storage in the standardization tanks if it is unnecessary.

$$\sum_{t\in\mathcal{T}}\sum_{j\in\mathcal{J}_i^{\text{FL}}} R_{ijt}\cdot cap_j \geq D_i,\ \forall i\in\mathcal{I} \tag{1}$$

$$R_{ij,t+1} = \sum_{j'\in\mathcal{J}_i^{\text{FS}}} E^{\text{fill}}_{ijj't} + \sum_{b\in\mathcal{B}}\sum_{j'\in\mathcal{J}_i^{\text{FS}}} Ref_{ijbj',t+1},\ \forall i\in\mathcal{I}, j\in\mathcal{J}_i^{\text{FL}}, t\in\mathcal{T}\backslash\{|\mathcal{T}|\} \tag{2}$$

$$L_{ij,t+1} = L_{ijt} + E_{ijt} - \sum_{j'\in\mathcal{J}_i^{\text{FS}}} S^{\text{fill}}_{ijj',t+1} - \sum_{b\in\mathcal{B}}\sum_{j'\in\mathcal{J}_i^{\text{FS}}} Ref_{ijbj',t+1},\quad \forall i\in\mathcal{I}, j\in\mathcal{J}_i^{\text{FL}}, t\in\mathcal{T}\backslash\{|\mathcal{T}|\} \tag{3}$$

$$X_{ij,t+1} = X_{ij,t} + S_{ij,t+1} - E_{ijt},\ \forall i\in\mathcal{I}, j\in\mathcal{J}_i^{\text{FL}}, t\in\mathcal{T}\backslash\{|\mathcal{T}|\} \tag{4}$$

$$I_{ibj,t+1} = I_{ibjt} + \sum_{j'\in\mathcal{J}_i^{\text{FL}}} Ref_{ij'bj,t+1}\cdot p_{ijj'} - Y_{ibjt},\ \forall i\in\mathcal{I}, b\in\mathcal{B}, j\in\mathcal{J}_i^{\text{FS}} \tag{5}$$

$$I_{ibjt} \leq cap_{ibj},\ \forall i\in\mathcal{I}, b\in\mathcal{B}, j\in\mathcal{J}_i^{\text{FS}}, t\in\mathcal{T} \tag{6}$$

$$\min\ \frac{1}{2}\cdot\sum_{i\in\mathcal{I}}\sum_{j\in\mathcal{J}_i^{\text{FL}}}\sum_{j'\in\mathcal{J}_i^{\text{FS}}}\sum_{t\in\mathcal{T}}\left(E^{\text{fill}}_{ijj't} + S^{\text{fill}}_{ijj't}\right) + \sum_{i\in\mathcal{I}}\sum_{b\in\mathcal{B}}\sum_{j\in\mathcal{J}_i^{\text{FS}}}\sum_{t\in\mathcal{T}}\frac{1}{w_{ij}}\cdot Y_{ibjt}\cdot t + \sum_{i\in\mathcal{I}}\sum_{j\in\mathcal{J}_i^{\text{FL}}}\sum_{t\in\mathcal{T}} L_{ijt} \tag{7}$$

3.2. Decomposition

Due to its size and complexity the model cannot be solved in a monolithic fashion. To generate feasible schedules in a time efficient manner an order decomposition approach, similar to Yfantis et al. (2019), is employed. The orders are scheduled iteratively while preventing overlaps through constraints. These infeasible allocations can easily be identified since each machine possesses an active binary variable at each time point where an operation is being performed, instead of just using a single binary variable for the start of an operation. The night shifts of the filling stations are modeled in a similar way. In contrast to the approaches in Yfantis et al. (2019) and Klanke et al. (2021b) no batch decomposition is needed, as the model can schedule orders that consist of a large number of

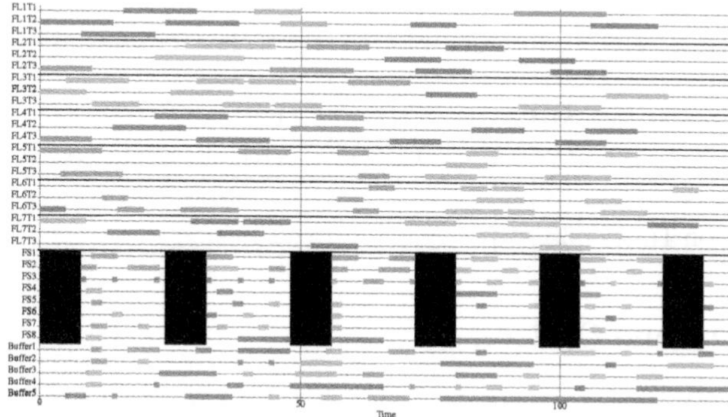

Figure 2: Gantt chart of the schedule generated with the proposed ILP-based approach.

batches efficiently. Furthermore, no two-step optimization approach is necessary, as the operations are already shifted to the left through the chosen objective function. Lastly, the time horizon is shifted to the end of the next day from the current makespan. If the subproblem is infeasible the time horizon is shifted by an additional day until a solution is found.

4. Results

The presented ILP-based solution approach was evaluated on the case study presented in Yfantis et al. (2019) and Klanke et al. (2021b). The setup consists of 7 formulation lines, each containing 3 standardization tanks, 8 filling stations and 5 buffer tanks. In total, 20 orders of different quantities, resulting in 78 batches are scheduled. A time horizon of one week, divided into 1-hour intervals, is considered. The solution approach was implemented in the programming language Julia (Bezanson et al., 2017). The ILP was solved using Gurobi on a Desktop PC (AMD Ryzen 5 3600 6-Core Processor @3.6 GHz). The subproblems were all solved to a 0 % optimality gap. The generated Gantt chart is depicted in Figure 2. It represents the batches on each standardization tank of the formulation lines, separated by the black solid lines, the filling stations, and the buffer tanks. Furthermore, the night shifts of the filling stations are illustrated as black regions. A makespan of 133 h is obtained, which is equal to the results obtained by the previous solution approaches. However, the benefit of the proposed ILP-based approach can be seen in the required computation time (cf. Table 1). The superior performance of the ILP model is further underlined by the fact, that no batch-based decomposition is needed. Instead, only an order decomposition is performed, so that a single subproblem can require scheduling a large number of batches, which would render it intractable for the previous approaches. The computation time is further enhanced by the lack of a two-step optimization approach, due to the chosen objective function, which results in fewer idle times than a makespan minimization. The superior performance can be attributed to the multiple active binary variables for a given schedule. In the MILP-based approach of Yfantis et al. (2019) binary variables only indicate the start of an operation, resulting in far less active binary variables. The tightly constrained active binary variables of the ILP aid the search procedure of the solver.

Table 1: Comparison between different solution approaches for scheduling of the industrial formulation plant.

Model	MILP (Yfantis et al., 2019)	CP (Klanke et al., 2021b)	ILP
Makespan	133 h	133 h	133 h
Computation Time	38 min	23 min	51 s

5. Conclusion and Outlook

This work presented a novel ILP-based formulation for the scheduling of an industrial formulation plant. In contrast to previous approaches, the model only employs integer variables, which greatly enhances its computational performance. Instead of minimizing the makespan, an objective function that discourages idle times is formulated, eliminating the need for a two-step optimization approach. The structure of the model enables a monolithic optimization without running into memory limitation issues. However, then the solution times are prohibitive for a real application. Nevertheless, in future work a monolithic optimization can be performed on specialized hardware to provide a reference for the decomposition approaches and other solution methods.

Acknowledgements

This work was partially funded by the European Regional Development Fund (ERDF) in the context of the project OptiProd.NRW (https://www.optiprod.nrw/en).

References

J. Bezanson, A. Edelman, S. Karpinski, V. B. Shah, 2017. Julia: A fresh approach to numerical computing. SIAM Review 59 (1), pp. 65–98.

A.P. Elekidis, F. Corominas, M.C. Georgiadis, 2019. Production Scheduling of Consumer Goods Industries. Industrial & Engineering Chemistry Research 58, pp. 23261-23275.

A. Elkamel, M. Zentner, J.F. Pekny, G.V. Reklaitis, 1997. A Decomposition Heuristic for Scheduling the General Batch Chemical Plant. Engineering Optimization 28 (4), pp. 299-330.

C. Klanke, D. Bleidorn, C. Koslowski, C. Sonntag, S. Engell, 2021a. Simulation-based scheduling of a large-scale industrial formulation plant using a heuristics-assisted genetic algorithm. GECCO '21: Proceedings of the Genetic and Evolutionary Computation Conference Companion, pp. 1587–1595.

C. Klanke, D. Bleidorn, V. Yfantis, S. Engell, 2021b. Combining Constraint Programming and Temporal Decomposition Approaches - Scheduling of an Industrial Formulation Plant. Lecture Notes in Computer Science, Vol. 12735, pp. 133-148.

V. Yfantis, T. Siwczyk, M. Lampe, N. Kloye, M. Remelhe, S. Engell, 2019. Iterative Medium-Term Production Scheduling of an Industrial Formulation Plant. In: Computer Aided Chemical Engineering, Vol. 46, pp. 19–24.

Proceedings of the 14th International Symposium on Process Systems Engineering – PSE 2021+
June 19-23, 2022, Kyoto, Japan
http://dx.doi.org/10.1016/B978-0-323-85159-6.50082-8

Optimal Sourcing, Supply and Development of Carbon Dioxide Networks for Enhanced Oil Recovery in CCUS Systems

Demian J. Presser[a,b], Vanina G. Cafaro[a,b], Diego C. Cafaro[a,b,*]

[a]*INTEC (UNL-CONICET), Guemes 3450, 3000 Santa Fe, Argentina*
[b]*Fac. de Ing. Química (UNL), Santiago del Estero 2829, 3000 Santa Fe, Argentina*
dcafaro@fiq.unl.edu.ar

Abstract

Carbon capture, utilization and storage (CCUS) is one of the most promising technologies for mitigating anthropogenic CO_2 emissions. The deployment of CUUS typically requires heavy capital investments that need to be offset by the benefits of carbon utilization. Carbon dioxide enhanced oil recovery (EOR-CO_2) consists on injecting large quantities of CO_2 into mature oil reservoirs to boost hydrocarbon recovery. It is one of the most effective ways to bring economic viability to CCUS projects, also providing the means for the geological sequestration of CO_2. The planning of CCUS coupled to EOR comprises interrelated decisions aiming to maximize oil production and CO_2 sequestration. In this work, we propose a novel optimization approach to allocate CO_2 from capture sources to oil fields according to their potential, and determine how these reservoirs should be developed over time. To this end, we seek for the optimal design of pipeline networks, as well as the injection plan in each reservoir according to the CO_2 availability. The results show that the coordinated operation of EOR-CO_2 in several oil reservoirs is crucial to the success of a CCUS project. An illustrative case study of 3 reservoirs and 2 sources (power plants) is presented. The production strategy yields up to 40% reduction in carbon emissions from the power plants and a positive net present value of 74 million USD in five years.

Keywords: EOR, Supply Chain, Carbon Dioxide, Optimization, CCUS, MINLP

1. Introduction

Greenhouse gas emissions (GHG) are expected to have their second largest increase in history due to global economies recovering from the COVID pandemic (IEA, 2021). Reducing CO_2 emissions is an indispensable requirement to achieve the goals of the Paris Agreement (2015), and carbon capture, utilization and storage (CCUS) systems are the most promising option to meet the targets. CCUS refers to the set of techniques to capture large amounts of CO_2 emissions from flue gas of fossil power plants and industrial processes, to subsequently transport CO_2 to utilization points, and finally guarantee its permanent sequestering. Although CCUS systems have been recognized for decades as one of the most promising technologies in the pursuit of net-zero emissions, progress has been relatively slow due to economic drawbacks (Nuñez and Moskal, 2019). Carbon dioxide enhanced oil recovery (EOR-CO_2) is a production technique consisting on injecting large quantities of CO_2 into mature oil reservoirs to extend their economic lifespan. CO_2 facilitates the displacement of the residual oil that remains trapped after primary and secondary production by reducing interfacial and surface tension, swelling oil, decreasing viscosity and improving mobility ratio (Lake, 1989). Moreover, EOR-CO_2 provides an efficient path for permanently sequestering massive amounts of GHG. Numerous studies conclude on the capability of EOR- CO_2 to achieve net zero (and even negative) emissions (Cuéllar and Azapagic, 2015).

So far, EOR-CO_2 has allowed large-scale, economic deployment of CCUS (Mavar et al., 2021). Nevertheless, proper planning of CCUS-EOR projects is required to address the allocation of CO_2 over time, the design of CO_2 pipeline networks, and the balance between maximizing oil recovery and GHG sequestration. Several contributions related to CCUS design and EOR planning have been published in recent years, although none of them tackle both problems in an integrated manner (Tapia, 2018). Turk et al. (1987) present one of the first formulations for the optimal allocation of CO_2, assuming a fixed economic value for its use. Middleton and Bielicki (2009) propose a mixed integer linear model (MILP) for the design of CO_2 capture and sequestration networks, setting a target value for the amount of CO_2 to store. Tan et al. (2013) present a multiperiod MILP to find the best matches between sources and sinks, accounting for injection rates and time windows. Tapia et al. (2016) solve the optimal allocation of CO_2 between a power plant and multiple reservoirs by means of a general scheduling framework. A fixed decreasing production yield is assumed, with no more details on the reservoir depletion behavior. On the other hand, forecasting production is a key feature for the development of optimization models. Capacitance Resistance Models (CRM) predict the fraction of the flow injected into a well that is conveyed to another well, from historical data (Yousef et al., 2005). Coupling CRM and fractional flow models allows high-level optimization of the reservoir development and preliminary assessment of the field production. Eshraghi et al. (2016) propose different heuristic approaches to establish the best injection strategy for a set of wells in a reservoir. Tao and Bryant (2015) take advantage of CRM to optimize CO_2 sequestering in an aquifer accounting for different injection rates. In 2021, Presser et al. combine CRM and a fractional flow approach to optimize polymer flooding production strategies in mature oil fields.

In this work, we propose the first mathematical programming approach to optimally plan the design and development of CCUS-EOR projects in an integrated fashion. Decisions addressed by the model include the allocation of CO_2 from sources to EOR reservoirs, pipeline network design and oil field development strategies. An illustrative case study is presented to show the potential of the tool and draw conclusions.

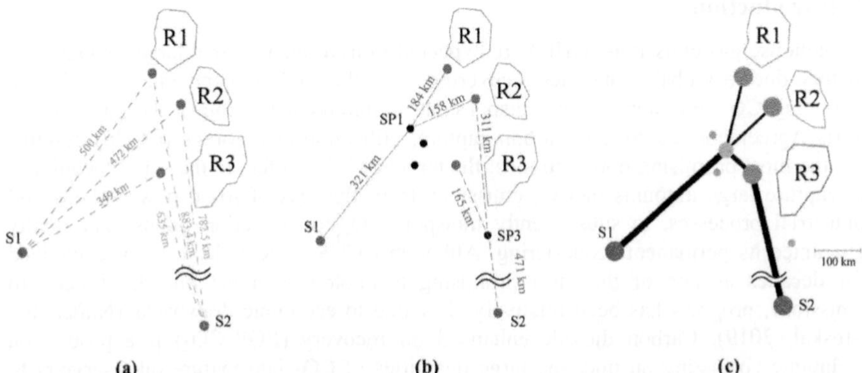

Figure 1 – (a) Layout and distances between sources S and reservoirs R. (b) Distances between nodes and intermediate points SP. (c) Best configuration found.

2. Problem Statement

The problem addressed in this work can be stated as follows: Given *n* CO_2 sources (e.g., power plants) venting flue gas at a certain rate, *m* depleted reservoirs to be developed through CO_2-EOR, potential locations for CO_2 pipelines (see Figure 1), reservoirs characterization in terms of selectable wells to be operated, forecasted decline curves and connectivities between the wells; we aim to optimally determine: (a) the allocation of CO_2 flows between sources and reservoirs, (b) the pipeline network design, (c) the wells to be operated as injectors and producers in each field, (d) the timing for operating each of these wells, and (e) the CO_2 injection rates in order to maximize the net present value of the CCUS-EOR project. The objective function accounts for the benefits from crude oil sales, as well as from CO_2 sequestration.

3. Mathematical Formulation

The formulation integrates two well-known reservoir prediction models: CRM and Gentil fractional flow (GFF) (Gentil, 2005). CRM allows for the characterization of the reservoir by assigning connectivities and time constants to every pair of wells based on history matching, while GFF assesses the production decline for each producer with respect to the cumulative injection of CO_2 reaching its drainage volume through a semi-empirical power-law function. We assume that connectivities and time constants have been inferred from secondary production, and the decline curve for each producing well is also known. The mathematical formulation is based on the set $t \in T$ representing time periods (typically semesters or years). Let $s \in S$ stand for CO_2 sources (e.g., power plants) with a known maximum supply rate $co2r_{s,t}$ (Mt/y), and $r \in R$ be reservoirs for EOR-CO_2 exploitation. Elements $p \in P$ represent pipes of different diameters and flow capacities, and $sp \in SP$ stand for intermediate points between *s* and *r* where pipelines can be joined or branched. Finally, $sc \in SC$ account for production schemes, comprising subsets of active injection wells *i* and producers *j* in reservoir *r*.
Eqs. (1) to (4) calculate the volume of CO_2 received by well *j* from the injection in well *i*, according to the selected production scheme and connectivities. Parameter $fs_{i,j,sc}$ stands for the connectivity between *i* and *j* under production scheme *sc*. The 0-1 variable $xsc_{r,sc,t}$ equals 1 if *sc* is the scheme selected for time *t* in reservoir *r* (0 otherwise).

$$QRE_{i,j,t} = \sum_{sc \in SC_{i,j}} QINJ'_{i,t,sc}\, fs_{i,j,sc} \quad \forall r, i \in I_r, j \in J_r, t \tag{1}$$

$$QINJ'_{i,t,sc} \leq \sum_s co2r_{s,t}\ \ xsc_{r,sc,t} \quad \forall r, sc, i \in I_r \cap I_{sc}, t \tag{2}$$

$$\sum_{sc \in SC_i} QINJ'_{i,t,sc} = QINJ_{i,t} \quad \forall r, i \in I_r, t \tag{3}$$

$$\sum_{sc \in SC} xsc_{r,sc,t} \leq 1 \quad \forall r, t \tag{4}$$

For simplicity, if under the production scheme *sc* a producing well is inactive, flows are proportionally redistributed among the remaining wells, as in Eq. (5). Connectivity factors are defined in advance and can be adjusted following any other criterion.

$$fs_{i,j,sc} = f_{i,j} / \sum_{j \in J_{sc}} f_{i,j} \quad \forall r, i \in I_r, j \in J_r \tag{5}$$

According to DFF, the productivity of each producing well decreases as a function of the cumulative volume of CO_2 received in its drainage volume, as modelled by Eqs. (6) and (7). $CGIA_{i,t}$ is a continuous variable accounting for the cumulative amount of CO_2 that has reached the drainage volume of *j* up to time *t*, $F^o_{j,t}$ stands for the fraction of oil in the production flow, and $Q^o_{j,t}$ is the oil production rate from *j* during time step *t*.

$$QTR_{j,t} = \sum_{i \in I_r} QRE_{i,j,t} \ ; \qquad CGIA_{j,t} \geq CGIA_{j,t-1} + QTR_{j,t} \qquad \forall r, j \in J_r, t \qquad (6)$$

$$F^o_{j,t} \leq \frac{1}{1+\alpha_j \ CGIA_{j,t}{}^{\beta_j}} \ ; \qquad Q^o_{j,t} \leq F^o_{j,t} \ QTR_{j,t} \qquad \forall r, j \in J_r, t \qquad (7)$$

Eq. (8) identifies the conversion of well i from production to injection mode at time t through the binary $ycv_{i,t}$. Note that the values of $xpr_{i,t}$ and $xinj_{i,t}$ can be directly calculated from $xsc_{r,sc,t}$ (the selected production scheme).

$$ycv_{i,t} \geq xinj_{i,t} - xpr_{i,t-1} \qquad \forall r, i \in I_r, t \qquad (8)$$

The supply of CO_2 to active reservoirs depends on injection decisions. Eq. (9) shows how CO_2 demand can be met from the selected sources ($PCO2_{r,t}$) or from recycling ($RCO2_{r,t}$), as in Eq. (10). In these volume balances, rec_r computes the proportion of the non-oil production stream that can be reconditioned and reinjected.

$$\sum_{i \in I_r} QINJ_{i,t} \leq PCO2_{r,t} + RCO2_{r,t} \qquad \forall r, t \qquad (9)$$

$$RCO2_{r,t} \leq rec_r \left(\sum_{j \in J_r} QTR_{j,t} - Q^o_{j,t} \right) \qquad \forall r, t \qquad (10)$$

Connecting sources with reservoirs through pipelines is a model decision, allowing for the allocation of CO_2 flows. The reservoirs can be fed directly from the sources or through intermediate nodes, as in Eq. (11). Eqs. (12) to (14) stand for the selection of pipeline diameters/capacities (psl_p) for the links *s-r*, *sp-r* and *s-sp*, respectively. Finally, Eq. (15) imposes the volume balance at the intermediate nodes.

$$PCO2_{r,t} = \sum_{s \in S_r} DCO2_{s,r,t} + \sum_{sp \in SP_r} ICO2_{sp,r,t} \qquad \forall r, t \qquad (11)$$

$$DCO2_{s,r,t} \leq \sum_{p \in P} psl_p \ ysr_{s,r,p} \qquad \forall s, r, t \qquad (12)$$

$$ICO2_{sp,r,t} \leq \sum_{p \in P} psl_p \ yspr_{sp,r,p} \qquad \forall sp, r, t \qquad (13)$$

$$FCO2_{s,sp,t} \leq \sum_{p \in P} psl_p \ yssp_{s,sp,p} \qquad \forall s, sp, t \qquad (14)$$

$$\sum_{r \in R} ICO2_{sp,r,t} = \sum_{s \in S} FCO2_{s,sp,t} \qquad \forall sp, t \qquad (15)$$

Where $ysr_{s,r,p}$, $yspr_{sp,r,p}$ and $yssp_{s,sp,p}$ are 0-1 variables. On the other hand, Eq. (16) estimates the amount of CO_2 produced in the sources that is not used for EOR, and therefore is economically penalized in the objective function.

$$\sum_r DCO2_{s,r,t} + \sum_{sp} FCO2_{s,sp,t} + CO2V_{s,t} = co2r_{s,t} \qquad \forall s, t \qquad (16)$$

The objective of this mixed integer nonlinear programming (MINLP) model seeks to maximize the net present value (Eq. 17), where r is the discount rate. Incomes (INC_t) are determined by the oil prices times the predicted production over t, adding credits for CO_2 sequestering. In turn, capital investments ($CAPEX_t$) comprise drilling and completion costs for new wells, conversion and shut-in charges. We also include a fixed term ($SCAPEX$) for pipeline and EOR facilities construction at the initial time. Operating expenditures ($OPEX_t$) involve injection and production costs for active wells, CO_2 acquisition, pumping, conditioning and recycling, and produced flows carrying and processing charges. Finally, we add a penalty cost term for not using CO_2 from sources ($SPEX_t$). Note that by Eqs. (6) and (7), the MINLP yields a nonconvex relaxation.

$$\text{Max}\, z = \sum_t (1+r)^{t-1} (INC_t - CAPEX_t - OPEX_t - SPEX_t) - SCAPEX \qquad (17)$$

4. Results

An illustrative case study is proposed to show the capabilities of the model. Two sources, three reservoirs and four potential split points are addressed, as shown in Figure 1. For clarity, only some distances are presented although all other connections are also possible. The arrangement of wells in each reservoir and their connectivities are displayed in Figure 2. Each of the potential producing wells has a pair of parameters α_j and β_j defining how fast oil productivity declines. Regarding CO_2 sourcing and network design, three pipeline sections are assessed, with transportation capacities ranging from 2 to 8 kt/day. The time horizon is discretized into 10 semesters. Oil price is assumed to increase over time and CO_2 acquisition costs are expected to decrease due to scalability and expertise in the capture and conditioning process. CO_2 recycling rates are set to 50%, 60% and 45% for reservoir 1, 2 and 3, respectively.

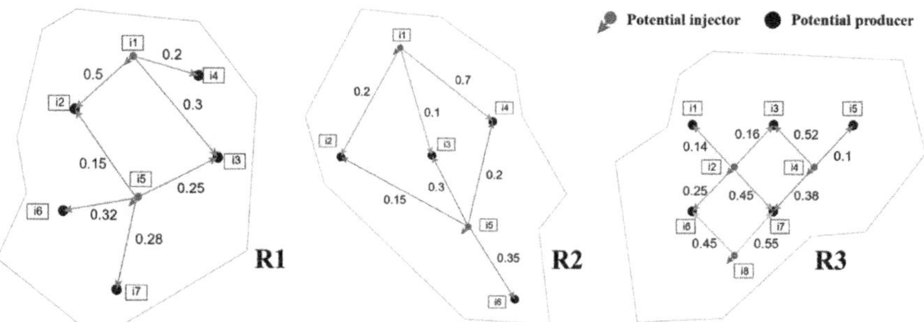

Figure 2 – Arrangement of wells in each reservoir and connectivity coefficients.

The nonconvex MINLP model is implemented in GAMS and solved through DICOPT, using CONOPT4 and CPLEX for NLP and MIP subproblems respectively. The model comprises 4,561 eqs, 1,417 0-1 vars and 2,231 cont. vars. The algorithm reaches a solution amounting to 74 MMUSD as NPV in 25 minutes of CPU. Given that DICOPT does not guarantee the global optimality, a tailored MILP relaxation is proposed to estimate the optimality gap. This relaxation yields results 10% higher than the solution obtained with DICOPT. The results of the source allocation and supply chain design are shown at the right of Figure 1. The best-found configuration suggests that S1 must supply the three reservoirs simultaneously through the splitting point SP2, while S2 should only feed R3 through a mainline of capacity *pl3*. Another mainline of capacity *pl3* connects S1 with SP2, while two pipes *pl1* connect SP2 with R1 and R2, and a pipe of capacity *pl2* feeds R3. In addition, the development strategies for injectors and producers for each of the reservoirs are presented in Figure 3. This figure shows that the most promising production schemes are exploited earlier, requiring less CO_2 for high production, while the wells with high potential but low initial connectivity (e.g., I3 in R2) are isolated to increase flow to them over the end of the horizon. Other schemes with good potential but higher CO_2 requirements are also tapped in later periods.

5. Conclusions

A novel MINLP formulation has been developed for the integration of CO_2 supply and EOR production planning decisions for the optimization of CCUS-EOR initiatives. Results suggest that the coordinated planning of several reservoirs is critical for the economic viability of these projects. The simultaneous optimization of production strategies may allow exploiting the most promising regions of each reservoir with no need to delay the start of EOR projects by restricting themselves to the need for rigid supplies. The model also facilitates the evaluation of large-scale CCUS systems involving multiple sources and sinks in a generalized framework, providing further guidance on the environmental impacts of the initiatives. Results for an illustrative case show an economic benefit of 74 MMUSD, using and finally sequestering 40% of CO_2 emissions from the sources (43 Mt of CO_2 over 5 years). Finally, accounting for the possibility of delaying investments in processing facilities in future works may bring further economic benefits to the strategies. In addition, addressing uncertainties of oil and CO_2 prices and the productive behaviour of the wells is another possible extension.

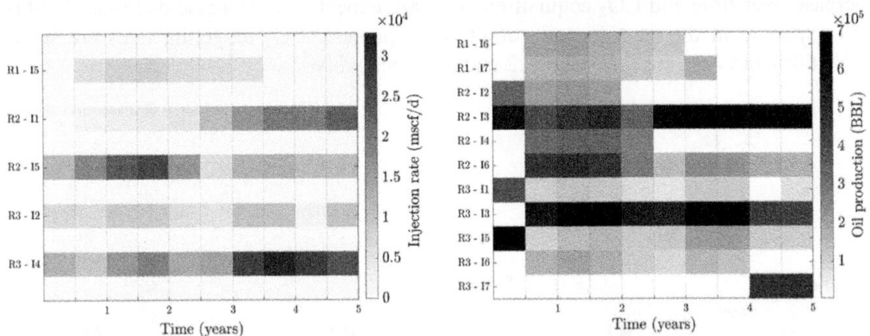

Figure 3 – Injection rate strategy and expected production in the best solution found.

6. References

R. M. Cuéllar-Franca, A. Azapagic, 2015, Carbon capture, storage and utilisation technologies: A critical analysis and comparison of their life cycle envir. impacts, J. of CO_2 Util., 9, 82–102.

S. E. Eshraghi, M. Rasaei, S. Zendehboudi, 2016, Opt. of mis. CO_2 EOR and strg. using heur. meth. comb. w. cap/res and Gentil fract. flow models, J. of Nat, Gas Sci & Eng, 32, 304–318.

P. H. Gentil, 2005, The Use of Multilinear Regression Models in Patterned Waterfloods: Physical Meaning of the Regression Coefficients, MSc thesis, University of Texas, Austin, TX, US.

L. W. Lake, 1989, Enhanced Oil Recovery, Prentice Hall: Englewood Cliffs, NJ, US.

R. S. Middleton, J. M. Bielicki, 2009, A compr. carbon capt. and strg. infrast. model, Energy Proc., 1(1), 1611–1616.

K. Novak Mavar, N. Gaurina-Međimurec, L. Hrnčević, 2021, Significance of Enhanced Oil Recovery in Carbon Dioxide Emission Reduction. Sust., 13(4), 1800.

V. Núñez-López, E. Moskal, 2019, Pot. of CO_2-EOR for Near-Term Decarb., Front. Clim., https://doi.org/10.3389/fclim.2019.00005.

D. J. Presser, V. G. Cafaro, D. C. Cafaro, 2021, Optimal Prod. Strategies for the Development of Mature Oil Fields through Polymer Flooding, Ind. & Eng. Chem. Res., 60(28), 10235–10253.

R. R. Tan, K. B. Aviso, S. Bandyopadhyay, D. K. Ng, 2013, Opt. sour.-sink match. in carb. capt. and strg. sys. with time, inj. rate, and cap. const., Envir. Prog. & Sust. Energy, 32(2), 411–416.

Q. Tao, S. L. Bryant, 2015, Optimizing Carbon Sequestration With the Capacitance/Resistance Model, SPE Journal, 20(05), 1094–1102.

J. F. D. Tapia, J. Y. Lee, R. E. Ooi, D. C. Foo, R. R. Tan, 2016, Optimal CO_2 allocation and scheduling in enhanced oil recovery (EOR) operations. Applied Energy, 184, 337–345.

J. F. D. Tapia, J. Y. Lee, R. E. Ooi, D. C. Foo, R. R. Tan, 2018, A rev. of opt. and dec.-making models for the plan. of CO2 capt., util. and strg. (CCUS) sys., Sust. Prod. and Cons., 13, 1–15.

G. A.Turk, T. B. Cobb, D. J. Jankowski, A. M. Wolsky, F. T. Sparrow, 1987, CO_2 Transport: A new application of the assignment problem, Energy, 12(2), 123-130.

A. A. Yousef, P. H. Gentil, J. L. Jensen, L. W. Lake, 2005, A Capacit. Model To Infer Interwell Connect. From Prod. and Inj. Rate Fluct., SPE Annual Tec. Conf. and Exhib., Dallas, TX, US.

Proceedings of the 14th International Symposium on Process Systems Engineering – PSE 2021+
June 19-23, 2022, Kyoto, Japan
http://dx.doi.org/10.1016/B978-0-323-85159-6.50083-X

Production scheduling in multiproduct multistage semicontinuous processes. A constraint programming approach

Lautaro D. Marcolini[a], Franco M. Novara[a], Gabriela P. Henning[a,b,*].

[a] Facultad de Ingeniería Química, Universidad Nacional del Litoral, Santa Fe 3000, Argentina
[b] INTEC (Universidad Nacional del Litoral, CONICET), Santa Fe 3000, Argentina

[*]*Corresponding Author's E-mail: ghenning@intec.unl.edu.ar*

Abstract

An expressive constraint programming (CP) formulation has been proposed to address the scheduling problem of a make-and-pack process. The resulting CP model is able to consider the typical processing stages of food industries in an integrated fashion, while capturing many features found in the industrial practice. The proposed CP formulation has been extensively tested and compared with other existing approaches. The results have shown that the model can efficiently solve medium and large-scale problem instances with multiple constraining features. The examples that have been solved show that the proposed formulation is computationally efficient

Keywords: Production scheduling; Constraint programming; Multiproduct Multistage Semicontinuous Processes; Make-and-Pack; Food industry.

1. Introduction

The production scheduling of multiproduct multistage semicontinuous facilities is addressed in this contribution. Many food production processes have three main stages: (i) processing of raw materials into intermediate products, (ii) storage of these intermediate products, which may require an additional operation (e.g., fermentation, aging), and (iii) packing of the final products. In consequence, in such processing facilities, batch and continuous operations interplay in the manufacturing route, leading to a semicontinuous production mode. In particular, the short term scheduling problem of a real-world multistage food process previously studied by other authors (Kopanos et al., 2011; 2012) is considered in this work. The process being tackled is derived from a real-world ice-cream production facility, which was originally introduced by Bongers and Bakker (2006). In many food processing plants, scheduling just focuses on the packing units for which an efficient schedule is sought. Once such agenda is obtained, it is propagated upstream to the other processing stages. However, such approach is only appropriate when there is a unique bottleneck in the process and it is associated to the packing stage units, independently of the product mix. Unfortunately, this assumption is not always valid. Therefore, it is necessary to address the scheduling problem of all the processing stages in an integrated fashion, leading to a defying problem, whose combinatorial complexity increases significantly with the number of products and their demands (higher number of batches), as well as the consideration of changeover times.

2. Methodology

Constraint Programming (CP) techniques have been successfully applied to scheduling problems by the Process Systems Engineering (PSE) community. Most approaches have been devoted to the scheduling of multiproduct multistage batch plants (Novara et al., 2016), leaving aside semicontinuous processes. An expressive constraint programming formulation has been proposed to address the challenging problem described in the previous paragraphs. The resulting CP model is able to consider the typical processing stages of food industries in an integrated fashion, while capturing many features found in the industrial practice. The proposal is based on the ILOG-IBM OPL language and the CP Optimizer, which are embedded within the CPLEX Optimization Studio (IBM ILOG, 2013).

3. CP model

Sets/Indexes. *B/b:* batches to be produced. *Bp/-:* batches of products *p*. C_p/*c:* possible campaigns of product *p*. *P/p:* products to be manufactured. *S/s:* processing stages. *Sa/-:* subset of aging/storage stages. *Sp/-:* subset of production stages. *U/u:* equipment units. U_s/*us:* set of units belonging to stage *s*, *s* = *Card(S)*

Parameters. $changeOverTime_{u,p,p'}$: changeover time between products *p* and *p'* in unit *u*. $maxAgingT_p$: maximum aging time for product *p*. *cleaningTime:* final cleaning time. $pt_{p,u}$: processing time required by a batch of product *p* in unit *u*.

Variables. $campaign_{p,us,c}$: interval variable that spans over all the processing tasks that belong to a campaign *c* of product *p* carried out in unit *us* that belongs to the packing stage. $campaignSeq_{us}$: sequence variable defined for each unit *us* belonging to packing stage. It represents an ordering of campaign interval variables associated with *u*. Each interval variable in this sequence is characterized by a type that is equal to the campaign product. $stTask_{b,s}$: interval variable that represents the processing of batch *b* at stage *s*. $task_{b,u}$: interval variable representing the execution of batch *b* in unit *u*. $taskSeq_u$: sequence variable capturing the ordering of the $task_{b,u}$ activities that take place in unit *u*.

Constraints. Constraint (1) prescribes that each batch must be assigned to just one processing unit at each stage; i.e. just one instance of $task_{b,u}$ will be part of the schedule and its interval will be the same of $stTask_{b,s}$. Constraint (2) works in s similar way regarding the tasks of the last stage, which are executed under a campaign mode.

$$Alternative\left(stTask_{b,s}, all(u \in Us)\ task_{b,u}\right), \quad \forall b \in B, \forall s \in S \tag{1}$$

$$Alternative\left(stTask_{b,s}, all\left(u \in Us, c \in C_p\right) task_{b,u,c}\right), \quad \forall b \in B, s = card(S) \tag{2}$$

Constraints (3) and (4) establish appropriate timing relationships between the first two adjacent tasks associated with any batch *b*. They synchronize the start of the first manufacturing stage, which is a continuous one, with the beginning of the second stage, which is a batch aging and storage activity.

$$startAtStart\left(task_{b,u}, task_{b,u'}\right), \quad \forall b \in B, \forall u \in U_S, \forall u' \in U_{S'}, s \in Sp, s' \in Sa, s' = s + 1 \tag{3}$$

$$startAtStart(stTask_{b,s}, stTask_{b,s'}), \forall b \in B, \forall s \in Sp, s' \in Sa, s' = s + 1 \quad (4)$$

Similarly, constraints (5) and (6) synchronize the finishing of the storage/aging activity and the packing one, prescribing that both must end at the same time, i.e. when the packaging task has already consumed all the material.

$$endAtEnd(task_{b,u}, task_{b,u',c}), \forall b \in B, \forall u \in U_S, \forall u' \in U_{S'}, \forall s \in Sa, \\ c \in C_p, s' = card(S) \quad (5)$$

$$endAtEnd(stTask_{b,s}, stTask_{b,s'}), \forall b \in B, \forall s \in Sa, s' = card(S) \quad (6)$$

Constraint (7) prescribes that the duration of each processing task depends on the unit assigned to it.

$$sizeOf(task_{b,u}) = pt_{p,u} \cdot presenceOf(task_{b,u}), \\ \forall p \in P, \forall b \in B_P, \forall u \in U_S, \forall s \in Sp \quad (7)$$

For storage/aging tasks, limits on their duration must be imposed. A batch should remain in aging vessels a minimum processing/aging time, captured by Expression (8), and no longer than its corresponding shelf-life, which is represented by constraint (9).

$$sizeOf(task_{b,u}) \geq pt_{p,u} \cdot presenceOf(task_{b,u}), \\ \forall p \in P, \forall b \in B_P, \forall u \in U_S, \forall s \in Sa \quad (8)$$

$$sizeOf(task_{b,u}) \leq maxAgingT_p \cdot presenceOf(task_{b,u}), \\ \forall p \in P, \forall b \in B_P, \forall u \in U_S, \forall s \in Sa \quad (9)$$

Constraints (10) to (13) capture the campaign operation mode of the last stage, where any packing activity $task_{b,us,c}$ must be part of a campaign. The variable $campaign_{p,us,c}$ represents a campaign *c* associated with product *p* in unit *us* belonging to the packing stage. By resorting to the *span* CP construct, expression (10) ensures that each packing task associated with a campaign of a certain product *p* takes place within the spanning interval of such campaign.

$$span(campaign_{p,us,c}, all(b \in B_P)\ task_{b,us,c}), \\ \forall p \in P, \forall c \in C_p, \forall us \in U_s, s = Card(S) \quad (10)$$

Expression (11) enforces all the campaign variables associated with a given unit not to overlap with each other.

$$noOverlap(campaignSeq_{us}), \qquad \forall us \in Us, s = Card(S) \quad (11)$$

In addition, constraint (12) prescribes that if the interval variable $task_{b,us,c}$ representing the packing task of batch *b* in unit *us*, associated with the campaign *c*, is included in the solution, the corresponding interval variable representing the packing campaign has to be included too.

$$presenceOf(task_{b,us,c}) \geq presenceOf(campaign_{p,us,c}), \\ \forall p \in P, \forall c \in C_p, \forall b \in B_P, \forall us \in Us, s = Card(S) \quad (12)$$

Constraint (13) avoids overlapping the execution of tasks in any unit u and simultaneously inserts the corresponding changeover time between consecutive tasks assigned to the unit.

$$noOverlap(taskSeq_u, changeOverTime_{p,p',u}), \quad \forall u \in U, \forall p, p' \in P \qquad (13)$$

Constraints (14) and (15) reduce the search space and improve the computational performance of the formulation by removing mathematical symmetries. For each unit u, if more than one batch that belongs to a given product p, is assigned to it, those batches must be processed following an increasing *id* number sequence.

$$startBeforeStart(task_{b,u}, task_{b',u}), \quad \forall u \in U_S, \forall s \in Sa, \forall b, b' \in B_P, b' = b + 1, b \neq card(b) \qquad (14)$$

$$startBeforeStart(stTask_{b,s}, stTask_{b',s}), \quad \forall s \in Sa, \forall b, b' \in B_P, b' = b + 1, b \neq card(b) \qquad (15)$$

Expression (16) represents the objective function to be minimized, which is makespan. The expression adds a final cleaning time which must be performed in the packing lines.

$$max\left(endOf(stTask_{b,s})\right) + cleaningTime, \forall b \in B, \forall s \in S \qquad (16)$$

4. Results

The proposed model has been tested by means of the well-known case-study originally introduced by Bongers and Bakker (2006). In addition, a comparison with the results reported by Kopanos et al. (2012) has been made.

The process corresponds to an ice-cream production facility, which manufactures eight different products, named A to H. The plant layout is depicted in Fig. 1. As seen, it has three stages: (i) processing of raw materials into intermediate products, (ii) storage and aging of these intermediate products, and (iii) packing of the final products. At the first stage only one manufacturing line is available. The second stage has six vessels and the last one has two packing lines. At stage 1 and 3 sequence dependent changeover activities must be considered. Changeovers at stage 2 are negligible; however, minimum and maximum aging times must be considered at this stage. Finally, to improve the efficiency of the last packing stage, a campaign operation mode must be enforced in it.

In order to test the CP formulation 20 different problems instances (P.01 to P.20) of this case study have been solved, varying the number of batches needed to fulfil increasing product demands. In fact, from problems P.01 to P.20, the number of batches raises from 70 to 180. The examples were solved on a computer having 16 GB of RAM memory and AMD Ryzen 3 3200G processor. Optimal solutions were reached in 13 out the 20 instances with low computational effort (29 to 734 seconds of CPU time) and only 7 good quality suboptimal solutions were reached. A limit of 3600 s of CPU time was imposed.

Table 1 presents the values of the objective function that were obtained by means of this proposal and the ones that were reported by Kopanos et al. (2012). It can be seen that in nine instances better values have been reached and in two cases the same values have been obtained. The worst quality solution that was reached has a makespan value that is only 0.23% greater that the corresponding optimal solution.

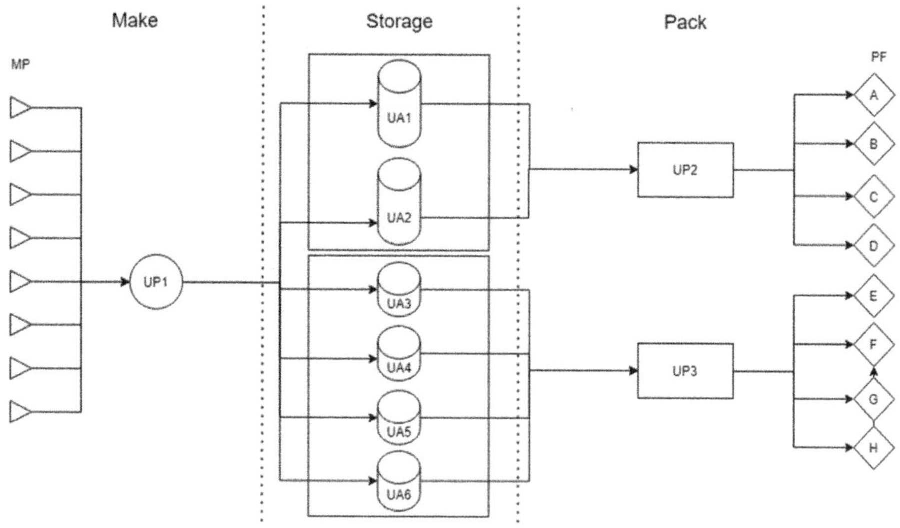

Fig. 1. Manufacturing process that corresponds to the case study under consideration.

Table 1. Objective function values obtained by means of this proposal and the ones of Kopanos et al. (2012).

Instance	Solution Approach		
	Proposed CP Model	**MIP-R***	**MIP BasB***
P.01	**120.28**	120.33	120.33
P.02	119.48	**118.17**	**118.17**
P.03	131.62	**131.48**	**131.48**
P.04	**142.07**	142.10	142.10
P.05	**149.65**	149.66	149.66
P.06	152.88	**152.34**	**152.34**
P.07	162.50	**161.47**	**161.47**
P.08	**171.35**	171.37	171.37
P.09	176.23	**175.82**	**175.82**
P.10	**187.75**	**187.75**	**187.75**
P.11	**191.18**	191.25	191.25
P.12	**206.42**	**206.42**	**206.42**
P.13	202.67	**201.76**	**201.76**
P.14	**223.55**	223.56	223.56
P.15	**224.68**	224.71	224.71
P.16	222.58	**222.06**	**222.06**
P.17	238.48	**238.04**	**238.04**
P.18	251.98	**251.49**	**251.49**
P.19	**260.45**	260.52	260.52
P.20	**291.72**	291.75	291.75

Bold numbers represent the best value of the objective function corresponding to each instance.

Fig. 2 depicts the Gantt diagram corresponding to the largest problem instance, having 180 batches.

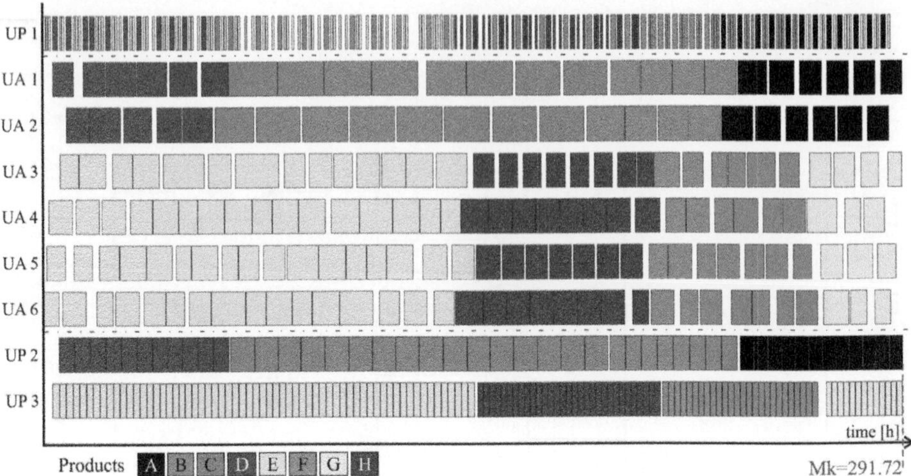

Fig. 2. Gantt diagram corresponding to problem instance P.20.

5. Conclusions and future work

Until now, most constraint programming models addressing industrial scheduling problems have focused on batch plants. In this contribution, an efficient CP model was developed to address the scheduling problem of make-and-pack plants, in which batch groupings into campaigns are considered in the last packing stage. It was applied to twenty instances of a case study, corresponding to an ice cream producer company, ranging from 70 to 180 batches. Despite the significant increase in the number of batches (157%), the performance of the model did not degrade because the rise of the number of variables was limited (138%). A comparison with the results reported by Kopanos et al. (2012) has been made, which allows concluding that the model is competitive. Future work will include the extension of the proposal to consider more complex industrial processes. In addition, the stochastic nature of certain variables, such as the processing rates/times, will be taken into account.

References

Bongers P.M.M., Bakker B.H., Application of multi-stage scheduling. In: Marquardt W., Pantelides C.C. (Eds.), 16th European Symposium on Computer Aided Process Engineering and 9th International Symposium on Process Systems Engineering, Elsevier. 1917-1922 (2006).

IBM ILOG, IBM ILOG CPLEX Optimization Studio. http://www-01.ibm.com/software/integration/optimization/cplex-optimization-studio/ (2013).

Kopanos G.M., Puigjaner L., Georgiadis M.C., Production scheduling in multiproduct multistage semicontinuous food processes. *Industrial Engineering & Chemistry Research*, 50, 6316-6324, (2011).

Kopanos G.M., Puigjaner L., Georgiadis M.C., Efficient mathematical frameworks for detailed production scheduling in food processing industries, *Computers and Chemical Enginnering,* 42, 206–216 (2012).

Novara, F.M., Novas, J.M., Henning, G.P., A novel constraint programming model for large-scale scheduling problems in multiproduct multistage batch plants: Limited resources and campaign-based operation, *Computers and Chemical Enginnering,* 93, 101–117 (2016).

Proceedings of the 14th International Symposium on Process Systems Engineering – PSE 2021+
June 19-23, 2022, Kyoto, Japan
http://dx.doi.org/10.1016/B978-0-323-85159-6.50084-1

Maintenance scheduling optimization for decaying performance nonlinear dynamic processes

Bogdan Dorneanu[a], Vassilios S. Vassiliadis[b], Harvey Arellano-Garcia[a,*]

[a]LS Prozess- und Anlagentechnik, Brandenburgische Teschnische Universität Cottbus-Senftenberg, Cottbus, D-03044, Germany
[b]Cambridge Simulation Solutions Ltd., Larnaca 7550, Cyprus
arellano@b-tu.de

Abstract

A first contribution of this paper is an overview of the research efforts and contributions over several decades in the area of scheduling maintenance optimization for decaying performance dynamic processes. Following breakthrough ideas and implementation in the area of heat exchanger networks for optimal scheduling of cleaning actions subject to exchanger surface fouling, these concepts were transferred successfully to the area of scheduling catalyst replacement actions in catalytic reactor networks. This necessary overview leads to the main, second contribution aimed with this work: its application to restorative maintenance scheduling in the area of RON regeneration actions planning, as well as point to new areas where this approach can be fruitfully applied to and extended into in the near future – particularly enhancing model descriptions that include general types of planning uncertainty. The effectiveness and efficacy of the approach is demonstrated computationally in this work.

Keywords: maintenance scheduling optimization, decaying performance processes, multistage optimal control, bang-bang optimal control, reverse osmosis networks.

1. Introduction

Modern engineering systems and manufacturing processes are nowadays very complex, with the demand for integration and multitasking processing being an ever-increasing trend so as to facilitate flexible manufacturing over multiple products, increase efficiency, reduce costs and environmental impact, as well as to secure safe operation. Production facilities thus involve numerous interactions and dependencies between components, and operate in highly dynamic environments. The operation of processes with decaying performance over time gives rise to challenging modelling and optimization problems. As the performance degrades over time, process shutdown for unit cleaning (reverse osmosis networks (Saif et al. 2019), heat exchanger networks (Al Ismaili et al. 2019)) or catalyst changeovers (catalytic processes) (Adloor & Vassiliadis, 2021) must be planned to restore it.

In order to avoid this, parallel processing lines are used to manufacture the products. This set up can improve the flexibility of the production process by allowing the shut-down of one unit for cleaning purposes, while the remaining units continue to meet the products' demand. While this maintenance action does improve the product yield, there are negative impacts associated with this operation, such as loss of production time, or energy and labour costs to restore the performance (Adloor & Vassiliadis, 2020). This leads to a trade-off to be addressed for each unit: while frequently cleaning results in high production rates, large maintenance costs and loss in production occur. This trade-off can be optimally managed by developing maintenance schedules that specify the optimum units to be used and the optimal use time of each unit in the parallel set up, over a fixed time horizon. The schedule may also be required to fulfil a constraint that no two units undergo cleaning action at the same time due to production requirements or labour and equipment availability (Al Ismaili et al. 2018).

Additionally, it is also necessary to identify the optimal operating conditions, as well as to ensure that the maintenance schedule and the process operation are tailored to produce an adequate inventory of product to effectively meet varying demand across the time horizon, while also avoiding excessively high storage costs. An integrated execution of all these decisions in an optimal manner can greatly minimise the negative effects of the performance decaying process, and thereby maximise the profit (Adloor & Vassiliadis, 2020).

The following sections present an overview of research efforts and contributions over several decades in the area of scheduling optimization for decaying performance dynamic processes, with particular focus on RON regeneration, as well as new areas of application and extension.

2. Maintenance scheduling of decaying performance processes

Two approaches are commonly employed in dealing with the maintenance scheduling (Santamaria & Macchietto, 2018):

a) *Optimal scheduling problem*, with binary decision variables associated with the operating states of the units (cleaning/operating) and the timing and sequencing of the task. The problem is combinatorial in nature and it is typically addressed using (pseudo-)steady-state models.

b) *Dynamic optimal scheduling problem* involving differential-algebraic equations (DAEs). In this case, the result is a (mixed-integer) nonlinear programming problem, but offers the flexibility of accommodating various types of models (Assis et al., 2015).

Furthermore, the accuracy of the process models used is of paramount importance. Rigorous models, capturing the full representation of the physical phenomena can be computationally expensive for a large-scale scheduling problem. Yet, inadequately describing the physics of the process may affect the validity of the obtained maintenance schedules, and the result may end up being useless for practical application (Van Horenbeek et al. 2010).

In the following, the underlying scheduling problem is reformulated as a dynamic multistage optimization (optimal control) model, and cast in a form that promotes bang-bang type solutions for the control variables associated with restorative action periods. This bang-bang behaviour is entirely equivalent to having a Boolean variable (integer, binary) within an otherwise smoothly represented dynamic optimisation model.

This approach has been successfully applied for solving maintenance scheduling problems for HENs (Al Ismaili et al., 2018) and catalytic reactor networks (Adloor & Vassiliadis, 2020). Furthermore, it has enabled reliable inclusion of process uncertainty to be included realistically in the resulting models (Al Ismaili et al., 2019; Adloor &

Vassiliadis, 2021). In the following, the application of the approach on the maintenance scheduling of a RON will be demonstrated as an original contribution of this work.

3. Maintenance scheduling of reverse osmosis networks (RONs)

Reverse osmosis (RO) is a well-established technology for water desalination. A commercial RO desalination system consists of seawater intake, seawater pre-treatment, main RO separation and post-treatment sections, which include several RO passes with auxiliary equipment, e.g., high-pressure pumps, energy recovery, etc. (Saif et al. 2019).

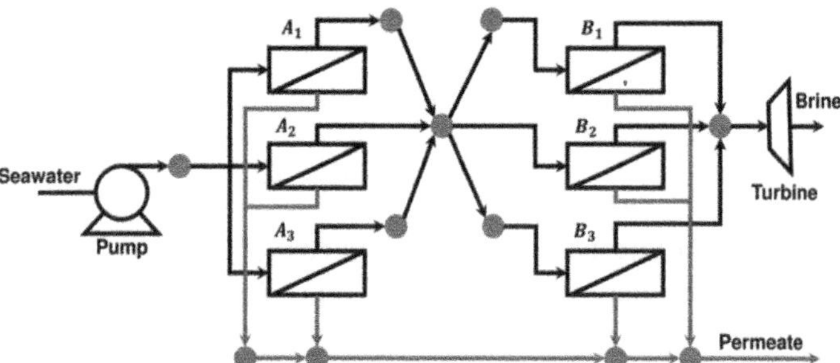

Figure 1: Reverse osmosis network considered

For the case study, a RON with 2 stages of 3 individual modules, with a total of 6 RO units, illustrated in Figure 2, is considered. Each RO unit has a membrane area, A of 152 m^2 and a permeate recovery ratio of 0.65. The RON processes a total flowrate of 5,004 m^3/h of sea water, with a salt content of 34,800 ppm. Other parameters for the RON operation (*e.g.*, membrane permeability decay constant – γ, solute transport parameters, initial water permeability, etc.) are taken from See et al. 2004.

3.1. Mathematical model

The decay in the unit's performance is defined as:

$$-\frac{dK_i}{dt} = Y_i \cdot \frac{K_i}{\gamma} \qquad i = 1, \dots, 6 \qquad (1)$$

Where K = the membrane permeability [kg m^{-2}], Y = a binary variable, equal to 1 if the RO unit is in operation or 0 if the unit is in cleaning action, and i = the RO module number.

The flowrates of the RO module inlet streams, F are determined from the total flowrate, F_{total}, as follows:

$$F_i = \frac{1}{3} \cdot Y_i \cdot F_{total} \qquad i = 1, \dots, 3 \qquad (2)$$

$$F_j = \frac{1}{3} \cdot Y_j \cdot R_k \qquad j = 4, \dots, 6 \qquad k = 1, \dots, 3 \qquad (3)$$

Where R = reject flowrate [m^3 day^{-1}].

The permeate flowrate, P_i is determined based on the permeate recovery ratio from:

$$P_i = Y_i \cdot \alpha \cdot F_i \quad (4)$$

Where α = the permeate recovery ratio.

The concentration of the permeate, $C_{P,i}$ is calculated based on the solute transport parameter, D, the pressure drop, ΔP and the osmotic pressure, $\Delta\pi$ as:

$$C_{P,i} = \frac{D \cdot C_{F,i}}{\Gamma \cdot K_i \cdot (\Delta P_i - \Delta\pi_i)} \quad (5)$$

Where Γ = the membrane geometry correction factor, and C_F = the concentration of the RO module inlet stream.

The pressure drop over a RO module is determined as:

$$\Delta P_i = Y_i \cdot \left(\frac{P_i}{A \cdot \Gamma \cdot K_i} + \Delta\pi_i\right) \qquad i = 1, \dots, 6 \quad (6)$$

The scheduling of the maintenance actions is defined as an optimisation problem having as decision variables the binary variables Y_i. The objective function to be optimised is the total cost of operating the RON, calculated as:

$$J = Income_{Sale} - Cost_{Cleaning} - Cost_{Energy} \quad (7)$$

With the income from permeate sales determined as:

$$Income_{Sale} = cost_{permeate} \cdot \sum_i P_i \qquad i = 1, \dots, 6 \quad (8)$$

The cost of cleaning as:

$$Cost_{Cleaning} = cost_{cleaning\ action} \cdot N_{CleaningPeriods} \quad (9)$$

And the energy cost:

$$Cost_{Energy} = cost_{electricity} \cdot \frac{\sum_i F_i \cdot \Delta P_i}{\eta_{pump}} \quad (10)$$

Where η_{pump} = pump energy efficiency.

The cost of electricity is assumed equal to 0.30 € kWh^{-1}, the cost of the cleaning action is 100 € unit^{-1} cleaning action^{-1}, while the permeate is sold at 0.48 € m^{-3}. The dynamic model of the RON presented above is implemented as a multiperiod simulation model, with a planning horizon equal to 26 weeks. This long planning horizon has been selected to even out economic effects. The optimization is implemented using a heuristic penalty scheme, to enforce binary values or the controls. A multiple start policy with 50 cycles is considered in order to determine the spread of the local solutions.

3.2. Results and discussion

The optimisation problem is implemented in Python v3.8 and solved on an Intel Core i7-8550U CPU @1.80GHz, 16.0 GB RAM. The *minimize* solver from *scipy.optimize* is used. Both linear and nonlinear constraints are implemented. The CPU time is 163.97 minutes. Out of the 50 multiple start cycles considered, 13 were successful (an optimal solution is found), with the value of the objective between €7.275 and €7.565 million. From the results in Figure 2 it can be observed that each of these solutions is being obtained more than once, hence the advantage of using the multiple start policy in identifying a better solution.

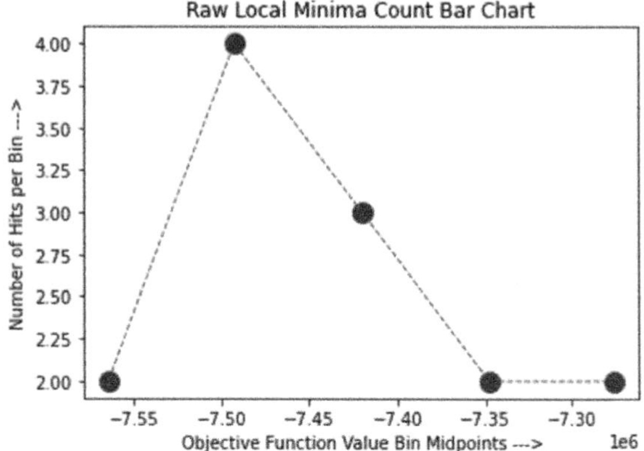

Figure 2: Local minima for the successful optimization cycles

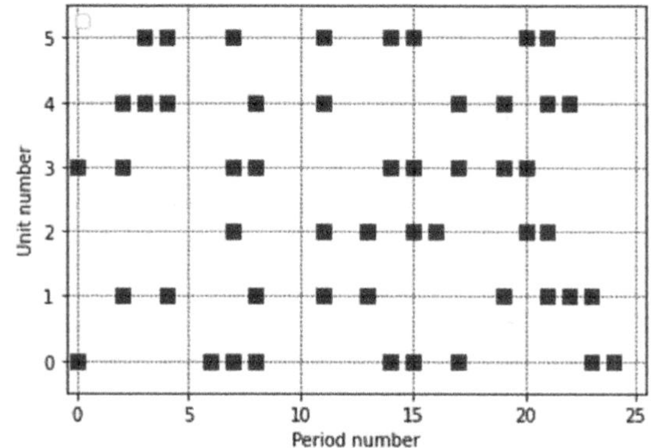

Figure 3: Cleaning schedule for the RON

The best point, with a value of the objective function of €7.565 million. The resulting maintenance schedule is presented in Figure 3. For most of the heat exchangers, there is no cleaning action near the start and at the end of the operating horizon, a similar behaviour observed by Al Ismaili et al. (2018) for HENs. This is because there is very little incentive to increase the cleaning cost further.

The number of cleaning actions varies between 7 (for RO module 3) and 9 (RO modules 1,2, 4, and 5). This could indicate that these modules are more important in the network.

4. Future directions for maintenance scheduling optimization

The maintenance scheduling of RONs can be further investigated to account for uncertainty in the sensor data regarding equipment degradation. Furthermore, comparisons with similar studies using mixed-integer formulations should be considered. The optimal control approach for scheduling maintenance and production can be further applied to other similar processes with decaying performance, such as biopharmaceutical manufacturing under performance decay (Liu et al. 2014) or chromatography-based processes (Vieira et al. 2017). Parallel production lines able to process multiple feeds and produce multiple products should be investigated as well, to overcome the combinatorial nature of the mixed-integer methodology (Adloor & Vassiliadis, 2020).

5. Conclusions

This work provides an overview of the optimal control approach for scheduling maintenance of decaying performance processes. An original case study of RONs is presented to illustrate the application of this procedure, based on the formulation of the scheduling task as a multistage mixed-integer optimal control problem, considering a dynamic model of the process. The requirement for an integer variable handling solution algorithm (*e.g.,* Branch-and-Bound) is not needed, although it is not always possible to ensure the necessary condition that each resulting case will exhibit such bang-bang behaviour.

Nonetheless, for significant portions of the observed solution profiles, over many applications over the course of years, it has been observed that mild penalization heuristic schemes work sufficiently well and very reliably over a multitude of published case study solutions.

References

S. Adloor & V.S. Vassiliadis, 2020, An optimal control approach to scheduling maintenance and production in parallel lines of reactors using decaying catalysts, Computers and Chemical Engineering 142, 107025

S. Adloor & V.S. Vassiliadis, 2021, An optimal control approach to considering uncertainties in kinetic parameters in the maintenance scheduling and production of a process using decaying catalysts, Computers and Chemical Engineering 149, 107277

R. Al Ismaili et al., 2018, Heat exchanger network cleaning scheduling: From optimal control to mixed-integer decision making, Computer and Chemical Engineering 111, pp. 1-15

R. Al Ismaili et al., 2019, Optimisation of heat exchanger network cleaning schedules: Incorporating uncertainty in fouling and cleaning model parameters, Computers and Chemical Engineering 121, pp. 409-421

B.C.G. Assis et al., 2015, Dynamic optmization of the flow rate distribution in heat exchanger networks for fouling mitigation, I&EC Research 54, pp. 6497-6507

S. Liu et al., 2014, Optimal production and maintenance planning of biopharmaceutical manufacturing under performance decay, I&EC Research 53, pp. 17075-17091

Y. Saif et al., 2019, MINLP model for reverse osmosis network design under time-variant operation constraints, I&EC Research 58, pp. 22315-22323

F. L. Santamaria & S. Macchietto, 2018, Integration of optimal cleaning scheduling and control of heat exchanger network undergoing fouling: Model and formulation, I&EC Research 57, pp. 12842-12860

H.J. See et al., 2004, Design of reverse osmosis (RO) water treatment networks subject to fouling, Water Science and Technology 49 (2), pp. 263-270

A. Van Horenbeek, et al., 2010, Maintenance optimization models and criteria, Int. J. Syst. Assur. Eng. Manag. 1(3), pp. 189-200

M. Vieira et al., 2017, Production and maintenance planning optimization in biopharmaceutical processes under performance decay using a continuous-time formulation: A multi-objective approach, Computers and Chemical Engineering 107, pp. 111-139

Proceedings of the 14th International Symposium on Process Systems Engineering – PSE 2021+
June 19-23, 2022, Kyoto, Japan
http://dx.doi.org/10.1016/B978-0-323-85159-6.50085-3

Cleaning schedule for heat exchanger networks subjected to maintenance constraints

Parag Patil[a], Babji Srinivasan[b,d], Rajagopalan Srinivasan[c,d*]

[a]*Department of Chemical Engineering, Indian Institute of Technology Gandhinagar, Gandhinagar382355, India*
[b]*Department of Applied Mechanics, Indian Institute of Technology Madras, Chennai, 600036, India*
[c]*Department of Chemical Engineering, Indian Institute of Technology Madras, Chennai, 600036, India*
[d]*American Express Lab for Data Analytics, Risk and Technology, Indian Institute of Technology Madras,Chennai Tamil Nadu, 600036, India*
**raj@iitm.ac.in*

Abstract

Fouling degrades the overall efficiency of the heat exchanger networks (HENs), which results in a significant economic loss. The mitigation of fouling in an operational HEN is carried out by optimizing the cleaning schedules of the heat exchangers. Although such approach can save costs, it is subjected to the exact implementation of the optimal cleaning schedule. Usually, the small and medium-scale process industries face difficulties in implementing such solutions due to limited resources, which forces them to rely on suboptimal cleaning schedules, such as postponing or avoiding few cleaning tasks. This work addresses this gap by optimizing the cleaning schedule considering the maintenance resource limitation. Our approach considers a mixed-integer linear programming (MILP) based optimization considering groupings of heat exchangers based on their spatial locations for ease of maintenance The proposed formulation is applied on a HEN with linear and asymptotic fouling, with and without cleaning cost. The results show that the approach can prevent a considerable economic loss, which would incur due to suboptimal cleaning schedules due to resource limitations.

Keywords: Heat exchanger network, fouling, cleaning schedule, MILP, maintenance constraints

1. Introduction

The HENs are present in almost all process industries, such as oil refineries, pulp, paper mills, sugar factories, etc. (Trafczynski et al., 2021). Such networks are mainly employed to recover the waste energy from hot process outlet streams to the cold process inlet streams in the process plant. As the operation progresses, the foulant in the streams starts depositing in the heat exchangers. The thermal conductivities of the foulant are usually lower than the material of construction of the heat exchangers; thus, their deposition results in reduced heat transfer rates. Moreover, the cross-sectional areas in the heat exchangers also reduce due to foulant deposition, increasing the pressure drops. Overall, the fouling affects thermal and hydraulic efficiencies of the HENs. Extra pumping power and utility consumption are required to compensate for this efficiency reduction, resulting in substantial economic loss. In 2015, the total cost of fouling in preheat trains in US refineries was reported to be about $2.26 billion (Coletti et al., 2015). Thus, fouling mitigation is essential to prevent such huge economic losses.

Generally, fouling in HENs is mitigated at two levels: (1) at the design or retrofit stage, where the heat exchanger geometries and HEN structures are optimized to minimize foulant deposition; (2) At the operational stage, where mass flowrates and heat exchanger cleaning schedules are optimized to reduce the additional utility and cleaning costs. The current work is focused on the existing networks; hence falls under the latter type. Several studies in this category formulate it as an optimization problem, considering the operating variables and cleaning activities as continuous and binary variables, respectively. The independent and simultaneous consideration of the variables in the optimization framework results in nonlinear programming (NLP) and mixed-integer nonlinear/linear programming problems(MINLP/MILP). Several authors have formulated the optimization of cleaning schedules as MINLP and MILP problems (Georgiadis et al., 2000, Smaili et al., 2002). Optimization based on simultaneous consideration of cleaning schedules and flow distribution has also been studied (Santamaria and Macchietto, 2020). Although these studies have shown the potential to save costs due to fouling, the saving is only possible with effective implementation of the obtained solutions. However, the small and medium-scale process industries usually face difficulties in implementing optimal solutions due to limited resources such as low maintenance budgets (Wang, 2016). Therefore, they tend to follow a suboptimal cleaning schedule by skipping or postponing the cleaning of heat exchangers, which results in higher utility consumption. Thus, obtaining the optimal cleaning schedules considering maintenance resource constraints is necessary. To our knowledge, no fouling mitigation studies have evaluated these limitations.

This work addresses the described gap by modelling the cleaning schedule of HENs with maintenance resource limitations. The heat exchangers in HENs can be either grouped based on similarities of the type of cleaning required, such as mechanical and chemical methods, or based on their spatial locations for ease of maintenance. This work proposes an MILP formulation for cleaning of HENs considering heat exchanger groups. The grouping is modelled using linear constraints. Next, we describe the MILP formulation used.

2. MILP problem formulation description

The HEN is modelled by the digraph method, where the edges are streams (s), and vertices are process equipment (E). The set of streams(s) is divided in the subset of cold streams (c_s) and hot streams (h_s) . The set of equipment is divided into subsets of supply units (Su_E), demand units (Du_E), heat exchangers (Hx_E), mixers (Mx_E), splitters (Sp_E) and an additional heater (He_E) . The overall operating time is discretized into sub-periods, denoted by τ. Following is a brief discussion about the constraints and objective functions:

a) *Mass balance constraints*: The mass flow rates in each stream (m_s) are assumed to be constant during the operational. The mass balance in the network is simulated based on the Equations (18) to (23) from Assis et al. (2013).
b) *Energy balance constraints*:
   - The energy balance across all the equipment is simulated as per Equations (26) to (31) from Assis et al. (2013).
   - The heat transfer across the heat exchangers are modelled by lumped-parametric model of $P-NTU$ method as follows:

$$P_{hx,\tau}(1-y_{hx,\tau})T_{hx,\tau}^{c,i}+(1-P_{hx,\tau})(1-y_{hx,\tau})T_{hx,\tau}^{h,i}-T_{hx,\tau}^{h,o}=0 \tag{1}$$

$$T_{hx,\tau}^{c,i}-T_{hx,\tau}^{c,o}-CR_{hx,\tau}(T_{hx,\tau}^{h,i}-T_{hx,\tau}^{h,o})=0 \tag{2}$$

where, $P_{hx,\tau}$ is the heat exchanger effectiveness parameter in the interval (τ), based on the number of transfer units $(NTU_{hxv,\tau})$. $CR_{hx,\tau}$ is ratio of heat capacity of the flowrates. $y_{hx,\tau}$ is binary variable, representing state of the heat exchanger: $y_{hx,\tau}$=1denotes cleaning and $y_{hx,\tau}$=0 denotes under operation. $T_{hx,\tau}^{c,i}$, $T_{hx,\tau}^{c,o}$ and $T_{hx,\tau}^{h,i}$, $T_{hx,\tau}^{h,o}$ are inlet and outlet temperatures of cold and hot streams in the heat exchangers (hx) in τ interval, respectively. It can be observed that equation (1) contains the terms $y_{hx,\tau}T_{hx,\tau}^{c,i}$ and $y_{hx,\tau}T_{hx,\tau}^{h,i}$, which are bilinear, which are linearized using a set of linear inequalities (Floudas, 1995). Also, $P_{hx,\tau}$ is a nonlinear function of thermal resistance due to fouling $\left(R_{f\,hx,\tau}\right)$. Thus, $P_{hx,\tau}$ introduces fouling in the energy balance through Equation (1). It is to be noted that, both the cold and hot streams across the heat exchangers are bypassed during their cleaning.

c) *Incorporation of fouling*: We consider linear and asymptotic nature of fouling based on the following respective equations:

$$R_{f\,hx,\tau}=K_{hx}*\tau \tag{3}$$

$$R_{f\,hx,\tau}=R_{f\,hx}^{\infty}(1-\exp -\tau/\Gamma) \tag{4}$$

where, K_{hx}, $R_{f\,hx}^{\infty}$ and Γ are the fouling parameters with appropriate units.

d) *Objective function*: It is sum of the additional utility cost and cleaning cost of each heat exchanger in network, as follows:

$$fobj=\sum_{\tau=1}^{\tau_f}\frac{m_sCp_s}{\zeta}(T_{targ}-T_{\tau,s'})+\sum_{hx=1}^{n}\sum_{\tau=1}^{\tau_f}C_{hx}y_{hx,\tau} \tag{5}$$

where T_{targ} is the target temperature, s' is the target stream and C_{hx} is the cleaning cost of each heat exchanger. ζ is the efficiency of the heater. $fobj$ is the overall cost, which has to be minimized by the optimization formulation by providing an optimal cleaning schedule using the proposed MILP formulation. Following section demonstrates a case study based on proposed MILP approach.

3. Case study

In this section, we apply MILP optimization formulation explained in section (2) on a HEN, shown in Fig.1 (Assis et al. 2013). It consists of four supply units, four demand units, six heat exchangers, four flow splitters, four mixers and a fired heater. All the heat exchangers have heat transfer area of 400 m^2 and the overall heat transfer coefficient of

253 W/m^2 in the clean condition. The overall heat transfer rates in each heat exchangers

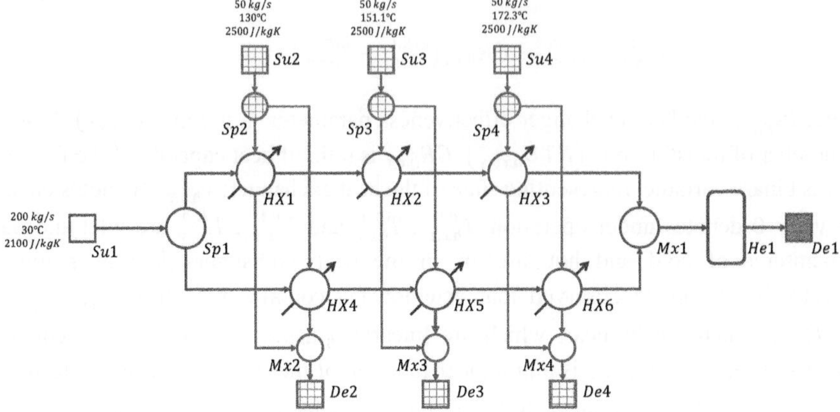

Figure 1: Schematic of the HEN used in the case study (adopted from Assis et al., 2013)

is 4.44 MW. The cold and hot fluids are flowing through the tubes and shell sides, respectively. The split fractions in each of the splitter is 0.5. The nominal temperature of the stream entering fired heater is 97.06°C. Heater provides additional energy in case if this temperature falls below its nominal value due to fouling or if any heat exchanger is taken offline for cleaning. The cost of utility, supplied to the heater is assumed to be 0.01 $£/kWh$ with 75% efficiency.

Two cases of linear and asymptotic fouling depositions based on Equations (3) and (4) are considered here. Further, two scenarios in each of the fouling cases are considered. In one, the cleaning cost of the heat exchanger is neglected, while in another, it is considered £ 4,000 per cleaning. Thus, four scenarios are generated as follows:

a) *Scenario 1*: Linear fouling with cleaning cost
b) *Scenario 2*: Linear fouling without cleaning costs
c) *Scenario 3*: Asymptotic fouling with cleaning cost
d) *Scenario 4*: Asymptotic fouling without cleaning cost

An operational period of 12 months is considered in each scenario. The optimization formulation described in the section (2) is applied in all the scenarios. The obtained schedules for three scenarios (except scenario 3) are shown in Fig.2. Scenario 3 does not have the cleaning schedule for any heat exchanger. The overall costs incurred in each scenario are tabulated in Table 1. It can be observed that the number of cleanings in the scenarios considering cleaning costs is less than the scenarios without cleaning costs. Also, the costs in the scenarios with linear fouling are lower than those with asymptotic fouling. It is to be noted that, the optimization in scenario 3 denotes no cleaning of any heat exchanger.

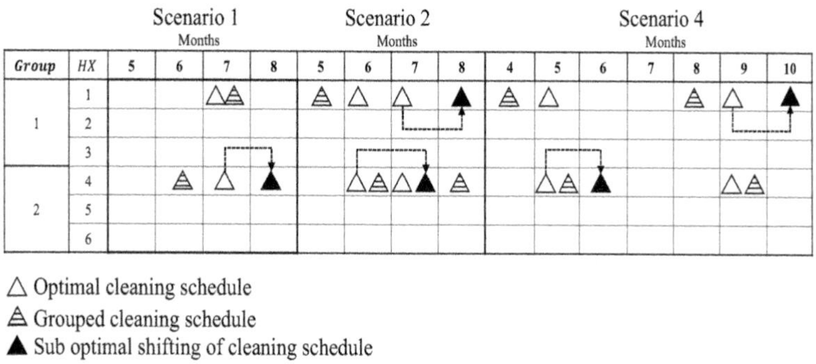

Scenario 1 Months
Scenario 2 Months
Scenario 4 Months

△ Optimal cleaning schedule
Grouped cleaning schedule
▲ Sub optimal shifting of cleaning schedule

Figure 2: Cleaning schedule for scenarios 1, 2 and 4 without grouping, with grouping and with resource constraints.

Table 1: Costs in various scenarios in optimal and suboptimal conditions

Scenarios	Cost with optimal schedule without group (£)	Cost with suboptimal schedule (£)	Cost with optimal schedule with group (£)	Saving, %
1	90,643	91,110	90,716	84.4
2	80,500	82,145	81,433	43.3
3	1,49,560	1,49,560	1,49,560	-
4	1,44,400	1,44,450	1,44,850	88.9

As discussed in section (2), the maintenance teams in the process industries may not consistently implement the obtained optimal cleaning schedules due to resource limitations. They may end up skipping or postponing the cleaning of a few heat exchangers, resulting in suboptimal cleaning schedules resulting in higher costs. One of the approaches to tackle this problem is to group the heat exchangers based on the similarity of type of foulant being deposited in the heat exchangers or the locations of the heat exchangers. By grouping the heat exchangers, the maintenance team can easily perform the cleaning activities, following the optimal schedule obtained. For the considered network, we assume that the heat exchangers $HX1$ to $HX3$ and $HX4$ to $HX6$ are spatially located near each other. Thus, two groups based on their locations are defined as follows:

a) Group 1: $HX1 - HX3$
b) Group 2: $HX4 - HX6$.

The maintenance team can perform cleaning of multiple heat exchangers if they belong to a same group. Whereas, the cleaning activities would get postponed or skipped if the multiple heat exchangers from different groups are in the cleaning schedule. It can be seen from Fig. 2 that $HX1$ and $HX4$ have to be cleaned simultaneously in 7th month for scenario 1. However, they belong to different groups. If cleaning of these heat exchangers is postponed by a month, it may result in higher cost of £ 91,110 due to sub-optimality (The cost for optimal cleaning schedule is £ 90,643). Whereas, if optimization is carried out with defined groups, the obtained schedule allows the maintenance team to clean the heat exchangers based on their limitations. The cost in this case is £ 90,716, which reduces the economic loss by 84.4 %, comparing the suboptimal schedule. All the other scenarios show a similar observation.

4. Conclusion and future work

Fouling in operational HENs is tackled by optimizing the mass flow distribution and cleaning schedule of the heat exchangers using MINLP or MILP frameworks. However, implementations of obtained optimal solutions is dependent on the limitations of the maintenance teams, particularly in the small and medium scale industries. This paper takes into account the maintenance resource limitations while considering the HEN cleaning optimization problem.

We formulate the problem using the MILP approach. Further, we obtained the optimal cleaning schedule in a HEN with six heat exchangers under various scenarios of linear and asymptotic fouling, with and without cleaning costs. We assume additional constraints of grouping the heat exchangers as per their spatial locations. Our results reveal that the proposed approach can prevent a considerable economic loss due to possible sub-optimal cleaning schedule, which are commonly followed by the maintenance teams due to resource limitations.

In future, we are planning to extend the proposed methodology to larger networks, where multiple grouping is possible. Apart from locations, the grouping will be also carried out based on fouling type, as different foulants require different cleaning methods.

Acknowledgement

This work is partially funded by American Express Lab for Data Analytics, Risk and Technology, Indian Institute of Technology Madras, Chennai, India.

References

Assis, B. C., Lemos, J. C., Queiroz, E. M., Pessoa, F. L., Liporace, F. S., Oliveira, S. G., & Costa, A. L. (2013). Optimal allocation of cleanings in heat exchanger networks. *Applied thermal engineering*, *58*(1-2), 605-614.

Coletti, F., Joshi, H. M., Macchietto, S., & Hewitt, G. F. (2015). Introduction. In Crude Oil Fouling: Deposit Characterization, Measurements, and Modeling (pp. 1–22). Elsevier Inc.

Floudas, C. A. (1995). *Nonlinear and mixed-integer optimization: fundamentals and applications*. Oxford University Press.

Georgiadis, Michael C., Lazaros G. Papageorgiou, and Sandro Macchietto. "Optimal cleaning policies in heat exchanger networks under rapid fouling." Industrial & engineering chemistry research 39.2 (2000): 441-454.

Ishiyama, E. M., Heins, A. V., Paterson, W. R., Spinelli, L., & Wilson, D. I. (2010). Scheduling cleaning in a crude oil preheat train subject to fouling: Incorporating desalter control. Applied Thermal Engineering, 30(13), 1852–1862.

Santamaria, F. L., & Macchietto, S. (2020). Online Integration of Optimal Cleaning Scheduling and Control of Heat Exchanger Networks under Fouling. Industrial and Engineering Chemistry Research, 59(6), 2471–2490.

Trafczynski, M., Markowski, M., Urbaniec, K., Trzcinski, P., Alabrudzinski, S., & Suchecki, W. (2021). Estimation of thermal effects of fouling growth for application in the scheduling of heat exchangers cleaning. *Applied Thermal Engineering*, *182*, 116103.

Wang, Y. (2016). What are the biggest obstacles to growth of SMEs in developing countries? – An empirical evidence from an enterprise survey. *Borsa Istanbul Review*, *16*(3), 167–176.

Proceedings of the 14th International Symposium on Process Systems Engineering – PSE 2021+
June 19-23, 2022, Kyoto, Japan
http://dx.doi.org/10.1016/B978-0-323-85159-6.50086-5

Estimating Energy Market Schedules using Historical Price Data

Nicole Cortes[a], Xian Gao[a], Bernard Knueven[b], and Alexander W. Dowling[a*]

[a]*Department of Chemical and Biomolecular Engineering, University of Notre Dame, Notre Dame, IN 46556, USA*
[b]*Computational Science Center, National Renewable Energy Laboratory, Golden, CO 80401, USA*
**adowling@nd.edu*

Abstract

The global climate crisis is expected to reshape the energy generation landscape in the coming decades. Increasing integration of non-dispatchable renewable energy resources into energy infrastructures and markets creates uncertainty as well as new opportunities for flexible energy systems. To conduct proper economic evaluation of flexible energy systems, such as integrated energy systems (IES), advancements in modelling of market interactions, such as bidding, is crucial. This work presents a shortcut algorithm which uses two mixed integer linear programs to compute dispatch schedules (e.g., hourly power production targets) that are constrained by the resource's bid information and characteristics (e.g., minimum up and down times) based on historical locational marginal price (LMP) data. The proposed algorithm is approximately 100 times faster and uses orders of magnitude less data than a full production cost model (PCM). We find the shortcut simulator recapitulates generator dispatch signals for the Prescient PCM with approximately 4% error for the RTS-GMLC test system.

Keywords: Electricity Generation, Energy Markets, Integrated Energy Systems, Multiscale Simulation

1. Introduction

Governments around the world have pledged to lower their carbon emissions in response to climate change. Incorporating more variable renewable energy (VRE) sources, such as wind and solar, into power systems is critical to meet these goals. While VRE resources have many benefits such as low to zero emissions and operating costs, their unpredictable nature is challenging for electric grid operations. They increase price variability (Seel et al. 2018) and create strong incentives for more flexible energy generation and consumption. Using historical market price data, Dowling et al. 2017a showed that energy systems can more than double their profits by participating in faster market timescales. Many new promising technologies, including integrated energy systems (IES) which exploit the synergy between multiple technologies (e.g., renewables, nuclear, fossil-based with CO_2 capture, energy storage) by tightly coupling them into single systems (Arent et al. 2021) can provide flexibility to enhance grid reliability and resilience with high VRE utilization. But properly valuing the flexibility of these new technology concepts requires analysis that directly considers interactions between IESs and energy markets. Traditional energy system value metrics, such as levelized cost of electricity (LCOE), do not capture the value created in the market (Dowling et al. 2017b).

Wholesale energy markets coordinate the generation and consumption of electricity from an increasingly diverse set of technologies. The markets set energy prices in a two-settlement system: a day-ahead market (DAM) to meet forecasted demand and a balancing real-time market (RTM) for fast adjustments. Market participants, providing energy generation or ancillary services (various reserves or frequency regulation), can interact with the market via self-scheduling or bidding. A resource that self-schedules creates its own power generation schedule over its preferred planning horizon and is subject to the cleared market price. In contrast, bidding requires participants to submit a set of power-price pairs to the independent service operator (ISO). The power-price pairs reflect the resource's marginal costs and generation flexibility to the ISO. With all the submitted bids, generation is scheduled by optimizing the bids and clearing the market in order of cost. Once enough generation has been scheduled to meet forecasted energy demand for the considered horizon (following day for DAM or following hours for RTM), the locational marginal price (LMP), or price per MWh produced, is set by the highest cost resource to clear the market. Ela et al. 2014 found self-scheduling, although popular for market-based technoeconomic analysis, results in lower profits than bidding. Despite this fact, much of the current technoeconomic analysis of novel, more flexible energy concepts are done via self-schedule and their value may not be fully estimated.

Bids submitted by generators enable flexibility in the system's power output and schedule, and with more flexibility, the market has more options to meet ever-increasing demand. Therefore, for the technoeconomic analysis of flexible energy system concepts, simulating their market performance while bidding is essential. But this evaluation requires models to predict energy dispatch calculated from resource bids. Unfortunately, Production Cost Models (PCMs), which mimic market clearing by ISOs, are 'data-hungry'; they require knowledge of all generation resources in the grid, network topology, demand, and renewables forecasts, etc. Much of this required data is private or protected, which makes PCMs challenging to use for economic evaluation.

To address this challenge, we propose a shortcut algorithm to estimate dispatch schedules for individual market participants, requiring only generator characteristics, bid curves, and historical LMPs. Figure 1 shows the three-step process, which includes solving two mixed integer linear programs (MILP). To evaluate the proposed method, we simulate a single generator in the open-source RTS-GMLC data set ("GridMod/RTS-GMLC") over a month-long horizon using a rolling-horizon algorithm. The resulting dispatch is then compared to results from conducting a full market clearing using the open-source Pyomo-based PCM Prescient ("Prescient").

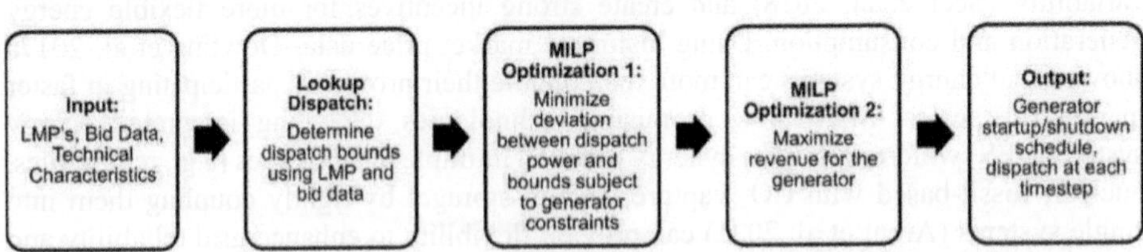

Figure 1: Shortcut Market Simulator Process

2. Methods

Figure 1 summarizes the proposed shortcut market simulator algorithm. The input data are: π_h^{real}, historical LMPs; piecewise "bid curve", a set of power, B_{hl}, and price, π_{hl}, pairs that communicate the total operational costs for the generator; and, technical characteristics including minimum and maximum power output, uptime and downtime constraints, and ramping limits. The latter are used in the thermal generator MILP model adapted from Arroyo and Conejo (2000) and Carrión and Arroyo (2006). The MILP optimization problems shown in Figure 1 are described below. The full simulation can be conducted in one-shot or using a rolling horizon algorithm. The rolling horizon algorithm solved a 24-hour horizon subproblem (from hour 0 to hour 23), saving the results of the first timestep, fixing that timestep, and solving another 24-hour horizon beginning at the next hour (from hour 1 to hour 24 with hour 1 fixed).

2.1. *Sets and Variables*

All equations in the MILP models are indexed over 2 sets: set $h \in H$ represents the timesteps in the horizon and set $l \in L$ represents the points on the bid curve, or each individual power-price pair. The MILP models include five sets of decision variables. Variable p_h represents the power output of the generator and time h. Variable B_h represents the bid power (bound by the lookup dispatch algorithm) for the generator at time h. Both p_h, and B_h are continuous variables. The remaining three variables are discrete: y_h represents the on/off state of the generator at timestep h (0 is off, 1 is on), y_h^{SU} represents if the generator *is* starting up at timestep h, and y_h^{SD} represents if the generator is shutting down at timestep h.

2.2. *Lookup Dispatch Algorithm*

The lookup dispatch algorithm compares the LMP, π_h^{real}, to the generator's bid curve prices, π_{hl}, at each timestep of the horizon (the bid curves may be either static, i.e., time-invariant, or indexed by time). The algorithm sets upper and lower bounds, $\underline{B_h}$ and $\overline{B_h}$, on the bid power at that timestep, B_h, according to where on the bid curve the LMP falls. If the LMP is larger than the highest price on the bid curve, the generator has low marginal costs and has cleared the market for that timestep, therefore will be constrained to maximum power output,P^{max}. If the LMP is lower than the lowest point on the bid curve, the generators marginal costs are higher than electricity price at that timestep, so the generator is constrained to either shutdown (zero power output) or operate at minimum power,P^{min}. If the LMP falls between two points on the bid curve, the dispatch of that generator is expected to fall between the associated power values of those points ($B_{hl} \leq B_h \leq B_{h(l+1)}$).

2.3. *MILP Optimization Problem*

After the bid power bounds are set, a multiobjective optimization problem is solved for the final dispatch of each generator:

$$\min \quad \Delta \tag{1a}$$

$$\max \quad \sum_{h \in H} \underbrace{\pi_h^{real} p_h}_{A} - \underbrace{(\pi_h^0 B_h^0) y_h}_{B} - \underbrace{\sum_{l=1}^{N} \pi_h^l \delta_{hl}}_{C} - \underbrace{c^{SU} y_h^{SU}}_{D} \tag{1b}$$

$$\text{s.t.} \quad \underline{B_h} \leq B_h \leq \overline{B_h} \;\; \forall h \tag{1c}$$

$$\Delta = \sum_{h \in H} |p_h - B_h| \tag{1d}$$

$$0 \le \delta_{hl} \le B_{hl} - B_{h(l-1)} \quad \forall h, l \tag{1e}$$

$$p_h = p^{min} y_h + \sum_{l=1}^{N} \delta_{hl} \quad \forall h \tag{1f}$$

$$\sum_{h \in H} |p_h - B_h| \le \Delta^* + \varepsilon \tag{1g}$$

The first objective function Eq.(1a) minimizes the sum of deviations for the generator, Δ. The second objective function Eq.(1b) maximizes the revenue of the generator over the entire horizon. Term A represents the profit from the final dispatch, term B represents the minimum operating costs which are represented by the first point on the bid curve, term C is a linear representation of the bid curve of the generator, and term D is the start-up cost (this term is zero if generator is not starting up at timestep h i.e. $y_h^{SU} = 0$) It is constrained by Eq.(1c), bounds on the bid power for each timestep, and Eq.(1d), the definition of deviation between final dispatch, p_h, and bid power, B_h. The continuous auxiliary variable δ_{jhl} is a linear correction for the piecewise bid curve. Eq.(1e) and Eq.(1f) describe the variable's behavior, which allows the selection of the proper segment of the piecewise bid curve when π_{hl} is increasing in l, i.e., the piecewise cost curve is convex. The thermal generator model also adds constraints to the problem and includes all the discrete decisions for the generator (whether it is on/off, starting up, or shutting down at each timestep). To solve the problem, objective functions are solved using lexicographic ordering, placing full priority on Eq.(1a) first, then optimizing with the second objective. To ensure the minimum deviation value is enforced in the second objective, constraint Eq.(1g) is added to constrain the deviation between the optimized first objective, Δ^*, and a small number ε (approximately 10^{-2}).

3. Results and Discussion

To test the shortcut market simulator algorithm, we analyze a single node from the RTS-GMLC data set named "Adams". One month of the node's dispatch was simulated using a rolling horizon algorithm. The historical LMPs came from a full market clearing simulation in Prescient. The dispatch results from the shortcut simulation and Prescient were then compared. Problems M1 and M2 were formulated in Pyomo (Hart et al. 2017) and solved using Gurobi. The optimization problem contained 194 variables (122 continuous, 72 binary) for the 24-hour sub problem solved during the rolling horizon. The total 31-day shortcut market simulator algorithm took ~532 seconds. In small-scale tests, we found the shortcut market simulator algorithm was approximately 100-times faster than conducting a full market clearing in Prescient.

Comparing the results of Prescient with the shortcut simulation revealed the accuracy of our proposed approximation. Figure 2 (left) shows the generator dispatch schedules from the shortcut simulator (solid line) and Prescient (dotted line) for one quarter of the 31-day rolling horizon case study (hours 186-372). Only three time periods in this portion of the simulation, circled in red, show differences in the dispatch profiles. When analyzing the points where the shortcut simulator's dispatch did not match Prescient's dispatch, we observed two main trends. First, the shortcut simulator heavily

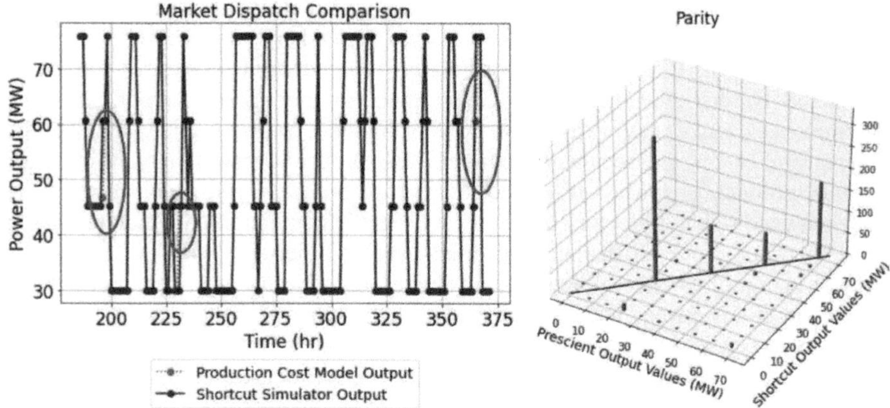

Figure 2: (left) generator dispatch schedule, comparing dispatch results from production cost model (red, dotted line) and shortcut market simulator (blue, solid line) for hours 182-372 of the 31-day simulation. The three red ovals show small discrepancies between output of the shortcut simulator and Prescient PCM. (right) parity between dispatch results from production cost model and shortcut market simulator.

favors the upper bound on bid power, set in the lookup dispatch step. Second, because Prescient makes unit commitment decisions (start-up/shut-down) in the DAM, the shortcut simulator finds different unit commitment while considering RTM prices. Figure 2 (right) shows a 3D parity plot, demonstrating the frequency of timesteps that match exactly. Approximately 67% of the dispatch points match within <1 MW. Overall, the shortcut simulator predictions had approximately 4% error in cumulative power output (summed over the entire horizon) as compared to Prescient.

4. Conclusions and Future Work

The case study provides initial validation of the proposed shortcut simulator to approach dispatch schedules using only historical LMPs, bid curves, and generator characteristics. Coupled with market participation optimization formulations (e.g., Dowling, 2017a), this can enable new approaches to estimate the economic performance of new technologies such as integrated energy systems when participating in markets. Ongoing work includes analysing all nodes of the RTS-GMLC dataset to further benchmark the accuracy of this proposed method including alternate MILP formulations. Moreover, the proposed shortcut simulator can be used to improve the realism of technoeconomic evaluations by considering bidding, the dominant mode to participating in markets, instead of the common self-schedule assumption.

Acknowledgements

This research was conducted as part of the Institute for the Design of Advanced Energy Systems (IDAES) and Design and Optimization Infrastructure for Tightly Coupled Hybrid Systems (DISPATCHES) projects. It was supported by (1) the Simulation-Based Engineering, Crosscutting Research Program within the U.S. Department of Energy's Office of Fossil Energy and Carbon Management and (2) the Grid Modernization Initiative of the U.S. Department of Energy as part of its Grid Modernization Laboratory Consortium, a strategic partnership between DOE and the national laboratories to bring together leading experts, technologies, and resources to collaborate on the goal of modernizing the nation's grid. This work was authored in part by the National Renewable Energy Laboratory, operated by Alliance for Sustainable Energy, LLC, for the U.S. Department of Energy (DOE) under Contract No. DE-AC36-08GO28308. Neither the United States Government nor any agency thereof, nor any of their employees, makes any warranty, express or implied, or assumes any legal liability or responsibility for the accuracy, completeness, or usefulness of any information, apparatus, product, or process disclosed, or represents that its use would not infringe privately owned rights. Reference herein to any specific commercial product, process, or service by trade name, trademark, manufacturer, or otherwise does not necessarily constitute or imply its endorsement, recommendation, or favoring by the United States Government or any agency thereof. The views and opinions of authors expressed herein do not necessarily state or reflect those of the United States Government or any agency thereof.

References

Arent, Douglas J., Shannon M. Bragg-Sitton, David C. Miller, Thomas J. Tarka, Jill A. Engel-Cox, Richard D. Boardman, Peter C. Balash, Mark F. Ruth, Jordan Cox, and David J. Garfield. 2021. "Multi-Input, Multi-Output Hybrid Energy Systems." *Joule* 5 (1): 47–58.

Arroyo, J. M., and A. J. Conejo. 2000. "Optimal Response of a Thermal Unit to an Electricity Spot Market." *IEEE Transactions on Power Systems* 15 (3): 1098–1104.

Carrión, Miguel, and José Manuel Arroyo. 2006. "A Computationally Efficient Mixed-Integer Linear Formulation for the Thermal Unit Commitment Problem." *IEEE Transactions on Power Systems* 21 (3): 1371–78.

Dowling, Alexander W., Ranjeet Kumar, and Victor M. Zavala. 2017. "A Multi-Scale Optimization Framework for Electricity Market Participation." *Applied Energy* 190 (March): 147–64.

Dowling, Alexander W., Tian Zheng, and Victor M. Zavala. 2017. "Economic Assessment of Concentrated Solar Power Technologies: A Review." *Renewable and Sustainable Energy Reviews* 72 (June 2016): 1019–32.

Ela, E, M Milligan, A Bloom, A Botterud, A Townsend, and T Levin. 2014. "Evolution of Wholesale Electricity Market Design with Increasing Levels of Renewable Generation," no. September: 1–139.

"GridMod/RTS-GMLC: Reliability Test System - Grid Modernization Lab Consortium." n.d. https://github.com/GridMod/RTS-GMLC.

Hart, William E., Carl D. Laird, Jean-Paul Watson, David L. Woodruff, Gabriel A. Hackebeil, Bethany L. Nicholson, and John D. Siirola. 2017. *Pyomo — Optimization Modeling in Python*. Vol. 67. Springer Optimization and Its Applications. Cham: Springer International Publishing.

"Prescient." n.d. https://github.com/grid-parity-exchange/Prescient.

Seel, Joachim, Andrew Mills, Ryan Wiser, Sidart Deb, Aarthi Asokkumar, Mohammad Hassanzadeh, and Amirsaman Aarabali. 2018. "Impacts of High Variable Renewable Energy Futures on Wholesale Electricity Prices, and on Electric-Sector Decision Making." https://emp.lbl.gov/publications/impacts-high-variable-renewable.

Proceedings of the 14th International Symposium on Process Systems Engineering – PSE 2021+
June 19-23, 2022, Kyoto, Japan
http://dx.doi.org/10.1016/B978-0-323-85159-6.50087-7

Scheduling of Material and Information Flows in the Manufacturing of Chemicals for the Order-to-Cash Process of a Digital Supply Chain

Hector D. Perez[a], John M. Wassick[b], Ignacio E. Grossmann[a*]

[a]Carnegie Mellon University, 5000 Forbes Ave., Pittsburgh 15213, USA
[b]The Dow Chemical Company, 2211 H.H. Dow Way, Midland 48674, USA
grossmann@cmu.edu

Abstract

A scheduling model is proposed to schedule order transactions and manufacturing operations in the order-to-cash process of a digital supply chain. The proposed model is compared to scheduling models that focus on either the order transactions or the manufacturing operations. The advantage of the integrated approach is found in the accuracy of the solutions attained, whereas the purely transactional model is found to be suboptimal, and the production scheduling model is found to be infeasible under certain circumstances. An illustrative example is presented where the integrated model is shown to increase both the system revenue (60% increase) and order-fulfilment (100% increase), compared to the transactional model. The production scheduling model is shown to be infeasible and overestimate the system revenue.

Keywords: Scheduling, Business Processes, Supply Chain.

1. Introduction

With the advent and widespread drive towards digitalization in the fourth industrial revolution, a clear opportunity has emerged for a more holistic approach to supply chain management. This endeavour requires reimagining supply networks as systems that unite physical, information, and financial flows, with multiple interactions across the enterprise where material, data, humans, and intelligent agents interact in a coordinated fashion (Büyüközkan and Göçer, 2018). Within the PSE community, Laínez and Puigjaner (2012) have called for an integrated approach to Supply Chain Management (SCM), with a shift from operations-based decision support systems to decision frameworks that integrate operational, financial, and environmental models.

In the last two decades, research has begun to respond to these trends and address this need for integration. One such study in this space is that of Guillen, et al. (2006), who present a planning/scheduling model for a chemical supply chain that integrates process operations and financial decisions. This work highlights the value obtained when financial and material flows are integrated in the scheduling decisions. However, their approach does not consider information flows in the supply chain, which is an area that has not received much attention. Information flows are captured in business processes, which model the transactions that occur on requests to the system involved. In supply chain, these requests can be external customer orders, such as in the order-to-cash process, or replenishment orders, such as in the procure-to-pay process. Scheduling events in business processes has been studied by the computer science and information systems communities (Xu, et al., 2010). The business process scheduling done in these works targets purely transactional business processes, such as banking processes that are executed in the cloud (Hoenisch, et al., 2016). However, when physical goods are involved, such as in material procurement or physical goods sales, the associated business processes become tightly coupled with the material flows in the system. Although scheduling business processes in this context has not received much attention, their close integration with physical flows is critical in chemical supply chains, where business processes like the order-to-cash process depend on the availability of inventory and the manufacturing of goods.

The scheduling of business process transactions in supply chain has been the focus of previous work by the authors. In their prior work, scheduling models have been applied to optimize the performance of the order-to-cash business process in a digital supply chain (Perez et al. 2020; 2021). However, the models have been applied primarily to the information flows in the supply chain and represent any physical processes as nodes in the transactional process network with a lumped processing time. The goal in this work is to extend what has been done previously by integrating a batch chemical manufacturing scheduling model with the order fulfilment supply chain model. The aim is to provide a more complete and accurate view of the supply chain by coupling material flows from chemical processing with the information flows from business processes. Thus, this work takes a step forward in the development of holistic decision support systems for digital supply chains.

2. Problem Statement

The order-to-cash business process manages the sequence of transactions that occur when a customer places an order. At each step, one or more agents is capable of performing certain transaction on an order. These agents can be human agents (e.g., planner, freight forwarder, customer service representative) or digital agents (for automated steps). Agents can be dedicated to a specific transaction, or they can be flexible such that they can perform transactions at different steps in the business process.

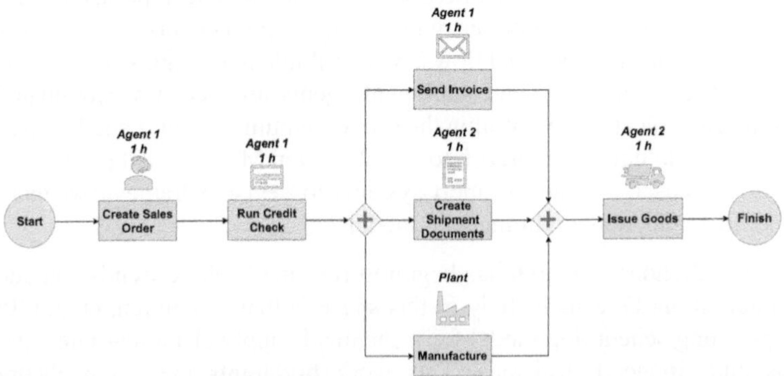

Figure 1. Illustrative order fulfilment process in a chemical supply chain

Consider the illustrative example in Figure 1, which shows a simplified customer order fulfilment process with five business transactions and one manufacturing step. The credit check step is a representation of many things that could hold or delay an order from being released to manufacturing. The invoice creation, shipment document creation, and manufacturing steps can be performed in parallel. Two agents are available to perform the five transactions on the orders as indicated in Figure 1. The manufacturing node can represent a batch chemical plant as the one in Kondili, et al. (1993), shown in Figure 2. The plant flowsheet involves a heating step, three reaction pathways, and a purification step to produce products P1 and P2 from raw materials A, B, and C. The main equipment in the batch plant includes a heating vessel with 100 kg capacity, two reactors with 50 and 80 kg capacities, and a distillation column (still) with 200 kg capacity. Intermediate storage tanks include a 100 kg tank for hot A, a 150 kg tank for BC, a 200 kg tank for AB, and a 100 kg tank for E. Raw material and final product storage are uncapacitated. Processing times are indicated next to each transaction in Figure 1 and each manufacturing step in Figure 2.

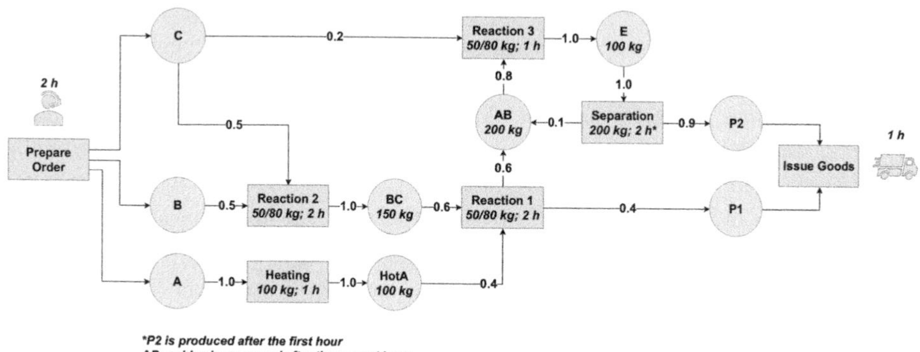

Figure 2. Flowsheet for batch chemical plant

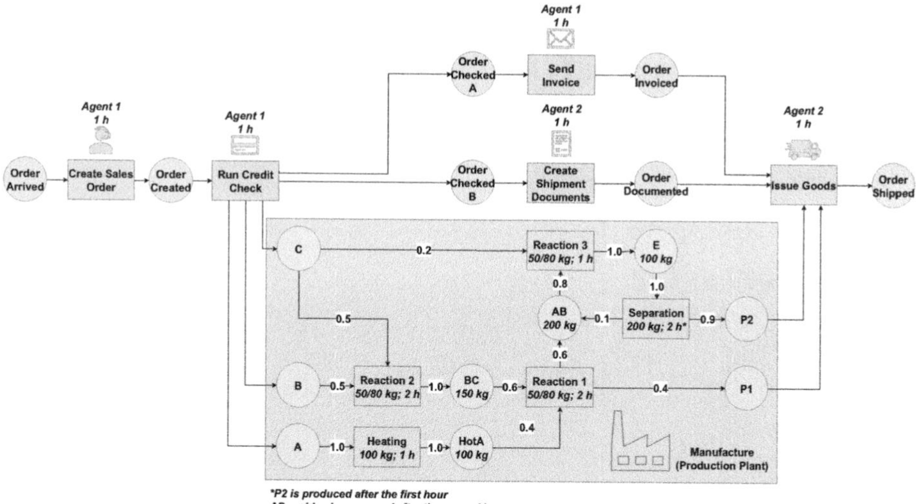

Figure 3. State-Task Network representation for the integrated model

3. Mathematical Model

The process can be modelled as purely transactional, as shown in Figure 1, by viewing the manufacturing node as a transactional step with a fixed processing type for each product type (4 h for P1 and 6 h for P2). Alternatively, from a purely plant operations standpoint, the system can be modelled using the flowsheet in Figure 2, adding a 2 h delay after an order enters the system and a 1 h delay after a batch of product is produced to account for the first two and last order transactions, respectively. A third option, the proposed approach, is to model the system holistically, accounting for the order transactions and the detailed chemical plant model as shown in Figure 3. In this approach, the stochiometric amount of each raw material for each order quantity is made available when the credit check step is completed. Producing one unit of P1, requires one unit of A, 0.75 units of B, and 0.75 units of C. Produce one unit of P2, requires 0.59 units of A, 0.44 units of B, and 0.66 units of C. For each of the three modelling approaches, a State-Task Network (STN) model (Shah, et al., 1993) is used to schedule the system events.

The objective function of the optimization models is to maximize the revenue as indicated by the first term in Eq. (1). For the purely physical model (plant model) and the integrated model (transactions + plant model), a small ϵ penalty (10^{-4}) is assigned to the binary task triggering variables for the plant tasks (heating, reactions, and separation) to force the optimizer to favour fewer large batches over many small batches. The margin (revenue) for each order is modelled as a monotonically decreasing piecewise linear function. Eq. (2) gives the upper bound on the order margin (z_o), where T_o^{fulfil} is the time that order o is fulfilled, and $m_{i,o}$ and $b_{i,o}$ are the slope and intercept parameters for each linear function i. The discontinuity in the order margin function occurs at the order due date (t_o^{due}), where a penalty is assessed because of backordering ($m_{1,o} \cdot t_o^{due} + b_{1,o} \geq m_{2,o} \cdot t_o^{due} + b_{2,o}$). The fulfilment time, T_o^{fulfil}, is constrained by Eq. 3, where $D_{o,t}$ is a binary variable used to indicate that order o was completed at time t and leaves the State-Task Network (external consumption term in the state balance). Backordering is governed by the binary variable B_o as shown in Eq. 4. Eq. 5 forces unfulfilled orders to have zero revenue. F_o is a binary variable that indicates if an order was fulfilled within the scheduling horizon, as shown in Eq. 6. The disjunctions in Eq. (2) and Eq. (5) are reformulated using Big-M constraints.

$$\max \sum_o z_o - \sum_{k \in K^{plant}} \sum_{r \in R_k} \sum_t \epsilon \cdot W_{k,r,t} \quad (1)$$

$$\begin{bmatrix} \neg B_o \\ z_o \leq m_{1,o} \cdot T_o^{fulfil} + b_{1,o} \end{bmatrix} \vee \begin{bmatrix} B_o \\ z_o \leq m_{2,o} \cdot T_o^{fulfil} + b_{2,o} \end{bmatrix} \quad \forall o \quad (2)$$

$$D_{o,t} \cdot t \leq T_o^{fulfil} \quad \forall o, t \quad (3)$$

$$B_o = 1 - \sum_{t \leq t_o^{due}} D_{o,t} \quad \forall o \quad (4)$$

$$\begin{bmatrix} F_o \\ z_o \leq z_o^{UB} \end{bmatrix} \vee \begin{bmatrix} \neg F_o \\ z_o \leq 0 \end{bmatrix} \quad \forall o \quad (5)$$

$$F_o = \sum_t D_{o,t} \quad \forall o \quad (6)$$

4. Illustrative Example

In the illustrative example depicted in Figure 1, five orders are generated with random due dates and order margin parameters. Orders 2, 3, and 4 are for material P1, and orders 1 and 5 are for material P2. The demand of each material is also sampled randomly with a mean of 25 kg. A scheduling horizon of 15 h is used. The three modelling approaches (purely transactional with lumped plant processing times, purely physical plant model with upstream and downstream delays, and the integrated model) are implemented in JuMP 0.21 (Julia 1.6), using CPLEX 20.1 as the optimizer on a PC with an Intel i7, 1.9 GHz processor with 24 GB of RAM. CPLEX is allowed to access all 8 threads. The problem is relatively small (approximately 1,400 binary variables, 290 continuous variables, and 4,200 constraints for the integrated model), and solves within 1 s or less.

Figure 4 shows the results for each of the three scheduling approaches. The limitations of the purely transactional or purely physical models are seen in the results obtained. The purely transactional model ignores the integration of physical flows, making it suboptimal. Because intermediate AB, which is required to produce P2, is a by-product of P1 and P2, the time to produce P2 can be decreased when a batch of P1 has already been produced or is being processed alongside an order for P2. On the other hand, the purely physical model ignores the resource constraints on the transactional side, producing an infeasible schedule. The infeasibility arises from the fact that there are not enough agents to perform the first two steps on each order in the first 2 hours of the schedule. Thus, the production of intermediates for all orders cannot begin at t = 2 h. Furthermore, the model assumes that there are enough agents to issue goods once they are ready, which overestimates the system revenue as not all orders can be fulfilled immediately after the material is produced. In contrast, the integrated model finds the optimal schedule which fulfils 80% of the orders in the 15 h horizon, accounting for both agent availability and process integration at the plant.

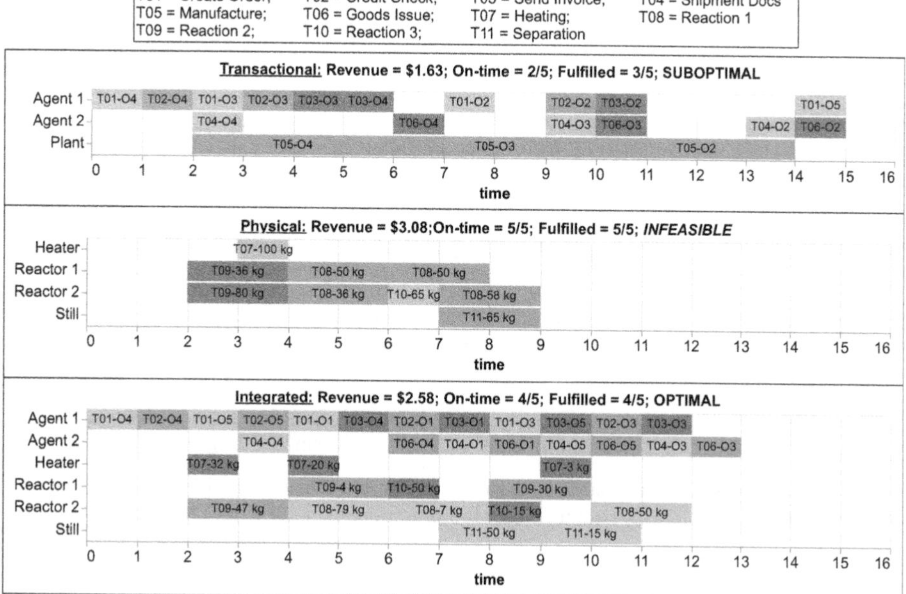

5. Conclusions

An STN-based scheduling model is proposed to schedule orders in the order-to-cash process of a chemical supply chain. The information flows in the order-to-cash process are integrated with the physical flows of the manufacturing facility. An illustrative example is given, in which the model that integrates the transactional and the material flows is shown to attain a 60% improvement in terms of revenue over the model that lumps the material flows in a single manufacturing node. The integrated model also doubles the number of orders fulfilled in the scheduling horizon. The manufacturing-only model that lumps the initial order transactions and the goods issue step, is shown to yield infeasible schedules in a make-to-order system when the transactional steps are resource constrained. The infeasibility demonstrated in the illustrative example is indicative of actual circumstances encountered in industrial supply chains. The lack of rigorous coordination between manufacturing scheduling and order processing often leads to telephone calls and email exchanges between the scheduler and customer service representative to ultimately resolve conflicts between their respective domains. The proposed modelling approach is a first attempt to integrate the different flows involved in a digital supply chain. Future work will include adding financial flows (accounting ledger), and extending the material flows to those in a multi-echelon supply network.

References

Büyüközkan, G., Göçer, F., 2018, Digital Supply Chain: Literature Review and a Proposed Framework for Future Research, Computers in Industry, 97, 157–77.

Guillén, G., Badell, M., Espuña, A., Puigjaner, L., 2006, Simultaneous optimization of process operations and financial decisions to enhance the integrated planning/scheduling of chemical supply chains, Computers and Chemical Engineering, 30, 421-436.

Hoenisch, P., Schuller, D., Schulte, S., Hochreiner, C., Dustdar, S., 2016, Optimization of complex elastic processes, IEEE Transactions on Services Computing, 9, 700-713.

Laínez, J.M., Puigjaner, L., 2012, Prospective and perspective review in integrated supply chain modeling for the chemical process industry, Current Opinion in Hcemical Engineering, 1, 430-445.

Kondili, E., Pantelides, C.C., Sargent, R.W.H., 1993, A general algorithm for short-term scheduling of batch operations-I. MILP formulation, Computers and Chemical Engineering, 17, 211–227.

Perez, H.D., Amaran, S., Erisen, E., Wassick, J.M., Grossmann, I.E., 2020, Optimization of Business Transactional Processes in a Digital Supply Chain, Computer Aided Chemical Engineering, 48, 1159–1164.

Perez, H.D., Amaran, S., Erisen, E., Wassick, J.M., Grossmann, I.E., 2021, A Digital Twin Framework for Business Transactional Processes in Supply Chains, Computer Aided Chemical Engineering, 50, 1755–1760.

Shah, N., Pantelides, C.C., Sargent, R.W.H., 1993, A general algorithm for short-term scheduling of batch operations-II. Computational issues, Computers and Chemical Engineering, 17, 229-244.

Xu, J., Liu, C., Zhao, X., Yongchareon, S., Business Process Scheduling with Resource Availability Constraints, 2010, Lecture Notes in Computer Science, 6426, 419-427.

Proceedings of the 14th International Symposium on Process Systems Engineering – PSE 2021+
June 19-23, 2022, Kyoto, Japan
http://dx.doi.org/10.1016/B978-0-323-85159-6.50088-9

Optimization of Maximum Completion Time of Polymerization Section Based on Improved Estimation of Distribution Algorithm

Jian Su[a], Yuhong Wang[a*], Su Zhang[a], Xiaoyong Gao[b]

[a]College of Control Science and Engineering, China University of Petroleum, Qingdao 266580, Shandong, China;
[b]Department of Automation, China University of Petroleum, Beijing 102249, China
Y.H.Wang@upc.edu.cn

Abstract

The polymerization section is an essential link in the production process of PVC, and the quality of its scheduling tasks directly affects the benefits of the enterprise. Given the scheduling optimization problems of unreasonable allocation of tasks and low efficiency, an improved estimation of distribution algorithm (IEDA) is proposed in this study to minimize the maximum completion time. The elitism strategy and the binary search strategy are employed to improve the global search ability and the solution speed of the estimation of distribution algorithm (EDA). Then the effectiveness of the proposed algorithm is verified in a case. The result of comparison demonstrates that compared with the EDA, the maximum completion time of the 3×5SP problem solved by the IEDA is reduced by 1.31% on average, and the speed of convergence is accelerated, which verified the accuracy and effectiveness of the IEDA in solving the scheduling problem of the PVC polymerization section.

Keywords: Process systems; Estimation of distribution algorithm; Polymerization; PVC; Scheduling optimization

1. Introduction

Polyvinyl chloride (PVC) is made of vinyl chloride monomer polymerization. The polymerization section is an imperative link. It is essential to develop a scientific and reasonable scheduling scheme to make full use of existing resources, and improve the economic benefits of enterprises.

PVC polymerization section is a batch production with large-scale and high complexity processes. How to optimize the solution of its model and improve the efficiency has attracted more attention. Wang et al. (2016) established the whole process model of PVC production, proposed an optimal decomposition algorithm based on hierarchical division, and decomposed the complex MINLP problems into MILP and NLP problems for solving. Gao et al. (2017) introduced a planning optimization model based on piecewise linear approximation to process the nonlinear characteristics in actual production, reducing the complexity of the model and improving the solving efficiency. However, it becomes difficult for the exact solution based on mathematical programming to adapt to the demand for the rapid solution with the increase of solution scale in the actual production environment. The EDA is a commonly used heuristic approach in project scheduling and related areas (Zhou et al., 2021). Research reveals that EDA breaks the pattern of traditional optimization algorithms, avoids premature convergence that frequently occurs in overcoming complex optimization problems, and has strong chain learning ability and evolutionary orientation. Therefore, it is of practical significance to solve the problem of PVC scheduling using EDA.

In this paper, the scheduling model of the PVC aggregation section is firstly described, and several strategies are proposed to improve EDA. Then, the IEDA is applied to the scheduling optimization problem to minimize the maximum completion time. Finally, a case is provided for analysis.

2. Scheduling model of PVC polymerization section

2.1. Modeling hypotheses

1) The number of polymerization reactors, PVC grades, and orders are known, each polymerization reactor can process any grade of PVC.
2) Each polymerization reactor can only produce PVC of the same grade in the same batch.
3) The same polymerization reactor can produce different grades of PVC within a scheduling period, the kettle and other operations should be cleaned when switching between different grades of PVC, resulting in waiting time.
4) The polymerization reaction time depends on the factors such as PVC grade and catalyst, temperature and pressure in the polymerization reactor.

2.2. Mathematical model

(1) Optimization objective

Assuming that the completion time on the j-th polymerization reactor is TE_j, the mathematical description of the optimization objective to minimize the maximum completion time T is:

$$T = min(max(TE_j)) \tag{1}$$

(2) Constraints

$$TE_j = \sum TH_{j,i_1,i_2} + \sum TP_{j,i}\,, i \in MP \tag{2}$$

$$TP_{j,i} = N_{j,i} \times T_{j,i} \tag{3}$$

$$\sum_{j=1}^{n} N_{j,i} = ceil\left(\frac{D_i}{FS \times \alpha_i}\right) \tag{4}$$

$$TS_{j,i} = TH_{j,i_1,i_2} + TC_{j,i_1} \tag{5}$$

$$TC_{j,i} = TS_{j,i} + TP_{j,i} \tag{6}$$

$$N_{j,i} \geq 0, D_i \geq 0, TS_{j,i} \geq TC_{j,i_1}, TC_{j,i} > 0, i \in MP \tag{7}$$

Eq.(1) presents the minimum completion time; Eq.(2) expresses the completion time constraint; Eq.(3) presents the polymerization time; Eq.(4) indicates the feed times constraint; Eq.(5) describes the constraints on the start time and end time of polymerization of the same grade in one polymerization reactor; Eq.(6) indicates the polymerization completion time; Eq.(7) describes the constraints on the number of feeding times, the total quantity of PVC of each grade in the order, and the start and end time of polymerization reactor processing.

3. Improved estimation of distribution algorithm

3.1. Improvement strategy

3.1.1. The elitism strategy

In the EDA, the proportion of selected dominant groups is fixed, which easily leads to local optimality. The number of dominant groups is adjusted based on the elitism strategy to more accurately express the information of solution space. Specifically, the individuals are sorted according to the fitness value; then the minimum value r_{min} and maximum value r_{max} of the ratio of the number of dominant population N to the total number of individuals in the population are set. Besides, M denotes the population size, I refers to the current iteration number, and K is the total iteration number. N is updated as:

$$N = M \times (r_{min} + (r_{max} - r_{min}) \times I/K) \tag{8}$$

3.1.2. Constructing probability model

The probability model was constructed in the following way to better describe the distribution of PVC production of different grades on the polymerization reactor. Suppose there are M individuals in the population, and N dominant individuals are selected to construct the probability model matrix P according to the fitness value function. Then, the feeding times of each grade of PVC in each polymerization reactor in dominant individuals are counted. The probability model matrix P is expressed as:

$$P = \begin{bmatrix} \frac{\sum_{k=1}^{N} b_{1,1,k}}{\sum_{k=1}^{N}\sum_{i=1}^{m} b_{i,1,k}} & \frac{\sum_{k=1}^{N} b_{1,2,k}}{\sum_{k=1}^{N}\sum_{i=1}^{m} b_{i,2,k}} & \cdots & \frac{\sum_{k=1}^{N} b_{1,n,k}}{\sum_{k=1}^{N}\sum_{i=1}^{m} b_{i,n,k}} \\ \frac{\sum_{k=1}^{N} b_{2,1,k}}{\sum_{k=1}^{N}\sum_{i=1}^{m} b_{i,1,k}} & \frac{\sum_{k=1}^{N} b_{2,2,k}}{\sum_{k=1}^{N}\sum_{i=1}^{m} b_{i,2,k}} & \cdots & \frac{\sum_{k=1}^{N} b_{2,n,k}}{\sum_{k=1}^{N}\sum_{i=1}^{m} b_{i,n,k}} \\ \vdots & \vdots & \cdots & \vdots \\ \frac{\sum_{k=1}^{N} b_{m,1,k}}{\sum_{k=1}^{N}\sum_{i=1}^{m} b_{i,1,k}} & \frac{\sum_{k=1}^{N} b_{m,2,k}}{\sum_{k=1}^{N}\sum_{i=1}^{m} b_{i,2,k}} & \cdots & \frac{\sum_{k=1}^{N} b_{m,n,k}}{\sum_{k=1}^{N}\sum_{i=1}^{m} b_{i,n,k}} \end{bmatrix} \tag{9}$$

Where, $1 \le i \le m$, $1 \le j \le n$, $1 \le k \le N$; $b_{i,j,k}$ represents the polymerization matrix code of the k-th individual in the dominant population, the feeding times of grade i PVC on the j-th polymerization reactor. The updating mode of P is shown in Eq.(10).

$$p_{i,j}(g+1) = (1-\beta)p_{i,j}(g) + \beta\frac{1}{N}\sum_{k=1}^{N} C_{i,j}^{k} \tag{10}$$

Where, $p_{i,j}(g)$ represents the probability matrix of the g-th generation, binary variable $C_{i,j}^{k}$ takes the value one when grade i PVC in the k-th individual is produced on the j-th polymerization kettle. β represents the learning rate of P, and the value is adaptive, as shown in Eq.(11), in which a_1 and a_2 are set to 0.7 and 0.4, respectively.

$$\beta = a_1 - a_2 \times (g/g_{\max}) \tag{11}$$

3.1.3. Binary search strategy

The binary search strategy is adopted to update individuals, so as to improve the breadth of algorithm search and the speed of convergence. The specific process is detailed as follows.

Firstly, the probability model matrix P and individual coding matrix B are constructed according to Eq.(12).

$$P=\begin{bmatrix} p_{1,1} & p_{1,2} & \cdots & p_{1,m} \\ p_{2,1} & p_{2,2} & \cdots & p_{2,m} \\ \vdots & \vdots & \cdots & \vdots \\ p_{n,1} & p_{n,2} & \cdots & p_{n,m} \end{bmatrix}, \quad B=\begin{bmatrix} b_{1,1} & b_{1,2} & \cdots & b_{1,m} \\ b_{2,1} & b_{2,2} & \cdots & b_{2,m} \\ \vdots & \vdots & \cdots & \vdots \\ b_{n,1} & b_{n,2} & \cdots & b_{n,m} \end{bmatrix} \tag{12}$$

Where, $p_{i,j}$ represents the probability of polymerization production of grade i PVC in the j-th polymerization reactor. The higher the probability value is, the more likely it is to choose this polymerization reactor for production, and the more the polymerization quantity is. And $b_{i,j}$ indicates the number of feeding times of grade i PVC in the j-th polymerization reactor.

Secondly, the maximum and minimum values corresponding to the i-th column of matrix B and matrix P and polymerization kettle number are determined. Finally, individual updates according to whether the PVC quantity corresponding to the individual and the distribution mode of the polymerization kettle comply with the combination mode described by the probability model.

3.2. IEDA

The steps for solving the PVC production scheduling problem are described as follows.

1) The initial population was randomly initialized using a coding method based on the sequence of aggregation and feed times.
2) The fitness value of each individual in the population was calculated according to the PVC production scheduling mathematical model.
3) The individuals with higher fitness values were selected to form the dominant group following the elitism strategy.
4) The probability matrix of different grades of PVC produced in different polymerization reactors was constructed depending on the dominant group obtained in step 3.
5) The coding mode of individuals in the population was transformed into aggregation matrix coding, and the binary search strategy was adopted to perform individual updating.
6) If the set number of iterations is reached, end the iteration, output the optimal individual and decode; otherwise, turn to step 2.

4. Case analysis

An actual industrial case study was conducted using MATLAB R2017b programming with the PVC polymerization section process as the research object to further verify the performance of IEDA. Experimental environment: Intel(R) Core(TM) i5-8400 CPU, 2.80GHz processor, 8.00GB memory, operating system Win10.

4.1. Case parameters

Two examples are selected: one is scheduling optimization problem of 3 polymerization reactors with 5 grades of PVC (3×5PS), the order is {700, 950, 1500, 1100, 500}; the other is scheduling optimization problem of 4 polymerization reactors with 3 grades of PVC (4×3PS), the order is {700, 1100, 680}.

4.2. Analysis of simulation results

Simulation experiments were conducted to verify the effectiveness of IEDA in solving the PVC scheduling problem. Genetic algorithm (GA), particle swarm optimization (PSO) and estimation of distribution algorithm (EDA) were used for simulation comparison experiments. Their parameters are set as follows: the maximum number of iterations of the algorithms is 1000, the population size is 300, the mutation probability of GA is 0.09, and the crossover probability is 0.7. The two learning factors of PSO are 1.62, and the inertial weights are 0.5 and 0.8, respectively.

Table 1 presents the maximum (T_{max}), minimum (T_{min}), average (T_{avg}) completion time, relative value (*R*) of IEDA to EDA and standard deviation (δ) of completion time (*T*) obtained through 20 experiments conducted by the algorithms under two examples.

Table 1 Optimization results of the algorithms

cases	algorithms	T_{max}	T_{min}	T_{avg}	R	δ
4×3PS	GA	192.3	187.5	189.61	--	1.268
	PSO	190.6	187.1	188.17	--	1.026
	EDA	185.3	180.4	183.76	--	1.137
	IEDA	183.6	179.3	181.45	1.25%↓	1.015
3×5PS	GA	401.4	399.1	399.35	--	0.494
	PSO	402.1	400.7	401.28	--	0.473
	EDA	398.5	397.0	397.88	--	0.445
	IEDA	393.3	391.7	392.66	1.31%↓	0.389

As revealed in Tables 1, the completion time obtained by IEDA are shorter than those obtained by other algorithms in the comparative experiments, besides, as another important evaluation index of algorithm performance, the standard deviation of IEDA is lower than others, which demonstrates that IEDA has better convergence ability and solution stability.

With the purpose of directly reflecting the superiority of IEDA in optimal solution and convergence speed, the average convergence curves of GA, PSO, EDA and IEDA for solving 3×5PS scheduling optimization problems 20 times were drawn, as illustrated in Figure 1.

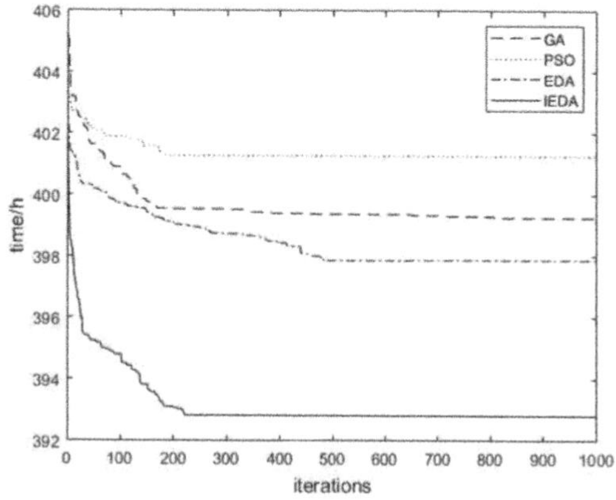

Fig.1 Optimization curves of the algorithms when solving 3×5PS problem

The convergence curves of the algorithms in Figure 1 suggest that after several iterations, the optimal solution solved by IEDA is superior to other algorithms, and the convergence speed and accuracy of IEDA are superior to EDA.

The Gantt chart corresponding to the optimal solution obtained by IEDA in 20 experiments is exhibited in Figure 2. Regarding the convenience of representation, a slash '/' and two groups of numbers before and after are used in the Gantt chart to indicate the PVC grade to be polymerized on each polymerization reactor and the feeding times.

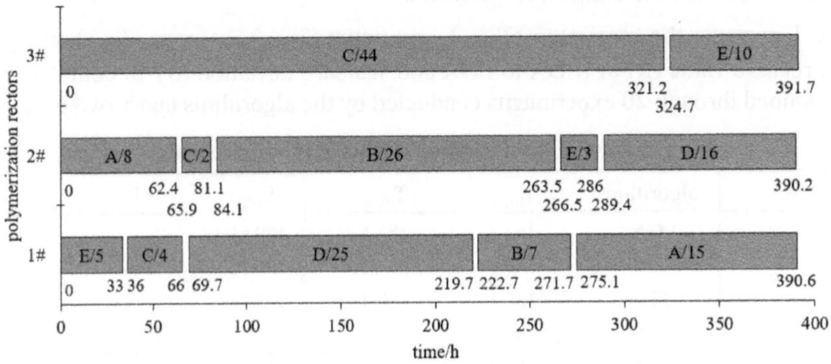

Fig.2 Optimal scheduling result of 3×5PS solved by IEDA algorithm

The analysis of completion time, evolution curve, and Gantt chart demonstrates that IEDA is superior to GA, PSO and EDA in terms of stability, convergence speed and accuracy, optimization performance, and comprehensive performance in solving PVC production scheduling problems. This verifies the effectiveness of IEDA in optimizing PVC production scheduling problems.

5. Conclusions

In this paper, a mathematical model of scheduling optimization problem of the PVC polymerization section is established, and IEDA is proposed to minimize the maximum completion time of polymerization. The results of the comparison of algorithms reflect that IEDA has higher convergence speed and optimization ability. Furthermore, as a general strategy, IEDA is applicable for the solution of PVC whole process production model and other similar process industries scheduling problems.

Reference

Y. H. Wang, X. Lian, X. Y. Gao, Z. H. Feng, D. X. Huang, T. Chan, S. S. Liu, J. X. Bai, 2016, Multiperiod Planning of a PVC Plant for the Optimization of Process Operation and Energy Consumption: An MINLP Approach, Industrial & Engineering Chemistry Research, 55, 48, 12430-12443.

X. Y. Gao, Z. H. Feng, Y. H. Wang, X. Huang, 2018, Decomposition algorithm for PVC plant planning optimization based on piecewise linear approximation, CIESC Journal, 69, 03, 953-961.

Y. F. Zhou, J. D. Miao, B. Yan, Z. S. Zhang, 2021, Stochastic resource-constrained project scheduling problem with time varying weather conditions and an improved estimation of distribution algorithm, Computers & Industrial Engineering, 157.

Proceedings of the 14th International Symposium on Process Systems Engineering – PSE 2021+
June 19-23, 2022, Kyoto, Japan
http://dx.doi.org/10.1016/B978-0-323-85159-6.50089-0

Evolutionary Algorithm-based Optimal Batch Production Scheduling

Christian Klanke[a*], Engelbert Pasieka[a*], Dominik Bleidorn[b], Christian Koslwoski[b], Christian Sonntag[b], Sebastian Engell[a]

[a]Process Dynamics and Operations Group, TU Dortmund University, Emil-Figge-Straße 70, 44227 Dortmund, Germany
[b]INOSIM Software GmbH, Joseph-von-Fraunhofer-Str. 20, 44227 Dortmund, Germany
{christian.klanke, engelbert.pasieka}@tu-dortmund.de

Abstract

In this work, a simulation-optimization strategy is applied to a benchmark scheduling problem from the pharmaceutical industry, as published by Kopanos, et al. (2010). The optimization is performed by a meta-heuristic using a commercial Discrete Event Simulation software as the schedule builder (simulation-optimization approach). Our work is motivated by commonly encountered real world scenarios where detailed simulation models of the production processes are available and can be used to validate and evaluate the schedules in the presence of many, often non-standard constraints. Moreover, the effort for re-modelling and for the maintenance is reduced by using the available simulator. The meta-heuristic applied here is an Evolutionary Algorithm and we discuss different variants of the encoding of the problem. It is demonstrated that for regular objectives the performance is similar to the tailored MILP-based solution strategy of Kopanos et al. (2010) where a two-stage decomposition strategy is employed.

Keywords: Batch Production Scheduling, Pharmaceutical Industry, Simulation-Optimization, Meta-heuristics, Evolutionary Algorithm, Discrete Event Simulation.

1. Introduction

Simulation-optimization (SO) is a versatile tool for the solution of planning and scheduling problems. In industrial practice, often simulation models of different degrees of accuracy are available from the plant design stage and/or used as a tool in operations for example to validate delivery promises and to determine bottlenecks. Some tools can represent complex constraints of the execution of the orders, include maintenance, the availability of personnel, feedstock and packing materials and the like. Also stochastic effects as e.g. disturbances or varying processing times can often be included. Usually such tools are implemented as Discrete Event Simulators (DES) where rules for the execution of the production can be implemented flexibly. Such simulators enable the end-user to model the production processes in detail and therefore to validate production schedules with respect to constraints which are difficult to formulate otherwise. The models that are built for commercial DES software are typically maintained by the industrial end users, which provides flexibility with respect to changing rules, constraints, recipes or even the set-up of the plant in an intuitive manner. If such a simulation is available for a given plant or process, it is often desired by the user to use it also for planning and scheduling purposes beyond manual generation of plans or schedules and

testing them in simulations. As the models do not conform to a specific mathematical formalism, combining simulation by the DES for the execution and performance evaluation of the schedules with meta-heuristics for schedule generation is an obvious approach. Clearly, this does not provide provably optimal or near-optimal solutions.
In contrast, mathematical programming (MP) provides exact solutions with performance guarantees. It can be applied even to large-scale problems (Harjunkoski, et al., 2014) but often the problem size and complexity leads to unacceptably long computation times or large optimality gaps. This issue is usually dealt with in a semi-heuristic manner, i.e. by employing decomposition approaches that exploit the problem structure in a tailored manner, generating sub-problems with reduced numbers of degrees of freedom. These sub-problems can be solved faster and their solutions are then combined to yield the solution of the full problem (Klanke, et al., 2021, Georgiadis, et al., 2019). MP yields solutions with a measure of optimality and the problems can be solved deterministically to proven optimality. However, as soon as decomposition approaches are used, a measure of optimality usually also is not provided, as only the optimality gaps of the sub-problems are known, but not the optimality gap of the final solution. In addition, the quality of the solutions depends on the heuristics that are employed to perform the decomposition, e.g., the assignments of orders to sub-problems in case of order-based decomposition. A major disadvantage of MP solutions is the need for expert knowledge to formulate the problem at hand and to maintain the models which is far less intuitive than parameterizing a DES.
In related work, a SO approach based on the same commercial simulator (Klanke, et al., 2021) was applied to a complex industrial make-and-pack scheduling problem for which no solutions from exact optimization approaches were available. In this work, we address the well-studied problem from Kopanos, et al., (2010), a large-scale benchmark batch scheduling problem from the pharmaceutical industry, to investigate the quality of the solutions obtained with the SO approach in comparison to those obtained from the tailored MP formulation in Kopanos, et al., (2010). There a two-step MILP decomposition strategy was proposed and the authors stated that "[…] a comparison of the solution method with elaborated metaheuristics would be of great interest." The remainder of this contribution is structured as follows: We start by giving a short overview of the case study and its key features in Section 2. Then, in Section 3, we introduce our methodology, including the representation of solutions and the genetic operators. In Section 4, we present the results of our approach for regular objectives and compare them with those obtained by Kopanos, et al. (2010). Additionally, we present and discuss results with our proposed approach for the non-regular Weighted Lateness objective where timing decisions had to be added to our approach. In the last Section we conclude our findings and present an outlook.

2. Case Study

The case study addressed in this work is taken from Kopanos, et al., (2010). It is a multiproduct batch plant with 17 units (machines) that are organized in 6 stages. The problem, which is a variant of a hybrid flow shop problem, comprises 12 instances that vary in the number of orders, the objectives, and in the storage policy. The features of the problem include limited product-unit flexibility, machine-dependent processing times, sequence-dependent changeover times, and product-specific recipes, meaning that certain jobs are not processed on some of the available stages.

This paper considers three problem instances with 30 orders, unlimited intermediate storage (UIS), and the objectives Makespan (C_{max}), Overall & Changeover Cost (O.&C.C.) and Weighted Lateness (W.L.), which are minimized. The objectives are defined as

$$C_{max} = \max(C_1,..,C_{|I|})\ [h] \tag{1}$$

$$O.\&C.C\ = \omega C_{max} + \Sigma_{i \in I}\ cc_i\ [h], \text{with } \omega = 0.9 \cdot 10^3 \tag{2}$$

$$W.L. = \Sigma_{i \in I}\ \alpha E_i + \beta T_i\ [h], \text{with } \alpha\ = 0.9 \text{ and } \beta\ 4.5 \tag{3}$$

C_i denotes the completion time of job i, cc_i denotes the sum of all changeover times multiplied with a sequence dependent impact factor associated with job i, and E_i and T_i denote the earliness and the tardiness of job i.

3. Methodology

In this section, a generic solution approach that works without decomposition of the problem is presented. We first focus on the regular objectives C_{max} and O.&C.C..
Our solution method uses modular representations for the different degrees of freedom that can be adapted according to the problem at hand. The case study has three generic degrees of freedom: the allocation of jobs or rather of their operations to units, the sequences of operations on units, and the timing of the operations. Our approach uses separate strings for all decisions similar to the approach presented in Chen, et al., (1999), to maintain flexibility in the choice of the representation. To reduce the search space, heuristics can replace some of these decisions. We tested different combinations of representations for the sequencing and the allocation. Encoding timing decisions explicitly was not necessary for the regular objectives, C_{max} and O.&C.C., because no improvements of the solution quality can be obtained if delays in the starting times of operations are included.

3.1. Encodings

For the two objectives C_{max} and O.&C.C., an encoding of the sequences and, depending on the applied strategy, an encoding of the allocation to units is used.
To keep the dimension of the search space manageable, the global sequence of orders, i.e. a single sequence $\pi = (\pi_1, \ldots, \pi_{|I|})$ permuting the set of jobs $i \in I$, which is imposed on all stages, is employed. In the simulation, this sequence is decoded by the DES software by processing the jobs in the order of appearance in the global sequence π. Consequently, the sequences of operations on each stage are tightly coupled, i.e., if job i follows i' on unit M01, i' cannot finish before i if they follow the same recipe and are therefore processed on the same units. However, as shown in (Kopanos, et al., 2010), in the schedule for the 30-product case, minimizing C_{max} under UIS-policy, better solutions can be obtained when the sequence of operations on the same units are swapped within two consecutive stages. However, encoding individual sequences for all stages S, would increase the search space significantly and lead to the need of a much larger number of calls of the simulator by the EA.
Two different ways to decide on the allocation of jobs to units were investigated. One option is to determine the allocation dynamically during the simulation using a rule that is implemented in the simulator such that the highest-priority operation is allocated to and executed by the machine that first becomes idle, and started as soon as it becomes idle,

leading to non-delay schedules. So the unit on which an operation is processed in each stage is determined by an EST heuristic.
In the second option, the allocation encoding assigns to every operation $o_i \in O_i$ of a job i a unit $u_s \in U_s$ in the corresponding stage $s \in S$. The allocation encoding $\alpha \subset O \times U$ therefore is a partial relation of the set of all operations $O = \bigcup_{i \in I} O_i$ and the set of all machines in all stages $U \in \bigcup_{s \in S} U_s$.
Employing these encodings two optimization strategies are obtained: *Strat1*, where the global sequence and the allocation are optimized simultaneously and *Strat2*, where the global sequence is optimized and the EST heuristic is used for the determination of the allocation during the simulation.
Weighted lateness is a non-regular objective where timing decisions are important, because the objective value is non-decreasing with the completion time of the scheduled jobs (Baker and Scudder, 1990). For the W.L. minimization, a simple heuristic improvement strategy was used for pre- and post-processing of the EA solutions. Prior to the optimization, the jobs were sorted according to their earliest due dates. The number of possible job permutations is still very high, because many jobs share the same due date. In a simple repair step, each operation on the last stage was delayed if it was early and the delay would not increase the tardiness of a following job.

3.2. Genetic operators

The parent and survivor selection operators are identical to those that were used in Klanke, et al. (2021), i.e. a rank-based parent selection and a rank-based/elitist survivor selection. In the latter operator, a fixed percentage of the best individuals are guaranteed to survive, while all remaining individuals are chosen via rank-based selection. Parameters for which the values are not stated explicitly in this work are also chosen as in Klanke, et al. (2021).
For the allocation chromosome, the Point Mutation operator that randomly picks an operation o and assigns it to a new unit of the same stage, and a Uniform Crossover operator that iterates over all products and stages and assigns a new unit, either from parent P1 or parent P2, with equal probability, is used.
As the mutation operator for the global sequence chromosome, we employ the Permutation Mutation operator from Eiben and Smith (2015) that cuts a sub-sequence of random length and permutes its elements before reinsertion into the chromosome. As the crossover operator, the Cycle Crossover, as reported in Larranga, et al. (1996) is used.

4. Results

In this section the solutions obtained by *Strat1* and *Strat2* are presented. The optimization was run on an i7-7700K Intel CPU under Windows 10 for approx. 2.5 h of computational time. As schedule builder, the commercial software INOSIM 13.0 which, on average, took about 2.5 seconds for a single fitness evaluation, is used. Within a computational time budget of 2.5 h, by parallelization of the fitness evaluation of all individuals of the same generation, in total 3040 evaluations could be performed per problem instance. The results of our approach are presented in Table 1 together with the results from Kopanos, et al. (2010), where the computation time was limited to 1 h. This led in some instances to non-feasible solutions for the monolithic approach (see O.&C.C. in Table 1 in Kopanos, et al. (2010)). The solutions found by the two-step MILP decomposition approach in Kopanos, et al. (2010), the construction (MILP decomp. 1st Step) and the improvement (MILP decomp. 2nd Step), serve as a benchmark for the strategies proposed in this paper. The runs for *Strat2* were repeated several times to evaluate the reproducibility of the solution. *Strat1* could barely reach the solution quality of the MILP monolithic approach for all three objectives, whereas the second strategy Strat2 outperformed the 1st step solution in Kopanos, et al. (2010), and leads to a solution quality between the 1st and 2nd step solutions of the MILP decomposition approach. The best solution that was observed with *Strat2* for the Makespan objective came very close to the 2nd step MILP solution. For the O.&C.C. objective, the best solution was slightly better than the 1st step solution from the decomposition approach. For the W.L. the best run led to a value of 47.22 h, which was reduced to 37.07 h after the repair step. Clearly here a tailored improvement strategy is needed.

Table 1: Results of the EA and MILP approaches for the 30 batches case from Kopanos, et al. (2010). $\mu^1 = 5$, $\lambda^2 = 40$ and ${N_{gen}}^3 = 600$

Solution Approach	Makespan [h]	O.&C.C. [h]	W.L. [h]
MILP monolithic	34.81	-	428.15
MILP decomp. 1st Step	28.51	66.16	48.16
MILP decomp. 2nd Step	26.56	62.91	19.09
Strat1 (Alloc. + Seq. Enc.)	35.02	77.49	693.71
Strat2 (EST + Seq. Enc.)[4]	27.90 ± 1.17	66.17±0.57	47.78±0.51
Best result from Strat2	26.72	65.59	47.22
After repair step	-	-	37.07

[1]Number of children, [2]Population size, [3]Number of generations, [4]Mean and standard deviation of three runs

5. Summary, Conclusion and Outlook

In this work, we investigated the potential of a simulation-optimization approach, combining an EA and DES, for a benchmark scheduling problem, from the pharmaceutical industry.

Our proposed approach benefits from the use of existing models and only encodes the essential degrees of freedom, while the detailed schedules are built by the simulation system. This has the advantage that all constraints that are implemented in the simulator are respected by the solution so the resulting schedule is executable to the best of the available knowledge of the processes in the plant.

For the case study under consideration, the allocation and the sequence degree of freedom were encoded explicitly (*Strat1*), or only the global sequence of jobs was encoded and the allocation was determined heuristically by the simulator (*Strat2*). The encoding of only the global sequence together with the heuristic allocation provided better results due to the smaller search space of the EA. For the three investigated objective functions, the best results are between the 1st and 2nd step solutions of the benchmark approach. From a practical point of view, the solution quality can be considered as sufficient and the small differences are outweighed by the advantages of the simulation-based approach of intuitive modelling, re-use of models and the ability to implement and modify all kinds of constraints in the execution of the schedule. For the W.L. objective, the optimization of a global sequence of the orders turned out to be insufficient. Here a tailored second-stage solution is needed where the allocation and sequencing decisions on the stages are considered explicitly.

The computation time of the detailed simulation models of a commercial simulation environment is significantly higher than that needed for computing a solution with a simple job-shop model due to the larger overhead that is caused by the possibility to implement more detailed models. It can be reduced significantly by a parallelization of the fitness evaluation. In our case, in a time span of 2.5 h the EA generated results that are similar to those obtained by the MILP decomposition approach for the Makespan objective.

Overall, the combination of a detailed discrete-event simulation and an evolutionary algorithm is attractive from an industrial point of view because of the flexibility to implement non-standard features in the simulation model, the fact that the modelling is more intuitive and the model can be modified and maintained by plant personnel. For timing-related objectives and large problem sizes, further work on suitable refinement strategies is needed.

Acknowledgements

This work was partially funded by the European Regional Development Fund (ERDF) in the context of the project OptiProd.NRW (https://www.optiprod.nrw/en).

References

Kenneth R. Baker and Gary D. Scudder, 1990, Sequencing with earliness and tardiness Penalties. A review, Operations Research, 38(1), 22–36

A.E. Eiben and J.E. Smith, 2015, Introduction to Evolutionary Computing, Springer-Verlag Berlin Heidelberg

Iiro Harjunkoski, Christos T. Maravelias, Peter Bongers, Pedro M. Castro, Sebastian Engell, Ignacio E. Grossmann, John Hooker, Carlos M´endez, Guido Sand, and John Wassick, 2014, Scope for industrial applications of production scheduling models and solution methods, Computers and Chemical Engineering, 62, 161–193

Christian Klanke, Dominik Bleidorn, Christian Koslowski, Christian Sonntag, and Sebastian Engell, 2021, Simulation-based Scheduling of a Large-scale Industrial Formulation Plant Using a Heuristics-assisted Genetic Algorithm, In GECCO '21: Proceedings of the Genetic and Evolutionary Computation Conference Companion, Association for Computing Machinery, 1587–1595

Christian Klanke, Vassilios Yfantis, Francesc Corominas, Sebastian Engell, 2021, Short-term scheduling of make-and-pack processes in the consumer goods industry using discrete-time and precedence-based MILP models, Computers and Chemical Engineering, 154, 107453

Georgios P. Georgiadis, Apostolos P. Elekidis, Michael C. Georgiadis, 2019, Optimization-Based scheduling for the Process Industries: From Theory to Real-Life Industrial Applications, 7(7), 438

Georgios M. Kopanos, Carlos A. Méndez, and Luis Puigjaner, 2010, MIP-based decomposition strategies for large-scale scheduling problems in multiproduct multistage batch plants: A benchmark scheduling problem of the pharmaceutical industry, European Journal of Operational Research, 207(2), 644–655

Pedro Larranaga, Cindy M. H. Kuijpers, Roberto H. Murga, and Yosu Yurra-Mendi, 1996, Learning Bayesian Network Structures by Searching for the Best Ordering with Genetic Algorithms, IEEE Transactions on Systems, Man, and, Cybernetics-Pakt A: System and Humans, 26(4), 487–493

Haoxun Chen, Jürgen Ihlow, Carsten Lehmann, 1999, A Genetic Algorithm for Flexible Job-Shop Scheduling, 1999 International Conference on Robotics & Automation, 1120-1125

Proceedings of the 14th International Symposium on Process Systems Engineering – PSE 2021+
June 19-23, 2022, Kyoto, Japan
http://dx.doi.org/10.1016/B978-0-323-85159-6.50090-7

Cream Cheese Fermentation Scheduling

Misagh Ebrahimpour[a], Wei Yu[a*], Brent Young[a]

[a] *Department of Chemical and Materials Engineering, The University of Auckland, Auckland 1142, AUCKLAND*
w.yu@auckland.ac.nz

Abstract

Maintaining high throughput with consistent quality is challenging in industrial cream cheese plants since batch fermentation time varies. However, determining the batch duration right from the batch start time is challenging. This makes the scheduling of this plant difficult. The characteristics of the plant, the main process challenges, and the resulting framework, which included adaptive modelling and scheduling, are presented.

Keywords: Cream cheese fermentation, Batch Scheduling, Online pH prediction

1. Introduction

Fermentation batches are challenging to schedule due to the high inherent biological variability. Batch fermentations are common in various industries such as food, chemical, and pharmaceutical processing; therefore, much work has been carried out to schedule such systems. Harjunkoski *et al.*, (2006) worked on scheduling a copper plant. Raw materials variation affected the reaction time, which made the plant operation challenging. Reaction modelling with raw material changes was used in a mixed-integer formulation for scheduling of the overall production process. Scheduling of penicillin fermentation was studied in Lau *et al.*, (2003). However, the authors did not consider the batch variation, and a nominal batch processing time was used in their scheduling formulation. Baldo *et al.*, (2014) presented a scheduling solution for a beverage plant in the brewing industry. They use a constant fermentation time which is much longer than the mean values for the scheduling time, however the fermentation time variation was not addressed. Their schedule significantly reduced the process throughput. Additionally, the fermentation liquid product could be stored in tanks for several days.

In cream cheese plants the variation of batch duration affects the downstream continuous production rate and quality. Furthermore, the fermentation curds cannot be stored for a long time since over acidification degrades the quality. To avoid batch interferences during cooking, engineers in industry set up the fermentation scheduling with a long buffer time between two fermentation vats. This assures quality; however, the production rate is reduced significantly. Better scheduling of batches can decrease their variation by reducing possible interferences between batches due to variations of their duration. A new framework is presented in this work that provides a primary schedule with updating each batch durations predicted by a fermentation model at each time step. This schedule was updated in real-time by using an adaptive model that predicted the batch duration along with the fermentation when enough measurements were available. A mixed-integer linear (MILP) programming optimization was formulated for real-time scheduling of the vats filling and draining. The constraints of the plant regarding the filling, draining, and cleaning of the vats were considered. The best configuration for scheduling was determined to minimize the cost and waste and improve the continuous operation of the plant.

2. Methodology

2.1. Scheduling framework

As Figure 1 (A) shows, the downstream and upstream units connected to vats are ideally in continuous operation. The objective is to schedule vats to maintain continuous operation while considering filling, draining, and cleaning constraints, and varying batch duration. As shown in Figure 1 (B), only one vat can be drained or filled at any time due to the draining and filling line architecture. Both filling and draining take 2 hours. After reaching the desired pH, batches should be cooked immediately to stop the fermentation. If one batch's pH reaches the desired value and the draining line is used by another vat, the batch can be cooled in the buffer tank and drained later. However, this will cause more energy consumption and extra cost for the plant. Therefore, interference between batches, as explained in the above example, should be avoided. These are two significant constraints that are considered in the optimization formulation. After the batch is drained, it should be cleaned for future usage. Dairy plants use the Cleaning in Place (CIP) term for cleaning. The CIP time also varies since it is monitored online and can be stopped based on CIP measurements. For this study we used a constant CIP value that was suggested by the plant.

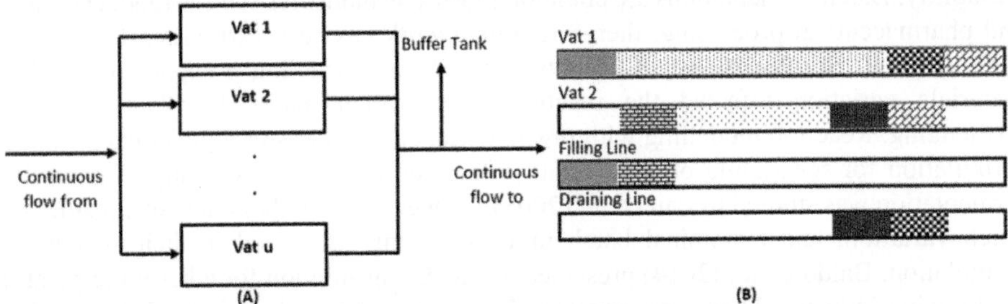

Figure 1. Unit operations: (A) Process flow diagram, (B) Vat operating conditions: filling shown by ■ and ▦, draining shown by ▩ and ⁘, and CIP shown by ⁄ .

The batch duration (the time required to reach the desired pH from the beginning of the batch) varies due to disturbances such as milk components changing from season to season due to cow nutrition and weather conditions. This makes the scheduling of vats a challenging task. A mixed-integer optimization has been applied for solving this scheduling problem. The scheduling routine is shown in Figure 2. When all vats are available, scheduling is carried out for all of them. The key problem is what batch duration time should we use? As mentioned before, batch duration varies. To deal with this problem, a default value is used first as the initial batch duration. The default value can be defined by engineers based on historical batch duration data. Different default values may impact the scheduling performance. Therefore, three default values, 12, 13 and 14 (hours), are investigated in this paper. After filling up the first batch, measurements from the batch beginning up to a specific time can be used in the pH prediction model to estimate the time for reaching the desired pH. This is important in the plant as the desired pH should be obtained at the end of batch draining, affecting the quality of the end-product. The updated batch duration will be used to reschedule the batches. Rescheduling will be repeated whenever enough data is available for determining the duration for each batch. The time needed to collect enough data for the pH prediction model and predict the actual batch duration can consequently affect the scheduling performance. The optimal estimate of the initial value of the batch duration is determined by evaluating the scheduling performance discussed in Section 3.

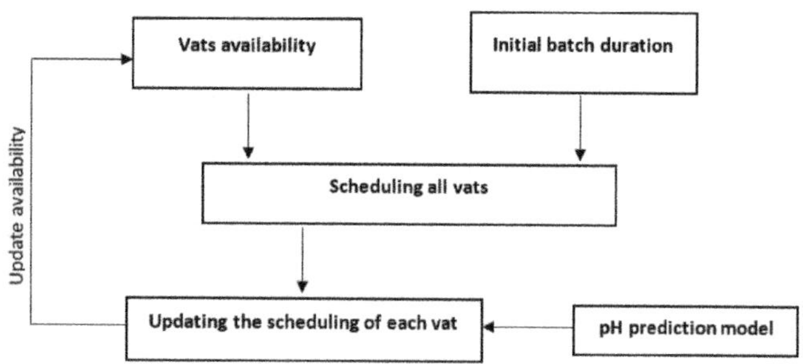

Figure 2. Scheduling framework

2.1.1 *pH prediction model*

Ebrahimpour *et al.*, (2021) studied the application of white, black, and grey box models for cream cheese pH prediction. A reliable pH prediction model was achieved by applying neural networks to pH dynamics. Additionally, a grey box model developed by Li *et al.* (2021) was discussed. Estimated biomass with measurements along the fermentation can make this model adaptive and improve the prediction. Both models can be used in the scheduling framework for cream cheese pH prediction.

2.1.2 *Scheduling formulation*

The operating conditions of the batch units were defined by two variables $W_{u,t}$ and $Y_{u,t}$ as shown in Table 1. The processing (fermentation) duration was defined between filling start time and the end of CIP. Variables $B_{u,t}$, $F_{u,t}$, $E_{u,t}$, $D_{u,t}$, and $G_{u,t}$ were used for distinguishing different occasions. The formulation and the details of the variables are given below.

$$C_{u,t} = C_{u,t-1} + W_{u,t} \qquad \forall u \in U, \forall t \in T : t > t_0 \qquad (1)$$

$$C_{u,tt} - C_{u,t} \leq (T_F - T_0) * (1 - B_{u,t}) \qquad \forall u \in U, \forall t \in T, \forall tt \in (t+1)...\min(t + P_u - 1, T_F) \qquad (2)$$

$$C_{u,t} - C_{u,t-P_u} \geq 1 \qquad \forall u \in U, \forall t \in T : \forall t \geq T_0 + P_u \qquad (3)$$

$$W_{u,t} + Y_{u,t} \geq 1 \qquad \forall u \in U, \forall t \in T \qquad (4)$$

$$Y_{u,t-1} - W_{u,t} \leq Y_{u,t} \leq Y_{u,t-1} + W_{u,t} \qquad \forall u \in U, \forall t \in T : t > t_0 \qquad (5)$$

$$W_{u,t} - Y_{u,t-1} \leq B_{u,t} \leq \frac{W_{u,t} + Y_{u,t}}{2} \qquad \forall u \in U, \forall t \in T \qquad (6)$$

$$F_{u,t+t_{FD}} = B_{u,t} \qquad \forall u \in U, \forall t \in T \quad (7) \qquad E_{u,t_{BD}} = B_{u,t} \qquad \forall u \in U, \forall t \in T \quad (8)$$

$$D_{u,t_{DD}} = E_{u,t} \qquad \forall u \in U, \forall t \in T \quad (9) \qquad G_{u,t_{CIPD}} = D_{u,t} \qquad \forall u \in U, \forall t \in T \quad (10)$$

$$\sum_{u=1}^{U} (B_{u,t} + F_{u,t}) = 1 \qquad \forall u \in U, \forall t \in T \quad (11) \qquad \sum_{u=1}^{U} (E_{u,t} + D_{u,t}) = 1 \quad \forall u \in U, \forall t \in T \quad (12)$$

T_0 : start of the solution horizon
T_F : end of the solution horizon
P_u : batch duration for batch unit u in U
U : domain of batch units 1…number of batch units
T : total time horizon from T_0 to T_F
$E_{u,t}$ = 1: if batch unit u starts draining a batch at time t, 0 otherwise (Boolean variable)
$C_{u,t}$: the number of batches and unit idle periods from time T_0 to t (integer variable)
u : batch unit number
t : time at any instant
$B_{u,t}$ = 1: if batch unit u starts filling a batch at time t, 0 otherwise (Boolean variable)
$F_{u,t}$ = 1: if batch unit u finishes filling at time t, 0 otherwise (Boolean variable)
$G_{u,t}$ = 1: if batch unit u is doing CIP at time t, 0 otherwise (Boolean variable)
$D_{u,t}$ = 1: if batch unit u finishes draining at time t, 0 otherwise (Boolean variable)

Equations (1)-(12) explanation:
Eq. (1): At any time, t, if a batch starts on a batch unit, u, or the unit is idle, a counter is incremented
Eqs. (2)-(3): Batch cycles times must be longer than the specified value
Eqs. (4)-(6): Boolean relationships for ensuring the feasibility (the Table 1 condition)
Eq. (7): Batch filling time duration specification; t_{FD} is the filling duration
Eq. (8): Batch complete time (from start time to reaching the desired pH)
Eq. (9): Batch draining time duration specification; t_{DD} is the draining duration
Eq. (10): Batch cleaning time duration specification; t_{CIPD} is the cleaning duration
Eq. (11): Batches filling constraint; only one vat can be filled at any time
Eq. (12): Batches draining constraint; only one vat can be drained at any time
The objective function maximizes the started vats which is equivalent to maximizing Y and W for all u vats at any time t.

$$Max \quad \sum_{u=1}^{U}\sum_{t=T_0}^{T_F} W_{u,t} + Y_{u,t} \tag{13}$$

Table 1. Operating conditions of a batch unit

Variable	Start filling a batch	Processing a batch	Unit is idle	Infeasible
$W_{u,t}$	1	0	1	0
$Y_{u,t}$	1	1	0	0

3. Results

The batch duration varies in the industrial case due to disturbances such as milk composition variation and bacteria activity. Since the batch duration cannot be predicted at the beginning of the batch, a default initial batch duration was assumed to schedule the vats. Three default batch durations (12, 13 and 14 hours) were selected for testing the impact of default batch duration on the scheduling performance. As soon as enough data was measured, the scheduling would be updated by the predicted fermentation time from the pH prediction model discussed in Section 2.1.1. The effect of updating time on the scheduling was tested by considering the pH prediction model output availability 5 and 8 hours after the batch start time.

3.1. Industrial scale scheduling

Batch duration data from a real cream cheese plant was used for testing the scheduling framework performance. The duration times of 20 batches in the sequence were used, which took approximately 70 operating hours in the plant. As shown in Figure 2, when all the vats are available, scheduling was carried out for all the vats.

As mentioned in previous sections, the batch duration cannot be determined before batches start. The initial batch duration in the scheduling algorithm was assumed to be a fixed value at the beginning of all batches run. For obtaining the best initial value, scheduling was applied to the industrial batch duration data. Scheduling was carried out by considering the default batch duration as 12, 13, and 14 hours. The initial batch duration was updated by the predictions from the pH prediction model. The pH model prediction output was assumed to be available 8 hours after the batch start time. The updated batch duration was used to update the scheduling of the vats.

Table 2 summarizes the scheduling results with different initial batch durations for five vats. The performance of the scheduling framework was studied by comparing three indicators - idle time, number of cooled batches, and number of waste batches. Idle time is the summation of hours in which the draining line is not in operation. This time should be minimized in the plant as continuous operation and consequently high throughput is desired. The number of cooled batches represents the draining interference of two batches when one is cooled and drained later. Wasted batches happen when more than two batches draining coincidence happens. One of the batches can be cooled at such a time, but the other one is wasted.

Table 2. Scheduling results with different initial default batch duration

Batch duration	Idle time (h)	Cooled batches	Wasted batches
12	22	3	1
13	20	4	1
14	24	4	2

Table 3. Scheduling results with different update availability

Update availability	Idle time	Cooled batches	Wasted batches
At 5 h	17	2	0
At 8 h	22	3	1

Table 2 shows that the 12 hours initial batch duration led to less cooled and wasted batches. This means that more energy and money are saved in the plant. However, the draining line idle time is more than 13 hours batch duration. The selection between the initial batch duration options should be made based on the plant's production, economic, and quality objectives. Without rescheduling, the idle time, number of cooled and wasted batches were 24 h, 4 and 3 respectively which shows the importance of rescheduling in improving the performance.

Figure 3 shows an example of the scheduling framework performance for the five vats with an initial batch duration of 12 hours. The top part of the Figure indicates the results for an initial batch duration of 12 hours for all vats at the batch start time. The scheduling update was carried out after determining the batch duration by pH prediction model. The bottom part of the Figure shows the actual batch duration. The vat filling time was updated after time step 13 according to the actual batch duration determined by the pH prediction model.

Scheduling performance can be improved by providing the batch duration prediction earlier. This has been studied by providing the batch predictions 5 and 8 hours after the batches start scheduling with the initial batch duration estimate of 12 hours. Table 3 shows that the earlier update of the scheduling using the pH prediction model outputs can decrease the idle time, and the number of cooled and wasted batches. This will improve the scheduling performance in terms of energy, economy, and quality.

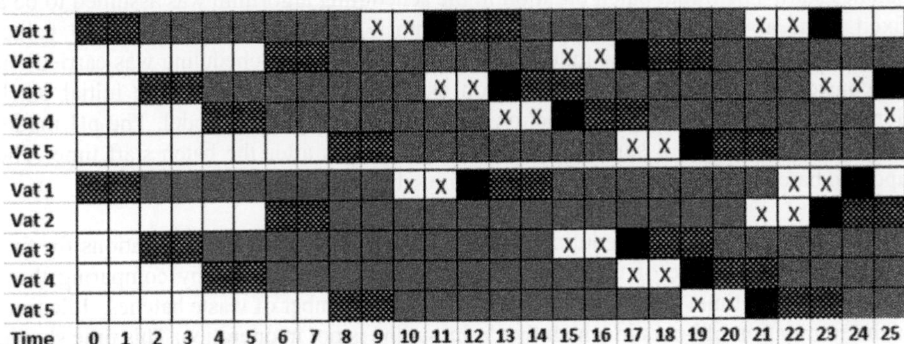

Figure 3. Scheduling of vats before (top) and after (bottom) the update. ■ is the initial batch duration, ■ is the actual batch duration, ▩ is the filling, × is draining, ■ is CIP

4. Conclusions

Scheduling cream cheese fermentation is challenging since batch duration varies. This work presented a scheduling framework that included an online pH prediction model along with MILP formulation. Online lactose and lactate measurements improved the pH prediction, which was achieved by reconciling the states. The formulation used the model output to reschedule the primary schedule, which was obtained by assuming a default initial batch duration. The framework performance was tested by scheduling 20 batches in sequence. Results showed that using 12 h as the default initial batch duration with batch prediction updating 5 hours after the fermentation started led to the minimum wasted and cooled batches.

References

M. Ebrahimpour, W. Yu, B. Young, 2021, Artificial neural network modelling for cream cheese fermentation pH prediction at lab and industrial scales, Food and Bioproducts Processing 126 (2021): 81-89.

B. Li, Y. Lin, W. Yu, D. Wilson, B. Young, 2021, Application of mechanistic modelling and machine learning for cream cheese fermentation pH prediction, Journal of Chemical Technology & Biotechnology 96, no. 1 (2021): 125-133.

Lau, S., Willis, M.J., Montague, G.A. and Glassey, J., 2004. Predictive scheduling of a penicillin bioprocess plant. IFAC Proceedings Volumes, 37(1), pp.463-468.

Baldo, T.A., Santos, M.O., Almada-Lobo, B. and Morabito, R., 2014. An optimization approach for the lot sizing and scheduling problem in the brewery industry. Computers & Industrial Engineering, 72, pp.58-71.

Harjunkoski, I., Borchers, H.W. and Fahl, M., 2006. Simultaneous scheduling and optimization of a copper plant. In Computer Aided Chemical Engineering (Vol. 21, pp. 1197-1202). Elsevier.

Proceedings of the 14th International Symposium on Process Systems Engineering – PSE 2021+
June 19-23, 2022, Kyoto, Japan
http://dx.doi.org/10.1016/B978-0-323-85159-6.50091-9

Multi-Objective Optimization of Production Cost and Carbon Loss in the U.S. Petrochemicals Industry

Ioannis Giannikopoulos[a], Alkiviadis Skouteris[a], David T. Allen[a,b], Michael Baldea[a,c] and Mark A. Stadtherr[a*]

[a]McKetta Department of Chemical Engineering, The University of Texas at Austin, 200 East Dean Keeton Street, Austin, Texas 78712-1589, United States
[b]Center for Energy and Environmental Resources, The University of Texas at Austin, 10100 Burnet Road, Bldg. 133, R7100, Austin, Texas 78758, United States
[c]Oden Institute for Computational Engineering and Sciences, The University of Texas at Austin, 201 East 24th Street, Austin, Texas 78712, United States

markst@che.utexas.edu

Abstract

The U.S. petrochemicals industry has been strongly influenced by the shale hydrocarbon boom commenced more than a decade ago. Newly available resources and emerging technologies spurred research focused on new pathways and technologies for producing chemicals. The adoption and deployment of these technologies by the manufacturing industry is driven by the need to minimize costs while meeting demand for chemical products. However, cost minimization is a unilateral objective that may conflict with other societal, environmental or economic goals and constraints. Motivated by this, in this paper we study the optimal configuration of the U.S. petrochemicals industry by considering both economic and environmental objectives. Our work is based on a comprehensive model representing the U.S. industry as a whole, and on multi-objective optimization problem formulations that allow us to elucidate the trade-off between economic costs and net carbon loss. A Pareto-optimal set of solutions is obtained and a comparison between the two extreme cases is performed.

Keywords: Sustainability; Chemical manufacturing; Supply chain; Network modeling

1. Introduction

Advances in hydraulic fracturing and horizontal drilling have led to significant growth in the U.S. petrochemicals industry. Oil and gas production have rapidly increased in the U.S., particularly from shale formations (U.S. Energy Information Administration, 2021a). An important consequence of the shale hydrocarbon boom has been the increased production of natural gas liquids (NGLs), which are often abundant in shale gas. NGLs are composed of ethane, propane, *n*-butane, isobutene and small amounts of less volatile hydrocarbons, molecules that are valuable feedstocks for chemical manufacturing (Siirola, 2014). The increase in the availability of shale gas and associated NGLs has thus provided a unique opportunity to expand the U.S. chemical manufacturing industry. In this paper, we aim to study optimal directions for this historic industry expansion, considering a trade-off between economic and environmental objectives.

We consider this industrial sector at the level of the entire United States, and use a computational model that comprises several hundred of the highest-volume chemicals and a library of hundreds of potential technologies for producing and processing them (DeRosa and Allen, 2016; Skouteris et al., 2021). The model is formulated as a superstructure that allows for determining the optimal configuration of the industrial sector by solving an optimization problem to minimize a given industry-wide objective, subject to material balance constraints as well as supply limitations and demand requirements. The solution of the optimization problem determines the optimal production levels for each process technology, as well as material flows in the network. In this paper, we consider two industry objectives: production cost minimization and minimization of carbon loss (e.g., as CO_2 emissions). In determining carbon loss, both feedstock carbon and the carbon cost of energy used are considered.

2. Background and Problem Definition

Optimization-based network superstructure models of chemical manufacturing originated in the work of Stadtherr and Rudd (1976), and many variations of this approach, with various focuses, have appeared since. Cost minimization is a commonly used industry objective in such studies and can be used to determine an optimal network configuration (i.e., the technologies in the superstructure that have nonzero utilization). In recent work (Skouteris, et al., 2021), we developed a nonlinear, cost-based industry model that propagates cost and price changes within the network as new technology is introduced. However, there are other objectives that may affect industry behavior, such as safety and environmental performance, leading to the use of multi-objective optimization. For example, Fathi-Afshar and Yang (1985) focused on the effect of gross toxicity in process selection and how it conflicts with the minimization of cost for the industry. Similarly, Chang and Allen (1997) studied trade-offs between chlorine usage and industry costs. Here we will use an industry network model with multi-objective optimization to study trade-offs between cost minimization and carbon usage.

In the network model, the industry is represented as a directed graph, where chemical processes are the nodes and the edges correspond to material and utility flows. The data for the model (e.g., process stoichiometries and costs) have been obtained from the IHS 2012 Process Economic Yearbook (IHS Markit, 2012). The model used in this work involves 887 processes, 892 materials and 7 utility types, aiming to represent the bulk petrochemicals industry, including polymer products, in the United States. The methodology can also be used to study the chemical industries in other countries or even different industrial networks within the U.S., provided that the data are adjusted accordingly. The core model consists of balance equations for all materials, and supply and demand constraints. The balance equations for every material *i* are of the form:

$$F_i + \sum_j a_{i,j} X_j - Q_i = 0 \tag{1}$$

where F_i is the exogenous flow rate of material *i* as a primary raw material into the network, $a_{i,j}$ is the input-output coefficient for *i* in process *j* (positive if *i* is produced, negative if *i* is consumed, and unity if *i* is the main product), X_j is the utilization level of process *j* (in terms of flow rate of main product), and Q_i is the exogenous flow rate of *i* as a final product out of the network. The supply and demand constraints are:

$$0 \leq F_i \leq S_i \tag{2}$$

$$Q_i = D_i \geq 0 \tag{3}$$

where S_i and D_i are specified exogenous raw material supply and final product demand rates for i, respectively.

Two objective functions for optimizing the industry behavior are considered. The first objective is minimization of total processing cost (equivalent to maximization of profit since output is fixed by Eq. (3)):

$$\min_{X_j,F_i} C = \sum_j C_j X_j \tag{4}$$

where C_j is the net unit cost of process j (cents/lb of main product), including raw materials and utility costs, fixed capital investment depreciated over a 10-year period, and other fixed operating costs. The second objective is net carbon loss:

$$\min_{X_j,F_i} L = \sum_i F_i w_{C,i} + \sum_k w_{C,k} \sum_j u_{k,j} X_j - \sum_i Q_i w_{C,i} \tag{5}$$

Here, $w_{C,i}$ is the weight fraction of carbon in material i, $w_{C,k}$ is the carbon cost per unit of utility k, and $u_{k,j}$ is usage of utility k per unit of production from process j. To determine $w_{C,k}$ we consider the actual carbon content of an energy-equivalent amount of natural gas. This means that, for example, 1 kWh of electricity (equivalent to 3412 BTUs) is assumed to have the same carbon content as 3412 BTUs of natural gas. Information on the energy content of utilities used is taken from the U.S. Energy Information Administration (2021b). The first term in Eq. (5) represents the feedstock carbon input to the industry, the second term the carbon cost of utilities used, and the last term the carbon outputs (constant here due to fixed industry output). Thus, L represents the industry-wide loss of carbon (e.g., as CO_2 emissions). As formulated here, the carbon loss function L does not consider the possible generation of energy, and thus a carbon credit, by a production process. An alternative formulation for L that accounts for energy production can be considered and will be the subject of our future research. Both objective functions are linear so the underlying problem is a linear program (LP). Here we use these two objectives to consider a multi-objective optimization problem. We seek to determine the Pareto optimal set for this problem using the weighted sum and ε-constrained methods.

3. Solution Strategies

The LP problem defined above was first solved separately with each individual objective to obtain the two single-objective optimal configurations, indicating that the two objectives are indeed in conflict. To obtain Pareto optimal solutions using the weighted sum method, the two functions were scalarized into a single objective by assigning each function a defined weight; the weights are then varied to obtain a set of Pareto-optimal solutions:

$$\min_{X_j,F_i} f = w_1 \frac{C}{C^*} + w_2 \frac{L}{L^*}, \quad \text{with } w_1 + w_2 = 1 \tag{6}$$

Here each objective function has also been scaled using the minimum values C^* and L^* obtained by solving the two single-objective LPs.

Additional Pareto-optimal solutions were generated using the ε-constrained method, in which the LP is solved for one objective, while bounding the other objective through an additional constraint:

$$\min_{X_j, F_i} C \tag{7}$$

$$\text{s.t. } L \le \varepsilon_1, \quad \text{where } L^* \le \varepsilon_1 \le L^0$$

or alternatively:

$$\min_{X_j, F_i} L \tag{8}$$

$$\text{s.t. } C \le \varepsilon_2, \quad \text{where } C^* \le \varepsilon_2 \le C^0$$

Here C^0 and L^0 correspond to the value each objective function takes when the other objective is minimized. Varying ε_1 and ε_2 within their given ranges will result in several additional Pareto-optimal solutions.

4. Case Study

Proceeding as described above, we found the optimal industry configurations for the two conflicting objectives defined by Eqs. (4) and (5), and determined the Pareto-optimal front, namely the set of non-inferior solutions for the multi-objective problem.

The Pareto front is shown in Figure 1. Here, point A represents the optimal industry configuration when minimizing the total production cost as a single objective, regardless of the carbon loss. This point corresponds to a minimum total production cost of 187 billion dollars per year and is accompanied by a carbon loss of 90.6 billion lbs per year. Similarly, point C represents the optimal configuration when minimizing the net carbon loss as a single objective, without considering the total production cost. At this point, the minimum net carbon loss is 62.8 billion lbs per year, requiring a total production cost of 258 billion dollars per year. All other Pareto-optimal solutions between these two extreme cases represent trade-offs between minimizing production cost or carbon loss, based on the varying importance levels given to each objective. An overall trade-off can be determined by comparing the two extreme solutions. In moving from point A to C to achieve the minimum carbon loss, the total industry production cost increases by approximately 37%, while moving in the opposite direction to achieve the minimum production cost, the net carbon loss increases by approximately 42%.

Point U in Figure 1 refers to the utopia point, which is an ideal solution corresponding to the minimum values found for both objectives, but which never can be reached for these two conflicting objectives. Ideally, though, it is desirable that the Pareto front be as close as possible to the utopia point. In this case, the closeness to U will depend on the "steepness" of the slope of the Pareto front in the vicinity of point C and the "flatness" of the slope in the vicinity of point A. We note that moving leftward from point A, significant reductions of the net carbon loss can be obtained with only small increases in the production cost. Similarly, moving downward from point C, significant reductions of the production cost can be obtained with only small increases in the carbon loss.

The changes that occur in moving along the Pareto front stem from changes in the industry network configuration. Here we highlight some of the most important changes observed between the extreme points, A and C. At point C, there is high production of methanol from natural gas, which is then used for producing olefins, such as ethylene and propylene. In contrast, at point A, propylene is produced from naphtha, and ethylene is produced from propane and ethane by steam cracking. Also, there is significantly higher production of ethylene at point C and its downstream usage differs between the two extreme points. In both cases, ethylene is used for the production of 1-butylene, polyolefin elastomer, EPDM rubber, ethylene dichloride ethylene/vinyl alcohol barrier resin, 1-hexene, polyethylenes, vinyl acetate-ethylene copolymer and vinylidene chloride. However, at point A, ethylene is also used for the production of ABS resin, methyl methacrylate, polystyrene, ethylene glycol and vinyl chloride, whereas it is used for production of ethanol, ethylene oxide and styrene at point C. These changes take place gradually throughout the network, as we move along the Pareto front. Consider, for example, point B, which is obtained from the weighted sum method when equal importance is given to both objectives. Here, ethylene is produced from a combination of steam cracking and methanol-to-olefins processes, with the production rates of these two types of processes being about the same. A similar behavior can be observed for several other chemicals in the network.

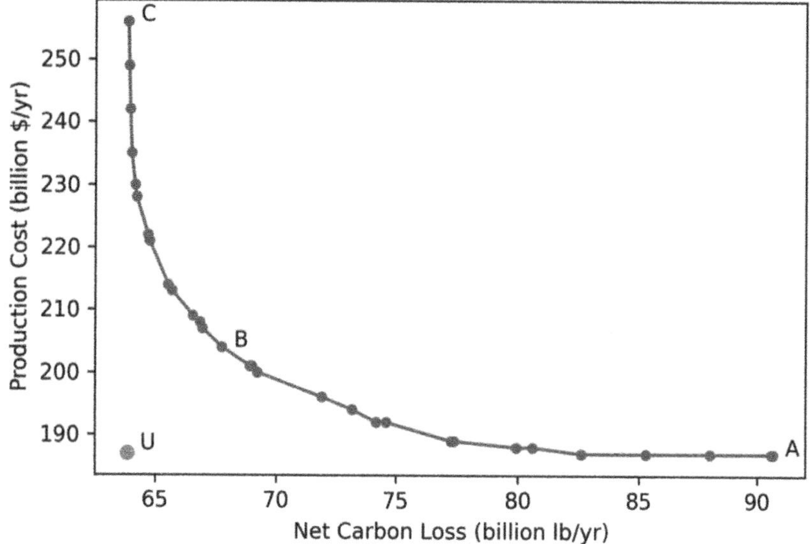

Figure 1: Pareto front and utopia point for the multi-objective optimization problem.

Comparing the amount and type of feedstock carbon that the industry network utilizes in each case is also of interest. Specifically, at point A, when production cost is the sole driving force behind the optimal industry configuration, a higher amount of feedstock carbon is utilized, compared to point C, when lost carbon content is the sole driving force. Moreover, feedstocks with lower carbon weight fraction see increased importance at point C. This leads to a situation at point C in which there is little loss of feedstock carbon, with the carbon loss function L being dominated by the carbon cost of utilities. In contrast, at point A, the contributions of feedstock carbon loss and utility carbon cost to L are roughly the same. This suggests that there may be environmental benefits to prioritizing efficient raw material usage, even if that means more usage of energy utilities. This observation will be reinforced as energy utilities are increasingly decarbonized.

5. Conclusions

In this work, we used a superstructure network model of the U.S. refining and chemical manufacturing industry, and formulated a multi-objective linear program with two conflicting objectives, total industry production cost and net industry carbon loss. The model was first solved for each objective separately, and then the weighted sum and ε-constraint methods were employed to obtain the Pareto-optimal set of solutions. Moving along the Pareto front towards the minimum carbon loss point causes a number of structural changes in the industry network, notably a shift towards natural-gas-derived methanol used for production of olefins. Results also suggest that there may be environmental benefits to prioritizing efficient raw material usage, even if that means more usage of energy utilities, especially as these utilities can be and will likely become increasingly decarbonized.

Acknowledgement

This paper is based on work supported primarily by the National Science Foundation under Cooperative Agreement No. EEC-1647722 (CISTAR: NSF Engineering Research Center for Innovative and Strategic Transformation of Alkane Resources). Any opinions, findings and conclusions or recommendations expressed in this material are those of the authors and do not necessarily reflect the views of the National Science Foundation.

References

D. Chang and D. T. Allen, 1997, Minimizing Chlorine Use: Assessing the Trade-offs between Cost and Chlorine Reduction in Chemical Manufacturing, Journal of Industry Ecology, 1, 111–134

S. E. DeRosa; D. T. Allen, 2016, Impact of New Manufacturing Technologies on the Petrochemical Industry in the United States: A Methane-to-Aromatics Case Study, Industrial & Engineering Chemistry Research, 55, 18, 5366-5372

S. Fathi-Afshar and J. C. Yang, 1985, Designing the Optimal Structure of the Petrochemical Industry for Minimum Cost and Least Gross Toxicity of Chemical Production, Chemical Engineering Science, 40, 5, 781–797

IHS Markit, 2012, IHS 2012 Process Economics Program Yearbook, https://ihsmarkit.com/products/chemical-technology-pep-index.html

J.J. Siirola, 2014, The Impact of Shale Gas in the Chemical Industry, AIChE Journal, 60, 3, 810-819

A. Skouteris, I. Giannikopoulos, T. F. Edgar, M. Baldea, D. T. Allen, and M. A. Stadtherr, 2021, Systems Analysis of Natural Gas Liquid Resources for Chemical Manufacturing: Strategic Utilization of Ethane, Industrial & Engineering Chemistry Research, 60, 33, 12377-12389

M. A. Stadtherr and D. F. Rudd, 1976, Systems Study of the Petrochemical Industry, Chemical Engineering Science, 31, 1019-1028

U.S. Energy Information Administration, 2021a, Natural Gas Explained: Where Our Natural Gas Comes From. [Online]. https://www.eia.gov/energyexplained/natural-gas/where-our-natural-gas-comes-from.php

U.S. Energy Information Administration, 2021, Units and Calculators Explained: British Thermal Units (Btu). [Online]. https://www.eia.gov/energyexplained/units-and-calculators/british-thermal-units.php

Proceedings of the14th International Symposium on Process Systems Engineering – PSE 2021+
June 19–23, 2022, Kyoto, Japan
http://dx.doi.org/10.1016/B978-0-323-85159-6.50092-0

Mapping Anthropogenic Carbon Mobilization through Chemical Process and Manufacturing Industries

Amrita Sen[a], George Stephanopoulos[b,c], Bhavik R Bakshi[a*]

[a]*William G Lowrie Department of Chemical Engineering, The Ohio State University, Columbus Ohio 43210, USA*
[b]*The Global KAITEKI Center, Arizona State University, Tempe, Arizona 85287, USA*
[c]*Department of Chemical Engineering, Massachusetts Institute of Technology, Cambridge, MA 02139, USA*

bakshi.2@osu.edu

Abstract

The long-term impact of global warming and the resulting climate crisis, brought about by human-induced emission of greenhouse gases, is an imminent environmental concern. The Paris Agreement aims to limit global temperature rise to below 2° C over pre-industrial levels, to curb this impact. Meeting this limit necessitates reaching carbon neutrality by 2050, which imply no net transport of carbon dioxide to the atmosphere. The chemical process industry along with associated manufacturing industries such as iron and steel, cement and aluminum contributes significantly towards global carbon dioxide emissions. Mapping the precise routes of Carbon mobilization is the first step towards establishment of a sustainable, circular and Carbon neutral chemical industry. There exist no C flow models for aforementioned energy intensive industries. Current published literature also does not account for C mobilized to meet the energetic needs of global chemical processes. They also do not account for the emissions offset by material exchange between different production processes. In this work, we develop a steady state model of Carbon flow through chemical process and associated industries. Our model traces the flow of carbon from fossil feedstock, to energy carriers and chemical intermediates, and finally valuable products, by-products and emissions. This model makes use of process data, life-cycle inventories models developed by existing studies on the chemical and petrochemical industries, government databases, greenhouse gas emissions data and economy models . Fundamental laws like mass and energy balance are used in conjunction with stoichiometric calculations to estimate missing data and reconcile incorrect data. We represent this model as a Sankey Diagram to better facilitate visualization of the process network and identify scope of process improvement. We elaborate how this model helps the placement of process alternatives such as use of renewables, electrification, green hydrogen and carbon capture and storage in the value chain. These alternatives can be highly energy intensive, requiring a large amount of "net zero" electricity to function. The dependence of renewably sourced electricity on land area availability necessitates its efficient use. Thus, the integration of fossil alternatives in the model paves the path for their targeted and optimal usage towards decarbonization.

Keywords: Decarbonization, Modelling, Supply chain, Sustainability

1. Introduction

As global average temperature continues to rise and predictions for climate change turn more grim with every new assessment, closing the global anthropogenic carbon (referred to as "C" from here on) cycle has become more important than ever. Reducing the production of materials for consumption, infrastructure and healthcare in the face of a rising global population, or bringing about drastic reduction in consumptive behaviour overnight, is unlikely. Therefore, focussing on emissions reduction while still maintaining production volumes (or establishing a circular economy of materials) may arguably have better payoffs in the immediate future.

The efficiency (yield or selectivity) of conventional chemical processes cannot be increased indefinitely. Thus, there is a minimum C emission associated with all products. Any further reduction requires us to choose alternate pathways or retrofit mitigation technologies to conventional pathways. Many innovative technologies have been developed to leverage both these options. [8, 7, 1, 10] The general idea behind carbon neutral technologies is to limit CO_2 emissions to the atmosphere. With prices of renewable electricity dropping steadily, electrically powered emerging technologies show promise in competing with incumbent routes of production. Examples of such processes include electrochemical means of converting CO_2, that would otherwise be emitted to the atmosphere,to value added chemicals, or electrification of H_2 production. While renewables and emerging technologies may lower emissions to their credit, their usage does not absolve industries of all environmental concerns. C capture itself might increase energy needs of a process enough, to offset its C credits. Renewables also raise issues of waste management of noble materials, land use concerns. Thus, the application of these technologies needs to be weighed in with its tradeoffs to guide policymaking.

Attempts at large scale, sector-wide decarbonization imply the implementation of alternate low carbon pathways wherever possible, and C capture from exhaust gases elsewhere. This naturally requires a thorough knowledge of C flows, sources and sinks. A superficial knowledge of emissions from the chemical industry is not very useful in this regard. The contribution of different processes, pathways and fuels is needed to target processes with the highest decarbonization potential. The US EPA traces a majority of US greenhouse gas (GHG) emissions back to the transportation sector, followed closely by electricity generation and industrial sectors. Many existing works break down these emissions across manufacturing and process industries. These diagrams however, suffer from various inadequacies of their own. The diagram developed by Lawrence Livermore National Lab uses data from the US Energy Information Administration (EIA) and does not distinguish between different processes in the industrial sector. [3] The diagram by Global Climate and Energy Project (GCEP) at Stanford, while much more detailed still lumps all chemicals into one node and does not provide any insight into the individual consumption or emission of processes.[9, 2] The mass flow balance on the process network in the chemical industry developed by Levi et al. while comprehensive, does not have information on the energetic needs of these processes. Finally, there is a distinct need for and lack of distinction between the direct and indirect C requirements of a process. The decarbonization potential of a process changes significantly depending on whether C is required as feedstock for the process, or simply for its energy or heating needs. This insight is valuable and missing from the current literature.

The current major scientific efforts in this field focus on development of decarbonization technologies. However, this reductionist approach may have rebound effects, whereby increase in consumptive behaviour offsets the marginal benefits of emissions reduction, and may hinder the longer scale goals of establishing a circular, sustainable chemical industry which is still carbon neutral. For example, attempts at electrification of ammonia, source hydrogen from electrolytic processes and attempt to electrify the operation of Haber Bosch process, to avoid releasing carbon dioxide as a co-product of fossil sourced hydrogen. A superficial analysis may reveal the abatement of a large fraction of greenhouse gad emissions when such production routes are taken. However, as we see in the results of our work, other processes like methanol, urea and acetic acid production are dependent on this carbon monoxide for their feedstock. Decarbonizing these sectors thus becomes much harder. This insight is easy to miss in traditional reductionist thinking and may lead us to grossly overestimating the emissions reduction. This incites the need of development of more holistic models which will accurately reflect the dependence of different processes in the network and avoid chances of shifting impacts and inadvertently increasing the environmental burden. In this work, we build a model that captures the co-dependence of different processes and outline a protocol for resolving the feedstock and utility C needs of the chemicals and material industries, while distinguishing between different processes and pathways of production.

2. Methodology

This model traces most conventional processes centering the chemical industry. We outline the C flows in the feedstock, product as well as that associated with energy requirement of the process. For all cases, we begin with a process description and a stoichiometric model of the ideal process. Yield and selectivity data collected from published surveys of operational plants lets us calculate realistic values of feedstock. Energy data is estimated from specific energy consumption (SEC) values or from life-cycle data. C content of these material and energy flows is then determined. Finally, we put these intensive flows into global perspective using production tonnage of each material. [11, 12] These calculations are demonstrated below for methyl alcohol.

Synthesis	$CO + 2H_2 \rightarrow CH_3OH$	(1)
Coal/Oil POX	$CH_n + H_2O \rightarrow CO + \frac{n+2}{2}H_2$	(2)
NG SMR	$2CH_n + O_2 \rightarrow 2CO + nH_2$	(3)
WGS	$CO + H_2O \rightarrow H_2 + CO_2$	(4)
RWGS	$H_2 + CO_2 \rightarrow CO + H_2O$	(5)
SMR to methanol	$2CH_n + \frac{n-2}{3}CO_2 + \frac{8-n}{3}H_2O \rightarrow \frac{4+n}{3}CH_3OH$	(6)
POX to methanol	$2CH_n + O_2 + \frac{4-n}{3}H_2O \rightarrow \frac{2+n}{3}CH_3OH + \frac{4-n}{3}CO_2$	(7)

To estimate feedstock requirement of methanol production, we use chemical synthesis route as shown in Eq.(1). The feedstock for methanol synthesis are sourced from syngas. Syngas can be generated by steam methane reforming of natural gas or coal gasification or partial oxidation of oil, as shown in Eq.(2) and Eq.(3) respectively. The kind of fossil feedstock used, determines the ratio of CO and H_2 in syngas. This ratio can be corrected by water gas shift or reverse water gas shift reactions for direct use in the synthesis process, depending on which gas is in excess. This is illustrated in Eq.(4) and Eq.(5). The value of 'n' can be approximated as 0.456 for coal, 1.873 for oil and 3.951 for natural gas. Thus, while syngas produced from coal and oil have excess CO and need to be subjected to water gas shift, NG sourced syngas is lean in CO and is followed up with reverse water gas shift. The final equations for methanol production, combining syngas generation, WGS/RWGS and methanol synthesis can be represented as Eq.(6) for NG and Eq.(7) for coal/oil.[6]

As can be observed from Eq.(6) and (7), the SMR/POX reactions coupled with WGS/RWGS reactions have two sources of C flows. The first is associated with the fossil feedstock requirement and the second is process emissions of CO_2. The coal/oil POX process emits CO_2 which is released to the atmosphere. On the other hand, the NG SMR process consumes CO_2 which we assume is sourced from ammonia plants nearby. Ammonia plants use only H_2 from syngas mixture. Thus, CO, which is generated as co-product of this H_2, can be separated and oxidized, according to Eq. (4), to provide feedstock to the methanol plants.

We assume an efficiency of 0.99 for the synthesis route (η_s) and 0.861 (NG), 0.808 (oil) and 0.76 (coal) for syngas generation steps (η_c). [6] Thus, the yield data along with stoichiometric information lets us calculate feedstock demand and C input thereof for methanol generation. [6] These calculations for process C of methanol are elucidated in Table 2 .

For energy requirement, we consider specific energy consumption (SEC) data for different feedstocks. Methanol generated from NG SMR has an SEC of 24 GJ/ton whereas partial oxidation of coal or oil lead to an energy consumption of 13.9 GJ/ton methanol. [5] To estimate the emissions associated with energy use, emisson coefficients associated with each fuel are used. The final calculations are shown in Table 3.

	Feedstock $\frac{CH_n}{CH_3OH}$	CO_2 input $\frac{CO_2}{CH_3OH}$	η_c	η_s	n	Actual feed $\frac{kg}{kgCH4O}$	Actual CO2 $\frac{kg}{kgCH4O}$
Coal	$\frac{6}{2+n}$	$-\frac{4-n}{2+n}$	0.76	0.99	0.456	1.26	-2.004
Oil	$\frac{6}{2+n}$	$-\frac{4-n}{2+n}$	0.808	0.99	1.873	0.84	-0.763
Natural Gas	$\frac{6}{4+n}$	$\frac{n-2}{4+n}$	0.861	0.99	3.951	0.44	0.396

	SEC for feedstock use $\frac{GJ}{ton\ CH_3OH}$	Feedstock fraction %	Emissions for energy use $\frac{kg\ CO2}{MJ}$	Energy fraction %
Coal	24	20.5	0.091	50
NG	13.9	71	0.013	50

Finally, these intensive product flow calculations are scaled up for global production tonnages. Currently, the annual production capacity of methanol stands at 102 million metric tonnes. [4] Of this, we estimate 71% is sourced from natural gas derived, 8.5% from oil derived and the remaining from coal derived syngas. [6] The flows are scaled accordingly and thus we arrive at the total C flows associated with fulfilling the global demand of methanol. The treatment of process C follows a protocol illustrated by Levi et al. [6]

3. Results and Discussion

Fig 1 shows the mobilization of C in feedstocks for manufacture of major chemicals. All flows shown here correspond to mass units of C. Their relative values are scaled by their annual global production capacities i.e. the flows are extensive in nature. Therefore, in this case, the production tonnage and specific C consumption both dictate magnitude of the flows. Process flows resulting in output of C flows are shown to be released to the environment. Unreacted reactants or leakages are grouped together in a separate category as "loss".

The diagram starts with fossil resources like crude oil, natural gas and coal. Refining processes yield primary hydrocarbons like olefins, aromatics, cyclic compounds and alkanes. Transformative reactions alter the relative production of these compounds. For example, toluene hydrodealkylation (THD) and toluene disproportionation (TDP) convert toluene to xylenes and benzene, ethylene and butene get converted to propylene via metathesis, and propane on dehydrogenation produces propylene. Alongside, we also show the synthesis of urea and methanol. The next stages show the production of platform chemicals like cumene, acrylonitrile, caprolactam, phenol, ethylene glycol, terephthalic acid, vinyl chloride monomer, acetic acid, formaldehyde etc from hydrocarbons. This is followed by production of polymers like polyethylene, polypropylene, polyvinyl chloride, polyethylene terephthalate, polystyrene etc. Finally, we track the end uses of some of these polymers to their major products. The diagram shows a large amount of C embodied in products used by the packaging industry, consumer goods and so on.

Large volume polymers like polyethylene, polypropylene, PET sequester C through their long half lives whereas C embodied in solvents such as acetone, ethylene glycol, toluene are either incinerated or disposed off. While attempts to circularize use of such stable plastics is underway, efforts can be made to source their feedstock C from non-fossil sources. While captured C or biogenic C can replace their fossil counterpart for use as feedstock, substituting the hydrogen or energy requirement of such processes presents a formidable task. Since captured C is only available as CO_2, it does not have any value as fuel. While the diagram itself only represents C flows, co-product flows are captured in process models. This information is indispensable in searching for lower C pathways of production.

We also observe a significant amount of process loss, throughout the industry. This can be attributed to unconverted reactants or inefficient separation of products. When the consumption of process and energy C are compared, we see emissions distributed similarly across both categories. This points to the vast decarbonization potential of the chemicals industry whereby energy can be alternately sourced from non emitting resoources.

4. Conclusions

Visualization of the C Flow model points us to the industries with greatest C footprint and the best ways to retrofit decarbonization technologies to these specific cases. This model is a stepping stone towards possibly answering bigger questions about the deep decarbonization of the chemicals industry. The data used in this model, can be used in conjunction with data on emerging technologies to optimize the economics and electricity demand of a decarbonized chemical industry. Additionally, the need for innovation and the direction in which it is needed may also be investigated. Eventually, the need for a policy change to support and affect the shift to decarbonized technologies can be supported with models such as this one. Thus, this model is a foundation in the vision of a sustainable, circular and C neutral chemical industry.

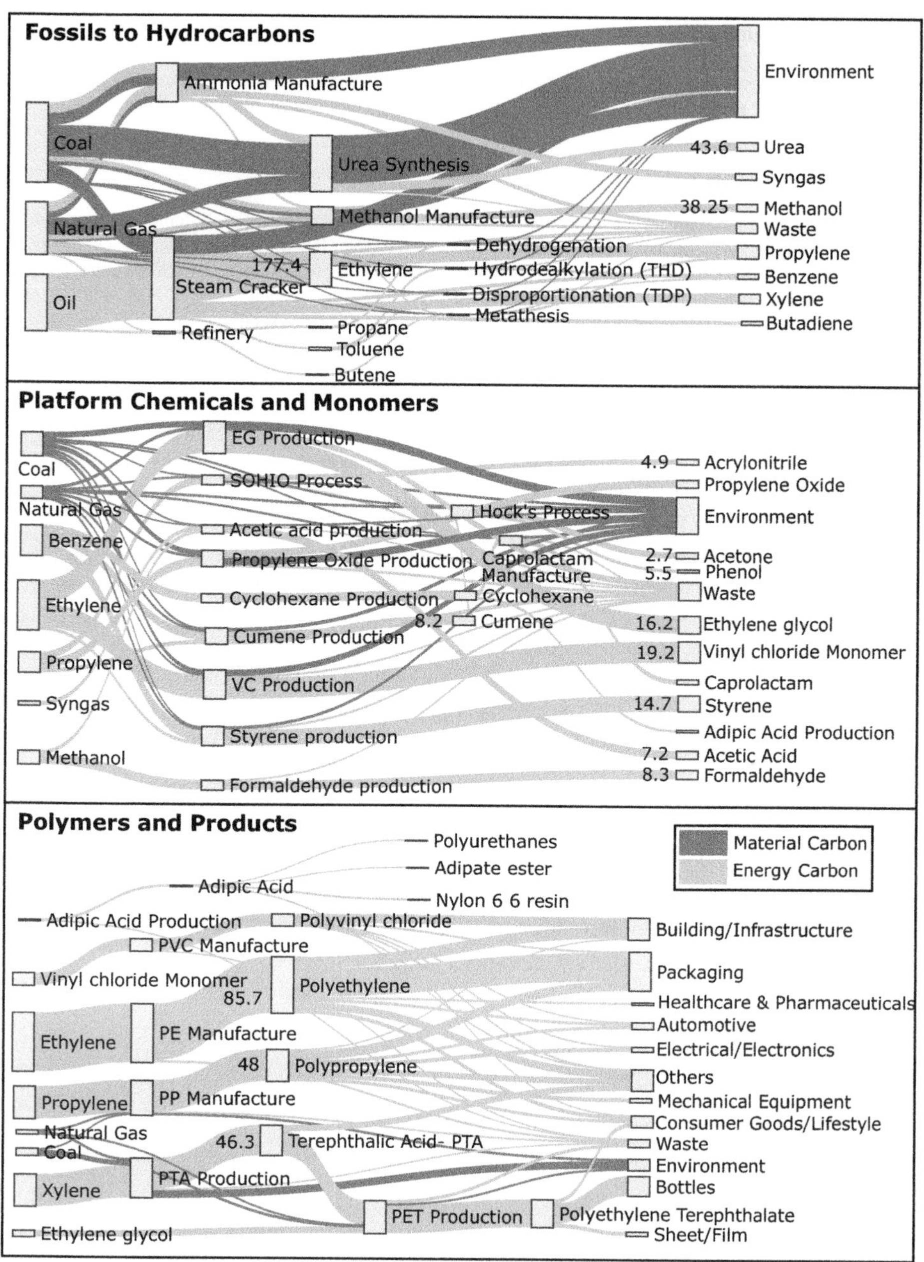

Figure 1: Flow of Fossil C through the Chemical Industry for in 2018 (in million metric tonnes of C)

5. Acknowledgments

Partial financial support was provided by "The Global KAITEKI Center" at Arizona State University (ASU), a university-industry partnership between ASU and The KAITEKI Institute of Mitsubishi Chemical Holdings Corporation.

References

[1] Mai Bui, Claire S. Adjiman, André Bardow, Edward J. Anthony, Andy Boston, Solomon Brown, Paul S. Fennell, Sabine Fuss, Amparo Galindo, Leigh A. Hackett, Jason P. Hallett, Howard J. Herzog, George Jackson, Jasmin Kemper, Samuel Krevor, Geoffrey C. Maitland, Michael Matuszewski, Ian S. Metcalfe, Camille Petit, Graeme Puxty, Jeffrey Reimer, David M. Reiner, Edward S. Rubin, Stuart A. Scott, Nilay Shah, Berend Smit, J. P. Martin Trusler, Paul Webley, Jennifer Wilcox, and Niall Mac Dowell. Carbon capture and storage (CCS): the way forward. *Energy & Environmental Science*, 11(5):1062–1176, 2018.

[2] W HERMANN. Quantifying global exergy resources. *Energy*, 31(12):1685–1702, sep 2006.

[3] https://www.llnl.gov/. Lawrence Livermore National Laboratory: C Emissions and Energy Flow Charts.

[4] https://www.methanol.org. Methanol Institute.

[5] IEA. Energy and GHG Reductions in the Chemical Industry via Catalytic Processes. 2013.

[6] Peter G. Levi and Jonathan M. Cullen. Mapping Global Flows of Chemicals: From Fossil Fuel Feedstocks to Chemical Products. *Environmental Science and Technology*, 52(4):1725–1734, feb 2018.

[7] Hélène Pilorgé, Noah McQueen, Daniel Maynard, Peter Psarras, Jiajun He, Tecle Rufael, and Jennifer Wilcox. Cost Analysis of Carbon Capture and Sequestration of Process Emissions from the U.S. Industrial Sector. *Environmental Science & Technology*, 54(12):7524–7532, jun 2020.

[8] Giulia Realmonte, Laurent Drouet, Ajay Gambhir, James Glynn, Adam Hawkes, Alexandre C. Köberle, and Massimo Tavoni. An inter-model assessment of the role of direct air capture in deep mitigation pathways. *Nature Communications*, 10(1):3277, dec 2019.

[9] Richard E Sassoon, Weston A Hermann, I-Chun Hsiao, Ljuba Milkovic, Aaron J Simon, and Sally M Benson. Quantifying the Flow of Exergy and Carbon through the Natural and Human Systems. *MRS Proceedings*, 1170:1170–R01–03, jan 2009.

[10] Nils Thonemann and Massimo Pizzol. Consequential life cycle assessment of carbon capture and utilization technologies within the chemical industry. *Energy & Environmental Science*, 12(7):2253–2263, 2019.

[11] www.ihsmarkit.com. IHS Markit Production Market Analysis.

[12] www.statista.com. Statista: Global Production Capacity Forecasts.

Proceedings of the 14th International Symposium on Process Systems Engineering – PSE 2021+
June 19-23, 2022, Kyoto, Japan
http://dx.doi.org/10.1016/B978-0-323-85159-6.50093-2

Optimal Designing and Planning of Ethiopia's Biomass-to-Biofuel Supply Chain Considering Economic and Environmental Dimensions under Strategic and Tactical Levels

Brook Tesfamichael[a,b,c], Ludovic Montastruc[a,b,*], Stéphane Negny[a,b], Abubeker Yimam[c]

[a]*Université de Toulouse, INP-ENSIACET, 4, allée Emile Monso, F-31432 Toulouse Cedex 04, France*
[b]*CNRS, LGC (Laboratoire de Génie Chimique), F-31432 Toulouse Cedex 04, France*
[c]*School of Chemical and Bio Engineering, Addis Ababa Institut of Technology, Addis Ababa University, Addis Ababa, Ethiopia*
**ludovic.montastruc@ensiacet.fr*

Abstract

This contribution provides an optimization-based decision support model of biomass to biofuels supply chain (BBSC) in order to offer optimal strategic decisions and tactical plans in the entire supply chain. This model is designed for long-term planning studies, in that it is utilized to optimize the Ethiopian BBSC over a 20-year horizon. Moreover, a comprehensive LCA is conducted on the BBSC by broadening the assessed impact categories adverse to most of the previous economic-environment models, which considers only one type of impact. To this end, through the LCA method and ecocost approach, an effort is made here to evaluate the environmental impacts associated with different biomass preprocessing technologies (drying and size reduction, mechanical and solvent extractions), biorefinery technologies (biochemical and thermochemical conversions, and homogeneous and heterogeneous transesterification) and material transportations along the BBSC. Since this planning problem relies on two objective functions, namely, profit and ecocost, a set of optimal solutions are generated to come up with the best compromise solution between the two antagonistic objectives.

Keywords: Biomass-to-biofuel supply chain (BBSC), economic-environment optimization, life cycle assessment, long-term planning.

1. Introduction

Over the last decade, biofuels are of rapidly growing interest in Ethiopia for reasons of saving foreign currency, export earning, job creation and greenhouse gas mitigation. However, the implementation of biomass-to-biofuel projects is in its infancy despite there is abundant biomass availability in the country [1]. Moreover, the existing infant biomass-to-biofuel supply chain (BBSC) is not carried out in a sustainable manner. This is majorly associated with the numerous economic and environmental challenges along the supply chain. Therefore, policymakers and other actors in the biofuel sector require a framework, which supports them to make scientifically valid and sustainable strategic decisions and tactical planning.

These days, numerous process systems engineering tools have been developed to assist decision making in the design and plan of various supply chains, of which optimization-based mathematical models take the largest share [2]. Based on the model outputs, recommendations had been forwarded for political decision-makers as well as for potential investors. Several strategic-tactical level models are formulated with objectives of maximizing economic and environmental benefits of supply chain in general and BBSC in particular. However, the models developed so far are not comprehensive and realistic enough to be applied at national level for long term planning of the biofuel sector. Some of the drawbacks include addressing the BBSC in a partial way (focusing on either upstream or midstream or downstream activities), dealing only on one type of biofuel product in a single supply chain and focusing on a one-year planning period. Moreover, the environmental concern in most of the previous studies emphasis on global warming, greenhouse gas (GHG) emissions and fossil energy consumption [3]. Nevertheless, these are not the only environmental impacts generated from the lifecycle of biofuel supply chain, which results in the importance of broadening the impact categories considered while dealing BBSC.

Henceforth, to address the limitations stated above, this work provides a comprehensive optimization-based decision support model in order to design and plan both bioethanol and biodiesel supply chain over a long-term. The objective of the model relies on both economic and environmental aspects, in that it aims to maximize the profit and minimize the ecocost of the BBSC. The model is applied to the real case of Ethiopia to offer optimal strategic and tactical decisions along the BBSC over 20-years horizon. Moreover, this study tries to make a comprehensive LCA along the supply chain of corn stover-, molasses-, and bagasse-based bioethanol and jatropha-, and castor-based biodiesel by broadening the assessed impacts. The impacts considered in this study are broadly classified into four; namely, carbon footprint (global warming potential), ecosystem (acidification, eutrophication and fresh water aquatic ecotoxicity potentials), human health (fine dust, human toxicity and photochemical oxidants potentials) and resource scarcity (metal and water scarcity, fossil fuel depletion and waste generation potentials).

2. Methodologies

2.1. Life cycle environmental assessment

The LCA method, which consists of goal and scope definition, life cycle inventory, and impact assessment, is considered in this work to analyze the BBSC impact on the environment. The LCA is applied herein is from biomass supplier (farm) gate to biofuel market. The BBSC stages considered in this work include biomass feedstocks transportation and preprocessing, preprocessed biomasses transportation, biofuels production and transportation. The technologies considered to preprocess bioethanol feedstocks is drying and size reduction, whereas mechanical and solvent extraction technologies are considered to preprocess the biodiesel feedstocks. Furthermore, the two biorefinery technologies considered for bioethanol production are biochemical and thermochemical conversions. Besides, homogeneous and heterogeneous base-catalyzed transesterification technologies are considered for biodiesel production. One ton of raw or prepocessed biomass is taken as the functional unit for this study. The life cycle inventory, which quantifies the amount of raw materials and product as well as energy requirements, of each biomass preprocessing and biofuel production (biorefinery) technology are estimated based on previous works. The GHG and other criteria pollutant emissions for the different technologies by taking into account each type of biomass and preprocessed biomass are obtained from the GREET model. On the other hand, previous researches are used to estimate the GHG and other criteria pollutants emissions from vehicles used in transporting materials along the supply chain, i.e., Euro II trailer truck and Euro III tanker truck for transportation of solid and liquid materials respectively. Then, based on the emission, inventory and utility consumption data, the impacts of all activities of the BBSC on the environment is analyzed through the ecocost method. This method is developed based on the marginal prevention costs needed to control the negative impact of toxic emissions. The total ecocost of a product or activity is the sum of ecocosts natural resources depletion, ecosystem, human health and carbon footprint during its life cycle.

2.2. Model formulation

The intention of this study is to provide a comprehensive mathematical model of BBSC, which includes all the principal supply-chain components upstream and downstream of the biorefineries. This model is designed for long-term planning studies, in that it is utilized to optimize the Ethiopian BBSC over a 20-year horizon. To account the whole BBSC behavior, the problem is designed as a spatially explicit, multi-product, multi-feedstock, multi-period, and multi-echelon MILP modeling framework. The model considers yearly and monthly time periods. The design mechanism is perceived as a multi-objective optimization problem that intends to maximize the profit and minimize the ecocost of the BBSC. The profit as illustrated in equation (1) is calculated by taking into account the cash inflow (total annual revenue) and cash outflows (total annual cost and investment cost) in a specific year. Moreover, the total ecocost is given as the sum of the ecocosts of biomass preprocessing, biofuel production and material transportation, as indicated in equation (2).

$$Profit = \sum_{n=1}^{Y} \left(\left[\frac{1}{(1+ir)^{y}} \left(Total\ Revenue_{\ y} - Total\ Cost_{\ y} \right) \right] \right) \tag{1}$$

Where ir is the discount rate

$$Total\ EcoCost = \sum_{y} \left[Ecocost\ Preprocessing_{\ y} + Ecocost\ Production_{\ y} + Ecocost\ Transportation_{\ y} \right] \tag{2}$$

Moreover, constraints and mass balances that needs to be fulfilled at each stage of the BBSC are formulated, including: supply and demand satisfaction, inventory balance, production amount, binary and non-negativity decision variables, and storage and weight capacity constraints. The expected output of the model refers to strategic decisions in the BBSC, which includes the network configuration, capacity, technology, and location of the biorefineries and preprocessing units as well as the capacity and location of distribution centers. Moreover, optimum decisions related to annual production, inventory, and transportation of materials along the BBSC are expected results of the model. The model is described on [4].

2.3. Case Study

The developed model in this study is applied to the real case of Ethiopia. All the assumptions taken and detail technical and economic data of the case study are available on [4]. These data include biomass feedstocks availability and purchasing price, biofuels and coproduct demand and selling price, investment and production costs as well as storage and processing capacities of each BBSC components, conversion factors of each candidate technology, transportation distance between different zones of the country and transportation cost of materials in the supply chain.

2.4. Solution method for multi-objective optimization

The MILP model was solved using the ILOG CPLEX solver. The antagonistic nature between the economic and environmental objectives was solved using the following procedure. First, the profit was maximized to obtain the resulting optimal profit (upper bound of profit) and the ecocost value (upper bound of ecocost). Second, the ecocost was minimized to obtain the resulting profit value (lower bound of profit) and the optimal ecocost (lower bound of ecocost). Then, the profit was maximized 10 times by constraining the ecocost in different ranges between the lower and upper bound. Similarly, the ecocost was minimized 10 times by constraining the profit in different ranges between the lower and upper bound. To this end, a set of efficient solutions ware generated.

3. Result and Discussion

3.1. Environmental impact

Based on the GREET outputs, utility consumption data and inventory analysis, the environmental impacts (ecocost) associated with biomass preprocessing, biofuel production and material transportation are calculated. The ecocosts associated with biomass preprocessing via drying and size reduction, mechanical and solvent extraction are depicted in Figure 1. Similarly, Figure 2 presents the ecocosts of bioethanol and biodiesel production via biochemical or thermochemical conversion, and homogenous or heterogeneous transesterification.

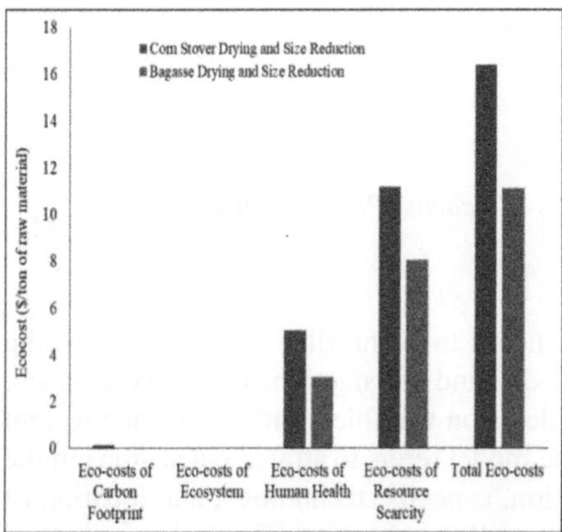

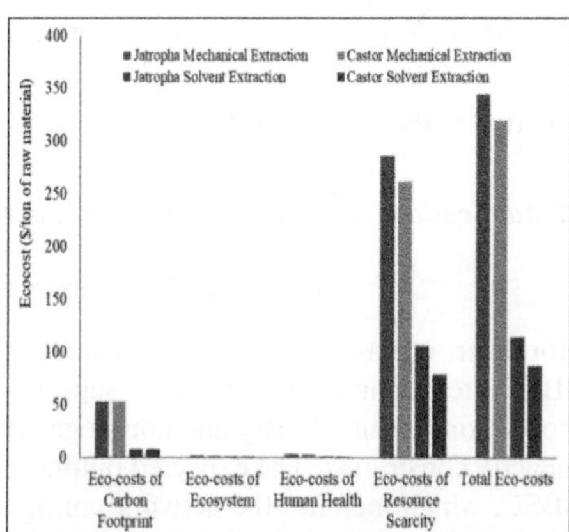

Figure 1: Ecocosts of carbon footprint, ecosystem, human health and resource scarcity for preprocessing corn stover and bagasse using drying and size reduction (left) and for preprocessing jatropha and castor using mechanical and solvent extraction (right)

In the drying and size reduction unit, ecocosts of human health and resource scarcity are significant among others as there is considerable fine dust emission during size reduction of the feedstocks and the requirement of energy by the hammer mill. Due to the higher energy demand in mechanical and solvent extraction, the resource scarcity ecocost is significant in these two preprocessing technologies compared with other ecocost types.

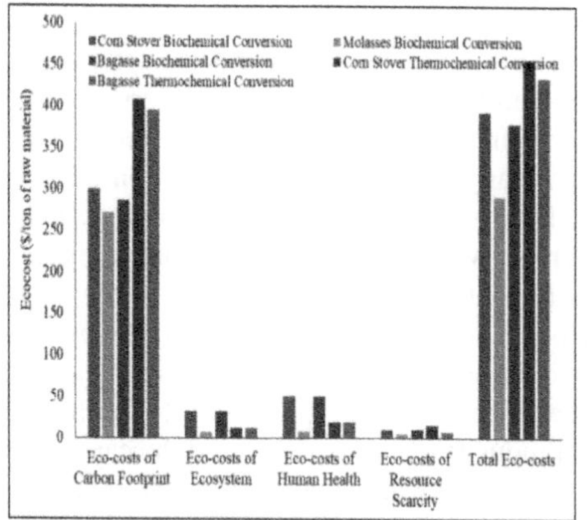

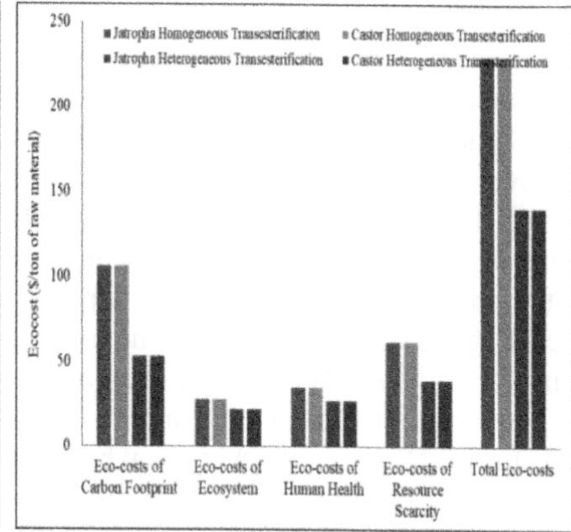

Figure 2: Ecocosts of carbon footprint, ecosystem, human health and resource scarcity for corn stover-, molasses- and bagasse-based bioethanol production using biochemical and thermochemical conversion (left) and jatropha oil-, and castor oil-based biodiesel production using homogeneous and heterogeneous base-catalyzed transesterification (right)

Biochemical and thermochemical conversions are the highest ecocost contributor compared with the other activities due to the highest GHG, specifically CO_2, emission generated from the two processes, in which the latter technology contributes more. Similar to the bioethanol technologies, the carbon footprint ecocost of biodiesel producing technologies (homogeneous and heterogeneous transesterification) are the most significant ones because of their higher energy requirement that is fulfilled by fossil fuel combustion, which is responsible for emission of CO_2 and other criteria pollutants.

The significant amount of CO_2, NOx, CO and VOC emissions from the vehicles, especially in the Euro II trailer truck, has resulted in a considerable contribution of ecocosts of human health, ecosystem and carbon footprint on the total ecocost.

3.2. Multi-objective optimization results

Each run of the MILP model had 1,348,768 constraints and 2,404,604 continuous decision variables of which 174 were binary variables. Optimal solutions were found between 58.42-102.42 minutes on an Intel 2.60-GHz processor. The set of solutions generated to show the tradeoff between the two objectives of the BBSC are depicted in Figure 3.

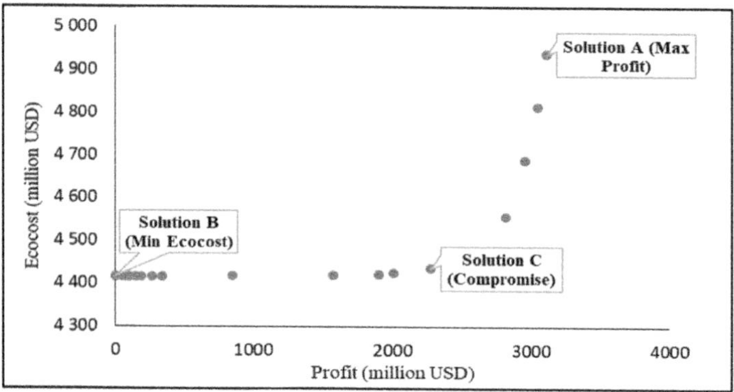

Figure 3: Set of solutions for profit maximization vs ecocost minimization

3.3. Optimum strategic decisions

The optimum solution (Solution C of Figure 3) promotes molasses and jatropha as the only biomass feedstock to address the bioethanol and biodiesel demand of Ethiopia in the next 10 and 5 years respectively, which is then joined by the other biomass feedstocks. Moreover, the optimal solution does not promote any drying and size reduction unit for the first 10 years and solvent extraction technology is mainly preferred to preprocess the biodiesel feedstocks in the entire planning period. Most of the preprocessing units are located proximate to the feedstock supply centers although not necessarily in the same zones. Regarding the biorefinery, the installation of biochemical refineries is proposed to attain the required amount of bioethanol production in the next 10 years, which is joined by thermochemical refineries after a decade. The locations proposed to build the biochemical refineries are in zones where sugar industries are available and the capacities are driven by the molasses availability. Besides, the model prescribes heterogeneous-transesterification refineries installation throughout the planning period for producing biodiesel.

4. Conclusions

To provide optimal strategic decisions and tactical plans of biomass to biofuels supply chain (BBSC), this study aims to develop an optimization-based decision support model. It is a long-term planning model with objectives of maximizing both economic and environmental benefits. The model is utilized to optimize the Ethiopian BBSC over a 20-year horizon. Unlike to previous researches, a number of environmental impact categories are considered to assess the impact of the BBSC on the environment. The addressed impact categories include carbon footprint, human health, ecosystem and resource scarcity potential of the BBSC. To this end, all these impacts are evaluated on each activities of the supply chain (biomass preprocessing, biofuel production and material transportation) by taking the type of biomasses and technologies into consideration. The results have indicated that biofuel production via biochemical or thermochemical conversions is the highest environmental impact contributor in case of bioethanol supply chain. Contrary, in supply chain of biodiesel, the highest impact is generated from biomass preprocessing using mechanical or solvent extraction. Since this planning problem relies on two objective functions, namely, profit and ecocost, a set of optimal solutions are generated to come up with the best compromise solution between the two antagonistic objectives.

References

[1] M. Berhanu, S.A. Jabasingh, Z. Kifile, Expanding sustenance in Ethiopia based on renewable energy resources – A comprehensive review, Renew. Sustain. Energy Rev. 75 (2017) 1035–1045. https://doi.org/10.1016/j.rser.2016.11.082.

[2] A.P. Barbosa-Póvoa, C. da Silva, A. Carvalho, Opportunities and challenges in sustainable supply chain: An operations research perspective, Eur. J. Oper. Res. 268 (2018) 399–431. https://doi.org/10.1016/j.ejor.2017.10.036.

[3] S. Soam, R. Kumar, R.P. Gupta, P.K. Sharma, D.K. Tuli, B. Das, Life cycle assessment of fuel ethanol from sugarcane molasses innorthern and western India and its impact on Indian biofuel programme, Energy. 83 (2015) 307–315. https://doi.org/10.1016/j.energy.2015.02.025.

[4] B. Tesfamichael, L. Montastruc, S. Negny, A. Yimam, Designing and planning of Ethiopia ' s biomass-to-biofuel supply chain through integrated strategic-tactical optimization model considering economic dimension, Comput. Chem. Eng. 153 (2021) 107425. https://doi.org/10.1016/j.compchemeng.2021.107425.

Proceedings of the 14th International Symposium on Process Systems Engineering – PSE 2021+
June 19-23, 2022, Kyoto, Japan
http://dx.doi.org/10.1016/B978-0-323-85159-6.50094-4

A Novel Integrated Optimal Scheduling Framework for Holistic Refinery Supply Chain Management

Li Yu, Qiang Xu*

Dan F. Smith Department of Chemical & Biomolecular Engineering, Lamar University, Beaumont, Texas 77710, USA
Qiang.xu@lamar.edu

Abstract

The refinery supply chain management is critically important. It covers three highly correlated sub problems: the front-end crude-oil management sub problem (CM), the refinery manufacturing sub problem (RM), and the multi oil-product pipeline distribution sub problem (MOPD). By coordinating the management and operations of the three sub problems, it can greatly minimize the operating cost of the entire supply chain. In this paper, a continuous-time and continuous-volume based general integrated optimal MINLP scheduling framework for holistic refinery supply chain covering the crude-oil management, the refinery manufacturing, and the multi oil-product pipeline distribution has been developed (CM&RM&MOPD). The objective is to minimize the total operating cost subject to various constraints such as operating rules, product specifications, inventory limits, delivery constraints, and oil-product demands at each oil depot. The efficacy of the developed CM&RM&MOPD model has been demonstrated by a large-scale case study.

Keywords: Integrated scheduling, MINLP, Holistic refinery supply chain, Crude-oil unloading and transferring, Refinery manufacturing, Pipeline distribution.

1. Introduction

The refinery supply chain management is critically important to the oil industry. It contains three subsystems as shown in Figure 1, starting from the crude-oil vessels unloading at ports to the oil-product exported to local consumer markets. Specifically, the first subsystem includes crude-oil unloading from vessels to storage tanks, transferring crude-oil to charging tanks, blending, and feeding to crude distillation units (CDUs); the second subsystem involves the refinery manufacturing process, including major refinery processing units such as crude distillation, catalytic reforming, fluid catalytic cracking, hydrocracking, delayed coking, hydrotreating, gas fraction, alkylation, hydrogen pooling, blending, as well as sulfur recovery facilities; the third subsystem is about refinery oil-product distribution, which consists of inventory management at the refinery product tank farm, multi oil-product pipeline transportation, as well as oil-product receiving, exporting, and inventory management at different depots. The three subsystems are highly correlated. According to Chima (2007), each subsystem should respond quickly to the exact demand of its downstream customers, protecting itself from problems with suppliers, and buffering its operations from both demand and supply uncertainty. Thus, by coordinating the management and operations of the three subsystems can greatly maximize the potential benefit margin of the entire refinery supply-chain. There exists a lot of works explicitly and deeply exploited and studied these subsystems separately, e.g., some for the front-end crude-oil management (Zhang and Xu, 2015; Qu et al., 2019), some for oil-product pipeline distribution (Cafaro and Cerdá, 2010; Yu et al., 2020), and some works have simultaneously considered the first two subsystems (Yang et al., 2020; Xu et al., 2017). However, few studies addressed these three sub systems simultaneously. Guyonnet et al. (2009) studied the simplified crude oil unloading, production planning, and distribution sub models on a tactical decision level by solving each part in a sequential push or pull manner, where the planning horizon is discretized into a day or a week. Generally, systematic studies for the integrated scheduling the holistic refinery supply chain are still lacking.

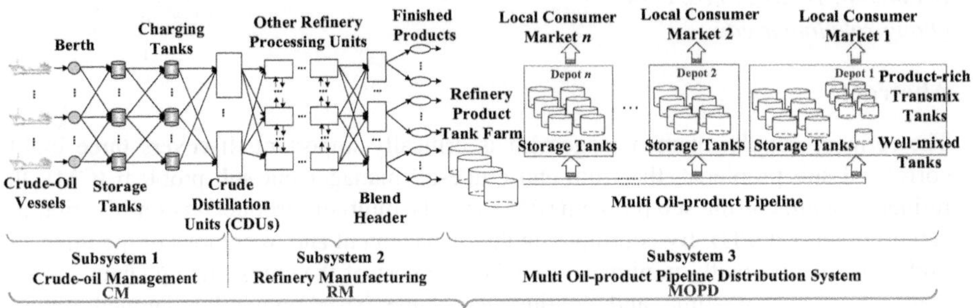

Figure 1. The studied scope of this study.

In this paper, a general integrated optimal scheduling model for the crude-oil management, the refinery manufacturing, and the multi oil-product pipeline distribution has been developed (CM&RM&MOPD). It consists of five sub-models: (i) a crude-oil management (CM) sub-model including the crude-oil unlading, transferring, and charging CDUs; (ii) a refinery manufacturing (RM) sub-model covering all major refinery processing units; (iii) a joint sub-model coupling the CM sub-model and its downstream RM sub-model; (iv) a new multi oil-product pipeline distribution (MOPD) sub-model that considers comprehensive handling measures for oil transmix including downgrading, blending, and distillation operations; and (v) a joint sub-model coupling the upstream RM and the downstream MOPD. The developed CM&RM&MOPD model is a large-scale continuous-time and continuous-volume based MINLP model, where the objective is to minimize the total operating cost subject to various constraints such as operating rules, product specifications, inventory limits, delivery constraints, and oil-product demands at each oil depot.

2. CM&RM&MOPD model

The detailed CM sub-model is remodeled from a previous study (Zhang and Xu, 2014); the RM sub-model is based on the study of Xu et al. (2017); while the MOPD sub-model involves the comprehensive TM handling measures and tanks inventory management is based on the MOPD sub-model development (Yu et al., 2020) with modest modifications. Due to the limited space, more detailed model equations and assumptions could be referred to these three corresponding articles.

2.1. CM&RM joint sub-model

Equation (1) is employed to mathematically connect the CDU charging amount at the front-end CM outlet and the RM inlet. For example, the CDU charging amount at the CM outlet during time event one (n=1) will be equal to the CDU charging amount at the RM inlet during the injection of the first new slug (i=i_0+1) into the downstream pipeline.

$$Fed_{i,c,unt} = F^{c}(unt,c,n), \ \ \forall i \in I^{new}, 1 \le n < |N|, \\ n = the\ order\ of\ new\ slug\ i, c \in C, unt \in DU \tag{1}$$

2.2. RM&MOPD joint sub-model

Sub-models RM and MOPD are materially linked through the mass balance of refinery storage tanks as shown in Eq. (2). Once the new slug *ii* is fed into the pipeline, Eq. (2) will calculate the leftover inventory of the refinery storage tank containing the oil product *p* ($Invp_{ii,p,rst}$), which is equal to the previous inventory after feeding slug *ii*-1 ($Invp_{ii-1,p,rst}$) plus the amount of oil product produced by refinery during the time period of feeding new slug *ii* ($Bldp_{ii,p}$), and minus the amount of oil product injected into the pipeline during the same time period ($Fedp_{ii,p}$). Eq. (3) constraints both the lower and upper bound of the refinery storage tanks.

$$Invp_{ii,p,rst} = Invp_{ii-1,p,rst} + Bldp_{ii,p} - Fedp_{ii,p}, \ \ \forall ii \in I^{new}, p \in P, rst \in RST \tag{2}$$

$$Invp^{lo}_{ii,p,rst} \le Invp_{ii,p,rst} \le Invp^{up}_{ii,p,rst}, \ \ \forall ii \in I^{new}, p \in P, rst \in RST \tag{3}$$

2.3. Objective function

The objective function of the CM&RM&MOPD model is to minimize the total process cost, which is defined in Eq. (4). It contains three main items representing the cost for the three sub problems, specifically, the first item *Cost_CM* represents the total CM sub-problem cost, the second item *Cost_RM* represents the total RM sub-problem cost, while the third item *Cost_MOPD* represents the total MOPD sub-problem cost.

$$\min Cost\_Holistic = (Cost\_CM) + (Cost\_RM) + (Cost\_MOPD) \tag{4}$$

3. Case study

The scope of the scheduling problem consists of (i) three single-parcel vessels carrying their respective crudes, one single docking berth, four storage tanks, four charging tanks; (ii) a refinery plant processing two types of crudes and producing four blending oil products and four corresponding refinery storage tanks; (iii) one long-distance pipeline connected to four oil depots; (iv) each depot has two storage tanks for each oil product; and (v) the farthest depot along the pipeline has nine additional storage tanks, including two product-rich transmix tanks for storing rich-product of each type of oil product (i.e., eight tanks) and one well-mixed tank storing well-mixed *ic*-TMs.

3.1. Computational performance and economic analysis

Based on our study, the developed CM&RM&MOPD model has been programmed with GAMS v25.1.2 and implemented on Intel 3.4 GHz Windows PC with 16.0 GB memory. The optimization solver DICOPT (based on the extensions of the outer-approximation algorithm) is adopted to solve the MINLP problems (Duran and Grossmann, 1986), where CPLEX and CONOPT4 are employed as the sub solvers for MIP and NLP sub problems, respectively. The problem size and results of economic and computational performance are summarized in Table 1. Note that the objective only considers the utility cost and various operating cost, while other costs like crude-oil purchasing cost, labor, maintenance, and royalties are not considered.

Table 1. Economic and computational performance results for the CM&RM&MOPD case

Problem Size and Solution Efforts			
No. of constraints	25,552	No. of binary var.	3,698
No. of continuous var.	16,132	Non-zeros	107,878
Optimality Gap	0.001%	CPU time (s)	2,038
Economic Results (k$)			
Total cost (objective)	281,471.68	MOPD sub-problem cost	226,911.55
CM sub-problem cost	430.54	Blending credit	-771.25
RM sub-problem cost	54,129.59		

3.2. Results of crude-oil management scheduling

The CM scheduling results is shown in Figure 3, where the numbers above bars represent transferred crude-oil volumes (Mbbl). Various filling patterns indicate the source units/facilities of crude-oils; while different colors denote specific time events when operations occur. Small solid black schedule bars represent the RPST time (Xu et al. 2017). Overall, four time events are employed for the CM scheduling. The first blue bar in the figure, for example, it means at time event 2, a total volume of 1,000 Mbbl crude-oil is transferred from parcel 1 to storage tank 2 from day 0 to day1.1. As shown, two refinery CDUs have received different types of crude blends from charging tanks at different time events. Thus, a RPST time is located between any pair of time events.

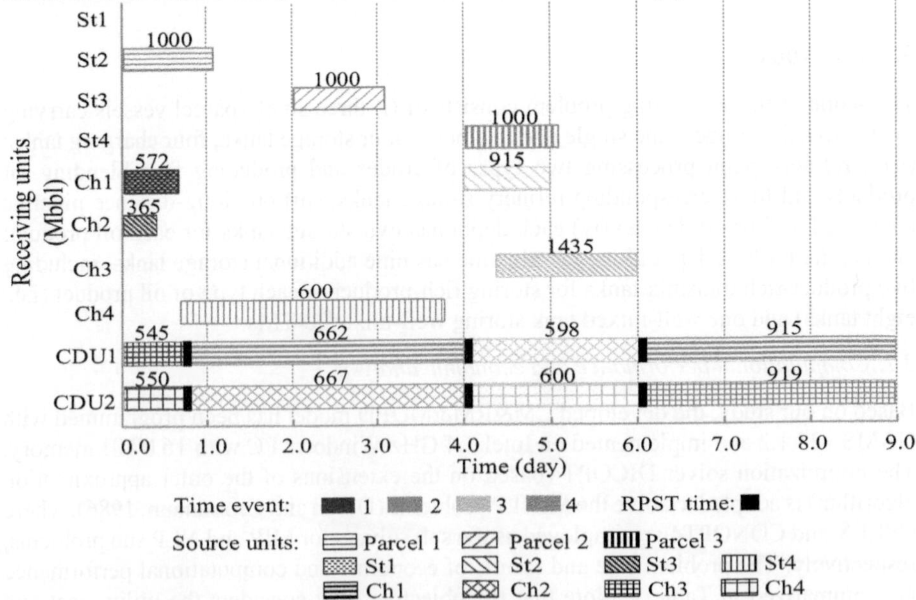

Figure 3. Scheduling result by considering the RPST time.

3.3. Results of refinery manufacturing scheduling

The scheduling results of the RM sub-problem are presented in Figures 4. It displays the production profiles of the blended oil products, where the colour of the 3-D column represents the scheduling time duration. The overall inventory based on the holistic scheduling are constrained within their capacity constraints.

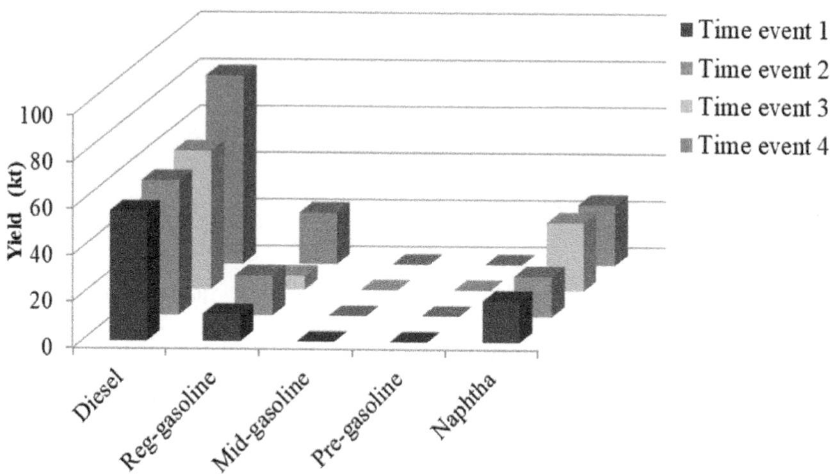

Figure 4. Production profiles of refinery blending product.

3.4. Results of multi oil-product pipeline distribution scheduling

The Gantt charts for the scheduling results of MOPD sub-problem is shown in Figure 5. The filling color of bars and arrows represents the type of oil product. The solution values of injected oil-product type, volume, and time duration are marked near the patterned horizontal arrows at the pipeline inlet. A recycling operation and the recycled volume of an *ic*-TM at the farthest depot are specifically denoted by a bent arrow with a volume value. The *ic*-TMs inside the pipeline during scheduling are represented by short and slash-patterned bars. The delivery operations and delivered volumes of oil products to corresponding depots are denoted by vertical arrows and values above.

4. Conclusions

In this paper, a continuous-time and continuous-volume based general integrated optimal scheduling framework for holistic refinery supply chain covering the crude-oil management, the refinery manufacturing, and the multi oil-product pipeline distribution has been developed. The objective is to minimize the total operating cost subject to various operating constraints. It can simultaneously provide optimal solutions for crude-oil vessels unloading, transfer connections, timings, and volumes; refinery unit operations, production profiles; oil-product inventory management at refinery and depots, oil slug movement profiles inside pipeline, as well as oil-product discharging strategies from pipeline to multiple tanks at different depots.

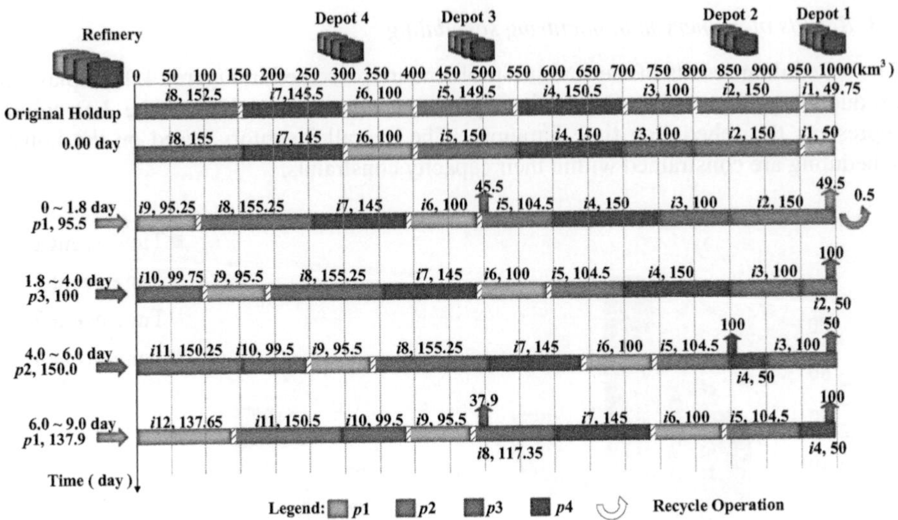

Figure 5. MOPD schedule and pipeline profiles.

Acknowledgements: This work was supported in parts by The Center for Midstream Management and Science (CMMS) and The Center for Advances in Port Management (CAPM) at Lamar University in Beaumont, Texas, USA.

References

Cafaro, D. C., & Cerdá, J. (2010). Operational scheduling of refined products pipeline networks with simultaneous batch injections. Computers & Chemical Engineering, 34(10), 1687-1704.

Chima, C. M. (2007). Supply-chain management issues in the oil and gas industry. Journal of Business & Economics Research (JBER), 5(6).

Duran, M. A., & I. E. Grossmann (1986). An outer-approximation algorithm for a class of mixed-integer nonlinear programs. Mathematical Programming 36(3): 307-339.

Guyonnet, P., Grant, F. H., & Bagajewicz, M. J. (2009). Integrated model for refinery planning, oil procuring, and product distribution. Industrial & Engineering Chemistry Research, 48(1), 463-482.

Qu, H., Wang, S., & Xu, Q. (2019). Integrated proactive and reactive scheduling for refinery front-end crude movement with consideration of unit maintenance. Industrial & Engineering Chemistry Research, 58(27), 12192-12206.

Xu, J., Zhang, S., Zhang, J., Wang, S., & Xu, Q. (2017). Simultaneous scheduling of front-end crude transfer and refinery processing. Computers & Chemical Engineering, 96, 212-236.

Yang, H., Bernal, D. E., Franzoi, R. E., Engineer, F. G., Kwon, K., Lee, S., & Grossmann, I. E. (2020). Integration of crude-oil scheduling and refinery planning by Lagrangean Decomposition. Computers & Chemical Engineering, 138, 106812.

Yu, L., Chen, M., & Xu, Q. (2020). Simultaneous scheduling of multi-product pipeline distribution and depot inventory management for petroleum refineries. Chemical Engineering Science, 220, 115618.

Zhang, S., & Xu, Q. (2015). Refinery continuous-time crude scheduling with consideration of long-distance pipeline transportation. Computers & Chemical Engineering, 75, 74-94.

Proceedings of the 14th International Symposium on Process Systems Engineering – PSE 2021+
June 19-23, 2022, Kyoto, Japan
http://dx.doi.org/10.1016/B978-0-323-85159-6.50095-6

Roadmap to digital supply chain resilience

Adnan Al-Banna[a,b], Robert E. Franzoi[a], Brenno C. Menezes[a*], Ahad Al-Enazi[a,c], Simon Rogers[d], Jeffrey D. Kelly[e]

[a]*Division of Engineering Management and Decision Sciences, College of Science and Engineering, Hamad Bin Khalifa University, Qatar Foundation, Doha, Qatar*
[b]*Department of Logistics and Supply Chain, Milaha, Doha, Qatar*
[c]*Commercial Planning and Optimization, QatarGas, Doha, Qatar*
[d]*Digital Solutions, Yokogawa, Tokyo, Japan*
[e]*Industrial Algorithms Ltd., 15 St. Andrews Road, Toronto M1P 4C3, Canada*
bmenezes@hbku.edu.qa

Abstract

As supply chains evolve from local trading entities to global physical and virtual markets, today's organizations are privileged with enhanced access to unprecedented opportunities in volume, variety, deliver time, transportation mode, of resources and goods. However, given today's level of interdependence of these entities that permits reduced mismatches in their processes, such organizations are more susceptive to disruptions in their networks. Over the past decades, global economies have experienced several crises induced by irrepressible circumstances that are either human-influenced, such as geopolitical conflicts and cyber-attacks, or provoked by nature, such as natural disasters and pandemic outbreaks. Hence, organizations have been placing substantial emphasis on supply chain resilience (SCR), with the objective of mitigating the impact of unforeseen risks on their supply chains, logistics, and their subsequent consequences on cost control and revenue maximization. Conventional SCR relied on increased safety stock levels, partial order allocations, supplier's diversifications, among others. On contrary, next generation of resilient supply chain operations can be reached by the digital transformation of its elements into the SCR modeling and control. The objective of this paper is twofold. First, it introduces the role of the digital transformation, advanced analytics, automation, and augmentation of the SCR with the support of cyber-physical systems and security (CPSS) solutions from the industry 4.0 age. Second, it provides a structured view on artificial intelligence (AI) and internet of things (IoT) technologies, aiming to establish a robust, timely, and successful digital supply chain resilience (DSCR). We believe the discussion provided and provoked herein will aid organizations towards addressing proper digital capabilities for achieving higher levels of visibility and control, enhanced revenues, reduced costs, and improved supply chain resilience augmented by the power of digitalization, automation, and artificial intelligence.

Keywords: Supply chain management, digital transformation, digital supply chain resilience, artificial intelligence, internet of things.

1. Introduction

The prerequisites of efficient business management are not limited to human and financial resources and their supporting ecosystem. Instead, organizational survival and success are underpinned by supply chain resilience (SCR), which encompasses the abilities to predict, avoid, contain, manage, recover from, and eventually alleviate adverse impacts of continuous disruptions and uncertainties (Melnyk et al., 2014). Previous literature has predominantly addressed the conventional supply chain efficiency (SCE) strategies involving multiple sourcing, partial order allocation, and extra inventory stocks (Tang, 2006; Vanany et al., 2009). Although the aforementioned strategies could have been sufficient to manage organizational risks in the previous decades, limiting the current organizational resilience toolbox to SCE strategies may lead to incurring losses due to a lack of no costly responsiveness to sudden events. Schreckling et al. (2017) highlight that for most industries, regardless of the field, location, and application, it is fundamental to advance towards enhanced digital transformation capabilities to interconnect entities and levels of the supply chain (ELSC). Agrawal (2018) emphasizes that digital transformation is not a choice in the current world of globalization, but it is imperative for all industries to find synergies of a collection of companies' segments and avoid the pitfalls of segregated ELSC. Most scholars addressed SCE and SCR in isolation, while few works have acknowledged their interconnected nature. In contrast, the distinctive approach of Dolgui et al. (2020) provides a concise differentiation of SCE and SCR and elaborates on their interconnections with digital supply chain (DSC) and sustainable supply chain (SSC), as illustrated in Figure 1, which shows the main strategies of the DSC, SCR, SSC, and SCE interplays. Although Dolgui et al. (2020) offer an efficient representation of the interconnectedness of these supply chain (SC) frameworks, it is noteworthy to mention that most previous works have not addressed their correlation.

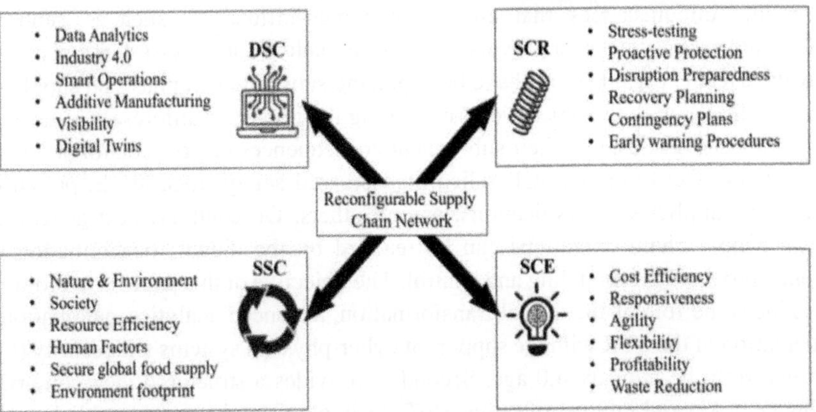

Figure 1. The reconfigurable supply chain network (adapted from Dolgui et al., 2020).

The main contributions of this work rely on addressing a multi-domain supply chain, which involves the interconnectedness of SCE, SCR, DSCE, and DSCR. We emphasize that DSCR elements must be embedded in the organization processes throughout its suppliers-input-process-outcome-customer (SIPOC) workflows. This ensures optimum preparedness to build enhanced: i) resistance against disruptions by employing avoidance and containment strategies; and ii) recovery capabilities by stabilizing and returning to the pre-disruption and pre-disturbance performance levels.

Early publications on SC have predominantly focused on SCE, whereas concepts of SCR have only recently been addressed and studied. Researchers have primarily addressed the impact of digitalization in the supply chain as SCE and later focused on its influence as SCR; therefore, most of the research is found in the SCE domain. Literature indicates a significant evolution in the supply chain research over the past decades, primarily because of the fast expansion of global markets and their associated opportunities and threats. However, DSCE and DSCR remain to be premature research areas where significant opportunities exist. The digital transformation of companies must be augmented with the relevant resilience and associated optimality that involve automation and digitalization of business processes to capture the status of the ecosystems and provide the necessary scalability and evolution into optimized and automated operations and controls (Menezes et al., 2019a). Gartner (2018) predicts that in 2022, 85% of all artificial intelligence projects are expected to fail due to data inconsistencies, inappropriate algorithms, and inefficient human capital. Hence, there is a fundamental need for a robust roadmap of digital transformation towards a supply chain resilient state.

2. Stages towards the digital transformation

2.1. First stage: SIPOC (suppliers-input-process-outcome-customer) integration

The first stage of any digital transformation project demands a detailed gap analysis that considers the overall SIPOC processes and interdependencies, whereby the current digital standpoint, desired ultimate organization status, and project milestones are identified. Hence, the strategic macro-level visions and operational micro-level requirements should be carefully envisioned, discussed, and outlined to allow future scalability and straightforward implementation. This should be ideally performed in a cross-departmental fashion and under strong sponsorship from top leadership to achieve a company-wide project environment. Similarly, the success of digital transformation projects requires critical factors, including competent human capital, adequate technology selection, efficient implementation, top management sponsorship, sufficient training and incentives for technology adoption, enterprise resources planning (ERP) integration capabilities, optimizing on-premise versus cloud storage, adequate data migration and protection, robust cybersecurity policies and infrastructure, clear KPI's with margins-of-error and escalation mechanisms and strategies for minimizing staff resistance to changes. The aforementioned factors are summarized by Bascur (2020) in three distinct domains, namely: a) people, b) business processes, and c) adopted technologies, whereby the importance of creating a digital transformation environment is highlighted as well. These three domains are considered the corner stones for the digital transformation success triangle and are required to provide optimal results.

2.2. Second stage: SIPOC autonomy

Once the digital transformation roadmap is established, agile organizations can use the aforementioned approach to combine their knowledge of economy, finance, technology, market dynamics, and business resilience. This provides efficient capabilities for handling continuous risks and uncertainties and progressively enhancing business resilience measures with the support of cyber-physical systems and security (CPSS) solutions. Throughout the transformation process, organizations need to acknowledge the interconnection of DSCR with the capabilities provided by artificial intelligence (AI) and the Industrial Internet of Things (IIoT). However, DSCR is expected to be as reliable as its weakest Industry 4.0 components. Hence, the concept of IIoT ecosystem trustworthiness is fundamental at all levels within digital ecosystems. Sharma et al. (2020) categorize an IIoT ecosystem into four interconnected layers, as illustrated in Figure 2, encompassing the internet, devices, support, and applications. The trustworthiness of any IIoT ecosystem depends on the proper and continuous functioning of all layers to enable the sensors to acquire information correctly. Information is transferred through the internet in a timely and holistically fashion. The support layer efficiently receives and decodes it to allow the application layer to display, process, and present it on the associated user interface for an appropriate decision-making process. We propose the addition of a fifth layer, which is integrated to the other layers towards decoding and converting data and information into a decision-making process.

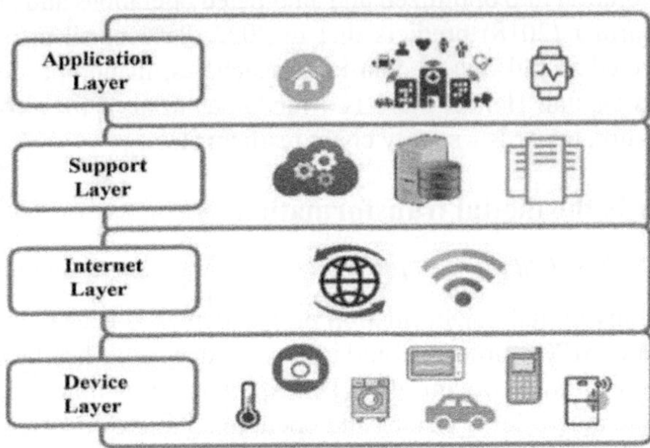

Figure 2. Four-layer architecture of IIoT ecosystem (adapted from Sharma et al., 2020).

The growth of connected IIoT devices is expected to generate increasing amounts of data, emphasizing the high need for a better-managed cybersecurity infrastructure that shields data integrity (IDC, 2019). This highlights the importance of adopting a regular reviews and PDCA (Plan-Do-Check-Act) cycles to continuously ensure data reliability and efficient decision-making. Rocher et al. (2019) adopts this concept and argues that cyber-physical systems should be continuously evaluated to ensure their reliability. The digital ecosystem vulnerability is further amplified whenever the instantaneous SCA (Sense-Calculate-Actuate) cycle is used (Menezes et al., 2019b). This becomes especially critical as the IIoT transforms into the state of AoT (Automation-of-Things). The ecosystem automatically manages the operation by sensing, calculating, and actuating more intelligently and autonomously, without human intervention, within seconds or minutes, depending on the business and industry applications. Such technologies provide capabilities to identify opportunities of (re-) designing and (re-) implementing supply chains to improve the production state within an online closed-loop fashion (Franzoi et al., 2021). The massive potential explains the increasing global spending on IIoT, estimated to surpass 1 trillion US dollars in 2023 (IDC, 2020). Hence, digital transformation in supply chains is expected to provide further insights beyond intrinsic knowledge and historical experience, which can be enhanced by ubiquitous visibility and connectivity among relevant systems.

3. Continuous evolution towards the digital supply chain resilience

Organizations are not more myopic to the importance of continuous evolution for the complete digital transformation on their supply chains. They rely on continuously exploring new advanced solutions and alternatives that could deliver higher reliability, reduced costs, higher efficiency, enhanced resilience, etc. For example, customers have been satisfied with monitoring of the geographical locations of their shipments a decade ago, but now they are able to monitor the shipments location, temperature, humidity, and visually. The IoT devices of a decade ago had to undergo many challenges of limited battery life, expensive data transfer charges, harsh weather, among other. While today's equipment and advances in technologies have eased these challenges. The fast-paced environment of our Society 5.0 and Industry 4.0 leads to sudden innovation changes, in which today's state-of-the-art technology shall soon become obsolete. Hence, organizations are encouraged to continuously transform and evolve their digital capabilities in their supply chains to avoid being among the 40% expected to fade away in their processes (Schreckling et al., 2017).

4. Conclusions

The development and continuous evolution of digital supply chain resilience is fundamental for today's organizations survival and success. DSCR and its prerequisites of digital transformation and automation success relies on three cornerstones related to human capital, business processes, and adopted technologies. In the human capital realm, the relevant stakeholders responsible for designing, implementing, and managing the digital transformation should be up to date with state-of-the-art technologies and continuously explore new inventions and trends. It is imperative to introduce training and incentive strategies for employees with the objective of enhancing employees' technological literacy and adoption rates within an organization. In the business processes realm, it is a must to conduct a detailed gap analysis of the organizational business requirements that serves the organization strategic vision, in an agnostic perspective that's receptive to innovative solutions and new methodologies with the objective to create an efficient SIPOC that meets the customer requirements, reduces costs, and maximizes revenues. The drawback of ignoring the business processes of the digital transformation triangle yields a mere digitalization project without tangible digital transformation. In the adopted technologies realm, it is critical to explore the organizational digital and technological requirements that meet the previously established business processes substantiated by SIPOC reviews and structured analysis of the right technologies, ERP, licenses, implementation, data storage, right cybersecurity measures, among others. This is crucial for building future technology scalability, enhancing efficiency, thereby decreasing costs, and increasing revenues. The above-mentioned success triangle supports digital supply chain resilience as it results in enhanced preparedness for achieving resistance against disruptions and disturbances (by employing avoidance and containment strategies) and recovery capabilities (by stabilizing and returning to the pre-disruption/disturbance performance). Nevertheless, AI and IoT ecosystems trustworthiness levels remain an imperative accompanying factor to be carefully considered. A key objective of augmenting organizational SCR with the SCA and AoT capabilities is to enhance real-time visibility, responsiveness, and control. However, there are multiple risks of malfunctions, cyber-attacks, and power failures, severely hindering reliability, robustness, and reliability. Hence, rigorous and continuous reviews and upgrades are required to ensure optimum results of DSCR technological elements. A multi-domain supply chain involving the SCE, SCR, DSCE, DSCR, and their interconnectedness are addressed herein, where DSCR elements are embedded in the organizational processes throughout SIPOC workflows. The proposed discussion guides the implementation of enhanced digital transformation capabilities towards better organizational visibility and control, and more efficient operations.

References

P. Agrawal, R. Narain, 2018, Digital supply chain management: an overview, IOP Conf. Series: Materials Science and Engineering, 455(1), 012074.

O. Bascur, 2020, Digital transformation for the process industries: a roadmap, CRC Press.

A. Dolgui, D. Ivanov, B. Sokolov, 2020, Reconfigurable supply chain: the X-network, International Journal of Production Research, 58(13), 4138–4163.

R. E. Franzoi, B. C. Menezes, J. D. Kelly, J. A.W. Gut, 2021, A moving horizon rescheduling framework for continuous nonlinear processes with disturbances. Chemical Engineering Research and Design, 174, 276-293.

Gartner, 2018, Gartner Says Nearly Half of CIOs Are Planning to Deploy Artificial Intelligence. Available at: https://www.gartner.com/en/newsroom/press-releases/2018-02-13-gartner-says-nearly-half-of-cios-are-planning-to-deploy-artificial-intelligence, accessed on 15 September, 2021.

International Data Corporation, 2019, Steady Commercial and Consumer Adoption Will Drive Worldwide Spending on the Internet of Things to $1.1 Trillion in 2023. Available at: https://www.idc.com/getdoc.jsp?containerId=prUS45197719, accessed on 15 September 2021.

International Data Corporation, 2020, Worldwide Spending on the Internet of Things Will Slow in 2020 Then Return to Double-Digit Growth. Available at: https://www.idc.com/getdoc.jsp?containerId=prUS46609320#:~:text=A%20new%20update%20to%20the,in%20the%20November%202019%20release.&text=Consumer%20spending%20on%20IoT%20solutions,year%20over%20year%20in%202020.https://www.idc.com/getdoc.jsp?containerId=prUS45197719, accessed on 15 September 2021.

L. Koh, G. Orzes, F. Jia, 2019, The fourth industrial revolution (Industry 4.0): technologies disruption on operations and supply chain management, International Journal of Operations and Production Management, 39, 817–828.

S. Melnyk, D. Closs, S. Griffis, C. Zobel, J. Macdonald, 2014, Understanding supply chain resilience, Supply Chain Management Review, 18(1), 34-41.

B. C. Menezes, J. D. Kelly, A. G. Leal, G. C. Le Roux, 2019a, Predictive, prescriptive, and detective analytics for smart manufacturing in the information age. IFAC Papers Online, 52(1), 568-573.

B. C. Menezes, J. D. Kelly, A. G. Leal, 2019b, Identification and design of Industry 4.0 opportunities in manufacturing: examples from mature industries to laboratory level systems. IFAC-PapersOnLine, 52(13), 2494-2500.

G. Rocher, J. Y. Tigli, S. Lavirotte, N. Le Thanh, 2018, A possibilistic i/o hidden semi-markov model for assessing cyber-physical systems effectiveness, IEEE International Conference on Fuzzy Systems, 1-9.

C. K. Sahu, C. Young, R. Rai, 2020, Artificial intelligence (AI) in augmented reality (AR)-assisted manufacturing applications: a review, International Journal of Production Research, 59(16), 4903-4959.

E. Schreckling, C. Steiger, 2017, Digitalize or drown. In Shaping the digital enterprise: trends and use cases in digital innovation and transformation, Springer Cham, 3-27.

A. Sharma, E. S. Pilli, A. P. Mazumdar, P. Gera, 2020, Towards trustworthy Internet of Things: A survey on Trust Management applications and schemes, Computer Communication, 160, 475–493.

C. S. Tang, 2006, Perspectives in supply chain risk management, International Journal of Production Economics, 103(2), 451-488.

I. Vanany, S. Zailani, N. Pujawan, 2009, Supply chain risk management: literature review and future research, International Journal of Information Systems and Supply Chain Management, 2(1), 16-33.

Proceedings of the 14th International Symposium on Process Systems Engineering – PSE 2021+
June 19-23, 2022, Kyoto, Japan
http://dx.doi.org/10.1016/B978-0-323-85159-6.50096-8

Development of Flexible Framework for Biomass Supply Chain Optimisation

Ken-Ichiro Sotowa

Dept. of Chemical Engineering, Kyoto University, Nishikyo-ku, Kyoto 615-8510 Japan
sotowa@cheme.kyoto-u.ac.jp

Abstract

Many studies are being conducted to develop methods for the conversion of biomass into useful chemicals. To exploit the results from these studies and realise a biomass-based chemical industry, an appropriate supply chain system must be designed. It is therefore necessary to select the best factory locations and reaction pathways as well as derive the best operational strategy. When biomass is used as feed stock, seasonal variations in the amount of available biomass induces variations in the amount of materials flowing in the system. Thus, several thousands of variables and equations are involved in such design problems. In this study, different elements in supply chain networks were classified into four types according to the feature of their mathematical representations: storage, conversion, transport, and utility models. This abstraction enabled us to model a wide class of supply chain networks in a unified framework. An optimal design system for a supply chain system based on this concept was implemented as a web system.

Keywords: biomass, supply chain, seasonal variation, optimisation.

1. Introduction

Biomass has been attracting a significant amount of attention as a raw material for the chemical industry. There are several substances that can be chemically extracted or synthesised from biomass, and synthetic methods for various substances starting from biomass are currently being developed (Serrano-Ruiz *et al.*, 2010, Gérardy *et al.*, 2020). If a system capable of producing high-value chemical substances can be implemented, the dependence of the chemical industry on petroleum resources can be reduced, thereby contributing to the building of a sustainable society highly based on renewable resources.

When implementing a technology for the conversion of biomass to chemical products, it is necessary to construct an optimal supply chain network starting from obtaining raw materials to the production and delivery of the products. The network should be designed by considering the characteristics of the area to which the network is to be implemented. This is due to the characteristics of chemical production systems that utilise biomass as a raw material. Because biomass is widely dispersed in an area, it is necessary to optimally select the location of the processing factories. The amount of available biomass varies seasonally. For a biomass-based energy system, there is only one product, that is, energy. However, for a chemical production system, multiple products with different prices and demands must be manufactured. It is therefore necessary to select the optimal reaction pathways from many possible alternatives. The reuse of waste energy and heat should also be considered.

Several researchers working in the field of biomass supply chain formulate the design problem as an MILP and solve it using optimisation software. By using a superstructure of the supply chain network covering all possible factory locations, reaction pathways, and transport of materials, the design problem can be described as an MILP. However, the number of variables and formulas that appear in MILP often exceeds thousands because there are several types of substances and seasonal fluctuations that must be considered. Even a small modification of the problem, such as the incorporation of new reaction techniques or changing the candidate location of the factory, requires a significant amount of effort. However, to implement a biomass-based manufacturing process for chemicals, various case studies must be conducted to evaluate the impact of any possible variations in the conditions. However, because the formulation and modification of the optimisation problem is extremely time-consuming, it is only possible to conduct several case studies.

In this study, we aimed to develop a technology that will enable us to formulate the optimisation problem quickly and subsequently derive the optimal design of a biomass supply chain network. Any change in the superstructure, number of reactions, and substances can be easily reflected in the system. In this presentation, we report on the key to the modelling method and the development of a web system based on this modelling approach.

2. Assumptions during model development

The following assumptions were made in the creation of the supply chain model.

- Each chemical substance whose state changes due to drying, chipping, and packaging is treated as a substance different from the one that has not undergone processing.
- To consider seasonal fluctuations, the target period is divided into N_t terms, and the change in the stored amount of a substance is calculated for each term.
- Only one substance can be stored in one storage.
- Only one type of substance can be transported via one transportation means at a time.
- Each utility is treated as a substance that cannot be stored.

3. Generalised representation of the supply chain elements

Several different types of operations are involved in the synthesis of chemical products from biomass in a supply chain. These operations are typically biomass harvesting,

Table 1 Four generalised elements in the supply chain network

Elements	Function	Usage
Conversion	Convert substance or utility to different ones	Chemical conversion, drying, chipping, separation and purification, packaging
Storage	Store substance according to the difference in the incoming and outgoing flow rates.	Storage of substance
Transport	Transfer substance from a storage to another	Transport, harvesting, product despatch, waste disposal
Utility	Supply or recover utilities	Supply, reuse, purchase and sale of utility

chipping, drying, storage, various reactions, transportation, sale, waste disposal, and purchase of utility. First, we considered the mathematical characteristics of these elements and classified them into four types, as presented in Table 1.

The elements included in a single category can be represented using a common mathematical model. The conversion model changes one substance or utility into another substance or utility and can be expressed by the following mathematical formula:

$$\sum_i r_{ri} R_{ri}(t) = \sum_i p_{ri} P_{ri}(t) \tag{1}$$

$R_{ri}(t)$ and $P_{ri}(t)$ are, respectively, the consumption and production rates of the raw material or utility i in the converter r in the period t, and r_{ri} and p_{ri} are the stoichiometric coefficients. Chipping or drying does not change the chemicals, but because it is assumed that these operations are treated as producing different substances, they can be expressed in this model.

The storage model is expressed using the following equation.

$$S_s(t) = S_s(t-1) - \sum_{r|s} R_{ri(s)}(t) + \sum_{r|s} P_{ri(s)}(t) + \sum_{y|s} \delta_{y|s} Y_{y(i(s))}(t) \tag{1}$$

$S_s(t)$ is the amount of substance in storage s at the end of period t. The substance stored in storage s is represented by $i(s)$. The second and third terms on the right side are the rate of increase or decrease of the substance $i(s)$ by the converter r connected to the storage s. The fourth term is the speed at which the substance enters and exits by means of transportation y, and $\delta y|s$ is +1 when y is brought into storage s and -1 when y is removed.

The transport model solely expresses the amount of transportation $Y_y(t)$ that occurs in y. For transport, it is usually necessary to define the start and end points; however, there are certain exceptions. Transportation with no defined starting point represents the external inputs to the supply chain network, such as biomass harvesting and electricity purchases. On the contrary, transportation without an endpoint represents the emission of a substance outside of the system, either as a product to be sold or as a waste that is discharged. For product dispatch, the cost associated with it is expressed as a negative value. Another rule for a transportation model is that it must always be connected to a storage model.

As stated in Section 2, a utility is treated as a substance that cannot be stored. A utility model is defined as a combination of storage and transport models to model the handling of a utility in a biomass supply chain system. The storage model is expressed by Eq. (2); however, $S_s(t)$ is always zero. Transportation models are used to express the purchase and sale of utilities.

Furthermore, in the conversion, storage, and transport models, the cost of operation is expressed as a function of the conversion rate, amount of storage, and transfer rate. For conversion and storage, the capital cost of the equipment is modelled as a function of the maximum capability.

4. Concept of site and path

By combining the abovementioned four elements, the design problem of a general biomass supply chain network can be easily modeled. In large optimisation problems, however, the superstructure network tends to be very complex owing to the large number of nodes and edges. Notably, in such problems, several candidate sites exist for factory locations, all of which have identical reaction networks. Therefore, in this study, the concept of site was introduced. In a single site, the reaction pathways can be defined using conversion, storage, and utility models; however, no transport models can be in it.

Several different types of substances are involved in a supply chain network; therefore, given a pair of sites, it must be possible to transport several substances between them. Those transport models have common origin and destination sites. A path was defined as a collection of such transport models. This path can be considered as a road connection between the two sites.

5. Formulation of the optimisation problem

The objective function of the supply chain optimisation problem is defined as the total annual cost of operation. The cost includes the depreciation cost of the equipment, in addition to the cost required for biomass collection, transportation, conversion, storage, and utility. The sale of products is subtracted from this cost. The optimisation variables are the transport rate, conversion rate, storage amount, and so on. Because the problem was formulated based on the superstructure, the selection of factory location and reaction pathways is possible with this framework.

Because the storage model connects the conversion and transport models, the mathematical formulation of the entire problem can be performed automatically when all the necessary information is collected. The conversion model consists of only stoichiometric relations and cost formulas. The transport model only expresses the cost mathematically. The storage model can be described using a mathematical formula to calculate the balance between the reaction and transport rate associated with it. Thus, using the concept of the four generalised elements, we can easily generate the mathematical equations for the optimal design of the biomass supply chain network. Because the equations can be obtained automatically from the collected data, this approach is expected to be a powerful tool in the development of optimal designs of systems involving several substances and reaction pathways and showing complex seasonal variations.

6. System development

To design a supply chain network capable of manufacturing chemical products from biomass, it is necessary to collect data from different industries such as agriculture and forestry, chemical industry, transportation industry, trading companies, and local governments. Because the amount of data to be collected is enormous, it is inefficient if a single person performs this task of collecting data and then providing it into the system. Therefore, a supply chain optimisation system was built as a system on a web, to ensure that anyone who owns the data for the supply chain design can enter them directly into the system. Figures 1-3 show an example of the browser screen of this system.

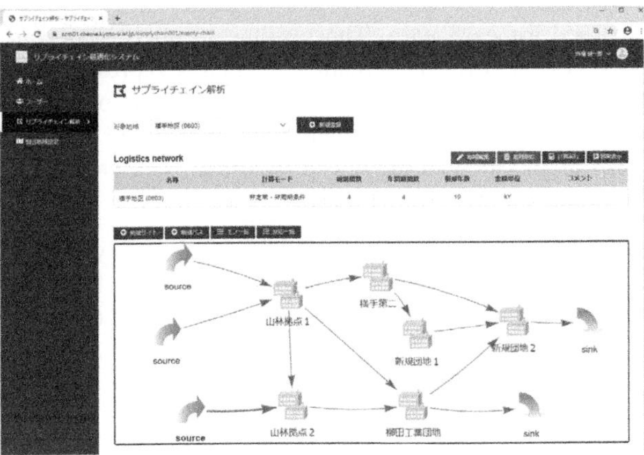

Figure 1 Example of the network comprising consisting of sites and paths (texts are in Japanese)

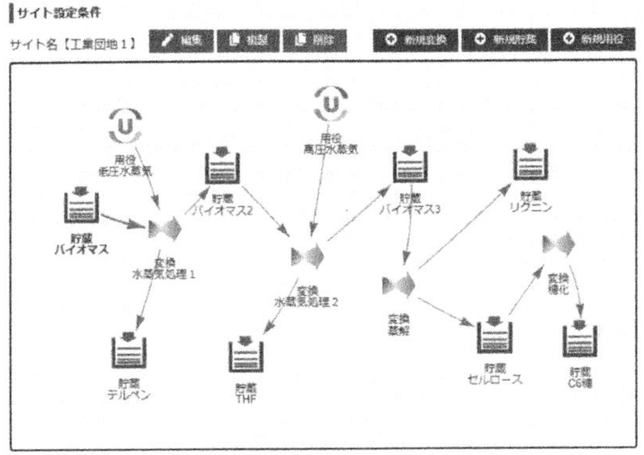

Figure 2 Example of the reaction path network in a site drawn using conversion, storage, and utility models. (texts are in Japanese)

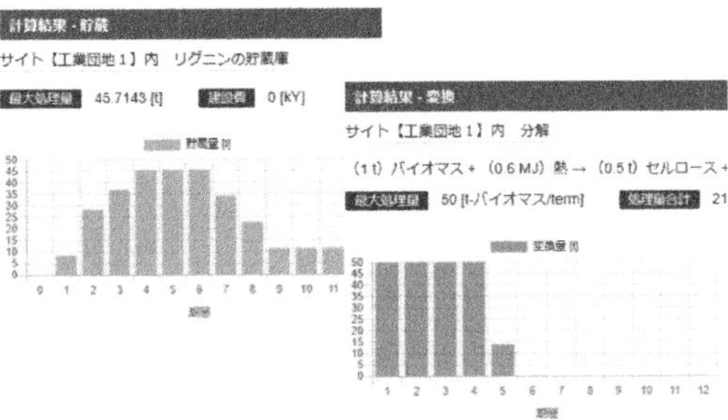

Figure 3 Example of graphical representation of the optimisation results. (texts are in Japanese)

The configuration of the superstructure can be input by a GUI on a web browser. The first step is to define the substances and the available conversion technologies. Then, a network of sites and paths is drawn (Figure 1). For each site, the reaction network is entered using the conversion, storage, and utility models (Figure 2). Transport models should then be defined for each path. The results can also be viewed using the GUI (Figure 3). In this system, the mathematical formulas representing each model are automatically generated based on the input data, and the optimisation problem is defined as MILP. The problem is solved using the lp_solve or IBM CPLEX software. The data and results are secured in the mysql database. Further, multiple problems can be handled by this system.

A case study was conducted to address the hypothetical supply chain design problem. The network establishment and data inputs were completed in two hours. The problem involved the use of 4626 variables and 4680 constraints. The optimisation calculation was completed within 10 s.

7. Conclusions

Four generalised elements for modelling the superstructure of a supply chain network were proposed. A web-based optimisation system was constructed based on this concept. The mathematical expression of the optimisation problem was automatically generated from the input data of the design problem. The impact of the developed system was demonstrated via a case study.

We plan to utilise this proposed system to design a biomass supply chain system for Yokote City in Japan, where abundant forest biomass exists. Since the proposed elements can also be used to model a wide range of supply chain networks, we plan to apply it to other problems, such as the evaluation of a resource recycling system and in the design of carbon-negative societies.

Acknowledgements

This work was supported by the Cabinet Office, Government of Japan, Cross-ministerial Strategic Innovation Promotion Program (SIP), "Technologies for creating next-generation agriculture, forestry and fisheries" (funding agency: Bio-oriented Technology Research Advancement Institution, NARO).

References

R. Gérardy, D. P. Debecker, J. Estager, P. Luis and J.-C. M. Monbaliu, 2020, "Continuous Flow Upgrading of Selected C_2–C_6 Platform Chemicals Derived From Biomass," Chem. Rev., **120**, 7219-7347.

J. C. Serrano-Ruiz, R. M. West and J. A. Dumesic, 2010, "Catalytic Conversion of Renewable Biomass Resources to Fuels and Chemicals," Annu. Rev. Chem. Biomol. Eng., **1**, 79-100.

Proceedings of the 14th International Symposium on Process Systems Engineering – PSE 2021+
June 19-23, 2022, Kyoto, Japan
http://dx.doi.org/10.1016/B978-0-323-85159-6.50097-X

Lagrangean Decomposition for Integrated Refinery-Petrochemical Short-term Planning

Ariel Uribe-Rodriguez[a,b], Pedro M. Castro[c], Gonzalo Guillén-Gosálbez[d] and Benoît Chachuat[b*]

[a] *Center for Innovation and Technology Colombian Petroleum Institute, Ecopetrol, Colombia*
[b] *Sargent Centre for Process Systems Engineering, Department of Chemical Engineering, Imperial College London, United Kingdom*
[c] *Centro de Matemática Aplicações Fundamentais e Investigação Operacional, Faculdade de Ciências, Universidade de Lisboa, Portugal*
[d] *Institute for Chemical and Bioengineering, Department of Chemistry and Applied Biosciences, ETH Zürich, Switzerland*
b.chachuat@imperial.ac.uk

Abstract

We present a methodology for the optimal integration of crude management (CM) and refinery-petrochemical (RP) planning operations. The physical coupling between both CM and RP optimization subproblems is via the flow rate, physical-chemical properties, and composition of the crude blends. For a given economic cost of the crude blends, which either provides a selling price for CM or a purchase price for RP, both subproblems can maximize their profits independently. But failure to integrate these two subproblems can create an imbalance between crude supply and demand. Optimizing CM and RP operations simultaneously entails the solution of large-scale, nonconvex quadratically-constrained quadratic programs (MIQCQPs). We apply a spatial Lagrangean decomposition algorithm to tackle these MIQCQPs and demonstrate it on a full-scale industrial facility. The results show that Lagrangean decomposition can outperform commercial global solvers BARON and ANTIGONE when applied to the monolithic MIQCQP. The Lagrangean decomposition can also reduce the optimality gap faster than with a clustering decomposition algorithm, leading to optimality gaps below 5% within 1 hour of CPU time.

Keywords: Lagrangean decomposition; nonconvex; planning; logistic.

1. Introduction

Integrated operations of petrochemical plants and crude oil refineries are more resilient to volatility of the hydrocarbons market than independent businesses for petrochemical commodities and fuel production. Such integration can be achieved by the exchange of by-products or intermediate streams from the refinery that are transformed into added-value products at the petrochemical units. Some by-products from petrochemical processes can also improve fuel quality at the refinery side. The refinery can provide part of the natural gas required by steam crackers and the petrochemical side can supply part of the hydrogen required by hydrotreating processes (Ketabchi, et al., 2019). Recently, deterministic global optimization and Lagrangean decomposition have been applied to short-term planning of integrated refining and petrochemical operations (Li, et. al, 2016;

Zhao, et. al, 2017; Uribe-Rodríguez, et. al, 2020), formulated as large-scale, nonconvex quadratically-constrained quadratic programs (MIQCQPs).

Herein, we investigate a spatial Lagrangean decomposition-based algorithm to solve such MIQCQPs. This problem is challenging for the following reasons: i) Compared to previous studies, a wider range of crudes are considered, which differ in terms of volume, quality, and cost; these crudes are transported by pipelines or river fleet, depending on their geographic location and can be blended to fulfill the volume and quality needs of the crude distillation units (CDUs). ii) Product demands are set for a large variety of fuels and petrochemical commodities. iii) Process units can be operated in exclusive or non-exclusive campaigns. iv) Higher connectivity between units and intermediate streams is considered in the process network. All these features lead to MIQCQPs with thousands of bilinear terms. Recently, Uribe-Rodríguez et al., (2020) tackled this problem with a deterministic global optimization approach based on process clustering decomposition (CL). Results for several scenarios have produced better incumbent solutions and smaller optimality gaps than BARON and ANTIGONE, but the optimality gap remains high for certain scenarios (11% on average). Therefore, a spatial Lagrangean decomposition-based algorithm is developed to further enhance solution quality and reduce the optimality gap.

2. Methodology

The monolithic short-term planning problem for the integrated refinery-petrochemical facility can be cast as the following MIQCQP:

$$\begin{aligned} z^* := \max\ & f_0(x,y) \\ \text{s.t.}\ & f_m(x,y) \leq 0\ \forall m \in \{1,\dots,M\} \\ & x \in [x^L, x^U] \subseteq \mathbb{R}_+^p, y \in \{0,1\}^q \end{aligned} \qquad \textbf{(P)}$$

where x are the non-negative continuous decision variables and y the binary decision variables used to select process operating conditions. The objective function and the constraints are furthermore quadratic in x and linear in y: $f_m(x,y) := \sum_{(i,j)\in BL_m} a_{ijm}x_ix_j + B_m x + C_m y + d_m\ \forall m \in \{0,\dots,M\}$. BL_m is an (i,j)-index set defining the bilinear terms x_ix_j, while a_{ijm}, d_m, B_m and C_m are parameters. Problem **P** can also describe optimization problems appearing in business units of the facility, subproblems that can be solved independently for a given economic incentive.

In the context of refinery operations, problem **P** exhibits a block structure, which makes it amenable to Lagrangean decomposition (Pinto, 2000). Figure 1 shows the material and economic flows between crude management (CM) and the refinery-petrochemical (RP) plant, which includes refinery (REF), petrochemical (PTQ) and fuel blending (FB) operations. CM includes the operations involved in the selection, transportation, blending and allocation of the crudes. CM buys crude oil from different sources (domestic or import) and sells crude blends to the refinery. CM maximizes profit by buying cheap crude oil on the market, minimizing the transportation cost, and producing crude blends to be sold at a price λ_u that is a function of their quality. The transformation of crude oil in RP involves operations such as crude oil fractionation at the CDUs, naphtha, jet, diesel and gas oil hydrotreating, gas oil catalytic cracking, etc. RP maximizes its profit by buying enough quantity of good-quality crude blends from CM at a cheap price (λ_u), without being concerned about delivering costs.

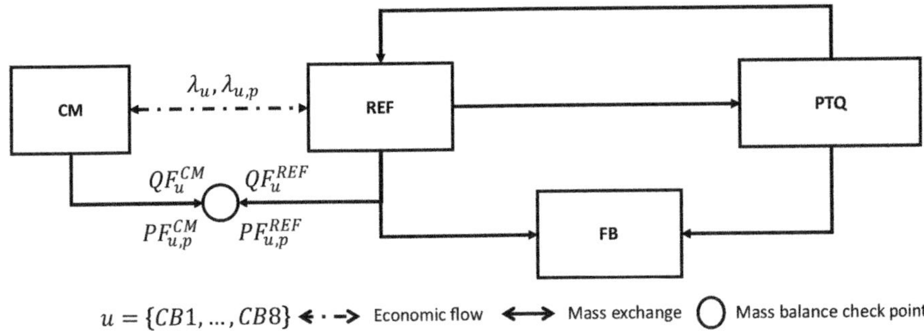

Figure 1. Subproblems derived from **P**.

2.1. Reformulation of problem **P**

Let the index set X denote the complicating variables (appearing in the mass balance check point in Figure 1) that are shared between subproblems 1 (CM) and 2 (RP). Problem **P'** is made equivalent to **P** (Guignard and Kim, 1987; Grossmann, 2021) after duplicating such variables and adding the constraints $x_e^1 = x_e^2 \ \forall e \in X$. Notice that the cost and constraints are also partitioned over the two subproblems. The reformulated problem **P'** is now amenable to Lagrangean decomposition.

$$z^* := \max \left\{ \sum_{i=1}^{2} f_0^i(x^i, y^i) \right\} \quad \textbf{(P')}$$
$$\text{s.t. } f_{m_i}^i(x^i, y^i) \le 0 \ \forall i \in \{1,2\}, m_i \in \{1, \ldots, M\}$$
$$x_e^1 - x_e^2 = 0 \ \forall e \in X$$

2.2. Lagrangean relaxation of problem **P'**

A Lagrangean relaxation (Guignard, 2003; Guignard and Siwhan, 1987) **LR**$_\lambda$ of problem **P'** is created by transferring each constraint $x_e^1 = x_e^2$ into the objective function, multiplied by a Lagrangean multiplier λ_e (unrestricted in sign).

$$z_\lambda^{LR*} := \max \left\{ \sum_{i=1}^{2} f_0^i(x^i, y^i) + \sum_{e \in X} \lambda_e (x_e^1 - x_e^2) \right\} \quad \textbf{(LR}_\lambda\textbf{)}$$
$$\text{s.t. } f_{m_i}^i(x^i, y^i) \le 0 \ \forall i \in \{1,2\}, m_i \in \{1, \ldots, M\}$$

2.3. Decomposition of $\boldsymbol{LR_\lambda}$

For fixed values of λ_e, problem **LR**$_\lambda$ can be decomposed into 2 parametric subproblems of type **LD**$_\lambda^i$, which can be solved independently. The optimal value z_λ^{LD*} is equal to $z_\lambda^{1,LD*} + z_\lambda^{2,LD*}$ and provides an upper bound UB on the optimal value z^* of problem **P**. To obtain the tightest relaxation possible, λ_e is updated by means of an iterative procedure. Herein, we adopt the hybrid method by Grossmann and co-workers (Mouret et al., 2011; F Oliveira et al., 2013; Yang et al., 2020) for updating the Lagrange multipliers, which is based on a subgradient method, cutting plane approach, trust-region method and volume algorithm. Note that the solutions from these subproblems provide good quality initial points to solve the monolithic problem **P** as well.

$$z_{\lambda}^{i,LD*} := \max \left\{ f_0^i(x^i, y^i) + \sum_{j=i+1}^{2} \sum_{e \in X} \lambda_e x_e^i - \sum_{j=1}^{i-1} \sum_{e \in X_{ji}} \lambda_e x_e^i \right\} \quad \text{s.t.}\ f_{m_i}^i(x^i, y^i) \le 0\ \forall m_i \in \{1, \dots, M\} \qquad (\mathbf{LD}_{\lambda}^{i})$$

3. Case study

The refinery-petrochemical facility produces several grades of gasoline, diesel and fuel oil, and a set of petrochemical processes for providing BTX, polyethylene, propylene, waxes, and specialty solvents. These commodities mostly supply the Colombian market, with only a small part being exported. A domestic petroleum production equal to 297 kbbl/day is assumed, involving 17 types of crude oil distributed over 8 geographical regions. The refinery can also import 7 types of crude, with up to 15 kbbl/day per crude. The total refining capacity is 248 kbbl/day and the logistic system for crude and commodities comprises 4 river fleet routes and a system of 9 pipelines. The refinery-petrochemical facility is composed of 60 industrial plants, represented by about 125 models. Crude mixing and fuel blending is done in a tank farm, modelled as 30 additional units. The complete model of the system leads to a MIQCQP model with 6975 equations, 35104 nonlinear terms, 9592 continuous and 279 discrete variables. The linking variables between both subproblems in the Lagrangean decomposition algorithm correspond to the flowrate and qualities of the $u \in U^{CRB} = \{CB1, \dots, CB8\}$ crude streams fed to the CDUs. Flowrates QF_u^{CM} and QF_u^{REF} are traded between CM and RP at the market price λ_u. Multipliers $\lambda_{u,p}$ are penalty costs associated with the $p = 1, \dots, 3$ crude blend qualities $PF_{u,p}^{CM}$ and $PF_{u,p}^{REF}$. In total, 57 Lagrange multipliers distributed into flowrates (8), bulk properties (24), and crude blend composition (25) are considered.

We define a minimum throughput to the RP of 100 kbbl/day, and set default values for the Lagrange multipliers ($\lambda_u = 0, \lambda_{u,p} = 0$) at the start of the algorithm. At zero crude blends cost, the RP profit is about 11.4 MUSD/day, whilst CM loses 3.5 MUSD/day (the income from selling crude blends is zero), leading to an upper bound (UB) of 7.9 MUSD/day. CM chooses to make 100 kbbl/day of CB7, with 20 API, 1.13 %wt sulfur content and 2.70 mg KOH/g crude oil. These features indicate that CB7 is a heavy, sour, and acidic crude oil with poor qualities for processing at the RP. In contrast, and because it is not paying for the crude blends, RP chooses to include all eight crudes in the basket, leading to a total refinery capacity of 203 kbbl/day. The crude oil throughput to the RP has 32 API, 0.66 %wt sulfur content and 1.25 mg KOH/g crude oil, much more suitable to process at the CDUs than the crude blend produced by CM.

The values of the Lagrange multipliers are updated at each iteration (Figure 2) aiming at tightening the relaxation bound on **P**. The objective function value for the CM subproblem increases (not necessarily monotonically) until reaching its maximum at iteration 17. At that point, CM supplies 240 kbbl/day of a crude basket composed by crude blends CB3 (11%), CB4 (2%), CB5 (10%), CB6 (19%), and CB7 (58%). It can be viewed as a medium crude blend (26 API), with 0.96 %wt sulfur content and 1.92 mg KOH/g crude oil. Likewise, the objective function for the RP subproblem decreases because of the increase in the cost of the crude blends. At iteration 17, the RP throughput is about 137 kbbl/day, with CB1 (23%), CB2 (18%), CB3 (20%), CB5 (18%), CB6 (3%), CB7 (17%) and CB8 (2%). Compared to iteration 1, the RP requires a crude blend with a lower mg KOH/g crude oil (0.53) and keeps the same figures for API and sulfur content. From iterations 18 to 37, the changes in the objective function of CM and RP are steadier.

Overall, finding the optimal values for λ_u^* and $\lambda_{u,p}^*$ determines a transfer price between the crude management and the integrated refinery-petrochemical complex, leading to a trade-off between the CM incomes and REF outcomes.

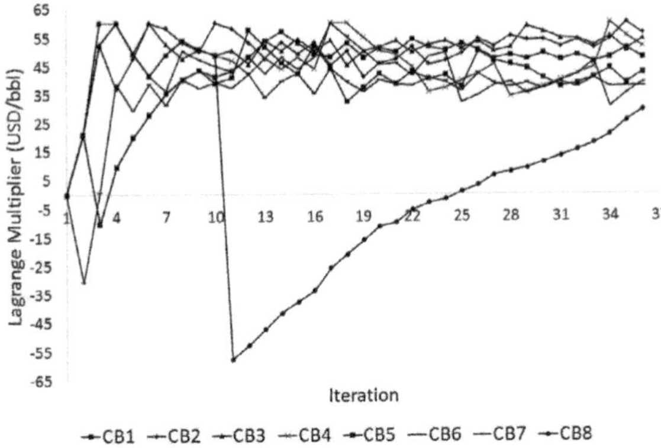

Figure 2. Lagrange multipliers associated with crude blend flowrates.

The performance of the spatial Lagrangean decomposition-based algorithm is summarized in Table 1. All the models used to address the short-term planning problem of the integrated refinery–petrochemical facility were implemented in GAMS 28.2. The CM subproblem was solved using ANTIGONE 1.1. The same is not true for the large-scale MIQCQP resulting from the RP subproblem. To address this challenge, the latter was solved by our process clustering decomposition approach (Uribe-Rodriguez et al., 2020), considering six clusters (crude distillation operations, vacuum and debutanizer columns, refinery units, petrochemical plants, fuels blending). Our Lagrangean decomposition-based approach reaches an optimal solution within 1 hour, with an optimality gap below 5%. Moreover, considering the lower bound reported by the clustering approach, the global optimal solution for this problem is enclosed between 2,964 kUSD/day and 3,063 kUSD/day.

Table 1. Performance comparison between global solvers

Approach	LB [kUSD/day]	UB [kUSD/day]	Gap [%]	Runtime [h]
Lagrangean Decomposition	2,932	3,063	4	0.8
Clustering Decomposition	2,964	3,205	8	5.7
ANTIGONE	2,634	3,898	48	10.0
BARON	2,687	4,250	58	10.0

4. Conclusions

This paper has presented a Lagrangean decomposition-based algorithm for large-scale MIQCQPs derived from the short-term planning problem of an existing integrated refinery-petrochemical facility. The high dimensionality makes it challenging to find high-quality solutions within a reasonable optimality gap. While all algorithms were able to identify feasible solutions, our approach outperforms the process clustering decomposition, BARON and ANTIGONE, in terms of profit, optimality gap and computational runtime.

Acknowledgments

Financial support from the Colombian Science Council (COLCIENCIAS), the Center for Innovation and Technology Colombian Petroleum Institute (Ecopetrol S.A.) and Fundação para a Ciência e Tecnologia through grants CEECIND/00730/2017 and UIBD/04561/2020.

References

Yang, H., Bernal E. D., Franzoi, R. E., Engineer., F. G., Kwon, K., Lee, S., and Grossmann, I, E., 2020, Integration of crude-oil scheduling and refinery planning by Lagrangean decomposition, Computers and Chemical Engineering, 106812. 138,

Uribe-Rodriguez, A., Castro M. P., Guillén-Gosálbez, G., and Chachuat, B., , 2020, Global Optimization of Large-scale MIQCQPs via Cluster Decomposition: Application to Short–Term Planning of an Integrated Refinery–Petrochemical Complex, Computers and Chemical Engineering 140, 106883.

Sahinidis, N. V., 2004, BARON: A general purpose global optimization software package. J. Glob. Optim. 8, 201–205.

Misener, R., Floudas, C.A., 2014, ANTIGONE: Algorithms for coNTinuous / Integer Global Optimization of Nonlinear Equations. J. Glob. Optim. 59, 503–526.

Ketabchi, E., Mechleri, E., Arellano-Garcia, H., 2019. Increasing operational efficiency through the integration of an oil refinery and an ethylene production plant. Chem. Eng. Res. Des. 152, 85–94.

Li, J., Xiao, X., Boukouvala, F., Floudas, C.A., Zhao, B., Du, G., Su, X., Liu, H., 2016. Data-driven mathematical modeling and global optimization framework for entire petrochemical planning operations. AIChE J. 62, 3020–3040.

Zhao, H., Ierapetritou, M.G., Shah, N.K., Rong, G., 2017. Integrated model of refining and petrochemical plant for enterprise-wide optimization. Comput. Chem. Eng. 97, 194–207.

Pinto, J.M., Joly, M., Moro, L.F.L., 2000. Planning and scheduling models for refinery operations. Comput. Chem. Eng. 24, 2259–2276.

Guignard, M., Siwhan Kim, 1987. Lagrangean decomposition: A model yielding stronger Lagrangean bounds. Math. Program. 39, 215–228.

Grossmann, I. (2021). Advanced Optimization for Process Systems Engineering (Cambridge Series in Chemical Engineering). Cambridge: Cambridge University Press.

Mouret, S., Grossmann, I.E., Pestiaux, P., 2011. A new Lagrangian decomposition approach applied to the integration of refinery planning and crude-oil scheduling. Comput. Chem. Eng. 35, 2750–2766.

Oliveira, F, Gupta, V., Hamacher, S., Grossmann, I.E., 2013. A Lagrangean decomposition approach for oil supply chain investment planning under uncertainty with risk considerations. Comput. Chem. Eng. 50, 184–195.

Proceedings of the 14th International Symposium on Process Systems Engineering – PSE 2021+
June 19–23, 2022, Kyoto, Japan
http://dx.doi.org/10.1016/B978-0-323-85159-6.50098-1

Green Ammonia Supply Chain Design for Maritime Transportation

Hanchu Wang[a], Prodromos Daoutidis[a*], Qi Zhang[a*]

[a] *Department of Chemical Engineering and Materials Science, University of Minnesota, Minneapolis, MN 55455, USA*

daout001@umn.edu, qizh@umn.edu

Abstract

Recently, there has been increased discussion about the potential of green ammonia as a carbon-free fuel for maritime transportation. If deployed at scale, the demand for ammonia from the shipping industry would be immense such that significant new investments had to be made in green ammonia infrastructure, including entire supply chains of new production sites and ammonia refueling ports. In this work, we develop an optimization model for the design of such a green ammonia supply chain. The proposed model integrates a large set of decisions, including the location of production plants and refueling ports, operational decisions related to green ammonia production using renewable energy, and ship routing decisions. This results in a complex mixed-integer linear programming formulation, which we apply to an illustrative case study to demonstrate its potential to address the given supply chain design problem.

Keywords: sustainability, green ammonia, maritime transportation, offshore wind

1. Introduction

Ammonia is one of the most produced commodity chemicals, and as the basis for most nitrogen fertilizers, it has been a key enabler for the sustained global population growth since the invention of the Haber-Bosch process. In recent years, ammonia has come under increased scrutiny due to the high carbon intensity of the conventional production process, and there have been various efforts in making its production more sustainable. One way to achieve this is to use renewable electricity to produce hydrogen via electrolysis and nitrogen via air separation and then react both chemicals to form ammonia. Ammonia that is produced in this manner is considered *green*. Green ammonia does not only have the potential to decarbonize fertilizer manufacturing, but can also be used as a carbon-free energy carrier [MacFarlane et al., 2020, Palys et al., 2021]. As such, it holds the promise to improve sustainability in multiple sectors. One exciting prospect is the use of ammonia as a marine fuel [de Vries, 2019]. The International Maritime Organization (IMO) has declared the goal of reducing the international shipping sector's annual greenhouse gas emissions by at least 50% compared to 2008 by 2050, which requires the use of alternative, less carbon-intensive fuels. Green ammonia is an ideal candidate as it does not cause any CO_2 emissions, neither in its production nor when it is combusted. In addition, it is sulfur-free, which ensures compliance with new IMO regulations.

In this work, we consider the design of green ammonia supply chains specifically for maritime transportation. For this purpose, we develop an optimization model that incorporates the production and distribution of green ammonia and its use as a marine fuel. Notably, in addition to ammonia produced on land, we also consider green ammonia that is produced on the open ocean using offshore wind. In our recent study [Wang et al., 2021], we have shown the techno-economic feasibility of such green offshore ammonia plants, which provide a means of harnessing wind energy far from the mainland. Here, such plants can further serve as offshore refueling stations, which would allow ships to carry less fuel when embarking on their trips across the ocean. This supply chain analysis aims to determine the optimal locations of ammonia production plants and refueling stations while considering the routing and scheduling of ship fleets as well as the production and storage of green ammonia. We propose a mixed-integer linear programming (MILP) formulation and apply it to an illustrative case study that demonstrates the main features of the model.

2. Mathematical Formulation

We consider a network consisting of a set of ports (including locations on the ocean) $\mathcal{M}$ and a set of ship fleets $\mathcal{V}$ where each fleet is defined by its origin and destination ports and the amount of cargo to be shipped. Each fleet can be split into multiple subfleets (or splits) that can travel on different routes. We consider a set of time periods $\mathcal{T}$ and adapt the arc-load continuous-time maritime inventory routing formulation proposd by Agra et al. [2017] to model the decisions associated with the routing of the subfleets. In the following, we briefly describe the main constraints of the proposed model.

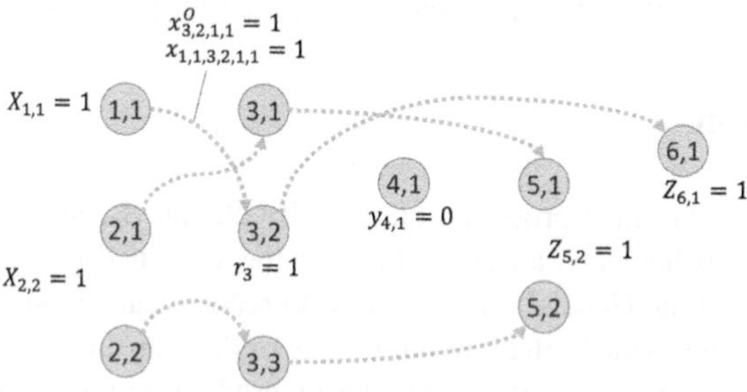

Figure 1: Illustration of the arc-load continuous-time formulation.

Figure 1 provides an illustration of the arc-load formulation. Here, each node is defined by a pair (i, m) representing port i visited the mth time (by any subfleet). We define a binary variable x_{imjnvk} that equals 1 if split k of ship fleet v travels from node (i, m) to node (j, n). Eq. (1) states that the sum of the split fractions, u_{vk}, for each fleet has to be 1. The binary variable h_{vk} equals 1 if fleet v is split. The binary variable w_{imvk} equals 1 if split k of fleet v visits port i at order m. Eqs. (3) and (4) state that each port visit and path traveled can be taken by one split only, and Eqs. (5)-(7) ensure that a port visit of a split only exits if the split exists, where z_{imvk} equals 1 if (i, m) is the terminal node visited by split k of fleet v. Eq. (8) ensures that all fleets travel from their origin ports to their destination ports, where set $\mathcal{O}$ contains all origin and destination ports of fleet v.

$$\sum_{k\in\mathcal{K}} u_{vk} = 1 \qquad \forall\, v \in \mathcal{V} \quad (1)$$

$$h_{vk}U_v^{\min} \le u_{vk}U_v^{\text{tot}} \le h_{vk}U_v^{\max} \qquad \forall\, v \in \mathcal{V},\ k \in \mathcal{K} \quad (2)$$

$$\sum_{v\in\mathcal{V}}\sum_{k\in\mathcal{K}} w_{imvk} \le 1 \qquad \forall\,(i,m) \in S_v^A \quad (3)$$

$$\sum_{v\in\mathcal{V}}\sum_{k\in\mathcal{K}} x_{imjnvk} \le 1 \qquad \forall\,(i,m,v,k) \in S_v^X \quad (4)$$

$$\sum_{(i,m)\in S_v^A} w_{imvk} \ge h_{vk} \qquad \forall\, v \in \mathcal{V},\ k \in \mathcal{K} \quad (5)$$

$$\sum_{(j,m)\in S_v^A} x^O_{jmvk} = h_{vk} \qquad \forall\, i \in \mathcal{I},\ v \in \mathcal{V} : X_{iv} = 1,\ k \in \mathcal{K} \quad (6)$$

$$\sum_{m\in\mathcal{M}} z_{imvk} = h_{vk} \qquad \forall\, i \in \mathcal{I},\ v \in \mathcal{V} : Z_{iv} = 1,\ k \in \mathcal{K} \quad (7)$$

$$\sum_{m\in\mathcal{M}} w_{imvk} = h_{vk} \qquad \forall\, v \in \mathcal{V},\ (i,m) \in \mathcal{S}_v^A : (i,v) \in \mathcal{O},\ k \in \mathcal{K} \quad (8)$$

Eqs. (9)-(14) are additional routing constraints. The binary variable x^O_{jmvk} equals 1 if (j,m) is the first node visited by split k of fleet v, as stated in Eq. (9). Eqs. (10) and (11) are the flow conservation constraints. Eq. (12) ensures that a port visit is recorded by w_{imvk}, and Eq. (13) guarantees that at most one fleet visits node (i,m), where y_{im} equals 1 if port visit (i,m) is taken by a fleet, and the visiting order is constrained by Eq. (14).

$$\sum_{n\in\mathcal{M}} x_{injmvk} = x^O_{jmvk} \qquad \forall\, i \in \mathcal{I},\ v \in \mathcal{V} : X_{iv} = 1,\ k \in \mathcal{K} \quad (9)$$

$$w_{imvk} - \sum_{(j,n)\in\mathcal{S}_v^A} x_{jnimvk} = 0 \qquad \forall\, v \in \mathcal{V},\ (i,m) \in \mathcal{S}_v^A : X_{iv} = 0,\ k \in \mathcal{K} (10)$$

$$w_{imvk} - \sum_{(j,n)\in\mathcal{S}_v^A} x_{imjnvk} = 0 \qquad \forall\, v \in \mathcal{V},\ (i,m) \in \mathcal{S}_v^A : Z_{iv} = 0,\ k \in \mathcal{K} (11)$$

$$w_{imvk} \ge x^O_{imvk},\ w_{imvk} \ge z_{imvk} \qquad \forall\, v \in \mathcal{V},\ (i,m) \in \mathcal{S}_v^A :,\ k \in \mathcal{K} (12)$$

$$\sum_{v\in\mathcal{V}}\sum_{k\in\mathcal{K}} w_{imvk} = y_{im} \qquad \forall\,(i,m) \in \mathcal{S}_v^A (13)$$

$$y_{i,m-1} - y_{im} \ge 0 \qquad \forall\,(i,m) \in \mathcal{S}_v^A : m > 1 (14)$$

Eqs. (15)-(19) are the ship fuel inventory constraints. Eqs. (15) and (16) compute the ship fuel level, l_{imvk}, for each subfleet when it departs from port visit (i,m). Here, $\gamma_v T_{ij}$ is the fuel consumption rate for fleet v that travels from port i to j, and $\bar{f}_{jnvk}$ is the total amount of fuel that split (v,k) receives from port visit (j,n). The binary variable g_{imvkt} equals 1 if split (v,k) visits (i,m) at time t; only then refueling can take place.

$$\begin{aligned} -\bar{C}_{vk}(1 - x_{imjnvk}) &\le l_{imvk} + \bar{f}_{jnvk} - \gamma_v T_{ij} x_{imjnvk} u_{vk} - l_{jnvk} \\ &\le \bar{C}_{vk}(1 - x_{imjnvk}) \quad \forall\,(i,m,j,n) \in \mathcal{S}_v^X,\ k \in \mathcal{K} \end{aligned} \quad (15)$$

$$\begin{aligned} -\bar{C}_{vk}(1 - x^O_{jnvk}) &\le l^O_{vk} + \bar{f}_{jnvk} - \gamma_v T^O_{jv} x^O_{jnvk} u_{vk} - l_{jnvk} \\ &\le \bar{C}_{vk}(1 - x^O_{jnvk}) \quad \forall\,(j,n) \in \mathcal{S}_v^A,\ k \in \mathcal{K} \end{aligned} \quad (16)$$

$$\bar{f}_{imvk} = \sum_{t\in\mathcal{T}} f_{imvkt} \qquad \forall\, v \in \mathcal{V},\ (i,m) \in \mathcal{S}_v^A,\ k \in \mathcal{K} \quad (17)$$

$$f_{imvkt} \le M^{big} g_{imvkt} \qquad \forall\, v \in \mathcal{V},\ (i,m) \in \mathcal{S}_v^A,\ t \in \mathcal{T},\ k \in \mathcal{K} \quad (18)$$

$$g_{imvkt} \le w_{imvk} \qquad \forall\, v \in \mathcal{V},\ (i,m) \in \mathcal{S}_v^A,\ t \in \mathcal{T},\ k \in \mathcal{K} \quad (19)$$

Eqs. (20)-(25) are the scheduling constraints where t^E_{im} and t^E_{imvk} denote the arrival and departure time of visit (i,m) for split (v,k), respectively. The parameters T^Q_i, T^S_i, T^O_{iv}, and $\bar{T}$ are the time required to load one unit of fuel at port i, the time to prepare to refuel, the time required to travel from the origin to port i, and the length of the time horizon, respectively. Eq. (20) states that the waiting time at port (i,m) can only be nonzero if the port is visited. Eq. (21) ensures that a fleet can only arrive at the next port after its previous port visit is completed. Eqs. (22) and (23) constrain the time for arrival and departure to and from port (i,m). The disjunction in Eq. (24) states that the arrival and departure times of two consecutive port visits are determined according to the visiting order.

$$t^E_{im}y_{im} \geq t^A_{im} + \sum_{v\in\mathcal{V}}\sum_{k\in\mathcal{K}} T^Q_i \bar{f}_{imvk} + \sum_{v\in\mathcal{V}}\sum_{k\in\mathcal{K}} T^S_i w_{imvk}(1-Z_{iv})(1-X_{iv}) \quad \forall\,(i,m)\in\mathcal{S}^A_v \quad (20)$$

$$t^E_{im} + T_{ij} - t^A_{jn} \leq 2\bar{T}(1-x_{imjnvk}) \quad \forall\,v\in\mathcal{V},\ (i,m,j,n)\in\mathcal{S}^X_v,\ k\in\mathcal{K} \quad (21)$$

$$\sum_{v\in\mathcal{V}}\sum_{k\in\mathcal{K}} T^O_{iv}x^O_{imvk} \leq t^A_{im} \leq |\mathcal{H}|y_{im} \quad \forall\,(i,m)\in\mathcal{S}^A_v \quad (22)$$

$$t^E_{im} \leq |\mathcal{H}|y_{im} \quad \forall(i,m)\in S^A_v \quad (23)$$

$$\Big[y_{im}+y_{i,m-1}\leq 1\Big] \vee \begin{bmatrix} y_{im}=y_{i,m-1}=1 \\ t^A_{i,m-1}\leq t^A_{im} \\ t^E_{i,m-1}\leq t^E_{im} \\ t^E_{i,m-1}+TB_i y_{im}\leq t^A_{im} \end{bmatrix} \quad \forall\,(i,m)\in\mathcal{S}^A_v \quad (24)$$

$$\sum_{(i,m)\in S^A_v} g_{imvkt} \leq 1 \quad \forall\,v\in\mathcal{V},k\in\mathcal{K},\ t\in\mathcal{T} \quad (25)$$

Eqs. (26)-(28) are the port inventory constraints. The ammonia inventory level at port i at time t is denoted by s_{it}, P_{it} is the production rate at port i in time period t, and q_{ijt} is the amount of ammonia transported from port i to j in time period t.

$$s_{it} = s_{i,t-1} + P_{it} - \sum_{v\in\mathcal{V}}\sum_{k\in\mathcal{K}}\sum_{m\in M} f_{imvkt} - \sum_{j\in\mathcal{J}}(q_{ijt}-q_{jit}) \quad \forall\,i\in\mathcal{I},\ t\in\mathcal{T} \quad (26)$$

$$s_{i,|T|} \geq s_{i0} \quad \forall\,i\in\mathcal{I} \quad (27)$$

$$s_{i,t} \leq Q_i \leq Q^{\max}_i \quad \forall\,i\in\mathcal{I},\ t\in\mathcal{T} \quad (28)$$

Eqs. (29)-(32) are the ammonia production constraints. The binary variable o_{it} equals 1 if ammonia is produced at port i in time period t, p_i and r_i equal 1 if port i is an ammonia production site and refueling station, respectively. The production rate P_{it} is bounded by the ammonia plant's capacity C_i which is bounded by the maximum plant capacity. The production rate is a function of wind speed, ω_{it}, and the plant capacity.

$$o_{it} \leq p_i \quad \forall i\in\mathcal{I},t\in\mathcal{T} \quad (29)$$

$$0 \leq P_{it} \leq C_i \leq C^{\max}_i o_{it} \quad \forall i\in\mathcal{I},t\in\mathcal{T} \quad (30)$$

$$P_{it} = f(\omega_{it},C_i,o_{it}) \quad \forall i\in\mathcal{I},t\in\mathcal{T} \quad (31)$$

$$q_{ijt} \leq p_i,\ q_{ijt} \leq r_j \quad \forall\,i\in\mathcal{I},\ j\in\mathcal{I},\ t\in\mathcal{T} \quad (32)$$

Finally, the disjunction in Eq. (33) links the routing constraints with the production and inventory constraints. The overall problem can be formulated as an MILP.

$$\begin{bmatrix} t^A_{im} \le t \le t^E_{im} \\ w_{imvk} = 1 \\ g_{imvk} = 1 \end{bmatrix} \vee \begin{bmatrix} \neg \begin{bmatrix} t^A_{im} \le t \le t^E_{im} \\ w_{imvk} = 1 \end{bmatrix} \\ g_{imvk} = 1 \end{bmatrix} \qquad \forall (i,m) \in S^A_v,\ k \in \mathcal{K} \quad (33)$$

3. Computational Case Study

The objective is to minimize the overall cost, which includes both the capital and operating costs. The capital cost includes the cost of constructing the green ammonia production plants and refueling ports while the operating cost consists of the costs for producing, storing, and transporting ammonia as well as the cost of operating the ship fleets. In our case study, we consider two proxies for the shipping cost: travel time and fuel cost.

As shown in Figure 2a, we consider a network of six ports and two ship fleets, where one fleet has to transport cargo from Port 1 to Port 6 while the other one has to travel from Port 2 to Port 5. Ammonia can be produced at every port; however, Port 3 is assumed to be a location on the open ocean where wind speeds are significantly higher and steadier [Possner and Caldeira, 2017]. As a result, the cost of producing ammonia at Port 3 is lower than at the other locations. With a time horizon of 30 days (each day being one time period), we optimize the system for two cases. In Case 1, we apply a penalty on the total travel time, assuming that the operating cost of shipping and the opportunity cost of delivering more cargo mainly depend on the travel time. In Case 2, we only consider fuel cost as a proxy for shipping cost.

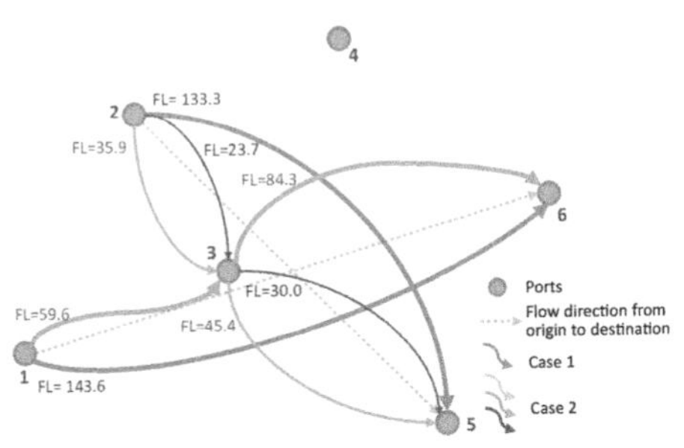

(a) Optimal routes for Cases 1 and 2

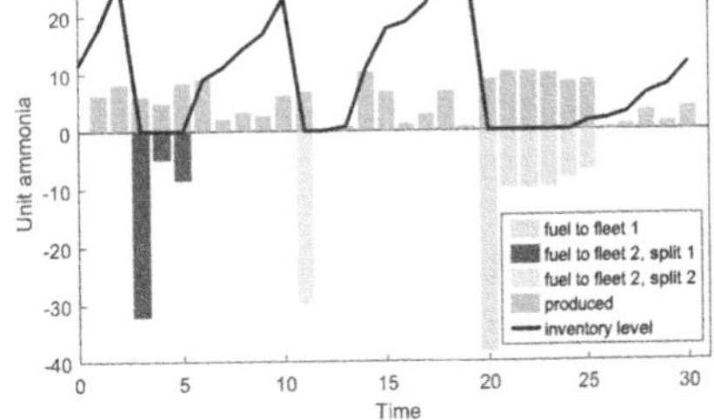

(b) Optimal ammonia schedule for Case 2

Figure 2: (a) Optimal routing decisions in Cases 1 and 2. Ports are depicted as grey nodes, grey dashed lines indicate the origin and destination ports. The blue arcs depict the optimal routes in Case 1 while the green and orange arcs represent the optimal routes in Case 2. (b) Ammonia production and refueling schedule and the resulting inventory profile at Port 3 in Case 2. Positive values indicate production while negative values indicate consumption.

Figure 2a shows the optimal routing decisions in both cases. In Case 1, the optimal route for each fleet is to simply go directly from its origin to its destination (blue arcs), which indicates that the shipping cost as a function of the travel time outweighs the benefit of producing ammonia at a lower cost at Port 3. In Case 2, the optimal route for each fleet involves stopping at Port 3 to refuel since part of the objective is to reduce fuel cost. Also, in this case, we see that all cargo is transported from Port 1 to Port 6 using one trip (orange arc), while two trips are required to transport all the cargo from Port 2 to Port 5 (green arcs). The reason is that, to reduce capital cost, the optimal solution suggests building an ammonia plant at Port 3 with a capacity that is not large enough to fuel the entire fleet that travels from Port 2 to Port 5. Hence, the fleet has to be split into two subfleets that arrive at Port 3 for refueling at different times. Figure 2b shows the optimal ammonia production and refueling schedule at Port 3. One can see that the three subfleets arrive at the port for refueling at different times such that there is enough time between two visits to replenish the ammonia inventory.

4. Conclusions

In this work, we considered the design of supply chains for the production of green ammonia and its use as a marine fuel in the shipping industry. This required the integration of maritime inventory routing and production scheduling decisions into a facility location formulation, which gives rise to a complex MILP model. We applied the proposed model to an illustrative case study, which demonstrates the model's ability to achieve solutions that optimally balance the costs of investment, shipping, and ammonia production. Future work will focus on the development of efficient solution algorithms that allow us to solve large-scale instances and draw conclusions about the potential benefit of green ammonia as a sustainable marine fuel at the industrial scale.

References

A. Agra, M. Christiansen, and A. Delgado, 2017. Discrete time and continuous time formulations for a short sea inventory routing problem. *Optimization and Engineering*, 18(1):269–297.

N. de Vries. *Safe and effective application of ammonia as a marine fuel.* Master thesis, TU Delft, 2019.

D. R. MacFarlane, P. V. Cherepanov, J. Choi, B. H. Suryanto, R. Y. Hodgetts, J. M. Bakker, F. M. Ferrero Vallana, and A. N. Simonov, 2020. A roadmap to the ammonia economy. *Joule*, 4(6):1186–1205.

M. J. Palys, H. Wang, Q. Zhang, and P. Daoutidis, 2021. Renewable ammonia for sustainable energy and agriculture: vision and systems engineering opportunities. *Current Opinion in Chemical Engineering*, 31:100667.

A. Possner and K. Caldeira, 2017. Geophysical potential for wind energy over the open oceans. *Proceedings of the National Academy of Sciences of the United States of America*, 114(43):11338–11343.

H. Wang, P. Daoutidis, and Q. Zhang, 2021. Harnessing the wind power of the ocean with green offshore ammonia. *ACS Sustainable Chemistry & Engineering*, 9(43):14605–14617.

Proceedings of the 14th International Symposium on Process Systems Engineering – PSE 2021+
June 19-23, 2022, Kyoto, Japan
http://dx.doi.org/10.1016/B978-0-323-85159-6.50099-3

Optimal agriculture residues revalorization as a biofuel alternative in electric power grids

Sergio Iván Martínez-Guido [a], Juan Fernando García-Trejo [a], Claudia Gutiérrez-Antonio [a*], and Fernando Israel Gómez-Castro [b]

[a]*Engineering Faculty, Universidad Autónoma de Querétaro, Campus Amazcala, El Marqués, Querétaro, 76265, Mexico*
[b]*Chemical Engineering Department, Universidad de Guanajuato, Guanajuato, Guanajuato, 36050, Mexico*
claugtez@gmail.com

Abstract

In the last years, the increase in energy demand along with depletion in the production of oil wells has driven the search of alternative energy sources. In addition, these sources must be renewable, in order to contribute to the solution of the climate change problem. Therefore, different alternatives have been proposed and evaluated to satisfy global energy demand. Among them, biomass has received higher attention due its availability, which places it as the third energy source, after crude and oil fuels. Particularly, the agricultural residues represent an option to obtain different biofuels, with the possibility to reduce between 78-94% greenhouse emissions by its use. Moreover, the integration of this kind of residues in new supply chains economies contributes to its valorisation, adding an economic benefit to its origin crop. Thus, it is necessary to evaluate the feasibility of using these biofuels, along with their environmental impact. Hence, this work was optimized the supply chain for the production of solid fuels from different agriculture residues along with its integration into the electric power grid; as a case of study, it was considered the agriculture residues generated in Mexico and its electric power grid. Results show that is possible to generate 140,673,599 GJ, and at the same time achieve a reduction of 20% of CO_2 emissions.

Keywords: Solid biofuels, optimization, supply chain, environmental impact.

1. Introduction

Due to the current increase in energy demand around the world, different bio-energy sources have received higher attention, being biomass waste one of the most promising sources (Schawarzböck et al., 2016). In this way, agro-industrial sector contributes different kinds of residual biomass, which are derived from all the operations or activities involved in the supply chains involved. In this context, agriculture industrial waste can be classified into four main groups (Kumar-Chhetri et al., 2020):

- Crop cultivation waste (stalk, silk, stem, seed, pod, root, weeds, etc.)
- Food loss/waste (edible and non-edible or unprocessed food, spoiled food, etc.)
- Industrial food processing waste (husk, seed, bagasse, fruit, peel, rind, etc.)
- Livestock rising aqua/microbial culture waste (excreta and carcasses dead cell, waste-water, etc.)

Particularly, crop cultivation waste impacts the environment due to these residues are mostly burned in the fields or put into landfills, being used only a lower percent as fodder.

Therefore, some works have focused on finding the optimal alternative to add value to these kinds of residues; highlighting that these kinds of residues are a promising raw material in biofuels processes production (Martínez-Guido et al., 2019). According to Debnath & Babu (2019) biofuels can be produced from different types and forms of biomass and residual biomass. Particularly, agricultural residues have an attractive potential to be used raw material in pellets (solid biofuel) production supply chains (Tauro et al., 2018), incorporating the advantages as overcome the issue with a lower energy per volume unit, easy management, transportation, handling cost, storage, and a better economic efficiency relation in comparison with liquid biofuels (Theppitak et al., 2020). Therefore, the pellets are part of the current renewable alternative sources for electric generation (Sandberg et al., 2019); however, nowadays only a few studies have been focused on the use of pellets obtained from agricultural and into electric power grids, incorporating this process as an agriculture residues revalorization strategy (Martínez-Guido et al., 2019). Hence, in this work is proposed the use of different agricultural residues (obtained from diverse Mexican crops), which nowadays doesn't have any use of the market, as raw material for pellets production. Moreover, the possible supply chain configuration to use these solid biofuels into the electric power grid of México is also analysed.

2. Problem statement

According to Kaza et al. (2018), around the world are generated almost 2.01 billion tonnes/y of solid wastes, and it is expected that this volume increase by 40% by 2050. Particularly, Mexico contributes with approximately 72,172 tonnes of agricultural residues per year (ANBIO, 2020); this residual biomass is constituted by chemical compounds of high value as cellulose, hemicellulose and lignin (Santiago del Rosa et al., 2018). However, as Pradhan et al. (2019) indicated these kinds of residues are left in the fields or even burned, mainly in developing countries. Therefore, the use of these residues as raw material for the pellets production could be a strategy with diverse benefits, such as the dependence on oils reduction, fuels with lower emissions, avoid the scarcity of conventional fuels, and, at the same time, to promote the circular economy. The goal in agriculture residues pelletization is to produce a cheaper and sustainable biofuel with the capacity to satisfy the Mexican electric energy demand. However, is not possible to take into consideration the pellets integrations in all the national electric power plants, due to the available technology in each electric plant; thus, for the analysis only 62% of national demand was considered. Hence, the design, planning and scheduling of a new supply chain for the integration of these kinds of residues into the electric power grid involving the economic, social, and environmental aspects is required (See Figure 1). Therefore, the optimal design could offer a win-win situation where both agriculture residues management and energy security issues are achieved, which is demonstrated through a case study of the electricity supply chain in Mexico.

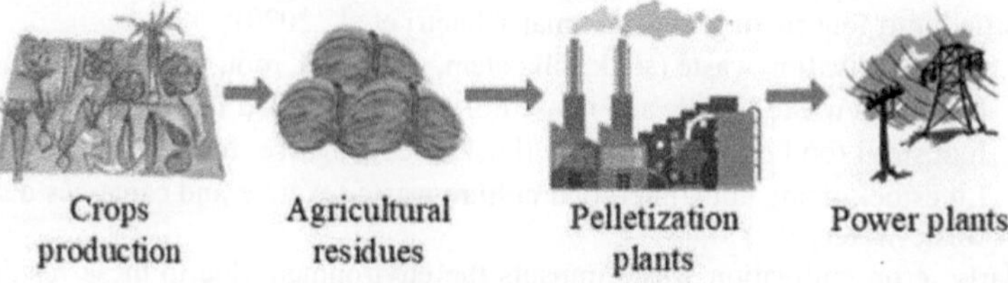

Figure 1. Agro-residues revalorization.

3. Methodology

As it was mentioned before, the proposed approach was performed using the current situation of the Mexican electrical energy demand as a case study. In this way, agricultural residues from the 18 crops (i), shown in Table 1, were analyzed in terms of seasonal availability and flux production in the 32 states (k) that constitute Mexico; since it would be wrong to take into consideration a constant flow of residues throughout the year.

Table 1. Agriculture residues considering in this work

Agave	Broad Beans	Coffee bean	Kidney beans	Peanut	Sorghum
Banana	Chickpea	Cotton	Lentil	Rice	Sugar Cane
Barley	Cocoa	Fodder	Oats	Sesame	Wheat

Hence, using Eq. (1) was possible to calculate the flow of residues of each crop produced $\left(FR_{i,k,w}^{AGr}\right)$ per week (w), biomass flux is directly linked with the respective parameter, yield of ton of residue per a ton of crop cultivated $\left(P_{i,k,w}^{AGry}\right)$ and the area used for the harvesting $\left(A_{i,k,w}^{harv}\right)$.

$$FR_{i,k,w}^{AGr} = A_{i,k,w}^{harv} * P_{i,k,w}^{AGry}, \forall\, i \in I, k \in K, w \in W \qquad (1)$$

Considering the agriculture residues availability, these can be collected in each harvesting site and transported to the pelletization plant. The installation of the pelletization plant is considered for each state in Mexico; however, the decision of the existence is constrained by the installation cost, and the residues availability in each state, a binary variable was used to identify in which states are installed a pelletization plant. This binary variable $\left(Y_{i,m}^{bv}\right)$ is multiplied by the fixed installation cost $\left(IC_{i,m}^{fix}\right)$, a value that added to the variable cost $\left(IC_{i,m}^{var}\right)$ multiplied by the process flow capacity $\left(RF_{i,m}^{proc}\right)$, gives the total installation cost of each pelletization plant $\left(TI_{i,m}^{cost}\right)$.

$$TI_{i,m}^{cost} = IC_{i,m}^{fix} * Y_{i,m}^{bv} + IC_{i,m}^{var} * RF_{i,m}^{proc}, \forall\, i \in I,\ m \in M \qquad (2)$$

With the flux of pellets $\left(Pe_{i,j,w}^{flo}\right)$ obtained in each installed plant, is possible to produce electricity in each selected power plant, and satisfy the electrical energy demand in each state $\left(EE_{j,w}^{prod}\right)$; however, if a state doesn't have enough solid biofuel, hence the conventional fuel $\left(CF_{l,j,w}^{flo}\right)$ is used to satisfy the required rest, as is described by Eq. (3).

$$EE_{j,w}^{prod} = \sum_i Pe_{i,j,w}^{flo} * FE_i^{gene} + \sum_l CF_{l,j,w}^{flo} * FE_l^{gene}, \forall\, j \in J, w \in W \qquad (3)$$

In order to obtain the optimal supply chain configurations, the proposed mathematical model included residues collection, transportation, transformation, and pellet distribution balances as mathematic equations. Additionally, equations as economic balances and emissions balances were proposed. Consequently, optimal solutions were obtained having as multi-objective function the CO_2 emissions and total cost minimization, and the social impact maximization, as is described in Eq. (4).

$$OF = Min\ CO_2^{Emis}, Min\ TOTC, Max\ TSI \qquad (4)$$

Therefore, multi-objective problem was codified at GAMS platform and solved using the ε constraint method (Diwekar, 2010), in which one of the objective functions is optimized using the others objectives functions as constrains, leading to finding the extreme solution at the feasible region. Afterward, the rest of the objective functions are optimizing under the same criteria. In this way, were analyzed five different scenarios, for each solution (scenario) the model calculates 608 discrete variables, 513,774 continuous variables under 68,718 constraints. The CPU execution time per assay was 2.265 seconds in an Intel 336 processor running at 2.40 GHz with 8 GB of RAM memory, using CPLEX as the solver.

4. Results

Mainly results obtained from the five scenarios analyzed are shown in Table 2. Particularly, scenario A represents the solution with the lower amount of CO_2 emissions in comparison with the rest of the solutions, even in comparison with the current situation of electricity production in Mexico. In this way, according to SENER (2016) the supply of 62% of national electric energy demand in Mexico (using only conventional fuels as energy sources) involves the release of 114,911,336 ton CO_2/y; hence, solution A represents 22.15% of emissions reduction, while the emissions in solution E are 6.58% lower in comparison with the current situation. Therefore, a reduction from 7,561,165-25,452,860 ton CO_2/y is possible to achieve if the agriculture residues revalorization is carried out. However, to achieve any of these percent's of emissions reduction is required money investment. As it is possible to notice in Table 2, scenario A needs the major investment (approximately 428,734,538 USD); nevertheless, for all the obtained solutions 80% of the total cost is given by the production cost, which is constituted by the pelletization plant installation and the transformation costs. In this way, the highest cost makes sense due that currently there are not any pelletization plant installed in Mexico; moreover, in solution A 32 new plants are installed to satisfy 62% of the national electrical energy demand. The 20% of the total money invested is given by transportation costs and taxes added to the new economic activity.

Table 2. Mainly results obtained in the different scenarios analyzed

		Difference with scenario A (%)			
	A	**B**	**C**	**D**	**E**
Invested money (USD/y)	428,734,538	-1.525	-4.261	-4.444	-4.574
Human development index (% of invested money)	12.96	-2.022	-6.420	-9.568	-11.574
Emissions (ton CO_2/y)	89,451,365	+7.69	+12.63	+16.29	+20.01

On the other hand, as it is shown in Table 2, the installation of 32 new industrial plants focused on solid biofuel production (scenario A) requires the higher investment; nonetheless, in this scenario is obtained a social benefit, which is represented by the money invested in social security, education and per-capita income variables which has a direct impact on the human development index. In this way, due that a new economic activity is developed; hence, new employees and as consequence new salaries are created, salaries to which taxes are deducted. Additionally, a taxes deduction over the new implanted industries is considered. So, from all the deducted taxes is possible to take into consideration a new national flux of money invested to human development activities; in this context, scenario A achieves 12.96% more invested money than that considered in the current national situation, while scenario E is possible to achieve only 1.38% more invested money.

Table 3 shown the economic comparison with the current conventional fuels used in the Mexican power grid; as it is possible to notice, each tone of pellets is 38% more expensive than the carbon prices (the cheaper conventional fuel alternative). However, in comparison with the Gas LP (the expensive conventional fuel alternative) and fossil diesel, each tone of pellets is 96% and 95% cheaper, respectively. In this way, according to Olguin-Muciel et al. (2020) the biofuel's potential is directly linked with the cost-competitively with conventional fuels; hence, this argument is achieved when pellets are compared with diesel and gas but is not reached with carbon. On the other hand, CO_2 emissions per MWh generated by the pellets are 20% higher than emissions released by the use of gas LP (conventional fuel with lower CO_2 emissions); but pellets emissions are 36% and 27% lower in comparison with the emissions generated by the use of diesel (conventional fuel with higher CO_2 emissions) and carbon, respectively. Nevertheless, emissions listed in Table 3 for conventional fuels do not take into consideration the CO_2 emitted by the extraction of the fuels, only are quantified the emissions released by the combustion (use); the reported CO_2 emissions by the use of pellets take into consideration all the emissions generated in the complete life cycle.

Table 3. Economic and emissions comparison

Energy source	USD/ton	CO_2 ton/MWh produced
Carbon	34	0.603
Diesel	1,275	0.692
Gas	1,398	0.352
Pellets	55	0.44

In the CO_2 emissions context, transportation activities in the pellets supply chain represent the process with the higher released emissions. In solution A, biomass transportation and pellets distribution contribute with 88% of the total generated emissions, while in scenario E these activities contribute with 68% of total emissions. Similarly, the pellets production release 10% of the total emissions in scenario A, while in scenario E this activity contributes with only 7%. However, in scenario E 20% of the energy sources used to satisfy the 62% of electrical energy demand comes from conventional fuels; therefore, 24% of the total emissions in this solution are given by the combustion of conventional fuels, while in scenario A the 62% of electricity national demand is satisfied only with pellets.

5. Conclusions

Agriculture residues revalorization throughout pellets production is a green alternative that can be used in the Mexican electricity grid, satisfying almost 62% of national electricity demand. Additionally, residues transformation into solid biofuel is an alternative to reduce dependence on fossil fuels under a circular economy development, having beneficial impact on the human development index. Fuel pellets production supply chain is a complex system due to all the activities involved to achieve the process goal; hence, the use of the mathematical model approach allows to obtain different system configurations, which results in attractive solutions from the economic, social, and environmental points of view.

Acknowledgements

Financial support provided by Secretaría de Educación Pública (SEP), through grant PRODEP-UAQ/332/19, for Sergio Iván Martínez-Guido is gratefully acknowledged.

References

ANBIO-National Atlas of Biomass, 2018, Atlas Nacional de Biomasa. Available on: https://dgel.energia.gob.mx/ANBIO/

D. Debnath, S. Babu, 2019, Biofuels, Bioenergy andk Food Security; Technology, Institutions and Policies, first ed., ELSEVIER, London, United Kindong

E. Olguin-Muciel, A. Singh, R. Cable-Villacis, R. Tapia-Tussell, H.A. Ruiz, 2020. Consolidated Bioprocessing, an Innovative Strategy towards Sustainability for Biofuels Production from Crop Residues: An Overview, Agronomy, 10, 1834

E. Sandberg, J.G. Kirkerud, E. Tømborg, T.F. Bolkejø, 2019, Energy system impacts of grid tariff structures for flexible power to district heat, Energy, 168, 772-781

N. Santiago-De La Rosa, G. González-Cardoso, J de J. Figueroa-Lara, M. Gutiérrez-Arzaluz, C. Octaviano-Villasana, I.F. Ramírez-Hernández, V. Mugica-Álvarez, 2018, Emission factors of atmospheric and climatic pollutants from crop residues burning, Journal of the Air & Waste Management Association, 68, 849-865

P. Pradhan, P. Gadkari, A. Arora, S.M. Mahajani, 2019, Economic feasibility of agro waste pelletization as an energy option in rural India, Energy Procedia, 158, 3405-3410

R. Kumar-Chhetri, N. Aryal, S. Kharel, R. Chandra-Poudel, D. Pant, 2020, Current Developments in Biotechnology and Bioengineering: Sustainable Bioresources for the Emerging Bioeconomy, first ed., ELSEVIER, Amsterdam, Netherlands (Chapter 5)

R. Tauro, C.A. García, M. Skutsch, O. Masera, 2018, The potential for sustainable biomass pellets in México: An analysis of energy potential, logistic cost and market demand, Renewable and Sustainable Energy Reviews, 82, 380-389

S. Kaza, L. Yao, P. Bhada-Tata, F. Van-Woerden, 2018, What a waste 2.0: A Global snapshot of solid waste management to 2050, World Bank Group, Available on: https://openknowledge.worldbank.org/handle/10986/30317

S. Theppitak, D. Hungwe, L. Ding, D. Xin, G. Yu, K. Yoshikawa, 2020, Comparison on solid biofuel production from wet and dry carbonization processes of food wastes, Applied Energy, 272, 115264

S.I. Martínez-Guido, I.M. Ríos-Badrán, C. Gutiérrez-Antonio, J.M. Ponce-Ortega, 2019, Strategic planning for the use of waste biomass pellets in Mexican power plants, Renewable Energy 130, 622-632

SENER "Energy Secretary" México, 2016, Development program of the national energy system. https://www.gob.mx/cms/uploads/attachment/file/98308/PRODESEN-2016-2030_1.pdf, (accessed on February 2020).

T. Schwarzböck, H. Rechberger, O. Cenic, J. Fellner, 2016, Determining national greenhouse gas emissions from waste-to-energy using the Balance Method, Waste Management, 49, 263-271

U. Diwekar, 2010, Introduction to Applied Optimization, Second ed, Springer, 10.1007/978-0-387-76635-5

Proceedings of the 14th International Symposium on Process Systems Engineering – PSE 2021+
June 19-23, 2022, Kyoto, Japan
http://dx.doi.org/10.1016/B978-0-323-85159-6.50100-7

Global Supply Chain Optimization for COVID-19 Vaccine under COVAX initiative

Katragadda Apoorva[a], IA Karimi[a]* and Xiaonan WANG[b]*
[a]*Department of Chemical and Biomolecular Engineering, National University of Singapore, Singapore 117585 Singapore*
[b] *Department of Chemical Engineering, Tsinghua University, Beijing 100084, China*
wangxiaonan@mail.tsinghua.edu.cn

Abstract

After the onset of the COVID-19 pandemic, World Health Organization (WHO) launched COVAX in April 2020 to bring together countries and vaccine manufacturers and provide innovative and equitable access to COVID-19 vaccines. We developed a global supply chain model to optimize the production of the vaccines and allocation to different countries worldwide. The global COVID-19 vaccine supply chain of COVAX should be resilient to various disruptions and risks. In this work, we develop an optimization model with risk mitigation strategies to determine the procurement of vaccines from production centers and distribution to different countries when the supply chain is subjected to various disruptions. Our case study demonstrates how different risk mitigation strategies would enable COVAX to meet the demand amid multiple disruptions. It indicates that it is feasible to meet the vaccine demand and help participating countries overcome the global pandemic.

Keywords: add three to five keywords here.

1. Introduction

The only way to overcome the ongoing pandemic and achieve herd immunity is to vaccinate people worldwide. After the accelerated vaccine development, several vaccines have been approved globally. However, to overcome the challenge of coordinating the procurement and distribution of vaccines globally, the COVAX initiative was set up. It is co-led by WHO, Gavi (an organization that works towards getting people from developing countries vaccinated), and Coalition for Epidemic Preparedness Innovations (CEPI), a Gates Foundation-funded project that aims to make more vaccines available during an outbreak, was setup. Under the COVAX initiative, funding from rich countries was supposed to pool to invest in multiple vaccine development to increase the chances of effective vaccine development and approval. In addition, the funding was intended to provide vaccines for poorer countries. COVAX initiative handles the procurement and distribution of COVID-19 vaccines without discriminating between participating countries based on income [1] (Figure 1). However, after the approval of several COVID-19 vaccines, the global delivery has been successful but limited to rich countries. Due to unprecedented demand for vaccines, there has been a shortage of vaccines to the COVAX initiative as the rich countries procured vaccines through bilateral deals. [2]. COVAX deliveries have been hindered but slowly accelerating. COVAX has been making efforts to address and mitigate various risks. Therefore, optimizing the supply chain under various uncertain disruptions is crucial to minimize the overall cost and utilize the resources best.

Stochastic supply chain optimization has been studied to optimize the supply chains of vaccines in the past. However, a recent study [3] reported a lack of existing academic publications on vaccine supply chain resilience. Few papers have been published partially addressing the challenges for the COVID-19 vaccine supply chain [4,5]. To account for the potential disruptions of vaccine production and delivery, we establish a stochastic model to capture different scenarios and minimize the overall cost. The objective function also has a term quantifying the supply chain's resilience. This work first provides insights into various setbacks faced by the COVAX facility in section 2. Section 3 describes the mathematical model in detail, and the solution for optimistic deterministic cases and scenarios with various disruptions are presented in section 4. Finally, the conclusion and future work is mentioned in Section 5.

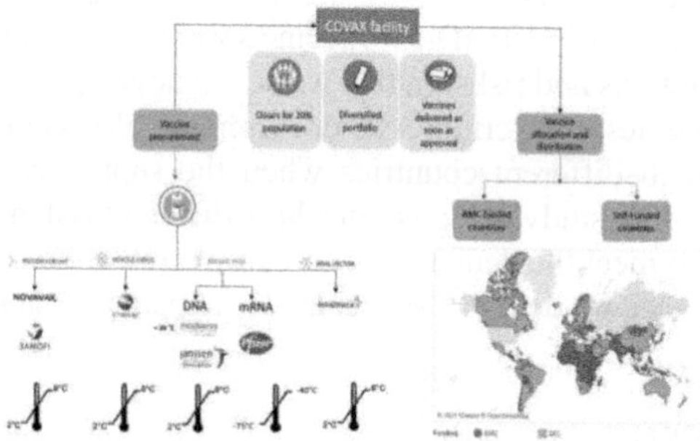

Figure 1. The schematic of the COVAX facility involves vaccine procurement and global distribution.

2. Challenges faced by COVAX

To achieve the objectives of COVAX, they made investments for the development of several vaccines during the development phase and then signed deals with various manufacturers to deliver vaccines once approved. Once the vaccines are procured, COVAX is responsible for transporting the vaccines from the manufacturing center to the Countries' central hub. However, even after the successful approval of the vaccines, COVAX has failed to meet its objectives. Since its launch, it has been subjected to various setbacks, and the most crucial ones are as follows: 1) Production facilities are not adhering to the promised doses. For example, COVAX depended mainly on the Serum Institute in India for vaccines for 2021 (~50%). The second wave of COVID-19 in India resulted in a halt in the supply of doses to COVAX [6], 2) Lack of transportation capacity and various transportation disruptions: With the unprecedented demand for vaccines, available transportation capacity is not enough. In addition, when the rich countries came forward for donation, the freight and storage had to be taken care of by the COVAX [7], 3) Vaccine nationalism: Rich countries have procured the vaccines, and none are left for the low- and middle-income countries under the COVAX facility. After 18 months of the launch of the COVAX initiative, 98% of people in low-income countries remain unvaccinated [8].

3. Problem Statement

This paper considers a two-echelon production-distribution network for vaccine distribution under COVAX. The COVID-19 vaccine delivery from the manufacturer to the country's central hub is carried through direct shipment to the point of use without any distribution centers in the middle. As part of the initiative, there are various manufacturers m, manufacturing set of vaccines v and delivering them to different countries c in the world through transportation links (TLs) using storage containers type s based on the storage requirements of vaccines. The risk mitigation strategies for different disruptions are as follows: 1) In case of a risk involved with the production facility, we employ two mitigation strategies: a) More investment should be made in scaling up the production capacity. If the production capacity is reduced, investment should be made to restore the capacity for the next round of allocation. In addition, instead of ordering the exact amount initially, COVAX should have a deal for extra doses as a buffer, b) Streamline the donation process: Coordinate with rich countries and plan the delivery of the vaccines. Rich countries are wasting several million unused doses. COVAX should tap into these countries and sign deals for donations. In other words, putting efforts to connect donating countries (backup nodes) when the primary manufacturer is not available. These mitigation strategies will help deal with the above-mentioned (Section 2) challenges with the procurement of doses. During the disruption in the cold chain transportation of the vaccines or sudden requirement of transportation fleet when a country agrees to donate, the COVAX facility should employee backup, i.e., 3PL, to take care of the vaccine distribution. This would ensure that the facility is prepared for the transportation of vaccines without any capacity constraints, would also enable that no vaccines are damaged during transport, and ensure that the donations are well-received.

4. Supply chain optimization

Decision-making in vaccine production and allocation is formulated as a mixed-integer linear programming (MILP) model. The objective functions and constraints are mentioned in table 1. The objective function is divided into two parts: one corresponding to minimizing the design costs based on pre-disruption decisions, and the second is the cost during expected worst-case after the realization of the disruptions. The worst case is incorporated in our model via the conditional Value at Risk (cVaR) measure. Stochastic optimization aims to minimize the total cost. Pre-disruptions design costs include establishing transportation links with the fleet and investment in procurement, such as signing more deals with donors to scale up the production capacity and contracting 3PL as backup transportation. The second part of the objective function is the expected worst-case cost, including transportation costs, storage costs, vaccine procurement costs, and recovery costs for restoring production and transportation capacities after disruptions. The optimization constraint includes capacity constraints, supply-demand balance, and other logical constraints. (Eq 6 – 9, Table 1).

5. Case study

We have considered the demand for nine countries (India, Pakistan, Nigeria, Mexico, Ethiopia, Egypt, DRC, Iran, and Thailand), 50% of COVAX demand. The vaccine portfolio of 9 vaccines is also considered. These vaccines broadly fall into four categories (Figure 1). The vaccines differ in price per dose, the number of doses per person, storage requirement, and production sites where each vaccine is produced. The production centers are fixed based on the deals with the vaccine manufacturers. Various costs such as storage cost, transportation per unit distance, and selling price of vaccines are fixed and taken from literature. However, few costs such as contracting 3PL, cost of restoration of production capacity, and setting up a contract between a production center and a country for vaccine delivery are assumed. Through our case study, we want to demonstrate the effectiveness of our model over the basic model employed by the COVAX facility currently. The production and transportation capacities are subjected to various disruptions and are expressed in the percentage of available capacity. We define four

Table 1. Mathematical model formulation as designed for the optimization problem

	Index	Mathematical Formulation	Description
Objective function			
	(1)	$\sum_p \sum_c \sum_m C^{install}_{p,c,m} Z_{p,c,m}$	Design Costs
	(2)	$\sum_p C^{extra\ capacity}_p w_p + \sum_c C^{contract}_c z^{contract}_c$	Resilience Enhancing Investment
	(4)	$\sum_m C^{vaccine}_v \left(\sum_c \left(\sum_p \sum_t \sum_m C^{vaccine}_v y^s_{v,p,c,t,m} F^{AMC}_c \right) \right)$	Cost of vaccines
	(5)	$\sum_v \sum_p \sum_c \sum_t \sum_m tr_{v,p,c,m} y^s_{v,p,c,t,m} + \sum_v \sum_p \sum_c \sum_t \sum_m C^{storage}_m y^s_{v,p,c,t,m}$	Cost of transportation and storage
	(6)	$\sum_m \sum_p \sum_c \sum_t C^{restore}_p rp^s_{p,t,v}$	Cost of transportation by 3PL
Constraints			
	(6)	$y^s_{v,p,c,t,m} \leq MZ_{p,c,m}$	Logical constraints
	(7)	$\sum_c \left[\sum_m (y^s_{v,p,c,t,m}) + (yb^s_{v,p,c,t} + rb^s_{v,p,c,t}) \right] \leq x^s_{v,p,t}$	Balance constraints
	(8)	$x^s_{v,p,t} \leq M * VP(v,p)$	Vaccine-production matching
	(9)	$D_{c,t} - \sum_p \sum_m \sum_v \frac{y^s_{v,p,c,t,m}}{Dose_v} - \sum_p \frac{yb^s_{v,p,c,t}}{Dose_v} - \sum_p \sum_m \sum_v \frac{rb^s_{v,p,c,t}}{Dose_v} = q^s_{c,t}$	Overall Supply-demand balance

independent scenarios for production and transportation disruptions each i.e., 100%, 80%, 60% and 40% capacities. Therefore, we have a total of 4^4 = 64 scenarios, each with an equal probability of occurrence. The demand for each country is fixed at 20% of its population, which was the goal of COVAX in 2021 [1].

6. Results

Evaluating the deterministic base supply chain model without any risk mitigation strategies: First, we optimized the base supply chain model without risk mitigation strategies. We have solved the problem for the ideal (optimistic) scenario which COVAX had expected. Under the ideal scenario, all the deals with the manufacturers are delivered without any delay and the transportation is not subjected to any disruptions. Then we optimized the model for the actual situation faced by the COVAX facility, accounting for all the production and transportation disruptions. Results demonstrate how the supply chain model failed when subjected to disruptions. This is validated by the fact that COVAX is far behind in fulfilling its objectives. Based on the results, it was found that these disruptions have led to around 64% of the unmet demand (Figure 2b). Based on the deals made by the facility, the allocation results indicate that countries are served by more than one production center. The allocation is not only based on the transportation and storage cost but based on the selling price of the vaccines. Vaccines provided to the AMC-funded countries are cheaper than the ones provided to the self-funding countries. On the other hand, the cost distribution indicates that vaccine cost is the main contributing factor compared to other costs (Figure 2a).

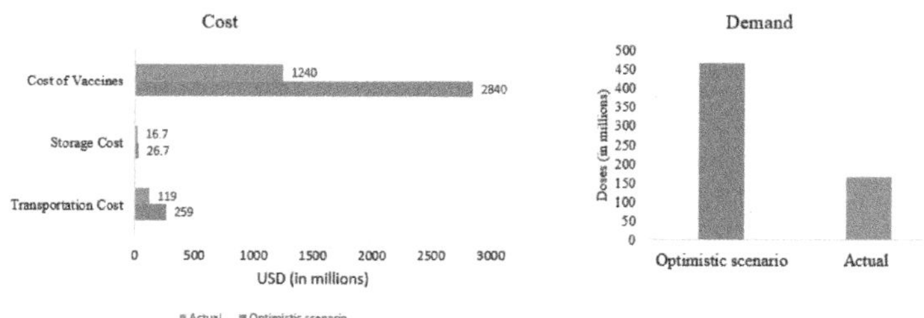

Figure 2. a) Cost distribution for basic supply chain model for optimistic scenario and actual case, b) The demand satisfied under each scenario.

5.2 Evaluating the performance of our model for the 2021 case study: We have successfully demonstrated the performance of our model as 100% demand is met and the cost is optimized (Table 2). Results support the claim that the vaccine demand can be met by having well-coordinated donations as backup production centers, restoring the production capacity after disruption, and having deals for buffer doses. We also studied the effect of disruption on different costs and found out that disruptions lead to an increase in the overall cost (Table 2). However, which cost factors will increase is not certain and is subjected to the nature of disruption. The cost distribution is illustrated in Figure 3. As we see that the major cost driver is the cost of vaccines, followed by the 3PL transportation cost. This is because 3PL handles the transportation of donations from various countries. Surprisingly, the results also demonstrate that the optimized cost for our model is only 13% higher than the ideal scenario. This proves that the COVAX facility does not have to spend a lot of extra money to meet the demand, rather should focus on coordinating and procuring donations effectively.

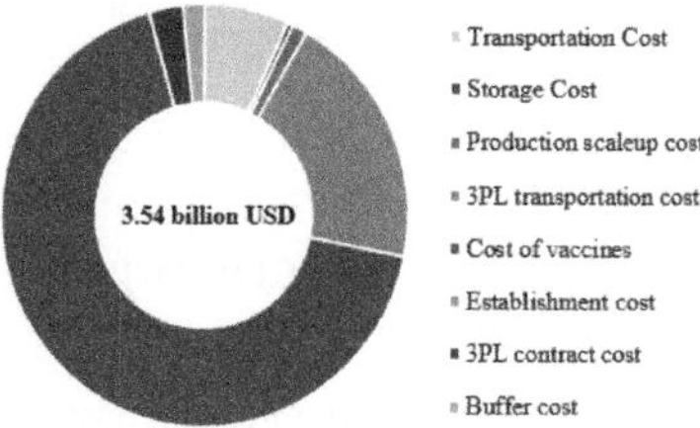

Figure 3. Cost distribution for our supply chain model for actual scenario of 2021 case study

Table 1. Optimization results of scenarios considering various disruptions.

Scenario	Total Cost (USD in billions)	Demand Satisfied
Optimistic scenario (Base model)	3.13	100%
Actual (Base model)	1.48	35.7%
Actual (Our model)	3.54	100%

7. Conclusions

The case study of 2021 has been used to study the performance of our supply chain model. Through our proposed model, we demonstrated that different risk mitigation strategies are crucial in order to successfully deliver the vaccines worldwide. In the absence of such measures, it is observed that the demand is not met, and the low- and middle-income countries are suffering the most. To handle various disruptions, a two-stage scenario-based MILP s programming model is presented. Scaling up the production facilities, coordinating donations, contracting 3PL to manage sudden transportation requirements are considered as the mitigation (i.e., resilience-enhancing) strategies. Furthermore, the COVAX facility also should invest in restoring the disrupted capacitates. The model demonstrates how COVAX could have battled various challenges it faced during 2021, and these strategies should be employed for 2022 to effectively deliver the vaccines to all the countries. Future work is to use this model and determine the strategies that COVAX should adopt for 2022 to meet the delivery promises. The future work is to forecast the dynamics of the virus in different countries through compartmental modeling and determine the vaccine demand to attain herd immunity and use our model to plan the production and distribution of the vaccines.

References

1. World Health Organization. "Fair allocation mechanism for COVID-19 vaccines through the COVAX Facility." Final working version-9 September (2020).
2. ECCLESTON-TURNER, M. A. R. K., and Harry Upton. "International Collaboration to Ensure Equitable Access to Vaccines for COVID-19: The ACT-Accelerator and the COVAX Facility." The Milbank Quarterly (2021).
3. Golan, Maureen S., et al. "The vaccine supply chain: a call for resilience analytics to support COVID-19 vaccine production and distribution." COVID-19: Systemic Risk and Resilience. Springer, Cham, 2021. 389-437.
4. Georgiadis, Georgios P., and Michael C. Georgiadis. "Optimal planning of the COVID-19 vaccine supply chain." Vaccine 39.37 (2021): 5302-5312.
5. DeRoo, Sarah Schaffer, Natalie J. Pudalov, and Linda Y. Fu. "Planning for a COVID-19 vaccination program." Jama 323.24 (2020): 2458-2459.
6. Burki, Talha Khan. "Challenges in the rollout of COVID-19 vaccines worldwide." The Lancet Respiratory Medicine 9.4 (2021): e42-e43.
7. Spadaro, Benedetta. "COVID-19 vaccines: challenges and promises of trials, manufacturing and allocation of doses." (2020): FDD.
8. Asundi, Archana, Colin O'Leary, and Nahid Bhadelia. "Global COVID-19 vaccine inequity: The scope, the impact, and the challenges." Cell Host & Microbe 29.7 (2021): 1036-1039

Proceedings of the 14th International Symposium on Process Systems Engineering – PSE 2021+
June 19-23, 2022, Kyoto, Japan
http://dx.doi.org/10.1016/B978-0-323-85159-6.50101-9

Optimal Liquefied Natural Gas (LNG) Annual Delivery Program Reflecting both Supplier and Customer Perspectives

Dnyanesh Deshpande[a], Mohd Shahrukh[a], Rajagopalan Srinivasan[a*], I.A Karimi[b]

[a]*Department of Chemical Engineering, Indian Institute of Technology Madras, Chennai - 600036, India*
[b]*Department of Chemical & Biomolecular Engineering, National University of Singapore, 119077, Singapore*
raj@iitm.ac.in

Abstract

Liquefied Natural Gas (LNG) is a convenient way of storing and transporting natural gas. Traditionally, LNG is traded via Long Term Contract (LTC) signed between the suppliers and the customers. But recently share of the spot market has increased significantly. This makes the development of a suitable delivery strategy of LNG shipments complex for the supplier. Therefore, the supplier develops an annual schedule of delivery for the upcoming year known as the Annual Delivery Program (ADP). In this paper, we present an ADP planning problem for an LNG supplier. A mixed-integer linear programming (MILP) model is developed with the objective to minimize the cost of delivering LNG shipments.

Keywords: Liquefied Natural Gas, Annual Delivery Program, Scheduling, Mixed Integer Linear Programming

1. Introduction

The demand for natural gas is increasing rapidly due to environmental considerations. However, transportation of natural gas from producing regions to customers around the world via pipelines is economically unattractive. Therefore, natural gas is liquefied to -162 °C at atmospheric pressure to form Liquefied Natural Gas (LNG), making it convenient for storage and transportation. Traditionally, LNG is traded through Long Term Contract (LTC) signed between supplier and customer. But due to an increase in the number of suppliers and customers around the world, a spot market for LNG trade has emerged in recent years.

LTCs guarantee supply security to the customers but they do not offer flexibility due to the presence of strict clauses in the contract (Shahrukh et al.,2021). Ensuring customer satisfaction and their reliability on the supplier in future is crucial. This motivates the supplier to come up with a strategy of delivering LNG shipments to its customers at the accepted delivery dates throughout the planning horizon. In order to plan for the LNG shipment deliveries, the supplier creates an Annual Delivery Program (ADP). An ADP is the list of scheduled voyages with information about the long-term contract served, ships nominated to serve the contracts, customer terminals nominated to receive delivery, date of ship loading etc. In this paper, we present an ADP planning problem with an objective to create an ADP which satisfies customers' demands at minimum cost.

1.1. Literature Survey

The ADP planning problem has been thoroughly studied in the literature. Stålhane et al. (2011) developed a Mixed Integer Programming (MIP) formulation and a construction and improvement heuristic (CIH) to solve the problem. Rakke et al. (2011) developed a rolling horizon heuristic (RHH) for creating ADPs. Andersson et al. (2010) solved two problems, one for a supplier of LNG and one for a vertically integrated company. Mathematical models for each problem are presented, and solution methods are discussed, but the computational results are not given. Mutlu et al. (2015) presented an ADP planning problem that allowed split delivery for delivering LNG shipments. The proposed model was computationally very expensive to solve. So, they proposed an efficient vehicle routing heuristic (VRH) which gave cost-effective solutions and outperformed commercial optimizers.

Generally, ADP planning problems in literature have focused on inventory and berth management at the supplier's terminal. They have considered that the supplier can deliver only one grade of LNG to a customer. These models are unable to satisfy customers' demands as they allow under-supply. Therefore, in this paper, we present a MILP model for the ADP planning problem considering inventory and berth management at the customer terminals, allowing the supplier to produce and deliver multiple grades of LNG and satisfying customer's demands with a reasonable over-supply.

2. Problem Description

The ADP planning problem has a supplier of LNG. The supplier produces multiple grades of LNG at a variable production rate. The supplier serves multiple LTC customers. Every customer has a slot-wise demand for one or more than one grade of LNG. When the supplier delivers more than the demand, the customer is said to be over-supplied. The supplier is penalized for over-supplying the customer and ensures that the over-supply is minimal. The supplier owns a heterogeneous fleet of ships. The supplier takes decisions regarding the determination of the production rate of every LNG grade and scheduling of the fleet. Scheduling of fleet involves taking decisions regarding loading and maintenance of ships. Loading of a ship takes place at a berth of the supplier terminal. Maintenance of ships is carried out at a maintenance terminal located near the supplier terminal. After maintenance, the ship undergoes a purge and cool down operation at the berth of the supplier's terminal. The objective of the problem is to create an ADP to satisfy the customer demands at minimum cost. The cost incurred by the supplier in delivering LNG shipments is the sum of transportation and penalty cost.

The sets of LTC customers, ship capacities in the heterogeneous fleet, planning horizon, initial inventory at the supplier and customer terminals, minimum and maximum storage capacities at the supplier and customer terminals, minimum and maximum production rates for each grade of LNG are known. Transportation time, slot wise demand at all customer terminals, time window and duration of maintenance, transportation cost of ships in \$ per slot and penalty in \$ per m^3 of oversupply to a customer are also known.

3. Mathematical Model

3.1. Modelling inventory and berth management at the customer terminals

The proposed model for ADP planning problem considers inventory and berth management at the supplier terminal, production of multiple LNG grades, over-supply and maintenance of ships. These aspects were modelled based on the models developed by Andersson et al. (2010), Rakke et al. (2011), Stålhane et al. (2011) in literature. But models in literature do not consider inventory and berth management at the customer terminals and delivery of multiple grades of LNG. For modelling inventory and berth management, we consider a set of customer terminals LTC (LTC = 1, 2, ...C) with every terminal having demand for one or multiple grades of LNG. D_{tgc} is the slot-wise demand of grade g LNG at customer $c's$ terminal. Inventory for every grade of LNG is stored in separate storage tanks. At every customer terminal c inventory level in storage tanks is monitored for every grade g at the end of every slot t and is denoted by I_{cgt}. So, inventory balance at customer terminals is written as follows:

$$I_{cgt} = I_{cg(t-1)} - D_{tgc} + \sum_{v \in V} C_v . x_{cgv(t-TT_{cv}-1)} \quad \forall c \in LTC, g \in G, t \in T \tag{1}$$

where x_{cgvt} is equal to 1 if ship v loads at the start of slot t to serve customer c having demand for grade g LNG and C_v is the capacity of ship v in m^3

The inventory of each grade of LNG must be maintained between the minimum and the maximum storage capacities of the terminal. This is ensured by writing the following constraint:

$$I_{cg}^{min} \leq I_{cgt} \leq I_{cg}^{max} \qquad \forall\ c \in LTC, g \in G,\ t \in T \tag{2}$$

The entire fleet of ships is divided into Q-Flex and Q-Max ships based on their capacities. Q-Flex and Q- Max ships are allotted different berths for unloading at the customer terminal. Now every customer terminal has a fixed number of berths available for unloading of ships. So, the number of ships unloading in every slot should not exceed the number of berths available at the customer terminal. This is called as the berth capacity constraint and is modelled as follows:

$$\sum_{g \in G} \sum_{v \in QF} x_{cgv(t-TT_{cv}-1)} \leq B1_c \quad \forall\ c \in LTC,\ t \in T \tag{3}$$

$$\sum_{g \in G} \sum_{v \in QM} x_{cgv(t-TT_{cv}-1)} \leq B2_c \quad \forall\ c \in LTC, t \in T \tag{4}$$

Here QF and QM are the set of Q-Flex and Q-Max ships in the heterogeneous fleet and $B1_c$ and $B2_c$ are the number of berths available for unloading of Q-flex and Q-max ships at customer terminal c respectively.

Every ship can serve a single customer in a given voyage. We call this the regular delivery constraint. It is modelled as follows:

$$\sum_{c\in LTC}\sum_{g\in G}\sum_{k=t}^{t+2TT_{pv}+1} x_{cgvk} \leq 1 \quad \forall\, p \in LTC, v \in V, t \in T \tag{5}$$

Whenever the supplier delivers LNG more than the customer's demand, the customer is said to be oversupplied. Oversupply of grade g LNG for customer c is denoted by os_{cg} and is modelled as follows:

$$os_{cg} = \sum_{v\in V}\sum_{t\in T} C_v . x_{cgv(t-TT_{cv}-1)} - \sum_{t\in T} D_{tgc} \quad \forall\, c \in LTC, g \in G \tag{6}$$

Over-supply should be non – negative. This is ensured by the following constraint:

$$os_{cg} \geq 0 \;\; \forall\; c \in LTC, g \in G \tag{7}$$

3.2. Objective Function

The objective is to minimize the cost incurred by the supplier in delivering LNG shipments to its customers over the planning horizon. The cost incurred by the supplier is the sum of transportation cost and penalty cost. CR is the transportation cost of ships in \$ per slot, TT_{cv} is the one-way transportation time in slots required for ship v to reach customer $c's$ terminal, P is the penalty in \$ per m^3 of oversupply to the customer. Then the objective function is formulated as follows:

$$\begin{aligned} Cost = &\sum_{c\in LTC}\sum_{g\in G}\sum_{v\in V}\sum_{t\in H} CR * (2TT_{cv} + 1) * x_{cgvt} \\ &+ \sum_{c\in LTC}\sum_{g\in G} P * os_{cg} \end{aligned} \tag{8}$$

4. Results

4.1. Illustrative Example

The example presented in this section considers a supplier of LNG serving two LTC customers. The supplier has a heterogenous fleet of 12 ships. The supplier produces two grades of LNG, namely Lean LNG (LNGL - G1) and Rich LNG (LNGR – G2). The production rate of each grade of LNG is known and varies between known limits. The supplier serves 2 LTC customers. In this example, we have taken that customer 1 (C1) has demand for both the grades, customer 2 (C2) has demand for LNGL only. The planning horizon is of 60 days. The entire planning horizon is divided into 60 uniform slots having a duration of 1 day. The duration for both loading and unloading of ships at the supplier and customer terminals is considered as 1 slot. The chartering rate considered for evaluating the transportation cost for delivering LNG is $ 80,000 per slot. The penalty per m^3 of oversupply is taken as $25.The transportation and penalty cost incurred by the supplier over the planning horizon is $37,760,000 and $1,79,000, respectively. The supplier delivers total 15 LNG shipments out of which 10 shipments are delivered to C1(5 shipments of LNGL and 5 shipments of LNGR) while 5 shipments are delivered to C2. Table 1 shows the ship schedule obtained by solving the illustrative example. The production rate for both the grades of LNG is almost constant over the planning horizon. The supplier operates at the upper limit of production rate for LNGL (G1) and then operates at the lower limit while for LNGR (G2) it almost operates at the lower limit. The supplier is able to satisfy the LTC customers demand with less than 1 % oversupply. The percentage over-supply for C1 for LNGL and LNGR is 0.2 % and 0.13%, respectively and that for C2 for LNGL is 0.67 %. The LNG shipment deliveries are fairly evenly spread over the planning horizon, which maintains the inventory at the customer terminals within the operational limits.

Table 1:Table giving the ship schedule for both the customers over the planning horizon

Customer	Grade of LNG	Ship Number	Loading Slot	Volume of Shipment (m^3)
C1	LNGR	12	1	259,789
C2	LNGL	8	1	181,454
C2	LNGL	11	3	252,597
C1	LNGL	9	4	237,919
C1	LNGR	10	5	244,826
C1	LNGR	4	6	157,154
C2	LNGL	7	11	173,859
C1	LNGL	5	15	163,395
C1	LNGL	6	28	168,550
C2	LNGL	8	32	181,454
C1	LNGR	1	37	138,270
C2	LNGL	12	39	259,789
C1	LNGL	11	41	252,597
C1	LNGR	10	42	244,826
C1	LNGL	9	44	237,919

4.2. Computational Results

The illustrative example was implemented in IBM ILOG CPLEX Optimization Studio 12.10.0 on a Dell Workstation with Intel(R) Xeon(R) Silver 4114 CPU@2.20 GHz with 32 GB RAM. While solving the example, we have considered a relative convergence criterion of 0.5 % with a global time limit of 86,400 seconds. Also, we have considered Depth First Search (DFS) as the node selection strategy and enabled solution polishing after a relative gap of 10 %. It took 31.82 seconds to solve the 2-month example with a relative gap of 0.47 %. The example had 3,668 binary and 490 continuous variables, 3,578 constraints, and the optimal cost obtained was $ 37,939,000.

5. Conclusions

In this paper, we present an ADP planning problem for a supplier of LNG. The objective of the problem was to develop a ship schedule which would satisfy LTC customers' demand at minimum cost. In this regard, a mixed integer linear programming (MILP) model is developed. ADP planning problems in literature did not focus on inventory and berth management at the customer's terminal which may lead to the violation of customer inventory resources which in effect will lead to a change in the developed ADP. Hence, our model reduces the probability of this change in ADP by considering customer inventory and berth availability. This consideration of resources at customer terminals also leads to a reduction in oversupply as compared to models proposed in the literature. Reduction in oversupply reduces the penalty cost incurred by the supplier. These incentives of our model are explained by solving an illustrative example, and the computational results of the example are also reported. In the future, we aim to develop an ADP considering spot market sales along with LTCs.

References

F. Mutlu, M. K. Msakni, H. Yildiz, E. Sönmez, and S. Pokharel, "A comprehensive annual delivery program for upstream liquefied natural gas supply chain," *European Journal of Operational Research*, vol. 250, no. 1, pp. 120–130, Apr. 2016.

H. Andersson, M. Christiansen, and K. Fagerholt, "Transportation Planning and Inventory Management in the LNG Supply Chain," in *Energy, Natural Resources and Environmental Economics*, E. Bjørndal, M. Bjørndal, P. M. Pardalos, and M. Rönnqvist, Eds. Berlin, Heidelberg: Springer, 2010, pp. 427–439.

J. G. Rakke *et al.*, "A rolling horizon heuristic for creating a liquefied natural gas annual delivery program," *Transportation Research Part C: Emerging Technologies*, vol. 19, no. 5, pp. 896–911, Aug. 2011.

M. Shahrukh, R. Srinivasan, and I. A. Karimi, "Optimal Procurement of Liquefied Natural Gas Cargos from Long-Term Contracts and Spot Market through Mathematical Programming," Ind. Eng. Chem. Res., vol. 60, no. 9, pp. 3658–3669, Mar. 2021.

M. Stålhane, J. G. Rakke, C. R. Moe, H. Andersson, M. Christiansen, and K. Fagerholt, "A construction and improvement heuristic for a liquefied natural gas inventory routing problem," *Computers & Industrial Engineering*, vol. 62, no. 1, pp. 245–255, Feb. 2012.

Proceedings of the 14th International Symposium on Process Systems Engineering – PSE 2021+
June 19-23, 2022, Kyoto, Japan
http://dx.doi.org/10.1016/B978-0-323-85159-6.50102-0

The Waste-to-Resource Game: Informed Decision-Making for Plastic Waste Transformers

Fabian Lechtenberg[a*], Antonio Espuña[a], Moisès Graells[a]

[a] *Department of Chemical Engineering, Universitat Politècnica de Catalunya, Barcelona 08019, Spain*
[*]fabian.lechtenberg@upc.edu

Abstract

Upgrading waste to recovered resources requires a (chemical) transformation process. Thus, waste transformers, waste providers and potential customers of such added-value resources, are essential actors in the game of circular economy. Hence, this work presents a decision-making framework addressing the definition and solution of multi-leader-follower games to find bargaining outcomes between these actors. The potential of the approach is illustrated through the case of a transformer who operates a pyrolysis process producing char, oil and gas fractions from plastic waste. A novel process model is used to aid the agents in making informed decisions. Results reveal that satisfactory natural bargaining outcomes may not exist in the interaction between the agents. Hence, the need of an authority altering the rules of the game and ensuring win-win situations is stressed.

Keywords: Plastic Waste; Pyrolysis; Game Theory; Surrogate Model; Decision-Making

1. Introduction

Rethinking waste products as suboptimally allocated resources is an essential part of sustainable development. Taking advantage of this unused potential to enable circularity in the supply chains often needs a waste transformer that performs the upgrading of wastes to added-value materials. Multiple objectives need to be considered accordingly. However, the fact that these objectives represent agents that are competing and making decisions based on their individual profit cannot be overlooked. Thus, the PSE community has adopted Game Theory as a powerful complement to multi-objective optimization and derive realistic bargaining outcomes (Avraamidou et al., 2020).
This work studies the bargaining process between a Waste Provider (WP), a Waste Transformer (WT) and a set of potential customers, and develops a strategy to obtain satisfactory situations in which no objective can be improved by unilaterally changing a decision. To that end, multi-leader-follower games (Aussel and Senvsson, 2020) are defined and solved through their corresponding bi-level optimization problems (Beykal et al., 2021).
Thus, this work proposes (1) a general modelling framework for finding "equilibrium" bargaining outcomes in which waste transformers are integrated to extend the lifespan of a product (resource) or to close a supply chain and (2) a process model for the pyrolysis process for plastic conversion. The latter is related to the case study, dealing with the conversion of plastic waste into added-value products. The knowledge captured in this model discloses the existence of satisfactory bargaining outcomes between the waste transformer and its customers under some restricted conditions.

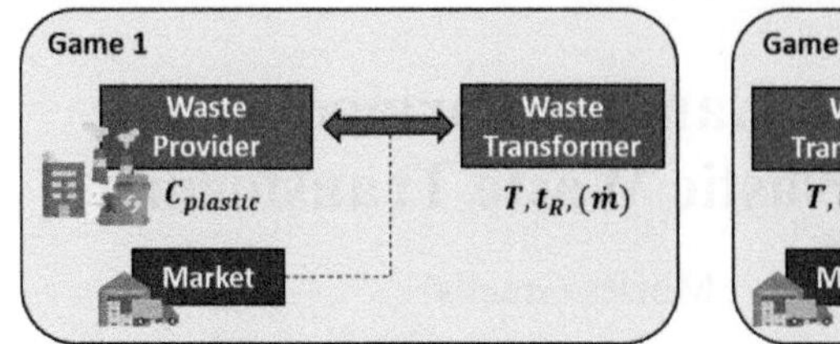

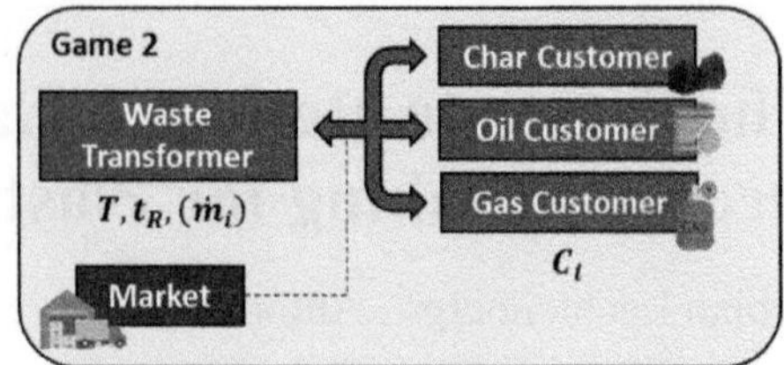

Figure 1. Bargaining interaction between the considered stakeholders in this work: Waste Provider (WP), Waste Transformer (WT) and customers.

2. Problem Statement

The problem and system boundaries considered in this contribution are illustrated in Fig. 1 and can be summarized as follows. Given:

- A Waste Provider (WP) producing, collecting and/or pre-treating plastic waste
- A Waste Transformer (WT) that has the technology and facilities for processing waste into added-value resources (e.g. the WT is willing to buy the pre-treated plastic waste and transform it into valuable products such as char, oil and gas)
- A set of customers (CUST) that buy the products produced by the WT
- A set of alternative strategies that can be taken by each of these agents.

Find optimal strategy sets of the agents and bargaining outcomes. All agents intend to maximize an economic objective. Here, two sequential Stackelberg competition scenarios are considered that, once solved, yield optimal pricing strategies and operational schemes. The pricing strategy, if existent, can be understood as the "equilibrium cost" of plastic waste and added-value products, which is conditioned by the process model of the WT and the market conditions.

3. Bargaining Game

The bargaining between WT, WP and customers is expressed as multi-leader follower games. A general form of the corresponding bi-level structure is given below:

$$\begin{aligned} &\max_x f_i^{leader}(x,y) \\ &\quad \text{s.t.} \quad g_i^{leader}(x,y) \geq 0 \qquad\qquad i \in I^{leaders} \\ &\qquad\quad y \; solves \; \max_y f_j^{follower}(x,y) \\ &\qquad\qquad\quad \text{s.t.} \quad g_j^{follower}(x,y) \geq 0 \qquad j \in J^{followers} \end{aligned} \tag{OP1}$$

The objective function of the WP is the maximization of its own profit:

$$f^{WP} = \dot{m}_{Waste}^{WP} \cdot C_{Waste} \tag{1}$$

With $\dot{m}_{Waste}^{WP}$ being the mass bought by the WT and C_{Waste} the price of the waste proposed by the WP. The objective function of the customers can be similarly expressed through the maximization of the savings over buying from the market:

$$f_k^{CUST} = \dot{m}_k \cdot (C_k^{market} - C_k) \qquad k = \text{customers} \tag{2}$$

Where $\dot{m}_k$ is the amount of product the WT sells to the customers and C_k is the price proposed by the customers. Since the amount $\dot{m}_k$ depends on C_k, the customers must strategize on how to choose a price that maximizes their benefit.

Finally, the objective of the WT is expressed as the maximization of its revenue:

$$f^{WT} = \dot{m}_{Waste}^{WP} \cdot \left(\sum_{k} \eta^{k} \cdot C_{k} - C_{Waste}^{WP} \right) \tag{3}$$

Here, η^k is the conversion of plastic waste into added-value products k. Utility costs (electricity, pumping ...) could be included. The limits on the decision variables (strategies) and other constraints are stated in $g_{i/j}(x, y)$. The possible leader-follower relations in this three-actor system are summarized in Tab. 1.

Table 1. Bargaining games constellation

Game	Leader	Follower	Type
1.1	WT	WP	Single-Leader Single-Follower (SLSF)
1.2	WP	WT	Single-Leader Single-Follower (SLSF)
2.1	WT	CUST	Single-Leader Multi-Follower (SLMF)
2.2	CUST	WT	Multi-Leader Single-Follower (MLSF)

4. Pyrolysis Model

For each case (i.e. for each different WT considered), a specific model for the transformation process will be required. This model may be available or may need to be developed. The particular case study addressed in this work corresponds to the chemical upcycling of plastic waste through a pyrolysis process. There are only few models that describe the pyrolysis of plastic waste and those that are available are often limited to a single set of operating conditions. The distribution of pyrolysis products strongly depends on key operating conditions like the residence time and reaction temperature (Miandad et al., 2016). This allows the plant operator to change the operating conditions to maximize the expected value of the product portfolio.

The pyrolysis process model developed herein extends the one presented by Fivga and Dimitriou (2018) through the incorporation of temperature and residence time dependent product yields in the reactor model. The reactor is assumed to be a fluidized bed reactor that can vary the residence time t_R and reaction temperature within some limited bounds by manipulating the recycle stream and the furnace operating conditions. A cyclone acts as solid separator to obtain the char product. The non-recycled gaseous product is cooled down to 25 °C to obtain the oil and gas products. Part of the gas product is burned in a furnace to supply the heat of reaction, so no external fuel is needed to drive the reaction.

In order to be able to evaluate the economic objective function of the WT it is necessary to quantify how much char, oil and gas is produced (η^k). Experimental data for the non-catalytic conversion of polyethylene (PE) waste was taken from Quesada et al. (2019). The authors report oil and char yield of experiments performed at 15 different temperature, residence time and heating rate combinations. Based on this data, a set of metamodels is trained to predict oil and char yields at the non-measured conditions. It is found that Gaussian Process Regressor (GPR) models and second- and third-degree polynomials exhibit desirable prediction and interpolation capabilities, exceeding those of the ANFIS and second-degree polynomials considered by Quesada et al. (2019).

For a fixed mass flow $\dot{m}^{plastic}$ the oil and char products can be directly calculated from the yield correlations $\eta^{char}(t_R, T)$ and $\eta^{oil}(t_R, T)$ described by the trained metamodels. Note, that the heating rate dependence has been omitted here due to the small influence

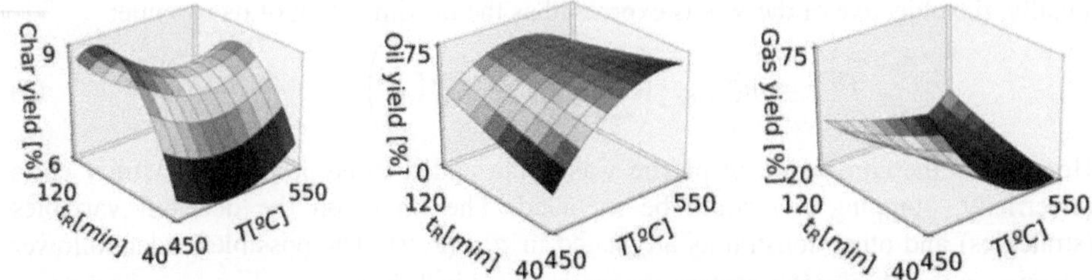

Figure 2. Char, oil and gas yield response surfaces (3rd degree polynomials).

on the yields. A similar correlation for the gaseous product has been obtained from repeated simulation of the flowsheet at different operating conditions. See Fig. 2 for the response surfaces.

By fixing the reference enthalpy of the plastic inlet, it is imposed that at nominal operating conditions (500 °C, 80 min) the heat of reaction equals 1316 kJ/mol (Fivga and Dimitriou, 2018). Following the same authors' example, it is assumed that the pyrolysis product can be sufficiently well represented by carbon and six selected hydrocarbons in the range of C_2-C_{30}. Then, a first-order decomposition (Eq. 4) was assumed and the kinetic constants were fitted to include the reported compositions.

$$\text{Plastic} \xrightarrow{k1} \text{n-C30} \xrightarrow{k2} \text{n-C25} \xrightarrow{k3} \text{n-C18} \xrightarrow{k4} \text{n-C14} \xrightarrow{k5} \text{n-C8} \xrightarrow{k6} \text{C2} \tag{4}$$

By doing so, a lookup table for the reactor outlet composition is obtained correlating the pyrolysis product composition with the temperature and residence time.

5. Case Study

We consider an operational problem of a plant that has been designed for treating 4 t/h of municipal PE plastic waste. The amount bought by the WT is not part of its strategy. The bounds on the prices proposed by the WP are lower bounded ($C_{plastic}^{low}$) by the cost that he would usually pay/receive for treating its waste and upper bounded ($C_{plastic}^{up}$) by the cost of virgin PE or the revenue of the highest value product of the WP. The prices that can be proposed by the customers are bounded ($C_k^{low/up}$) by some lower bound that is subject of investigation (> 0 €/kg) and the market price of the virgin raw material. To illustrate the effect of different (ratios of) values of the products we arbitrarily chose their market prices to be equal at 1 €/kg. The operational limits of the WT (T, t_R) stem from the range used to train the metamodels (450 – 550 °C, 40 – 120 min) and can be justified by the kinetics of the reaction and technical limitations of the reactor.

6. Results and Discussion

The bi-level problems can be solved through various approaches such as multi-parametric programming or data-driven optimization (Beykal et al., 2021). Since the complexity of the problem strongly depends on the configuration and constraints considered, here, different strategies are used for each game.

The solutions to games 1.1 and 2.1 are straightforward: The follower's problem (WP and customers) comprise a linear problem with box constraints on the decision variable which can be substituted by its KKT optimality conditions. Since the follower has no conjecture about the leader's decision, its safest bet is to decide on the price that would maximize its objective for a fixed $\dot{m}_i$. In the case of the WP this limit is the market price raw plastic price $C_{plastic}^{up}$ and for the customers the low bound C_k^{low} (see Tab. 3).

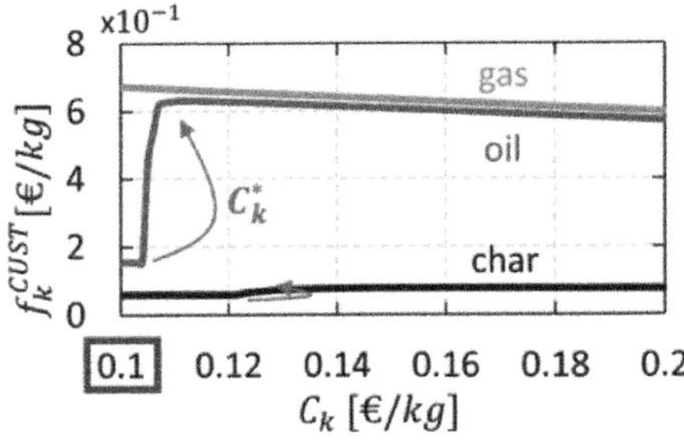

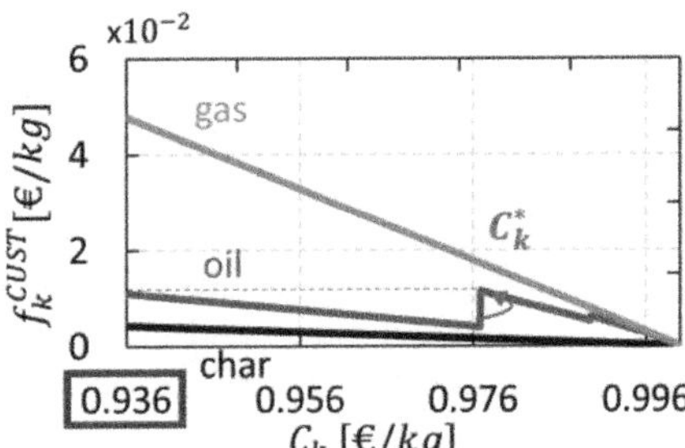

Figure 3. (left) Customer objectives depending on unilateral changes of proposed prices at C_k^{low}= 0.1 €/kg. (right) Customers do not improve their objectives by deviating from C_k^{low}=0.936 €/kg.

It has to be acknowledged that these solutions cannot be considered satisfactory. The WT would not buy the waste plastic at the same price as virgin plastic and it would also not sell the products for 0 €/kg.

When changing the role of the leader and the follower (WT as follower), it is assumed that the leader has full knowledge about how the follower will react to its decisions. In the case of game 1.2 this knowledge does not add any additional value to the bargaining since we assume that the exchanged mass is fixed and not part of the follower's strategy. As a result, the WT has no way of influencing the WP's decision, leading him to choose again the highest possible price. Neither game 1.1 nor 1.2 yield satisfactory bargaining outcomes. A potential authority setting rules or redirecting taxes and/or incentives could resolve this situation (e.g. by introducing an incentive that stems from the avoided cost of municipal waste treatment).

In the case of game 2.2 the knowledge of the customers about the WTs reaction can be exploited by them to make an informed decision on the price that they propose. Fig. 3 (left) illustrates how changing the proposed price influences the agent's objective. It can be seen that when every agent proposes the same price (0.1 €/kg) the WT will operate at those conditions with the overall highest yield (least amount of gas burned). This situation favours the gas customer. However, the oil and char customers can react by proposing a slightly higher price that convinces the WT to operate at different conditions and produce more oil or char respectively.

The bi-level game was reformulated into an NLP problem following the description by Leyffer and Munson (2010) and solved using BARON in GAMS. Not all properties (e.g. convexity of follower's problem) are fulfilled to qualify the solution as an equilibrium point. Thus, a numerical test has been conducted. It is found that, due to the specific characteristics of the WT production process (model), a strict mathematical equilibrium point only exists when the lower bound (C_k^{low}) is forced to be ≥ 0.936 €/kg for all agents. In this situation, any bid from the char or oil customers will not improve their objective despite the WT changing its operating conditions (C_k^*) (Fig 3. (right)).

Table 2. Summary of equilibrium solutions in the studied bargaining games.

Game	Leader	Follower
1.1	$T^{opt}, t_R^{opt} = f(C_{plastic}^{up})$	$C_{plastic} = C_{plastic}^{up}$
1.2	$C_{plastic} = C_{plastic}^{up}$	$T^{opt}, t_R^{opt} = f(C_{plastic}^{up})$
2.1	$T^{opt}(C_k^{low}), t_R^{opt}(C_k^{low})$	$C_k = C_k^{low}$
2.2	$T^{opt}(C_k^{eq*}), t_R^{opt}(C_k^{eq*})$	$C_k = C_k^{eq*}$ (Fig 3)

This points again towards the need of an authority that sets the initially arbitrarily defined bound (C_k^{low}) to this "forced equilibrium" bound. The solution could be regarded as satisfactory from all agents' points of view: The WT can sell its recovered added value products at a price slightly below the market price of virgin or fossil-sourced materials while the customers win by paying less than the market price.
Table 2 summarizes the results of the studied case. These results are conditioned by the underlying process model and market assumptions and can be very different for other cases (e.g. different chemical recycling process, recovery of used solvents …).

7. Conclusions

The presented work introduces a general bargaining framework between waste transformers, waste providers and customers of the added-value materials. Applying this framework to a chemical recycling of waste plastic case study reveals that one-to-one bargaining between a waste provider and a waste transformer leads to outcomes that are not acceptable for either of the agents. The interaction between waste transformer and customers neither yields acceptable results if the customers choose their minimum acceptable price too ambitiously. Both situations point towards the need of an authority that sets the rules of the games so that win-win situations are enforced, despite the agents' effort to maximize their own profit. The knowledge captured in the proposed WT's process model enables the determination of a reasonable lower bound on the customers' pricing strategies. Future work should explicitly consider such an authority in the modelling framework. Moreover, this authority should follow strategies that focus not only on economic but also environmental and social sustainability.

Acknowledgements: Financial support from the Spanish "Ministerio de Ciencia e Innovación" and the European Regional Development Fund, both funding the Project CEPI (PID2020-116051RB-I00) is fully acknowledged. F.L. gratefully acknowledges the Universitat Politècnica de Catalunya for the financial support of his predoctoral grant FPU-UPC, with the collaboration of Banco de Santander.

References

D. Aussel, A. Svensson, 2020, A Short State of the Art on Multi-Leader-Follower Games, Bilevel Optimization, 53-76

S. Avraamidou, S.G. Baratsas, Y. Tian, E.N. Pistikopoulos, 2020, Circular Economy - A challenge and an opportunity for Process Systems Engineering, Computers & Chemical Engineering, 133

B. Beykal, S. Avraamidou, E.N. Pistikopoulos, 2021, Bi-level Mixed-Integer Data-Driven Optimization of Integrated Planning and Scheduling Problems, Computer Aided Chemical Engineering , 50, 1707-1713

R. Miandad, M. Barakat, A. Aburiazaira, M. Rehan, A. Nizami, 2016, Catalytic pyrolysis of plastic waste: A review, Process Safety and Environmental Protection, 120, 822-838

A. Fivga, I. Dimitriou, 2018, Pyrolysis of plastic waste for production of heavy fuel substitute: A techno-economic assessment, Energy, 149, 865-874

L. Quesada, A. Pérez, V. Godoy, F.J. Peula, M. Calero, G. Blázquez, 2019, Optimization of the pyrolysis process of a plastic waste to obtain a liquid fuel using different mathematical models, Energy Conversion and Management, 188, 19-26

S. Leyffer, T. Munson, 2010, Solving Multi-Leader-Common Follower Games, Optimisation Methods & Software, 601-623

Proceedings of the 14th International Symposium on Process Systems Engineering – PSE 2021+
June 19-23, 2022, Kyoto, Japan
http://dx.doi.org/10.1016/B978-0-323-85159-6.50103-2

Implications of Optimal BECCS Supply Chains on Absolute Sustainability

Valentina Negri[a], Gonzalo Guillén-Gosálbez[a*]

[a]*Institute for Chemical and Bioengineering, Department of Chemistry and Applied Biosciences, ETH Zürich, Vladimir-Prelog-Weg 1, 8093 Zürich, Switzerland*
gonzalo.guillen.gosalbez@chem.ethz.ch

Abstract

Carbon dioxide removal technologies are expected to play a decisive role in meeting the target of 1.5 °C, yet their broad sustainability implications remain unclear. Among those, bioenergy with carbon capture and storage (BECCS) has attracted growing interest, as it can remove CO_2 while providing energy. This study presents an optimization approach to design and evaluate BECCS supply chains based on absolute sustainability criteria. We analyze the solution to a minimum cost scenario removing 0.61 $GtCO_2$ in the European Union, assessing the impacts with the Environmental Footprint method and interpreting the results using the planetary boundaries linked to the United Nations Sustainable Development Goals. We find that BECCS could indeed be implemented within the safe operating space but would consume large amounts of global ecological shares due to burden-shifting on some categories.

Keywords: bioenergy with carbon capture and storage, supply chain, optimization, planetary boundaries, Sustainable Development Goals.

Introduction

The IPCC pathways that limit the global temperature rise by 2100 to well below 2 °C above pre-industrial levels indicate that a large deployment of negative emissions technologies and practices (NETPs) is required to compensate for the emissions from hard-to-abate sectors (IPCC, 2018).

Bioenergy with carbon capture and storage (BECCS) has been identified as the most promising nature-based NETPs because it contributes to CO_2 removal (CDR) while providing a clean, reliable energy source. BECCS, defined as the coupling of bioenergy production with carbon capture and storage (CCS) (Canadell and Schulze, 2014), has been extensively studied in the literature from a techno-economic standpoint.

From an environmental perspective, BECCS has proven to have the capacity to be implemented at a large scale and contribute substantially to achieving the CDR required to meet the Paris Agreement goal. Nevertheless, it depletes resources such as water and land (Heck et al., 2018), ultimately competing with food production (van Vuuren et al., 2018). The severity of these impacts can be assessed following a life cycle assessment (LCA) approach. However, standard LCA studies lack reference values to interpret the results and, consequently, they provide limited insights into the broad implications of deploying NETPs at a large scale.

In recent years, absolute sustainability assessments based on LCA principles were put forward to quantify impacts relative to the planet's carrying capacity. Such methods are based on the planetary boundaries (PB) concept (Rockström et al., 2009), which defines a set of biophysical limits of the Earth system that should never be surpassed to operate our planet safely. Recently, Sala et al. (2020) built on existing literature to map 16

indicators of the Environmental Footprint (EF) method to five Sustainable Development Goals (SDGs). Despite sustainability assessments are emerging in the literature, especially for what concerns supply chains (SCs) (Mota et al., 2013 and 2017, Barbosa-Póvoa, 2009), their application to CDR technologies is at the very beginning.
In this contribution, we quantify the performance of BECCS on five SDGs, previously studied by qualitative approaches alone (Honegger et al., 2020 for CDR options in general and Smith et al., 2019 for land-based solutions in particular).

Methods

In a previous work (Negri et al., 2021), we presented a highly detailed BECCS SC model (NETCOM, Negative Emissions Technologies COoperative Model) that identifies the optimal SC configuration in the European Union (EU) for a net global yearly CDR target retrieved from Peters and Geden (2017). The model includes all EU Member States as of 2018 (28) and assumes full cooperation among the countries to meet the climate target. Following a life cycle optimization approach, the model optimizes costs, emissions and impacts on the Recipe 2016 endpoints. The input data are given specifically for the five echelons of the SC included in NETCOM, connected by transportation. They comprise unitary costs, crop yield and carbon intensities, physical limits for biomass cultivation and growth, and environmental impacts.
Here we enlarge the scope of a cost-driven optimization in NETCOM to include a set of metrics that evaluates the impact of deploying BECCS on the PB linked to five SDGs, providing a more detailed picture of the implications of deploying CDR at a large scale on sustainable development. Yet, the model is still a linear programming, which guarantees a global optimum solution.
Figure 1 provides a sketch of the updated NETCOM. This mathematical model consists of mass and energy balances at each stage of the SC and calculates the total cost, emissions and life cycle impacts.

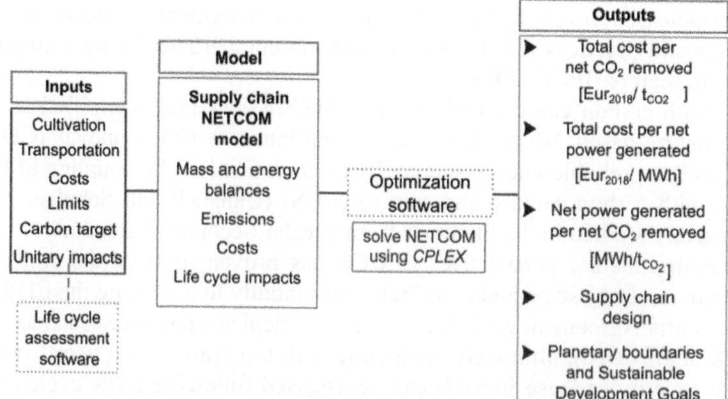

Figure 1. Structure of the NETCOM model. Input data, equations, solver, and outputs included in the model.

To this end, we quantify the total impact on a set of LCA metrics k connected to the PBs and five SDGs, summing up the impacts of all the activities in the SC. Each of them is determined by multiplying an ecovector defined for every activity with the corresponding functional unit, as shown in Eq.(1).

$$\mathrm{eimp_k} = \sum_{i} \mathrm{fu_i}\ \mathrm{IMP_{ik}}\ \forall\, \mathrm{k} \in \mathrm{K} \tag{1}$$

where $\mathrm{eimp_k}$ is the total environmental impact of the BECCS SC on metric k, calculated as the sum of each activity i characterized by its functional unit ($\mathrm{fu_i}$). The ecovector $\mathrm{IMP_{ik}}$ denotes the impact per unit of activity i in each metric k, calculated by implementing a full LCA of the activity in SimaPro v.9.0.0.48.
We refer to the original work (Negri et al.) for detailed information about NETCOM. In the analysis presented hereafter, we update the cost of CO_2 transportation via pipeline to \$ 3.60/tCO_2/250 km from Budinis et al. (2018).

Eq.(1) provides the impact of the SC, which needs to be evaluated relative to the global carrying capacity (i.e., safe operating space). Sala et al. provided life cycle impact assessment-based limits referred to the EF method. The human health-related limits, namely human cancer and non-cancer effects, particulate matter and ionizing radiation, depend on the population and have been updated for 2018. In order to assess the impact of BECCS in the EU, we downscale the global limits by applying an egalitarian-based sharing principle, similarly to Wheeler et al. (2020), obtaining shares of the safe operating space for EU ($\mathrm{PB^{EU}}$). Then, the transgression level ($\mathrm{tl_k}$) of the SC on the metric k is calculated as in Eq.(2).

$$\mathrm{tl_k} = \frac{\mathrm{eimp_k}}{\mathrm{PB_k^{EU}}}\ \forall\, \mathrm{k} \in \mathrm{K} \tag{2}$$

Later, the transgression level is incorporated into the original optimization model's objective function, which includes mass balances, capacity constraints, and other techno-economic and environmental equations of the BECCS SC for each EU country.

The problem, comprising 756,298 variables and 712,381 equations, was solved in GAMS 35.1 with CPLEX on an Intel CoreTM i7-10510U machine at 1.80 GHz and 16 GB RAM running Windows 10.

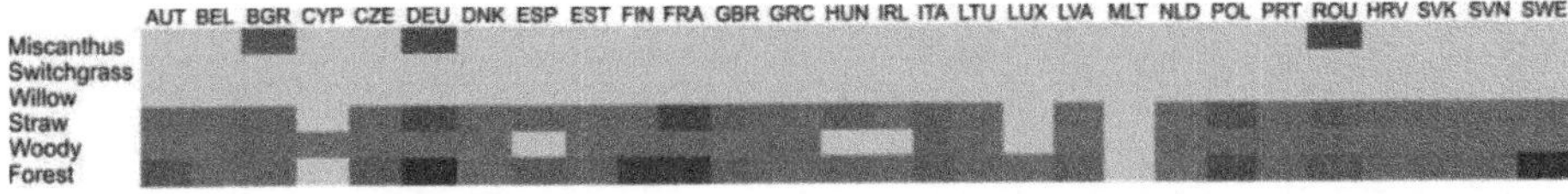

Figure 2. Heat map of the feedstock distribution in the EU-28 countries. The light grey cells represent no use of the corresponding biomass type in that country. Straw, woody and forest residues dominate, while only Miscanthus is selected among the energy crops available.

Results

We ran NETCOM to minimize the total cost of the SC subject to a minimum net removal of 0.61 $GtCO_2$. The minimum cost is 74 billion Euros, with the CDR constraint being active. The largest cost contributions include biomass combustion (58 %), transportation (13 %) and pelleting (10 %). The latter two are also the main contributors to the SC emissions, each one accounting for 30 % of the total amount. The net electricity production is 511 TWh, which accounts for the energy penalty associated with the CCS system at the biomass combustion stage. Here we do not integrate BECCS in the EU energy system; therefore, the electricity generation is considered in the functional unit together with the annual CO_2 removal.

The total feedstock is 562 Mt of biomass, consisting of 88 % of residues (straw cereals, woody and forest) complemented by the energy crop Miscanthus. The latter is cultivated in Bulgaria, Germany and Romania, taking up only 8 % of the total land available in the EU due to its high carbon content (%C in wet biomass) and higher yield compared to other crops. The feedstock distribution is visualized in the heat map in Figure 2. The optimal SC is centralized in Bulgaria and Poland. The solution is driven by the local costs, computed using the purchasing power parity metric, which stand below the European average. The biomass is firstly transported from most EU countries to Bulgaria and Poland mainly by train and, for what concerns the latter, also by ship. At these locations, the biomass is converted into pellets and then combusted. The CO_2 captured at the power generation plants is then distributed in the EU via pipeline and injected in suitable storage sites (depleted carbon fields or aquifers). The transportation of biomass from the land to the processing site and the CO_2 pipeline network are given in Figure 3.

The total impact on the metrics linked to the SDGs is obtained by summing up the impacts in Eq.(1) of the activities modeled in the entire supply chain. Then, we compare the performance of the SC with respect to the safe operating space assigned to the EU (PB^{EU}). We find that none of the PBs is transgressed in the EU, but significant burden-shifting occurs when reducing climate change impacts, as shown in Figure 4. Notably, respiratory inorganics (particulate matter) is the most critical impact, occupying roughly 50 % of the EU safe operating space. Non-cancer human health also shows a 17 % of the EU threshold. The negative implications on these categories can be mainly attributed to the pelleting activity and transportation, which were already identified as hotspots in Negri et al. by performing a standard LCA analysis. We recall that the model relies primarily on residues feedstock, leading to low impacts on water consumption and land use

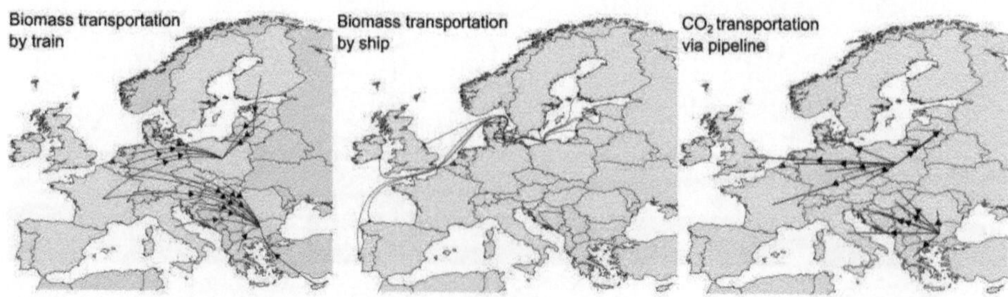

Figure 3. Links of transportation by train, by ship and CO_2 by pipeline among countries in the optimal supply chain. Intra-country connections are not represented.

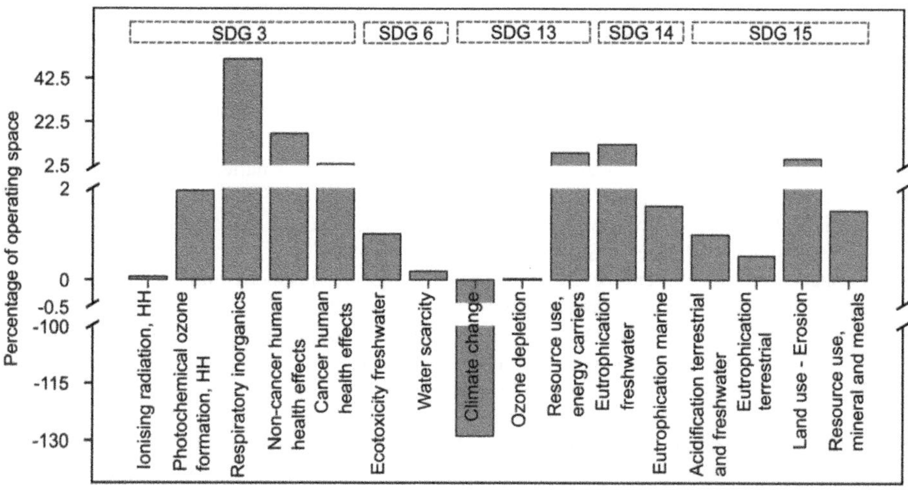

Figure 4. Total impact of the BECCS supply chain on the planetary boundaries considered. At the top we group the impacts per corresponding SDG according to Sala et al.

categories. Nonetheless, eutrophication freshwater also presents a non-negligible burden-shifting, with 14 % of the PB^{EU} occupied.

Contextualizing the results from an SDGs perspective, we find that improving climate action (SDG 13) worsens good health and wellbeing (SDG 3) due to respiratory inorganics and non-cancer human health effects. Similarly, life below water (SDG 14) worsens due to the impact on eutrophication freshwater. Lastly, the most considerable contributions affecting life on land (SDG 15) are land erosion and resource use, minerals and metals.

Conclusions

Here we studied the broad implications of deploying BECCS at a large scale on sustainable development. The minimum cost solution of a BECCS supply chain in the European Union was sought using the NETCOM optimization model, which was enlarged in scope to include planetary boundaries-based metrics. The total cost amounted to 74 billion Euros for a net removal of 0.61 tCO_2 in one year, without considering the credits from a net electricity production of 511 TWh. The optimal solution relies on residues and a centralized supply chain. The environmental assessment showed that the BECCS supply chain could operate within the safe operating space. Yet, delivering negative emissions to mitigate climate change inevitably exacerbates other indicators. This is particularly evident in the case of respiratory inorganics, where the BECCS supply chain took half of the share allocated to the European Union. Note that this safe operating space should be shared among all economic activities, such as chemical production and the energy sector, which raises concerns about the feasibility of BECCS at a large scale. Additionally, given that the yearly CO_2 target is reached using biomass residues, future research should investigate more ambitious removal and different types of feedstock, which could eventually lead to the transgression of the safe operating space. When looking at the effect on the Sustainable Development Goals, negative emissions benefited climate action (SDG 13) at the expense of good health and wellbeing (SDG 3) and life below water (SDG 14). Overall, this work shows that impacts should be quantified from a life cycle perspective and considering absolute limits to interpret the results from a global sustainability viewpoint.

References

A. P. Barbosa-Póvoa, 2009, Sustainable Supply Chains: Key Challenges, Computer Aided Chemical Engineering, 27, 127-132

S. Budinis, S. Krevor, N. Mac Dowell, N. Brandon, A. Hawkes, 2018, An assessment of CCS costs, barriers and potential, Energy Strategy Reviews, 22, 61-81

J. G. Canadell and E. D. Schulze, 2014, Global potential of biospheric carbon management for climate mitigation, Nature Communications, 5,1-12

V. Heck, D. Gerten, W. Lucht, A. Popp, 2018, Biomass-based negative emissions difficult to reconcile with planetary boundaries, Nature Climate Change, 8, 151-155

M. Honegger, A. Michaelowa, J. Roy, 2020, Potential implications of carbon dioxide removal for the sustainable development goals, Climate Policy, 21, 678-698

IPCC, 2018, Mitigation Pathways Compatible with 1.5°C in the Context of Sustainable Development. In Global Warming of 1.5°C. An IPCC Special Report on the impacts of global warming of 1.5°C above pre-industrial levels and related global greenhouse gas emission pathways, in the context of strengthening the global response to the threat of climate change, sustainable development, and efforts to eradicate poverty

B. Mota, M. I. Gomes, A. Barbosa-Póvoa, 2013, Towards supply chain sustainability: balancing costs with environmental and social impacts, Computer Aided Chemical Engineering, 32, 895-900

B. Mota, A. Carvalho, M. I. Gomes, A. Barbosa-Póvoa, 2017, Sustainable supply chain design and planning: the importance of life cycle scope definition, Computer Aided Chemical Engineering, 40, 541-546

V. Negri, A. Galán-Martín, C. Pozo, M. Fajardy, D. M. Reiner, N. Mac Dowell, G. Guillén-Gosálbez, 2021, Life cycle optimization of BECCS supply chains in the European Union, Applied Energy, 298, 117252

G.P. Peters and O. Geden, 2017, Catalysing a political shift from low to negative carbon. Nature Climate Change, 7,619–621

J. Rockström, W. Steffen, K Noone, Å. Persson, F. Stuart III Chapin , E. Lambin, T. M. Lenton, M. Scheffer, C. Folke, H. Joachim Schellnhuber, B. Nykvist, C. A. de Wit, T. Hughes, S. van der Leeuw, H. Rodhe, S. Sörlin, P. K. Snyder, R. Costanza, U. Svedin, M Falkenmark, L. Karlberg, R. W. Corell, V. J. Fabry, J. Hansen, B. Walker, D. Liverman, K. Richardson, P. Crutzen, J. Foley, 2009, Planetary boundaries: Exploring the safe operating space for humanity, Ecology and Society, 14

S. Sala, E. Crenna, M. Secchi, E. Sany-Mengual, 2020, Environmental sustainability of European production and consumption assessed against planetary boundaries, Journal of Environmental Management, 269, 110686

P. Smith, J. Adams, D. J. Beerling, T. Beringer, K. V. Calvin, S. Fuss, B. Griscom, N. Hagemann, C. Kammann, F. Kraxner, J. C. Minx, A. Popp, P. Renforth, J. Luis Vicente Vicente, S. Keesstra, 2019, Land-Management Options for Greenhouse Gas Removal and Their Impacts on Ecosystem Services and the Sustainable Development Goals, Annual Review of Environment and Resources, 44, 255–86

United Nations, Sustainable Development Goals https://sdgs.un.org/goals.

D. P. van Vuuren, E. Stehfest, D. E. H. J. Gernaat, M. van den Berg, D. L. Bijl, H. Sytze de Boer, V. Daioglou, J. C. Doelman, O. Y. Edelenbosch, M. Harmsen, A. F. Hof, M. A. E. van Sluisveld, 2018, Alternative pathways to the 1.5 °C target reduce the need for negative emission technologies, Nature Climate Change 8, 391–397

J. Wheeler, Á. Galán Martín, F. D. Mele, G. Guillén-Gosálbez, 2020, Supply Chain Design Optimization within Planetary Boundaries, Computer Aided Chemical Engineering, 48, 1489-1494

Proceedings of the 14th International Symposium on Process Systems Engineering – PSE 2021+
June 19-23, 2022, Kyoto, Japan
http://dx.doi.org/10.1016/B978-0-323-85159-6.50104-4

A Multi-disciplinary Assessment of Innovations to Improve Grocery Bag Circularity

Kevin Dooley[a*], Vyom Thakker[b], Bhavik Bakshi[b], Matt Scholz[a], Fatima Hafsa[a], George Basile[a], Raj Buch[a]

[a]*The Global Kaiteki Center, The Julie Anne Wrigley Global Futures Lab, Arizona State University, Tempe, Arizona 85287, USA*
[b]*Department of Chemical & Biolmolecular Engineering, The Ohio State University, Columbus, Ohio 43210, USA*
Kevin.Dooley@asu.edu

Abstract

While demand for plastic increases because of its broad application base, the negative environmental consequences of plastic production must be minimized through effective value chain design. Plastic production creates GHG emissions, and its inadequate disposal can generate water or air pollution. Plastic packaging makes up over 40 percent of all plastic made, and within that category, plastic grocery bags have been a focal point for reduction of impacts. This paper explores the types of innovations needed to make grocery bags more circular, i.e., increased recycling and reuse. In similar studies, researchers have used one type of model or theoretical frame to address the question, such as life cycle assessment or economics. In this paper, we use the multi-disciplinary approach of convergence science to address this question. We consider a baseline scenario involving single-use plastic grocery bags, and then explore alternatives from the perspectives of life cycle assessment (LCA), policy, economics, and supply chain management. Integration of these perspective highlights the necessary interdependency of circular innovations needed to bring about systemic improvement.

Keywords: Plastic; Packaging; Sustainability; Circular Economy; Recycling

1. The need for more circular grocery bags

Society calling for the plastic economy to be more circular by reducing plastic usage and reusing or recycling the plastic that we consume (Ellen MacArthur Foundation, 2017). Plastics posea particularly significant circular economy challenge given their pervasiveness. Plastic production creates GHG emissions (Zheng & Suh, 2019), and its inadequate disposal can pollute local water sources and generate air pollution (Verma et al., 2016). These externalities can be mitigated by establishing a more circular economy for plastics, but less than 10 percent of plastic of all plastic ever produced has been recycled and data on plastic reduction and reuse efforts are scarce (Geyer et al., 2017).

Among different plastic products, plastic packaging constitutes 42 percent of plastic production and 47 percent of the plastic waste stream (Ritchie, 2018). Less than 20 percent of plastic packaging is recycled globally, the rest is either landfilled, incinerated, or leaked. Our previous research has identified seven different classes of circular-economy innovation: polymer design and production, packaging design, packaging reuse, packaging disposal, waste collection and sorting, waste treatment, and recycled content use. An eighth type, policy, is added and may have implications at any of the value chain stages (Hafsa et al., 2020).

The question remains, which innovations will be most impactful or necessary to make the plastic packaging value chain more circular? In many similar studies, researchers have used one type of model or theoretical frame to address the question, such as life cycle assessment or economics. In this paper, we use the multi-disciplinary approach of convergence science to address this question.

To scope our research, we will apply this research question to the domain of grocery bags. We consider a baseline scenario involving single-use plastic grocery bags, and then explore alternatives, including different materials. We will use the following lenses to address the research question, and then synthesize by identifying common themes and disciplinary differences.

- Life cycle assessment (LCA) will be used to model the environmental trade-offs between different types of grocery bag materials, and the impact of different levels of reuse and recycling (Thakker and Bakshi, 2021).
- Policy analysis will be used to identify the regulatory and market mechanisms that have been used to reduce grocery bags' negative impacts and assess the effectiveness of these policies.
- Economic analysis will be used to assess the downstream market for recycled plastic grocery bags, which will vary by plastic type and attributes as well as region of the market.
- Supply chain management research will be used to understand the opportunities and constraints concerning the logistics of plastic bag collection, recycling, and remanufacturing.

2. Baseline model

The model that underlies our analysis is shown in Figure 1 (Thakker and Bakshi, 2021). At the top left, plastic feedstock is extracted, processed, and manufactured into grocery bags of four different possible plastic types: high density polyethylene (HDPE), low density polyethylene (LDPE), polypropylene (PP), or bioplastic polylactic acid (PLA). These are distributed to consumers (households) and may be one-use or multi-use. They are then collected either through waste management (trucks) or consumers (cars), and a certain number of bags are assumed lost to the environment. Then they are transported to a material recovery facility (MRF) where they are either landfilled; chemically recycled via pyrolysis; incinerated for energy; or segregated for composting, recycling, or upcycling to plastic lumber or cement clinker. This model has three decision points: which material portfolio to choose, how to collect the bags, and how to treat bags at end of life. From a system standpoint, one can use bag design to increase the number of uses per bag; policy and consumer education to incentivize more flow of bags into appropriate recovery channels; technologies at waste processing that minimize environmental impacts, especially related to energy use; more infrastructure to handle increased volume of flow through recycling channels; and more efficient production processes to make the bag itself.

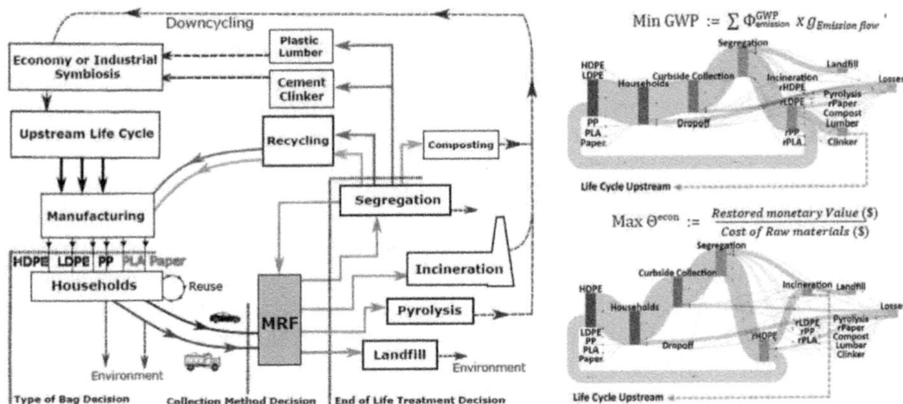

Figure 1 LCA optimization model of grocery bags

3. Life cycle assessment

Life cycle assessment and optimization methods were used to quantify the environmental impacts associated with different pathways and system designs. For any given objective function, the modeling yields an optimal bag combination and subsequent waste collection and management strategies, as shown in the Sankey diagrams in Figure 1. The optimal pathways are chosen among all life-cycle alternatives for objectives from three dimensions: circularity (Θ), environmental impact (Global Warming Potential, GWP), and cost (not shown). The trade-offs between objectives are quantified using pareto fronts, and optimality is identified. The conclusions from our modeling are:

- The scenario with least global warming potential and economic cost is the manufacture of reusable LDPE bags, followed by household littering to the environment without collection or treatment. This is a somewhat trivial answer, in that it would make little sense to accept a system that only littered to the environment; but since littering is an uncaptured externality in most LCA models, this solution highlights society's own incentives to minimize leakage.
- After considering the trade-offs between objectives of the three dimensions, the following value chain is found to be optimal under current technosphere conditions: Manufacture and use of reusable PP and LDPE, curbside collection by a truck, followed by segregation and recycling. The surplus generated recycled resin is used as cement clinker and incinerated.
- If adequate infrastructure existed to process more compostable material, the optimal shifts to a combination of corn-based PLA and PP bags. The shift of technosphere from current waste management scenario to the flexible technosphere yield win-win solutions in all three dimensions.

4. Policy

An array of policy interventions, both mandatory and voluntary, have been enacted or considered for reducing the consumption of plastic grocery bags and subsequent litter and waste. Policy makers have targeted governments, producers, retailers, consumers, and waste managers with diverse measures that include prescribed product design specifications, taxes, subsidies, bans, quotas, awareness campaigns, and extended producer responsibility (EPR) programs, wherein producers individually or collectively subsidize the cost of managing the final disposition of their products. A substantial body of empirical literature—and indeed much theoretical literature—has been developed around these topics, and several reviews can be consulted (e.g., Abbott, 2019).

Taxes on plastic carrier bags have been implemented by at least 30 countries spread across all habitable continents and are often coupled to campaigns to promote the adoption of reusable bags. While taxes can be assessed at the producer level, they typically take the form of levies that are either imposed upon or voluntarily adopted by retailers, who may pass the fees on to consumers at the point of sale. Programs vary in the cost of the fee, its frequency, and on what thickness of bag it is assessed. An oft-cited example of a popular and successful levy program is the Irish PlasTax, which was originally levied in 2002 and led to use reduction on the order of 90% and marked decreases in plastic bag litter (Convery, 2007).

Bans are equally ubiquitous and appear to be more common than taxes in Africa, Australia, and the US. These can take several forms, but outright bans on plastic bags at point-of-sale appear most common (United Nations Environment Programme, 2018). Often these bans permit thicker bags, which are presumed reusable, and there are frequent exemptions for certain uses, such as wrapping fresh meat. Soft bans also exist where consumers only receive bags when they specifically request them. Another type of ban is the landfill ban that prohibits the disposal of plastic waste in landfills—a type of ban that has become popular in many northern European and Scandinavian countries (Steensgaard, 2017).

Perhaps the most concise statement of the effectiveness of various policy interventions for reducing the environmental impacts of plastic carrier bags is provided by the IMF: "No single policy approach is ideal for all contexts, and regulatory and economic instruments can serve as complements as well as substitutes" (Matheson, 2019). The available data seem to support the effectiveness of bans and taxes on plastic bag use at reducing their consumption, litter, and waste.

5. Economics

The economic incentives to collect and process used grocery bags must be sufficient to overcome the default of simply disposing them in landfill. For other types of products or packaging materials, such a metal or paper fibre, the economic incentives are high, in that recovering the material is so much less expensive than the cost of making it anew; in other words, recycled content is less expensive than virgin content. There are also functional requirements – the recycled content must be of high enough quality that it can meet the engineering needs of its use. Finally, recycled content is more valuable if it has fewer impurities

These desired objectives are not well met by the current plastic recycling market. In part because of the pandemic and in part due to a reduced cost of petroleum – the feedstock most often used to make virgin plastic – plastic recycling prices for some types of plastics became inverted in 2021. Data was collected from the publication Plastic News, and in June 2021, the price of virgin HDPE in the U.S. was around 85 cents per pound, while scrap clear HDPE was 110 cents per pound. On one hand, this does increase profit per pound to companies in the recycling stream. However, the much lower cost of purchasing virgin HDPE leads to less use and demand for recycled HDPE, so overall profits decline as volumes decrease.

Our LCA studies suggest that because of HDPE's larger environmental impact, a more sustainable portfolio would consist of either PP and LDPE bags or PLA bags. Unfortunately, these solutions run up against economic constraints. PP and LPDE are both materials where recycled content costs less than virgin content, as expected. However, their recovery is so low that it is a disincentive to communities to collect it. In the U.S., PP has historically been collected curbside, but the poor recycling value has caused many cities to stop collection.

Economics also do not currently support a move to PLA bags. Until there is broad infrastructure to separate and collect compostable material, too many compostable bags would end up in recycling bins, thus acting as a contaminant, and reducing the margins associated with collecting recyclable material.

6. Supply chain management

Modern waste management systems are designed and operated on the basis that large volumes need to be collected and aggregated to take advantage of strong economies of scale. Large capital investments are required for infrastructure, and the impact of the large, fixed cost is reduced as volume of waste managed increases. On the revenue side, especially for plastic recycled content, margins are small, so large volumes must be amassed to waste management businesses to make sufficient total profit.

There is also a conflict between the material pathways that LCA modelling prescribes and the constraints that supply chain management issues pose with prescribed materials. Because of the relatively higher rate that HDPE is collected curb side in the US, compared to LDPE and PP, the latter suffer from the need to aggregate even greater volumes of recycled content, which leads to increasing logistics costs and environmental impact. Plastic in general, and LDPE specifically, are also less attractive to material handling companies such as warehouses because the value of the recycled content relative to its physical footprint is poor. Per tonne, it takes up more volume in the truck or warehouse but has less value per storage unit.

7. Conclusion

In conclusion, as one would expect in any complex system, there is no single or dominant optimal solution. LCA modelling demonstrates that different stakeholders, represented by different utility or objective functions, will assess different circular solutions and material pathways in different ways. Maximizing circularity will not necessarily minimize environmental impacts or direct material costs. Likewise, the optimality of many solutions depends on a bundle of innovations to be implemented. For example, the attractiveness of PLA based solutions increases as we have more composting infrastructure available.

When we combine multiple disciplinary perspectives to this problem, we further highlight the trade-offs that exist between any decision pathways. LCA modelling suggests that PP and LDPE may be strong alternatives to HPDE for grocery bag. But economic and supply chain analysis suggest that because of recycled HDPE's larger price per tonne, it may still be a better solution for companies in the recycling sector. Policy analysis suggests that there are pre-competitive mechanisms that can yield either consumers or manufacturers to be more committed to collecting recyclable packaging, but that the success of such policy mechanisms may be different for different packaging applications, formats, material types, and regions. We encourage other scholars and practitioners to bring an interdisciplinary lens when exploring solutions for a more circular economy.

In this study, we developed a proprietary LCA optimization model to examine the impact of different circular innovations, and then qualitatively examined whether other perspectives aligned with or contradicted the conclusions from the LCA model. In the future, the LCA model can be expanded to take these additional dimensions (e.g., economics, policy) directly into account within the computational model.

References

Abbott, J.K., Sumaila, U.R., 2019. Reducing Marine Plastic Pollution: Policy Insights from Economics. Review of Environmental Economics and Policy 13, 327–336. https://doi.org/10.1093/reep/rez007

Convery, F., McDonnell, S., Ferreira, S., 2007. The most popular tax in Europe? Lessons from the Irish plastic bags levy. Environ Resource Econ 38, 1–11. https://doi.org/10.1007/s10640-006-9059-2

Ellen MacArthur Foundation, 2017. The New Plastics Economy: Rethinking the Future of Plastics & Catalysing Action. Ellen MacArthur Foundation.

Geyer, R., Jambeck, J., & Law, K. L., 2017. Production, use, and fate of all plastics ever made. Science Advances, 3(7), e1700782. https://doi.org/10.1126/sciadv.1700782

Hafsa, F., Dooley, K., Basile, G., and Buch, R., 2020, Innovation pathways for more circular plastic packaging, AIChE Sustainable Packaging Conference.

Matheson, T., 2019. Disposal is Not Free: Fiscal Instruments to Internalize the Environmental Costs of Solid Waste. IMF Working Papers 19. https://doi.org/10.5089/9781513521589.001

Steensgaard, I.M., Syberg, K., Rist, S., Hartmann, N.B., Boldrin, A., Hansen, S.F., 2017. From macro- to microplastics - Analysis of EU regulation along the life cycle of plastic bags. Environmental Pollution 224, 289–299. https://doi.org/10.1016/j.envpol.2017.02.007

Thakker, V. and Bakshi, B., 2021, Toward sustainable circular economies: A computational framework for assessment and design, Journal of Cleaner Production, Vol. 295, https://www.sciencedirect.com/science/article/abs/pii/S0959652621005734

United Nations Environment Programme, 2018. Single-Use Plastics: A Roadmap for Sustainability. Available at https://www.euractiv.com/wp-content/uploads/sites/2/2018/06/WED-REPORT-SINGLE-USE-PLASTICS.pdf.

Verma, R., Vinoda, K. S., Papireddy, M., & Gowda, A. N. S., 2016. Toxic pollutants from plastic waste-a review. Procedia Environmental Sciences, 35, 701–708. https://doi.org/10.1016/j.proenv.2016.07.069

Zheng, J., & Suh, S., 2019. Strategies to reduce the global carbon footprint of plastics. Nature Climate Change, 9(5), 374–378. https://doi.org/10.1038/s41558-019-0459-z

Acknowledgements

The authors gratefully acknowledge the support of the research that led to this publication, from "The Global KAITEKI Center" at Arizona State University (ASU), a university-industry partnership between ASU and The KAITEKI Institute of Mitsubishi Chemical Holdings Corporation.

Proceedings of the 14th International Symposium on Process Systems Engineering – PSE 2021+
June 19-23, 2022, Kyoto, Japan
http://dx.doi.org/10.1016/B978-0-323-85159-6.50105-6

Process Sustainable Supply Chain: integrating monetization strategies in the design and planning

Cátia da Silva[a]*, Ana Barbosa-Póvoa[a], and Ana Carvalho[a]

[a]*CEG-IST, Instituto Superior Técnico, University of Lisbon, Lisbon 1049-001, PORTUGAL*
**catia.silva@tecnico.ulisboa.pt*

Abstract

Several wrong human actions have compromised future generations leading to growing concerns on environmental and social issues. As a result, the industry became aware of the need to integrate these concerns into its decision-making process. This is crucial within the process supply chains (that deal with process design with the aim of converting raw materials into final products), due to the type of process and products that they deal with. Though, quantifying both environmental and social impacts of the supply chain is not easy and understanding their units is challenging, particularly for decision-makers. In this way, this work intends to develop an optimization-based decision support tool that: i) models possible decisions taken throughout the supply chain, while considering demand uncertainty; ii) translates both environmental and social impacts of the supply chain into the same monetary unit so as to optimize the design and planning of economic, environmental, and social performances of the supply chain in the same unit. Considering that decision-makers are used to dealing with money when managing their supply chain, this innovative decision-support tool simplifies the decision-making process as all supply chain performances are quantified in an understandable monetary unit, which can constitute an asset to inform decision-makers. This innovative decision support tool is validated considering a real case study of a process supply chain.

Keywords: Sustainable supply chain; Design and planning; Optimization; Monetization; Uncertainty.

1. Introduction

All companies want to improve their supply chain (SC) as only through its effective management is it possible to obtain beneficial results for the company. Furthermore, in the current situation of great competition among companies, an optimized management of the SC is essential for complete customer satisfaction. In this scenario the main focus of companies ceased to be exclusively an economic performance, but environmental and social issues are very important to the proper functioning of SCs. In fact, the integration of the three pillars of sustainability (i.e., economic, environmental, and social) in the SC management has become essential (Barbosa-Póvoa et al., 2018). The World Commission on Environment and Development recognized sustainable SCs as a form of optimizing customer value and reach a market's competitive advantage. However, SC management concerning sustainable and effective goals is challenging, particularly when its design and planning are considered. Considering that sustainability involves a focus on the economic, environmental, and social performance, the most challenging are the ones associated with environmental and social quantification. In fact, the economic performance of the SC has been evaluated by decision-makers for a long time and is the one that they find it most easy to understand. On the other hand, environmental and social performances are not easily perceived by decision-makers, and its quantification often does not help this understanding. Thus, monetization can help in understanding these abstract impacts, as it allows to translate environmental and social impacts into monetary units, which facilitates the perception of the value of these abstract impacts in the SC and can facilitate the management of decision-making. It is also important to highlight that besides studying SC economic and social impacts, the major focus of this work will be on environmental aspects as they are truly critical within the process SC. This paper presents a MILP that accounts for the economic, environmental, and social concerns in the same objective function by monetizing both environmental and social impacts and considering demand uncertainty.

2. Environmental and social monetization methodologies

Regarding the environmental impacts' assessment, it appears that the life cycle assessment (LCA) is the most used methodology in the literature. LCA is composed by four main phases. The first one includes the goal and scope definition, where the context of the study is set out. The second phase is related to inventory analysis, which involves creating flows' inventory from and to nature for a system. The third step is the life cycle impact assessment (LCIA) phase that aims to evaluate the significance of potential environmental impacts based on the life cycle inventory flow results. However, this is a critical phase, where decision-makers must assign weights to factors, which may not be easy for most decision-makers. In addition, there is many environmental quantification methods, which also makes it difficult to choose the best one to use. Among the methods that exist, it appears that some of them quantify environmental impacts in abstract units or scores, while others monetize them. Monetizing means quantifying the impact in monetary units. Although there are many methods capable of translating environmental impacts into money, the European Commission (2010) considers EPS 2000 to be a very adequate and complete method when compared to other LCIA methods, having its uncertainties fully specified (Steen, 2000). The fourth phase is the life cycle interpretation that allows the identification, quantification, check and evaluation of the information from the LCA results.

Considering the social impacts' quantification, many works related to sustainable SC focus mainly on the environmental pillar while neglecting the social one. In fact, social performance of the SC has been the least explored one, which resulted in a relevant research gap in this area. In this set, companies have difficulties to assess and quantify their social performance (Beske-Janssen, Johnson, and Schaltegger 2015). Generally, social indicators are associated with safety, health, human rights, community initiatives, child labour, labour issues, and employment benefit. Global Reporting Initiative (GRI) identified labour practices and decent work, human rights, society, and product responsibility as important categories in the social component. It is important to mention that there is no consensus in the scientific community, particularly when defining social indicators. In this way, the identification of the suitable social indicators to be applied within the SC and its quantification is urgent to support the decision-making process. For this reason, translating social impacts into monetary units so that they are easily understood by decision-makers can be an important contribution to explore these research gaps.

3. Problem description and model characterization

This problem considers a generic SC that includes the flow of suppliers in which raw materials are sent to factories and the final products are obtained. Final products can move to warehouses or directly to markets. At markets, the end-of-life products can be recovered and sent to warehouses or directly remanufactured in factories. Given the possible set of locations of SC entities, production and remanufacturing technologies, possible transportation modes between entities, and products within the SC, the main objective is to obtain the SC network structure, supply and purchase levels, entities' capacities, transportation network, production, remanufacturing and storage levels, supply flow amounts, and product recovery levels, to maximize profit and social performance, while minimizing environmental impact. To solve this problem a MILP model was developed, which is based on da Silva et al. (2020). This model was extended to also consider the impact of SC social performance. Eq. (1) represents the first objective function, which is the maximization of the expected economic, environmental, and social performances of the SC, namely the expected net present value (eNPV), the expected social impact (eSoImpact), and the expected environmental impact (eEnvImpact). The economic performance is assessed through the eNPV (represented by Eq (2)), which is obtained through the sum of each node's probability multiplied by the discounted cash flows (CF_{Nt}) in each period *t* and for each node *N* at a given interest rate (*ir*). These CF_{Nt} are obtained from de net earnings (difference between incomes and costs). There are several costs included, namely raw material costs, product recovery costs, production/remanufacturing operating costs, transportation costs, contracted costs with airline or freight, handling costs at the hub terminal, inventory costs, and labour costs. In addition, for the last time period, it is considered the salvage values of the SC (FCIγ). The environmental performance is assessed through the eEnvImpact (represented by Eq. (3)), LCA is performed on the transportation modes and on entities installed in the SC boundaries, using EPS 2015. The Life Cycle Inventory is retrieved from the Ecoinvent database (through SimaPro 8.4.0 software). The LCA results are expressed in Environmental Load Units (ELU) and used as input data (*ei*) in Eq. (3), particularly in the environmental impact of transportation (first term), and entity (second term). Moreover, considering that the main focus of European Commission is to bet on promoting job creation and regional development, the social performance here considered is represented by Eq. (4), where $\frac{LProd_t}{GProd_t}$ corresponds to the ratio between labour productivity and global productivity; GDP_i is the gross domestic product of a country or sector where the SC is inserted; α_i represents an impact regional factor, which can assume different values according to the intended purpose of the study; and Y_i is a binary variable (which returns 1 if entity i is opened). Global productivity is given by $GProd_t = \sum_j \frac{GDP_j}{NEmpl_j}$ and labour productivity is given by $LProd_t = \sum_i \sum_j \frac{€prod_{ij}}{Nwor_{ij}}$ where j is a given country or sector where the SC is inserted; GDP_j corresponds to the gross domestic product of a country or sector j where the SC is inserted; and $NEmpl_j$ is the number of people employed in country or sector j where the SC is implanted and $Nwor_{ij}$ is the number of workers that the company or the SC owns. The model also considers several constraints regarding mass balance, capacity, transportation, and technology (for more details, please see da Silva et al. (2020)).

$$\max\,(e\mathrm{NPV}_N + e\mathrm{So\,Impact}_N - e\mathrm{Env\,Impact}_N) \tag{1}$$

$$\mathrm{eNPV_N} = \sum_N pb_N \left(\sum_{t\in T}\frac{CF_{Nt}}{(1+ir)^t} - \sum_{\gamma} FCI_{\gamma}\right) \tag{2}$$

$$\mathrm{eEnvImpact_N} = \sum_N pb_N \left(\sum_{\substack{t\in T\\(a,m,i,j)\in NetP}} ei_{ac}pw_m d_{ij}X_{maijtN} + \sum_{i\in I_f\cup I_w} ei_{ic}YC_i\right) \tag{3}$$

$$\mathrm{eSoImpact_N} = \sum_N pb_N \left(\sum_i\sum_j \frac{L\mathrm{Prod}_t}{G\mathrm{Prod}_t}.\frac{1}{GDP_j}.\alpha_i.Y_i\right) \tag{4}$$

4. Case study

The model is applied to a chemical components' producer located in Lyon, France (Silva et.al., 2020). The company's suppliers are local and placed in Lyon. It supplies three main markets that are in different European countries: Portugal, France, and Germany. France is the market that owns the highest percentage of company's sales (38.9%), followed by Germany (33.7%), and Portugal with 27.4% of company's sales. Considering the willingness of the company's decision-makers to expand its SC, to three new markets (Ireland, Spain, and Canada), the company wants to know what changes could result from this expansion in financial terms. Currently, transportation is only performed by road, namely by truck. However, with the expansion, there is the need to combine road transportation with air and sea transportation modes. Regarding company's characterization, it is important to mention that it sells three different types of chemical products (fp1, fp2, fp3) that can be sold within the chemical industry and to other industries. In the current production, three technologies (pr1, pr2, pr3) are used that produce respectively products fp1, fp2, and fp3. Furthermore, end-of-life products can be recovered and remanufactured into final products. This work accounts for product's demand uncertainty through a stochastic approach since this method allows the discretization of stochastic data over the time horizon and can be adjusted during the planning horizon. A scenario three was considered (Figure 1), where node N characterizes a possible state and the arcs represent the evolutions it may have. Each node has a specific probability and a path from the root to a leaf node represents a scenario.

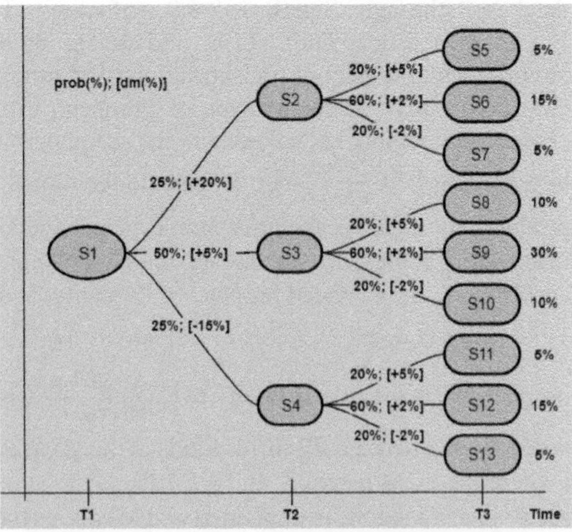

Figure 1- Scenario tree - values for probability and demand (D) variation are represented

4.1. Results

Initially, the model was solved considering each objective function individually, which means that the three goals are considered separately. In addition, the three goals were also analysed within the same function (single objective function). Thus, four cases are studied to understand the results obtained with the proposed approach:

- Case A: analyses the case-study results that represents the optimal economic performance as major goal;
- Case B: analyses the case-study results that represents the optimal social performance as major goal;
- Case C: analyses the case-study results that represents the optimal environmental performance as major goal, evaluated through EPS;
- Case D: analyses the case-study results that represent the optimal trade-off between social, environmental, and economic performances.

As a result, the values for the total expected net present value, social impact, and environmental impact obtained in each case are shown in Table 1.

Table 1 Outcomes for the economic, social, and environmental impacts.

Obj. Function	**Case A**	**Case B**	**Case C**	**Case D**
	Max eNPV	Max eSoImpact	Min eEImpact	Max (eNPV + eSoImpact - eEnvImpact)
eNPV	**$1.5203x10^9$ €**	$1.4905x10^9$€	$1.1979x10^9$ €	$1.5098x10^9$ €
eSoImpact	$8.1700x10^{-12}$€	**$3.1150x10^{-11}$€**	$1.6100x10^{-11}$€	$5.2567x10^{-12}$ €
eEImpact	$1.0149x10^9$ €	$1.1057x10^9$€	**$9.3470x10^8$ €**	$9.8220x10^8$ €

Regarding the results, it is noted that case A is associated with the biggest value for eNPV, which arises from the fact that its objective function is maximized, while returns the lowest social benefit. Case B considers the maximization of the social performance and has the highest value for eSoImpact that corresponds to $3.1150x10^{-11}$€ and the lowest value of economic performance. In contrast, case C that consider the minimization of the eEImpact (assessed through EPS method) has the lowest eNPV value and an expected environmental impact that corresponds to $9,3470x10^8$ €. Finally, case D that considers the three performances simultaneously, which is only possible thanks to the social and environmental impacts' monetization process. It can be seen that global profit is decreased in 1 million euros when comparing cases A with D, but the impact of environment increased by nearly 32.7 million euros that can only be accomplished by using the single objective approach. On the other hand, the value achieved for social performance in case D, is between the values of case A and B. Furthermore, it is possible to note that global profit improved further than 300 million euros between cases C and D, whereas the impact of environment is worst at nearly 48 million. In other words, with the aim of maximizing the global profit, the single objective approach allows to improve 3.33% in environmental performance and to improve 55% in the social performance, while ENPV only decreases 0.7%. Table 2 shows SC design decisions considering the results depicted in Table 1 for case D. Additionally to the existent factory, one new factory is installed. The results also show that there is the need to expand the existing capacity by opening new warehouses. Regarding suppliers' allocation, all factories are supplied by all suppliers, which results from the balance between the lower costs of raw materials and fewer transportation costs. Regarding transportation, the truck with more capacity (Truck2) is preferred in all cases since this has a lower environmental impact. In terms of intermodal transportation, sea option is preferred, while air transportation is not used.

Table 2 Supply chain network structure for case D

Allocation of suppliers		Closest suppliers supply all factories plus Bremen supplier
Factories		Lyon and Galway
Warehouses		Lyon
Production		The majority of fp1 production is in the current factory
		The majority of fp2 production is shared between factories
		Most production of fp3 is in the opening factories
Remanufacture		Most of rp1 is in the existing facility (around 70%)
		rp2 and rp3 are only performed in the existing facility
Technologies		Alternative one is preferred for fp1 and fp2 in the opening factories
Inventory	fp1	43% in Lyon and 57% in Galway
	fp2	65% in Lyon and 35% in Galway
	fp3	30% in Lyon and 70% in Galway
Transportation		Road: 8 trucks; Air: Not adopted; Sea: Adopted

5. Conclusions

This study intended to develop a decision support tool for the design and planning of a generic SC, where the economic, environmental, and social performances are considered under uncertainty on the product's demand. Economic performance is assessed by using the expected NPV. In addition, environmental performance was evaluated through the LCA methodology. Considering the social performance, job creation was the indicator considered in our first social approach. This analysis was only possible due to the monetization, which was able to quantify both environmental and social impacts in a monetary unit. This allowed to include in the same objective function the economic, the environmental and the social impacts. Moreover, from the analysis made, it was clear that results are influenced by social and environmental impacts, and this proves the importance of considering these issues in solving real-life problems. For future work, further research should be done on this topic to better explore monetization approaches to be a reliable alternative to evaluate environmental and social impacts. Also, an extension of this work should consider different social indicators and a more comprehensive study of uncertainty to conclude on its adequacy even better.

Acknowledgements

The authors acknowledge the support provided by FCT and PORTUGAL2020 under the project PTDC/EGE-OGE/28071/2017, Lisboa -01.0145-Feder-28071.

References

A. Barbosa-Póvoa, Cátia da Silva, and Ana Carvalho. 2018. "Opportunities and Challenges in Sustainable Supply Chain: An Operations Research Perspective." European Journal of Operational Research 268 (2): 399–431.

P. Beske-Janssen, Matthew Phillip Johnson, and Stefan Schaltegger. 2015. "20 Years of Performance Measurement in Sustainable Supply Chain Management – What Has Been Achieved?" Supply Chain Management: An International Journal 20 (6): 664–80.

C. da Silva, Ana Barbosa-Póvoa, and Ana Carvalho. 2020. "Environmental Monetization and Risk Assessment in Supply Chain Design and Planning." Journal of Cleaner Production, 270, 121552.

European Commission. 2010. "Joint Research Centre – Institute for Environment and Sustainability: International Reference Life Cycle Data System (ILCD) Handbook – General Guide for Life Cycle Assessment – Detailed Guidance. Publications Office of the European Union".

Proceedings of the 14th International Symposium on Process Systems Engineering – PSE 2021+
June 19-23, 2022, Kyoto, Japan
http://dx.doi.org/10.1016/B978-0-323-85159-6.50106-8

Systematically Identifying Energy-Efficient and Attractive Multicomponent Distillation Configurations

Tony Joseph Mathew[a], Mohit Tawarmalani[b], Rakesh Agrawal[a*]

[a]*Davidson School of Chemical Engineering, Purdue University, West Lafayette, IN-47907, USA*
[b]*Krannert School of Management, Purdue University, West Lafayette, IN-47907, USA*
agrawalr@purdue.edu

Abstract

Thousands of configurations exist for multicomponent distillation, making it laborious to use standard process simulators for identifying which among this plenitude are energy-efficient for a given separation. Shortcut models quickly screen the wide search space, but their development has been limited by various obstacles. In this work, we overcome three challenges: assumptions of constant relative volatilities and constant molar overflow, and utilizing heat integration. We incorporate our solutions into an optimization formulation and subsequently demonstrate its ability to identify energy-efficient and heat-integrated configurations on a case study. We also demonstrate how process intensification can be used to raise the value of the selected configuration.

Keywords: Multicomponent Distillation; Optimization; Process Synthesis; Process Intensification.

1. Introduction

Ubiquitous in the chemical and petrochemical industries, distillation is a staple unit operation in the separation of various mixtures such as crude petroleum, air, natural gas liquids, alcohols, and aromatics. However, these separations come with substantial energy expenses which have a by-product of greenhouse gas emissions. Therefore, it is of vital importance to identify new distillation arrangements with lower energy consumption for separations.

For multicomponent separations, there is a vast search space of configurations possible. For example, 6,128 configurations exist for separating just five components in a mixture (Shah and Agrawal, 2010). A systematic analysis (with optimization) and comparison is required to determine which of these are energy-efficient for a given separation. But performing such an analysis in a standard process simulator is impractical due to the computational challenges of optimizing with the complex thermodynamics and exorbitant time spent in evaluations (Madenoor Ramapriya et al., 2018). Hence, we use a simplified model for energy optimization to quickly screen through the vast search space of configurations, identifying a handful of candidates for further analysis in the process simulator.

Although several simplified models exist for distillation in the literature (Caballero and Grossmann, 2006; Nallasivam et al., 2016; Tumbalam Gooty et al., 2018; Ryu and Maravelias, 2020), they make various assumptions which, while granting them computational simplicity, limit their accuracy. For example, the Underwood method (Underwood, 1948) is often used to estimate the minimum reflux in columns. However, the method was derived based on two vital assumptions, constant relative volatilities (CRV) and constant molar overflow (CMO), which do not hold for many real separations. Moreover, these models face computational difficulties incorporating important elements of process flowsheets. For example, heat integration (the re-use of heat) is invaluable for energy reductions. However, its feasibility checks can hamper global optimization when complex equations are used to calculate temperatures. In this paper, we present our solutions to the aforementioned limitations and demonstrate the optimization formulation in which they have been incorporated to identify energy-efficient and heat-integrated distillation configurations. We also demonstrate process intensification techniques to improve the attractiveness of the chosen configuration.

2. Optimization Model

2.1. Base Model

First, we describe the base model of Nallasivam et al. (2016), upon which we have incorporated our advances. Implemented in a nonlinear program, it determines the minimum vapor duty (sum of the reboiler vapor duties) of regular-column (n columns for n-component separation) distillation configurations. It employs assumptions of ideal and zeotropic mixtures, CRV, and the standard McCabe-Thiele assumptions (which result in CMO). Each configuration is uniquely identified by the set of streams present. Columns with multiple feeds are modelled as a collection of pseudo-columns for the split of each feed stream. These pseudo-columns are stacked vertically, with the common products of adjacent splits being withdrawn as sidedraws.

The variables in the base model are component and vapor flowrates of each stream and column section, and the Underwood roots of each split. Mass and vapor balances are applied at the product and feed ends of each stream. The Underwood method (Underwood, 1948) is utilized to constrain minimum vapor flows in columns and ensure feasible component distributions in sloppy splits. The vapor flowrate of a stream is constrained according to its nature, viz., associated with a heat exchanger, sidedraw, or thermally coupled.

2.2. Estimating Better Relative Volatilities

The relative volatility of component i, α_i, is a measure of how this component distributes between the phases of a vapor-liquid equilibrium (VLE) compared to the heaviest component n in the mixture. When α_i are constants (the direct result of the CRV assumption), the following equation (written to predict vapor composition, y_i, from liquid composition, x_i) is sufficient to characterize the VLE.

$$y_i = \frac{\alpha_i x_i}{\sum_{j=1}^{n} \alpha_j x_j} \quad (1)$$

But in general, component relative volatilities vary with the specifications of the mixture, i.e., composition, temperature, and pressure. For this reason, CRV (and thereby the above simplified VLE) has been viewed as a poor assumption in distillation models. However, even if the physical values of relative volatilities vary widely, there can exist constant mathematical values which capture these variations. Instead of the common perception that Eq.(1) is only valid for ideal mixtures, we advocate interpreting it as a surrogate VLE. α_i are then to be determined by parameter estimation, so that this surrogate VLE best approximates the true VLE (Anderson & Doherty, 1984).

The method we propose for estimating α_i is as follows (Mathew et al., 2020). Generate a systematic spread of VLE training data in x_i and y_i, by considering each component to be either lean or rich, as well as the pressure to be low or high. Then regress α_i in Eq.(1) via non-linear least squares. This yields values for α_i which can capture the VLE through Eq.(1), and therefore be employed in methods assuming CRV, such as the Underwood method, while accounting for the variations in relative volatilities.

2.3. Relaxing Constant Molar Overflow

CMO is valuable in shortcut models as it simplifies complex energy balances over enthalpy into simple linear balances over vapor and liquid flowrates. A critical requirement for CMO is that all components have the same latent heat of vaporization, λ_i. However, λ_i can have a wide spread in many separations, such as for crude oil. To account for different latent heats, researchers such as Mole (1950) have derived the following simple variable transformation from molar variables to latent heat variables (^{LH}) for component flowrate (f), total flowrate (F), and composition (z).

$$f_i^{\text{LH}} = f_i\lambda_i, \quad F^{\text{LH}} = F\sum_{j=1}^{n} z_j\lambda_j, \quad z_i^{LH} = \frac{z_i\lambda_i}{\sum_{j=1}^{n} z_j\lambda_j} \tag{2}$$

The benefit of this particular transformation is that, when the different latent heats are accounted for, the resulting model written in latent heat variables is mathematically equivalent to the usual CMO model in molar variables. Thus, the transformation allows us to implicitly account for different latent heats but while retaining the computational simplicity of the CMO equations. We applied the above transformation in our formulation to not only relax the CMO assumption but also determine the minimum heat duty of configurations, which is a more accurate proxy for energy consumption than vapor duty which the base model determines.

2.4. Heat Integration to Reduce Energy Consumption

One opportunity for heat integration in distillation is to transfer heat from the condenser of one column to the reboiler of another. Such a heat transfer is allowed only if the temperature of the source (condenser) is greater than that of the sink (reboiler). This implies that temperatures would need to be calculated during optimization while checking for feasible heat integrations. However, such checks can hamper convergence to global optimality when complex thermodynamic equations are used. To address this, we developed a shortcut criterion for feasibility of heat integration (Mathew et al., 2021).

Using Raoult's and Dalton's laws for partial pressures, along with Eq.(1), we derived a new metric (pressure-scaled pseudo relative volatility, ρ) that monotonically decreases with temperature. Therefore, we utilize ρ as an inverse proxy for temperature which is computationally cheaper to calculate during optimization. The shortcut criterion is shown below. ρ is first calculated, in Eq.(3), for each stream at its bubble and dew points, using only component relative volatilities (α_i), composition (z_i), and pressure (P). Then, heat transfer (Q) is permitted via Eq.(4) only if ρ of the condensing stream (c) is less than that of the boiling stream (b), implying that the condensing stream is hotter than the boiling stream.

Table 1: Feed data for case study. Feed is saturated liquid at 1 atm.

	Components				
	A	B	C	D	E
Species	Benzene	Toluene	Ethylbenzene	p-Xylene	o-Xylene
Feed Flowrate, f (kmol/h)	30	30	5	5	30
Relative Volatility α	5.61	2.43	1.25	1.17	1
Latent Heat λ (kJ/mol)	30.0	32.5	34.7	34.9	35.7

$$\rho^{\text{bub}} = \frac{1}{P}\sum_{j=1}^{n} \alpha_j z_j, \quad \rho^{\text{dew}} = \left[P\sum_{j=1}^{n} \frac{z_j}{\alpha_j}\right]^{-1} \tag{3}$$

$$Q\left(\rho_c^{\text{bub}} - \rho_b^{\text{bub}}\right) \leq 0, \quad Q\left(\rho_c^{\text{dew}} - \rho_b^{\text{dew}}\right) \leq 0 \tag{4}$$

3. Case Study

We now demonstrate our formulation on a five-component aromatics separation, with feed data shown in Table 1. We solved our shortcut model for each of the 6,128 different regular-column configurations possible for this separation (Shah and Agrawal, 2010), while considering heat integration opportunities and allowing column pressures to vary between 1 atm and 2 atm.

The configuration in Figure 1(a) was predicted to have the least heat duty of 1.82 MW among all the configurations optimized. It uses two heat integrations of condenser (filled circle) of stream CD supplying heat to the reboiler (hollow circle) of stream CDE, and condenser C supplying heat to reboiler DE. To make these heat integrations feasible, columns 1 and 2 are operated at the feed pressure of 1 atm while columns 3 and 4 are operated at higher pressures of 1.4 atm and 2 atm respectively.

To improve the structural attractiveness of this configuration, we apply a variety of transformation techniques which fall under the broad umbrella of process intensification (PI) (Jiang and Agrawal, 2019). First, we horizontally consolidate columns I and II into a single shell with a vertical partition in between, forming a dividing wall column (DWC) (Agrawal, 2001; Madenoor Ramapriya et al., 2018b). Then, the three column shells are vertically consolidated into a single shell (I-II, III, then IV), with the heat integrations performed internally using multi-effect technology (Agrawal, 2000).

The final configuration is shown in Figure 1(b). An important feature of the transformation techniques we employed is that they maintain thermodynamic equivalence. Thus, the process-intensified configuration in Figure 1(b) has the same least heat duty of 1.82 MW as that of Figure 1(a) but with greater structural attractiveness. We remark that the configuration performs a five-component separation in a single shell. It is a triple-effect column, with the topmost column being a DWC. The vapor-split at the bottom of the partition in this part can be indirectly controlled via pressures in the condensers of A and B. Thus, this type 2 DWC is more operable compared to the conventional type 1 DWC where the partitions lie in the middle of the shell (Chen and Agrawal, 2020).

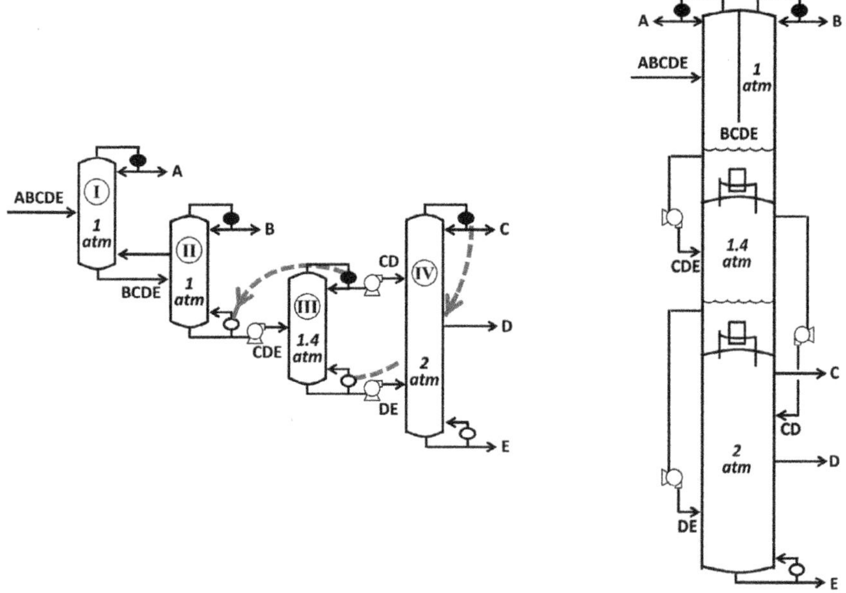

(a) Heat-integrated configuration with least heat duty

(b) After process intensification

Figure 1: Configurations identified by formulation for case study. Column number and pressure are indicated in roman and arabic numerals respectively.

4. Conclusions

Shortcut models are invaluable in screening the vast search space of possible configurations for energy demand, since a systematic analysis and comparison using standard process simulators is impractical. However, such models have been limited in their accuracy and the flowsheet features that they could capture. In this work, we presented solutions to three challenges faced by current shortcut models for distillation during global optimization: 1) accounting for the variations in component relative volatilities, 2) accounting for different latent heats of vaporization, and 3) searching for heat integration opportunities. We incorporated these advances in our optimization formulation, and it is now capable of quickly identifying energy-efficient and heat-integrated distillation configurations with greater accuracy, as demonstrated on a five-component separation of aromatics. Furthermore, we demonstrated how various PI techniques can improve the structural attractiveness of selected configurations without comprising on their energy benefits through thermodynamic equivalence. The PI techniques we used, and several others, are general and can be applied to a wide number of configurations in addition to the one we showed. This work will aid the process engineer in more reliably finding valuable and novel configurations for their separations.

Acknowledgments

We thank the US Department of Energy (Award number: DE -- EE0005768) for financial support. We also thank Dr. Radhakrishna Tumbalam Gooty for his input during discussions of the work in this paper.

References

R. Agrawal, 2000, Multieffect Distillation for Thermally Coupled Configurations. AIChE Journal, 46(11), pp.2211–2224.

R. Agrawal, 2001, Multicomponent Distillation Columns with Partitions and Multiple Reboilers and Condensers. Industrial Engineering & Chemistry Research, 40(20), pp.4258-4266.

N. J. Anderson, and M. F. Doherty, 1984, An Approximate Model for Binary Azeotropic Distillation Design, Chemical Engineering Science, 39(1), pp.11-19.

J. A. Caballero, and I. E. Grossmann, 2006, Structural considerations and modeling in the synthesis of heat-integrated thermally coupled distillation sequences, Industrial Engineering & Chemistry Research, 45(25), pp.8454-8474.

Z. Chen, and R. Agrawal, 2020, Classification and Comparison of Dividing Walls for Distillation Columns. Processes, 8(6), p.699.

Z. Jiang, and R. Agrawal, 2019, Process intensification in multicomponent distillation: A review of recent advancements, Chemical Engineering Research Design, 147, pp.122-145.

G. Madenoor Ramapriya, A. Selvarajah, L. E. Jimenez Cucaita, J. Huff, M. Tawarmalani, and R. Agrawal, 2018a, Short-Cut Methods versus Rigorous Methods for Performance-Evaluation of Distillation Configurations, Industrial & Engineering Chemistry Research, 57(22), pp.7726–7731.

G. Madenoor Ramapriya, M. Tawarmalani, and R. Agrawal, 2018b, A Systematic Method to Synthesize All Dividing Wall Columns n-Component Separation — Part I, AIChE Journal, 64(2), pp.649–659.

T. J. Mathew, R. Tumbalam Gooty, M. Tawarmalani, and R. Agrawal, 2020, Quickly Assess Distillation Columns, Chemical Engineering Progress, 116(12), pp.27-34.

T. J. Mathew, R. Tumbalam Gooty, M. Tawarmalani, and R. Agrawal, 2021, A simple criterion for feasibility of heat integration between distillation streams based on relative volatilities, Industrial & Engineering Chemistry Research, 60(28), 10286-10302.

P. Mole, 1958, A unified theory for ideal separation processes. Chemical Engineering Science, 8(3), pp.236-243.

U. Nallasivam, V. H. Shah, A. A. Shenvi, J. Huff, M. Tawarmalani, and R. Agrawal, 2016, Global optimization of multicomponent distillation configurations: 2. Enumeration based global minimization algorithm, AIChE Journal, 62(6), pp.2071-2086.

J. Ryu and C. T. Maravelias, 2020, Computationally efficient optimization models for preliminary distillation column design and separation energy targeting, Computers and Chemical Engineering, 143, 107072.

V. H. Shah and R. Agrawal, 2010, A matrix method for multicomponent distillation sequences, AIChE journal, 56(7), pp.1759-1775.

R. Tumbalam Gooty, M. Tawarmalani, and R. Agrawal, 2018, Optimal Multicomponent Distillation Column Sequencing: Software and Case Studies, Computer Aided Chemical Engineering, 44(2), pp.660–672.

A. J. V. Underwood, 1948, Fractional distillation of multi-component mixtures, Chemical Engineering Progress, 44, pp.223–228.

Proceedings of the 14th International Symposium on Process Systems Engineering – PSE 2021+
June 19-23, 2022, Kyoto, Japan
http://dx.doi.org/10.1016/B978-0-323-85159-6.50107-X

Synthesis of Advanced Reactive Distillation Technologies: Early-Stage Assessment Based on Thermodynamic Properties and Kinetics

Isabel Pazmiño-Mayorga[a*], A.A. Kiss,[a] M. Jobson[a]

[a] *Centre for Process Integration, Department of Chemical Engineering, The University of Manchester, M13 9PL, Manchester, United Kingdom*

isabel.pazminomayorga@manchester.ac.uk

Abstract

In the early stages of process design, the design space is enormous, often requiring simplified models that are based on conventional unit operations with their inherent strengths and limitations. In this paper, we present a novel conceptual framework and a synthesis methodology applied to a specific design problem featuring an equilibrium-limited reaction or a separation that can benefit from the introduction of a reactive separating agent to use intensified technologies following the success of reactive distillation. Two case studies (related to lactic acid and dimethyl ether production) illustrate the application of the synthesis methodology, and the outcomes are verified with conceptual design studies reported in the literature.

Keywords: Process synthesis; Reactive distillation; Process intensification; Feasibility methodology; Fluid separations

1. Introduction

Chemical industries face multiple challenges due to the increasing competitiveness, tighter regulations, and more stringent technical, commercial, safety and environmental requirements. Conventional process synthesis and design approaches to serve chemical industries generally apply established unit operations that are continuously challenged to reach new targets. Also, the increase in computing power has benefited the development of complex superstructure optimization methods combining synthesis and design simultaneously and including economic and sustainability indicators. As a result, the increased complexity requires numerous assumptions to simplify the models and often neglect important characteristics of the system that may impact process design at later stages. On the other hand, understanding a chemical system is crucial in the early stages of process design, for example, during flowsheet development.

Therefore, this work focuses on a much smaller subset of the design problem and proposes a methodology for early-stage process design to quickly evaluate advanced reactive distillation technologies that incorporate additional intensification features to reactive distillation (RD). These advanced RD technologies can be applied to equilibrium-limited reactive systems in the liquid phase or fluid separations that can benefit from the introduction of a reactive separating agent (RSA) to facilitate the separation. Decision making for process synthesis is guided by high-level questions about the chemical system of interest, which can be answered by knowing basic thermodynamic properties and kinetic data and using experience or experts' knowledge from conventional RD applications.

2. Advanced reactive distillation technologies

The technologies included in the scope of the synthesis methodology were developed following the success of RD by evaluating additional intensification features to expand the operating window and find potential new applications. The technologies included in this study are reactive dividing-wall column (R-DWC), catalytic cyclic distillation (CCD), reactive internally heat-integrated distillation (R-HIDiC), reactive high-gravity distillation (R-HiGee), and membrane-assisted reactive distillation (MA-RD). Figure 1 illustrates the key features of the five technologies included in the scope of this study and highlights their advantages compared to RD.

3. Research approach, conceptual framework and scope

3.1. Research approach

Kiss et al. (2019) noted that advanced RD technologies have not reached maturity due to the lack of robust methods and tools for process design and simulation, process dynamics and control, lack of pilot and industrial tests, and because of practical challenges related to ease of implementation. However, the range of applications of conventional reactive distillation is well established for equilibrium-limited reaction systems that have been studied on a laboratory, pilot or industrial scale (Luyben, 2013; Skiborowski, 2018). The ongoing research and developments about advanced distillation technologies (Kiss, 2013) and the knowledge and understanding of various chemical systems – feed and product specification, kinetics, phase equilibria, catalysts and operating conditions – are the basis for the decision-making methodology that aims to include advanced RD technologies in the early stages of process design.

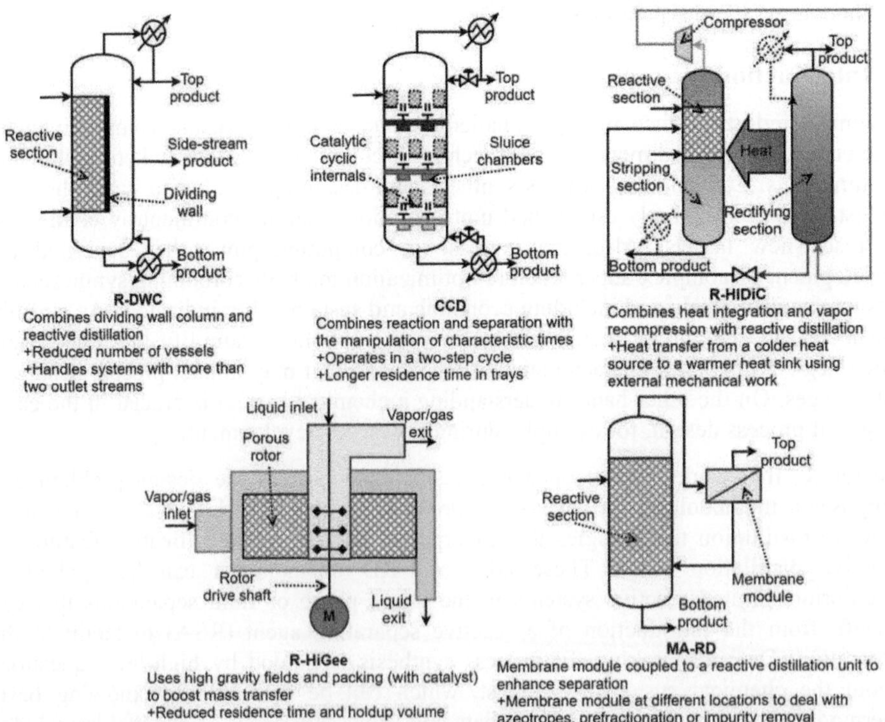

Figure 1. Main features of the five advanced reactive distillation technologies

3.2. Conceptual framework and scope

The methodology aims to be general enough to cover a wide range of equilibrium-limited reaction systems and their characteristics relevant to large-scale industrial applications (e.g., azeotropes, impurities and trace components, difficult separations). These characteristics are often simplified in laboratory-scale investigations, such as considering pure feeds, a large amount of solvent, and not accounting for the type of utilities needed. As a result, these characteristics usually lead to the need for multiple processing steps. However, intensified technologies that combine reaction and separation may overcome these challenging characteristics resulting in more compact and efficient processing units.

Figure 2 shows the conceptual framework of the decision-making methodology proposed in this work, which prompts high-level questions to the user to know the chemical system better. These questions can be answered given the thermodynamic properties and the kinetic parameters. The most common sources of information are also indicated.

Thermodynamic property data of pure compounds and mixtures include process stream compositions (feeds and products), basic physical properties and phase equilibrium information. These data can be easily gathered from databases and handbooks, from experiments or robust equations of state and activity coefficient models.

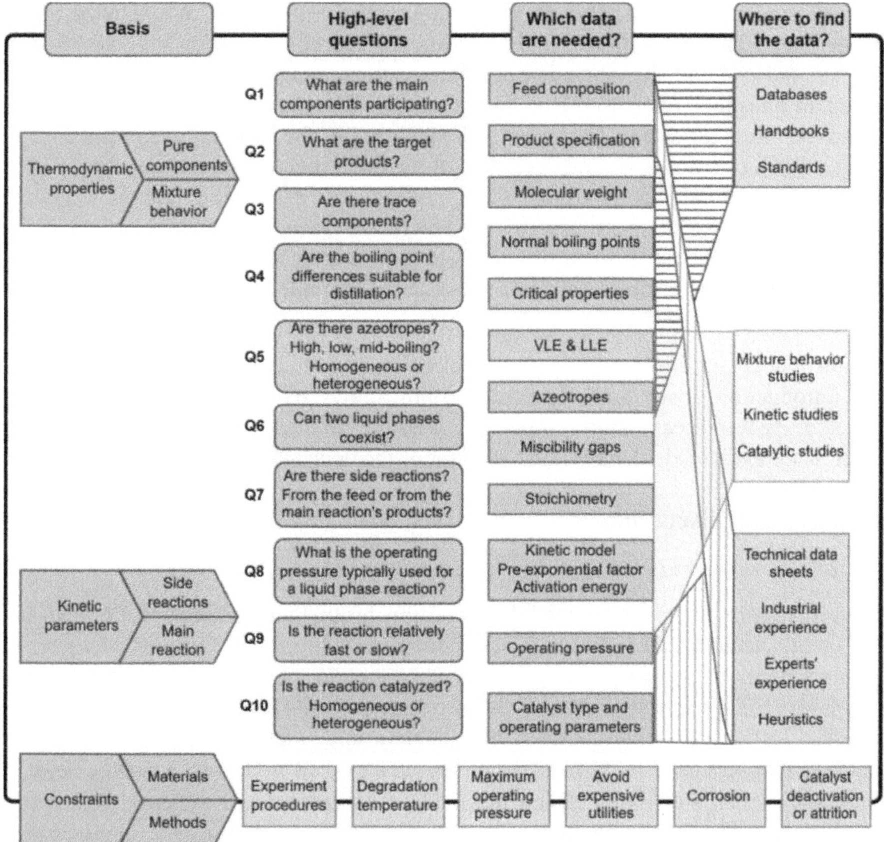

Figure 2. Conceptual framework for the synthesis of advanced reactive distillation technologies

The kinetic parameters of the main reaction must be carefully identified along with relevant side reactions that are often neglected in the conceptual design phase. For example, a parallel reaction can compete with the main reaction (consuming a reactant), or a series reaction can consume a product. Therefore, potential side reactions and their impact must be thoroughly understood at early stages because neglecting them can drive the decision-making process towards infeasible designs that may not be able to handle or overcome such complexities.

Information about thermodynamic properties and kinetics parameters can guide selection, but decisions also need to take into account constraints imposed by materials (i.e., catalysts, materials of construction) and methods (e.g., laboratory experiments). The materials constraint accounts for the chemicals used, the catalyst (functions, robustness against deactivation, thermal and mechanical performance, availability for large scale applications), and the materials used for vessels, column internals, membranes, and fluid handling system. The methods constraint includes laboratory procedures to evaluate kinetics or mixture behavior, or methods to conduct equipment sizing especially when severe conditions are required: operating pressure and temperature, moving parts, corrosive environment, or abrasive materials.

4. Decision-making methodology applied to two case studies

The high-level questions shown in Figure 2 are the backbone of the decision-making methodology. These questions firstly address the feed composition and the expected products and by-products, considering dilution, trace components and impurities. The next set of questions refers to the operating conditions: operating pressure and the range of temperatures expected. The next step deals with the reactions identified in the system. The forward reaction rate constant of the main reaction is evaluated at 363.15 K to categorize its rate as relatively slow, average, or fast. Side reactions are then evaluated according to the source of the reactants: from the feed stream, which can drive parallel reactions; or from the main reaction products, which can trigger a series reaction. Finally, the mixture behavior is evaluated by understanding the phases present and the existence of azeotropes.

We illustrate the application of the decision-making methodology in two case studies. A brief introduction about each chemical system allows the high-level questions to be answered. In each case study, relevant decision points that guide the technology selection are examined, along with an excerpt of the decision-making flowchart.

5. Results and discussion

5.1. Concentration and purification of lactic acid

The feed consists of a pre-treated fermentation broth that contains lactic acid (LA) (30 % wt.), succinic acid (5 % wt., reactive impurity), and a large amount of water. The design problem involves separating water and other acid impurities to obtain food-grade LA (88 % wt.). We introduced a reactive separating agent (RSA), methanol, to promote the esterification LA to produce methyl lactate and water with a heterogeneously catalyzed equilibrium-limited reaction of the type $A + B \rightleftharpoons C + D$. Succinic acid also reacts to produce succinates. Once the heavier succinates are removed, the reverse hydrolysis reaction is promoted by providing sufficient water in the liquid phase to obtain LA on specification and free from the impurity.

Relevant answers used in the decision-making flowchart are that the feed is diluted (Q1); the streams identified are product, by-product, excess water, and the RSA (Q2); the operating pressure should be sub-atmospheric to avoid thermal degradation (Q8); the existence of parallel side reaction from the impurity in the feed (Q7); the existence of homogenous mid boiling azeotropes (Q5), which are presented in an excerpt of the decision-making flowchart in Figure 3a.

The main outcomes are that a preconcentration step is required to remove excess water. Among the advanced RD technologies evaluated, the R-DWC is deemed suitable due to the number of outlet streams required, the side reaction by-products and the presence of mid-boiling azeotropes that can be consumed in the reactive sections. In addition, R-HIDiC and CCD are discarded because of their limitations to operate under vacuum. These outcomes were supported with conceptual design studies about thermally coupled configurations (Kim et al., 2017) and a dual R-DWC (Pazmiño-Mayorga et al., 2021), which demonstrated energy savings compared to a conventional RD.

5.2. Production of dimethyl ether (DME)

A feed of pure methanol reacts to produce water and dimethyl ether (99.5% mol). Conventional DME production requires high temperatures and pressures and several unit operations. The design problem involves a heterogeneously catalyzed liquid-phase reaction of the type $A \rightleftharpoons B + C$.

The main characteristics driving decisions for technology selection are illustrated in Figure 3b. The reaction rate constant is relatively slow in the framework of RD applications (Q9), the presence of a small two-phase liquid region (Q6) and the absence of azeotropes (Q5).

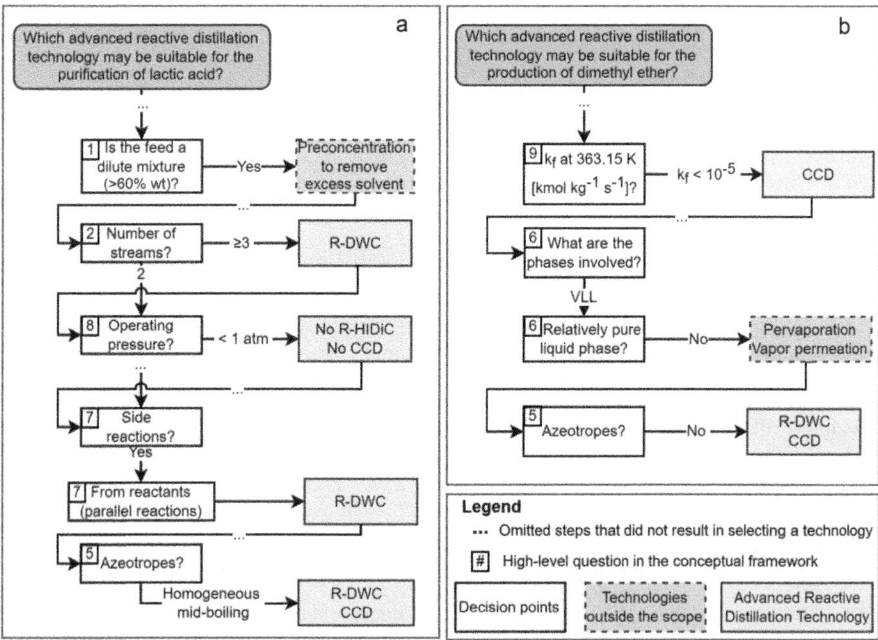

Figure 3. Excerpt of the decision-making methodology and outcomes a) lactic acid purification b) dimethyl ether production

The technologies deemed suitable for DME production are CCD as larger holdups allow longer residence times suitable for the relatively slow reaction. The absence of azeotropes enables the application of R-DWC and CCD without risking the purity of the outlet streams. However, the existence of a small two-phase region suggests that auxiliary equipment may be needed to remove water, such as a membrane. These outcomes were demonstrated with the conceptual design study of an R-DWC that showed energy saving compared with conventional RD (Kiss and Suszwalak, 2012). Also, DME production in a CCD has been studied at the conceptual level (including a patent), indicating that higher purities can be achieved with fewer stages and a lower vapor flow rate (Pătruţ et al., 2014; Kiss et al., 2015).

6. Conclusions

This work showcases a decision-making methodology for the synthesis of advanced RD technologies using chemical system data that can be easily obtained at early stages during flowsheet development. The highlights are the inclusion of novel intensified technologies that are often dismissed in traditional process design settings, the use of thermodynamic properties and kinetic parameters of the chemical systems and a set of heuristics from recent research about RD and advanced distillation. The methodology is demonstrated in two case studies. The results of published studies verify the outcomes of the methodology. A more detailed description of the methodology is under preparation with further case studies to evidence its range of applicability.

Acknowledgements

IPM gratefully acknowledges the full fund support from SENESCYT-Ecuador.

References

Kim, S.Y., Kim, D.M., Lee, B., 2017. Process simulation for the recovery of lactic acid using thermally coupled distillation columns to mitigate the remixing effect. Korean J. Chem. Eng. 34, 1310–1318.

Kiss, A.A., 2013. Advanced distillation technologies: design, control, and applications. Wiley, Chichester, West Sussex, United Kingdom.

Kiss, A.A., Bîldea, C.S., Pătruţ, C., 2015. Process and installation for the production of dialkyl ether. CA2936291A1.

Kiss, A.A., Jobson, M., Gao, X., 2019. Reactive Distillation: Stepping Up to the Next Level of Process Intensification. Ind. Eng. Chem. Res. 58, 5909–5918.

Kiss, A.A., Suszwalak, D.J.-P.C., 2012. Innovative dimethyl ether synthesis in a reactive dividing-wall column. Comput. Chem. Eng. 38, 74–81.

Luyben, W.L., 2013. Distillation design and control using Aspen simulation, 2nd ed. ed. Wiley, Hoboken, N.J.

Pătruţ, C., Bîldea, C.S., Kiss, A.A., 2014. Catalytic cyclic distillation – A novel process intensification approach in reactive separations. Chem. Eng. Process. 81, 1–12.

Pazmiño-Mayorga, I., Jobson, M., Kiss, A.A., 2021. Conceptual design of a dual reactive dividing wall column for downstream processing of lactic acid. Chem. Eng. Process. 164, 108402.

Skiborowski, M., 2018. Process synthesis and design methods for process intensification. Curr. Opin. Chem. Eng., Biotechnology and bioprocess engineering 22, 216–225.

Proceedings of the 14th International Symposium on Process Systems Engineering – PSE 2021+
June 19-23, 2022, Kyoto, Japan
http://dx.doi.org/10.1016/B978-0-323-85159-6.50108-1

Process Synthesis and Intensification for Upgrading Natural Gas Liquids in Shale Gas

Zewei Chen[a], Edwin Andres Rodriguez Gil[a], Rakesh Agrawal[a*]

[a]*Davidson School of Chemical Engineering, Purude University, West Lafayette, Indiana, USA*
agrawalr@purdue.edu

Abstract

In the past two decades, natural gas flaring and venting have increased due to the lack of transforming or transportation infrastructure in emerging shale-gas-producing regions. To reduce carbon emissions and wastage of shale resources, we recently reported several innovative flowsheets for natural gas liquid (NGL) to liquid fuel processes on a small scale near the wellhead (Chen et al., 2021). These processes consist of a direct shale gas dehydrogenation reactor followed by an oligomerization reactor. In this work we perform thermodynamic analysis on both dehydrogenation and oligomerization reactors and demonstrate the benefits of our proposed processes over other processes alternatives. This study also provides a systematic procedure for the synthesis of economically attractive processes for small scale shale gas valorization.

Keywords: shale gas, natural gas liquid, process intensification

1. Introduction

Shale gas is a promising energy resource and chemical feedstock for the transition period towards a sustainable economy and has the potential to be a carbon source for the long term. However, huge amount of shale gas at remote shale gas basins is directly flared (Fisher et al. 2019) due to the lack of infrastructure to transport the gas from well heads to the central processing plant. To avoid long distance transportation, it is essential to convert shale gas to value-added and easily transportable products on site at a distributed scale. Liquid fuel with high market value and large market demand, such as gasoline and diesel are our target products. Unlike current shale gas process where large scales are preferred, simple and intensified processes with least processing steps and least pieces of equipment are favoured for remote shale plays.

Natural gas liquids contained in shale gas are especially of our interest since they are comparably easier to activate and transform to liquid products. While conventional shale gas processing usually follows a hierarchy of “Front-end Separation, NGL activation, NGL upgrading” (He and You 2014), we recently showed that a new process hierarchy of “NGL activation, NGL upgrading, Back-end separation” has significant advantages for small scale installation (Chen et al., 2021a). In this work, we carry out a systematic analysis of the proposed process hierarchy to illustrate its benefits and provide an evolution procedure from the conventional process to the novel processes.

Our process designs evolve from NGL co-processing (Ridha et al., 2018) wherein the NGL mixture after recovery is directly activated and upgraded to liquid fuel, to switched NGL activation and recovery, wherein the NGL recovery step takes place after the NGL activation step. Finally at the backend NGL recovery step, where the NGL recovery step takes place after the NGL has been upgraded to liquid fuel. A two-step conversion of NGL to liquid hydrocarbons via dehydrogenation followed by oligomerization is used as an example to show how these innovative process designs evolve. We synthesize process configurations corresponding to each step in the evolution and illustrate the merits and shortcomings of each configuration through thermodynamic analysis on both dehydrogenation and oligomerization reactors. Higher yield of liquid products, fewer processing steps, reduced numbers of equipment pieces and elimination of energy and capital-intensive units can be achieved. The intensification of these processes would benefit the modularization of shale gas plants and make it possible for onsite distributed production of liquid hydrocarbons for remote shale locations.

2. Base Case Flowsheet

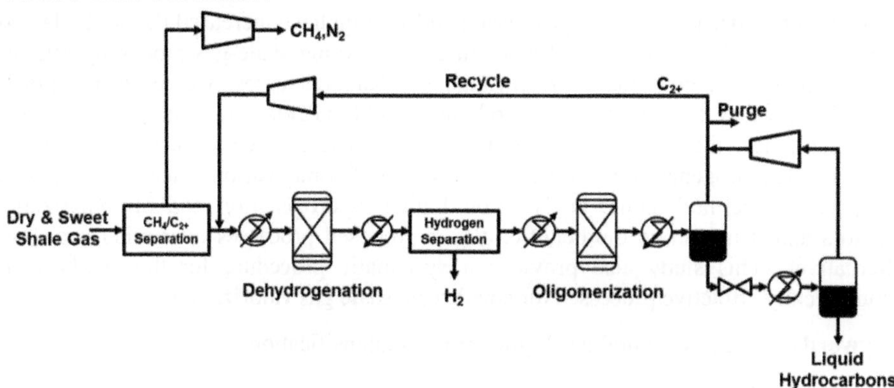

Figure 1: Process I: NGL co-processing proposed by Ridha et al. (2018)

We start with Process I (NGL co-processing) synthesized by Ridha et al., as depicted in Figure 1. In the configuration, the dry and sweet shale gas first goes through a CH_4/C_{2+} separation to separate CH_4 from natural gas liquids. The CH_4/C_{2+} separation unit is a conventional cryogenic demethanizer (Getu et al., 2013). NGL in this stream is then preheated and sent to the catalytic dehydrogenation unit wherein a portion of NGL is converted to their corresponding olefins. The effluent stream is sent to a hydrogen separation unit for hydrogen removal and then the oligomerization unit wherein olefins are converted into longer chain molecules which are liquid in the ambient state. The separation between C_{5+} liquid and light hydrocarbons (C_2-C_5) in stream is performed in a simple two-flash system. In process I (NGL co-processing), NGL and its corresponding olefins are directly sent to the oligomerization reactor without paraffin-olefin separation, and a much simpler separation between C_{5+} liquid and light hydrocarbons is employed. This design is already much simpler than the conventional shale gas process (He and You, 2014).

However, the configuration in Figure 1 is still not economically attractive for a 10 million standard cubic feet per day (MMSCFD) small scale plant at the gas gathering station, due to the following reasons: 1) The front-end separation consists of a series of energy intensive and costly unit operations, especially the cryogenic demethanizer, 2) The catalytic dehydrogenation reactor has limited conversion and selectivity, and 3) There are significant C_{2+} losses at multiple locations of the flowsheet, including the hydrogen membrane, CH_4/C_{2+} separation, and purge stream. In section 3, we will perform a systematic analysis on the dehydrogenation and oligomerization to show how we overcome these drawbacks step by step.

3. Systematic Analysis and Evolution of Process Configurations

We perform a thermodynamic analysis on the dehydrogenation reactor in Figure 1. There are two state-of-the-art methods for dehydrogenation: thermal dehydrogenation, and catalytic dehydrogenation. Catalytic dehydrogenation is operated at a relatively low temperature, usually below 700 ^{0}C and has a high selectivity towards olefins. For example, propane catalytic dehydrogenation is a widely used process for propylene production. Thermal dehydrogenation, on the other hand, is operated at a higher temperature and has a low selectivity due to cracking. A good example of this is steam cracking for olefin production. Although there are multiple efforts in literature studying catalytic ethane dehydrogenation (Dai et al., 2021), this technology is not suitable for a simple plug flow reactor due to equilibrium limitation. Figure 2 shows the equilibrium conversion for a pure ethane feed at different operating conditions. Equilibrium conversion curves show that the maximum conversion of ethane is only around 40% at 700 ^{0}C and 1 bar. The equilibrium conversion marks the highest conversion possible, while in a real catalytic dehydrogenation reactor, the conversion tends to be lower than this value. To achieve a higher conversion, one can either operate the reactor at a lower partial pressure or at a higher temperature. However, when operated at a higher temperature, thermal dehydrogenation is already fast enough and there is no need for the catalyst. The conventional ethane steam cracker only has a residence time of 0.2s and practitioners must quench the effluent stream to stop side reactions (Karimzadeh et al., 2009). Further decreasing the total pressure of the reactor results in vacuum operation, which is also not a good idea for hydrocarbon reactions. While ethane catalytic dehydrogenation may be incorporated in an advanced reactor design, such as membrane reactor to overcome the equilibrium conversion limit (Champagnie et al., 1992), complex reactor designs are not suitable options for small scale installation due to limited capital expenditure.

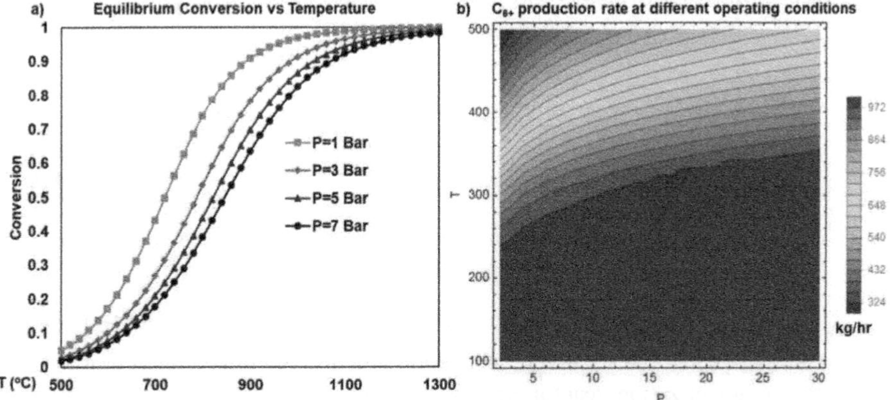

Figure 2: Sensitivity analysis over the dehydrogenation and oligomerization reactors. a) Ethane conversion as a function of operating temperature at different operating pressures, and b) C_{6+} production rate (kg/h) at different temperatures and pressures in the oligomerization reactor.

To achieve high conversion, thermal dehydrogenation is the only option to keep a simple reactor design. The conventional steam cracker is usually operated at 850 ^{0}C with 1:3 mass ratio of water to hydrocarbon in the cracker. The partial pressure of hydrocarbons in the steam cracker is around 1 bar, which indicates around 85%

conversion in Figure 2. In the steam cracking system, steam serves as an inert to decrease the partial pressure of hydrocarbons. However, steam cracker contains a complex system for steam generation, preheating, and post-reaction dehydration, which is also not suitable for small scale installation.

To overcome the thermodynamic as well as economic challenge, it is essential to identify an alternative inert in the system which could decrease the partial pressure of hydrocarbons without introducing additional complexity to the process design. CH_4, which is already mixed with the NGL in the shale gas from a well and a byproduct in the ethane thermal dehydrogenation becomes the perfect choice. Rather than separating CH_4 before dehydrogenation, leaving CH_4 in the feed to the reactor significantly simplifies the entire process. Process II (Switched NGL recovery and activation), the switched NGL recovery and activation, is a process containing such a process sequence (Figure 3). In this configuration, the dry and sweet shale gas is directly sent to thermal dehydrogenation unit and the CH_4/NGL separation takes place after the thermal dehydrogenation step. For a Bakken shale gas containing 57.8% CH_4, 20.0% C_2H_6, 11.4% C_3H_8, and 5.1% heavier components, when the total pressure of the reactor is 2 bar, the partial pressure of NGL components is only 0.6 bar, leading to a higher conversion and selectivity towards olefins.

Furthermore, the conventional steam cracker is followed by a demethanizer to remove CH_4, which is produced in the steam cracker as a byproduct. This demethanizer is a duplication of the front-end demethanizer, resulting in increased capital cost. In Process II (Switched NGL recovery and activation), the repeated demethanizer is now eliminated (Figure 3). The C_{2+} loss in this configuration is also significantly reduced because this process does not have a H_2/NGL separation and a purge stream as in Process I (NGL co-processing), which could be the sources of C_{2+} loss.

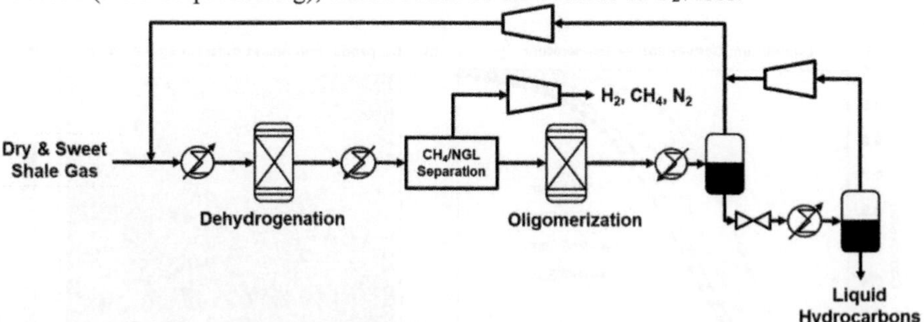

Figure 3: Process II: process configuration with switched NGL recovery and activation

We can further switch the CH_4/NGL separation unit and oligomerization unit. CH_4 and H_2 in the oligomerization reactor serve as thermal mass to somewhat mitigate the temperature increase and as a result, less reactor beds are needed for the process (Chen et al., 2021a). However, it results in reduced partial pressure of olefins, leading to a decreased conversion. Again, we performed a sensitivity analysis on the oligomerization reactor at different temperatures and pressures. The analysis is performed for a 1000 kg/h pure ethylene feed, using RGibbs model in Aspen Plus and assuming olefins from C_2 to C_{20} are produced. From the analysis, we observe that the C_{6+} yield is a weak function of pressure. At an operating temperature of 200 ^{0}C ~ 300 ^{0}C, almost all ethylene is converted to C_{6+}, even if operated at a low pressure. This analysis confirmed that it is beneficial to further switch the order between the CH_4/NGL separation unit and oligomerization reactor.

Figure 4 shows Process III (Backend separation) wherein the oligomerization takes place before any separations, and it is denoted as back-end NGL recovery configuration. In this configuration, objective of the separation task is to separate the effluent stream from the oligomerization reactor into three streams, a gaseous stream containing H_2, CH_4, N_2 which could be further treated in a membrane separation unit to obtain pipeline natural gas, a recycle stream sent back to the dehydrogenation reactor, and a liquid hydrocarbon product stream containing C_{6+}. An absorption column using a portion of the liquid product stream as the absorbent is used for the separation of CH_4 and NGL. Readers may refer to Chen et al.'s work for detail description of this process. This backend separation system is much simpler and less costly than the conventional front-end demethanizer. The reason being that, as all the separations are performed together in the end, the separation task could become easier, and synergies could be identified among all separations. In Process III (Backend separation), if we denote the feed stream as ABC, in which A is H_2, CH_4, N_2, B is C_2-C_5 hydrocarbons, C is C_{6+} liquid hydrocarbons, then the separation in Process III (Backend separation) could be perceived as sloppy separation A/ABC and ABC/C. While in Process I (NGL co-processing) and II (Switched NGL recovery and activation), all the separations are sharp separations. The sloppy separations could be less energy intensive than the sharp separations, with the only penalty of slightly increasing the recycle ratio.

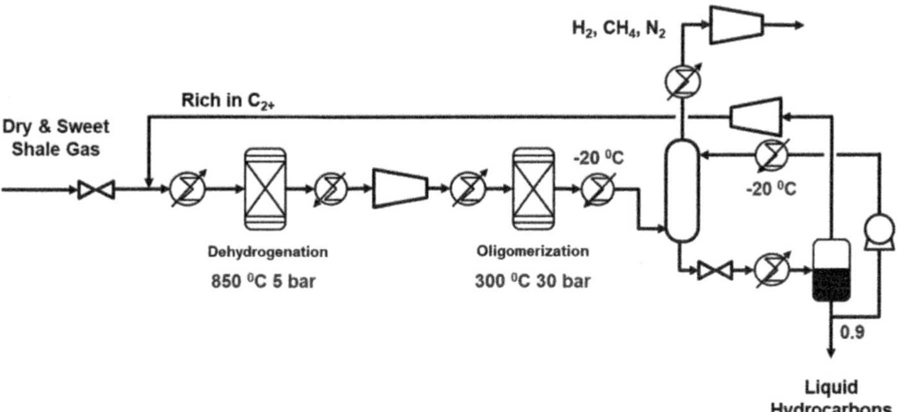

Figure 4: Process III: our process configuration with backend separation (Chen et al., 2021a)

From the simulations and thermodynamic analysis results above, we can conclude several general principles for process synthesis and intensification: when a feed mixture contains inert components and has constituents that are also created in downstream processing, which must be separated downstream, then one should carefully evaluate the merit of (1) avoiding upstream separation of the constituents from the feed mixture, and (2) arranging the processing sequence so the duplication of separation between any two components is avoided, (3) arranging the process sequence for the maximum thermodynamic benefits and (4) arranging most of the separations next to each other and identifying synergies among them. Furthermore, potential advantages of the inert in the feed for the downstream endothermic reactions, which are unfavoured according to the Le Chatelier's principle, should be carefully explored against the increase in the cost due to an increase in the equipment size. Using these principles, we recently proposed an efficient and cost-effective process for propylene and ethylene production from shale gas (Chen and Agrawal, 2021b).

4. Conclusions

In this work, we described a series of processes for shale gas valorization at remote shale gas basins evolving from NGL co-processing (Ridha et al., 2018) wherein the NGL mixture is directly activated and upgraded to liquid fuel. However, we switched NGL recovery and activation steps and used the CH_4 present in the shale gas as inert for the NGL dehydrogenation step. Finally, unconverted NGLs and methane are separated in one simple separation step after conversion of olefins to liquid fuel. We performed sensitivity analysis on both dehydrogenation and oligomerization reactors and revealed the effects of operating pressure and temperature over the performance of the reactor. In terms of this, we made decisions whether to switch the order between separations and reactions and demonstrated that the backend NGL recovery process has advantages over the other two previous methods and hence more suitable for small scale installation. We also summarized several general principles for process intensification which could be potentially applied to other reaction-separation networks.

References

A. M. Champagnie, T. T. Tsotsis, R. G., Minet, and E. Wagner, 1992, The study of ethane dehydrogenation in a catalytic membrane reactor. Journal of Catalysis, 134(2), 713-730.

Z. Chen, Y. Li, W. P. Oladipupo, A. R. Edwin Gil, G. Sawyer, R. Agrawal, 2021a, Alternative ordering of process hierarchy for more efficient and cost-effective valorization of shale resources. Cell Reports Physical Science, 100581.

Z. Chen, R. Agrawal, 2021b, Alternative Processing Sequence for Process Simplification, Cost Reduction, and Enhanced Light Olefin Recovery from Shale Gas. ACS Sustainable Chemistry & Engineering, 9, 41, 13893–13901

Y. Dai, X. Gao, Q. Wang, X. Wan, C. Zhou, Y. Yang, 2021, Recent progress in heterogeneous metal and metal oxide catalysts for direct dehydrogenation of ethane and propane. Chemical Society Reviews, 50, 5590-5630.

D. Fisher, M. J. Wooster, 2019, Multi-decade global gas flaring change inventoried using the ATSR-1, ATSR-2, AATSR and SLSTR data records. Remote Sensing of Environment, 232, 111298.

M. Getu, S. Mahadzir, N. V. D. Long, M. Lee, 2013, Techno-economic analysis of potential natural gas liquid (NGL) recovery processes under variations of feed compositions. Chemical Engineering Research and Design, 91(7), 1272-1283.

C. He, F. You, 2014, Shale gas processing integrated with ethylene production: novel process designs, exergy analysis, and techno-economic analysis. Industrial & Engineering Chemistry Research, 53(28), 11442-11459.

R. Karimzadeh, H. R., Godini, M. Ghashghaee, 2009, Flowsheeting of steam cracking furnaces. Chemical Engineering Research and Design, 87(1), 36-46.

T. Ridha, Y. Li, E. Gençer, J. J. Siirola, J. T. Miller, F. H., Ribeiro, R. Agrawal, 2018, Valorization of shale gas condensate to liquid hydrocarbons through catalytic dehydrogenation and oligomerization. Processes, 6(9), 139

Proceedings of the 14th International Symposium on Process Systems Engineering – PSE 2021+
June 19-23, 2022, Kyoto, Japan
http://dx.doi.org/10.1016/B978-0-323-85159-6.50109-3

Energy-Efficient Direct Cyclohexene to Cyclohexanol Process by Heat Pump Assisted Reactive Distillation

Xinyan Liu[a], Yang Lei[a], Hao Luo [a*], Xiaoqin Wu[a] and Rafiqul Gani[b]
[a] Department of Chemical & Chemical Engineering, Wuhan University of Science and Technology, Wuhan 430081, China
[b]PSE for SPEED, Skyttemosen 6, DK-3450 Allerod, Denmark
haoluo@wust.edu.cn

Abstract

Cyclohexanol is regarded as an important raw material to produce many useful chemicals such as hexanedioic acid, hexamethylenediamine, and caprolactam. However, it's production usually leads to high energy consumption. Traditional technologies include three routes: oxidation of cyclohexane, hydrogenation of phenol and direct hydration of cyclohexene. Avoiding the risk of explosion and a low price of raw material, the direct hydration of cyclohexene route is selected in this paper. To enhance the energy efficiency, a novel heat-pump-assisted reactive distillation process (HPRD) is proposed and simulated through AspenPlus. The discharge compressor pressure is optimized to be 3.2 bar to minimize the cost. For purposes of comparison, two conventional processes, aqueous-phase-refluxed reactive distillation with a stripper (ARDS) and organic-phase-refluxed reactive distillation with a stripper (ORDS), are also simulated and optimized through sensitivity analysis. All these three processes are evaluated through energy and economic analysis. The results show that the ORDS process saves the total energy and annualized cost by 15% and 12%, respectively, compared with the ARDS process, while the heat-pump-assisted process realizes a significant energy saving of 65% and achieves 33% reduction in total annualized cost, demonstrating a high economic feasibility.

Keywords: Cyclohexene to cyclohexanol; Direct hydration; Reactive distillation; Heat-pump; Process optimization.

1. Introduction

Cyclohexanol, as an important intermediate chemical, has been widely used in the production of hexanedioic acid, hexamethylenediamine, caprolactam and many more. These chemicals are the main raw materials for producing polymers such as Nylon 6,6 and Nylon 6. Therefore, cyclohexanol is usually a raw material in huge demand in the chemical industry and receives much attention in terms of their synthesis approaches and catalysts research. One of the main traditional routes for cyclohexanol production is the direct hydration of cyclohexene, overcoming the risk of explosion and high cost, has been identified as the main research direction for cyclohexanol production.

The direct hydration method allows cyclohexene contacting with water by an additive reaction to produce cyclohexanol. However, the reaction occurs in the liquid phase, and the immiscibility of cyclohexene and water leads to a low conversion rate. What's more, the equilibrium reaction would also result in low production efficiency. In order to reduce energy consumption, reactive distillation, as one of the technologies for process intensification, has been applied in previous studies. The production rate of cyclohexanol could achieve a significant increase through the continuous removal, breaking the limitation of equilibrium reaction and promoting the reaction to the forward direction. Chen et al. (2014) proposed a reactive distillation process making full use of liquid-liquid splitting of the binary cyclohexanol-water azeotrope. Ye et al. (2014) introduced a side reactor configuration. Both strategies could achieve significant energy-efficiency and cost-saving. Although direct cyclohexene hydration as an alternative has been suggested, overall process simulation and evaluation as well as detailed analysis of energy and economic aspects are still scarce. To improve the energy efficiency, some novel technologies such as heat pump, extractive distillation and different flowsheet configurations with different phase reflux options could also be considered.

In this work, a novel heat-pump-assisted reactive distillation process (HPRD), combining two technologies: reactive distillation and vapor recompression (VRC) heat pump, is proposed for direct hydration cyclohexene to cyclohexanol, thus allowing a significant reduction of the energy requirements for cyclohexanol purification. The process is simulated with rigorous AspenPlus modules. For a comprehensive comparison, two conventional reactive distillation processes with different phase reflux options (aqueous and organic phase), ARDS (aqueous-phase-refluxed reactive distillation with a stripper) and ORDS (organic-phase-refluxed reactive distillation with a stripper) are also simulated. All these three processes are evaluated by energy and economic analysis.

2. Problem Statement

As a useful material for surfactant production and other industrial utilization, cyclohexanol (NOL) should have a minimum purity of 99 wt%, but this specification requires high energy consumption, leading to a large energy penalty. Using aqueous-phase-refluxed reactive distillation (RD) with a stripper, owing to the enhanced equilibrium conversion and full use of liquid-liquid separation, the energy requirements could be reduced by 46.76% from 2603 kJ/(kg NOL) to 1386 kJ/ (kg NOL) (Ye et al., 2014). However, the energy and economic costs needed for cyclohexanol production are still considerably high, especially when taking into account the price gap between cyclohexane and cyclohexanol. To address this issue, we integrate a heat-pump into the top of the RD-column because, conceptually, less energy would be needed in the reboiler through heat integration, compared with the conventional reactive distillation process. Also, the objective is to confirm previously published results with another thermodynamic model as well as the integrated heat-pump design by studying different integration schemes.

3. Reaction kinetics and phase equilibrium model

The parameters of kinetic models are obtained from Sun et al., (2021). The reaction of direct hydration of cyclohexene (ENE) with water to produce cyclohexanol (NOL) is given by Eq. (1) and the kinetic equation for this reaction is given by Eq. (2):

$$\text{ENE} + \text{W} \rightleftharpoons \text{NOL} \tag{1}$$

$$-r = -\frac{dC_{W}}{mdt} = 54775.19\exp\left(\frac{-57894.54}{R_{g}T}\right)C_{ENE}C_{W} - 1.7327\exp\left(\frac{-16451.74}{R_{g}T}\right)C_{NOL} \quad (2)$$

Where, r is reaction rate in mol/(L s gcat), m is mass of the catalyst in g, T is temperature in K, CENE is water concentration mol/L, CW is the concentration of water mol/L, CNOL is the concentration of NOL mol/L.Rgis the ideal gas constant, 8.314 J/(mol.K). It is assumed that the catalyst occupies half of the total hold of each reactive tray, and 90% of the tray area is considered as the active area to consider the space for downcomer. The column diameter is obtained from Column Internals in AspenPlus. The catalyst is Amberlyst 36 cation exchange resin and its density is assumed to be 770 kg/m^3.

The Universal Quasi–Chemical/Hayden-O'Connell equation of state with Henry's law (UNIQUAC-HOC) property model is selected as an appropriate model in ApsenPlus to describe the vapor-liquid-liquid equilibrium. Table 1 lists the UNIQUAC binary parameters. Table 2 compares the model predicted azeotropic composition with that reported in the literature and also with the NRTL model reported in our published work (Liu et al., 2022), the relative error is smaller than 3% and the two models demonstrate almost the same results. Therefore, it is reasonable to use UNIQUAC-HOC model for process simulation.

Table 1 the UNIQUAC binary parameters in the system

Component *i*	Component *j*	a_{ij}	a_{ji}	b_{ij}	b_{ji}
C_6H_{10}	H_2O	0	0	-1024.1	-466.35
$C_6H_{12}O$	H_2O	0	0	-342.857	26.0981

Table 2 the comparison of boiling point for different systems

Component	Literature values (Gould, 1973)		Calculated values using NRTL (Liu et al., 2022)		Calculated values using UNIQUAC	
	T/°C	Molar composition	T/°C	Molar composition	T/°C	Molar composition
ENE	82.75	-	82.88	-	82.88	-
W	100.00	-	100.02	-	100.02	-
(ENE-W)	70.80	(0.308,0.692)	70.62	(0.314,0.686)	70.58	(0.314,0.686)
NOL	160.65	-	160.84	-	160.84	-
(NOL-W)	97.80	(0.927,0.073)	98.24	(0.929,0.071)	98.46	(0.929,0.071)

Note: ENE denotes cyclohexene; W denotes water; NOL denotes cyclohexanol

4. Process Simulation

In this work, for all processes described below, including the ARDS, ORDS and HPRD. The process simulations were conducted using the rigorous modules (RADFRAC). in AspenPlus. The productivity of cyclohexanol is set to 10016 kg/hr (100 kmol/hr).

4.1. Aqueous-phase-refluxed reactive distillation with a stripper (ARDS)

The ARDS process contains two distillation columns, one is reactive distillation (RD), the other is a distillation stripper in which the product (NOL) is purified. The aqueous phase from the RD-column decanter is fully refluxed to the top of the RD-column, thereby, the organic phase from the decanter is 99.75% cyclohexene, which can be recycled to the RD-column with its make-up, the bottom outlet is the cyclohexanol-water mixture, which is separated by a decanter after cooling. The aqueous phase from the decanter is recycled back with fresh water into the RD-column, the organic phase is fed into a stripper to obtain 99.9 wt% cyclohexanol. A small heat exchanger is used to heat the recycled water stream to reduce the reboiler duty (691 kW) of the RD-column. In this process, the temperature of the RD-reboiler is 121.45 °C and that of the stripper is 161.74 °C, thereby low pressure (LP, 6atm 159 °C) steam and medium pressure (MP, 11 atm, 184 °C) steam are required. The original detailed flowsheet is given in Liu et al. (2022).

4.2. Organic-phase-refluxed reactive distillation with a stripper (ORDS)

The flowsheet of ORDS also contains reactive distillation and a stripper, similar to that of ARDS. The main difference is that the organic phase from the decanter is fully recycled back to the top of the RD-column. Therefore, the bottom outlet is a mixture of cyclohexene, cyclohexanol, and H_2O with a lower reboiler temperature (105.59 °C). Unlike ARDS, where the second decanter is used to split the cyclohexanol-water mixture, in ORDS it is used to split the cyclohexanol-water-cyclohexene mixture, therefore, the remaining organic phase is the mixture of cyclohexene-cyclohexanol, which is further separated by a stripper with an additional decanter. It should be noted that the temperature difference between the RD-column condenser and reboiler in ORDS is smaller than that of ARDS. Also, organic-phase-refluxed method results in a higher cyclohexene concentration in the RD-column, leading to a better energy utilization efficiency of the reactive distillation column. The original detailed flowsheet is given in Liu et al. (2022).

4.3. Heat-pump-assisted reactive distillation (HPRD)

Figure 1 presents the flowsheet of heat-pump-assisted reactive distillation with its mass and energy balance from AspenPlus simulation. The results are almost the same with that reported in our previous work (Liu et al., 2022) in which the NRTL model is used. Compared with the ORDS process, the main difference is that a heat pump is used to compress the vapor phase to 3.2 atm at the top of the reactive distillation column to increase the stream temperature so that it could be used to heat the reboiler at the bottom, thereby an extra heat exchanger is required. A flash tank is also used to provide the bottom vapor phase for the RD-column.

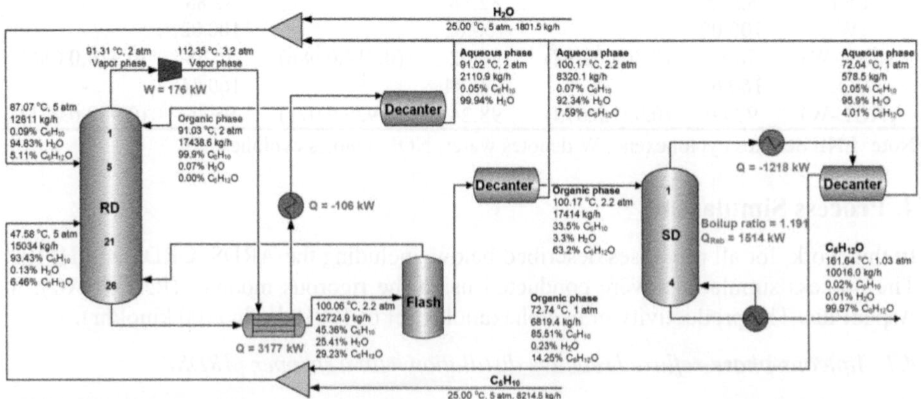

Figure 1 The flowsheet of the novel heat-pump assisted reactive distillation column

5. Process Evaluation

5.1. Evaluation method

Energy analysis: To assess the total energy consumption under the same criterion, the electricity is converted into the equivalent heat duty through a coefficient (see Eq. (3)).

$$TEC = W_e/\eta + Q_{th} \tag{3}$$

Where, We is the electricity consumption in pump and compressor, Q_{th} is the heat duty in flash and stripper, η is the conversion efficiency of thermal energy (heat duty) to electricity, which is usually around 0.3~0.4 (Luo et al., 2015).

Economic analysis: For the economic analysis, the total cost is often calculated from the sum of the annualized capital cost (ACC) and the total operating expenditure (OPEX). The ACC is computed by translating the total capital expenditure (CAPEX) into annualized ones. All the ACC, CAPEX and OPEX are calculated based on the procedure given by (Liu et al., 2021). The purchased equipment cost and utility cost in OPEX are computed from Aspen Process Economic Analyzer (APEA). Considering the same productivity of the different processes, the raw material (cyclohexene and fresh water) is not included in the comparison.

5.2. Evaluation results

For the energy consumption, the total energy consumption (TEC) of the three processes, including electricity (converted by equivalent heat) and heat duty are shown in Figure 2a. Compared with ARDS process, the ORDS process shows a reduction of 15% in TEC, demonstrating the advantage of the process with organic reflux, which could increase the concentration of ENE, enhancing the conversion rate. For the HPRD process, the TEC saving becomes 65%, which is a remarkable figure, implying a very high energy efficiency. Through economic evaluation, As shown in Figure 2b, it can be observed that the annualized capital cost (ACC) contributes little (< 3%) of the total cost compared with the operational expenditure (OPEX) containing the fixed operation cost (FOC) and variable operation cost (VOC) in three processes, indicating the predominance of OPEX in total annualized cost and the importance on energy saving. Compared with the ARDS, ORDS process, the HPRD process achieves a reduction of 23%, 33%, respectively, realizing significant economic-saving. The new analysis confirms the HPRD results reported earlier as the best among the different alternatives studied.

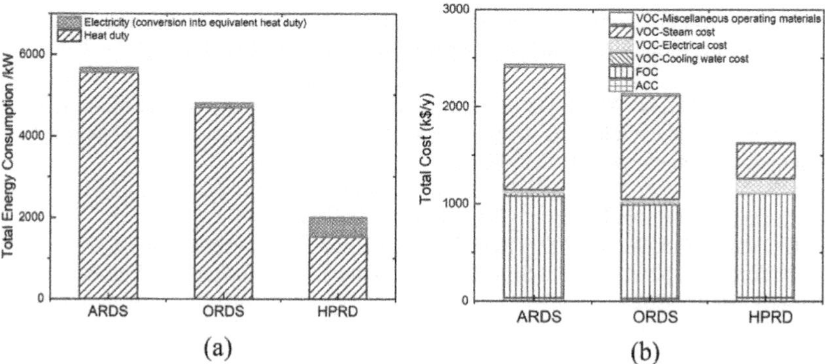

Figure 2 Total energy and economic results in three processes (a) total energy consumption (b) total cost

6. Conclusion

In this work, with cyclohexanol in a huge demand in current industry, the reactive distillation (RD) process for direct hydration of cyclohexene to cyclohexanol has been studied. The parameters of reaction kinetic model and phase equilibrium models are obtained from reported data in published papers and the database in AspenPlus. The prediction of phase equilibrium, which plays a very important role in this study, has been cross-checked not only with available data but also with different property models. The UNIQUAC model has been found to give similar results as the NRTL model. Two reactive distillation processes with conventional flowsheet are simulated and assessed, one is aqueous-phase-refluxed reactive distillation with a stripper (ARDS), the other is organic-phase-refluxed reactive distillation with a stripper (ORDS). To improve the energy efficiency, different heat-pump-assisted reactive distillation process (HPRD) alternatives have been studied and a novel scheme has been identified. The key operation parameters are optimized through sensitivity analysis. Different alternatives have been compared through rigorous process simulation and evaluated in terms of energy and economic data. Results show that the performance of ORDS is better due to a slightly higher conversion of cyclohexene to cyclohexanol. The HPRD process, however, realizes a significant energy saving of 58% and achieves a 23% reduction in total energy consumption and total annualized cost, as compared to ORDS, indicating the possibility of a good economic-saving and environmentally friendly technology.

Acknowledgements

This study was financially supported by the National Undergraduate Training Program for Innovation and Entrepreneurship (No. S202110488032) and the Scientific Research Foundation from Wuhan University of Science and Technology (No.1050038; No.1050040).

References

B. C. Chen, B. Y. Yu, Y. L. Lin, H. P. Huang, I.L. Chien, 2014. Reactive-Distillation Process for Direct Hydration of Cyclohexene to Produce Cyclohexanol. Industrial & Engineering Chemistry Research 53, 7079-7086.

R.F. Gould, 1973. Azeotropic Data—III, Copyright, Advances in Chemistry Series.

X. Liu, Y. Chen, S. Zeng, X. Zhang, X. Liang, R. Gani, G.M. Kontogeorgis, 2021. Separation of NH_3 /CO_2 from melamine tail gas with ionic liquid: Process evaluation and thermodynamic properties modelling. Separation and Purification Technology 274, 119007.

X. Liu, H. Luo, Y. Lei, X. Wu, R. Gani, 2022. Heat-pump-assisted reactive distillation for direct hydration of cyclohexene to cyclohexanol: a sustainable alternative. Separation and Purification Technology 280, 119808.

H. Luo, C.S. Bildea, A.A. Kiss, 2015. Novel Heat-Pump-Assisted Extractive Distillation for Bioethanol Purification. Ind. Eng. Chem. Res. 54, 2208-2213.

D. Sun, H. Tian, J. Sun, W. Xu, 2021. Reactive Distillation for the Production of Cyclohexanol: Experiments and Simulations. Chemical and Biochemical Engineering Quarterly 34, 223-232.

J. Ye, J. Li, Y. Sha, H. Lin, D. Zhou, 2014. Evaluation of Reactive Distillation and Side Reactor Configuration for Direct Hydration of Cyclohexene to Cyclohexanol. Industrial & Engineering Chemistry Research 53, 1461-1469.

Proceedings of the 14th International Symposium on Process Systems Engineering – PSE 2021+
June 19-23, 2022, Kyoto, Japan
http://dx.doi.org/10.1016/B978-0-323-85159-6.50110-X

Sustainable Process Intensification of Refrigerant Mixture Separation and Management: A Multiscale Material Screening and Process Design Approach

Mohammed Sadaf Monjur, Ashfaq Iftakher, M. M. Faruque Hasan*

Artie McFerrin Department of Chemical Engineering, Texas A&M University, College Station, TX 77843-3122, USA.
hasan@tamu.edu

Abstract

High global warming potential of refrigerant gases have prompted immediate attention to ensure minimum usage and recovery of hydrofluorocarbons (HFCs). Due to the azeotropic nature of HFC mixtures, advanced separation processes are required for selective separation and recovery. We perform a multiscale separation, intensification and material-to-process systems analysis of R-410A, which is a HFC mixture of R-32 and R-125 refrigerants, using extractive distillation (ED) and ionic liquids (ILs) as solvents. Under different design objectives, we demonstrate improved process performance of the obtained flowsheets in terms of process economics, energy consumption and sustainability. Specifically, when minimization the overall separation cost, we achieve upto 21% lower cost than that of a base design. Additionally, when minimizing CO_2-eqv emission, we achieve process configurations with up to 60% and 50% reductions in energy and emission, respectively. We also performed an IL-process performance mapping considering both cost and equivalent energy consumption as functions of IL-selectivity. Our analysis shows that R-32 selective ILs would lead to processes with better performances. For such cases, the optimal IL candidates would most likely have Henry's constant between 0.4 and 1.6 MPa with energy consumption as low as 500 kJ/kg of HFC mixture.

Keywords: Sustainable Process Intensification; Process Synthesis; Material Screening; Refrigerant Separation; Extractive Distillation

1. Introduction

R-410A belongs to a family of hydrofluorocarbons (HFCs) which are commonly used as refrigerants in domestic and commercial cooling systems. Due to lower ozone depletion potentials, HFCs are predominantly used to replace chlorofluorocarbons (CFCs). However, high global warming potential (GWP) plagues the sustainable usage of HFCs. About 2–3% of the total global greenhouse gas (GHG) emission is due to the millions of tons of worldwide HFC emission (Purohit and Höglund-Isaksson, 2017). To combat this issue, the Kigali Amendment to the Montreal Protocol recommended cutting the global HFC emissions by 80–85% by 2047 (Pardo et al., 2021). In addition, low GWP refrigerants (e.g., hydrofluoroolefins, hydrocarbons, etc.) are proposed to be used in place of HFCs. Therefore, it is desirable to minimize the amount of already existing HFCs. Incineration is not a practical option since it would result in the release of a large amount of CO_2 into the atmosphere. Recycling, on the other hand, may have a market value of more than a billion dollars in the U.S. At the same time, HFCs can be chemically converted to low GWP hydrofluoroolefins (Pardo et al., 2021). However, recycling HFCs pose a significant challenge as they often form azeotropes or close-boiling mixtures that often behave as single fluid. Consequently, conventional separation techniques, such as cryogenic distillation are highly energy and cost-intensive, and pose significant operational challenges (Pardo et al., 2021). Process intensification techniques, such as extractive distillation (ED), can be used to resolve these challenges (Tian et al., 2018; Demirel et al., 2019). ED processes depend on suitable solvent selection. To combat this issue, ionic liquids (ILs) have garnered significant attention as potential solvents for ED-based separation of the azeotropic HFC mixtures. More specifically, ILs can selectively absorb a particular refrigerant from a mixture of HFCs, thereby improving the efficiency of absorption refrigeration processes. In addition, the negligible vapor pressure of ILs ensures that the toxicity and the contamination of the refrigerant gas with solvent can be prevented (Faúndez et al., 2013).

Although, several works have been reported in the literature on extractive separation applications (Finberg and Shiflett, 2021; Faúndez et al., 2013), there is a need for systematic analysis of ED performance for different ILs as solvents. In this work, we report SPICE_ED (Synthesis and Process Intensification of Chemical Enterprises Involving Extractive Distillation) framework for detailed process synthesis, intensification and optimization. We demonstrate the framework using two ILs, namely $[C_4C_1im][PF_6]$ and $[C_4C_1im][BF_4]$ and carry out rigorous ED modeling and analysis to investigate the process performance in terms of energy requirement, sustainability, and process economics. We extend our analysis to hypothetical ILs by utilizing the temperature dependent binary interaction parameters of vapor-liquid equilibrium (VLE) thermodynamics and perform a material-property-process-performance mapping. We anticipate that such a mapping will direct the experimental efforts in synthesizing new ILs with superior performance.

2. Problem Representation

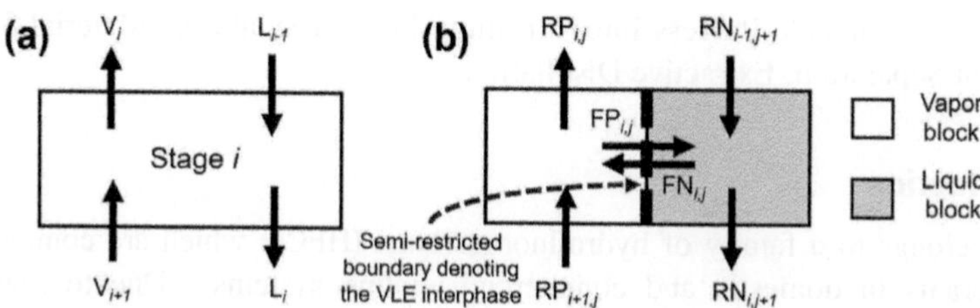

Figure 1: Distillation column tray: (a) conventional representation, (b) equivalent building block-based representation.

In this section, we provide a brief overview of the SPICE_ED framework which is then used for the detailed synthesis and optimization of R-410A separation process. In this framework, we express the physicochemical phenomena through the building-block based representation (Demirel et al., 2017; Monjur et al., 2021a,b), where sets of blocks are arranged in a two-dimensional grid to represent a superstructure. Eqs. 1–4 provide a simplified (not exhaustive) formulation of the superstructure. We denote the position of blocks in the superstructure by i (row number) and j (column number). Figure 1a depicts the conventional representation of a single ED column tray, whereas Figure 1b depicts building block-based representation of a single tray. Two blocks are used to represent the two phases, and the dashed vertical line between the blocks represent the phase boundary. In this manner, we require two series of blocks to represent the whole ED column. We represent the material balance for each component k (Eq. 1), where material flow rates in vertical and horizontal directions are denoted by $R_{i,j,k}$ and $F_{i,j,k}$, respectively. We denote flow rates of fresh feed f, product p, and jump streams from block (i, j) to block (i', j') by $M_{i,j,k,f}$, $N_{i,j,k,p}$, and $J_{i,j,i',j',k}$ respectively. We express the energy balance for each block (Eq. 2), which considers stream enthalpies along with work and heat from external utility sources.

$$\begin{aligned} &F_{i,j-1,k} + R_{i-1,j,k} - F_{i,j,k} - R_{i,j,k} + \sum_{f \in FS} M_{i,j,k,f} - \sum_{p \in PS} N_{i,j,k,p} \\ &+ \sum_{(i',j') \in Link} J_{i',j',i,j,k} - \sum_{(i',j') \in Link} J_{i,j,i',j',k} = 0, \quad \forall\ i,j,k \end{aligned} \tag{1}$$

$$\begin{aligned} &EF_{i,j-1} + ER_{i-1,j} - EF_{i,j} - ER_{i,j} + EM_{i,j} - EN_{i,j} + EJ^{f}_{i,j} - EJ^{p}_{i,j} \\ &+ W^{comp}_{i,j} - W^{exp}_{i,j} + W^{pump}_{i,j} - W^{val}_{i,j} + Q^{h}_{i,j} - Q^{c}_{i,j} = 0, \quad \forall\ i,j \end{aligned} \tag{2}$$

$$\mathbf{f}^{ph}_{i,j,k,ph} = \mathbf{f}^{equil}(K^{eq}_{i,j,k,ph}, T_{i,j}, P_{i,j}, y_{i,j,k}, y_{i,j+1,k}, z_{i,j,ph}), \quad \forall\ i,j,k,\ \ ph \in Equil \tag{3}$$

$$\mathbf{f}^{ph}_{i,j,k,ph} - M(1 - z_{i,j,ph}) \leq y_{i,j,k} \leq \mathbf{f}^{ph}_{i,j,k,ph} + M(1 - z_{i,j,ph}), \quad \forall\ i,j,k,ph \tag{4}$$

For the R-410A separation process, we rely on VLE based ED process. Therefore, the phenomena set ph in Eq. 3 contains VLE-based separation phenomena. The equilibrium based separation depends upon equilibrium rate constant, temperature, pressure, and composition, which are denoted by $K^{eq}_{i,j,k,ph}$, $T_{i,j}$, $P_{i,j}$, and $y_{i,j,k}$, respectively. Based on the value of the binary variable, $z_{i,j,ph} \in \{0, 1\}$, the appropriate separation phenomena is activated (Eq. 4). Following previous work (Shiflett and Yokozeki, 2006), we model the solubility of the HFCs in the IL using the Gamma-Phi based method, where the liquid phase activity coefficient is estimated by the NRTL model.

3. Extractive Distillation Process Synthesis for R-410A Separation

3.1. Base Design

For the separation of R-410A mixture, we consider a typical ED based process configuration as base case design, which is shown in Figure 2. $[C_4C_1im][PF_6]$ is used as the solvent to break the azeotrope. R-410A enters the ED column at stage 21 with a flow rate of 100 kg/h, while the recirculating IL enters at stage 2. The ED column operates at 10 bar with a reflux ratio of 0.25 and has total 28 stages. As R-32 is more soluble in $[C_4C_1im][PF_6]$, it leaves the column with the IL at the bottom while the less soluble R-125 separates out as distillate product at the top. The rich IL from the bottom of the ED column is sent to two sequential flash separators for regeneration, which operate at 1 bar and 0.1 bar, respectively. The combined vapor product from the flash separators has a R-32 purity of 99.9 mol%. The IL from Flash 2 is sent back to the ED after being pumped and cooled.

The overall process has equivalent energy consumption of 2078 kJ/kg R-410A, 0.073 kg CO_2-eqv/kg R-410A emission, and separation cost of \$0.081/kg R-410A.

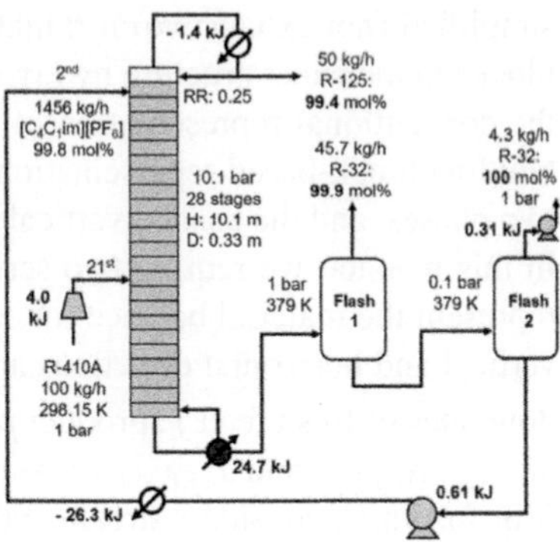

Figure 2: Process flowsheet of base design.

3.2. Process Optimization

We optimize the base design by taking into consideration the detailed phenomena level process synthesis. Here, we limit our process-scale analysis to two commonly used ILs as absorbents, $[C_4C_1im][PF_6]$ and $[C_4C_1im][BF_4]$. For each of the cases, we vary the number of trays between 15 and 40 and allow R-410A to enter at any tray. We also consider heat integration between the hot and the cold process streams. The minimum purity that must be achieved is set to be at least 99.5 mol% for both R-32 and R-125.

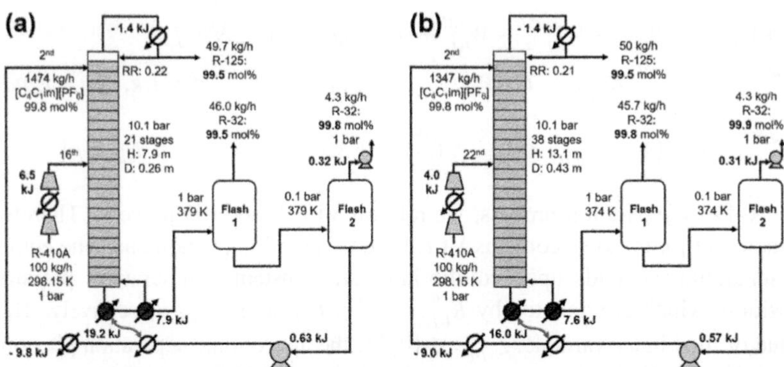

Figure 3: Optimized extractive distillation process with $[C_4C_1im][PF_6]$ as solvent for R-410A separation. Design targets are (a) minimum separation cost, and (b) minimum CO_2-eqv emission.

When $[C_4C_1im][PF_6]$ is used as solvent, Figure 3a shows the optimized process flow sheet with 21 total stages for the design objective of minimization of separation cost (\$0.071/kg R-410A). As shown in Table 1, it offers 12% lower separation cost than that of the base design. It also achieves 60% reduction in energy consumption. Due to the heat integration, 70% of the re-boiler duty is supplied from the circulating IL, while 66% of the cooling duty for the IL is provided by the re-boiler. Consequently, the required sizes of the heat exchanger and re-boiler reduce. We then set CO_2-eqv emission as the design target, and obtain a process flowsheet with 38 stages (Figure 3b). Note that, an increase in the number of equilibrium stages (i.e. trays) improves the separation and consumes less energy. Compared to the base design, we achieve 50% and 60% reduction in CO_2-eqv emission and energy consumption, respectively. However, the increased number of trays increases the capital cost and results in increased separation cost.

Table 1: Process Performance Comparison.

Design targets	Base design	$[C_4C_1im][PF_6]$	Improvement (%)	$[C_4C_1im][BF_4]$	Improvement (%)
Equivalent energy (kJ/kg R-410A)	2078	824	**60**	852	59
CO_2 emission (kg/kg R-410A)	0.073	0.036	**50**	0.038	48
Separation cost ($/kg R-410A)	0.081	0.071	12	0.063	**21**

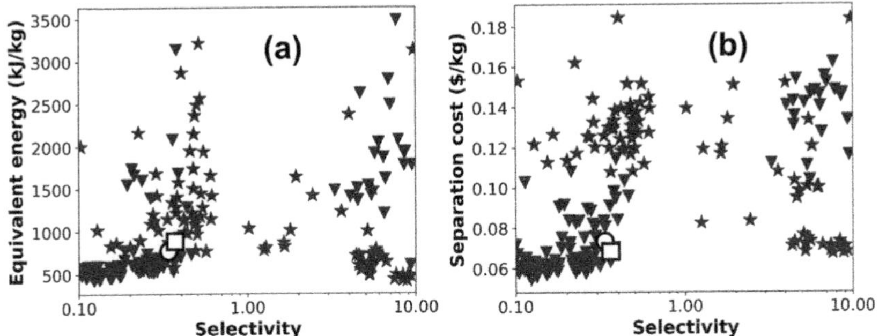

Figure 4: Selectivity mapping of ILs for (a) minimum equivalent energy, and (b) minimum separation cost. The triangle (▼) represent the designs with 99.5 mol% minimum purity and the star (★) denote the designs with 97 mol% minimum purity. $[C_4C_1im][PF_6]$ is represented by the circle (○) and $[C_4C_1im][BF_4]$ by the square (□).

Next, we consider $[C_4C_1im][BF_4]$ as solvent, and perform similar optimization. As shown in Table 1, when the design target is the minimization of separation cost, we achieve 21% reduction compared to the base design. The corresponding ED column requires 20 stages. Unlike the previous designs, here the R-410A enters in two different trays (trays no. 16 and 17). Notably, we achieve 48% reduction in CO_2-eqv emission compared to the base design under the design target of CO_2-eqv emission minimization. The corresponding process configuration requires ED column with 37 trays.

3.3. Mapping of IL Selectivity, Separation Energy and Cost

As the cations and the anions forming an IL can be arranged in many different combinations, it is possible to consider millions of hypothetical ILs. However, exhaustive synthesis and the corresponding process-scale analysis of all the ILs is impractical. To address this issue, we aim to reduce the search space of optimal ILs for R-410A separation. The motivation arises from the need to construct hypothetical ILs and predict the corresponding process performance to direct the experimental efforts. It is well known that the binary interaction parameters of a particular IL/HFC system dictates its solubility. Therefore, we focus on generating feasible binary interaction parameters via latin hypercube sampling, and construct nearly 3000 hypothetical ILs. When each of the ILs are used as solvents in the SPICE_ED optimization framework, not all are able to achieve the required R-32 and R-125 purity. For example, out of 3000 ILs, only 200 satisfy 97 mol% purity while only 117 ILs satisfy 99.5 mol% purity constraint. The equivalent energy consumption and separation cost of all the ILs (200 hypothetical, $[C_4C_1im][PF_6]$, $[C_4C_1im][BF_4]$) are shown in Figure 4. Note that the selectivity is defined as the ratio of Henry's constant of R-32 over R-125 at 298.15 K. By definition, when the selectivity < 1, R-32 is more soluble in the IL and vice versa. We deduce three key points: a) when the selectivity is between 0.5 and 2.0, IL may not be a suitable solvent candidate for HFC separation, since the required 99.5 mol% purity is not achieved, (b) R-32 favourable (more selective) IL is desired, as the corresponding process consumes less energy and requires less separation cost, (c) The Henry's constant value of R-32 is of particular importance, since for the same selectivity, ILs can have different equivalent energy consumption. Interestingly, when the target is less than 1000 kJ/kg R-410A equivalent energy with 99.5 mol% purity, more than 86% ILs have Henry's constant value of R-32 between 0.4 and 1.6 MPa. It is worth noting that, prediction of important IL properties (e.g., viscosity, heat capacity, and heat of absorption) which might impact the overall process performance, is beyond scope of this study.

4. Conclusions

Due to the azeotropic nature of HFC mixtures, conventional separation technologies are not suitable. In an effort to address this issue, we employed extractive distillation as a means for HFC separation process intensification. Many favourable properties of ionic liquids make them an attractive candidates as solvent for the absorption of selective refrigerants in HFC mixtures in ED columns. We developed SPICE_ED framework to achieve improved process configurations for IL-based extractive distillation. Our analysis show that use of $[C_4C_1im][BF_4]$ would result in lower separation cost, while $[C_4C_1im][PF_6]$ would result in lower energy consumption and emission. We extended our analysis to hypothetical ILs by utilizing the temperature dependent binary interaction parameters and performed a multiscale mapping of IL selectivity and energy/cost. We conclude that ILs offering more solubility towards R-32 would lead to better process performance in terms of energy consumption. We also conclude that the optimal IL candidates would most likely have exhibit Henry's constants between 0.4 to 1.6 MPa for R-32. The overall energy consumption can be also reduced to as low as 500 kJ/kg and separation cost as low as $0.06/kg of HFC.

5. Acknowledgment

The authors gratefully acknowledge the support from NSF EFRI DChem Award 2029354.

References

S. E. Demirel, J. Li, M. M. F. Hasan, 2017. Comput. & Chem. Eng. 105, 2–38.

S. E. Demirel, J. Li, M. M. F. Hasan, 2019. Current Opinion in Chemical Engineering 25, 108–113.

C. A. Faúndez, L. A. Barrientos, J. O. Valderrama, 2013. Int. J. of Refrigeration 36 (8), 2242–2250.

E. A. Finberg, M. B. Shiflett, 2021. Ind. Eng. Chem. Res.

M. S. Monjur, S. E. Demirel, J. Li, M. M. F. Hasan, 2021a. Ind. Eng. Chem. Res.

M. S. Monjur, S. E. Demirel, J. Li, M. M. F. Hasan, 2021b. Comput. Aided Chem. Eng 50, 287–293.

F. Pardo, S. V. Gutiérrez-Hernández, G. Zarca, A. Urtiaga, 2021. ACS Sust. Chem. Eng 9 (20), 7012–7021.

P. Purohit, L. Höglund-Isaksson, 2017. Atmos. Chem. Phy. 17 (4), 2795–2816.

M. B. Shiflett, A. Yokozeki, 2006. AIChE J. 52 (3), 1205–1219.

Y. Tian, S. E. Demirel, M. M. F. Hasan, E. N. Pistikopoulos, 2018. Chem. Eng. Proc. Proc. Int 133, 160–210.

Proceedings of the 14th International Symposium on Process Systems Engineering – PSE 2021+
June 19-23, 2022, Kyoto, Japan
http://dx.doi.org/10.1016/B978-0-323-85159-6.50111-1

A systematic methodology for the optimisation, control and consideration of uncertainty of reactive distillation

A. Tsatse[a], S. R. G. Oudenhoven[b], A. J. B. ten Kate[b], E. Sorensen[a]*

[a]*Department of Chemical Engineering, University College London, Torrington Place, WC1E 7JE London, UK;*
[b]*Nouryon, Zutphenseweg 10, 7418 AJ Deventer, the Netherlands*
e.sorensen@ucl.ac.uk

Abstract

The main goal of this work is the development of a structured optimisation strategy for reactive distillation systems in order to prevent production failures due to operational disturbances and/or uncertainties in the design input. The framework developed is demonstrated using a case study of industrial interest, based on a systematic evaluation of optimal design and control alternatives, offering the possibility of revising the design and/or operation of the process in order to minimise the risk of production failures. This framework can be used in an early design stage to quantify the impact of specific input parameters such as kinetics on process performance and costs, and it can therefore be used to focus the experimental effort on determining the most critical parameters for the performance of a reactive distillation process.

Keywords: reactive distillation, design, operation, control, uncertainty

1. Introduction

Reactive distillation is an intensified process where reaction and separation are integrated into a single unit. However, the large difference in time scales of the two processes, where reaction typically requires minutes for significant conversion whilst VLE is almost instantaneous, means that the design and control strategies cannot be easily extended from conventional distillation. This challenge is even further amplified when disturbances and design uncertainties are considered within the process.

Various optimisation methods have been applied in the open literature for the design of reactive distillation processes (e.g. Ciric and Gu 1994, Tian et al. 2020 etc.), some of which considering process control as part of the optimisation problem (e.g. Contreras-Zarazúa et al. 2017, Bernal et al. 2018 etc.). A few contributions have discussed the impact of process design on controllability (e.g. Mansouri et al. 2015, Georgiadis et al. 2002 etc.) whilst others have focused on the design of reactive distillation processes capable to successfully operate under uncertainty (e.g. Paramasivan and Kienle 2012, Tian et al. 2020 etc.).

Although reactive distillation design, controllability and uncertainty have all been previously studied, no systematic methodology has combined all those elements to investigate potential process modifications to improve performance under process disturbances and/or market changes. This is therefore the aim of this work, to provide a framework for the design of reactive distillation processes which are capable of dealing with production failures due to design and/or operational deficiencies. The framework and associated benefits will be demonstrated here by considering input uncertainty (particularly in reaction kinetics) on an optimal reactive distillation process.

2. Methodology

The methodology demonstrated in this work is presented in Figure 1. The methodology starts with determining the optimal design and operational parameters of the process, for instance using a methodology based on superstructure optimisation (Tsatse et al. 2021), then different process control configurations are evaluated. If, given the control scheme and the process disturbances considered, the system is not able to meet specifications and tolerate the (short-term) disturbances introduced, then the design must be revised in order to improve its control performance. If, however, specifications are met and disturbances are tolerated, the design is provisionally acceptable. In the final step, which is the focus of this work, the performance of the process is evaluated under input uncertainty. Process disturbances can be considered simultaneously with input uncertainty, although only the latter is the focus of this work. If the system cannot tolerate these (i.e. is failing to meet specifications) then the design and/or its control configuration must be revised to increase its flexibility (i.e. tolerance to uncertainties). If the system is not sensitive to the uncertainties, then the engineer can be confident that the process designed is not only economically attractive, but also capable of mitigating production failure issues due to design and/or operational deficiencies and model parameter uncertainties. The software used in this work for process simulation, optimisation and control is gPROMS ProcessBuilder v1.3.1 (Process Systems Enterprise 2021). For the uncertainty simulations in particular, the Global System Analysis (GSA) tool within ProcessBuilder was additionally used. The GSA tool is used to perform multiple model evaluations (simulations) with selected (i.e. uncertain) model input, as will be shown in section 4.

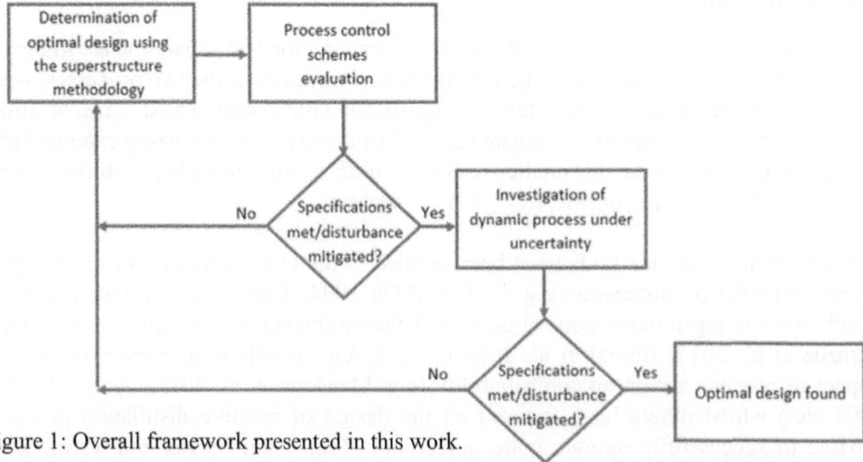

Figure 1: Overall framework presented in this work.

3. Case study

In this section, the case study used for the demonstration of the methodology is presented. This case study will only focus on the investigation of input uncertainty as the optimal design and control of the process have been previously considered in separate investigations.

A quaternary system is considered, in which the following auto-catalysed reversible reaction occurs in the liquid phase with component D as the desired product:

$$A + B \leftrightarrow C + D$$

The kinetic expressions for the forward (f) and backward (b) reaction rates are the following:

$$r_f = k_{f0} e^{-Ea_f/RT} C_A C_B$$
$$r_b = k_{b0} e^{-Ea_b/RT} C_C C_D$$

where reaction rate, r, is expressed in kmol/(m^3·s), pre-exponential kinetic factors, k_{f0} and k_{b0}, are expressed in m^3/(kmol·s), activation energy, E_a, is expressed in kJ/mol (assumed to be 80 kJ/mol for both directions), and component concentration C_i is expressed in kmol/m^3. Heat of reaction was assumed to be negligible, thus the activation energy is the same for both reaction directions and K_{eq} is independent of temperature, based on the previous assumptions. More details for the system considered and the underlying assumptions can be found in Tsatse et al. (2021) for Case study 15 in particular.

The feed streams to the overall system were one stream of reactant B of flow rate 12.6 kmol/hr, and one stream of reactant A below of the same flow rate (1:1 feed molar ratio). This corresponds to approximately 5 ktn/year of product D for full reactant conversion, which is met for production rates larger than 12.55 kmol/hr of component D. The feeds were assumed to be at their boiling points at 1 atm. Liquid hold-up of the reactive distillation column was assumed equal for all reactive stages, fixed at 0.1 m^3/reactive tray.

V-only control was applied to the system, where pressure at the top of the column (stage 2) is controlled by the condenser duty (PI control, $K_c = 20$ and $\tau = 12$ min) and the liquid levels of the reflux drum (P-only, $K_c = 2$) and the sump (P-only, $K_c = 2$) are controlled by the distillate flow rate and bottoms flow rate, respectively. Reboiler duty is manipulated in order to control bottom product purity (PI control, $K_c = 3$ and $\tau = 25$ min).

In this work, process disturbances such as feed composition change etc. (second step of the framework presented in Figure 1) will not be considered, in order to focus on input uncertainties only. For reactive distillation, critical input is mainly reaction kinetics and VLE and in early design stages, these are typically known with limited accuracy. Proper understanding of their impact on process performance and cost can therefore contribute to focused experimental effort, leading to a carefully designed and rigorous process.

Uncertainty in reaction kinetics is considered for the controlled process, using two cases (case a: uncertainty in k_{f0} so varying k_{b0} in order to keep K_{eq} at the base case value, case b: uncertainty in K_{eq} so fixing k_{f0} and varying k_{b0} to form the desired K_{eq} uncertainty values as $K_{eq}=k_{f0}/k_{b0}$)). For both cases, the uncertainty range considered was ±50% based on industrial experience and the two pre-exponential factors were grouped and varied as a multivariate enumerated set (i.e. 100 pairs or samples of the predefined values of the two pre-exponential factors to uniformly cover the uncertainty range). Based on the base-case values presented in Table 1, the value ranges considered are therefore:

a) $15.138 < k_{f0} = 30.276 < 45.414$ (10^9 m^3/(kmol·hr)) so
$6.728 < k_{b0} = 13.456 < 20.184$ (10^9 m^3/(kmol·hr)) to keep K_{eq} constant at 2.25

b) $1.125 < K_{eq} = 2.25 < 3.375$, and since $k_{f0} = 30.276 \cdot 10^9$ $m^3/(kmol \cdot hr)$
$8.971 < k_{b0} = 13.456 < 26.912$ (10^9 $m^3/(kmol \cdot hr)$)

The Key Performance Indicators (KPIs) for the case study considered were the bottom product purity ($x_{B,D}$), which should be maintained at 0.99 mol/mol; bottom production rate (B), which should be higher than 12.55 kmol/hr; condenser (Q_C) and reboiler (Q_R) duties; as well as the total cost of the process (Production TAC) .

4. Results and Discussion

In this work, the uncertainty simulations using GSA in gPROMS ProcessBuilder v1.3.1 (Process Systems Enterprise 2021) needed approximately 0.2-5 min CPU time. The short times are due to the fact that the number of samples (100) and the number of factors (k_{f0} and k_{b0}) and responses (controlled and manipulated variables, objective function value) was moderate, as was the complexity of the flowsheet (a single reactive distillation column in this case). The initial optimal design of the case study considered was found based on the superstructure methodology and a cost objective function, subject to product quality constraints, whilst the main product of interest was component D (see Tsatse et al. 2021 for more details). The base-case input as well as the initial optimal results are presented in Table 1.

Figure 2 shows the results of the simulations when considering uncertainty in reaction kinetics (left: case a, right: case b) for the initial (lines indicated as *initial*) as well as the flexible (lines indicated as *flexible*) system. Note that *flexible system* refers to the revised process, as presented in Table 1.

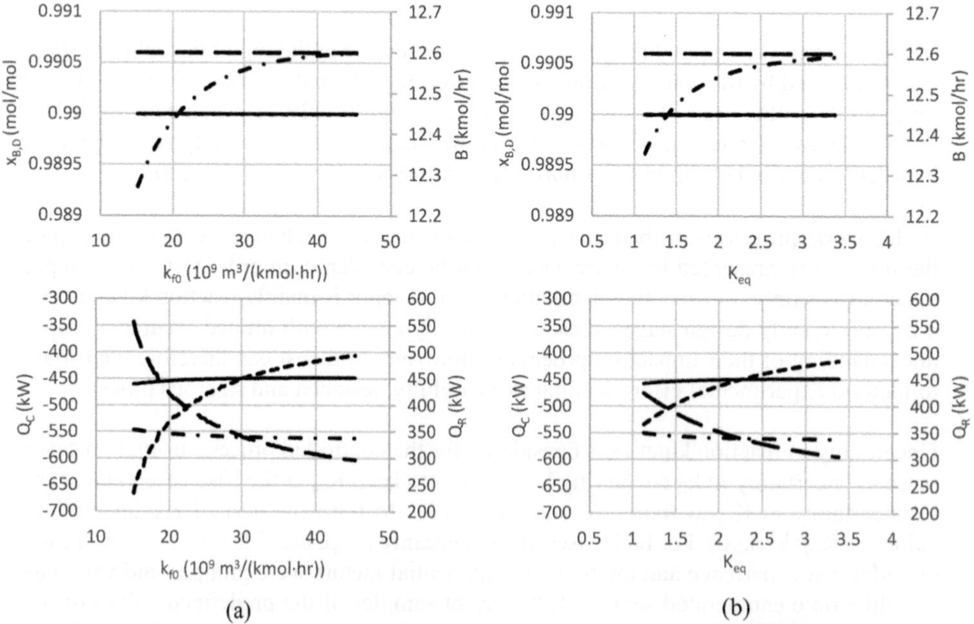

Figure 2: Uncertainty simulations. Product purity ($x_{B,D}$) together with bottom production rate (B), condenser (Q_C) and reboiler (Q_R) duties and flexible optimal dynamic controlled (V-only) design. Uncertainty in kinetics (case a-left, case b-right) is considered.

Initial design is indicated as: —— for left y-axis, and as: — · — for right y-axis. Flexible design is indicated as: – – for left y-axis, and as: —— —— for right y-axis.

Figure 2 (left: case a, right: case b) shows that under the uncertainty considered, the product purity ($x_{B,D}$) is maintained (top of Figure 2) by the V-only controlled system, but this is only possible by reducing the bottom production rate (i.e. B < 12.55 kmol/hr) when k_{f0} drops below $28.6 \cdot 10^9$ m^3/(kmol·hr)). This means that with the initial optimal design and control configuration, slower kinetics (case a) down to $28.6 \cdot 10^9$ m^3/(kmol·hr)) can be mitigated by control action alone. Similarly, lower chemical equilibrium (down to 2.08) can be mitigated by control action whilst lower values lead to violation of the desired production flow rate (right in Figure 2). Figure 2 shows that for this design and parameter set and the uncertainties considered, slower kinetics (k_{f0}) have a more significant impact on the performance than lower K_{eq}. The 50% uncertainty range considered for K_{eq} corresponds to a range of 51.5% to 64.8% conversion (the base case conversion, i.e. for K_{eq}=2.25, is 60%) which is not a broad range and can easily occur.

As the initial optimal design is not able to tolerate the entire range of uncertainty considered, a mitigation strategy must be applied which in this case is revision of column design. Re-optimising the reactive distillation column using the methodology described in Tsatse et al. (2021) leads to the optimal parameters of the new, flexible process as shown in Table 1. The uncertainty range is now re-considered, this time in the new flexible V-only controlled system and the results are shown in Figure 2. The system is now able to tolerate the entire range of uncertainty in kinetics considered, not only in terms of product purity (note that $x_{B,D}$ lines of initial and flexible design overlap) but also maintaining production rate at the desired level. Changes in condenser and reboiler duties are more significant for slow kinetics than for lower chemical equilibrium.

Table 1: Optimal results for the initial and flexible design for the case study considered (stages numbered from the top, condenser = 1, reboiler = N_T).

	Initial optimal design	**Flexible design**
k_{f0} (m^3/(kmol·hr))	$30.276 \cdot 10^9$	
K_{eq}	2.25	
α_{CA} - α_{AB} - α_{BD}	1.2 - 2.5 - 2	
	Values in optimal design	
Heavy feed (B) stage (N_{T1})	9	12
Light feed (A) stage (N_{T2})	23	26
Number of stages (N_T)	27	31
Reflux ratio (RR,-)	3.7	3.5
Bottoms flow rate (B, kmol/hr)	12.6	12.6
Reactive stages	2-26	2-30
Column diameter (D_C, m)	0.71	0.70
Bottom purity ($x_{B,D}$)	0.99	0.99
Operating cost (OPEX, M€/yr)	10.49	10.50
Capital cost (CAPEX, M€/yr)	0.31	0.41
Production TAC (€/kg)	2.150	2.167

This particular case study demonstrates revision of process design as the mitigation strategy is employed. However, alternative mitigation strategies, i.e. revision of control configuration and revision of the entire process including addition of ancillary units, are also supported within the framework. Since the entire range of uncertainty in reaction kinetics is now tolerated, the engineer can have confidence that the new flexible V-only controlled design can mitigate the uncertainty considered, here up to ±50% uncertainty in kinetics. Also, compared to the initial column design, the new flexible design includes four additional stages for reaction and separation to tolerate the uncertainty in kinetics considered, with less than a 1% increase (which mainly stems from the increase in capital cost) in the objective function as shown in Table 1 indicating a cost-effective alternative.

5. Conclusions

The findings indicate that, as uncertainty is expected in a reactive distillation process, a structured methodology to quantify its impact is essential as an economically optimal steady state design might nevertheless not operate successfully under process and input uncertainties leading to an unsuccessful project evaluation. Revision of its design and control strategy may therefore be required to improve its robustness. As this revision is associated with increased cost, the framework thus provides a basis to assess the relative benefits (process robustness vs cost) helping to make a more profound business decision.

References

D.E. Bernal, C. Carrillo-Diaz, J.M. Gómez and L.A. Ricardez-Sandoval, 2018, "Simultaneous Design and Control of Catalytic Distillation Columns Using Comprehensive Rigorous Dynamic Models." Industrial & Engineering Chemistry Research 57 (7), 2587– 2608.

A.R. Ciric and D. Gu, 1994, Synthesis of nonequilibrium reactivedistillation processes by MINLP optimization. AIChE J. 40 (9),1479–1487.

G. Contreras-Zarazúa, J.A. Vázquez-Castillo, C. Ramírez-Márquez, J.G. Segovia-Hernández and J.R. Alcántara-Ávila, 2017, "Multi-objective optimization involving cost and control properties in reactive distillation processes to produce diphenyl carbonate." Computers & Chemical Engineering 105: 185-196.

M.C. Georgiadis, M. Schenk, E.N. Pistikopoulos and R. Gani, 2002, "The interactions of design control and operability in reactive distillation systems." Computers & Chemical Engineering 26(4): 735-746.

S.S. Mansouri, M. Sales-Cruz, J.K Huusom, J.M. Woodley and R. Gani, 2015, "Integrated Process Design and Control of Reactive Distillation Processes." IFAC-PapersOnLine 48(8): 1120-1125.

G. Paramasivan and A. Kienle, 2012, "Decentralized Control System Design under Uncertainty Using Mixed-Integer Optimisation." Chemical Engineering & Technology 35(2): 261-271.

Process Systems Enterprise, 2021, gPROMS, https://www.psenterprise.com/products/gproms/process, 1997-2021.

Y. Tian, I. Pappas, B. Burnak, J. Katz, E.N. Pistikopoulos, 2020, ASystematic Framework for the synthesis of operable processintensification systems — reactive separation systems. Comput. Chem. Eng. 134, 106675.

A. Tsatse, S.R.G. Oudenhoven, A.J.B. ten Kate and E. Sorensen, 2021, "Optimal design and operation of reactive distillation systems based on a superstructure methodology." Chemical Engineering Research and Design, 170, 107-133.

Proceedings of the 14th International Symposium on Process Systems Engineering – PSE 2021+
June 19-23, 2022, Kyoto, Japan
http://dx.doi.org/10.1016/B978-0-323-85159-6.50112-3

Equation Oriented Optimization of Multi Stream Heat Exchanger Design and Operation in Natural Gas Liquefaction Process

Saif R. Kazi[a], Lorenz T. Biegler[a*], Rahul Gandhi[b]

[a]*Department of Chemical Engineering, Carnegie Mellon University, 5000 Forbes Avenue, Pittsburgh, PA 15232, USA*
[b]*Shell Technology Centre, Houston, TX 77032, USA*
lb01@andrew.cmu.edu

Abstract

The natural gas liquefaction process is a cryogenic energy intensive process which requires a complex designed multi-stream heat exchanger (MHEX). In this study, we present a discrete model for the detailed design of a spiral wound heat exchanger (SWHX) used in the natural gas liquefaction process. The design model is derived by discretizing first principles heat equation inside the heat exchanger for multiple refrigerant streams and natural gas. The phase change (liquefaction or vaporization) process is modeled using complementarity constraints which are reformulated and solved as a NLP.

The SWHX model is embedded and solved inside a flowsheet model with process constraints for feasible design operations. The optimization results show that the inclusion of detailed MHEX design inside process flowsheet models is imperative to obtain optimal solutions which can be achieved in actual process performance.

Keywords: Multi-Stream Heat Exchanger, Natural Gas, Optimization

1. Introduction

Natural gas has become the largest source of energy production in US over the last years. The increase in production has led to increase in US natural gas exports to other countries (Source: U.S. EIA, 2021). Natural gas is transported overseas in a liquefied state inside huge storage tanks as liquefied natural gas (LNG). The natural gas liquefaction (NGL) process is known to be a very energy intensive cryogenic process which can account upto 52% of the cost of LNG (Petrowiki, 2018).

There are mainly three types of natural gas liquefaction (NGL) processes i.e. a) cascade liquefaction process, b) mixed refrigerant liquefaction process and c) expander based liquefaction process. Cascade liquefaction processes consist of multiple independent pure refrigeration cycles where the natural gas is cooled using propane, ethylene and methane as refrigerants sequentially. The cascade liquefaction process has high energy efficiency compared to other type of liquefaction process but its capital costs are high because of its complex design and additional individual units required.

Mixed refrigerant (MR) liquefaction processes use a nitrogen and hydrocarbon mixture (methane, ethane, propane, i-butane and n-butane). They require fewer units than cascade refrigeration process and the energy consumption is significantly lower. MR liquefaction process can have single (SMR) (eg. PRICO process) or dual (DMR) refrigeration loop cycles. Another type of MR liquefaction process (C3MR) has a pre-cooling stage where liquid propane (C3) is used as a refrigerant to cool the natural gas before liquefying using the MR. This increases the energy efficiency of the process but requires more heat transfer and pressure control units. The expander based liquefaction process uses pure nitrogen or methane as the refrigerant in a single stage refrigeration cycle with multiple compressor stages. Unfortunately the method has lower energy efficiency than MR processes and is not suitable for high LNG yield.

Review papers (Austbø et al. (2014); Qyyum et al. (2108)) on optimization of natural gas liquefaction processes provide an extensive analysis of different methods and studies done on the topic. Most studies used process simulation software like Aspen Plus or Hysys combined with either stochastic or deterministic optimization solvers in MATLAB. Some studies have also used equation-oriented (EO) modeling in GAMS, AMPL or gPROMS with continuous and mixed-integer optimization tools like IPOPT, CONOPT and DICOPT. Previous studies (Watson et al., 2018) have used simple enthalpy balances to model the MHEX in the NGL process and neglect the effect of the exchanger design on the thermodynamic performance of the refrigerant cycles. This could severely affect the optimization results as the MHEX design has highly nonlinear correlations with the process variables and the energy efficiency of the process. To date, only Tsay et al. (2017) have presented an equation oriented model of natural gas liquefaction process with detailed multi-stream heat exchanger design. They used heat transfer coefficient and pressure drop correlations to model temperature and pressure variation inside the MHEX in the PRICO process flowsheet. Their MHEX design model was embedded inside the PRICO flowsheet and solved using a pseudo-transient EO approach which converts system of nonlinear equations into a nonlinear differential equation system. They used shooting methods in gPROMS to integrate the differential equations and the SQP algorithm as the optimization solver to solve the problem.

In this study, a new DAE-based design model is developed for multi-stream spiral wound heat exchanger (SWHX), the type of MHEX used in LNG processes. The DAE model is derived using the heat equation representing the heat transfer between the streams. The phase change inside the exchanger is modeled using complementarity constraints. Finally the DAE model is solved within a NG liquefaction flowsheet model as a simultaneous design optimization of the complete process.

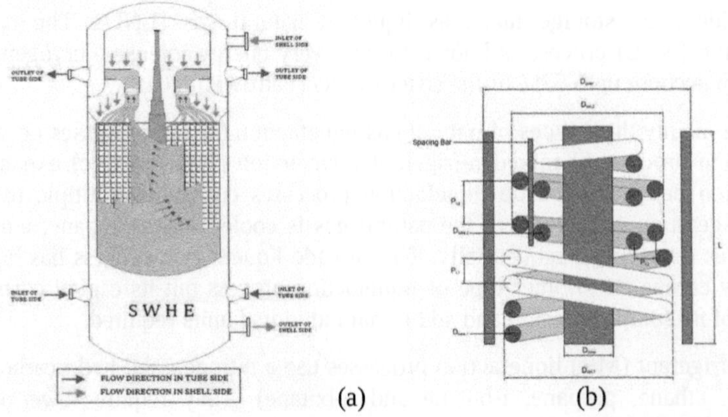

Figure 1: Inside and cross-section view of spiral wound heat exchanger

2. Model

2.1 MHEX DAE model

MHEX(s) have more complex design and geometry than single stream heat exchangers, which makes it difficult to build an optimization model for MHEX design. The SWHX consists of a central rod-like structure around which multiple tubes are coiled in a circular helix shape as shown in Figure 1a. The concentric coils have different radii and appear to form a spiral shape around the central rod. The tubeside and shellside streams enter the exchanger from opposite directions and exchange heat over the tube curved surface. Multiple streams in the tubeside (usually hot) and single stream on the shellside (usually cold) flow in a counter-current cross-flow pattern inside the MHEX as shown in Figure 2a.

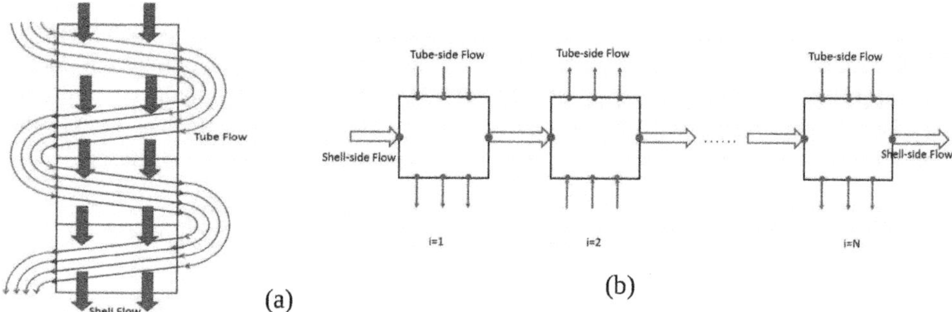

Figure 2: Discretization of SWHX into discrete finite elements

We propose a discrete model which discretizes the exchanger into discrete elements and solves energy balance using first principles heat equation inside each element as shown in Figure 2b and Figure 3.

2.2 Heat Equation

The heat equation for the streams inside SWHX is derived by discretizing the exchanger into multiple discrete finite elements. The steady-state heat equation for tubeside and shellside streams can be written as:

$$\rho_t C_t^p u_x \frac{dT_t}{dx} = -q_v \qquad \text{and} \qquad \rho_s C_s^p u_y \frac{dT_s}{dy} = q_v \tag{1}$$

where ρ is molar density, Cp is specific heat capacity, u is velocity, k is thermal conductivity, Tt , Ts are tube and shell temperature, and qv is the volumetric heat. The following assumptions are made: 1) Zero or negligible heat transfer by conduction and 2) Shell and coil side fluid flow are unidirectional.

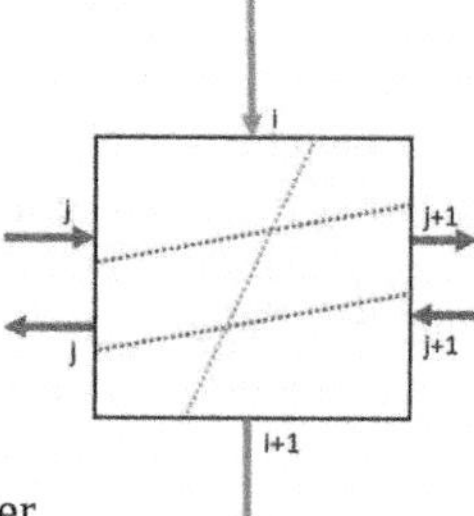

Figure 3: Discrete Element inside the exchanger

Since the streams are mixtures and are undergoing phase change, it is more meaningful to use enthalpy as the differential variable. The coupled ODE system Eq.(1) is discretized using the smaller discrete elements (shown in Figure 3) and FEM with hat functions as the basis functions resulting in the following set of equations:

For i=1...N

$$F_j\frac{(H_j^{i,2}-H_j^{i,1})}{2}+\frac{U_{j,s}\Delta A_{j,s}}{3}(T_j^{i,2}-T_s^{i+1})+\frac{U_{j,s}\Delta A_{j,s}}{6}(T_j^{i,1}-T_s^{i})=0 \quad \forall j\in S_c$$
$$F_s\frac{(H_s^{i+1}-H_s^{i})}{2}-\sum_{k}^{k\in S_c}\left[\frac{U_{k,s}\Delta A_{k,s}}{3}(T_k^{i,2}-T_s^{i+1})+\frac{U_{k,s}\Delta A_{k,s}}{6}(T_k^{i,1}-T_s^{i})\right]=0 \tag{2}$$

2.3 Phase Change

The condensation (liquefaction) and evaporation process for mixed component streams can be modeled using complementarity constraints. The pure vapor, liquid and two-phase (mix of liquid and vapor) streams are in a state of vapor-liquid equilibrium (VLE). As the streams exchange heat between them, they can be imagined as a PQ flash process. The flash equations for VLE for a mixed component stream are written as:

Flash VLE Equations

$$\begin{aligned} F_j &= L_j+V_j \\ z_{ij}F_j &= x_{ij}L_j+y_{ij}V_j \\ y_{ij} &= \beta_j K_{ij}(T_j,P_j)x_{ij} \\ \sum_i(y_{ij}-x_{ij}) &= 0 \end{aligned} \quad \text{and} \quad \begin{aligned} \beta_j-1 &\le sV_j \\ \beta_j-1 &\ge -sL_j \\ 0\le sV_j &\perp V_j\ge 0 \\ 0\le sL_j &\perp L_j\ge 0 \end{aligned} \tag{3}$$

The stream enthalpy (H) is written as function of its temperature (T), pressure (P) and composition (*x,y*) using equation of state (EOS). Additional constraints are stated to connect the state variables (H, T and P) at the element boundary as given in Kazi(2021). Also inlet and outlet temperatures are imposed as the boundary conditions.

2.4 Flowsheet

The natural gas liquefaction flowsheet is shown in Figure 4. The flowsheet model consists of mass and energy balance along with process constraints and flash equations to model the adiabatic valves. The objective function minimizes

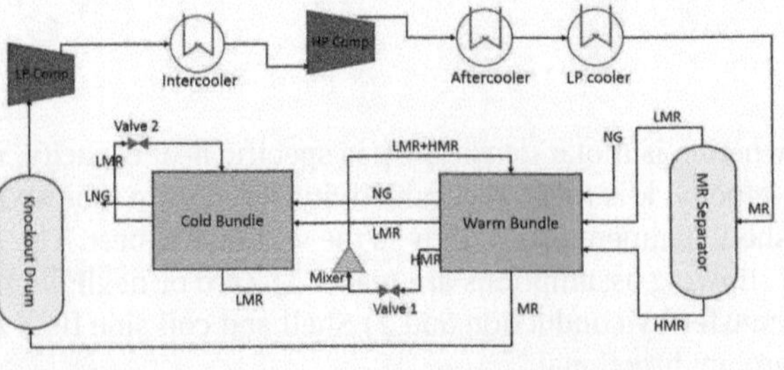

Figure 4: Natural Gas Liquefaction Flowsheet Diagram

the compressor power required to recycle the mixed refrigerant (MR) and provide enough refrigeration to liquefy natural gas. The degrees of freedom (DOF) in the optimization model are: 1) MR inlet temperature, pressure and composition, 2) Pressure drop across LMR and HMR valves and 3) Bundle break temperature (temperature between warm and cold bundles).

3. Methodology

The optimization of natural gas liquefaction process with the described MHEX DAE design model for SWHX and the NGL flowsheet model is a large scale optimization problem with nonlinearities and complementarity constraints. Therefore, it is imperative to provide a good initial point for convergence of the NLP solver. For this reason, the problem is solved in a step-by-step procedure as described:

- **Solve natural gas liquefaction flowsheet model:** The first step is solve the flowsheet model without the heat exchanger model. The model consists of only enthalpy and mass balances along with the process constraints such as EMAT, super-heated stream at compressor inlet etc.

- **Solve MHEX DAE design model:** The stream flowrates and temperatures from the flowsheet model solution are taken as inputs to the MHEX DAE design model. The DAE model is discretized and the complementarity constraints are relaxed and solved as a NLP model as in Kazi et al. (2019) .

- **Initialize and solve the combined flowsheet with detailed DAE model:** The solution from both the flowsheet and the MHEX models are used as the initial guess for the combined overall natural gas liquefaction model with detailed exchanger design. The combined optimization model is solved using standard NLP solvers such as CONOPT or IPOPT.

4. Optimization Results

The models are written using Pyomo – a Python based modeling language and the MHEX DAE model is discretized into N=20 elements each for warm and cold bundle respectively. The flowsheet model consists of 2,453 variables and 2,465 constraints, whereas the DAE model consists of 23,297 variables and 23,834 constraints. The solution time to solve the complete set of models comes to about 5 CPU min on a 16 GB RAM Intel Core i7 system with 2.70 GHz processor.

Variable	Value		MR Composition	Value
Pressure Energy Loss (Objective)	33,854.4 kW		Nitrogen	0.046
Pressure Drops (Valve 1 and 2)	3700 & 3840 kPa		Methane	0.404
Heat Duty (WB)	2,01,095 kW		Ethane	0.5
Heat Duty (CB)	97,376		Propane	0.05

Table 1: Optimal values for Flowsheet values and MR composition

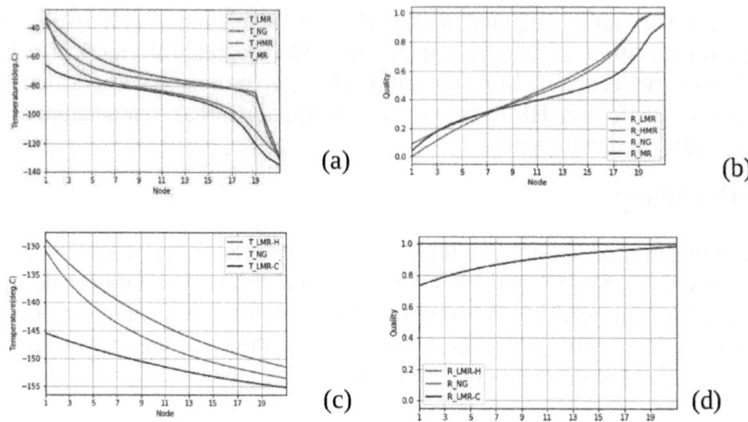

Figure 5: Temperature and liquid fraction profiles inside the exchanger ((a,b) - WB and (c,d) - CB)

5. Conclusions

A DAE model for SWHX-type MHEX is developed based on first principles heat equation. An initialization/solution strategy is presented to robustly and simultaneously solve the combined flowsheet with detailed MHEX design model. The results show that the inclusion of detailed exchanger design inside flowsheet models is able to reduce the objective value by 8% (36,840kW to 33,854kW of compressor power) as compared to the smaller flowsheet model without detailed DAE heat exchanger models. Future work will extend the DAE model to account for equipment design variables including shell & tube diameter, number of coils and geometric factors.

References

Source: U.S. Energy Information Administration, Sep 2021, Monthly Energy Review

PetroWiki, 2018, "Liquified Natural Gas" https://petrowiki.spe.org/Liquified_natural_gas_(LNG)

Bjørn Austbø, Sigurd Weidemann Løvseth, Truls Gundersen, 2014, "Annotated bibliography - Use of optimization in LNG process design and operation", *Computers & Chemical Engineering*, 71, 391-414,

Muhammad Abdul Qyyum, Kinza Qadeer, and Moonyong Lee, 2018, "Comprehensive Review of the Design Optimization of Natural Gas Liquefaction Processes: Current Status and Perspectives", *Industrial & Engineering Chemistry Research*, *57* (17), 5819-5844

H. A. Watson, M. Vikse, T. Gundersen, and P. I. Barton, 2018, "Optimization of single mixed-refrigerant natural gas liquefaction processes described by nondifferentiable models," Energy, 150, 860–876

C. Tsay, R. C. Pattison, and M. Baldea, 2017, "Equation-oriented simulation and optimization of process flowsheets incorporating detailed spiral-wound multistream heat exchanger models," AIChE Journal, 63, 9, 3778–3789

S. R. Kazi, L. T. Biegler, 2019, "Nonlinear Optimization of Detailed Heat Exchanger Models with Phase Change," Computer Aided Chemical Engineering, 47, 151–156

S. R. Kazi, "Mathematical Modeling and Optimization of Heat Exchanger Design in Process Flowsheets", PhD Thesis, Carnegie Mellon University, Pittsburgh, PA (2021)

Proceedings of the 14th International Symposium on Process Systems Engineering – PSE 2021+
June 19-23, 2022, Kyoto, Japan
http://dx.doi.org/10.1016/B978-0-323-85159-6.50113-5

Optimal Design of Extractive Dividing-Wall Column Using an Improved Sequential Least Squares Programming Algorithm

Yingjie Ma[a], Nan Zhang[a], Jie Li[a,*]

[a]*Centre for Process Integration, Department of Chemical Engineering, The University of Manchester, Manchester M13 9PL, UK*
jie.li-2@ manchester.ac.uk

Abstract

Extractive dividing wall column (EDWC) is an efficient and economic technique for separating azeotropic or close boiling-point mixtures. However, optimal design of EDWC using rigorous models is still challenging. In this work, we develop an improved sequential least squares programming (SLSQP)-based feasible path algorithm for such optimal design. The computational results show that the proposed algorithm can generate better solutions and reduce the computational time by around one order of magnitude.

Keywords: EDWC, SLSQP, feasible path algorithm, homotopy continuation

1. Introduction

Extractive dividing wall column (EDWC) is a promising intensification technique for separating azeotropic or close boiling-point mixtures, which can reduce both energy and capital costs significantly compared to the conventional extractive distillation. However, optimal design of EDWC is still challenging due to the complexity of its model with at least ten design and operating variables to be determined.

The sequential sensitivity analysis-based method is frequently used, but the method is hard to consider the interactions among variables, possibly getting a suboptimal solution. Although stochastic algorithms such as genetic algorithm (GA) have also been applied to optimize EDWC (Bravo-Bravo et al., 2010), these algorithms need a large number of simulations, leading to long computational time. The sequential quadratic programming (SQP)-based feasible path algorithm has also been reported for optimisation of EDWC using the sequential modular simulator (Yang et al., 2018). However, the convergence of the SQP algorithm in such environment is largely degraded due to inaccurate gradients used (Pattison and Baldea, 2014). To resolve such problem, Ma et al. (2020) proposed a hybrid steady-state and time-relaxation-based optimization algorithm for optimal design of EDWC in the equation-oriented environment, demonstrating a good convergence. However, the hybrid algorithm requires many pseudo-transient continuation (PTC) simulations (Pattison and Baldea, 2014). As the PTC simulation is usually much more time-consuming than the steady-state simulation, the hybrid algorithm is inefficient.

In this work, we develop an improved sequential least square programming (SLSQP)-based feasible path algorithm for optimal design of EDWC. We integrate the homotopy continuation (HC) technique with the line search to achieve effective and robust line search. The PTC simulation is activated to guarantee the convergence only when many

HC steps are needed. It is shown that the proposed algorithm can generate better solutions with the reduced computational effort by approximately one order of magnitude.

2. Problem Statement

Fig. 1a illustrates a typical EDWC, where the mixture *AB* is feed stream and *S* is the solvent. The EDWC can be modelled by the thermodynamically equivalent model with five column-sections shown in Fig. 1b, which is adapted from the model with six column-sections for DWC proposed by Pattison et al. (2016). The problem is stated below:

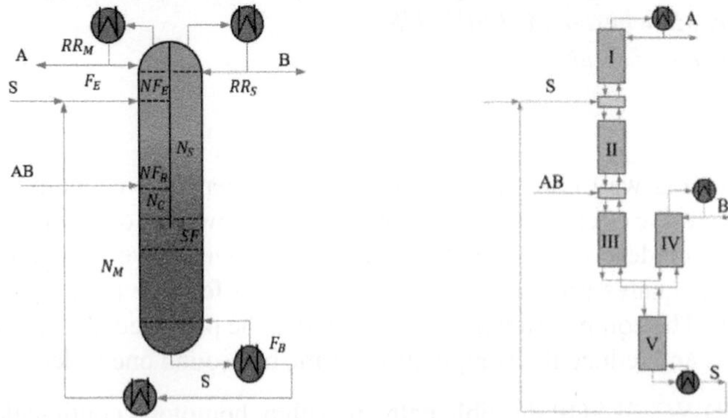

Fig. 1 a) Schematic of an extractive dividing wall column; b) thermodynamically equivalent model with five column-sections

Given: an azeotropic or close boiling-point mixture to be separated, the solvent adopted, the purity requirements of the products, and perhaps some other production requirements (such as the temperatures of some streams). Determine: solvent make-up flow rate (F_S), the number of stages in the five column-sections, reflux ratios of the main and side sections (RR_M, RR_S), split fraction of the vapour stream to the side column section (SF) and the flow rate (F_B) at the bottom. The objective is to minimise total annualised cost.

3. Mathematical Model

The EDWC is described by the rigorous equilibrium stage model with material balance, phase equilibrium, summation and enthalpy balance (MESH) equations applied to each stage. The bypass efficiency method (Dowling and Biegler, 2014) is adopted to determine the number of stages so that the current problem is a more tractable nonlinear programming (NLP) problem. Since we will use PTC simulations as safeguards of the line searches, the PTC model from Ma et al. (2017) is used for such simulations.

4. Solution method

4.1. SLSQP-based feasible path algorithm

Feasible path algorithms separate variables x in the optimisation problem as independent variables x_I and dependent variables x_D. For each given x_I, x_D (and possibly the sensitivity $\partial x_D / \partial x_I$) can be got through solving an nonlinear equation system,

$$F(x_I, x_D) = 0, \tag{1}$$

which is usually called simulation in engineering. Then, various optimisation algorithms can be applied to solve the problem in x_I space instead of the original high dimensional x space. SQP algorithm is often used in such setting as it usually requires less function evaluations (corresponding to simulations) (Schittkowski, 1982) that accounts of nearly all the computational time. As an variant of SQP, SLSQP (Schittkowski, 1982) has the same merit as SQP and is possibly more stable (Schittkowski, 1982), which is to solve a linear constrained linear least squares problem (LSQ) shown below to generate descent direction d^k at each major iteration.

$$\min \frac{1}{2}\|A^k d^k - b^k\|^2 \quad \text{(LSQ)}$$

$$s.t. E^k d^k - f^k = 0$$

$$G^k d^k - h^k \geq 0.$$

A typical SLSQP-based feasible path algorithm can be briefly stated as follows:

Step 1: set $k \leftarrow 0$. Given x_I^0 and corresponding b^0, E^0, f^0, G^0, h^0, which can be got according to the solution of the simulation problem $F(x_I^0, x_D^0) = 0$.
Step 2: solve LSQ subproblem for d^k and check convergence condition of the original NLP problem. If solution is found, go to step 5.
Step 3: conduct line searches with some simulations to get $x_I^{k+1}$and x_D^{k+1} satisfying the Armijio condition Eq. (2).
Step 4: update $A^{k+1}, b^{k+1}, E^{k+1}, f^{k+1}, G^{k+1}, h^{k+1}$ based on simulation results at x_I^{k+1} and BFGS formula. Set $k \leftarrow k+1$, then go back to Step 2.
Step 5: return x_I^k, x_D^k, f^k.

In step 3, the Armijio condition is as follows

$$P(x_I^{k+1}) \leq P(x_I^k) + \alpha\, \rho\, DP(0), \quad (2)$$

where $\rho \in (0, 0.5)$ is a constant, $P(x_I^k)$ is the L1 merit function considering the values of both objective function and constraint violations, and $DP(0)$ is the directional derivative of $P(x_I)$ along direction d_k at $\alpha = 0$.

One of the main difficulties in the feasible path algorithm is to conduct the line search reliably in step 3. In Section 4.2, the HC method will be used to resolve the problem.

4.2. Homotopy continuation (HC) enhanced line search

A typical backtrack line search procedure in a major iteration k of above feasible path algorithm is as follows, where we drop the superscript k to avoid the abused use of indices. Hence, x_I^0, x_D^0 in the current Section 4.2 is actually x_I^k, x_D^k in Section 4.1.

Step 3.1: set $i \leftarrow 0$. Given x_I^0, x_D^0, and an initial step length $\alpha^0 \in (0, 1]$.
Step 3.2: set $x_I^{i+1} \leftarrow x_I^0 + \alpha^i d$, conduct simulation $F(x_I^{i+1}, x_D^{i+1}) = 0$, and evaluate the merit function $P(x_I^{k+1})$ based on the simulation results.
Step 3.3: if Eq. (2) is satisfied, go to Step 3.5.
Step 3.4: generate an α^{i+1} smaller than α^i, set $i \leftarrow i+1$, then go back to Step 3.2.
Step 3.5: returnx_I^{i+1}, x_D^{i+1}.

The line search may fail to generate an α satisfying Eq. (2) or may generate a tiny step length if the simulations continue to fail and $P(x_I^{k+1})$ cannot be evaluated in step 3.2. The former causes the premature termination of the optimisation, while the latter leads to slow progress. The HC method can be used to resolve the problem, which is to start from the solution of an equation system that can be solved more easily and then approach the solution of the original problem. In that spirit, if a simulation problem $F(x_I^0 + \alpha^i d, x_D^{i+1}) = 0$ cannot be solved in Step 3.2, we define an intermediate step length

$$\bar{\alpha}^j = t^j \alpha^i, t^j \in (0,1], t^0 = 0. \tag{3}$$

We then gradually increase $\bar{\alpha}^j$ from 0 and solve a series of simulation problems $F(x_I^0 + \bar{\alpha}^j d, \bar{x}_D^j) = 0$ with the solution $(\bar{x}_D^{j'})$ at $\bar{\alpha}^{j'} < \bar{\alpha}^j$ $(j \geq 1)$ as the initial point until $\bar{\alpha}^j = \alpha^i$ $(t^j = 1)$, reaching to the solution of the original problem. In this way, when $\bar{\alpha}^j$ and $\bar{\alpha}^{j'}$ are close enough and the implicit function $x_D(x_I)$ is continuous with nonsingular Jacobian matrix, $\bar{x}_D^{j'}$ will be within the convergence basin of the Newton method for solving the simulation problem, leading to a converged simulation. Note that $\bar{\alpha}^0 = 0$, $\bar{x}_I^0 = x_I^0$ and $\bar{x}_D^0 = x_D^0$. Such process leads to a homotopy path as shown in Fig. 2a.

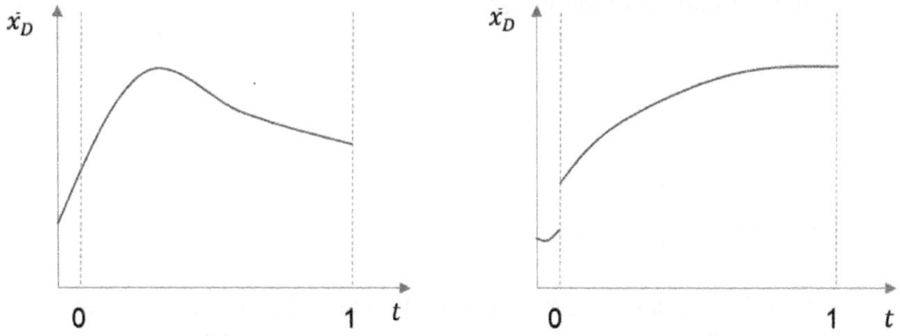

Fig 2. a) homotopy path without singular point, b) homotopy path with discontinuous point.

A merit of applying HC method in line search algorithm is that we have the chance to terminate the HC calculation before t^j reaches to 1 if the merit function $P(x_I^0 + \bar{\alpha}^j d)$ starts to increase. This is because a larger α will lead to a higher merit function under the assumption that $P(x_I^0 + \alpha d)$ has a single minimum along the direction d for $\alpha \in [0,1]$, while the aim of the whole line search algorithm is to find its minimum. The chance to terminate early is an advantage of the proposed HC method to the PTC method, which doesn't provide meaningful intermediate information before the PTC simulation finishes.

However, the HC method cannot guarantee a converged simulation if the assumptions of continuity and nonsingularity are not satisfied as shown in Fig. 2b, which frequently happens during the line search for the optimisation of EDWC. If x_I^0 is at or rather close to the discontinuous point, the HC method will be useless for promoting the convergence of the simulation for the first line search step. In such case, we have to use the PTC method to guarantee the convergence. When the number of HC steps (denoted as n_{HC}) is greater than a certain number (e.g. 10), the PTC method will be then activated. The proposed simultaneous homotopy continuation and line search method is given below,

Step 3.2.1: set $j \leftarrow 0$. Given x_I^0, x_D^0, $\alpha^i \in (0,1]$, n_{HC}; set $t^j \leftarrow 0.5$, $flag^{LS} \leftarrow False$, $\alpha^{LS} \leftarrow None$, $x_I^{LS} \leftarrow None$, $x_D^{LS} \leftarrow None$, $\alpha^{\min} \leftarrow 0$, $x_I^{\min} \leftarrow$, $P^{\min} \leftarrow \infty, t_c \leftarrow 0$,

Step 3.2.2: generate $\bar{\alpha}^j$ according to Eq. (3), $\bar{x}_I^j \leftarrow x_I^0 + \bar{\alpha}^j d$, conduct simulation $F(\bar{x}_I^j, \bar{x}_D^j) = 0$, and evaluate $P(\bar{x}_I^j)$ based on the simulation results.

Step 3.2.3 if the simulation converges, $t_c \leftarrow t^j$, go to Step 3.2.4; otherwise, go to Step 3.2.6.

Step 3.2.4: if Eq. (2) is satisfied, set $flag^{LS} \leftarrow True$, $\alpha^{LS} \leftarrow \bar{\alpha}^j$, $x_I^{LS} \leftarrow \bar{x}_I^j$, $x_D^{LS} \leftarrow \bar{x}_D^j$.

Step 3.2.5 if $P(\bar{x}_I^j) < P^{\min}$ and $t^j < 1$, set $P^{\min} \leftarrow P(\bar{x}_I^j)$, $\alpha^{\min} \leftarrow \bar{\alpha}^j$, $x_I^{\min} \leftarrow \bar{x}_I^j$, $x_D^{\min} \leftarrow \bar{x}_D^j$ and set $t^{j+1} \in (t_c, 1]$; otherwise, go to Step 3.2.7.

Step 3.2.6: if $j < n_{HC}$, set $t^{j+1} \in (t_c, t^j)$; otherwise, set $t^j \leftarrow 1$, apply the PTC method for simulation, evaluate $P(\bar{x}_I^j)$ and then go to Step 3.2.7;

Step 3.2.7: if $flag^{LS} = True$, return $flag^{LS}$, α^{LS}, x_I^{LS}, x_D^{LS}; otherwise, return $flag^{LS}$, $\alpha^{\min}$, $x_I^{\min}$, $x_D^{\min}$. Go to Step 3.3 of previous algorithm.

Here, $flag^{LS}$ indicates whether a step length satisfying Armijio condition has been found ($True$ if found; otherwise, $False$), and α^{LS}, x_I^{LS} and x_D^{LS} are the corresponding step length, independent and dependent variables. P^{min} denotes the minimum penalty function value obtained until the current iteration, and $\alpha^{\min}$, $x_I^{\min}$ and $x_D^{\min}$ are the corresponding step length, independent and dependent variables. t_c is the largest homotopy parameter leading to a converged simulation until the current iteration.

5. Case study

The separation of acetone and chloroform mixture using EDWC is used to illustrate the capability of the proposed algorithm. The optimal design of EDWC for the same separation has been reported in Ma et al. (2020). The example is solved on a desktop with 3.20 GHz Intel core i7 processor, 16 GB RAM and Windows 64-bit operating system. The optimisation problem involves 9399 equations, 16 inequality constraints and 10570 variables including 90 decision variables. The objective is to minimize total annualized cost (TAC). We conduct optimisations from six different initial points as with Ma et al. (2020). The results are shown in Table 1.

Table 1. Comparative results from the algorithm of Ma et al. (2020) and the proposed algorithm

Initial point		1	2	3	4	5	6
Time/s	Ma2020	1259	7722	2263	3698	1650	1714
	Ours	1498	587	903	380	1197	1519
Number of Simulations	Ma2020	239	302	409	509	380	262
	Ours	478	268	528	229	466	796
TAC/ (k\$ year^{-1})	Ma2020	6081	6116	6106	6124	6137	6097
	Ours	6076	6076	6076	6078	6094	6077

As seen from Table 1, both algorithms can find optimal solutions from all six initial points. The proposed algorithm needs much less computational time than the hybrid algorithm of Ma et al. (2020) from all initial points except from the initial point 1. For instance, starting from the second initial point, the proposed algorithm needs 587 CPU s, whilst the hybrid algorithm requires 7722 CPU s. More importantly, the proposed algorithm always obtains a bit better solution with TAC reduced by 0.08% ~ 0.75%, compared to the hybrid algorithm. In addition, the proposed algorithm often requires more simulations than the hybrid algorithm, which do not lead to higher computational time for the proposed algorithm because the time-consuming PTC simulations are used much less compared with the hybrid algorithm.

6. Conclusions

In this work we proposed an improved SLSQP-based feasible path optimisation algorithm for optimal design of EDWC using rigorous models. We integrate HC simulations with line searches to get step lengths satisfying Armijio condition reliably. To further improve the efficiency, we proposed a criteria to terminate the HC calculation early. To further guarantee the convergence of simulations, we use PTC simulations as the last safeguard. Finally, one case study from literature indicates the proposed algorithm can be 10 times faster than the state-of-art feasible path algorithm and also generates better solutions.

Acknowledgements

The authors acknowledge financial support from China Scholarship Council – The University of Manchester Joint Scholarship (201809120005)

References

Bravo-Bravo, C., Segovia-Hernández, J.G., Gutiérrez-Antonio, C., Durán, A.L., Bonilla-Petriciolet, A., Briones-Ramírez, A., 2010. Extractive Dividing Wall Column: Design and Optimization. Ind. Eng. Chem. Res. 49, 3672-3688.

Dowling, A.W., Biegler, L.T., 2014. Rigorous Optimization-based Synthesis of Distillation Cascades without Integer Variables, in: Jiří Jaromír Klemeš, P.S.V., Peng Yen, L. (Eds.), Comput. Aided Chem. Eng. Elsevier, pp. 55-60.

Ma, Y., Luo, Y., Yuan, X., 2017. Simultaneous Optimization of Complex Distillation Systems with a New Pseudo-transient Continuation Model. Ind. Eng. Chem. Res. 56, 6266-6274.

Ma, Y., Zhang, N., Li, J., Cao, C., 2020. Optimal design of extractive dividing-wall column using an efficient equation-oriented approach. Front. Chem. Sci. Eng. 15, 72-89.

Pattison, R.C., Baldea, M., 2014. Equation-Oriented Flowsheet Simulation and Optimization Using Pseudo-Transient Models. AIChE J. 60, 4104-4123.

Pattison, R.C., Gupta, A.M., Baldea, M., 2016. Equation-oriented optimization of process flowsheets with dividing-wall columns. AIChE J. 62, 704-716.

Schittkowski, K., 1982. The nonlinear programming method of Wilson, Han, and Powell with an augmented Lagrangian type line search function. Numer. Math. 38, 115-127.

Yang, A., Wei, R., Sun, S., Wei, S.a., Shen, W., Chien, I.L., 2018. Energy-Saving Optimal Design and Effective Control of Heat Integration-Extractive Dividing Wall Column for Separating Heterogeneous Mixture Methanol/Toluene/Water with Multiazeotropes. Ind. Eng. Chem. Res. 57, 8036-8056.

Proceedings of the 14th International Symposium on Process Systems Engineering – PSE 2021+
June 19-23, 2022, Kyoto, Japan
http://dx.doi.org/10.1016/B978-0-323-85159-6.50114-7

Biphasic Dehydration of Sugars to 5-Hydroxymethylfurfural and Furfural—Multiscale Modeling for Easier Optimization and More Accurate Solvent Selection

Abhimanyu Pudi[a,b], Martin P. Andersson[a], Seyed Soheil Mansouri[a*]

[a]*Department of Chemical and Biochemical Engineering, Technical University of Denmark, Søltofts Plads 228A, Kgs. Lyngby, DK-2800, Denmark*
[b] *Sino-Danish College, University of Chinese Academy of Sciences, 19A Yuquan Road, Shijingshan District, Beijing, 100049, China*
seso@kt.dtu.dk

Abstract

An integrated and multiscale modeling framework is introduced to accurately model the biphasic dehydration of a mixed carbohydrate feed from typical lignocellulosic waste biomass to form 5-hydroxymethylfurfural and furfural. This modeling framework integrates computational chemistry into a process model, allowing for a greater exploration space for process design. Moreover, this multiscale model is used to demonstrate more accurate solvent selection that is in line experimental data, unlike the existing solvent screening methods. For this purpose, a pool of five commonly used organic solvents for this system are considered, which are 1-butanol, 2-butanol, methyl isobutyl ketone, 2-methyltetrahydrofuran, and tetrahydrofuran.

Keywords: green chemistry, process intensification, computational chemistry, mathematical modeling, lignocellulosic biomass valorization.

1. Introduction

The current global scenario for energy and chemicals consumption features the impending exhaustion of fossil resources and the undeniable threat of global warming as major challenges to be tackled by mankind. Due to the escalating demands for energy, bulk chemicals and materials, alternative sources of feedstock are restlessly sought after. In the recent decades, the biorefinery concept has emerged as an alternative for the generation of these goods via the sustainable processing of biomass of diverse nature following chemical, thermochemical, enzymatic or fermentative pathways (Corma et al., 2007). Conversion of biomass into fuels and chemicals bids a potential opportunity to fulfill the energy needs of the upcoming decades. Owing to their relevance in synthesis, 5-hydroxymethylfurfural (HMF) and furfural have been considered as outstanding building blocks for chemicals and fuels in the US Department of Energy's list of top value-added chemicals from biomass (Bozell and Petersen, 2010). Both these compounds offer great possibilities considering their chemical functionality and allow the production of a wide array of chemicals with very diverse applications. Putten et al. (2013) reviewed thoroughly the synthetic pathways starting from HMF leading to products with applications as: monomers for subsequent polymerization, highlighting diols from HMF, 2,5-diformylfuran, 2,5-furandicarboxylic acid or 5-hydroxymethyl-2-furan carboxylic acid; fine chemicals, including products of interest as pharmaceuticals, agrochemicals, flavors and fragrances; and fuel components, such as dimethylfuran, levulinic acid or methyl tetrahydrofuran.

Much of the earlier work on the synthesis of these building block chemicals is reported in monophasic systems which suffer from thermodynamic limitations, low selectivity, low yield, or undesired side-products. A smart strategy to overcome some, if not all, of these hurdles is the use of a multiphase reaction-extraction system. However, the design and optimization of such systems is hardly straightforward. For instance, the choice of the organic solvent in the aqueous biphasic system to produce HMF and furfural from sugars is a crucial factor for both process economics and sustainability. Mathematical modeling can be valuable for efficiently analyzing and designing these complex systems. For example, solution and reaction properties of the many chemicals involved (reactants, solvents, products, coproducts, and catalysts) need to be described; the extent of miscibility (totally, partially, or effectively immiscible) must be established; the phases where reactions occur need to be identified; and the reaction and mass transfer mechanisms must be established. Also, the effects of chemically inert species on partitioning and of mixture composition on reaction rates must be characterized. However, the commonly used thermodynamic models lack the necessary thermodynamic parameters for every case and are inherently limited to the portion of the chemical design space for which every binary interaction parameter is available.

In this respect, COSMO-based models, such as COSMO-RS (Klamt, 1995; Klamt et al., 1998), are valuable alternatives for describing liquid-phase thermodynamics since they do not require any binary interaction parameters. Furthermore, such models allows for easy integration of quantum chemical calculations into a process modeling framework, greatly expanding the envelope of chemical species that can be modeled at a high level of accuracy. Here, an integrated and multiscale modeling architecture (Pudi et al., 2020) is employed to design and simulate the biphasic process based on COSMO-based thermodynamic models that do not require any binary interaction parameters. This modeling approach allows for not only easier optimization of reaction conditions but also more accurate solvent selection compared to the existing screening methods.

2. Multiscale modeling approach

This multiscale approach was first presented in an earlier work (Pudi et al., 2020). With python as the high-level interface, three different tools are employed at three different scales: density functional theory for the description of individual molecules, COSMO-RS for the description of individual physicochemical phenomena, and mathematical modeling for the description of all the interlinked phenomena in a biphasic reactive system.

3. Biphasic system

In an effort to achieve carbon neutrality and circular economy, lignocellulosic waste biomass has been identified as a promising carbon source and widely studied for the production of HMF and furfural. Therefore, a typical composition of rice straw (20% xylose, 35% fructose, and 45% lignin and other inert materials) is considered as feed (Amiri et al., 2010). Three reactions are considered in the system: xylose dehydration to furfural, fructose dehydration to HMF, and HMF rehydration to levulinic acid (LA) and formic acid (FA).

$$\text{xylose} \rightarrow \text{furfural} + 3H_2O \quad (1)$$

$$\text{fructose} \rightarrow \text{HMF} + 3H_2O \quad (2)$$

$$\text{HMF} + 2H_2O \rightarrow \text{LA} + \text{FA} \quad (3)$$

Other degradation reactions, including humin formation, have not been considered in this work. The calculations are carried out for a typical reaction temperature of 150 °C and 1:1 volume ratio of aqueous and organic phases. Five commonly used organic solvents for this process are considered to evaluate the impact of this choice on system performance and compare the accuracy of the multiscale model with experimental data and other solvent screening works. The candidates are 1-butanol, 2-butanol, methyl isobutyl ketone (MIBK), 2-methyltetrahydrofuran (2-MeTHF), and tetrahydrofuran (THF).

4. Results and discussion

4.1. Steady state properties of the system

Results from the multiscale process model are presented in Table 1. At equilibrium, the conversions of xylose and fructose are essentially 100 %. Since only reaction is considered for xylose, all of the converted reactant is converted to furfural. In the case of fructose, it appears that it is completely converted to LA and FA, leaving no presence of HMF. These results are unsurprising once the standard Gibbs' free energies of these reactions in the aqueous phase are considered: -164 kJ/mol for xylose dehydration to furfural, -182 kJ/mol for fructose dehydration to HMF, and -121 kJ/mol for HMF rehydration to LA and FA. These values remain do not decrease by more than 15–30 kJ/mol as the reaction proceeds from the feed composition to equilibrium. This explains the complete conversion of the feed reactants and HMF. Feed sugar conversions of >99% at equilibrium are also observed in experiments (Yang et al., 2012).

Table 1 Equilibrium results (in percentages) at 150 °C calculated using the multiscale model

Solvent	Furfural Yield	Furfural Extracted	HMF Yield	LA Yield	LA Extracted	FA Extracted
1-butanol	100	87	0	100	77	60
2-butanol	100	86	0	100	74	56
MIBK	100	81	0	100	58	40
2-MeTHF	100	83	0	100	62	50
THF	100	88	0	100	77	68

The biphasic system has minimal effect on the fundamental kinetics in the aqueous phase (Weingarten et al., 2010), but it is crucial to maximize product yield by extracting the desired products into the organic phase. Although the choice of the solvent also depends on other process objectives, this work only compares their extractive abilities. All the considered solvents extract more than 80% of the produced furfural. However, contrary to the results of other solvent screening works (Esteban et al., 2020), our results show that 1-butanol and 2-butanol extract higher percentage of furfural than MIBK and 2-MeTHF. Moreover, our results agree with experimental studies (Amiri et al., 2010). The strength of our multiscale model in comparison to other solvent screening works lies in the estimation of a solvent's extractive ability.

4.2. Extractive ability of the solvent candidates

Extractive ability of the organic solvent is crucial for a well-designed biphasic system that can capture as much of the desired products as possible. Table 2 presents a comparison between the partition coefficients of all the products in five different solvents at feed conditions. These coefficients (P_{OA}) are calculated as the ratio of mole fraction of a component in the organic phase to that in the aqueous phase. Earlier studies in solvent selection chose to calculate partition or distribution coefficients at room temperature and/or in a purely ternary solvent-water-solute system (Blumenthal et al., 2016; Esteban et al., 2020). However, partition coefficients could vary by significant margins at higher temperatures and in the presence of other compounds. In general, high partition coefficients are desired both at higher temperatures during the reaction (to maximize yield and selectivity) and at lower temperatures after the reaction (to maximize the amount of product in the extraction phase).

Although the values reported in this work cannot be quantitatively compared to the concentration-based partition coefficients usually reported in experimental studies, the general trends can be compared. Most of the commonly used organic solvents for this application provide a higher P_{OA} for furfural than HMF (Esteban et al., 2020), and this trend is also seen in the values reported in this work. However, comparing the partition coefficients in Table 2 to the amounts of products extracted in Table 1, there is no direct correlation. For example, MIBK has the highest P_{OA} for furfural but recovers the least amount of furfural.

Herein lies the reason for our multiscale model's better prediction of the real behavior observed in experiments. While all the solvent screening work published in the literature so far have based their results on partition coefficients at one particular state of the biphasic system (or worse, in pure ternary systems), our multiscale model takes into account the changing compositions. If necessary, it can also consider the change in temperatures if the reaction and settling are performed at different temperatures.

Table 2 Partition coefficients of all the products at feed composition and 150 °C

Solvent	HMF	Furfural	Levulinic Acid	Formic Acid
1-butanol	8.1	10.9	5.5	1.6
2-butanol	8.4	11.5	5.7	1.6
MIBK	11.2	19.4	6.7	1.8
2-MeTHF	10.2	15.6	6.0	1.9
THF	7.7	9.5	5.0	1.9

In addition to the partition coefficients, it is important to consider the degree of miscibility between the solvent and water. Most studies neglect the amount of water dissolved in the organic phase in their solvent selection process. However, the mole fraction of water partitioning into the organic phase is around 30–50% for all the commonly used organic solvents for this process. The solubility of one solvent in the other creates downstream separation and recycling challenges that should be considered in the overall process economics and sustainability analyses. A recent study has identified several alternatives in this aspect (Wang et al., 2021).

5. Current limitations

As noted earlier, only three reactions are considered in this work and only one of them is a degradation reaction. For example, no degradation reactions were considered for furfural, which caused 100% furfural yield. However, soluble and insoluble humins are known to form in this system, which reduces the yield of furfural and HMF. In addition, this process in practice is rarely taken to equilibrium in order to maximize the yield of desired products (Weingarten et al., 2010). Therefore, a more comprehensive study must include kinetics and assess the dynamic behavior of the system.

6. Conclusions

A multiscale modeling approach based on quantum chemistry and COSMO-RS is successfully employed in this work to model the steady state behavior of biphasic dehydration of sugars to valuable products such as HMF and furfural. This approach conforms to prior knowledge and experimental data. In addition, solvent selection based on this multiscale model presents more accurate results than the existing screening approaches that sometimes contradict experimental behavior. The presented approach paves the way for a more comprehensive work that can be used for systematic process optimization.

References

Amiri, H., Karimi, K., Roodpeyma, S., 2010. Production of furans from rice straw by single-phase and biphasic systems. Carbohydr. Res. 345, 2133–2138.

Blumenthal, L.C., Jens, C.M., Ulbrich, J., Schwering, F., Langrehr, V., Turek, T., Kunz, U., Leonhard, K., Palkovits, R., 2016. Systematic Identification of Solvents Optimal for the Extraction of 5-Hydroxymethylfurfural from Aqueous Reactive Solutions. ACS Sustain. Chem. Eng. 4, 228–235.

Bozell, J.J., Petersen, G.R., 2010. Technology development for the production of biobased products from biorefinery carbohydrates—the US Department of Energy's "Top 10" revisited. Green Chem. 12, 539–554.

Corma, A., Iborra, S., Velty, A., 2007. Chemical Routes for the Transformation of Biomass into Chemicals. Chem. Rev. 107, 2411–2502.

Esteban, J., Vorholt, A.J., Leitner, W., 2020. An overview of the biphasic dehydration of sugars to 5-hydroxymethylfurfural and furfural: A rational selection of solvents using COSMO-RS and selection guides. Green Chem. 22, 2097–2128.

Klamt, A., 1995. Conductor-like screening model for real solvents: A new approach to the quantitative calculation of solvation phenomena. J. Phys. Chem. 99, 2224–2235.

Klamt, A., Jonas, V., Bürger, T., Lohrenz, J.C.W., 1998. Refinement and parametrization of COSMO-RS. J. Phys. Chem. A 102, 5074–5085.

Pudi, A., Karcz, A.P., Shadravan, V., Andersson, M.P., Mansouri, S.S., 2020. Modeling of Liquid-Liquid Phase Transfer Catalysis: Process Intensification via Integration of Process Systems Engineering and Computational Chemistry, in: Pierucci, S., Manenti, F., Bozzano, G.L., Manca, D. (Eds.), Proceedings of the 30th European Symposium on Computer Aided Process Engineering (ESCAPE30). Elsevier B.V., pp. 43–48.

Putten, R.-J. van, Waal, J.C. van der, Jong, E. de, Rasrendra, C.B., Heeres, H.J., Vries, J.G. de, 2013. Hydroxymethylfurfural, A Versatile Platform Chemical Made from Renewable Resources. Chem. Rev. 113, 1499–1597.

Wang, Z., Bhattacharyya, S., Vlachos, D.G., 2021. Extraction of Furfural and Furfural/5-Hydroxymethylfurfural from Mixed Lignocellulosic Biomass-Derived Feedstocks. ACS Sustain. Chem. Eng. 9, 7489–7498.

Weingarten, R., Cho, J., Conner, W.C., Huber, G.W., 2010. Kinetics of furfural production by dehydration of xylose in a biphasic reactor with microwave heating. Green Chem. 12, 1423–1429.

Yang, Y., Hu, C.W., Abu-Omar, M.M., 2012. Synthesis of furfural from xylose, xylan, and biomass using AlCl 3·6H2O in biphasic media via xylose isomerization to xylulose. ChemSusChem 5, 405–410.

Proceedings of the 14th International Symposium on Process Systems Engineering – PSE 2021+
June 19-23, 2022, Kyoto, Japan
http://dx.doi.org/10.1016/B978-0-323-85159-6.50115-9

Study of Mass Transfer Coefficient of CO_2 Capture in different Solvents using Microchannel: A Comparative Study

Bushra Khatoon, Shabih-Ul-Hasan, and M. Siraj Alam*

Department of Chemical Engineering, MNNIT Allahabad, Prayagraj-21104, India
**msalam@mnnit.ac.in*

Abstract

Process intensification with micro channels is known for the lowest production cost, high efficiency, safest-clean production rate, and energy-saving equipment. It is well known that by replacing conventional channels with micro-level channels, CO_2 emission can be controlled efficiently with the comparatively high CO_2 removal rate. In the present study, we compare the CO_2 absorption rate in presence of different solvents like water, amino acids, mixture of amines, ammonia, NaOH, and KOH in terms of mass transfer coefficient that is based on different absorption phenomena and come-up with some guidelines. Also, an attempt is made to develop a correlation for the Sherwood number and the results obtained are compared with the predicted available co-relations in literature. This study concludes that the use of microchannels can enhance the mass transfer coefficient as well as CO_2 absorption rate several times in comparison to conventional channels and amines are proved to be a better solvent in comparison to other solvents for CO_2 removal in microchannels.

Keywords: Absorption, Mass transfer coefficient, Amines, CO_2, Microchannels.

1. Introduction

In this era, industrial growth is on boom due to rapid advancement and implementation of new techniques at the same time its growth is hampered significantly due to CO_2 emissions. Absorption of CO_2 in solvents like water, amino acids (MEA, DEA, and MDEA), mixture of amines (Mackowiak et al., 2018), ammonia, NaOH, and KOH is promising both by physically and chemically in micro-channels. Akkarawatkhoosith et al., (2020) shows that the chemisorption rate is lowest in conventional channels, and its value increases as the size of channel diameter decreases. It is well known that physisorption of CO_2 by water at low temperature and elevated pressure is comparatively low w.r.t chemisorption. However, the absorption rate can be enhanced by replacing the solvents, using some additive in existing solvents, varying the operating conditions such as flow rates (Q), concentration (C), etc., replacing physical absorption phenomena with chemical absorption, and by reducing the channel diameter to mini and micro level. As a result, we discuss the need of microchannels over conventional and mini contactors/reactors on the basis of mass transfer coefficients values in the next section.

2. Selection of system

2.1 Conventional, Mini, and Micro-channels

On the basis of mass transfer coefficients values we justify the need of microchannels over conventional channels/reactors. Figure 1 (a & b) shows a comparison of the values of mass transfer coefficient for conventional channels (e.g. packed columns, tray columns, trickle bed reactors), and microchannels (range: 200 μm $\geqq D_h > 10$ μm). Chemical absorption involves mass transfer rate and mass transfer coefficient can be enhanced by the parameters such as flow rates (Q), concentration (C), temperature (T), pressure (P) etc. (Al-Hindi et al., 2018). It can be easily seen in Figure 1 that the microchannels and a special type of microchannel gives a higher value of mass transfer coefficient than the conventional and mini-channels for the absorption process.

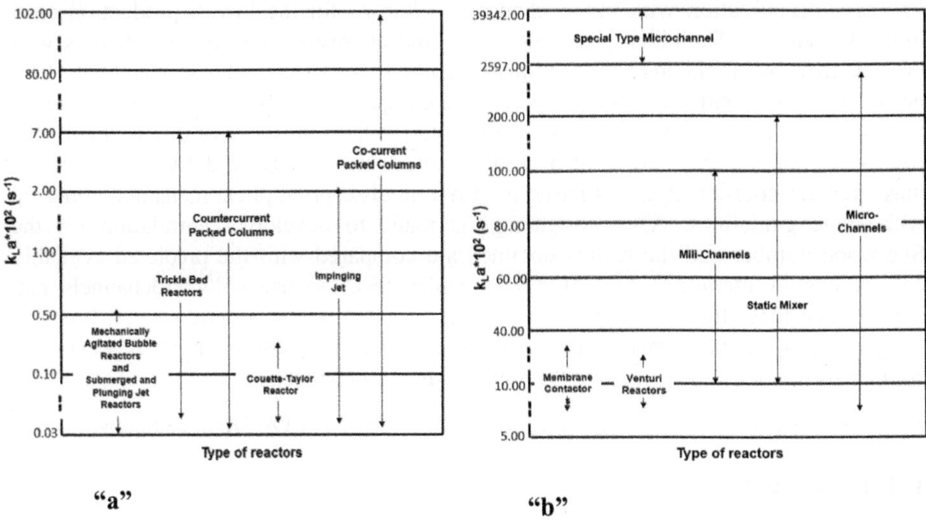

Figure 1: Schematic representation of mass transfer coefficient for different contactors and reactors.

2.2 Physical/Chemical Absorption

Dong et al., (2020) shows that the chemisorption of CO_2 has an absorption rate around 3 to 10 times greater than the physical absorption. As the diameter of the channels decreases (micro-channels) chemisorption always gives higher values of mass transfer coefficient over physical absorption (Akkarawatkhoosith et al., 2020). For microreactors, the range of mass transfer coefficient for physical absorption comes under the 0.3 - 7 s-1 and for chemisorption, the range extended from 0.7 - 100 s-1 for CO_2 absorption in amines (Yao et al., 2017).

2.3 Solvents

The solvents shown in Table 1 gives good absorption rate for conventional channels. These solvents can also give good absorption rate in mini and micro-channels as well provided channels should be clean before vaporization of solvents. Because absorption of CO_2 in water, NaOH, KOH, and ammonia forms soluble salts (Carbonates and Bicarbonates) may block the channels of small diameters. Thus, the amines and its blended solutions can be proved to be good solvents for the CO_2 absorption process in microchannels and a special type of microchannel (Figure 1).

Table 1: CO_2 absorption in different type of solvents reported in literature.

Authors	Absorption	Absorption mechanism
Elhajj et al., (2020)	Water	$CO_2 + H_2O \rightleftharpoons H_2CO_3; H_2CO_3 \rightleftharpoons HCO_3^- + H^+;$ $HCO_3^- \rightleftharpoons CO_3^{2-} + H^+$
Kraub et al., (2017)	NaOH	$CO_2 + 2OH^- \rightleftharpoons CO_3^{2-} + H_2O$
Liu et al., (2009)	Ammonia	$NH_3 + CO_2 + H_2O \rightleftharpoons NH_4HCO_3$
Kim et al., (2014)	MEA	$CO_2 + 2MEA \rightleftharpoons MEAH^+ + MEACOO^-$
Rinker et al., (1996)	DEA	$CO_2 + R_1R_2NH \rightleftharpoons R_1R_2NH^+COO^-$ $R_1R_2NH^+COO^- + B \rightleftharpoons R_1R_2NCOO^- + BH^+$
Donaldson et al. (1980)	MDEA	$(R)_3N + CO_2 + H_2O \rightleftharpoons (R)_3NH^+ + HCO_3^-$ Where $(R)_3N$ is any tertiary amine e.g., MDEA
Conway et al. (2015)	Mixture of Amines	$Amine_1 + Amine_2 + CO_2 \rightleftharpoons Amine_1CO_3^- + Amine_2H^+$

2.4 Concentration

When CO_2 absorbs in any solvent, several parameters affect the absorption rate like concentration, flow rates, temperature, pressure, channel diameter, type of absorption, and solvents. Section 2.1, 2.2, and 2.3 helps to decide the channel diameter range, type of absorption (physical/chemical absorption), and solvents. Table 2 shows low temperature and high pressure is a favorable condition for CO_2 loading (means mole of CO_2 load per mole of solvent). Table 3 indicates that higher absorption efficiency can be achieved with higher solvent rate and low value of CO_2 flow rate.

Table 2: CO_2 absorption in amines at different temperature and pressure.

Amines	Temperature (K)	Pressure (kPa)	CO_2 loading (mole/mole)	Authors
MEA	313	15.70	0.56	Prachi Singh (2011)
MEA	373	30.40	0.238	Guevara et al., (1993)
DEA	298	6.89	0.57	Lee et al., (1972)
DEA	313	10.70	0.59	Benamor et al., (2005)
MDEA	313	101.325	0.46-0.58	Chowdhary et al., (2013)

Table 3: CO_2 absorption in amines at different flow rates.

Amines	Liquid load (m^3/m^2-h)	Gas flow rate (L/h)	Removal Efficiency (%)	Authors
MEA, DEA, MDEA	10	-	90, 54, 04	Aroonwilas et al., (2004)
MEA, DEA, MDEA	4.8	-	43, 35, 03	Aroonwilas et al., (2004)
MDEA	-	100, 200, 300, 400	$< 40, \approx 20, < 10, < 05$	Pan et al., (2014)

2.5 Sherwood number

From section (2.1-2.4) that chemisorption in microchannels enhance mass transfer coefficient/absorption rate by using high flow rate of solvent (amines), low flow rate of

CO_2, low temperature, and high pressure. We represent mass transfer coefficient in terms of Sherwood number (Sh) for gas liquid-phase and use the method of Buckingham Pi theorem in which Sherwood number is a function of gaseous Reynolds number (Re_G), Reynolds number of liquid (Re_L), Schmidt number for gas (Sc_G), and the ratio of liquid to gas velocity (V_L/V_G) as given by Eq. (1 & 2).

$$Sh = f.(Re_G.Re_L.Sc_G.\frac{V_L}{V_G}) \quad (1)$$

$$Sh = n_1.Re_G^{n_2}.Re_L^{n_3}.Sc_G^{n_4}.\frac{V_L}{V_G}^{n_5} \quad (2)$$

In order to obtain a more accurate Sherwood number, the Schmidt number of gas is introduced in Eq. (2) in which n_1, n_2, n_3, n_4, and n_5 are the fitting parameters and their values taken are 0.084, 0.12, 0.385, 0.3, and 1 respectively. These values are obtained with the help of experimental data, performed in the laboratory and the parameters used in the experiment are given in Table 4. The final modified form of the equation is given by Eq. (3).

$$Sh = 0.084\,.Re_G^{0.12}Re_L^{0.385}Sc_G^{0.3}\frac{V_L}{V_G} \quad (3)$$

Table 4: Parameters used for the present study of experimental and theoretical work.

Parameters	Values	Parameters	Values	Parameters	Values
Gas	CO_2	Temperature	298, 313, and 338 K	Schmidt number	5891.684, 4359.327, and 3969.112
Amine	Aq. MEA	Model	Homogeneous mixture model	Reynolds number	$13 < Re_G < 193$ $90 < Re_L < 540$
Pressure	1 atm.	V_L/V_G	10	System	Microchannel

3. Results and discussion

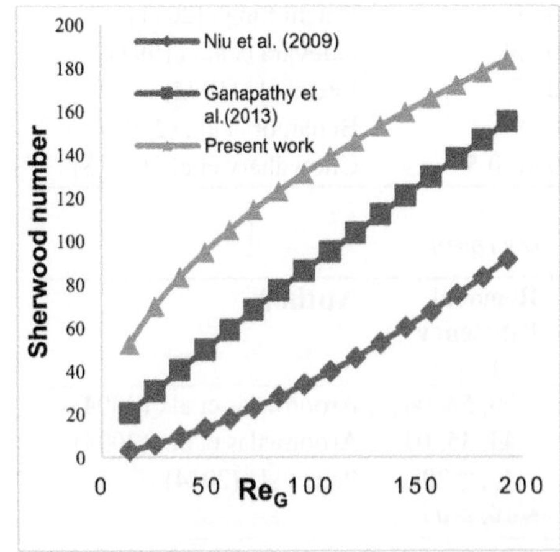

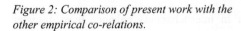

Figure 2: Comparison of present work with the other empirical co-relations.

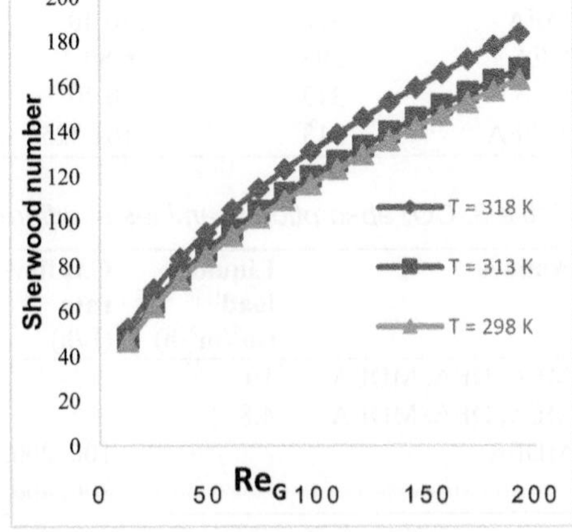

Figure 3: Study of Sherwood number at a different temperature, for CO_2 absorption in aq. MEA.

Figure 2 and Figure 3 shows the comparison of modified correlation given by Eq. (3) with that of Niu et al., (2009) and Ganapathy et al., (2013) which is mentioned in Eq. (4) and (5) respectively.

$$Sh.a.d_h = 0.11Re_G^{0.39}Re_L^{0.7}Sc_L^{0.5} \quad (4)$$

$$Sh.a.d_h = 10.201Re_G^{0.206}Re_L^{0.218}Sc_L^{0.5} \quad (5)$$

It can be clearly seen that the modified correlation outperforms in comparison to the others and gives higher values of Sherwood number throughout the range of Re_G (0-200) (Figure 2). It is also observed that replacing Sc_L with Sc_G gives the higher value of Sherwood number and thereby higher value of mass transfer coefficient as well. Figure 3 indicates that with increase in temperature, the value of the Sherwood number increases as a result the mass transfer coefficient also increases at higher temperature values.

4. Conclusions

The presented work investigates the conditions to enhance the higher rate of CO_2 removal and solvent selection, and equipment's based on literature review and also suggest a modified correlation of Sherwood number that gives higher values of mass transfer coefficient. The main findings are as follows:

- In conventional, mini and microchannel, it is found that microchannels/special type of microchannels provides a high value of mass transfer coefficient.
- It is found that chemisorption with amine solution gives high rate of absorption with low flow rate of CO_2, high flow rate of solvents, low temperature and high pressure. Amines are proved to be good solvent for microchannels because it doesn't form carbonates and bi-carbonates and thereby prevent choking problems in channels.
- On that basis of developed empirical co-relation, it can say that that the selection of Sc_G over Sc_L provides much better results than the other empirical co-relations which are also verified with the help of experimental work.
- At constant pressure, as the temperature increases the value of Sherwood number increases which leads to increase in the value of mass transfer coefficient. Thus, it can be concluded that the 318 K favours the chemisorption process of CO_2 in MEA.

References

Akkarawatkhoosith N., Nopcharoenkul W., Kaewchada A., Jaree A., 2020, Mass transfer correlation and optimization of carbon dioxide capture in a microchannel contactor: A case of CO_2 rich gas. Energies, 13, 5465.

Al-Hindi M., Azizi F., 2018, Absorption and desorption of carbon dioxide in several water types. The Canadian Journal of Chemical Engineering, 96, 274-284. Industrial and Engineering Chemistry Research, 43, 2228-2237.

Aroonwilas A., Veawab A., 2004, Characterization and comparison of the CO_2 absorption performance into single and blended alkanolamines in a packed column.

Benamor A., Aroua M. K., 2005, Modeling of CO_2 solubility and carbamate concentration in DEA, MDEA and their mixtures using the Deshmukh–Mather model. Fluid Phase Equilibria, 231, 150-162.

Chowdhary F. A., Yamada H., Higashi T., Matsuzaki Y., Kazama S., 2013, Synthesis and characterization of new absorbents for CO_2 capture. Energy Procedia, 37, 265-272.

Conway W., Bruggink S., Beyad Y., Luo W., Cabrera M. I., Puxty G., Feron P., (2015), CO_2 absorption into aqueous amine blended solutions containing monoethanolamine (MEA), N, N-dimethylethanolamine (DMEA), N, N-diethanolamine (DEEA) and 2-amino-2-methyl-1-propanol (AMP) for post-combustion capture process, Chemical Engineering Science, 126, 446-454.

Dong R., Chu Di., Sun Q., Jin Z., 2020, Numerical simulation of the mass transfer process of CO2 absorption by different solutions in a microchannel. The Canadian Journal of Chemical Engineering, 98, 2648-2664.

Donaldson T. L., Nguyen Y. N., 1980, Carbon dioxide reaction kinetics and transport in aqueous amine membranes. Ind. Engineering Chemical Fundamental, 19, 260-266.

Elhajj J., Al-Hindi M., Azizi M., 2020, A review of the absorption and desorption process of carbon dioxide in water systems. Industrial and Engineering Chemistry Research, 53, 2-22.

Guevara F. M., Libreros E. R., Trejo A., 1993, Gas solubility of carbon dioxide and hydrogen sulfide in mixtures of sulfolane with monoethanolamine. Fluid Phase Equilibria, 86, 225-231.

Ganapathy H., Al-Hajri E., Ohadi M., 2013, Mass transfer characteristics of gas-liquid absorption during Taylor flow in mini/microchannel reactors. Chemical Engineering Science, 101, 69–80.

Kim I., Hoff K. A., Mejdell T., Heat of absorption of CO_2 with aqueous solutions of MEA: new experimental data. Energy Procedia, 63, 1446-1455.

Kraub M., Rzehak R., 2017, Reactive absorption of CO_2 in NaOH: Detailed study of enhancement factor models. Chemical Engineering Sciences, 166, 193-209.

Lee, J. I., Otto, F. D., Mather, A. E., 1972, Solubility of carbon dioxide in aqueous diethanolamine solutions at high pressures. Journal of Chemical and Engineering Data, 17, 465-468.

Liu J., Wang S., Zhao B., Tong H., Chen C., 2009, Absorption of carbon dioxide in aqueous ammonia, Energy Procedia, 1, 933-940.

Mackowiak J. F., Syring K., Thomas A., Leimbrink M., Skiborowski M., Gorak A., Mackowiak J., 2018, Absorption of carbon dioxide using enzyme activated amine solution in columns with random packings. Chemical Engineering Transactions, 69, 2283-9216.

Niu H., Pan L., Wang S., 2009, Flow pattern and gas-liquid interfacial area in a microchannel contactor. Modern Chemical Industry, 29, 60-64.

Pan M. Y., Qian Z., Shao L., Arowo M., Chen J. F., Wang J. X., 2014, Absorption of carbon dioxide into N-methyldiethanolamine in a high-throughput microchannel reactor. Separation and Purification Technology, 125, 52-58.

Rinker E. B., Ashour S. S., Sandall O. C., 1996, Kinetics and Modeling of Carbon Dioxide Absorption into Aqueous Solutions of Diethanolamine. Industrial & Engineering Chemistry Research, 35, 1107-1114.

Singh P., Amine based solvent for CO_2 absorption form molecular structure process, Thesis. University of Twente, The Netherlands, 2011.

Yao C., Zhu K., Liu Y., Liu H., Jiao F., Chen G., 2017, Intensified CO_2 absorption in a microchannel reactor under elevated pressures. Chemical Engineering Journal, 319, 179-190.

Proceedings of the 14th International Symposium on Process Systems Engineering – PSE 2021+
June 19-23, 2022, Kyoto, Japan
http://dx.doi.org/10.1016/B978-0-323-85159-6.50116-0

Techno-Economic Study of Intensified Ethylene Oxide Production Using High Thermal Conductivity Microfibrous Entrapped Catalyst

Chinmoy B. Mukta[a], Nikhil R. Rayaprolu[a], Selen Cremaschi[a], Mario R. Eden[a*] and Bruce J. Tatarchuk[a,b]

[a]*Department of Chemical Engineering, Auburn University, Auburn, AL 36849, USA*
[b]*IntraMicron Inc.. 368 Industry Drive, Auburn AL 36832, USA*
edenmar@auburn.edu

Abstract

Ethylene oxide (EO), a high-volume chemical intermediate, is produced through highly exothermic partial oxidation reactions. It is one of the most energy-intensive and inefficient processes in the chemical process industry. Even a small increase in efficiency through process intensification can significantly reduce the harmful impact on the environment and improve economic performance. The exothermic partial oxidation reaction necessitates the use of a large number of long, small-diameter tubes inside the EO reactor to achieve fast convective heat removal. Moreover, localized hotspots can originate from flow channelling inside the reactor, causing some tubes to operate under runaway conditions, producing unwanted, complete oxidation of ethylene in the ignited tubes, resulting in much lower overall selectivity. The newly developed MicroFibrous Entrapped Catalysts (MFECs) is a non-woven microfibrous metal mesh made of either nickel, steel, or copper. MFECs provide better thermal management of the exothermic reactions through enhanced conductive instead of convective heat transfer inside the reactors. This work assesses the impact of using MFECs inside the EO reactor on the overall process. We have evaluated the effect of the number of ignited tubes (10%, 4%, 2%, 0%) inside the reactor for the conventional process and compared it to the MFEC configuration, which inherently avoids ignition. Avoiding ignited tubes results in higher EO production and reduced formation of CO_2, leading to reduced separation cost. The MFEC configuration leads to an overall product cost reduction of 18.4%.

Keywords: Intensification; Process Simulation; Derivative-free Optimization.

1. Introduction

The ever-growing use of commodity products is causing great demand for high-volume raw material intermediates such as ethylene oxides, which are extensively used in plastic bottles, anti-freeze, sports gear, detergents, and paints. In 2019 alone, the United States produced 2.8 million metric tons of ethylene oxides (EO) and is projected to increase 3-4% per year over the next decade. Ethylene oxidation is considered to have great potential for reducing of carbon emissions (Brueske *et al.*, 2015).

The newly developed MicroFibrous Entrapped Catalysts (MFECs) is a non-woven microfibrous metal mesh made of either Nickel, Steel, or Copper. MFECs provide better thermal management of the exothermic reactions through enhanced conductive instead of convective heat transfer inside the reactors. It also has a better ignition prevention capacity because of its ability to mitigate hotspots. The technology has been experimentally proven for a variety of exothermic reaction systems, including Fisher-Tropsch Synthesis (Choudhury *et al.*, 2020). Moreover, MFECs having a large surface area and high void space can help in even flow distribution along the reactor. All these properties of MFECs are advantageous in EO production, especially in terms of increased per pass ethylene conversion, prevention of hotspots, enhanced process safety, stable performance, and extended catalyst activity (Sheng *et al.*, 2013).

This work assesses the impact of using MFECs inside the EO reactor on the overall process. First, a plant-scale baseline simulation model of the conventional EO process has been developed using Aspen Plus™. The optimum design parameters are found using derivative-free optimization (DFO). Next, an economic analysis tool, ECON (Kalakul *et al.* 2014), is used to calculate capital and operating costs. We evaluated the effect of the number of ignited tubes (10%, 4%, 2%, 0%) inside the reactor for the conventional process and compared it to the MFEC configuration, which inherently avoids ignition.

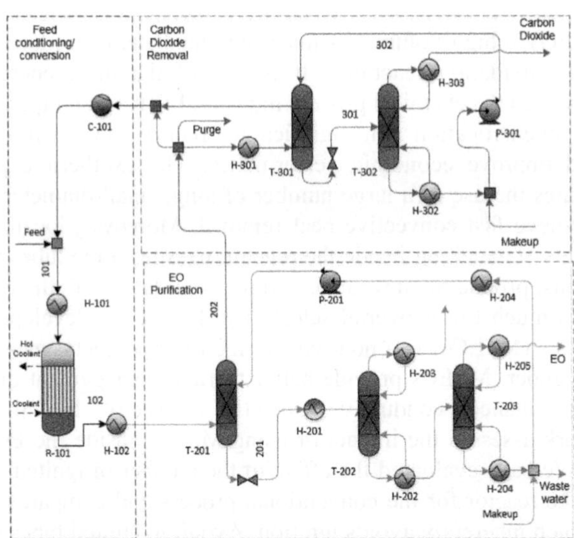

Figure 1. Ethylene oxide process PFD

2. Process Description and Design

2.1 Process description

The conventional oxygen-based process, which is reported to offer higher efficiency towards EO formation than the air-based process variant, was selected as the base-case design for later process intensification (Barecka *et al.*, 2017; Peschel *et al.*, 2012). Based on reported EO capacities, the typical product flowrate was selected as 100 kilotons per year with a purity of 99.1%. The reactor and EO feed conditioning and conversion sections are modeled using the UNIFAC group contribution method. Moreover, the model applicability was verified by comparing simulation results with process plant data. For the EO absorption and purification sections, SR-POLAR and experimentally regressed CPA models are used, respectively (Barecka *et al.*, 2017). The carbon dioxide separation sections are modeled by the Electrolyte Non-Random-Two-Liquid (ENRTL) model with the Redlich-Kwong (RK) equation for the vapor phase. Henry coefficients are used for modeling the solubility of gases.

2.2. Feed conditioning and conversion

The EO reactor (R-101) is modeled as a multitubular, packed-plug flow reactor. A silver-based catalyst was chosen based on its reported high selectivity and work rate (Kobe *et al.*, 2002). Typical reaction conditions for industrial EO production uses excess ethylene with 8% conversion of ethylene and 2% EO in the reactor outlet.

2.3. EO Purification

EO is absorbed in water under high pressure (20 bars) in a counter-current column (T-201). The water flow rate is adjusted to achieve total recovery of the diluted EO. The gas stream leaving the absorber, which is depleted in EO, is split into three streams: a fraction of the stream is sent to the CO_2 removal section, whereas the rest is directly recycled to the reactor to limit separation costs. A small fraction (<1%) of the gas stream is purged to avoid build-up of impurities. In column T-202, the dissolved gases are vented. Finally, in column T-203, EO is desorbed under lower pressure, reaching a purity of 99%.

2.4. Carbon dioxide removal

Carbon dioxide is scrubbed by physical and chemical absorption in hot potassium carbonate (K_2CO_3) solution (30% in water); MEAs are usually not used as they might form stable EO complexes. The reaction kinetics reported by Kothandaraman (2010) were used for modeling the absorption. The absorption column consists of several separation trays and operates at 20 bar, while the desorption column is operated at 1 bar. The purity of the CO_2 stream recovered as the top product was fixed at 95% to limit solvent loss.

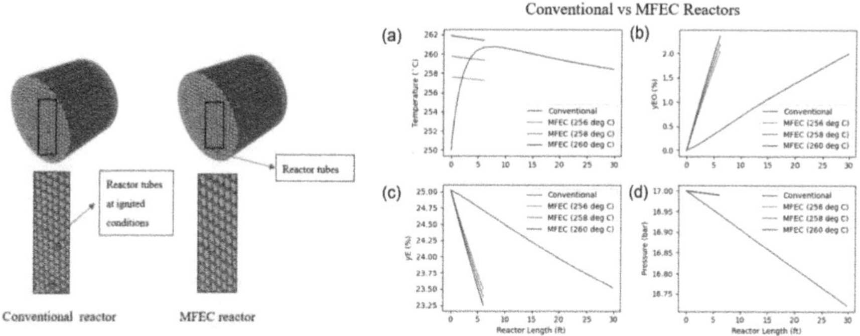

Figure 2. Ignited tubes inside conventional reactor vs. MFEC reactor (left) and its effect on reactor temperature, pressure and ethylene conversion (right)

2.5. Tube burnout inside EO reactor

The exothermic partial oxidation reaction necessitates the use of a large number of long, small-diameter tubes inside the EO reactor to achieve fast convective heat removal (Partopour & Dixon, 2016). Moreover, localized hotspots can originate from flow channeling inside the reactor, causing some tubes to operate under runaway conditions, producing unwanted, complete oxidation of ethylene in the ignited tubes, resulting in much lower overall selectivity (Geitenbeek *et al.*, 2018; Kimmerle *et al.*, 2009). As indicated in Figure 2 (left), EO reactors are continuously run even when a number of tubes are operating under ignited conditions which considerably impact reactor temperature profiles for conventional reactors. Ignited tubes inside the reactor result in waste of valuable raw materials and loss of product. Considerable amounts of excess waste CO_2 is produced inside the reactor. MFEC reactors which have better heat dissipation capabilities have the potential to prevent most of these problems. Figure 2(a) shows the reactor operating conditions for both MFEC and conventional reactor (Fogler, 2011). Figure 2(b-c) show the ethylene oxide (yEO) and ethylene (yE) mole fractions along the reactor, respectively. The figure shows six feet of tubes might be sufficient compared to thirty feet of conventional reactor with same number (24800) of tubes. Figure 2(d) shows the pressure drop along the reactor for both reactor configurations.

3. Optimization Algorithm

Figure 3 illustrates the DFO algorithm, a type of optimization algorithm which does not use derivatives to reach optimality. The objective function is treated as a black-box model or analytical equations, which provides the objective function values for a set of decision variables. Next, both a set of decision variables and the objective function combination is passed back to the DFO algorithm, where a new set of decision variables are calculated based on optimality direction and subsequently further evaluated. This process is carried until the termination criterion (number of iterations) is met.

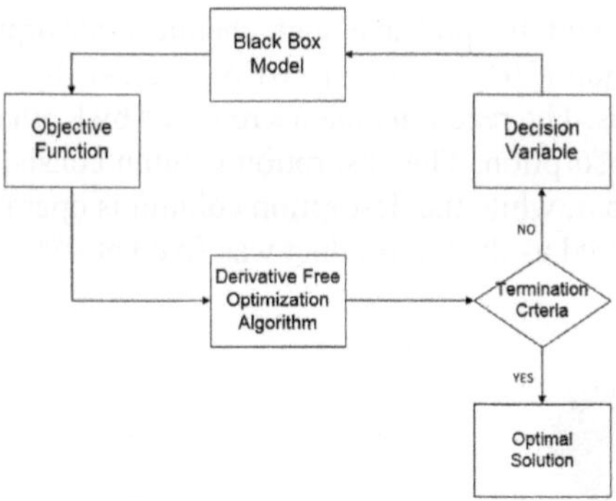

Figure 3. DFO algorithm

In this work, a DFO based algorithm named RBFOpt (Radial Basis Function) is used where a surrogate-model-based search method is employed to select the optimal design and operating conditions to achieve minimized objective function (Costa & Nannicini, 2018; Rios & Sahinidis, 2013). We used annualized cost as our objective function, which is calculated using Equations (1) - (8). The cost of each piece of equipment was calculated using standard cost coefficients from literature (Turton *et al.*, 2008). The raw material (EO and ethylene) cost has been calculated using a commodity chemical database (ICIS Chemical Business, October 2020).

$$min\text{: } TAC = \frac{i(i+1)^n}{(i+1)^n - 1} \times IC + AUC \tag{1}$$

$$st.\ IC = \sum_j Cost_j(q_{s,j}) \tag{2}$$

$$AUC = 24 \times 300 \times \sum_j Utility_j(q_{o,j}) \tag{3}$$

$$q = \theta\ (x,\ z,\ p(x)) \tag{4}$$

$$\sum_j Utility_j \leq Utility_0 \tag{5}$$

$$x_{product} \geq purity \tag{6}$$

$$x \in X \tag{7}$$

$$z \in Z \tag{8}$$

4. Results and Discussion

We used the DFO algorithm to find the optimum configuration for the overall EO process. The optimized process configuration parameters are given in Table 1 for varying degrees of tube ignition (note that BU indicates the bounds using during optimization). As CO_2 formation due to ignition increases inside the reactor, the requirements for the separation equipment increase. It can also be seen that the EO purification column (T-203) contributes most to the separation cost.

Table 1: Optimal process configuration for the EO process

	0%	2%	4%	10%	BU
No. Stages in EO Absorption Column, T-201	15	15	15	15	8-28
Solvent Flowrate in Column T-201 (ton/hr)	188	191	195	209	1-1000
No. Stages in EO Purifier Column, T-202	14	14	15	18	5-20
Feed Stage in EO Purifier Column, T-202	8	9	5	7	3-20
Pressure in EO Purifier Column, T-202 (bar)	2	2	2	2	1-15
No. Stages in EO Purifier Column, T-203	65	68	70	84	35-95
Feed Stage in EO Purifier Column, T-203	50	32	25	44	3-95
Reboiler Duty, T-203 (MW)	29	30	30	31	1-100
Pressure in EO Purifier Column-2, T-203 (bar)	1	1	1	1	1-15
No. Stages in CO_2 Absorption Column, T-301	6	5	5	5	4-7
Solvent Flowrate, T-301 (ton/hr)	21	26	31	48	1-100
No. Stages in CO_2 Desorption Column, T-302	9	11	13	20	3-22
Feed Stage in CO_2 Desorption Column, T-302	4	4	3	3	3-22

The capital and annualized cost for different varying levels of tube ignition in the EO process are shown in Table 2 (note that CV indicates the conventional reactor configuration). As the ignition percentage increases, the annualized cost also increases due to increased solvent requirements and an increase in the associated reboiler duties of the purification columns in Table 1. A larger overall cost reduction is found for the MFEC process mainly related to catalyst cost, as the MFEC system requires much less catalyst inside the reactor than the conventional process.

Table 2: Optimal process configuration for the EO Process

	0% MFEC	0% CV	2% CV	4% CV	10% CV
Capital Cost (10^6\$)	170.08	179.08	180.79	181.46	183.89
Annualized Cost (10^6\$)	167.45	179.05	180.96	181.78	184.84
EO Production (kton/year)	111.12	111.12	109.27	107.04	100.00
Cost of EO Production (\$/tons)	1506.93	1611.32	1656.08	1698.24	1848.40

5. Conclusions

In this paper, we have investigated various reactor ignition cases of the EO process and examined how the conditions inside the reactor and the use of MFEC can significantly impact the overall economics of the process. We have used DFO optimization to find the optimum process configuration in each case. If tube ignition can be avoided inside the reactor, the separation cost can be reduced for the intensified process by using MFEC, while also achieving optimum design and operating conditions. Moreover, our economic analysis clearly shows that the use of MFECs can significantly reduce the annualized cost of production from \$1,848/ton to \$1,506/ton, corresponding to a reduction of 18.4%.

References

Barecka, M. H., Skiborowski, M., & Górak, A. (2017). A novel approach for process retrofitting through process intensification: Ethylene oxide case study. Chemical Engineering Research and Design, 123, 295-316.

Brueske, S., Kramer, C., & Fisher, A. (2015). Bandwidth Study on Energy Use and Potential Energy Saving Opportunities in US Chemical Manufacturing (No. DOE/EE-1229). Energetics.

Choudhury, H. A., Cheng, X., Afzal, S., Prakash, A. V., Tatarchuk, B. J., & Elbashir, N. O. (2020). Understanding the deactivation process of a microfibrous entrapped cobalt catalyst in supercritical fluid Fischer-Tropsch synthesis. Catalysis Today, 343, 112-124.

Costa, A., & Nannicini, G. (2018). RBFOpt: an open-source library for black-box optimization with costly function evaluations. Mathematical Programming Computation, 10(4), 597-629.

Fogler, S. H. (2011). Essentials of chemical reaction engineering.

Geitenbeek, R. G., Nieuwelink, A. E., Jacobs, T. S., Salzmann, B. B., Goetze, J., Meijerink, A., & Weckhuysen, B. M. (2018). In situ luminescence thermometry to locally measure temperature gradients during catalytic reactions. ACS catalysis, 8(3), 2397-2401.

ICIS Chemical Business (2020): October 2020 Ethylene Oxide.

Kalakul, S., Malakul, P., Siemanond, K., & Gani, R. (2014). Integration of life cycle assessment software with tools for economic and sustainability analyses and process simulation for sustainable process design. Journal of cleaner production, 71, 98-109.

Kimmerle, B., Grunwaldt, J. D., Baiker, A., Glatzel, P., Boye, P., Stephan, S., & Schroer, C. G. (2009). Visualizing a catalyst at work during the ignition of the catalytic partial oxidation of methane. The Journal of Physical Chemistry C, 113(8), 3037-3040.

Kobe, J. M., Evans, W. E., June, R. L., & Lemanski, M. F. (2002). Epoxidation Industrial. Encyclopedia of catalysis.

Kothandaraman, A. (2010). Carbon dioxide capture by chemical absorption: a solvent comparison study (Vol. 72, No. 01).

Partopour, B., & Dixon, A. G. (2016). Reduced microkinetics model for computational fluid dynamics (CFD) simulation of the fixed-bed partial oxidation of ethylene. Industrial & Engineering Chemistry Research, 55(27), 7296-7306.

Peschel, A., Jörke, A., Sundmacher, K., & Freund, H. (2012). Optimal reaction concept and plant wide optimization of the ethylene oxide process. Chemical engineering journal, 207, 656-674.

Rios, L. M., & Sahinidis, N. V. (2013). Derivative-free optimization: a review of algorithms and comparison of software implementations. Journal of Global Optimization, 56(3), 1247-1293.

Turton, R., Bailie, R. C., Whiting, W. B., & Shaeiwitz, J. A. (2008). Analysis, synthesis and design of chemical processes. Pearson Education.

Sheng, M., Gonzalez, C. F., Yantz Jr, W. R., Cahela, D. R., Yang, H., Harris, D. R., & Tatarchuk, B. J. (2013). Micro scale heat transfer comparison between packed beds and microfibrous entrapped catalysts. Engineering Applications of Computational Fluid Mechanics, 7(4), 471-485.

Proceedings of the 14th International Symposium on Process Systems Engineering – PSE 2021+
June 19–23, 2022, Kyoto, Japan
http://dx.doi.org/10.1016/B978-0-323-85159-6.50117-2

Power Systems Infrastructure Planning with High Renewables Penetration

Can Li[a*], Antonio J. Conejo[b], Peng Liu[c], Benjamin P. Omell[c], John D. Siirola[d], Ignacio E. Grossmann[a]

[a]*Department of Chemical Engineering, Carnegie Mellon University, 5000 Forbes Ave, Pittsburgh, PA 15213, USA*
[b]*Department of Integrated Systems Engineering, The Ohio State University, 1971 Neil Avenue, Columbus, OH 43210,USA*
[c]*National Energy Technology Laboratory, Pittsburgh, PA 15236, United States*
[d]*Center for Computing Research, Sandia National Laboratories, P.O. 5800, Albuquerque, NM, 87185, USA*

canli.pse@gmail.com

Abstract

With the increasing penetration of renewable generating units, especially in remote areas not well connected with load demand, there is growing interest to co-optimize generation and transmission expansion planning (GTEP) in power systems. Due to the volatility in renewable generation, a planner needs to include the operating decisions into the planning model to guarantee feasibility. Three different formulations, i.e., a big-M formulation, a hull formulation, and an alternative big-M formulation, are reported for transmission expansion. To address the computational challenge, we propose a nested Benders decomposition algorithm and a tailored Benders decomposition algorithm that exploit the structure of the GTEP problem. Using a case study from Electric Reliability Council of Texas (ERCOT), we are able to show that the proposed tailored Benders decomposition outperforms the nested Benders decomposition. The coordination in the optimal generation and transmission expansion decisions from the ERCOT study implies that there is an additional value in solving GEP and TEP simultaneously. The detailed results of this paper has been published in Li et al. (2021).

Keywords: Power Systems, Generation Transmission Expansion, Mixed-integer Programming, Decomposition Algorithm

1. Introduction

Generation expansion planning (GEP) of power systems involves determining the optimal size, location, and construction time of new power generation plants, while minimizing the total cost over a long-term planning horizon (Conejo et al., 2016). There is a growing interest to use mathematical programming models to solve generation expansion planning problems (Lara et al., 2018; Tso et al., 2020). Conventional power units are dispatchable thermal power plants that can provide stable power output. However, with the increased penetration of renewable generation technologies, such as solar and wind, power systems nowadays need to be more flexible so as to adjust to the volatile power generation from renewables. In this case, operations decisions, such as unit commitment, ramping decisions, become important to assess system feasibility. Transmission expansion planning (TEP) refers to installing new transmission lines or expanding the capacities of existing transmission lines in a power system. Bahiense et al. (2001) propose a mixed integer disjunctive model for transmission network expansion. GEP and TEP are generally solved as two independent optimization problems. However, the significant penetration of renewables into power systems may lead to their concentration in remote areas not well connected to load demand. Therefore, installing renewables in those remote areas could compromise transmission expansion. The recognition of transmission's interaction with generation expansion has motivated the development of co-optimization methods to consider the tradeoffs between generation and transmission expansion (Krishnan et al., 2016). This paper is an extension of the GEP model reported in Lara et al. (2018) to a GTEP model. The long version of this paper has been published in Li et al. (2021).

2. Problem Statement

We are given different types of existing and known generating units and the generating units' nameplate (maximum) capacity; expected lifetime; fixed and variable operating costs; fixed and variable start-up cost; cost for extending their lifetimes; CO_2 emission factor and carbon tax, if applicable; fuel price, if applicable; and operating characteristics such as ramp-up/ramp-down rates, operating limits, contribution to spinning and quick start fraction for thermal generators, and capacity factor for renewable generators. Also given are existing and candidate transmission lines between any of the two neighboring buses. The susceptance, distance, and capacity of each transmission line are known. We use DC power flow equations to calculate the power flow in each transmission line. These equations are built based on Kirchhoff's voltage and current laws which differ from the network flow model used in the work of Lara et al. (2018). In the network flow model, the transmission network is represented similarly to pipelines where the flows only observe energy balance at each node while ignoring Kirchhoff's laws.

With the above input data, the spatial and temporal representations in Li et al. (2021), the proposed GTEP model is to decide: a) when and where to install new generators, storage units and transmission lines; b) when to retire generators and storage units; c) whether or not to extend the life of the generators that reached their expected lifetime; d) unit commitment of the thermal generators during the representative days; e) power generation of the generator clusters and power flows through the transmission lines. The objective is to minimize the overall cost including operating, investment, and environmental costs (e.g., carbon tax and renewable generation quota).

3. Transmission Expansion Formulation

One of the major constributions of this paper is to compare different formulations for transmission expansion. For the candidate transmission lines, we can write the following disjunction, where $NTE_{l,t}$ is a logic variable whose value can be True or False indicating whether or not transmission line l is installed in year t. If line l already exists in year t, the corresponding power flow has to satisfy DC power flow equation and upper and lower bounds. Otherwise, the corresponding power flow is zero. We assume that all the candidate transmission lines are standard. In other words, the susceptance of the candidate transmission lines B_l are parameters in the model.

$$\begin{bmatrix} NTE_{l,t} \\ p^{\text{flow}}_{l,t,d,s} = B_l(\theta_{s(l),t,d,s} - \theta_{r(l),t,d,s}) \\ -F^{\max}_l \le p^{\text{flow}}_{l,t,d,s} \le F^{\max}_l \end{bmatrix} \vee \begin{bmatrix} \neg NTE_{l,t} \\ p^{\text{flow}}_{l,t,d,s} = 0 \end{bmatrix} \quad \forall l \in \mathcal{L}^{\text{new}}, t, d, s \tag{1}$$

Standard approaches, i.e., big-M reformulation and hull reformulation (Grossmann and Trespalacios, 2013), are available to reformulate disjunctions (1) into mixed integer constraints.

The big-M formulation of the disjunction is,

$$-M_l(1-nte_{l,t}) \le p^{\text{flow}}_{l,t,d,s} - B_l(\theta_{s(l),t,d,s} - \theta_{r(l),t,d,s}) \le M_l(1-nte_{l,t}) \quad \forall l \in \mathcal{L}^{\text{new}}, t, d, s \tag{2}$$

$$-F^{\max}_l nte_{l,t} \le p^{\text{flow}}_{l,t,d,s} \le F^{\max}_l nte_{l,t} \quad \forall l \in \mathcal{L}^{\text{new}}, t, d, s \tag{3}$$

This big-M formulation is most commonly used in the literature (Conejo et al., 2016) for TEP.

The hull formulation is,

$$p^{\text{flow}}_{l,t,d,s} = B_l \Delta\theta^1_{l,t,d,s} \quad \forall l \in \mathcal{L}^{\text{new}}, t, d, s \tag{4}$$

$$\theta_{s(l),t,d,s} - \theta_{r(l),t,d,s} = \Delta\theta^1_{l,t,d,s} + \Delta\theta^2_{l,t,d,s} \quad \forall l \in \mathcal{L}^{\text{new}}, t, d, s \tag{5}$$

$$-\pi \cdot nte_{l,t} \le \Delta\theta^1_{l,t,d,s} \le \pi \cdot nte_{l,t} \quad \forall l \in \mathcal{L}^{\text{new}}, t, d, s \tag{6}$$

$$-\pi(1 - nte_{l,t}) \le \Delta\theta^2_{l,t,d,s} \le \pi(1 - nte_{l,t}) \quad \forall l \in \mathcal{L}^{\text{new}}, t, d, s \tag{7}$$

where $\Delta\theta^1_{l,t,d,s}$ and $\Delta\theta^2_{l,t,d,s}$ are disaggregated variables for the angle difference of transmission line l. Variable $\Delta\theta^1_{l,t,d,s}$ is equal to the angle difference if transmission line l has been installed in year t. Otherwise, $\Delta\theta^2_{l,t,d,s}$ equals to the angle difference. In addition to equations (4)-(7), equation (3) needs to be included in the hull formulation. The hull formulation has more continuous variables than the big-M formulation but it avoids using the big-M parameters of equations (2).

Alternative big-M formulation: Besides the big-M and hull formulations, an alternative big-M formulation is proposed by Bahiense et al. (2001). In this formulation, additional continuous variables $p^{\text{flow}+}_{l,t,d,s}$, $p^{\text{flow}-}_{l,t,d,s}$, $\Delta\theta^+_{l,t,d,s}$, $\Delta\theta^-_{l,t,d,s}$, are introduced, where the superscript '+' means that the flow is in the same direction as the nominal direction of transmission line l, i.e., from the sending-end node $s(l)$ to the receiving-end node $r(l)$; superscript '-' means the opposite direction. By defining these new continuous variables, equation (2) is replaced by equations (8a) to (8d) and equation (3) is replaced by equations (8g) and (8h).

$$p^{\text{flow}+}_{l,t,d,s} - B_l \Delta\theta^+_{l,t,d,s} \le 0 \quad \forall l \in \mathcal{L}^{\text{new}}, t, d, s \tag{8a}$$

$$p^{\text{flow}-}_{l,t,d,s} - B_l \Delta\theta^-_{l,t,d,s} \le 0 \quad \forall l \in \mathcal{L}^{\text{new}}, t, d, s \tag{8b}$$

$$p^{\text{flow}+}_{l,t,d,s} - B_l \Delta\theta^{+}_{l,t,d,s} \geq -M_l(1 - nte_{l,t}) \quad \forall l \in \mathcal{L}^{\text{new}}, t, d, s \tag{8c}$$

$$p^{\text{flow}-}_{l,t,d,s} - B_l \Delta\theta^{-}_{l,t,d,s} \geq -M_l(1 - nte_{l,t}) \quad \forall l \in \mathcal{L}^{\text{new}}, t, d, s \tag{8d}$$

$$p^{\text{flow}}_{l,t,d,s} = p^{\text{flow}+}_{l,t,d,s} - p^{\text{flow}-}_{l,t,d,s} \quad \forall l \in \mathcal{L}^{\text{new}}, t, d, s \tag{8e}$$

$$\theta_{s(l),t,d,s} - \theta_{r(l),t,d,s} = \Delta\theta^{+}_{l,t,d,s} - \Delta\theta^{-}_{l,t,d,s} \quad \forall l \in \mathcal{L}^{\text{new}}, t, d, s \tag{8f}$$

$$p^{\text{flow}+}_{l,t,d,s} \leq F^{\max}_l nte_{l,t} \quad \forall l \in \mathcal{L}^{\text{new}}, t, d, s \tag{8g}$$

$$p^{\text{flow}-}_{l,t,d,s} \leq F^{\max}_l nte_{l,t} \quad \forall l \in \mathcal{L}^{\text{new}}, t, d, s \tag{8h}$$

$$p^{\text{flow}+}_{l,t,d,s}, p^{\text{flow}-}_{l,t,d,s}, \Delta\theta^{+}_{l,t,d,s}, \Delta\theta^{-}_{l,t,d,s} \geq 0 \quad \forall l \in \mathcal{L}^{\text{new}}, t, d, s \tag{8i}$$

4. Proposed Algorithms

The proposed MILP GTEP model typically involves millions or tens of millions of variables, which makes the model not directly solvable by the commercial solvers. We propose two algorithms to efficiently solve this problem.

4.1. Nested Benders decomposition

Lara et al. (2018) apply a nested Benders decomposition algorithm to solve their GEP model. Like in the GEP model, the nested Benders decomposition algorithm decomposes the fullspace of the GTEP problem by year.

4.2. Benders decomposition

Instead of solving the GTEP problem sequentially by year as in the nested Benders decomposition, we treat all the investment-related variables as complicating variables and include all these variables in a single Benders master problem. The Benders algorithm iterates between the Benders master problem and the Benders subproblems.

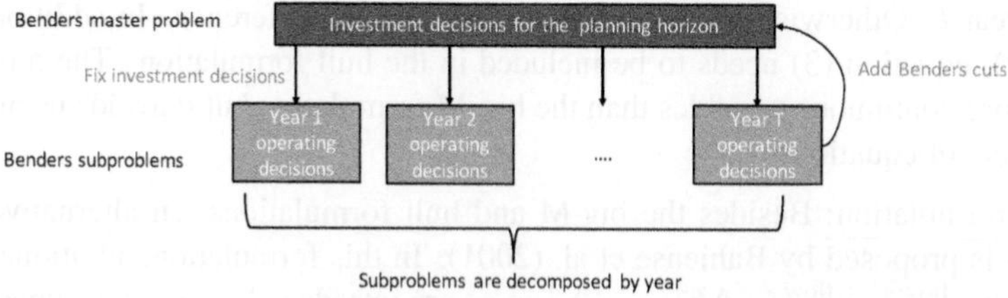

Figure 1: Tailored Benders decomposition algorithm applied to the GTEP problem

5. Results

We carry out a GTEP case study for ERCOT (Texas region in the US). It is divided into five geographical regions: Northeast, West, Coast, South, and Panhandle. We also test the two decomposition algorithms described in section 4. The nested Benders decomposition is implemented in Pyomo/Python (Hart et al., 2011). The tailored Benders decomposition implementation is from CPLEX. The computational results of the two proposed decomposition algorithms are shown in Table 1. The tailored Benders decomposition algorithm is able to solve all the three formulations to within 1% optimality gap within 10,000 seconds wall time (real wall clock time).

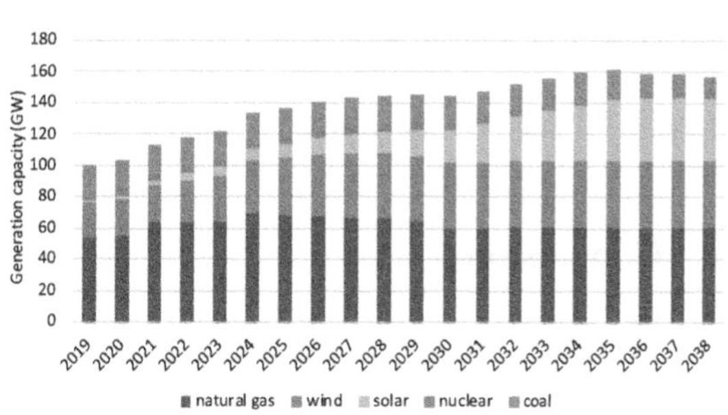

Figure 2: Aggregated generation expansion results

Table 1: Computational results of the two proposed decomposition algorithms using different formulations

Algorithm	Formulation	UB ($\$10^9$)	LB ($\$10^9$)	Gap	Wall time (secs)
tailored Benders	big-M	283.7	282.6	0.38%	5,115
tailored Benders	alternative big-M	283.9	281.6	0.82%	3,693
tailored Benders	hull	282.6	280.6	0.71%	8,418
nested Benders	big-M	295.7	268.9	9.98%	53,682
nested Benders	alternative big-M	294.2	265.5	10.81%	43,389
nested Benders	hull	288.0	269.3	6.97%	37,577

The capacities of different generation technologies from 2019 to 2038 are shown in Figure 2. The results include high capacities of solar and wind. The aggregated natural gas capacity of the five regions increases in the first few years, reaches its peak in 2024 and gradually decreases afterwards due to the retirement of old generators and the increase in carbon tax, which makes the natural gas generators less competitive compared with solar and wind generators. The nuclear capacities are unchanged throughout the planning horizon. The coal capacities are unchanged in the first few years

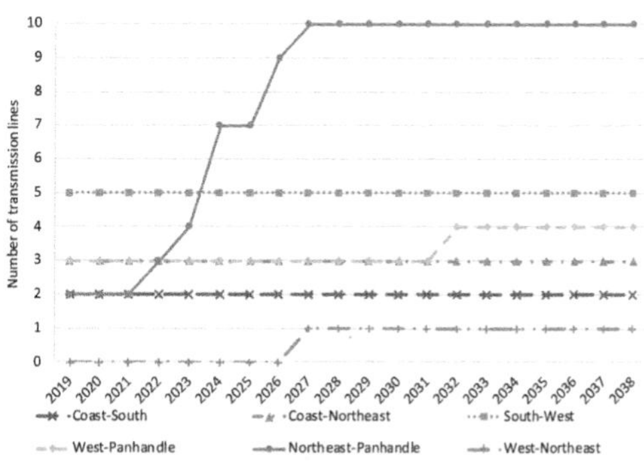

Figure 3: Transmission expansion results

and start decreasing in 2029 because of reaching their nominal lifetimes. No storage unit is installed. Therefore, the renewable generation when the net load is negative has to be curtailed. The total discounted renewable curtailment cost is $1.64 billion in 20 years. The number of transmission lines built over the planning horizon are shown in Figure 3. Most of the transmission lines are built for Northeast-Panhandle and South-West in order to transfer the power generated by the renewable sources in West and Panhandle to other regions.

6. Conclusions

We have developed models and algorithms for capacity expansion of power systems with high penetration of renewables. For PSE researchers, the capability to analyze power systems enables to study hybrid energy systems that have both electricity generators and electricity/heat consumers, such as chemical plants.

References

L. Bahiense, G. C. Oliveira, M. Pereira, and S. Granville. A mixed integer disjunctive model for transmission network expansion. *IEEE Transactions on Power Systems*, 16 (3):560–565, 2001.

A. J. Conejo, L. Baringo, S. J. Kazempour, and A. S. Sissiqui. *Investment in Electricity Generation and Transmission - Decision Making under Uncertainty*. Springer International Publishing, 2016. ISBN 978-3-319-29501-5. doi: 10.1007/978-3-319-29501-5.

I. E. Grossmann and F. Trespalacios. Systematic modeling of discrete-continuous optimization models through generalized disjunctive programming. *AIChE Journal*, 59(9): 3276–3295, 2013.

W. E. Hart, J.-P. Watson, and D. L. Woodruff. Pyomo: modeling and solving mathematical programs in python. *Mathematical Programming Computation*, 3(3):219, 2011.

V. Krishnan, J. Ho, B. F. Hobbs, A. L. Liu, J. D. McCalley, M. Shahidehpour, and Q. P. Zheng. Co-optimization of electricity transmission and generation resources for planning and policy analysis: review of concepts and modeling approaches. *Energy Systems*, 7(2):297–332, 2016. ISSN 1868-3975.

C. L. Lara, D. S. Mallapragada, D. J. Papageorgiou, A. Venkatesh, and I. E. Grossmann. Deterministic electric power infrastructure planning: Mixed-integer programming model and nested decomposition algorithm. *European Journal of Operational Research*, 271(3):1037–1054, 2018.

C. Li, A. J. Conejo, P. Liu, B. P. Omell, J. D. Siirola, and I. E. Grossmann. Mixed-integer linear programming models and algorithms for generation and transmission expansion planning of power systems. *European Journal of Operational Research*, 2021.

W. W. Tso, C. D. Demirhan, C. F. Heuberger, J. B. Powell, and E. N. Pistikopoulos. A hierarchical clustering decomposition algorithm for optimizing renewable power systems with storage. *Applied Energy*, 270:115190, 2020.

Proceedings of the 14th International Symposium on Process Systems Engineering – PSE 2021+
June 19-23, 2022, Kyoto, Japan
http://dx.doi.org/10.1016/B978-0-323-85159-6.50118-4

An Optimization Model for the Design and Operation of Reliable Power Generation Systems

Seolhee Cho[a] and Ignacio E. Grossmann[a*]

[a] *Department of Chemical Engineering, Carnegie Mellon University, Pittsburgh, PA 15213, USA*
* *Corresponding Author: grossmann@cmu.edu*

Abstract

This paper aims to develop a new optimization model for the design and operation of reliable power generation systems. This work optimizes the selection of redundant or backup units and operating units to maximize the reliability and to minimize the cost. In particular, every possible failure state that the power generation systems can have is investigated to evaluate the system reliability. To achieve this goal, we develop an optimization model that minimizes the total cost using Generalized Disjunctive Programming (GDP). The GDP model includes two decision variables: the first is a selection of redundant units with different sizes to increase the reliability of systems, and the second is a selection of operating units to satisfy the power demand. Specifically, the model determines the system reliability and corresponding expected power production by considering the number of redundant and operating units, and possible failure states under each design and operation mode. The model imposes a penalty when the demand is not satisfied, and the system has a low reliability. We have applied the proposed model in a small power plant (one stage with up to three generators) and verified through a sensitivity analysis that the model installs larger and more units to improve the system reliability as penalty rates increase.

Keywords: Redundancy, Reliability, Design, Operation, Optimization

1. Introduction

As evidenced by the Texas power crisis in 2021[1], the failure of power generation systems can lead to extreme events. Therefore, power generation systems should be designed to have high reliability to withstand failures of one or multiple components, and supply near uninterrupted electric power to industries and households. Reliability indicates the probability that a system will perform its required function properly even if one or multiple units fail (Sherwin et al., 2020). Since the goal of power generation systems is to consistently provide electric power, securing high reliability in their design and operation is a highly desirable objective. Numerous studies on the design/planning of power generation systems and reliability evaluation have been reported. However, previous works have dealt with these problems separately. Lara et al. (2018) have focused on optimizing the generation capacity to satisfy the power demand, whereas Amusat et al. (2016) have evaluated the reliability after designing the power generation systems. Studies that integrate design and reliability have also been reported, but they only consider a couple of generators or transmission lines failures (Moreira et al., 2016). Given the

---

[1] In February 2021, massive electricity generation systems in Texas were failed due to severe winter storms. Due to this, more than 4.5 million homes and businesses were left without power for several days, and at least 210 people were killed.

recent crisis, there is a strong motivation for a more comprehensive method to consider reliability in the design and operation phases of the power generation systems.

One method to improve reliability of the power generation systems at the design phase is to add redundant or backup units, which allows the systems to operate even if one or multiple generators fail (Kim et al., 2016). This approach is known as ‘reliability-based design optimization,’ and various studies on this topic have been conducted. Ye et al. (2018) develop a mixed integer nonlinear programming model for the optimal design of chemical process. Ortiz-Espinoza et al. (2021) present a multi-objective reliability-based design optimization model by combining economics, reliability, and safety. Chen et al. (2021) propose a two-stage stochastic generalized disjunctive programming (GDP) model by considering reliability and endogenous/exogenous uncertainties. Since these works assume that their target systems operate at a steady state, the authors mainly focus on optimizing the number of redundant units for the reliable design. However, since power systems operate in unsteady state due to time-varying power demand, reliability is also influenced by the operational strategies that the systems use to satisfy the load demand. Specifically, backup units can have a dual role in power generation systems. They can remain as backup units in case of low power demand or change to operating units when the power demand is high. Such dual purpose of redundant units depending on the load demand should be considered in the design and operation of reliable power generation systems. To our knowledge, this issue has not been addressed before in the literature for the design optimization of power generation systems with considerations of reliability.

This paper aims to develop a new optimization model for the design and operation of reliable power generation systems. This work optimizes the number of redundant units and operating units to maximize the reliability and to minimize the cost. In the remainder of this paper, we develop an optimization model using Generalized Disjunctive Programming (GDP), which is a high-level model representation that involves equations, disjunctions, and logic propositions. We then verify the effectiveness of the proposed model by solving an illustrative example.

2. Problem statement

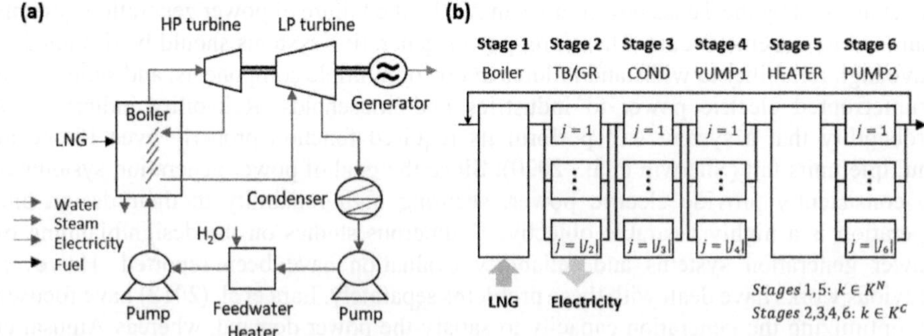

Figure 1. (a) Flow diagram of thermal power plant, (b) circular-parallel systems structure

Given is a natural gas power plant with multiple stages $k \in K$ including turbine, boiler, and pump, parallel identical units $j \in J_k$ for each stage k, and set of discrete capacities $c \in C_k$ of the units j in stages k. The stages can be classified into two groups: noncritical stage $k \in K^N$ that do not consider reliability, and critical stages $k \in K^C$ that do consider reliability. A set of stage designs $h \in H_k$ and corresponding operation modes $m \in M_{k,h}$, and time periods $t \in T$ are also given. Specifically, $h = 1$ means one unit installation and $h = H$ means all potential units are installed. Likewise, $m = 1$ represents one unit operation mode, $m = M$ refers to the mode in which all units are simultaneously operated. Each stage k has different failure states $s \in S_{m,k,h}$ depending on design h and operation mode m, which can be classified into (i) successful operation states $(S^F_{m,k,h})$ and (ii) partial operation states $(S^P_{m,k,h})$. There are also corresponding operating reliabilities: successful operation reliability $(R^F_{k,t})$ and partial operation reliability $(R^P_{k,t})$. While 'successful operation states' indicate the operation states in which the power generation capacity is sufficient to satisfy the load demand, 'partial operation states' refer to the operation states in which the power generation capacity is insufficient to meet the load demand, but still can produce electric power at a limited level. The $R^F_{k,t}$ and $R^P_{k,t}$ are probabilities that such successful or partial operation states exist in stage k in time t, respectively. The major assumptions used in the model are: (i) There is one unit in noncritical stages, which has sufficiently large capacity; (ii) A redundant unit can be a backup of any operating unit; (iii) Repair and maintenance processes are not considered.

3. Model formulation

The model is developed using Generalized Disjunctive Programming (GDP) (Grossmann and Trespalacios, 2013), which can be expressed in terms of Boolean and continuous variables, algebraic constraints, disjunctions, and logic propositions.

$$\bigvee_{h \in H_k} \left[\begin{array}{l} Z_{k,h} \\ \sum_{c \in C_k} y_{k,j,c} = i, \quad i = 1,\dots,h \\ \bigvee_{m \in M_{k,h}} \left[\begin{array}{l} W_{m,k,h,t} \\ \sum_{j \in J_k} \sum_{c \in C_k} x_{k,j,c,t} = i, \quad i = 1,\dots,m \\ \sum_{c \in C_k} \varepsilon_j \rho_{k,c} x_{k,j,c,t} \le AUC_{k,j,t} \quad \forall j \in J_k \\ AUC_{k,j,t} \le \sum_{c \in C_k} \rho_{k,c} x_{k,j,c,t} \quad \forall j \in J_k \\ R^F_{k,t} = \sum_{s \in S^F_{m,k,h}} \left\{ \prod_{j \in J^O_{s,m,h}} \lambda_{j,k} \prod_{j \in J^N_{s,m,h}} \sigma_{j,k} \right\} \\ R^P_{k,t} = \sum_{s \in S^P_{m,k,h}} \left\{ \prod_{j \in J^O_{s,m,h}} \lambda_{j,k} \prod_{j \in J^N_{s,m,h}} \sigma_{j,k} \right\} \\ EP^s_{k,t} \le \omega_t \sum_{j \in J^O_{s,m,h}} \sum_{c \in C_k} AUC_{k,j,t} R^s_{k,t} \quad s = 1 \\ EP^s_{k,t} = \omega_t \sum_{j \in J^N_{s,m,h}} IC_{k,j} R^s_{k,t} \quad \forall s \ne 1, s \in S_{m,k,h} \end{array} \right] t \in T \end{array} \right] k \in K^C$$

- (a) **Investment disjunction**
- (1) **Number of installed unit**
- (b) **Operation disjunction**
- (2) **Number of operating unit**
- (3) **Available operating capacity of unit in time**
- (4) **Successful and partial operation reliability**
- (5) **Expected production by successful operation**
- (6) **Expected production by partial operation**

$$\begin{cases} \sigma_{j,k} = 1 & \forall j \in J^B_{s,m,h}, k \in K \\ \sigma_{j,k} = (1 - \lambda_{j,k}) & \forall j \in J^F_{s,m,h}, k \in K \end{cases} \qquad \begin{array}{l} J^B_{s,m,h} \cup J^F_{s,m,h} = J^N_{s,m,h} \quad \forall j \in J_k \\ J^O_{s,m,h} \cup J^N_{s,m,h} = \emptyset \quad \forall j \in J_k \end{array} \qquad (7)$$

There are two Boolean variables related to investment and operation decisions. $Z_{k,h}$ is true if design h is selected for stage k; false otherwise (Equation (a)). $W_{m,k,h,t}$ is true if stage k is in operation mode m in time t for design h; false otherwise (Equation (b)). The binary variable $y_{k,j,c}$ indicates the installation of unit j with specified capacity c in stage k and $x_{k,j,c,t}$ indicates the operation of unit j with specificed capacity c in stage k and time t. $\lambda_{j,k}$ is a reliability of unit j in stage k and $\sigma_{j,k}$ defined in Eqn (7), states that when the unit j belongs to set of backup units in failure state s under design h and operation mode m ($J^B_{s,m,h}$), the unit reliability ($\lambda_{j,k}$) will be 1. If the unit j belongs to set of failed unit ($J^F_{s,m,h}$), the unit unreliability ($1-\lambda_{j,k}$) will be used to calculate system reliability.

$$\sum_{c\in C_k} y_{k,j,c} \le 1 \quad \forall k \in K^C, j \in J_k \quad \textbf{(8)} \qquad \sum_{c\in C_k} x_{k,j,c,t} \le 1 \quad \forall k \in K^C, j \in J_k, t \in T \quad \textbf{(9)}$$

$$IC_{k,j} = \sum_{c\in C_k} \rho_{k,c} y_{k,j,c} \quad \forall k \in K^C, j \in J_k \quad \textbf{(10)} \qquad TEP_{k,t} = \sum_{s\in S} EP^s_{k,t} \quad \forall k \in K^C, t \in T \quad \textbf{(11)}$$

$$ASC_{k,t} = \sum_{j\in J_k} AUC_{k,j,t} \quad \forall k \in K^C, t \in T \quad \textbf{(12)} \qquad DC_{k,t} = \xi R^P_{k,t} \quad \forall k \in K^C, t \in T \quad \textbf{(13)}$$

$$\left.\begin{array}{ll} \veebar_{h\in H_k} Z_{k,h} & \forall k \in K^C \\ Z_{k,h} \Leftrightarrow \veebar_{m\in M_{k,h,t}} W_{m,k,h,t} & \forall h \in H_k, k \in K^C, t \in T \end{array}\right\} \textbf{(14)} \qquad \left.\begin{array}{ll} y_{k,j+1,c} \le y_{k,j,c} & \forall k \in K^C, j \in J_k, c \in C_k \\ x_{k,j+1,c,t} \le x_{k,j,c,t} & \forall k \in K^C, j \in J_k, c \in C_k, t \in T \end{array}\right\} \textbf{(15)}$$

$$y_{k,j,c} \ge x_{k,j,c,t} \quad \forall k \in K^C, j \in J_k, c \in C_k, t \in T \quad \textbf{(16)} \qquad \left.\begin{array}{ll} ASC_{k,t} \le \psi_k & \forall k \in K^N, t \in T \\ TEP_{k,t} \le ASC_{k,t} & \forall k \in K^N, t \in T \end{array}\right\} \textbf{(17)}$$

$$TEP_{k+1,t} = \eta_k TEP_{k,t} \quad \forall k \in K, t \in T \quad \textbf{(18)}$$

$$Z_{k,h}, W_{m,k,h,t} \in \{True, False\};\ x_{k,j,c,t}, y_{k,j,c} \in \{0,1\};\ IC_{k,j}, AUC_{k,j,t}, ASC_{k,t}, R^s_{k,t}, EP^s_{k,t}, TEP_{k,t}, DC_{k,t}, F_t \ge 0$$

Eqns. (8) and (9) state that only one capacity can be installed and operated. Eqns. (10) – (12) indicate capacity of unit installed in stage k, total expected power production, and available capacity of stage k, respectively. Eqn. (13) is a downtime penalty and Eqn. (14) is a logic constraint for disjunction. Eqn. (15) are symmetry breaking constraints, meaning that a unit can only be selected if the one with higher priority is selected. Eqn. (16) indicates that installed units only can be used. Eqn. (17) constrains the expected production and operating capacity of noncritical stage $k \in K^N$. Eqn. (18) states that the expected production of stage $k+1$ is estimated by using expected production of stage k and conversion rate of stage k.

The objective function in (19) is to minimize the total cost, which includes the investment cost ($\delta_{k,c} y_{k,j,c}$), start-up cost ($\theta_{k,c} x_{k,j,c,t}$), expected fuel cost to purchase natural gas ($\pi_t F_t$), expected operating cost ($\gamma_k TEP_{k,t}$), downtime penalty ($DC_{k,t}$), and unmet demand penalty (PN_t). The system is charged penalties for the unmet demand, as shown by Equation (20). Rather than considering a bi-criterion optimization problem, we assume that shortfalls in power demand and low reliability are penalized so as to formulate the optimization problem as a single objective problem for cost minimization.

$$\min Z = \sum_{k\in K}\sum_{j\in J_k}\sum_{c\in C_k} \delta_{k,c} y_{k,j,c} + \sum_{k\in K}\sum_{j\in J_k}\sum_{c\in C_k}\sum_{t\in T} \theta_{k,c} x_{k,j,c,t} + \sum_{t\in T} \pi_t F_t + \sum_{k\in K}\sum_{t\in T} \gamma_k TEP_{k,t} + \sum_{k\in K}\sum_{t\in T} DC_{k,t} + \sum_{t\in T} PN_t \quad \textbf{(19)}$$

$$\left.\begin{array}{l} \begin{bmatrix} V_{1,t} \\ TEP_{k,t} < \omega_t D_t \\ PN_t = (\omega_t D_t - TEP_{k,t})\alpha \end{bmatrix} \vee \begin{bmatrix} V_{2,t} \\ TEP_{k,t} \ge \omega_t D_t \\ PN_t = 0 \end{bmatrix} \quad \forall k = GN, t \in T \\ V_{1,t} \veebar V_{2,t} \quad \forall t \in T \end{array}\right\} \textbf{(20)}$$

The GDP given by (1)–(20) can be transformed into a Mixed-Integer Nonlinear Programming (MINLP) using Big-M (BM) and/or Hull Reformulation (HR) (Grossmann and Trespalacios, 2013). This paper uses both methods, and Eqns. (5) and (6) are transformed into MILP constraints by using an exact linearization (Avraamidou and Pistikopoulos, 2019, and Garcia-Herreros et al., 2015).

4. Illustrative example

To verify the proposed model, the power system that has one stage ($k = 1$) involving up to three generators ($|J_k| = 3$) and three different sizes ($|C_k| = 3$) are analysed. Here the one stage stands for the generator stage. The total time horizon is 10 months, which is divided into 10 periods (i.e., 1 month). Table 1 shows the parameter values for the example.

Table 1. Parameter for illustrative example

Parameter	Symbol	Value	Parameters	Symbol	Value
Nameplate capacity (MW)	$\rho_{k,c}$	50,80, 100	Purchase cost of natural gas ($/MMBtu)	π_t	5
Minimum operating capacity (ratio of $\rho_{k,c}$, %)	ε_j	10	Production cost ($/MWh)	γ_k	5
Unit reliability	$\lambda_{j,k}$	0.97	Downtime penalty rate ($/hr)	ξ	1000
Conversion rate	η_k	0.4278	Installation cost (k$/unit)	$\delta_{k,c}$	10, 13, 15
Unmet demand penalty rate ($/MWh)	α	100	Start-up cost ($/unit)	$\theta_{k,c}$	100, 160, 200

Table 2. Numerical results of illustrative example

Solution method	MINLP		MILP	
Solver	BARON		CPLEX	
Cost (k$)	164.1		164.1	
Average reliability	**0.9758**		**0.9758**	
Reformulation	BM	HR	BM	HR
Equations	1,110	1,212	2,190	4,452
Cont. variables	267	1,083	627	2,883
Binary variables	108	360	108	360
CPU (sec.)	4.040	11.110	0.360	0.687

Figure 2. Optimal design and operation

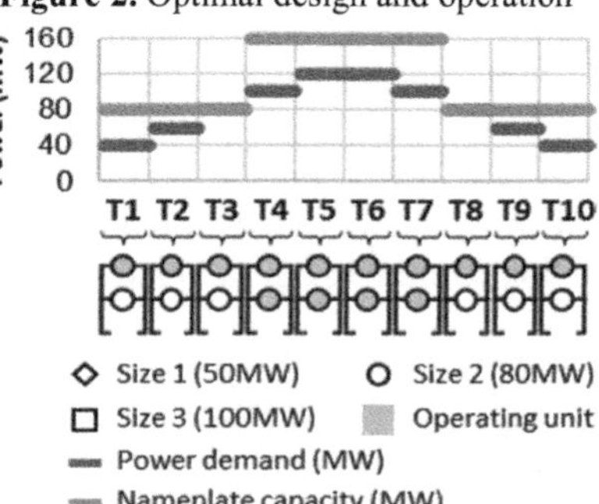

Table 2 shows the numerical results obtained with BARON and CPLEX in GAMS 32.1.0 on an Intel Core i7-10510U CPU, 1.80GHz. Although the sizes of the MILP reformulations are larger, their CPU times are significantly shorter than the MINLP. The proposed model predicts the total cost of $164,192 including unmet demand penalty of $144 and downtime penalty of $2,328. As shown in Figure 2, the model installs two medium size generators of 80 MW each yielding a total of 160MW. While the second generator remains as a backup when the demand is relatively low (from T1 – T3 and T8 – T10), both generators are used to meet the demand during T4 – T7.

5. Sensitivity analysis

To analyze the impact of unmet demand and downtime penalty rates on design and operation of reliable power systems, two alternative cases that have different penalty rates are suggested (Case 1: α = $500/MWh, ξ = $5,000/hr, Case 2: α = $1,000/MWh, ξ = $10,000/hr). As shown in Figure 3(a), the system with higher penalty rates than base case (c.f., Base case: α = $100/MWh, ξ = $1,000/hr) tends to install two larger units (each 100 MW) so as to improve reliability, and the cost is also increased to 171.9 k$. When the unmet and downtime penalties are significantly higher than other two cases (Base case and Case 1) (Figure 3(b)), the system decides to install three medium size generators (each 80 MW) and have one unit as a backup during all the periods, which results in the highest reliability (0.9989) and cost (175.1 k$).

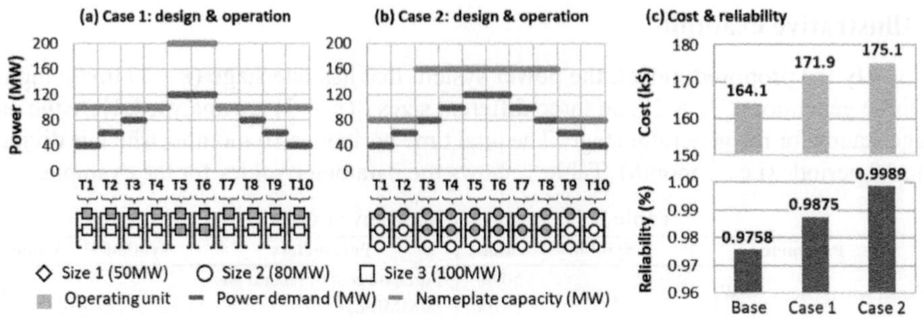

Figure 3. (a) and (b): Optimal design and operation of alternative cases, (c): total cost and average reliability of all cases

6. Conclusions

This paper has presented a mathematical optimization model for the design and operation of reliable power generation system. This work optimizes the number of redundant units and operating units to maximize the reliability and to minimize the cost. We propose a GDP formulation to represent the reliability and expected production, which are essential factors to determine the design and operation of power generation systems. Through a small example and sensitivity analysis, we found that the optimal system involves more and larger units to improve the system reliability as the penalty rates increase. Future work will involve other operation problems in power systems such as economic dispatch and unit commitment to evaluate the reliability more precisely by using a more rigorous reliability model such as Markov chain theory.

Acknowledgement

This work was conducted as part of the Institute for the Design of Advanced Energy Systems (IDAES) with support through the Simulation-Based Engineering, Crosscutting Research Program within the U.S. Department of Energy's Office of Fossil Energy and Carbon Management.

References

Amusat OO, Shearing PR, Fraga ES. Optimal integrated energy systems design incorporating variable renewable energy sources. Computers & Chemical Engineering, 2016

Avraamidou S, Pistikopoulos EN. A Bi-Level Formulation And Solution Method For The Integration of Process Design And Scheduling. Computer Aided Chemical Engineering, 2019

Chen Y, Ye Y, Grossmann IE, Chen B. Integrating Reliability and Uncertainty in Process Synthesis. Computer Aided Chemical Engineering, 2021

Garcia-Herreros P, Zhang L, Misra P, Arslan E, Mehta S, Grossmann IE. Mixed-integer bilevel opimization for capacity planning with rational markets, Computers and Chemical Engineering, 2015

Grossmann IE, Trespalacios F. Systematic modeling of discrete-continuous optimization models through generalized disjunctive programming. AIChE Journal, 2013.

Kim H, Kim P. Reliability–redundancy allocation problem considering optimal redundancy strategy using parallel genetic algorithm. Reliability Engineering & System Safety, 2017

Lara CL, Mallapragada DS, Papageorgiou DJ, Venkatesh A, Grossmann IE. Deterministic electric power infrastructure planning: Mixed-integer programming model and nested decomposition algorithm. European Journal of Operational Research, 2018.

Moreira A, Pozo D, Street A, Sauma E. Reliable Renewable Generation and Transmission Expansion Planning: Co-Optimizing System's Resources for Meeting Renewable Targets. IEEE Transactions on Power Systems, 2017.

Ortiz-Espinoza AP, Ye Y, Grossmann IE, Jiménez-Gutiérrez A. Multi-objective optimization for the incorporation of safety and reliability considerations in process design. Computer Aided Chemical Engineering, 2021

Sherwin DJ, Bossche A. The Reliability, Availability and Productiveness of Systems. Springer, 1993.

Ye Y, Grossmann IE, Pinto JM. Mixed-integer nonlinear programming models for optimal design of reliable chemical plants. Computers and Chemical Engineering, 2018

Proceedings of the 14th International Symposium on Process Systems Engineering – PSE 2021+
June 19-23, 2022, Kyoto, Japan
http://dx.doi.org/10.1016/B978-0-323-85159-6.50119-6

Rule-based Method for Retrofitting Conventional Processes with Integrated Units

Eduardo Perez-Cisneros[a], Mario R. Eden[b], Rafiqul Gani[c*]
[a]*Departmento de IPH, UAM-Iztapalapa, Mexico City, Mexico*
[b]*Department of Chemical Engineering, Auburn University, Auburn, AL 36849, USA*
[c]*PSE for SPEED Company, Ordup Jagtvej 42D, DK-2920 Charlottenlund, Denmark*
[*]*rgani2018@gmail.com*

Abstract

Targeted process improvements can be achieved through process intensification and/or integration. Three alternative options, depending on the reference, are highlighted in the paper. The rules needed, to establish when process intensification and/or integration are feasible pathways to improvement, are given and through case studies, their successful applications are highlighted.

Keywords: Reactive distillation; Divided wall columns, Hybrid distillation schemes; Intensification; Optimization; Integration

1. Introduction

Integrated technologies can perform multiple tasks simultaneously within the same physical unit or sequentially in separate physical units with the objective to achieve a set of performance improvement targets. In the case of the former, a reactive distillation column (RDC) is a well-known example, while in the case of the latter, a divided wall column (DWC) and a hybrid distillation scheme (HDS) are well-known examples. In RDCs, both reaction and separation tasks are performed simultaneously on one or more stages of the column (Tian *et al.*, 2018; Tula *et al.*, 2020). In DWCs multicomponent separations that normally require multiple distillation columns are performed in a single column by placing a partial vertical partition (pre-fractionator) inside the main column (Asprion and Kaibel, 2010). In HDSs, two-unit operations, where one is distillation, are combined to perform specific separation tasks such that each operates at their highest efficiencies (O'Connell *et al.*, 2019). Note that HDS is not membrane distillation.

Distillation is the common separation technique in RDC, DWC and/or HDS. However, separation by distillation is energy intensive and the majority of the separation operations found in the chemical and related industries are primarily distillation. Therefore, a large percentage of indirect emissions of carbon dioxide (CO_2) could also be attributed to distillation (Angelini *et al.*, 2005). Accordingly, the challenge of the energy-environment interactions requires consideration of options to perform the same separation tasks at lower energy consumptions (Pistikopoulos *et al.*, 2021). Opportunities exist for substantial reductions in CAPEX, OPEX, waste and CO_2 emission through simultaneous and/or sequential integration of operations.

Options to totally replace distillation as a separation technique by less energy intensive separation techniques have been proposed (Sholl and Lively, 2016), but their use depends on availability of, for example, materials that could serve as mass separating agents for membrane-based or for adsorption-desorption based separation techniques. Also, from a practical point of view, while it would be possible not to use distillation in future chemical processes, it would be practically impossible to replace the thousands of existing distillation columns that are currently in operation all over the world. A more pragmatic alternative is to employ intensification and/or integration options based on the currently used separation techniques together with new separation techniques in hybrid schemes.

In this paper, feasibility of employing integrated technologies and related issues is highlighted. That is, in which chemical processes the reaction and separation operations can be intensified into an RDC, or which separation operations can be combined into DWC units, or which distillation-based separation operations can be retrofitted by an HDS? Note that in all cases the objective is to improve energy demand and related sustainability metrics without changing the product specifications and the feed mixture. The first two options indicate the replacement of an existing design with a more sustainable design, while the third refers to use of retrofit options without removing existing equipment.

Here, we present a rule-based, three-step method, which assists designers in deciding whether a more sustainable RDC can be configured to represent (and replace) a known chemical process; or, which separation operations can be combined into DWC; or, which distillation columns can be modified to HDSs; together with results from case studies highlighting different features of the three-step method. In particular, the results from the case studies highlight the potential to significantly improve the process in terms of sustainability metrics. More sustainable alternatives mean increased profit, lower CO_2 emission and sensitive environmental impacts. The objective is to find non-tradeoff solutions, if feasible, within the limits of the equipment parameters.

2. Method

Very briefly, the work-flow for the method has three main steps: 1) check using the rule-based method, if any of the three alternatives satisfy a set of feasibility criteria; 2) if the answer is yes, then apply the respective design methods for the feasible candidates; 3) apply target-based process improvement methods to obtain the final sustainable process design. A sample of the rules employed by the work-flow of step-1 is given in Table 1 for the three options. For step-2, stages 1 & 2 of the sustainable design method (Tula *et al.*, 2017a) are applied, while for step-3, extended versions of stage-3 of the same method are applied. Therefore, the methods-tools for these steps are described here.

Table 1: Selected rules for process intensification and/or integration

Rules	Reactive Distillation	Divided Wall Column	Hybrid Distillation Scheme
1	Is the reaction exothermic?	Are there two or more distillation columns connected sequentially?	Are high purity products obtained as distillate?
2	Is there only one reaction?	Is it necessary to separate a multicomponent mixture?	Does the host column have 1 feed & 2 products?
3	Does the reaction and separation involve liquid and vapor phases?	Can the lightest & heaviest boiling products leave as top & bottom products in DWC?	Is the separation difficult (indicated by their driving force values)?
4	Does the separations involve azeotropes or close boiling pairs?	Is the number of high purity products less than or equal to 2 for a DWC?	Based on the cut-off equation (Eq 1), is the potential saving > 20%?
5	Does the separations involve 3 or more products?	Can the separations in the targeted columns be operated at similar pressures?	Is the feasibility of the other separation technique in HDS confirmed?
6	Are high purity products desired?	Does the targeted columns involve extraction and recovery operations?	The mixture to be separated does not involve azeotropes?
7	Are there energy intensive separations or waste issues?	Is the middle product flowrate low?	Are retrofit alternatives desired?

In step-1, based on the problem data and applying the rules, if the answer is yes to all the questions (for the RDC case), then the potential for generating a sustainable alternative employing RDC will exist. For DWC and HDS, additional rules and/or data are needed for rules 5-7. Step-2 involves the actual synthesis and design of the respective intensified-integrated alternative (Tula *et al.*, 2017a). Step-3 verifies and further refines the solution from step-2, and ranks the alternatives in terms of chosen sustainability metrics based on techno-economic analysis and process simulation. See Tula et al. (2017a) for more details.

3. Case Studies

Results from three case studies involving RDC, DWC and HDS are presented. Detailed results for all case studies can be obtained from the authors.

3.1. Application of RDC (replacement and/or retrofit of base case)

Process intensification issues are highlighted through a new case study involving the production of methyl chloride (MeCl), which is produced from the reversible gas-phase reaction between methanol and hydrogen chloride, also producing water. Dehydration of methanol may occur giving di-ethyl ether and water. As in the production of methyl acetate (Agreda & Partin, 1984) or dioxalane (Castillo-Landero *et al.*, 2018), this process can also be intensified to RDC because the answers to the rules in Table 1 are yes.

A base case process design exists for MeCl production (Dantus, 1999) and the goal is to produce the required amount of MeCl (90,000 metric tons/year), with a desired purity of MeCl (96-99.5 mol%). Design of the conventional process achieves these goals with higher operating and raw material costs. Figures 1 and 2 show two configurations generated by applying the established RDC synthesis and design methods (Sanchez-Daza *et al.*, 2003). The main differences between the two configurations are: i) configuration-1 (Fig 1) considers a chiller to process the top product (MeCl) containing surplus reagent (HCl) for later separation using a conventional distillation column to recover the pure product and the surplus reagent; ii) configuration-2 (Fig 2) has a side product, which is sent to a membrane-based separation unit from which the product (MeCl) is separated from the unreacted HCl.

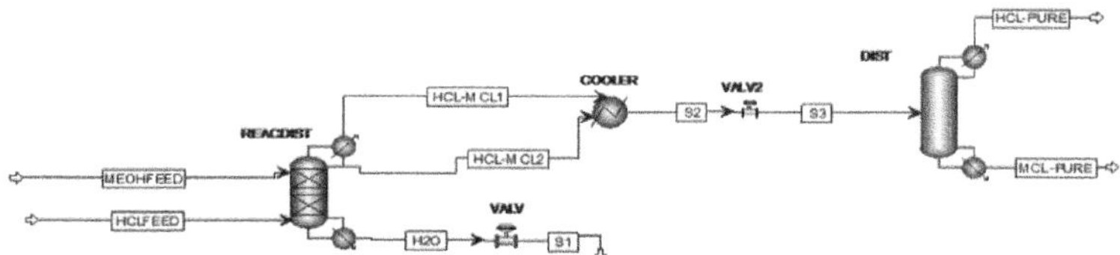

Figure 1: RDC configuration-1 for the production of methyl chloride

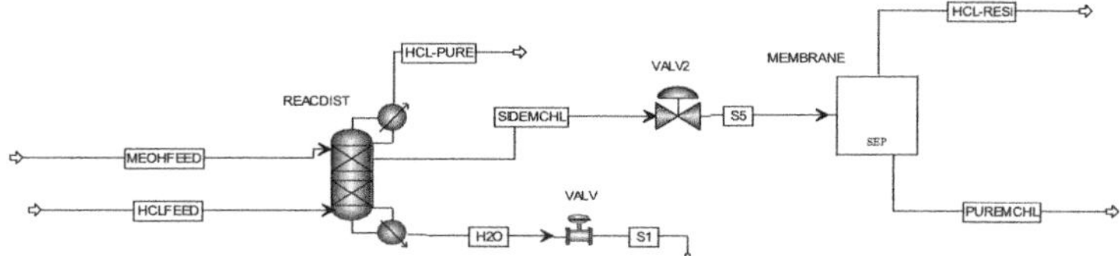

Figure 2: RDC configuration-2 for the production of methyl chloride

As the two reversible gas-phase reactions are exothermic, the heat produced by the reactions can be used to reach the boiling temperatures at each reactive stage. Therefore, the two RDC configurations require less energy than the base case process: configuration-1 requires -14.94 MW in the condenser and 14.44 MW in the reboiler, while, configuration-2 requires -15.53 MW in the condenser and 14.41 MW in the reboiler. The furnace energy consumption used to pre-heat the reactants in the base case process is around 146.54 MW. The savings in cost of capital and operation are significant, even after taking into consideration the investiment for the extra unit operation. Note that as a retrofit option, one of the three existing distillation columns could be used as the RDC as the number of stages match. The reactive stages would be packed with catalyst. Another advantage of process intensification is that the RDC configurations achieve a higher purity product (99.9% MeCl), compared to the base case of 96% purity.

3.2 Application of DWC (replacement of base case)

The feasibility of the application of a DWC is highlighted considering a simpler version of the separation problem (Tamuzi *et al.*, 2020), where a 6-compound hydrocarbon mixture consisting of C2, C3, iC4, nC4, C5+ is considered. There are 5 products, consisting of C2, C3, iC4, n-C4, C5+ and separation by distillation trains require a minimum of 4 columns corresponding to four separation tasks represented by splits of C2/C3, C3/i-C4, i-C4/n-C4 & n-C4/C5+. The answers to the rules from Table 1 are yes, and so any two of adjacent columns of the distillation train can be intensified into a DWC. Four possible configurations are feasible and the best is shown in Figure 3. All columns are designed by the reverse driving force based method in terms of sequence of the splits (separation task), the number of stages, feed location and product purities. Note that these are the minimum design variables that need to be specified to determine all other variables by simulation. Further reductions in energy could be achieved by adding separation units, as highlighted in Figure 3, in hybrid distillation schemes (described in section 3.3).

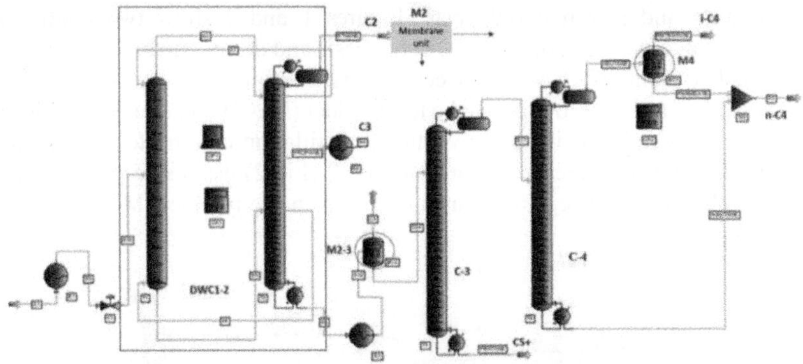

Figure 3: Flowsheet of a separation process with a DWC.

In Figure 3, the first two columns for the C2/C3 and C3/i-C4 splits are combined into one DWC. Membrane unit M2 purifies the distillate (top) product from DWC1-2 and M4 purifies the distillate top product from column C-4 by removing the high boiling compounds from their respective feed streams. Membrane unit M2-3 on the other hand, removes the low boiling compound from its feed stream. In all cases, the compound present in the smaller amount is removed, making the membrane unit feasible in terms of flux limitations and membrane area needed for the separation. It is able to reduce the energy consumption by around 45.32% compared to the optimized 4-column configuration. Other DWC combinations, such as two DWC (DWC1-2 and DWC 3-4; C1, DWC2-3, C4; C1, C2, DWC3-4, with or without membrane units, give lower reductions in energy consumptions.

3.3. Application of HDS (retrofit of base case)

In principle, any distillation column (also RDC and DWC) can be considered for HDS if the rules given in Table 1 give "yes" answers. Then, for the identified column (separation task), the work-flow involves selection of the operating pressure to determine the driving force and its maximum location for the binary pair of compounds defined as a key compound for the separation task. Next, for a column with fixed number of stages and feed location, simulation-based data is generated to obtain plots of reboiler duty versus distillate product purity as a function of driving force (O'Connell *et al.*, 2019). Next, the $Q_{cut\text{-}off}$ (the reboiler duty corresponding to a lower product purity) and $Q_{desired}$ (reboiler duty corresponding to the target high purity product) are located on the reboiler duty versus distillate purity plot and used to determine the likely energy savings, $Q_{savings}$:

$$Q_{savings} = \left(\frac{Q_{desired} - Q_{cut-off}}{Q_{desired}}\right) * 100 \quad (1)$$

If this value is > 20%, an HDS would be feasible, provided a separation technique for the further purification separation task can be found. For example, find a suitable membrane for a membrane-based separation. The synthesis-design of an HDS represents step-3 of the 3-step method. A typical HDS problem could be defined as:

Given - a mixture to be separated into two or more almost pure compounds; *Required* - design an appropriate hybrid distillation scheme that can deliver the specified products at lower energy consumption than a single distillation operation.

The work-flow for the above problem solution is given by O'Connell *et al.* (2019) and available in the ProCAFD software (Tula *et al.*, 2017b), which provides options for fast and reliable separation process design, including hybrid separation schemes for azeotropic as well as non-azeotropic mixtures. In this paper, some of the applicability issues are highlighted. Table 2 lists different distillation columns that have been retrofitted (based on their reported designs) to more sustainable HDS and verified through steady state simulation with AVEVA PRO/II (AVEVA, 2021).

Table 2: Hybrid distillation schemes reported in published papers

Problem	Mixture compounds	Energy saved	Reference
1	i-butane + n-butane*	44.4%	14
2	i-pentane + n-pentane*	37.6%	14
3	Methanol + water*	34.5%	14
4	2,2 dimethyl butane + n-hexane	25-45%	4
5	Styrene + ethylbenzene	25-45%	4
6	Benzene + cyclohexane*	42.5%	15
7	Acetonitrile + water	38.5	15

* One separation task in a multicomponent separation process or a multi-operation process

As an example, consider problem 1 in Table 2 (also, column C-4 in Fig 3). Using the data reported by Tula *et al.* (2017b), the available driving force for i-butane and n-butane is computed to be 0.095. From the corresponding reboiler duty versus distillate product purity, potential energy savings is calculated to be 44% (with $Q_{desired}$ as 32.33 GJ/hr and Q_{cutoff} as 17.98 GJ/hr). The distillate cut-off composition is 85.0% and the specified distillate purity is selected as 99.5%. The HDS for this mixture is shown in Fig 3 (column C-4). A membrane with permeabilities of 0.2196 kmole/(m^2 hr) for n-butane and 0.0008 kmole/(m^2 hr) for i-butane is available in the database. This gives a required membrane area of 109.24 m^2. Using a membrane cost of 2500 Euro/m^2, the additional CAPEX is calculated to be 273,100 Euro. Savings in energy costs is calculated to 114.1 Euro/hr, giving a payback time of 0.27 years. Details of this solution can be found in Tula *et al.* (2017b). Considering driving force values ranging from 0.085 to 0.095, with the lower value indicating actual column data, a range of energy savings data can be generated.

4. Conclusion

The intensification and integration options considered in this paper confirm their potential in terms of tackling the energy-environment nexus. The large number of energy intensive chemical processes and within them, distillation operations, should be targeted for improvement in terms of energy and environment where the additional investment could be recovered from the additional profit, without negatively impacting the environment. It should be noted that while the operations of some chemical processes are energy intensive, others are sensitive to environmental impacts but not energy intensive. Therefore, targeted improvements must address both these issues. The proposed rules and the three steps method are able to quickly identify the candidates for improvement, and opportunities for new advances in methods and associated tools to tackle the challenges. In this way, they add an intelligence feature to the current design methods. Current and future work is expanding the rules-based feasibility analysis as well as creating a database of solved problems that can serve as repository of knowledge and data to share with the community. The rules also need to be updated to avoid exceptions.

References

V. H. Agreda, L. R. Partin, 1984, Reactive distillation process for the production of methyl acetate. US Patent 4435595.

P. Angelini, 2005, Materials for Separation Technologies: Energy and Emission Reduction Opportunities, Industrial Technologies Program, DE-AC05-00OR22725. US DOE.

N. Asprion, G. Kaibel, 2010, Dividing wall columns: fundamentals and recent advances, *Chemical Engineering and Processing: Process Intensification,* 49, 139-146.

AVEVA, 2021, PRO/II User Manual.

A. Castillo-Landero, A. Jiménez-Gutiérrez, R. Gani, 2018, Intensification methodology to minimize the number of pieces of equipment and its application to a process to produce dioxolane products, *Industrial & Engineering Chemistry Research*, 57, 9810-9820.

M. Dantus, 1999, PhD Dissertation. Department of Chemical Engineering. Oklahoma State University, Stillwater, Oklahoma.

J. P. O'Connell, M. R. Eden, A. K. Tula, R. Gani, 2019, Retrofitting Distillation Columns with Membranes, *Chemical Engineering Progress*, 115; 41-49

E. N. Pistikopoulos, A. Barbosa-Povoa, J. H. Lee, R. Misener, A. Mitsos, G. V. Reklaitis, V. Venkatasubramanian, F. You, R. Gani, 2021, Process Systems Engineering–The Generation Next? *Computers & Chemical Engineering*, 147, 107252

O. Sánchez-Daza, E. S. Pérez-Cisneros, E. Bek-Pedersen, R. Gani, 2003, Graphical and stage-to-Stage methods for reactive distillation column design, *AIChE J.*, 49, 2822–2841.

D. S. Sholl, R. P. Lively, 2016, Seven chemical separations to change the world, *Nature*, 532, 435.

A. Tamuzi, N. Kasiri, A. Khalili-Garakani, 2020, A. Design and optimization of distillation column sequencing for NGL fractionation processes, *Journal of Natural Gas Science & Engineering*, 76, 103180.

Y. Tian, S. E. Demirel, M. M. F. Hasan, E. N. Pistikopoulos, 2018, An overview of process systems engineering approaches for process intensification: State of the art, *Chemical Engineering and Processing-Process Intensification,* 133, 160-210.

A. K. Tula, D. K. Babi, J. Bottlaender, M. R. Eden, R. Gani, 2017a, A computer-aided tool for sustainable process synthesis-intensification, *Comput & Chem Eng*. 105, 74-95.

A. K. Tula, B. Befort, N. Garg, K. V. Camarda, R. Gani, 2017b, Sustainable process design & analysis of hybrid separations, *Computers & Chemical Engineering*, 105, 96-104.

A. K. Tula, M. R. Eden, R. Gani, 2020. Computer-aided process intensification: Challenges, trends and opportunities. *AIChE Journal*, 66, e16819

R. Vooradi, S. P. Venkata, A. K. Tula, B. A. Sarath, M. R. Eden, R. Gani, 2018, Hybrid Separation Scheme for Azeotropic Mixtures–Sustainable Design Methodology, *Chemical Engineering Transactions*, 69, 637- 42.

Proceedings of the 14th International Symposium on Process Systems Engineering – PSE 2021+
June 19–23, 2022, Kyoto, Japan
http://dx.doi.org/10.1016/B978-0-323-85159-6.50120-2

Integration of Design and Operation for the CO_2-based Methanol Synthesis

Christian Hoffmann[a*], Erik Esche[a], Jens-Uwe Repke[a]

[a]*Process Dynamics and Operations Group, Technische Universität Berlin, Straße des 17. Juni 135, 10623 Berlin, Germany*

c.hoffmann@tu-berlin.de

Abstract

Conventionally, many approaches for process design are based on steady-state assumptions. Only in the last two decades, dynamic aspects have also been considered, but frameworks for large-scale systems are still scarce. Recently, we introduced our framework of a fully discretized dynamic model in combination with an optimal economic NMPC. In this contribution, we apply this framework on the CO_2-based methanol synthesis, which represents a large-scale case study of 50,000 continuous variables for a time horizon of around 1 h. Feed variability is modeled by an amplitude-modulated pseudo-random binary sequence to gain as much information on the dynamics as possible.

Keywords: Integration of Design and Operation, Methanol Synthesis, Economic NMPC.

1. Introduction

Process design is a fundamental aspect of process systems engineering. The design must ensure that all requirements regarding product purities are met. Additional constraints for process parameters, e.g., due to safety concerns, must hold as well. Conventionally, process design and control design are performed sequentially or as an iterative process (Seider et al., 2017). However, this approach may lead to dynamic constraint violations, hinder robust performance, or simply reduce the controllability of a process during plant operation (Malcolm et al., 2007). Therefore, performing these two subsequent tasks simultaneously by integration of design and operation (IDO) is highly desirable. The most common approaches have been summarized in several reviews, for example, by Vega et al. (2014). Previously, we suggested using the objective function of an economic nonlinear model-predictive controller (eNMPC) to account for the connection of economics and variability (Hoffmann et al., 2019). We also studied how parametric uncertainty can be included by using the Unscented Transform (Hoffmann et al., 2020). In this contribution, we apply our framework on a considerably larger example: the CO2-based methanol synthesis. In the next section, we describe our IDO-eNMPC framework. Afterward, we outline the dynamic process model of the case study. Finally, we present the results obtained with our framework and analyze them regarding their merit.

2. Framework

The mathematical structure of the IDO framework is given in Equation (1): An objective function that includes both investment and operating costs is minimized subject to equality and inequality constraints. The constraints are functions of states x, controls u, input variabilities ν, parameters θ, and design variables d (for example, the volume of equipment). In addition, constraints determining the initial states (subscript 0) and terminal states (subscript t) are necessary. In the framework, all equations are fully discretized using orthogonal collocation on finite elements. The indices represent the collocation point c_p and the finite element *fe*. States and controls must also lie within a certain domain $\mathcal{X}$ and $\mathcal{U}$, respectively:

$$\min_{u,d} \quad f\left(x_{cp,fe}, u_{cp,fe}, d\right) \tag{1a}$$

$$\text{s.t.} \quad 0 = g\left(x_{cp,fe}, u_{cp,fe}, \nu_{cp,fe}, \theta, d\right) \quad \text{(Dynamic process model)}, \tag{1b}$$

$$0 \leq h\left(x_{cp,fe}, u_{cp,fe}, \nu_{cp,fe}, \theta, d\right) \quad \text{(Path constraints)}, \tag{1c}$$

$$0 \leq h_0\left(x_0, u_0, \nu_0, \theta, d\right) \quad \text{(Initial constraints)}, \tag{1d}$$

$$0 \leq h_{\mathrm{t}}\left(x_{\mathrm{t}}, u_{\mathrm{t}}, \nu_{\mathrm{t}}, \theta, d\right) \quad \text{(Initial constraints)}, \tag{1e}$$

$$x_{cp,fe} \in \mathcal{X},\; u_{cp,fe} \in \mathcal{U} \quad \text{(Domain)} \tag{1f}$$

The input variability is represented by amplitude-modulated pseudo-random binary sequences (APRBS), a signal type that allows for high information gain and that is suitable for nonlinear systems (Nelles, 2001).

3. Model

The dynamic process model is based on the flowsheet in Figure 1. The feed gas (CO_2 and H_2) is compressed, potentially heated to reactor inlet temperature, and passes the fixed-bed reactor to form methanol and water. The products are condensed whereas the gases are re-compressed and recycled to the reactor. In the tank, liquid methanol and water are stored and the product stream is withdrawn.

3.1. Balance equations

The model consists of a two-dimensional (time and axial) model of reactor with dynamic mole, energy, and momentum balances (only the mole balance is shown here due to space limitations):

$$\varepsilon_{\text{cat}} \cdot \frac{\partial c_c}{\partial t} = -c_c \frac{\partial w}{\partial z} + w \frac{\partial c_c}{\partial z} + (1 - \varepsilon_{\text{cat}}) \cdot \rho_{\text{cat}} \cdot \sum_r \nu_{c,r} r_r \tag{2}$$

Therein, ε_{cat} is bed porosity, c_c is molar concentration of component c, w is velocity, ρ_{cat} is catalyst density, $\nu_{c,r}$ and r_r are stoichiometric coefficient and reaction rate, respectively. Here, the reaction kinetics by Slotboom et al. (2020) are used. The tank consists of dynamic mole balances. Heat exchangers and compressors are modeled under steady-state assumptions.

3.2. Cost functions

The cost of the equipment is determined from cost functions with degression exponent n:

$$C = C_{\text{ref}} \left(\frac{cap}{cap_{\text{ref}}} \right)^n. \tag{3}$$

Therein, C and C_{ref} are costs at capacity cap and reference capacity cap_{ref}, respectively. Operating costs are computed by multiplying the electricity or product costs with the integral mean of the respective material or energy stream.

3.3. Initial conditions

During the model formulation and first attempts to solve the system, it became clear that the large number of unfixed initial conditions in a spatially distributed system, i. e., the reactor, causes an additional challenge. If these are not assigned consistently by any method, the optimizer may choose huge initial concentrations of the product and thus artificially maximize the product yield. This cannot be resolved by simply bounding the initial conditions as they should also represent are realistic concentration, temperature, and velocity profiles. Also, fixing the initial conditions to an arbitrary value is impossible because they are inherently related to the design, which will change during the iterations. For this reason, a steady-state version of the model is also incorporated into the model, which is solved simultaneously with the dynamic model. The steady-state sub-model provides the initial conditions for the dynamic case, but it will also still depend on the same design variables.

3.4. Path constraints

Several path constraints are required to ensure a stable behavior: First, the temperature must always remain below 260 °C to avoid catalyst deactivation – this temperature is higher in reality; the value was chosen to achieve an active bound at the optimal solution. Second, stability must be ensured so that concentration profiles do not drift over time. This is achieved by demanding that the terminal states match the initial condition within a certain threshold. This is not required for every state of the model, but for key variables, such as the inlet pressure and temperature of the reactor, and the holdup of the tank, for example:

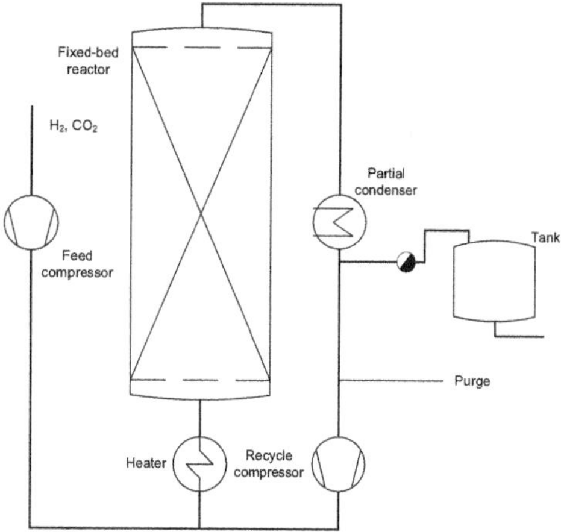

Figure 1: Flowsheet for the case study.

$$|HU_{\text{tank}}(t=0) - HU_{\text{tank}}(t=t_{\text{t}})| \leq \varepsilon_{\text{tank}} \tag{4}$$

This ensures the stability of the obtained trajectories under the respective input variability. In addition, the integral average of the produced flow should be close to the nominal product flow to achieve production goals:

$$\left| \frac{1}{t_{\text{t}}} \int_{t=0}^{t=t_{\text{t}}} F_{\text{prod}}(t)\,\text{d}t - F_{\text{prod,st-st}} \right| \leq \varepsilon_{\text{prod}} \tag{5}$$

The integral is evaluated with Radau quadrature using the same Radau collocation points as in the discretization scheme. In addition, the change between consecutive values of the same variable can be restricted, for example, the reactor's feed pressure:

$$|P_{\text{reactor}}(t = t_k) - P_{\text{reactor}}(t = t_{k+1})| \leq \varepsilon_{\text{pressure}} \tag{6}$$

3.5. Implementation and framework

The resulting partial differential equation system is discretized via orthogonal collocation in both the spatial coordinate of the reactor and the time coordinate. 20 spatial finite elements were chosen in preliminary trials. The number of finite elements for the time coordinate can be chosen freely. The system roughly scales to 50,000 variables per 10 finite elements in time. The model is formulated within AMPL (Fourer et al., 2003) and interfaced to Python via AMPLPy. AMPL is chosen because it allows the use of sets for model generation, includes a powerful tool for automatic differentiation to generate derivatives, and disposes of interfaces to many solvers. The external layer in Python provides the data (parameter and variable values), performs the initialization, manages loops and saves the results.

4. Results and discussion

In this contribution, both CO_2 and H_2 feed are assumed to be variable inputs $\nu_{cp,fe}$ that are represented by two APRBS, which means that their values at each collocation point are given by the APRBS. Both are assumed to have a standard deviation of the variability range of 20 mol s^{-1}. The APRBS are generated by our own sampling framework (Weigert et al., 2020).

4.1. Initialization

Even if the model is initialized at steady-state, an initialization strategy is required to solve Problem (1). For this purpose, an homotopy approach is taken so that the current input depends on an homotopy parameter φ:

$$F_{st=1,c} = \varphi \cdot F_{st=1,c}^{\text{APRBS}} + (1 - \varphi) \cdot F_{st=1,c}^{\text{nominal}} \tag{7}$$

Hence, Problem (1) is solved repeatedly with increasing φ from 0.1 to 1. In our experience, an increase of 0.1 per step suffices to converge the system. Should this not be the case, the step size can be made smaller.

4.2. Comparison of steady-state and dynamic results

The results obtained with the framework are compared to results obtained under steady-state conditions only. Exemplary numerical values for design decision are given in Table 1. In both cases, the tube diameter lies at the lower bound. The reactor inlet pressure is lower in the dynamically obtained design (lower costs for feed compression) whereas the inlet temperature is higher (faster kinetics) that are necessary in cases where the stoichiometry might no be ideal occasionally. The reactor length is significantly shorter in the dynamic case, which is compensated by higher recycle ratios and thus results in a larger energy

Table 1: Comparison of design based on steady-state and dynamic consideration. Results under dynamic conditions are average values or are given in ranges. Lower (LB) and upper bounds (UB) during the optimization are given if applicable.

Design variable / operating condition	LB	UB	Steady-state	Dynamic
Average feed compressor power, MW	0	–	12.7	11.1
Average reactor inlet pressure, bar	30	100	60	50
Reactor inlet temperature, K	273	–	320	384 – 426
Reactor length, m	0	–	5.3	2.6
Tube diameter, m	0.05	–	0.05	0.05
Number of tubes	10	–	14,400	25,600
Condenser area, m^2	0	–	1740	1200
Recycle compressor, MW	0	–	2.8	4.2
Recycle ratio	1.0	–	4.4	2.6 – 8.6

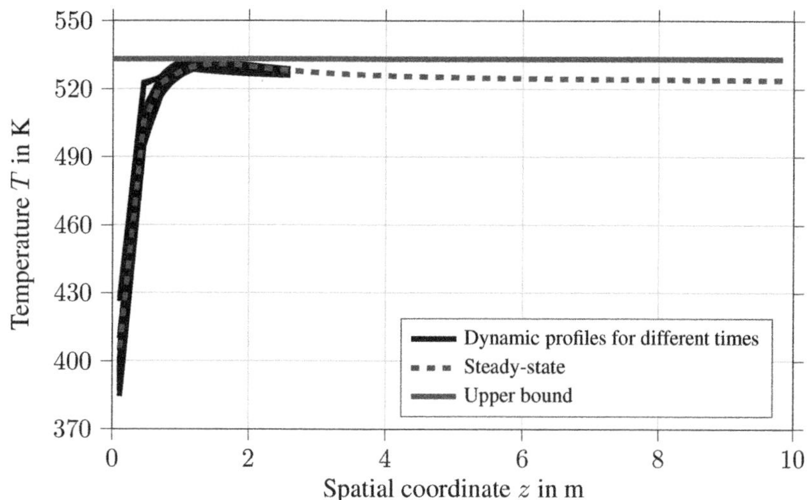

Figure 2: Comparison of axial temperature profiles at different times and the steady-state temperature profile.

consumption of the recycle compressor. Figure 2 shows a comparison between the steady-state temperature profile (long reactor) and the dynamic, axial temperatures for different times. For both profiles, the upper bound is never violated. In the case of the dynamic optimization, this is, however, only possible because the design has notably changed.

4.3. *Computational times*

The computations were performed on an Intel® Core™ i7-4770K CPU @ 3.50GHz running Ubuntu 18.04.6. AMPL version 20210326 in combination with IPOPT 3.12.6 was used to formulate and solve the optimization problems. Because a steady-state solution and a dynamic solution are looked at here, it is not a fair comparison in terms of the required computational time. However, the reader may get an impression of how the computational time scales with the system's size. The steady-state solution is usually obtained within a few seconds. This may vary with the quality of the initialization. The dynamic solution, which is always initialized at the steady-state solution, may require several days of computations. However, this is still deemed acceptable for design problems, which typical do not require the rapid solution that is demanded from online applications, such as model-predictive control.

5. Conclusion and outlook

This contribution applied a methodology for the integration of design and operation on a large-scale system. The results were obtained by full discretization of the dynamic process model with subsequent solution of the resulting nonlinear programming problem. We compared the obtained results with those obtained by a steady-state optimization and found significant differences in the design, e.g., the reactor length, which would justify to consider the dynamics during process design. However, the length of the time horizon might have significant impact on the results. Therefore, this must be investigated in the future.

References

R. Fourer, D. M. Gay, B. W. Kernighan, 2003, AMPL : a modeling language for mathematical programming, Thomson/Brooks/Cole, Pacific Grove, CA.

C. Hoffmann, E. Esche, J.-U. Repke, 2019, Integration of design and control based on large-scale NLP formulations and an optimal economic NMPC, Computer Aided Chemical Engineering, 47, 125–130.

C. Hoffmann, J. Weigert, E. Esche, J.-U. Repke, 2020, Integration of Design and Operation Using Dynamic Perturbation and Chance Constraints with Unscented Transform, Computer Aided Chemical Engineering, 48, 751–756.

A. Malcolm, J. Polan, L. Zhang, B. A. Ogunnaike, A. A. Linninger, 2007, Integrating systems design and control using dynamic flexibility analysis, AIChE Journal, 53, 2048–2061.

O. Nelles, 2001, Nonlinear system identification : from classical approaches to neural networks and fuzzy models, Springer-Verlag Berlin Heidelberg, Berlin, Heidelberg.

Y. Slotboom, M. J. Bos, J. Pieper, V. Vrieswijk, B. Likozar, S. R. A. Kersten, D. W. F. Brilman, 2020, Critical assessment of steady-state kinetic models for the synthesis of methanol over an industrial Cu/ZnO/Al2O3 catalyst, Chemical Engineering Journal, 389, 124181.

P. Vega, R. L. de Rocco, S. Revollar, M. Francisco, 2014, Integrated design and control of chemical processes – Part I: Revision and classification, Computers & Chemical Engineering, 71, 602–617.

J. Weigert, C. Hoffmann, E. Esche, J.-U. Repke, 2020, Enabling Dynamic Real-Time Optimization under Uncertainty using Data-Driven Chance Constraints, Computer Aided Chemical Engineering, 48. Elsevier, 1189–1194.

Proceedings of the 14th International Symposium on Process Systems Engineering – PSE 2021+
June 19-23, 2022, Kyoto, Japan
http://dx.doi.org/10.1016/B978-0-323-85159-6.50121-4

Blue Syngas Synthesis via the Integration of Gasification and Reforming Processes

Hussain A. Alibrahim[a], Siddig S. Khalafalla[a], Usama Ahmed[a,b] and Umer Zahid[a,c*]

[a] *Chemical Engineering Department, King Fahd University of Petroleum & Minerals (KFUPM), Dhahran 31261, Saudi Arabia*
[b] *Interdisciplinary Research Center for Hydrogen and Energy Storage, King Fahd University of Petroleum & Minerals (KFUPM), Dhahran 31261, Saudi Arabia*
[c] *Interdisciplinary Research Center for Membranes & Water Security, King Fahd University of Petroleum & Minerals (KFUPM), Dhahran 31261, Saudi Arabia*
uzahid@kfupm.edu.sa

Abstract

Syngas is an important intermediate feedstock to produce various downstream chemicals and clean fuels. In this study, two process models are developed by integrating the gasification and dry-reforming models in the parallel and series configuration to produce the syngas at the rate of 10,000 kmol/h with H_2/CO ratio of 2. The heat integration is also developed in a way to utilize the heat energy from the coal-derived syngas into the dry-reformer without any energy penalties. The proposed integrated designs can enable the utilization of fossil fuels in an environment friendly, technically feasible and an economical way.

Keywords: Integration; carbon capture and utilization; simulation; syngas.

1. Introduction

Synthesis gas commonly known as "syngas" is an important component for the synthesis of chemicals and fuels. It drives many industrial facilities including power generation, fertilizers, polymers, and production of bulk chemicals. Depending on the feedstock, oxidizing agent, desired syngas ratio and downstream application, multiple syngas production technologies exist. Gasification and reforming are the most commonly employed commercial technologies for the syngas production (Medrano-García et al., 2018). Generally, gasification is used for the solid feed stocks such as coal, coke, and biomass while reforming is the preferred process for the gaseous and liquid feed stocks. While coal is still the primary source of energy for many countries, coal based processes are usually associated with high carbon emissions (Alibrahim et al., 2019).

Reforming technologies may employ steam (in steam reforming), oxygen (partial oxidation reforming) or carbon dioxide (dry reforming) as the oxidant depending on the type of reforming process. Steam reforming (SR) and dry reforming (DR) are endothermic processes while partial oxidation (POX) of hydrocarbon is an exothermic process. Recently, a great attention has been given, particularly in the process and catalyst development, to the DR processes (Alenazey et al., 2021; Alibrahim et al., 2021). This is due to the fact that the DR consumes two major greenhouse gases in which methane or other higher hydrocarbons along with carbon dioxide can be converted to the syngas (Afzal et al., 2018). However, the commercialization of DR based processes have been hindered due to certain process limitations. The main problematic aspect of the DR technology is the deactivation of active catalyst surface due to carbon deposition at high temperature, along with high energy demand for the endothermic reactive system, low syngas ratio and equilibrium limitation due to the influence of reverse water gas shift reaction (RWGS). Elbashir et al. (Elbashir et al., 2018) reported that the operational limitations of DR process can be overcome by combining the DR with other reforming process such as SR and POX. Similarly, Man et al. (Man et al., 2014) studied the integration of SR, DR and gasification processes by utilizing the coke-oven gas for the coal-to-olefins (CTO) process. Their results showed that the coke-oven gas assisted process with the coal gasification improves the process efficiency by 10% compared to the conventional CTO process. Several studies in the past have focused on the integration of various reforming and gasification technologies in order to combine the synergies and suppress the imperfection of one technology to another (Balasubramanian et al., 2018; Carapellucci and Giordano, 2020; Summa et al., 2019; Wang et al., 2020). Qian et al. (Qian et al., 2015) evaluated the utilization of CO_2 supply from WGS reactor in the tri-reforming for the coal-to-methanol (CTM) process. They reported a decrease in the carbon emissions by 44% and an improvement of carbon utilization by 25% compared to the conventional CTM process. Chen et at. (Chen et al., 2019) investigated the integration of conventional coal gasification and coke-gasification processes to produce methanol product. They showed the integrated design to have 14.3% higher carbon utilization efficiency and 34.6% reduced carbon emissions compared to the conventional CTM process.

The goal of this work is to develop the conceptual design based on the process intensification techniques that can produce the syngas of varied composition by the integration of gasification and DR processes. The combination of an endothermic and exothermic processes for energy-effective utilization offers lower exergy destruction. The proposed designs offer an improved performance in terms of energy requirement, carbon emissions and cost due to the process intensification and synergies coupling. First, standalone simulation models are developed for the coal gasification and DR respectively to assess the performance in terms of efficiency and syngas quality. Then, two integrated process designs are proposed with series and parallel integration between gasification and DR process. In order to have a fair comparison among various designs, the syngas production capacity is set as 10,000 kmol/hr with a syngas ratio (H_2:CO) of 2 which is suitable for many downstream applications. Finally, a detailed techno-economic analysis has been performed in order to ascertain the performance and economic feasibility of the proposed designs.

2. Process description

2.1. Series integration

In the case of gasification and DR series integration, coal preparation and gasification units are similar to that of the standalone gasification process. However, the gas cleaning unit only contains H_2S removal system while the CO_2 removal unit is employed in the WGS unit after the shift reactors as shown in the figure 1. An important aspect of this design is the heat integration between the gasification and the reforming reactor. All the heat duty required by the DR reactor has been provided from the gasification reactor, hence making the net heat duty of the DR reactor zero. The DR unit is placed downstream of H_2S removal unit where it receives a bulk of gas mixture mainly containing syngas and CO_2. Given that H_2/CO ratio is below unity after coal gasification, high water-gas shift rate is expected. The CO_2 captured from the WGS section is sent back to the DR section as a feed to react with freshly fed methane. The syngas ratio at the exit of dry reforming process is 0.822 which is low compared to the target syngas ratio of 2. Therefore, a part of raw syngas stream is sent to the WGS unit where 99.6 % CO conversion is achieved. Rectisol process is used to capture the 99.7 mol. % CO_2 while the high purity H_2 is blended with the bypassed syngas to achieve the desired product syngas.

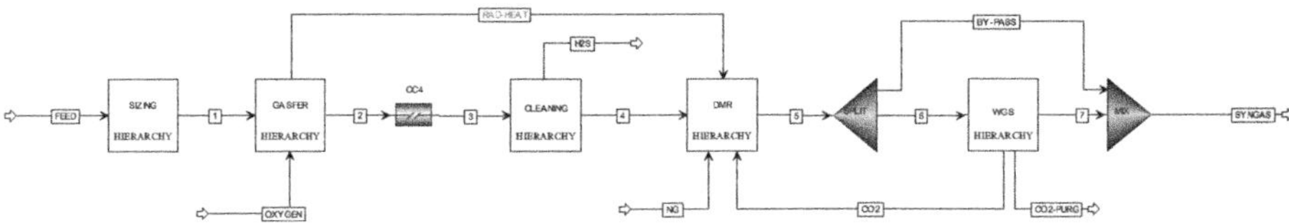

Figure 1. Series design integration of gasification and dry reforming for syngas production

2.2. Parallel integration

In the case of parallel integrated design, the coal preparation and gasification sections are the same as that of the standalone gasification process. The gas cleaning unit has H_2S removal and CO_2 removal sections employing the Rectisol process. The captured high purity (99.7 mol.%) CO_2 stream is sent to the dry reforming unit which is in parallel configuration with the gasification process. The raw syngas from the outlet of gas cleaning unit has a H_2 to CO ratio of 0.76 which is lower than the required syngas ratio of 2. Therefore, a part of the raw syngas is directed to the WGS unit in order to convert CO to H_2, while the remaining syngas bypasses the WGS unit. Design Spec function in Aspen Plus has been utilized to vary the split fraction in order to achieve the desired product syngas ratio. Since the syngas coming from the gasification and dry reforming sections is deficient in H_2 content, the Design Spec function calculates the amount of syngas that should be directed to the WGS, while the remaining syngas is bypassed. The second CO_2 capture unit is installed in the WGS unit to separate the produced CO_2 from the CO which is sent back to the DR unit. The bypassed syngas, syngas from the DR and high purity H_2 from the WGS are then mixed to produce the desired product syngas. Similar to the series integrated design, the parallel integration provides all the required DR heat duty from the gasification section as shown in the figure 2.

In this study, two cases (series and parallel) are demonstrated for the syngas production rate of 10,000 kmol/h with a H_2/CO ratio of 2. However, the proposed designs are flexible in terms of changing the quantity and/or quality of the product syngas. The feed coal and natural gas flowrates can be adjusted for a desired production rate of syngas in a way that the reformer net duty remains zero. Similarly, the quality of the syngas can be adjusted by changing the split fraction upstream of the WGS unit. However, it should be noted that any such change will affect the overall carbon utilization and emissions from the process.

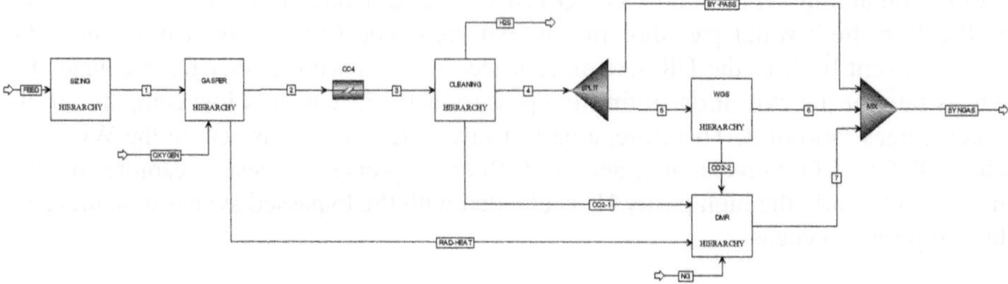

Figure 2. Parallel design integration of gasification and dry reforming for syngas production

3. Results

3.1. Energy analysis

Figure 3 shows the total energy requirement in terms of utilities for the four cases for the syngas production of 10,000 kmol/h with H_2 to CO ratio of 2. The results show that in the case of standalone DR, more than 62.8 % of the total energy requirement is in the form of heating. In the case of standalone gasification, both the heating and cooling requirements contributes significantly to the total energy demand. On the other hand, approximately 43.25 MW of net power is generated from the steam cycle. The electricity demand for the standalone DR process is the highest among all the designs. Since, the delivery pressure of the product syngas is set at 28 bar, the syngas produced from the DR process at 4 bar needs to be compressed to 28 bar requiring a three-stage compression train. The electrical energy consumed by the 3-stage compressor is 28.2 MW which is significantly higher than the pumping requirement of the gasification process. The integration of coal gasification and DR shows considerable reduction in the total energy input as shown in figure 3. The results show that the integrated designs reduce the heating requirement by 52.4% and 61.8% for the series and parallel designs respectively compared to the standalone DR. Figure 4 shows the breakdown of the total energy requirement for each section of the four cases. The reformer is the largest energy consumer in the case of standalone DR process requiring around 46.5% of the total energy. By performing an integration between the gasification and DR, the reformer duty is completely removed by supplying the required heat from the gasification. The net heat supplied from the gasification reactor in the series and parallel integration is equivalent to 82.16 MW and 81.92 MW respectively. Since, all the cases are designed for the production of an equimolar flowrate, the amount of feeds in the integrated design is considerably reduced compared to the standalone gasification case. The result reveals that an integrated design requires 45.2% and 54% less coal and natural gas feed rates respectively, compared to the standalone gasification and DR process.

3.2. Economic analysis

The analyses performed in the previous section clearly shows the technical feasibility for the design integration between the gasification and DR process. The results revealed a positive impact on the overall process performance in terms of carbon emissions and energy requirements for the series and parallel integrations. This section explores the economic viability of the integrated designs compared with the standalone gasification and DR process. A detailed economic analysis has been performed to calculate the fixed capital and operating costs. Aspen Economic Analyzer has been used to perform the sizing and capital cost estimation of the equipment.

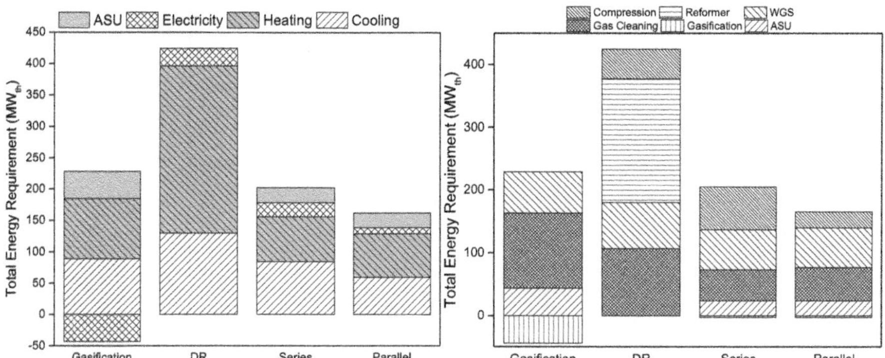

Figure 3. Utility-wise energy consumption for the standalone and integrated designs

Figure 4. Section wise energy consumption for the standalone and integrated designs

The result shows that the series design has the highest total capital cost while the parallel design offers the lowest capital cost. The high capital cost of series design is due to the series integration of the gasification and DR processes which resulted in the large equipment size. The results also reveal that the direct cost is in the range of 55 – 63% of the total capital cost. The operating cost calculation includes the raw materials, utilities, labor and supervisory costs, maintenance and general and administrative costs. The integrated series design offers the TAC of 100.4 M$ which is 16% higher than the integrated parallel design cost. The economic analysis shows that the series design is cost competitive with the standalone DR design. Since all the designs produce the same amount of syngas, per unit cost of syngas for the integrated designs is lower compared to the standalone designs as shown in figure 5.

4. Conclusions

In this study, two integrated models are proposed to produce 10,000 kmol/h of syngas with a H_2/CO ratio of 2 delivered at a pressure of 28 bar. The integrated designs eliminate the energy requirement of dry reformer by supplying the heat energy from the gasifier. The total energy requirement for series and parallel design is 202 and 162 MW respectively, compared to 424.3 MW energy requirement for the standalone DR process. The low energy requirement by the integrated designs is reflected in terms of high process efficiency of 83.63 % and 86.66 % for the series and parallel designs, respectively. The economic analysis shows that the raw materials cost has the highest share in the TAC for all the designs. Parallel design requires less CAPEX and OPEX of 17.7 M$ and 12.2 M$/y respectively compared to the series design. Among all the designs (standalone and integrated), parallel offers the lowest TAC of 86.4 M$/y which translates into unit product cost of $ 0.99.

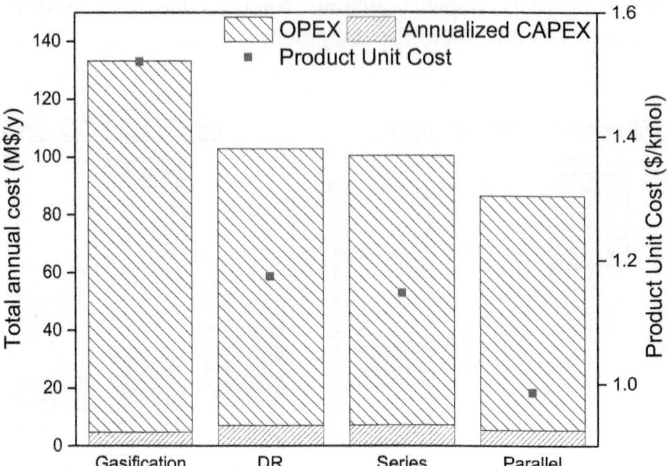

Figure 5. TAC and product cost for the standalone and integrated designs

References

Afzal, S., Sengupta, D., Sarkar, A., El-Halwagi, M., Elbashir, N., 2018. Optimization Approach to the Reduction of CO2 Emissions for Syngas Production Involving Dry Reforming. ACS Sustain. Chem. Eng. 6, 7532–7544.

Alenazey, F., AlOtaibi, B., Otaibi, R.A.L., Alyousef, Y., Alqahtania, S., Qazaq, A., Zahid, U., Vo, D.-V.N., Adesina, A., 2021. A Novel Carbon-Resistant Perovskite Catalyst for Hydrogen Production Using Methane Dry Reforming. Top. Catal. 1–9.

Alibrahim, H.A., Khalafalla, S.S., Ahmed, U., Park, S., Lee, C.-J., Zahid, U., 2021. Conceptual design of syngas production by the integration of gasification and dry-reforming technologies with CO2 capture and utilization. Energy Convers. Manag. 244, 114485.

Alibrahim, H.A., SeedAhmed, S., Ahmed, U., Zahid, U., 2019. Comparative analysis of gasification and reforming technologies for the syngas production, in: Computer Aided Chemical Engineering. Elsevier, pp. 1759–1764.

Balasubramanian, P., Bajaj, I., Hasan, M.M.F., 2018. Simulation and optimization of reforming reactors for carbon dioxide utilization using both rigorous and reduced models. J. CO2 Util. 23, 80–104.

Carapellucci, R., Giordano, L., 2020. Steam, dry and autothermal methane reforming for hydrogen production: A thermodynamic equilibrium analysis. J. Power Sources 469, 228391.

Chen, J., Yang, S., Qian, Y., 2019. A novel path for carbon-rich resource utilization with lower emission and higher efficiency: An integrated process of coal gasification and coking to methanol production. Energy 177, 304–318.

Elbashir, N.O., Challiwala, M.S., Sengupta, D., El-Halwagi, M.M., 2018. System and method for carbon and syngas production. World Intellect. Prop. Organ. Prod. Syst. Method Carbon Syngas, issued.

Man, Y., Yang, S., Zhang, J., Qian, Y., 2014. Conceptual design of coke-oven gas assisted coal to olefins process for high energy efficiency and low CO2 emission. Appl. Energy 133, 197–205.

Medrano-García, J.D., Ruiz-Femenia, R., Caballero, J.A., 2018. Multi-objective Optimization of a Carbon Dioxide Utilization Superstructure for the Synthesis of Formic and Acetic Acid, in: Computer Aided Chemical Engineering. Elsevier, pp. 1419–1424.

Qian, Y., Man, Y., Peng, L., Zhou, H., 2015. Integrated process of coke-oven gas tri-reforming and coal gasification to methanol with high carbon utilization and energy efficiency. Ind. Eng. Chem. Res. 54, 2519–2525.

Summa, P., Samojeden, B., Motak, M., 2019. Dry and steam reforming of methane. Comparison and analysis of recently investigated catalytic materials. A short review. Polish J. Chem. Technol. 21, 31–37.

Wang, H., Su, Y., Wang, D., Jin, S., Wei, S., Shen, W., 2020. Optimal Design and Energy-Saving Investigation of the Triple CO2 Feeds for Methanol Production System by Combining Steam and Dry Methane Reforming. Ind. Eng. Chem. Res. 59, 1596–1606.

Proceedings of the 14th International Symposium on Process Systems Engineering – PSE 2021+
June 19-23, 2022, Kyoto, Japan
http://dx.doi.org/10.1016/B978-0-323-85159-6.50122-6

Network optimization of the electrosynthesis of chemicals from CO_2

Ana Somoza-Tornos[a*], Omar J. Guerra[b], Wilson A. Smith[a,b], Bri-Mathias Hodge[a,b*]

[a]*Renewable and Sustainable Energy Institute, University of Colorado, Boulder, CO 80309, United States*
[b]*National Renewable Energy Laboratory, Golden, CO, United States*
[*]*ana.somozatornos@colorado.edu, brimathias.hodge@colorado.edu*

Abstract

Carbon dioxide electroreduction (ECO2R) is gaining attention due to its capacity to mitigate CO_2 emissions while using electricity that would otherwise be curtailed. Its foreseeable industrial implementation requires of holistic methods to assess the technological and economic performance of ECO2R processes and integrate them in current chemical supply chains and power systems.
Here, we combine techno-economic assessment and mathematical programming to find the optimal paths to electroreduce CO_2 into valuable chemicals under variable electricity prices. The proposed approach is tested with a case study addressing the CO_2 capture from flue gas or direct air and its electricity-powered reduction into carbon monoxide, formic acid or multi-carbon compounds. The results obtained demonstrate the ability of the framework to build ECO2R networks and provide operation profiles that respond to fluctuating electricity prices.

Keywords: electroreduction, carbon dioxide, techno-economic assessment, superstructure, optimization.

1. Introduction

The electroreduction of carbon dioxide (ECO2R) can play a pivotal role in the transition to carbon-free chemicals. Catalyst and reactor design have led to an interesting range of electrosynthesized chemicals from single-carbon syngas and formic acid to multi-carbon commodities (e.g. ethylene, ethanol or propanol). However, the integration of these chemicals into the current market remains a challenge, mainly due to the electricity-intensive nature of ECO2R. Renewably-powered ECO2R can lead not only to the mitigation of CO_2 emissions, but also contribute to the use of electricity that would otherwise be curtailed. Conversely, techno-economic estimations show that under current electricity prices, the cost shares to power the electrolyzer can represent up to a 78% of the total cost (Somoza-Tornos et al., 2021). Thus, current research efforts should focus on scaling up the technology to industrially-relevant scales while integrating it with renewable energy systems in an economically viable manner.

In this work, we present an optimization framework to assess the large-scale implementation of ECO2R and its integration with renewable energy systems based on process modeling, techno-economic assessment and network optimization. It is built upon previous experimental work on ECO2R (Ma et al., 2021); studies on the modeling and assessment of CCU and ECO2R (Jouny et al., 2018; Orella et al., 2019; Roh et al., 2020; Shin et al., 2021; Sisler et al., 2021; Zimmermann et al., 2020), hybrid fossil- and CO2-based routes (Ioannou et al., 2020) and supply chain optimization of carbon utilization processes (Leonzio et al., 2020; Zhang et al., 2020).

2. Modeling and techno-economic assessment of ECO2R processes

One of the main challenges of assessing the implementation of emerging ECO2R is the accurate evaluation of the costs that the technology will entail in short to mid-term time frames, when it is expected to be operated at industrial scales. To increase the accuracy of existing ECO2R techno-economic models, our framework includes a rigorous calculation of the mass balances of the systems under study, leading to better separation cost estimations. That is done through the calculation of the cell outlets based on the cell design and reaction mechanisms. Eq. 1, for instance, represents the global mass balance of the electrolyzer cell.

$$m_{cathode}^{in\ (gas)} + m_{electrolyte}^{in\ (aq)} = m_{cathode}^{out\ (gas)} + m_{electrolyte}^{out\ (aq)} + m_{anode}^{out\ (gas)} \tag{1}$$

The flows and compositions of the industrial-scale electrolyzer are later used in the techno-economic assessment to evaluate the unitary capital and non-energy operational costs, as well as the electricity and heat requirements. This data is then used as inputs for the optimization model in the next section.

3. Optimization model

In this section, the network optimization model for the combined design and operation of ECO2R systems is formally defined.

3.1. Problem statement

The problem addressed can be stated as follows: given are a set of CO_2 emissions sources (i.e. flue gas or air) and a set of technologies that enable the electricity-powered transformation of these emissions into valuable products (i.e. point source capture, direct air capture, and electroreduction of CO_2 and CO into chemicals including product purification) with their corresponding data on performance, cost and energy consumption. Given is also a yearly profile with hourly detail of electricity prices and other relevant economic parameters. Our goal is to find the optimal paths to best utilize CO_2 by its upcycling into commodity chemicals, tackling both design capacities and their operation according to fluctuating prices.

The elements of the network are represented through a superstructure, that provides all the paths to go from CO_2 emissions to carbon sinks, allowing for one and two-step electrosynthesis of products.

3.2. Mathematical formulation

The problem is formulated as a mixed-integer linear program (MILP) where the main variables are the capacity of technology j built (C_j) and its operational level at time period t (O_{jt}). The objective function to be minimized is the total cost (Eq. 2) including the capex and non-energy opex (calculated through the parameters for the unitary capex γ_j and opex σ_j), the electricity consumption (where θ_j denotes the unitary electricity consumption of each technology and ε_t the cost of electricity for time period t) and the heating costs (likewise, with ρ_j and τ). Eq. 3 denotes the material balance for each compound i, including the CO_2 sources utilized U_{it}, the transformation $\sum_j \mu_{ij}\, O_{jt}$ (where μ_{ij} is a parameter linking the consumed and produced yields of compound i for each technology j) and the sales of final products P_{it}. Eqs. 4-7 represent the algebraic constraints to the decision variables: the set of demands of compounds i δ_i should be satisfied (Eq. 4) while not exceeding the available CO_2 sources (Eq. 5); the capacity of each technology cannot exceed a maximum level which is based on feasible plant sizes ($\bar{C}_j^{max}$) (Eq. 6); and the operation of each technology in each time period has to be below or equal to its capacity (Eq. 7).

$$\min Cost = \sum_j C_j \gamma_j + \sum_{jt} O_{jt} \sigma_j + \sum_{jt} O_{jt} \theta_j \varepsilon_t + \sum_{jt} O_{jt} \rho_j \tau \tag{2}$$

s.t.

$$U_{it} + \sum_j \mu_{ij} O_{jt} = P_{it} \qquad \forall i, \forall t \tag{3}$$

$$\sum_t P_{it} \geq \delta_i \qquad \forall i \in I^{products} \tag{4}$$

$$\sum_t U_{it} \leq \varphi_i \qquad \forall i \in I^{feeds} \tag{5}$$

$$C_j \leq \bar{C}_j^{max} \qquad \forall j \tag{6}$$

$$O_{jt} \leq C_j \qquad \forall j, \forall t \tag{7}$$

4. Case study

To illustrate the capabilities of the model, we define a case study on the CO_2 capture from flue gas or direct air and its electrically-powered reduction into carbon monoxide, formic acid or multi-carbon chemicals (including routes from CO_2 and CO to evaluate the one-step and two-step electrolysis).

The costs for the economic models of CO_2 capture from flue gas and direct air are retrieved from reports on their simulation and techno-economic assessment (James et al., 2019; Keith et al., 2018) and the experimental results needed for the modelling and assessment of ECO2R technologies are gathered from diverse lab-scale contributions (Chen et al., 2020; J. Li et al., 2019; Y. C. Li et al., 2019; Ma et al., 2020; Wang et al., 2020) identified at the review by Ma et al. (2021).

As an illustrative example, flue gas from a natural gas power plant with a capacity of 1,036 MW and annual CO_2 emissions of 3.5 M tonnes (United States Environmental Protection Agency (EPA), 2021) is used as a flue gas source, together with an unlimited supply of air for direct air capture. The demands of one multi-carbon product (ethylene) and one single-carbon (formic acid) are also defined. A target on the demand of ethylene of a 10% of the maximum stoichiometric yield of that CO_2 stream is used. And since the same assumption for formic acid would exceed the national yearly demand, the latter is assigned. The electricity prices profile chosen for the assessment is the hourly purchase prices for Texas in 2019, to avoid the effect of the 2020 Covid pandemic.

5. Results

The model is implemented in GAMS and solved with CPLEX 20.1. The MILP involves 307,489 continuous variables and 210,872 constraints and was solved in 42.2 CPUs on an Intel® Core™ i5-8250U processor operating at 1.60GHz.

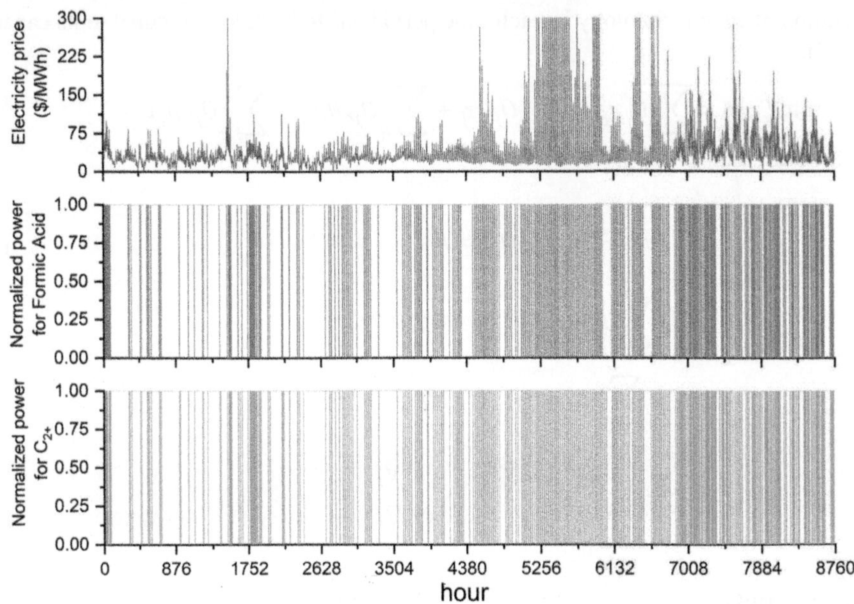

Figure 1. Hourly operation levels of the two selected technologies with respect to the electricity price profile.

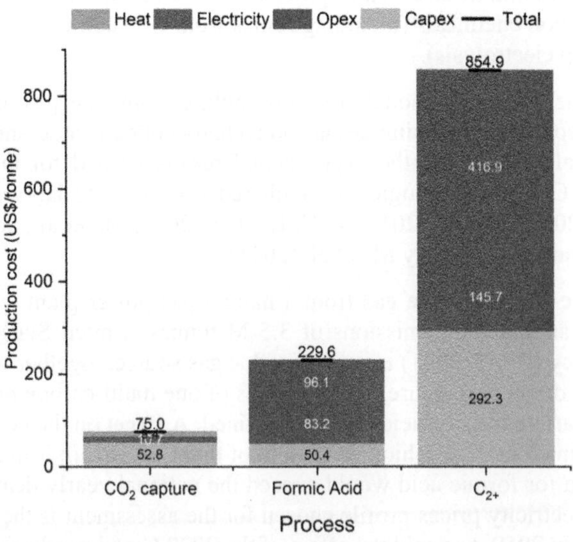

Figure 2. Production cost of the capture and ECO2R technologies resulting from the optimization.

The three technologies selected to satisfy the demands of ethylene and formic acid are the CO_2 capture from flue gas, the CO_2 reduction into formic acid, and one of the routes for the CO_2 reduction into multi-carbon products (with mass yields of 54% ethylene, 27% acetic acid, 13% ethanol, 3% n-propanol and 3% hydrogen). Figure 1 shows the result for the optimal operation of the two ECO2R plants as a result of the variable electricity prices, with capacity factors of 85% for the formic acid production and 84% for the multi-carbon plant. The threshold for the electricity price that causes plant shutdowns for the present case is 49 USD/MWh. Figure 2 depicts the production cost breakdowns for the three resulting technologies. While the cost driver of the CO_2 capture from flue gas is its capital costs (52.8%), electricity is the main driver of ECO2R processes (42% for the reduction into formic acid and 48% for the reduction into multi-carbon products).

6. Conclusions

The results obtained show that the model is a useful tool to identify the most promising routes to convert CO_2 into valuable chemicals and its operative response to fluctuating electricity prices. Such methodology is valuable for the multiple actors involved in the mitigation of emissions and the alternative synthesis of chemicals: from private companies, who can identify the most economically promising processes; to policymakers, who can identify which routes should be incentivized to promote carbon capture and utilization.

ECO2R-specific conclusions can also be drawn from the studied case. CO_2 capture is preferred over direct air capture due to its higher cost-effectiveness. Also, one-step electrolysis is selected over the two-step route, since the higher efficiency of the latter does not compensate the higher capital expenses of two electrolyzers.

Future work will address the assessment of the main sources of uncertainty at the electrolyzer operating parameters and the economic model and the integration of environmental criteria in the assessment.

References

Chen, C., Yan, X., Liu, S., Wu, Y., Wan, Q., Sun, X., Zhu, Q., Liu, H., Ma, J., Zheng, L., Wu, H., Han, B., 2020. Highly Efficient Electroreduction of CO 2 to C2+ Alcohols on Heterogeneous Dual Active Sites. Angew. Chemie Int. Ed. 59, 16459–16464. https://doi.org/10.1002/anie.202006847

Ioannou, I., D'Angelo, S.C., Martín, A.J., Pérez-Ramírez, J., Guillén-Gosálbez, G., 2020. Hybridization of Fossil- and CO 2 -Based Routes for Ethylene Production using Renewable Energy. ChemSusChem cssc.202001312. https://doi.org/10.1002/cssc.202001312

James, R.E., Kearins, D., Turner, M., Woods, M., Kuehn, N., Zoelle, A., 2019. Cost and Performance Baseline for Fossil Energy Plants Volume 1: Bituminous Coal and Natural Gas to Electricity. https://doi.org/10.2172/1569246

Jouny, M., Luc, W., Jiao, F., 2018. General Techno-Economic Analysis of CO 2 Electrolysis Systems. Ind. Eng. Chem. Res. 57, 2165–2177. https://doi.org/10.1021/acs.iecr.7b03514

Keith, D.W., Holmes, G., St. Angelo, D., Heidel, K., 2018. A Process for Capturing CO2 from the Atmosphere. Joule 2, 1573–1594. https://doi.org/10.1016/j.joule.2018.05.006

Leonzio, G., Foscolo, P.U., Zondervan, E., 2020. Optimization of CCUS Supply Chains for Some European Countries under the Uncertainty. Processes 8, 960. https://doi.org/10.3390/pr8080960

Li, J., Wang, Z., McCallum, C., Xu, Y., Li, F., Wang, Y., Gabardo, C.M., Dinh, C.-T., Zhuang,

T.-T., Wang, L., Howe, J.Y., Ren, Y., Sargent, E.H., Sinton, D., 2019. Constraining CO coverage on copper promotes high-efficiency ethylene electroproduction. Nat. Catal. 2, 1124–1131. https://doi.org/10.1038/s41929-019-0380-x

Li, Y.C., Wang, Z., Yuan, T., Nam, D.-H., Luo, M., Wicks, J., Chen, B., Li, J., Li, F., de Arquer, F.P.G., Wang, Y., Dinh, C.-T., Voznyy, O., Sinton, D., Sargent, E.H., 2019. Binding Site Diversity Promotes CO 2 Electroreduction to Ethanol. J. Am. Chem. Soc. 141, 8584–8591. https://doi.org/10.1021/jacs.9b02945

Ma, W., He, X., Wang, W., Xie, S., Zhang, Q., Wang, Y., 2021. Electrocatalytic reduction of CO 2 and CO to multi-carbon compounds over Cu-based catalysts. Chem. Soc. Rev. https://doi.org/10.1039/D1CS00535A

Ma, W., Xie, S., Liu, T., Fan, Q., Ye, J., Sun, F., Jiang, Z., Zhang, Q., Cheng, J., Wang, Y., 2020. Electrocatalytic reduction of CO2 to ethylene and ethanol through hydrogen-assisted C–C coupling over fluorine-modified copper. Nat. Catal. 3, 478–487. https://doi.org/10.1038/s41929-020-0450-0

Orella, M.J., Brown, S.M., Leonard, M.E., Román-Leshkov, Y., Brushett, F.R., 2019. A General Technoeconomic Model for Evaluating Emerging Electrolytic Processes. Energy Technol. 1900994. https://doi.org/10.1002/ente.201900994

Roh, K., Bardow, A., Bongartz, D., Burre, J., Chung, W., Deutz, S., Han, D., Heßelmann, M., Kohlhaas, Y., König, A., Lee, J.S., Meys, R., Völker, S., Wessling, M., Lee, J.H., Mitsos, A., 2020. Early-stage evaluation of emerging CO 2 utilization technologies at low technology readiness levels. Green Chem. 22, 3842–3859. https://doi.org/10.1039/C9GC04440J

Shin, H., Hansen, K.U., Jiao, F., 2021. Techno-economic assessment of low-temperature carbon dioxide electrolysis. Nat. Sustain. https://doi.org/10.1038/s41893-021-00739-x

Sisler, J., Khan, S., Ip, A.H., Schreiber, M.W., Jaffer, S.A., Bobicki, E.R., Dinh, C.-T., Sargent, E.H., 2021. Ethylene Electrosynthesis: A Comparative Techno-economic Analysis of Alkaline vs Membrane Electrode Assembly vs CO 2 –CO–C 2 H 4 Tandems. ACS Energy Lett. 6, 997–1002. https://doi.org/10.1021/acsenergylett.0c02633

Somoza-Tornos, A., Guerra, O.J., Crow, A.M., Smith, W.A., Hodge, B.-M., 2021. Process modeling, techno-economic assessment, and life cycle assessment of the electrochemical reduction of CO2: a review. iScience 102813. https://doi.org/10.1016/j.isci.2021.102813

United States Environmental Protection Agency (EPA), 2021. Emissions & Generation Resource Integrated Database (eGRID), 2019. Office of Atmospheric Programs, Clean Air Markets Division, Washington, DC.

Wang, Y., Wang, Z., Dinh, C.-T., Li, J., Ozden, A., Golam Kibria, M., Seifitokaldani, A., Tan, C.-S., Gabardo, C.M., Luo, M., Zhou, H., Li, F., Lum, Y., McCallum, C., Xu, Y., Liu, M., Proppe, A., Johnston, A., Todorovic, P., Zhuang, T.-T., Sinton, D., Kelley, S.O., Sargent, E.H., 2020. Catalyst synthesis under CO2 electroreduction favours faceting and promotes renewable fuels electrosynthesis. Nat. Catal. 3, 98–106. https://doi.org/10.1038/s41929-019-0397-1

Zhang, S., Zhuang, Y., Liu, L., Zhang, L., Du, J., 2020. Optimization-based approach for CO2 utilization in carbon capture, utilization and storage supply chain. Comput. Chem. Eng. 139, 106885. https://doi.org/10.1016/j.compchemeng.2020.106885

Zimmermann, A.W., Wunderlich, J., Müller, L., Buchner, G.A., Marxen, A., Michailos, S., Armstrong, K., Naims, H., McCord, S., Styring, P., Sick, V., Schomäcker, R., 2020. Techno-Economic Assessment Guidelines for CO2 Utilization. Front. Energy Res. 8. https://doi.org/10.3389/fenrg.2020.00005

Proceedings of the 14th International Symposium on Process Systems Engineering – PSE 2021+
June 19-23, 2022, Kyoto, Japan
http://dx.doi.org/10.1016/B978-0-323-85159-6.50123-8

A robust design of heat exchanger network for high temperature electrolysis systems

Hua Liu[a], Lasse Røngaard Clausen[b], Ligang Wang[c], and Ming Chen[a*]

[a] *Department of Energy Conversion and Storage, Technical University of Denmark, 2800 Kgs. Lyngby, Denmark*
[b] *Department of Mechanical Engineering, Technical University of Denmark, 2800 Kgs. Lyngby, Denmark*
[c] *Institute of Energy Power Innovation, North China Electric Power University, 100193, Beijing, China*
[*] *minc@dtu.dk*

Abstract

The solid oxide electrolysis cell (SOEC) has been recognized as a promising technology for producing green hydrogen utilizing renewable energy. However, due to various degradation phenomena, the electrochemical performance of SOEC will deteriorate over time. This degradation leads to varying heat duty and inefficient operation. Based on previously reported durability test data, we simulate and optimize a SOEC system with a robust heat exchanger network to address the degradation issue. Overall, a 45.9% redundancy heat exchanger area is designed into the system, which leads to a levelized cost of hydrogen (LCOH) of 4.23 \$/kg H_2. The system efficiency is 77.4% initially but drops to 63.2% due to degradation. The vaporizer consumes the most energy in the heat exchanger network.

Keywords: Solid oxide electrolysis cells; Potentiostatic; Degradation; System design.

1. Introduction

Climate neutrality is one of the most essential European policies today, and using green hydrogen is indispensable to achieve this goal (Espegren et al., 2021). Green hydrogen is produced from water electrolysis powered by solar or wind energy. Among various electrolysis technologies, the solid oxide electrolysis cell (SOEC) is the most promising in the future due to its high electrochemical efficiency compared to its low temperature competitors (Ebbesen et al., 2014). The SOEC is a multi-layer unit consist of fuel electrode, electrolyte, and oxygen electrode. Its efficiency is strongly impacted by the operating voltage, necessitating careful control. When SOEC operates at thermoneutral voltage (~1.285 V), it has near 100% stack efficiency as the Joule heat fully compensates for the heat demand of the endothermic electrolysis reaction. Operating the SOEC stacks at thermoneutral voltage makes it easier to manage heat balance because no extra heat is needed from or released to the system. It also reduces potential cell cracking caused by large temperature gradients and excessive thermal stress within the stack.

Even though constant voltage operation has several advantages, it is not immune to the problem of cell degradation. The most likely causes for the cell degradation include formation of ZrO_2 nano-particles in the fuel electrode, which deteriorates the active triple phase boundary, and O_2 bubble formation in the electrolyte near electrode/electrolyte interface (Chen et al., 2013; Knibbe et al., 2010). Yang et al. recently reported a potentiostatically operated SOEC durability test at thermoneutral voltage, which reveals the details of long-term cell degradation (Yang et al., 2021). As illustrated in Fig. 1, current density decreases dramatically over the first 300 hours and then stabilizes. Throughout the test, several unwanted interrupts and four load cycles occur, and the current density remains stable after each load cycle. This indicates that while SOEC degraded primarily during the initial stage, it is capable of remaining stable over time even when subjected to numerous load cycles.

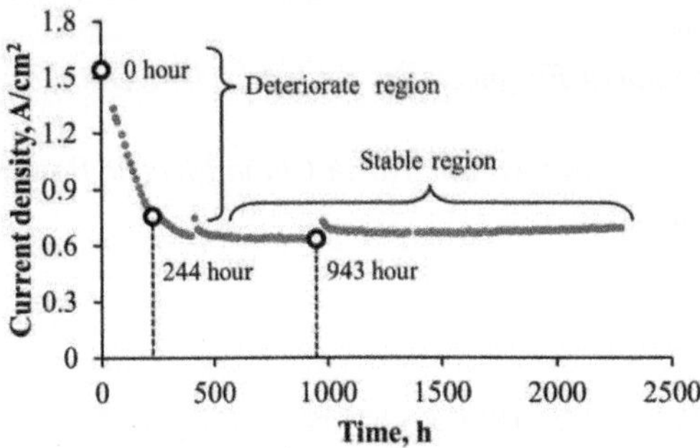

Fig. 1. Evolution of current density of an SOEC cell operated at 750°C and 1.29V for electrolysis of steam. Replotted based on the data reported by Yang et al., 2021.

From a system perspective, a decrease in current density results in a decrease in H_2 production and a change in the heat capacity of downstream flow. For efficiency and safety reasons, such uncertainty must be factored into the design stage. Given that the installed plant's SOEC effective cell area and heat exchange area are fixed, it requires a robust system designed to address the degradation issue and ensure the system's appropriate operation throughout its life. However, by designing an oversized heat exchange network, the system can achieve robustness efficiently and cost-effectively. (Chin et al., 2020; Kemp and Lim, 2020).

2. Process description

This paper proposes a robust SOEC system modified after the original design (AlZahrani and Dincer, 2017) as shown in Fig. 2. The system process is simulated and optimized based on the SOEC durability test profile (Yang et al., 2021). Table 1 presents the results of the durability test, including the current density. While data from the entire test period was used in the simulation, only those at the most critical time are listed here. The initial condition is set to 0 h, and the stable condition is set to 943 h. Data at 244 h are used solely for comparison purposes. The designed power $P_{el,des}$ is assumed to be 10 MW. As the stable region occupies most of the life cycle, the current density at the stable stage J_{stb} is used to estimate the cell area:

$$A_{cell} = \frac{P_{el,des}}{V_{th} J_{stb}} \tag{1}$$

During the test, the feedstock of the cathode is a mixture of 10% H_2 and 90% H_2O at 800 °C. Cathode feed stock flow rate is determined by the initial current density at thermal neutral voltage. To be more precise, the water molar flow rate $n_{cat,H2O}$ is:

$$n_{cat,H_2O} = \frac{J_{ini} A_{cell}}{2F \times SC_{des}} \tag{2}$$

where J_{ini} is initial current density, A_{cell} is cell area, F is Faraday constant, and SC_{des} is design steam conversion ratio, which is 85%. The feedstock flowrate remains constant throughout the test period. Meanwhile, because of degradation, current density decreases, along with the actual steam conversion ratio SC_{real} and electrolyze power $P_{el,real}$:

$$SC_{real} = \frac{J_i A_{cell}}{2F \times n_{cat,H_2O}} \tag{3}$$

$$P_{el,real} = J_i A_{cell} V_{th} \tag{4}$$

where J_i is current density at time i.

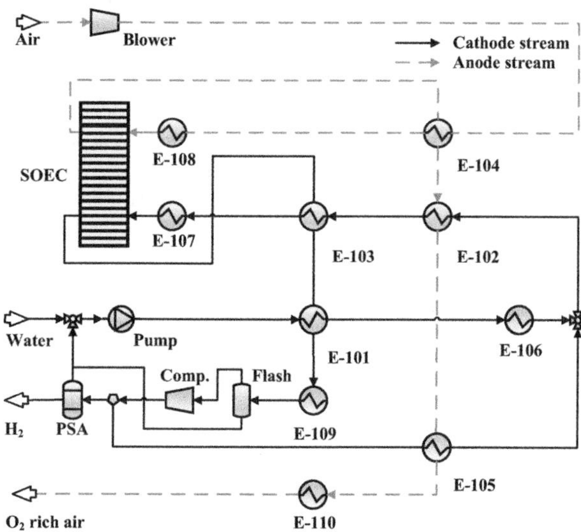

Fig. 2. Process flowsheet of the SOEC hydrogen production system.

Table 1. SOEC experiment profile from the durability test (Yang et al., 2021) and simulation respond at different time.

Time, h	Voltage, V	T, °C	J, A/cm^2	$n_{cat,H2O}$, mol/s	SC_{real}, %	$P_{el,real}$, MW
0	1.29	800	1.54	109.1	85.0	24.3
244	1.29	800	0.76	109.1	41.9	12.0
943	1.29	800	0.64	109.1	35.0	10.0

Before entering the SOEC at 800 °C, the water and air feedstocks are heated via a series of heat exchangers and an electric heater. Five of these heat exchangers (E-101~E-105) are configured for heat recovery. Given the current density deterioration, the optimal exchanger area will also shift over time. To get the optimal heat exchanger area, the temperature boundary of these five heat exchangers is optimized as a nonlinear constrained programme. The constraints include the mass and energy balance and the minimal temperature difference in the heat exchanger. The objective function is the total heat exchanger area. Then, for each heat exchanger, the design with the largest optimal exchange area over its life is chosen. Finally, the temperature settings in simulation are revoked, and the final oversized heat exchange areas are specified. Even though this increases the cost, it assures the system continues to run reliably over its entire life.

Besides the heat exchangers that improve robustness, the system involves other components such as evaporators, pre-heater, compressor, blower, and pump. The evaporator E-106 is an electric heater that vaporizes liquid water into steam. E-107 and E-108 are electric pre-heaters that ensure cathode and anode feedstock temperatures reach 800 °C. Anode product (O_2 rich air) is emitted into the environment after cooling down to room temperature by E-110. Considering the cost of purification, O_2 is inappropriate for separation and storage. Meanwhile, high commercial value product H_2 is treated another way. After being cooled by E-109, the cathode product is separated by a flash into two phases: the vapor and the liquid phase. The vapor phase is a mixture of H_2O and 98.2% H_2, which required a further purification by PSA. Liquid water from the flash and PSA are mixed with the makeup water before being fed to the system. A portion of the vapor phase from flash is heated and recycled to dilute the cathode feedstock to 90% H_2O.

3. Result and discussion

In this paper, a 10 MW SOEC system for hydrogen production is simulated in Aspen Hysys. Pinch analyses are evaluated in Aspen Energy Analyser. The optimization of the heat exchanger network is calculated in MATLAB. Optimal temperature set up and oversized UA is introduced from MATLAB into Aspen Hysys via COM interface following Hysys Customization Guide (AspenTech, 2011).

The grand composite curve of the SOEC system at both initial and steady stage are compared in Fig. 3. In both cases, the SOEC is operated in potentiostatic mode at thermal neutral voltage. As illustrated, water vaporization is the most energy intensive part in the heat exchanger network. The electricity consumption of vaporization accounts for 29.5% of the total system electricity consumption, while SOEC accounts for 67.0%. Apart from improving the efficiency of the SOEC stack, another way to save energy in this system is to rely on a cheap vaporization approach. The operation cost would be reduced if a less expensive heat source that can vaporize the water is available, such as abundant heat from fuel synthesis (Wang et al., 2018). To separate the water and hydrogen, the cathode product must be cooled to room temperature. Condensation cooling demand increases over time as the steam conversion ratio decreases and more water stays in the cathode product.

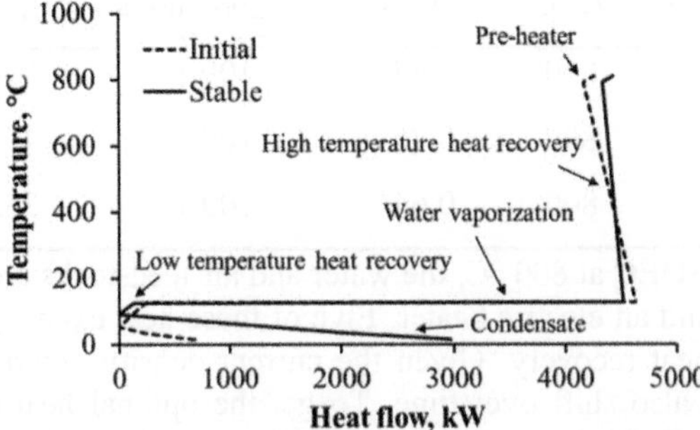

Fig. 3. Grand composite curve of the SOEC system in each degradation stage.

Due to degradation, both the composition and the heat capacity of the cathode product change, resulting in a variation in heat recovery duty, as well as a different optimal exchanger area for heat recovery. The varying optimal exchange areas of five heat recovery heaters (E-101~E-105) are depicted in Fig. 4. For example, the overall heat transfer coefficient (UA) of E-101 and E-103 decreased by 28.7% and 35.9%, respectively. Also, not all heat exchanger areas need to be reduced with degradation. At 244 hours, the optimal UA of E-102 is 4.09 kJ/°C/h, but it is only 1.84 kJ/°C/h at the start. This emphasizes the necessity of doing detailed robust heat exchanger network design as feasible for all stages of SOEC performance.

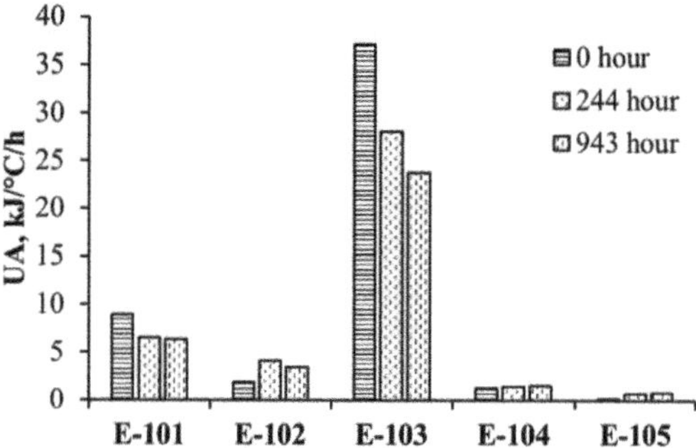

Fig. 4. Overall heat transfer coefficient (UA) of the heat exchangers at each time.

System efficiency (LHV) of the system is shown below, which is also depicted in Fig 5:

$$\eta_{sys} = \frac{H_2 \text{ combustion heat}}{\text{total electric power input}} \tag{5}$$

The SOEC system efficiency is deteriorating simultaneously as the current density. In the first 300 hours, the system efficiency also decreases by 14.2 %. Overall, the current density drops by 58.8 % from initial stage to stable stage, and the system efficiency decreases from 77.4% to 63.2%. Although the system efficiency reduces sharply over the first 300 hours, this problem can be mitigated in practice. The situation occurs because the initial water flow rate is too high and applying a lower water flow rate can improve efficiency. After each load cycle, SOEC recovers a little bit, which result in a rise of system efficiency. When the SOEC is restarted at 1000 h, the current density rises 0.09 A/cm^2, and the system efficiency enhances by 2.66%.

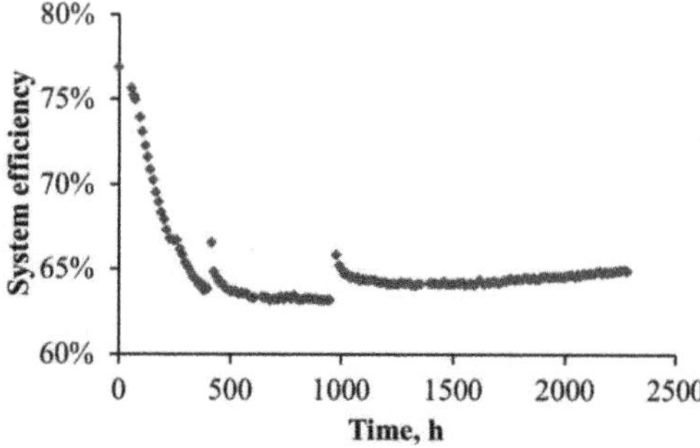

Fig. 5. System efficiency of the SOEC hydrogen production process.

This work also examines the economics of the robust SOEC system. It should be noted that the total capital cost (TPC) is calculated based on the oversized capacity of the components (particularly the heat exchanger). As a result, the system has a greater TPC than the conventional design. Simultaneously, a drop in current density results in a reduced rate of hydrogen production, thereby diminishes the revenue. The robust optimization prolongs the system's life by 1.6% at the cost of an 11% increase in equipment costs. In the life cycle, the levelized cost of hydrogen (LCOH) is \$4.25/kg H_2 and the net present value (NPV) is \$13.5 million.

4. Conclusions

In summary, this paper presents a SOEC hydrogen production system incorporates oversized heat exchangers to handle degradation concerns. SOEC degradation manifests as a decrease in current density during potentiostatic operation. Both electric power and system efficiency decline in lockstep with the trend of decreasing current density. Additionally, the optimal heat exchange area changes because of degradation, and 45.9% more heat exchange area can handle this uncertainty. Meanwhile, vaporizers consume most of the electricity in the heat exchange network. When other techniques for reducing evaporating costs are considered, the system still has the potential to increase profitability. In future studies, we will look at how to improve the SOEC system design and operating strategy to increase durability.

References

K. Espegren, S. Damman, P. Pisciella, I. Graabak and A. Tomasgard, 2021. The role of hydrogen in the transition from a petroleum economy to a low-carbon society. Int. J. Hydrogen Energ. 46, 23125–23138.

S. D. Ebbesen, S. H. Jensen, A. Hauch and M. B. Mogensen, 2014. High Temperature Electrolysis in Alkaline Cells, Solid Proton Conducting Cells, and Solid Oxide Cells. Chem. Rev. 114, 10697–10734.

M. Chen, Y.-L. Liu, J. J. Bentzen, W. Zhang, X. Sun, A. Hauch, Y. Tao, J. R. Bowen and P. V. Hendriksen, 2013. Microstructural Degradation of Ni/YSZ Electrodes in Solid Oxide Electrolysis Cells under High Current. J. Electrochem. Soc. 160, F883–F891.

R. Knibbe, M. L. Traulsen, A. Hauch, S. D. Ebbesen, & M. Mogensen, 2010. Solid Oxide Electrolysis Cells: Degradation at High Current Densities. J. Electrochem. Soc. 157, B1209.

Y. Yang, X. Tong, A. Hauch, X. Sun, Z. Yang, S. Peng and M. Chen, 2021. Study of solid oxide electrolysis cells operated in potentiostatic mode: Effect of operating temperature on durability. Chem. Eng. J. 417, 129260.

H. H. Chin, B. Wang, P. S. Varbanov, J. J. Klemeš, M. Zeng, and Q. Wang, 2020. Long-term investment and maintenance planning for heat exchanger network retrofit. Appl. Energ. 279, 115713.

I. C. Kemp, & J. S. Lim, 2020. Pinch Analysis for Energy and Carbon Footprint Reduction. 131–194

A. A. AlZahrani and I. Dincer, 2017. Thermodynamic and electrochemical analyses of a solid oxide electrolyzer for hydrogen production. Int. J. Hydrogen Energ. 42, 21404–21413.

AspenTech, 2010. Aspen HYSYS: Customization Guide.

L. Wang, M. Pérez-Fortes, H. Madi, S. Diethelm, J. V. herle and F. Maréchal, 2018, Optimal design of solid-oxide electrolyzer based power-to-methane systems: A comprehensive comparison between steam electrolysis and co-electrolysis, Appl Energ, 211, 1060–1079.

Proceedings of the 14th International Symposium on Process Systems Engineering – PSE 2021+
June 19-23, 2022, Kyoto, Japan
http://dx.doi.org/10.1016/B978-0-323-85159-6.50124-X

Techno-economic Assessment of Upstream and Downstream Process Alternatives for the Production of Monoclonal Antibodies

Sara Badr, Kozue Okamura, Nozomi Takahashi, Hirokazu Sugiyama*

Department of Chemical System Engineering, The University of Tokyo, 7-3-1, Hongo, Bunkyo-ku, 113-8656, Tokyo, Japan
sugiyama@chemsys.t.u-tokyo.ac.jp

Abstract

The rising demand for monoclonal antibodies is increasing the pressure for improving production efficiency and lowering costs. A high-resolution assessment of two bottleneck units is provided. Within the main cultivation unit, different cell lines were assessed at various production scales, and operating modes. In addition to operating costs, and production time, the generation of impurities, e.g., host cell proteins was also estimated using a hybrid model. A newly established cell line was shown to be highly productive, but presenting a trade-off between production costs and time, and generated impurity levels. A superstructure was built combining design and operating parameters of the capture chromatography unit. Scenarios regarding variations in inlet conditions based on upstream disturbances were analyzed. Process robustness was evaluated and mitigation measures suggested. This work provides a more comprehensive assessment framework that extends beyond cost and time to include quality, and potential operational problems. This could help guide process design and control efforts.

Keywords: Cell cultivation; Capture Chromatography; Continuous production; Process assessment; Biopharmaceutical production; Therapeutic proteins.

1. Introduction

Demand for therapeutic proteins, and especially monoclonal antibodies (mAb)s, is rising, having already increased many folds in the past decade (Walsh, 2018). Applications for mAbs are expanding for the treatment of diseases such as cancer and even most recently for COVID-19. The pandemic has placed the efficiency of biopharmaceutical manufacturing under scrutiny. Increasing productivity is now necessary to avoid bottlenecks and keep up with the rising demand, especially for plants already operating at near capacity. Another major challenge is to reduce production costs to increase accessibility and to fend off rising competition from biosimilars.

A typical mAb production process involves upstream cell cultivation to produce the required antibody product and downstream purification units to reach the required product profile as shown in Figure 1. Efforts to increase productivity include cell line modifications, manipulating operating conditions to improve cell productivity, or changing operating modes from batch to continuous. Continuous operations can potentially offer higher productivities, more flexibility as well as being more suitable for unstable products. However, they are also susceptible to increased operational difficulties, such as clogging, which could lead to fluctuations in downstream loads and longer process downtimes.

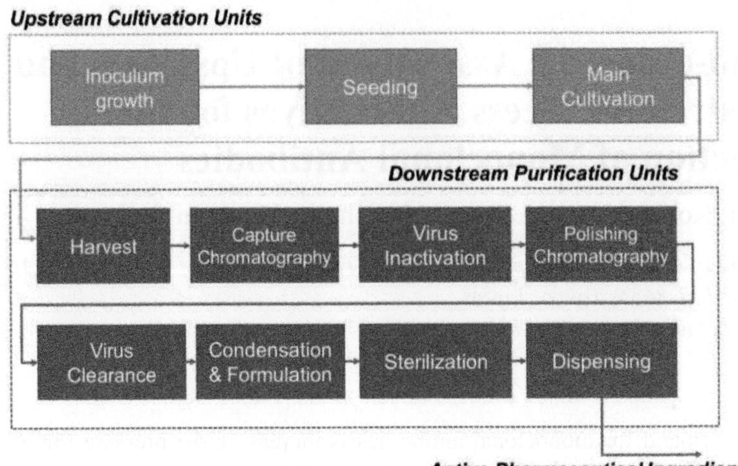

Figure 1: Typical mAb production process

Most studies comparing batch and continuous operations focus on ideal operations. A comprehensive framework is still needed for comparison including product quality and production robustness in addition to production time and costs.

This work offers an assessment of different upstream process alternatives involving variations in cell lines, operating conditions, and cultivation modes. A comparison is presented in terms of operating costs and expected product quality. Downstream capture chromatography is also investigated regarding differences in design and control parameters. Different scenarios of upstream changes are presented and their influence on capture costs and productivity. A discussion of measures needed to maintain productivity is also provided.

2. Simulation of process alternatives

2.1. Main cultivation unit

Simulated alternatives described in this work include fed-batch and perfusion cultivation (Karst et al., 2018). Fed-batch cultivation is where nutrient levels are maintained during operation to avoid cell death without removing product from the reactor. Perfusion cultivation is where continuous addition of nutrients is balanced with product and by-product removal to reach steady operation. Three different Chinese hamster ovary (CHO) cell lines are depicted in this work. Cell A is from a newly established cell line, which is proclaimed to be more productive than traditional cell lines. Further details can be found in Okamura et al. (2022). Simulations with Cell B were based on the fed-batch experiments presented in detail by Badr et al. (2021) at and Cell C on that presented by Xu and Chen (2016) with perfusion operation.

Cell cultivation models used in this work were based on the model presented by Badr et al. (2021). The model presented there was validated with experimental data generated from the Kobe GMP consolidated lab of the Manufacturing Technology Association of Biologics. The newly established cell line used as the basis for the Cell A simulations are more sensitive to lactate concentrations. A novel hybrid modelling approach is introduced in Okamura et al. (2022), where a data-driven module accounts for the impact of changes in experimental conditions on model parameters and acts to provide a dynamic correction for lactate concentrations. The generation of host cell proteins (HCP)s and other process-related impurities was accounted for through description of cell death and dissolution (Maruhashi et al., 1994).

2.2. Downstream capture chromatography

A comparison of batch and continuous operations in the capture unit is presented. While chromatography is typically conducted as batch, continuous operation can be achieved through running several columns together. An example of continuous capture chromatography is periodic counter current (PCC) operations, where one column is loaded while others go through cycles of washing and regeneration (Baur et al., 2016). A sensitivity analysis was carried out varying the column design and control parameters. Within this analysis a superstructure of process options was built, where operational costs and productivity of the capture unit were compared. The superstructure was used to identify promising alternatives. In addition to varying the operating mode from batch to continuous, the super structure also included changes in the number of columns, column dimensions, superficial velocity in the column, and the column switching criterion in continuous mode. The model presented in Badr et al. (2021) was used for flow description within the column and for estimating the costs and productivity.

Four different scenarios regarding inlet concentrations and flowrates were also tested in this analysis as shown in Figure 2. The scenarios represent different potential disturbances that can arise in upstream units. In the baseline scenario Sc. 1, a constant inlet was simulated based on the expected flowrates from a typical perfusion or fed-batch cultivation operation. Sc. 2 represents the impact of the start-up and shutdown phases within the continuous operation in a more realistic portrayal of the inlet form perfusion mode. In the absence of active control in the upstream units, concentration peaks and fluctuations can be observed as seen in Sc. 3 and 4, respectively. The impacts of such disturbances were investigated along with mitigation measures in the design and operation of the capture columns.

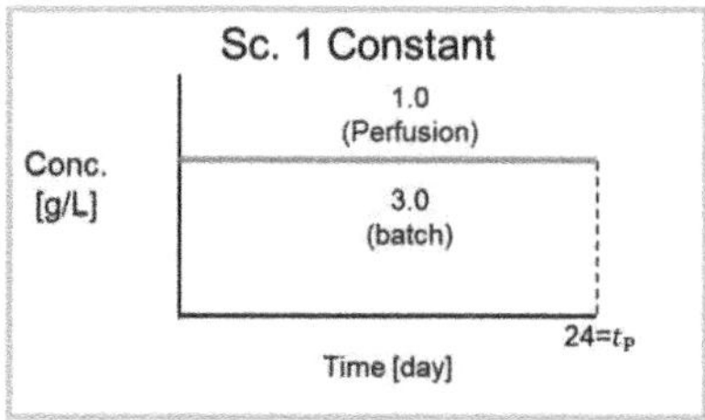

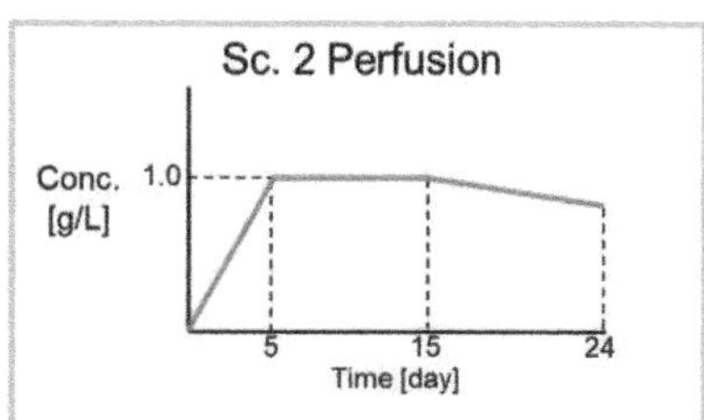

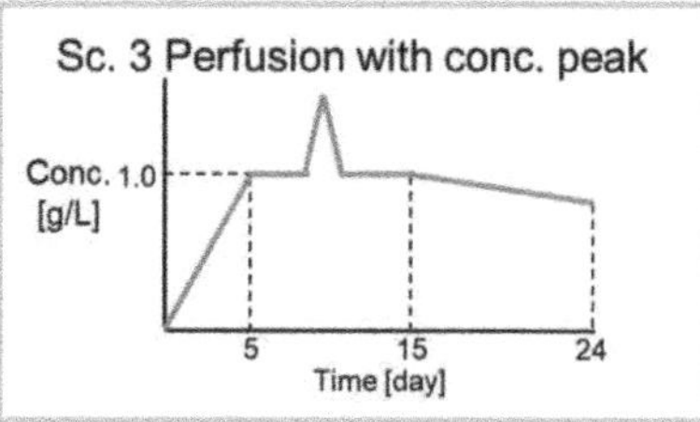

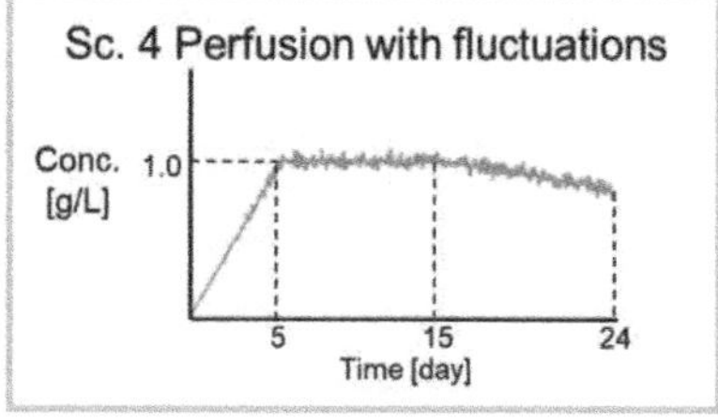

Figure 2: Downstream inlet scenarios

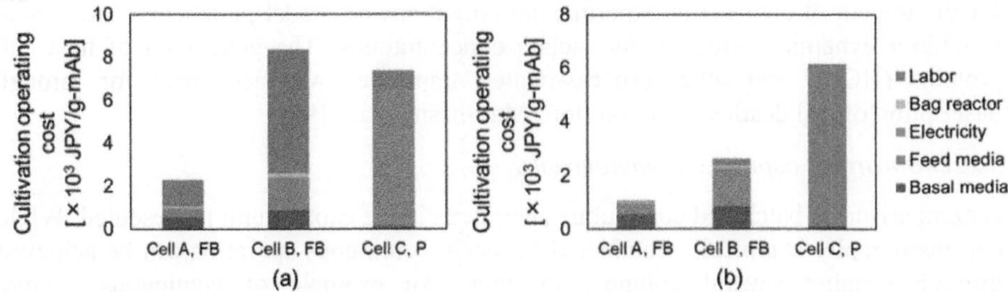

Figure 3: Cultivation operating costs for scenarios (a) 2 kg production scale in 50 L reactor and (b) 200 kg production scale in 2000 L reactor

3. Results and discussion

3.1. Cultivation unit

Figure 3 shows a comparison of cultivation operating costs and their breakdown at different production scales, reactor volumes, operating modes and cell lines. The newly established cell line (Cell A) resulted in the lowest overall costs per gram mAb produced. The higher productivity of this cell line also resulted in a reduced cultivation time (~4.4 times shorter than that of Cell B). The highest productivity and lowest cultivation time were achieved by the perfusion mode, followed closely by that of Cell A in fed-batch mode. However, perfusion mode also yielded the highest costs per gram at commercial scales, mainly due to the higher media consumption. At smaller scales and reactor volumes, labor costs were more pronounced for fed-batch units.

Figure 4 shows the calculated concentrations of HCPs in the reactor for Cells A and B. HCP concentrations as well as other process related impurities, such as DNA, were found to be higher for Cell A than for the other tested alternatives. Therefore, the load to downstream purification units from Cell A can be higher than the other candidates.

Further improvements can still be tested, for example, by using the more productive Cell A in perfusion mode. This could result in additional productivity gains, while maintaining the generated impurity concentrations at lower levels.

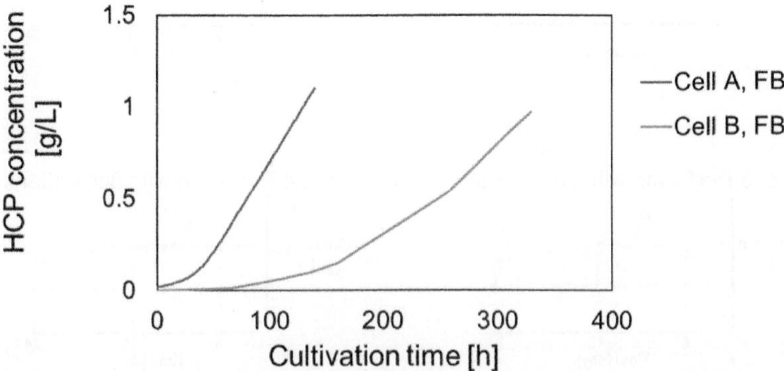

Figure 4: Simulated host cell protein concentrations in the reactor

3.2. Capture chromatography

In total 1,440 combinations of process alternatives were tested in the developed superstructure. Figure 5 shows the resulting pareto optimal alternatives considering operating capture costs and productivity for integrated batch options with fed-batch inlet and integrated continuous processes with perfusion inlet.

The superstructure results show that continuous options can offer lower costs compared to the batch alternatives. The lower productivity can also be attributed to the lower titers of the perfusion cultivation units, which results in a need to process larger volumes downstream to achieve the same product mass. Optimizing operating conditions can help increase productivity, e.g., increasing superficial velocity. However, care should be taken to avoid product losses especially when high velocities are coupled with short columns and slow switching between columns in PCC operations. Product losses lower the yield per cycle and lead to significant increases in costs. Product losses should thus be minimized for robust design. This effect is particularly highlighted when upstream disturbances are taken into account, especially for scenario Sc. 3 with the sudden concentration peaks. Therefore, the results from all scenario analysis should be carefully considered to reach a compromise between maintaining high productivity and robustness with upstream changes.

Ideally, one of the advantages of integrated continuous operations, would be eliminating the need for intermediate surge tanks. This could have a big impact on achieving reductions in process capital costs. However, surge tanks can still be beneficial for mitigating upstream disturbances, in particular concerning fluctuations in inlet flowrates and concentrations. Careful determination of the required surge tank volume is necessary to avoid suboptimal operation. The conducted scenario analysis is thus a crucial tool towards achieving this goal.

Overall, the analysis showed that hybrid alternatives with fed-batch upstream and continuous downstream options can outperform integrated batch or continuous operations. This is achieved by combining the advantages of both, with higher titers from upstream operations and more efficient continuous downstream conditions. However, there is still room for improvement with developments upstream, e.g., with using the more productive Cell A in perfusion mode, higher titers could be achieved.

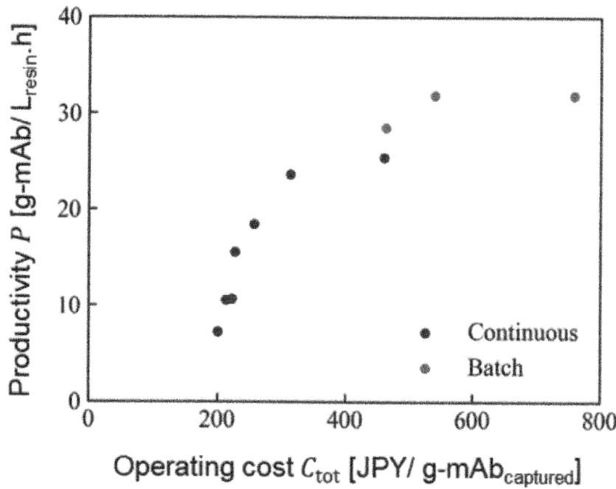

Figure 5: Pareto optimal design alternatives for the capture chromatography unit

4. Conclusions

In this work a high-resolution analysis was undertaken for two bottleneck units in mAb production. Within the upstream cultivation unit, the newly established cell line gave superior results in terms of operating costs and reasonable operating times even in fed-batch operation. The performance of this cell line should be investigated in more novel perfusion operation or in different experimental conditions to further enhance its performance in the established fed-batch operations. Cell A, however, resulted in a higher concentration of process related impurities (e.g., HCPs). This could cause increased loads on the downstream units. This work does not differentiate between different HCP structures though. A unified measure of quality between upstream and downstream units should still be determined. As downstream processing difficulties do not only arise from the increased volumes and concentrations but could also be influenced by similarities between the impurities to be removed and the main product.

The importance of incorporating expected upstream disturbances in the design of downstream units has been demonstrated. The analysis in this work was extended beyond costs and time to also include quality aspects in the upstream units and robustness downstream. This approach provides a comprehensive overview of performance under varying production scenarios, production scales, and possible operational issues. The analysis offers a deeper understanding of influential process parameters, the sources of disturbances in the system, their magnitudes, and potential mitigation measures.

Acknowledgements

This work was supported by the Japan Agency for Medical Research and Development (AMED) [grant No. JP21ae0121015, JP20ae0101064, JP20ae0101058].

References

Badr, S., Okamura, K., Takahashi, N., Ubbenjans, V., Shirahata, H., Sugiyama, H., 2021. Integrated design of biopharmaceutical manufacturing processes: Operation modes and process configurations for monoclonal antibody production. Comput. Chem. Eng. 153, 107422.

Baur, D., Angarita, M., Müller-Späth, T., Steinebach, F., Morbidelli, M., 2016. Comparison of batch and continuous multi-column protein A capture processes by optimal design. Biotechnol. J. 11, 920–931.

Karst, D.J., Steinebach, F., Morbidelli, M., 2018. Continuous integrated manufacturing of therapeutic proteins. Curr. Opin. Biotechnol. 53, 76–84.

Maruhashi, F., Murakami, S., Baba, K., 1994. Automated monitoring of cell concentration and viability using an image analysis system. Cytotechnology 15, 281–289.

Okamura, K., Badr, S., Murakami, S., Sugiyama, H., 2022. Hybrid modelling of CHO-MK cell cultivation in monoclonal antibody production. Submitted to the 14th International Symposium on Process Systems Engineering – PSE 2021+.

Walsh, G., 2018. Biopharmaceutical benchmarks 2018. Nat. Biotechnol. 36, 1136–1145.

Xu, S., Chen, H., 2016. High-density mammalian cell cultures in stirred-tank bioreactor without external pH control. J. Biotechnol. 231, 149–159.

Proceedings of the 14th International Symposium on Process Systems Engineering – PSE 2021+
June 19-23, 2022, Kyoto, Japan
http://dx.doi.org/10.1016/B978-0-323-85159-6.50125-1

Biomethane liquefaction followed by CO_2 solidification based biogas upgrading process

Ahmad Naquash[a], Muhammad Abdul Qyyum[b], and Moonyong Lee[a*]
[a]School of Chemical Engineering, Yeungnam University, Gyeongsan 712-749, Rep. of Korea
[b]Department of Petroleum & Chemical Engineering, Sultan Qaboos University, Muscat, Oman
mynlee@yu.ac.kr

Abstract

Energy consumption and climatic changes are challenging issues these days. Unlike fossil fuels, the utilization of renewable fuels such as biogas is a promising option to meet these challenges. Biogas upgraded form (biomethane) is an emerging potential alternative to natural gas. However, biomethane production is itself challenging because of the pros and cons of each biogas upgrading technology. In this study, a cryogenic technology is adopted because of its dual benefits; carbon dioxide (CO_2) removal and biomethane precooling due to its low-temperature operation. The CO_2 is removed from biogas through the CO_2 solidification process. The phase behavior of CO_2 is investigated and the specified conditions for CO_2 solidification (-68°C and 5.17 bar) are applied for biomethane production. After CO_2 removal, biomethane is liquefied. The refrigeration duty for upgrading and liquefaction is provided by a parallel nitrogen expansion cycle adopting pure nitrogen as a refrigerant. Aspen Hysys® v11 is used as a commercial simulator for process simulation and to evaluate CO_2 freezing behavior in the proposed study. The mixed optimization technique is employed to optimize the design variables of the proposed process. The proposed process shows energy and exergy savings of 17.4 and 29.7%, respectively. It is evaluated that the proposed integrated process depicts superior results than the conventional studies.

Keywords: Biomethane production; Liquified biomethane; CO_2 solidification; Anti-sublimation; Mixed optimization; Parallel nitrogen expansion cycle.

1. Introduction

Due to increasing energy demand and environmental challenges, the use of biogas has seen an increasing trend at a rate of 11.5% annually (International Energy Agency, 2020). Owing to its increasing production, transportation of biogas is becoming a matter of concern especially because of production at atmospheric pressure. Transportation at this pressure is uneconomical due to its low energy density (Krich et al., 2005). This energy density can be enhanced either through compression or liquefaction. Compression is beneficial only for shorter distances. For longer distances, liquefaction is an economical approach. However, the impurities must be removed before liquefaction to avoid carbon dioxide (CO_2) freezing or maintenance issues. Typically, CO_2 below 50 ppm is recommended in the upgraded biogas i.e., biomethane (Fan et al., 2018).

Biogas upgrading can be carried out through absorption, adsorption, membrane, and cryogenic technology. Amongst these technologies, cryogenic technology is the most viable technology if integrated with the liquefaction process, known as liquefied biomethane (LBM) production (Naquash et al., 2021). The cryogenic technology is of two types, depending on the state of CO_2 separated. The cryogenic distillation process is adopted to separate CO_2 in liquid form (Yousef et al., 2017) while anti-sublimation technology is adopted to separate CO_2 in solid-state (Spitoni et al., 2019). Separation of CO_2 in solid form is preferable because of high product purity. Various researchers have explored these technologies technically and economically. For example, the cryogenic and absorption-based biomethane production integrated with a liquefaction process was studied by (Pellegrini et al., 2018). Their results showed that the absorption upgrading, and liquefaction process requires 34.8% of the total energy to liquefy biomethane, which is significantly higher than cryogenic processes. Similarly, the absorption and cryogenic biogas upgrading processes integrated with liquefaction were analyzed by (Hashemi et al., 2019). Their results showed that the cryogenic process is more efficient, with lower specific energy consumption (SEC) of 2.07 kWh/kg bio-LNG than that of the absorption process (3.35 kWh/kg) (Hashemi et al., 2019). In another study, the CO_2 solidification-based biogas upgrading integrated with the liquefaction process was investigated and the reported SEC was 1.45 kWh/kg (Baccioli et al., 2018). Similarly, the CO_2 solidification-based biogas upgrading integrated with the liquefaction process under various feed compositions was also studied recently and the reported SEC ranged from 1.093 to 1.574 kWh/kg (Spitoni et al., 2019). Recently, another study was proposed in which a biogas upgrading process through CO_2 solidification followed by LBM production was investigated. The total SEC was 0.495 kWh/kg (Naquash et al., 2021).

It is analyzed from the literature review that the cryogenic upgrading process is energy-intensive and complex. In this study, a simple and energy-efficient process is proposed that adopts a single refrigeration cycle utilizing pure refrigerant to produce high purity LBM. The refrigeration cycle i.e., parallel nitrogen expansion cycle (PNEC) is a simple cycle utilizing pure N_2 as a refrigerant. The application of PNEC has already been explored in the liquefaction of natural gas (He et al., 2019). In this study, the application of PNEC is evaluated for cryogenic biogas upgrading and LBM production. The process is simulated in Aspen Hysys® v11. To explore energy-saving potential, the process is optimized through Aspen Hysys® v11 in-built optimizer using mixed optimization technique. The proposed process is analyzed through energy and exergy analyses to identify and locate process inefficiencies.

2. Process design and simulation

2.1. Process description

The process flow diagram of the proposed process is shown in Figure 2. The feed stream (Biogas) at 1.0 bar is first compressed to 6.97 bar by compressors (K1 and K2) assisted with aftercoolers (E1 and E2) before entering in CHX1. After CHX1, the feed stream temperature is dropped to -66°C at 5.17 bar in stream (5). The stream (5) is entered into the cold box (CB1) where the temperature is further decreased to -68°C. The CB1 conditions are selected according to the solidification conditions of CO_2. The phase diagram of the feed stream is prepared according to the data calculated by Aspen Hysys® v11, as shown in Figure 1. According to Figure 1 (enlarged version), the feed conditions at -68°C and 5.17 bar are in the region of CO_2 solidification.

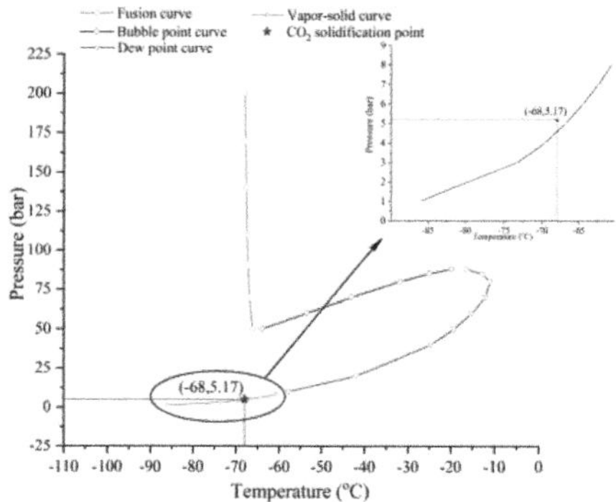

Figure 1 Pressure-Temperature phase diagram of biogas feed (CH_4/CO_2: 0.5/0.5)

In CB1, the CO_2 is separated in solid form and biomethane is separated from the top of CB1. For simplification, only one cold box is shown in Figure 2. Considering continuous operation of solidification process, another cold box configuration can be installed. Biomethane is then sent to CHX2 for liquefaction. At the outlet of CHX2, the biomethane is 100% liquefied. The pressure of LBM is reduced to 1.2 bar by passing through an expander (T3) for storage at liquid conditions. The cooling duty for biogas upgrading and biomethane liquefaction is provided by PNEC. In PNEC, pure nitrogen (N_2) is used as a refrigerant, which is compressed to 16.83 bar in a series of compressors. After compression, stream (18) is cooled to -66°C by passing through CHX1. After CHX1, the stream (19) is split into streams (20 and 21) by TEE2. Stream 21 pressure is reduced to 4.20 bar which further enters MIX2. Stream (20) is further cooled to -137.3°C by passing through CHX2 in stream (23). Stream (23) pressure is then reduced to 4.20 bar which reenters CHX2 to exchange its cold energy. Stream (25), leaving CHX2, is mixed with stream (22) in MIX2 and reenters CHX2 to further exchange its cold energy. After leaving CHX2, stream (27) at -88°C enters CHX1 to assist in temperature decrease of stream (4) and stream (18). After CHX1, stream 28 at 37.14°C and 3.90 bar is recycled back to complete the refrigeration loop.

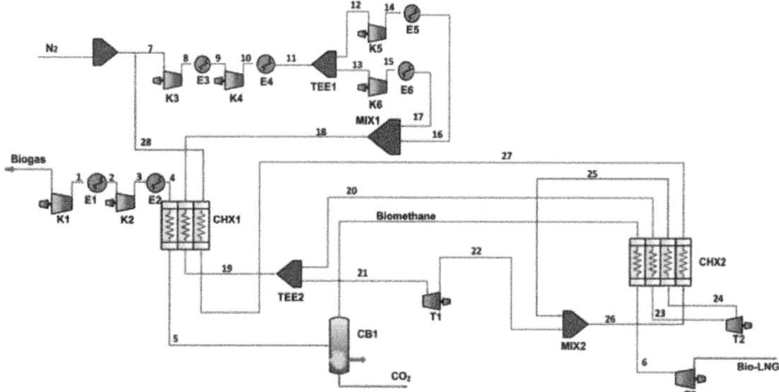

Figure 2 Process flow diagram of the proposed process

2.2. Process simulation

The process is simulated in Aspen Hysys® v11. Peng-Robinson is used as the equation of state (Peng and Robinson, 1929). The feed conditions and design parameters have opted from the Base case (Naquash et al., 2021). The following assumptions (Naquash et al., 2021) were taken in the simulation of this study:

1. The pressure drop in coolers is 0.25 bar.
2. The pressure drop in CHXs is 1.0 and 0.1 bar for the hot and cold sides, respectively.
3. It was assumed that CO_2 is completely solidified at -68°C and 5.17 bar.

The design parameters of the proposed process are presented in Table 1.

Table 1 Design parameters and constraints of proposed process

Design Parameters	**Values** (Naquash et al., 2021)
Feed biogas conditions	T: 35 °C P: 1 bar Flowrate: 308.2 kg/h
Feed biogas composition (mole)	CH_4: 0.5 CO_2: 0.5
Compressor efficiency	80%
Turbine efficiency	90%
Design constraints	
MITA value (°C)	1.0 ~ 3.0
Inlet temperature of compressors	$>T_{dew}$

3. Process optimization

The process was optimized in the in-built optimizer of Aspen Hysys® v11. In this study, a mixed (combination of BOX and SQP) optimization method was adopted to calculate the optimal values of design variables keeping the design constraint value within the range. The objective function is to reduce SEC while keeping the design constraint i.e., minimum internal temperature approach (MITA) in the range of 1 to 3°C. The values of refrigerant flow rate, suction and discharge pressure of refrigeration cycle, and split ratios of TEE1 and TEE2 are the design variables optimized through mixed technique.

4. Results and discussion: Process analysis

The energy and exergy analyses are performed which are discussed in the following sections.

4.1. Energy analysis

The energy analysis of a liquefaction process is typically described in terms of SEC and refrigerant flowrates. The values of refrigerant flowrates, SEC along suction and discharge pressure of refrigeration cycles of the base case and the optimized proposed process is presented in Table 2. It can be seen from Table 2 that the proposed process is energy efficient with 17.4% energy savings compared to the base case process. In the base case process, two separate refrigeration cycles were used whereas in the proposed process, a single refrigeration cycle is used with pure refrigerant to make a simple, and energy-efficient biomethane production and liquefaction process. However, as compared to the base case, the process consumes more refrigerant flowrate i.e., 2398 kg/h which is 33.4% more.

Table 2 Design variables values of base case (Naquash et al., 2021) and proposed case

Design variables	**Base case**	**Proposed process**
Biogas upgrading section		
m_{C1} (kg/h)	66.6	-
m_{C3} (kg/h)	87.5	-

m_{CO2} (kg/h)	718.1	-
Total refrigerant flowrate (kg/h)	872	-
Suction pressure (bar)	11.8	-
Discharge pressure (bar)	50.7	-
Specific energy consumption (kWh/kg)	0.162	-
Bio-LNG section		
m_{N2} (kg/h)	85	2398
m_{C1} (kg/h)	376	-
m_{C2} (kg/h)	165	-
m_{C3} (kg/h)	98	-
Total refrigerant flowrate (kg/h)	724	2398
Suction pressure (bar)	3.1	4.2
Discharge pressure (bar)	68.7	17.1
Specific energy consumption (kWh/kg)	0.333	
Total specific energy consumption (kWh/kg)	**0.495**	**0.408**
Relative energy savings (%)		**17.4**

4.2. Exergy analysis

The exergy analysis of the optimized process is performed. The equations adopted for exergy analysis are taken from (Venkatarathnam and Timmerhaus, 2008). The values of exergy destruction for each piece of equipment are presented in Figure 3.

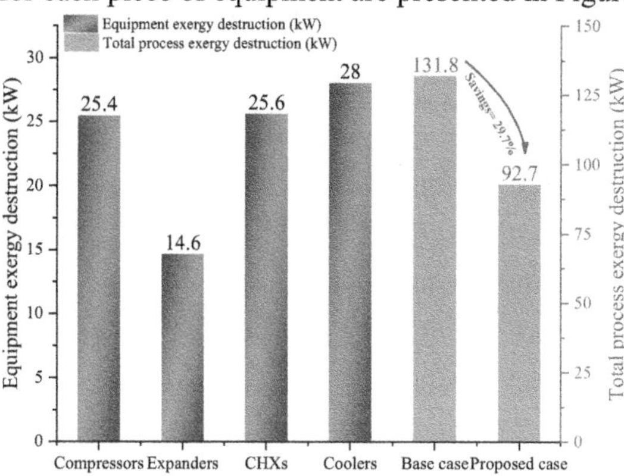

Figure 3 Total process and equipment exergy destruction values

The highest exergy destruction (28 kW) is attributed to coolers followed by compressors (25.4 kW) whereas expanders exhibit the lowest exergy destruction (14.6 kW). The main reason for high exergy destruction in compressors and coolers is due to high SEC by refrigeration cycle compressors. This high exergy destruction shows that there is large potential available for improvement. As compared to the base case, the overall exergy destruction is significantly lower with 29.7% savings.

5. Conclusions

The cryogenic biogas upgrading, and LBM production process is a complex and energy-intensive process. To reduce high SEC and process complexity, a simulation study considering CO_2 solidification-based biogas upgrading process followed by LBM production is proposed. The proposed process is simulated in Aspen Hysys® v11. The CO_2 solidification conditions are assessed from the phase diagram of biogas. The CO_2 is solidified at -68°C at 5.17 bar. The high purity biomethane is liquefied assisted by PNEC. The proposed process is analysed from energy and exergy aspects. From the results, it is concluded that the process has a low SEC of 0.408 kWh/kg with 17.4% energy savings compared to the base case. In terms of exergy, the proposed process is 29.7% efficient owing to less equipment and low SEC.

Acknowledgements

This work was supported by the National Research Foundation of Korea (NRF) grant funded by the Korea government (MSIT) (2021R1A2C1092152) and by Priority Research Centers Program through the National Research Foundation of Korea (NRF) funded by the Ministry of Education (2014R1A6A1031189).

References

Baccioli, A., Antonelli, M., Frigo, S., Desideri, U., Pasini, G., 2018. Small scale bio-LNG plant: Comparison of different biogas upgrading techniques. Appl. Energy 217, 328–335. https://doi.org/10.1016/j.apenergy.2018.02.149

Fan, Q.H., Li, H.Y., Jia, L.X., 2018. DESIGN AND ANALYSIS OF A SMALL-SCALE BIOGAS LIQUEFACTION CYCLE. https://doi.org/10.1063/1.2908468

Hashemi, S.E., Sarker, S., Lien, K.M., Schnell, S.K., Austbø, B., 2019. Cryogenic vs. absorption biogas upgrading in liquefied biomethane production – An energy efficiency analysis. Fuel 245, 294–304. https://doi.org/10.1016/j.fuel.2019.01.172

He, T., Liu, Z., Ju, Y., Parvez, A.M., 2019. A comprehensive optimization and comparison of modified single mixed refrigerant and parallel nitrogen expansion liquefaction process for small-scale mobile LNG plant. Energy 167, 1–12. https://doi.org/10.1016/j.energy.2018.10.169

International Energy Agency, 2020. Renewables Information - Overview (2020 Edition). IEA Stat. 497.

Krich, K., Augenstein, D., Batmale, J., Benemann, J., Rutledge, B., Salour, D., 2005. Storage and Transportation of Biogas and Biomethane. Biomethane from Dairy Waste A Sourceb. Prod. Use Renew. Nat. Gas Calif. 71–80.

Naquash, A., Qyyum, M.A., Haider, J., Lim, H., Lee, M., 2021. Renewable LNG production: Biogas upgrading through CO2 solidification integrated with single-loop mixed refrigerant biomethane liquefaction process. Energy Convers. Manag. 243, 114363. https://doi.org/10.1016/j.enconman.2021.114363

Pellegrini, L.A., De Guido, G., Langé, S., 2018. Biogas to liquefied biomethane via cryogenic upgrading technologies. Renew. Energy 124, 75–83. https://doi.org/10.1016/j.renene.2017.08.007

Peng, D., Robinson, D.B., 1929. A new equation of state. Nature 123, 507.

Spitoni, M., Pierantozzi, M., Comodi, G., Polonara, F., Arteconi, A., 2019. Theoretical evaluation and optimization of a cryogenic technology for carbon dioxide separation and methane liquefaction from biogas. J. Nat. Gas Sci. Eng. 62, 132–143. https://doi.org/10.1016/j.jngse.2018.12.007

Venkatarathnam, G., Timmerhaus, K.D., 2008. Cryogenic mixed refrigerant processes. Springer.

Yousef, A.M., Eldrainy, Y.A., El-Maghlany, W.M., Attia, A., 2017. Biogas upgrading process via low-temperature CO2 liquefaction and separation. J. Nat. Gas Sci. Eng. 45, 812–824. https://doi.org/10.1016/j.jngse.2017.07.001

Proceedings of the 14th International Symposium on Process Systems Engineering – PSE 2021+
June 19-23, 2022, Kyoto, Japan
http://dx.doi.org/10.1016/B978-0-323-85159-6.50126-3

Importance of interannual renewable energy variation in the design of green ammonia plants

Nicholas Salmon[a] and René Bañares-Alcántara[a*]

[a]*Department of Engineering, University of Oxford, Parks Road, Oxford, OX1 3PJ, UK*
**rene.banares@eng.ox.ac.uk*

Abstract

Green hydrogen and ammonia are critical technologies in our decarbonisation toolkit, but at present remain more expensive than traditional energy vectors. In order to increase their competitiveness with respect to fossil fuels, many authors have optimised production systems based on hourly solar and wind profiles and a range of technologies to maximise production and minimise costs. This optimisation problem, however, is enormous in scale: it requires consideration of a large number of possible production sites and their performance over many years. Failure to consider both spatial and temporal variation in green ammonia production costs may exclude excellent locations, or include sites that are unreliable due to interannual variation. In this work, we examine three techniques which can reduce the complexity of input data: time aggregation, hierarchical clustering, and K-means clustering. We compare the suitability of each of these approaches based on the extent to which they accelerate the solution of a green ammonia plant design optimisation problem, and the error between the simplified and actual solutions to the problem. Using these simplification approaches, we demonstrate the importance of considering interannual variation in green ammonia plant design.

Keywords: Data Clustering, MILP Optimisation, Green ammonia production, Renewable energy storage

1. Introduction

The decarbonisation of national power grids poses new energy storage challenges to provide reliable power during periods of high demand, or when renewable energy availability is low. While a range of technologies can be deployed on a very large scale for storage on an hours-days timescale (e.g. demand response, battery to grid, highly interconnected electrical grids with geographical diversity of energy sources), fewer technologies are available for storage on a months-years timescale.

Storage on a months-years timescale is necessary to provide sufficient storage (i) to meet seasonal peaks in energy usage, and (ii) to account for interannual variation in renewable energy availability. In the UK, for instance, the energy shortage at the start of autumn 2021 was exacerbated by a long-term wind-drought, the scale of which had not been observed since the early 1960s (Ambrose 2021); the frequency of such wind droughts is forecast to increase with climate change (Dawkins 2019).

Green ammonia is a promising solution for storage over large timescales. Compared to liquid hydrogen, it can be stored cheaply, and with much lower boil-off. Unlike gaseous hydrogen stored in salt caverns, it has much higher density, allowing import via ship. Recent publications have optimised the cost of green ammonia production and have demonstrated its cost is rapidly falling, and will soon be competitive with other technologies (Nayak-Luke and Bañares-Alcántara 2020; Fasihi et al. 2021).

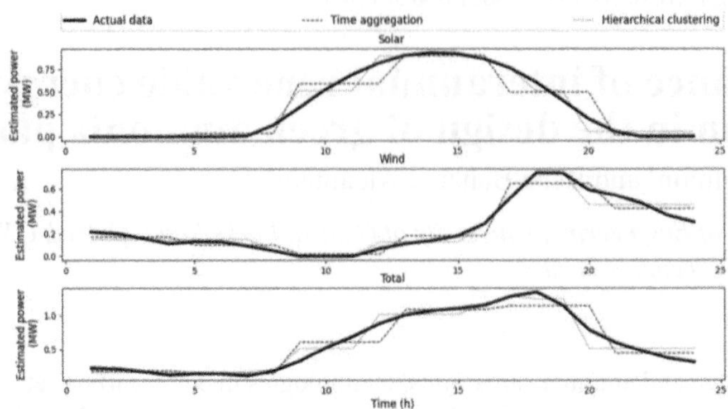

Figure 1 - Comparison of time aggregation and hierarchical clustering

However, the optimisation of green ammonia plants is computationally intensive, forcing researchers to either consider a comparatively small number of locations (Nayak-Luke and Bañares-Alcántara 2020), or to use only one year of weather data for plant design (Fasihi et al. 2021). Further complications emerge if other energy sources (e.g. electricity grids or hydro/nuclear power) are considered. Given the interannual weather variation described above, and the intended use of ammonia to store energy between years, larger volumes of weather data need to be processed to develop a robust ammonia economy.

This work explores three data clustering approaches which reduce the volume of weather data. It demonstrates that it is possible to significantly accelerate calculation without sacrificing accuracy. Several applications of accelerated calculation are then discussed.

2. Methodology

Green ammonia production uses renewable energy (from wind and/or solar plants) to power three core units: a water electrolyser to make hydrogen, an air separation unit to make nitrogen, and a Haber-Bosch loop which synthesises them into ammonia. Since it operates at high temperatures and pressures, the Haber-Bosch process requires back-up storage of power and hydrogen to sustain production above minimum rates. Here, back-up power is supplied from batteries, or from a fuel cell which cannibalises some of the stored hydrogen. The model may also connect the plant to the electricity grid, from which it can buy and sell power (capped at 175 MW by the limits of grid connection).

Rigorous existing models for ammonia plant design use hourly weather data to size each piece of equipment, subject to material and energy balances and technical constraints on equipment, mostly related to the inflexibility of the ammonia plant. However, in other energy optimisation analyses, some data clustering techniques have been attempted.

The Balmorel energy systems model, a popular open-source application, uses time aggregation, whereby larger time steps are used to reduce the data size (Wiese et al. 2018). Palys and Daoutidis (Palys and Daoutidis 2020) modelled a grid-based energy system which included ammonia that used a hierarchical approach, in which the most similar input data points are iteratively clustered until the data is reduced in size by a pre-specified factor. Not all time steps are the same size using this approach, so the model affords them different weights to determine the impact of a time-step on ammonia production, and the levels in energy and mass storage equipment. Figure 1 shows the difference between these two techniques. The former is simpler for both the coder and the computer to implement; the latter captures more dynamic variation in weather with the same number of time steps.

A third approach in the literature simplifies the data using representative days (van der Heijde et al. 2019); one technique used by Gabrielli et al. (Gabrielli et al. 2018) for selecting such days is K-means clustering, which uses a principal component analysis to classify days into clusters, and then represents each day in the cluster by its medoid.

To compare these options (time-aggregation, hierarchical aggregation and K-means clustering), we define the simplification factor (*SF*), which is the ratio of the number datapoints in the raw hourly data to the number of datapoints in the clustered data; for instance, data using a two-hourly time-step would have $SF = 2$. The model has eleven variables defined at all time steps (nine for power flows between plant components, and one for each of the inventories of the battery/hydrogen storage), nine continuous variables for the size of each unit in the process, and a binary variable indicating if grid connection is used. Thus for a model considering n years of data, the total number of variables is:

$$\frac{11}{SF}(8760n) + 10 \tag{1}$$

For K-means clustering, the storage inventories cannot be represented by their cluster's medoid, since this will cause discontinuities where two consecutive days are not in the same cluster. Therefore for the K-means cases, the number of variables is:

$$\left(\frac{9}{SF} + 2\right)(8760n) + 10 \tag{2}$$

An 8-core desktop computer with an i7 processor and 16 GB of RAM was used to solve the model for 701 locations in Australia (spread in a grid pattern across the country). Only three cores were parallelised; if more cores were used, very large convergence times were observed as the computer hit RAM limits. The concurrent and barrier methods of the Gurobi optimisation solver were used for the root and node relaxations respectively; these settings were found to give the fastest solutions.

3. Results

3.1. Comparison of performance

Figure 2 compares the techniques at different simplification factors to results at a simplification factor of 1. Each point represents results at one location; if the points form 45° lines, this indicates good agreement between the simplified model and actual results.

Time aggregation and hierarchical clustering perform well at low simplification factors. Performance starts to degrade around a simplification factor of 12, because the diurnal variation of solar panels begins to be smoothed into a near constant supply of electricity, which will underestimate the amount of energy storage required. As expected, the performance of time aggregation degrades more quickly than hierarchical clustering. In general, both techniques tend to slightly underestimate the LCOA; this is because the smoothing inherent to reducing the size of the time data provides more reliable electricity and therefore reduces the need for batteries, hydrogen storage, or back-up grid power.

The performance of K-means clustering is very poor at all simplification factors. While other techniques exist by which representative days can be selected, it is unlikely that a different selection of medoids would radically change the poor performance of this approach. To some extent, the poor performance is caused by the long-term nature of ammonia plant design, meaning the representative day is too short a time frame over which to base plant design. For instance, plant operation may need to be different on two days with identical weather based on the inventories of the hydrogen storage and battery.

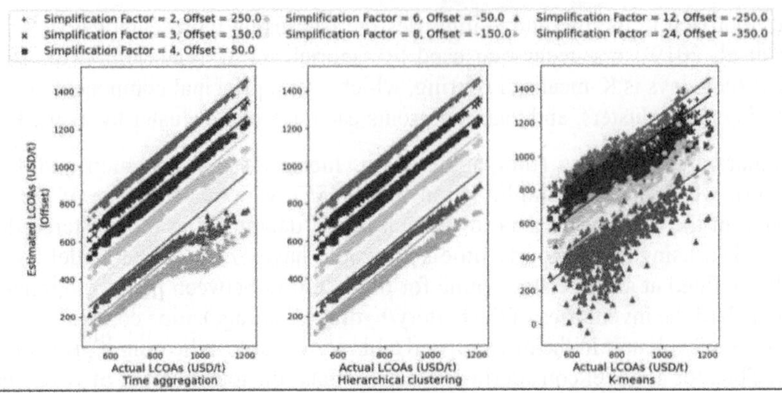

Figure 2 - x-y plots for estimated LCOA from simplified approaches compared to results from a one-hour time-step. Data are offset for readability; see legend. Each point represents a different location; offset x-y 45° lines are included for each series (a) - Left: Time aggregation. (b) - Centre: Hierarchical clustering. (c) - Right: K-means (Simplification Factor = 24 excluded for readability)

3.2. Comparison of speed

Figure 3 shows the relationship between the time taken for the model to converge in all of the 701 locations considered, and both the average and maximum error observed in the results compared to the result obtained using a one-hour time step.

Predictably, because of the results shown in Figure 2, the results for K-means clustering generate very high errors; additionally, they also take a long time to converge. This is because the dimensionality of the hydrogen and battery storage variables is not reduced by representative day clustering (since the model still needs to build a continuous storage profile). For the other two clustering techniques, higher simplification factors tend to result in shorter solution times and higher errors. In all cases, the error observed using the hierarchical clustering was lower than that observed using time aggregation at the same simplification factor, but the time required for convergence was greater.

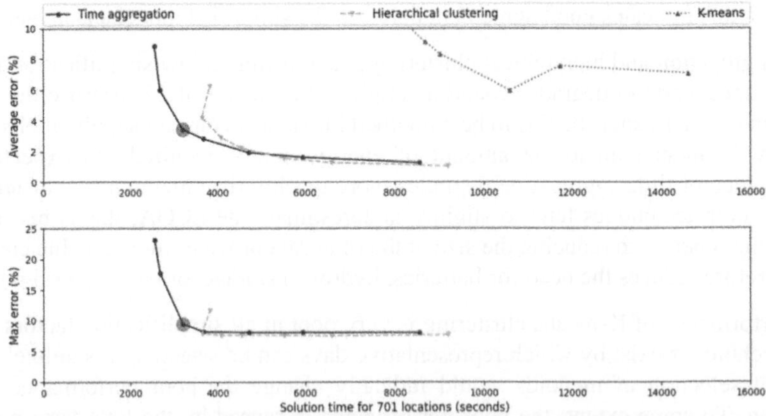

Figure 3 - Relationship between error and solution time. The highlighted marker is the option selected as optimal for further analysis. (a) – Top: Average error across all locations. (b) – Bottom: Maximum error across all locations; the axes in this subplot do not encompass K-means clustering due to the large errors observed with this method.

At low simplification factors, the majority of time taken for the model to converge is taken by the optimisation solver. However, as the simplification factor increases, the computational time required to simplify the data itself begins to increase, and the time required for the optimisation solver decreases. This limits the time taken for the model to converge to the time taken to perform the data clustering itself. Because the hierarchical clustering approach is more computationally challenging than time aggregation, this minimum limit on convergence time is higher; indeed, at the highest simplification used here (24), the model begins to take longer to converge than at the lower factor of 12.

The best option for further analysis will deliver a fast solution with an acceptably small error. The point selected is shown on Figure 3; it combines acceptable errors (~3.5% on average, 9.5% at most) with quick solution times (~3,500 s). More accurate results could have been obtained with a time penalty of ~ 20%, but the improvement is not large, particularly given the error implicit in the model due to input parameter estimation.

4. Historical Data Analysis

Green ammonia plants for energy storage need to operate under different conditions over a large time period (~30 years). Using time aggregation with a simplification factor of 8, the model was converged repeatedly using different starting years, and considering time periods of 1, 3, 5 and 10 years. Since long-term historical grid data is not available, grid connections were not allowed for these estimates. The LCOA results for a single representative location are plotted in Figure 4. They demonstrate that as more years of data are considered, the optimum value for the LCOA tends to converge around a single value; if only one year of data is used, there is a wide spread in the LCOA estimates.

Considering all locations for the cases where only one year of data was analysed, the average range between the minimum and maximum LCOAs estimated was 15% (substantially higher than the error introduced by clustering); in the worst case, it was more than a third of the total ammonia cost. When a larger number of years of data are considered, the results are much more stable over different time periods. Using ten years of input data, the average range between the minimum and maximum cases across all locations was only 2%, and the largest error observed was only 6%.

If the long term average LCOA is taken from the cases where a single year of data is used, the cheapest location for ammonia production is located near in central Western Australia. However, this site only has the cheapest production cost in ten of thirty years of individual data; in one poorly performing year, it was the 50th ranked site of the 701 considered.

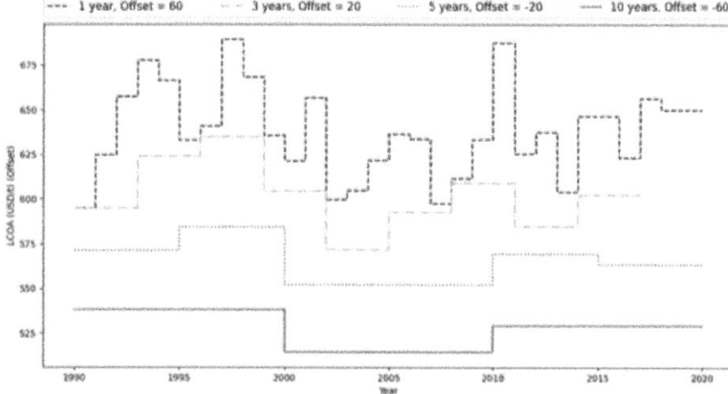

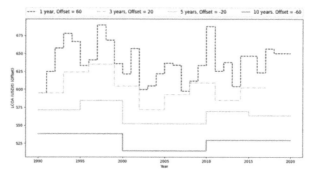

Figure 4 - Optimum LCOA for a given location in South Australia using different input weather data; data are offset from each other to improve readability.

There is a weak relationship between the number of years of data used for the optimization and its outcome. In 677 of the 701 cases considered, there was a positive correlation between the number of years of data considered and the LCOA; i.e. considering more years of data slightly increases the LCOA. Although this relationship is small (on average, the LCOA estimated increases by 10 USD/t when comparing average results from ten individual years to the results from one ten-year period), it does suggest that an engineering plant designed over a single year alone will be underdesigned.

5. Conclusions

To play a robust role as an energy storage medium on a months-years timescale, green ammonia plants must consider large time periods in system design. This research analysed three techniques to reduce the size of large weather datasets to enable plant design to be optimised rapidly over large time scales and in many locations.

The results demonstrate that a 'representative day' approach (e.g. K-means clustering) for data size reduction is not suitable for plant design; too much relevant data is excluded with little benefit to convergence time. However, both time aggregation and hierarchical clustering accelerate convergence while providing meaningful results. Since hierarchical clustering itself is slow, time aggregation provided the optimum balance of speed and accuracy for this work, but hierarchical clustering may be better suited for other problems.

Using the time aggregation approach, ammonia plant designs were considered for a range of different years of data. They demonstrated that considering only a single year of data may undersize ammonia plants, and may fail to identify the optimum production location.

The accelerated solutions enabled by time aggregation could facilitate significant further research. Two options would include (a) Monte-Carlo simulation of green ammonia plant design given the significant unknowns surrounding equipment cost and performance, and (b) consideration of climate forecasting (which returns a large array of possible outcomes) in future-proofing ammonia plant designs against various possible scenarios.

References

J. Ambrose, 2021, 'What caused the UK's energy crisis?', *The Guardian*.

L. Dawkins, 2019, 'Weather and Climate Related Sensitivities and Risks in a Highly Renewable UK Energy System: A Literature Review', Met Office, Accessed May 2021. https://nic.org.uk/app/uploads/MetOffice_NIC_LiteratureReview_2019.pdf.

M. Fasihi, R. Weiss, J. Savolainen, and C. Breyer, 2021, 'Global potential of green ammonia based on hybrid PV-wind power plants', *Applied Energy*, 294: 116170.

P. Gabrielli, M. Gazzani, E. Martelli, and M. Mazzotti, 2018, 'Optimal design of multi-energy systems with seasonal storage', *Applied Energy*, 219: 408-24.

R. Nayak-Luke, and R. Bañares-Alcántara, 2020, 'Techno-economic viability of islanded green ammonia as a carbon-free energy vector and as a substitute for conventional production', *Energy & Environmental Science*, 13: 2957-66.

M.J. Palys, and P. Daoutidis, 2020, 'Using hydrogen and ammonia for renewable energy storage: A geographically comprehensive techno-economic study', *Computers & Chemical Engineering*, 136.

B. van der Heijde, A. Vandermeulen, R. Salenbien, and L.Helsen, 2019, 'Representative days selection for district energy system optimisation: a solar district heating system with seasonal storage', *Applied Energy*, 248: 79-94.

F. Wiese, R. Bramstoft, H. Koduvere, A.P. Alonso, O. Balyk, J.G. Kirkerud, A. G. Tveten, T.F. Bolkesjø, M. Münster, and H. Ravn, 2018, 'Balmorel open source energy system model', *Energy Strategy Reviews*, 20: 26-34.

Proceedings of the 14th International Symposium on Process Systems Engineering – PSE 2021+
June 19-23, 2022, Kyoto, Japan
http://dx.doi.org/10.1016/B978-0-323-85159-6.50127-5

Integrating Carbon Negative Technologies in Industrial Clusters

Elizabeth J. Abraham, Dhabia M. Al-Mohannadi*, Patrick Linke

Department of Chemical Engineering, Texas A&M University at Qatar, Education City, PO Box 23874, Doha, Qatar
dhabia.al-mohannadi@qatar.tamu.edu

Abstract

Negative emission technologies (NETs) are an emerging innovation essential for tackling the climate crisis since decarbonization on its own will no longer suffice. While these technologies are crucial in limiting temperature rise by the end of the century, they bring their own set of unique feasibility and efficiency challenges. An innovative approach to overcoming these barriers is the development of eco-industrial parks (EIPs) or clusters, which can integrate several processes and technologies to achieve economic, environmental, and social benefits collectively. Furthermore, through the multiple interactions that can arise from exchanging resources and technical knowledge in these systems, technology spill overs can occur, allowing these parks to serve as a hub for process innovation. Thus, this work explores the integration of NETs into industrial clusters that can simultaneously exchange multiple resources over time. The multi-period model optimized network configurations for maximum net present value and determined park design across time. Two NETs, bioenergy with carbon capture and storage (BECCS) and direct air carbon capture and storage (DACCS), were integrated into a cluster to provide the carbon dioxide needed for methanol production, produced through either carbon hydrogenation or electrolysis. The optimization revealed that electrolysis required improved energy efficiency to compete with hydrogenation. Furthermore, significant reductions in capital costs are necessary for the NETs to become active in EIPs.

Keywords: Multi-period, Resource integration, Negative emission technologies, Industrial parks, Optimization

1. Introduction

Climate change mitigation is a daunting challenge whose slow progress now requires the reduction of greenhouse gases (GHGs) and their removal from the atmosphere to limit global warming temperature rise to less than 2 °C above pre-industrial levels (Gasser et al., 2015). While several strategies and technologies can effectively reduce GHGs, negative emissions technologies (NETs) that offset positive emissions have only begun to gain traction. To lower their atmospheric concentrations, NETs remove GHGs, particularly carbon dioxide (CO_2), from the atmosphere through various existing or proposed techniques and subsequently store them (McLaren, 2012). The extensive research on NETs currently explores different technologies, their feasibility, and comparative performance with other technologies, where two NETs, bioenergy with carbon capture and storage (BECCS) and direct air carbon capture and storage (DACCS) make up a significant portion of this literature. BECCS utilizes biomass or plant material that absorbs atmospheric CO_2 as it grows to produce bioenergy and then captures and stores any emissions released during production in geological formations (IPCC, 2018).

DACCS, on the other hand, directly extracts CO_2 from the atmosphere, typically using solid sorbents or basic aqueous solutions as the capture media, before storing them underground (Keith et al., 2018). While both NETs are in early commercialization stages, they encompass many uncertainties. Geological storage is a fundamental aspect of NETs, which though seemingly feasible at present, entails high costs and uncertainties over long-term storage (Norhasyima and Mahlia, 2018). In these scenarios, there is a proclivity to utilize and valorize the CO_2 captured (Norhasyima and Mahlia, 2018), which calls for the integration of NETs with carbon capture utilization and storage (CCUS), as shown by Tan et al. (2021) in carbon management networks integrated with enhanced weathering and biochar application.

Systematic methods that synthesize CCUS strategies by considering various CO_2 sources and sinks include optimization methods (Al-Mohannadi et al., 2016), graphical source-sink allocation approaches (Lameh et al., 2020), and others like the Mini-MAC approach that uses marginal abatement costs (Lameh et al., 2021). While these approaches focus on CO_2 as the primary material of interest, most utilization technologies require multiple material and energy resources. The recent resource integration approach developed by Ahmed et al. (2020) considers both material and energy resources simultaneously to design industrial clusters or eco-industrial parks (EIPs). This work uses a multi-period model based on this novel approach to identify challenges in integrating NETs and CCUS in clusters that can capture emissions from the atmosphere and itself.

2. Approach

The multi-period resource integration approach described in this work adopts the method proposed by Ahmed et al. (2020) to optimize industrial clusters while simultaneously considering all material and energy flows. The extension allows for assessing the evolution of such clusters over a time horizon, where each process considered, including the NETs, have a set of associated resources. The optimization is solved as a mixed-integer linear program (MILP) that determines the existence and capacities of processes along with the flow of its associated resources throughout the cluster in each period considered. The net present value (NPV) of the cluster, which accounts for the time value of money, is maximized as the objective function in this work as given by Eq. (1):

$$NPV_{EIP} = \sum_{Period} \frac{\sum_{Process} Revenue - Operating\ Cost - Capital\ Cost}{(1 + Discount\ Rate)^{Number\ of\ periods\ considered}} \tag{1}$$

The proposed model has several parameters that govern resource and cash flows throughout the cluster, such as process-specific cost and performance parameters, resource line specifications, resource prices, inflation rates, and NPV discount rates. Simply put, each process has specific capital and operating cost parameters, in addition to specific mass and energy balance parameters that define the flow of resources to and from it. These resources flow in the cluster through resource lines characterized by a unique set of specifications (temperature, pressure, quality, etc.). Thus, processes obtain input resources from certain resource lines and send output resources to their corresponding resource lines. In this way, resource lines can be associated with multiple processes with the same resource specifications, thereby facilitating resource integration. Variables in this model include process capacities and flows of fresh feed and output resources in each period considered. Furthermore, quality and inequality constraints are placed on the resource line balances and variables respectively to ensure non-negative values, while binaries implement logical decisions within the model. The optimization problem has been solved using LINDO "What'sBest!16.0.2.6" in Microsoft Excel 2019.

3. Illustrative example

3.1. Process data

The multi-period model is to design an industrial cluster that must integrate two NETs, bioenergy (BEC) and direct air (DAC) carbon captures, to capture the CO_2 required to produce 500,000 tons per period (tpp) of methanol (CH_3OH). For this, the cluster considers two innovative methanol production routes, namely, the emerging hydrogenation (CHR) route and the novel infeasible CO_2 electrolysis (CEM) route. The CHR process requires hydrogen (H_2), provided from a steam methane reformer (SMR) or water electrolyzer (WSE), in addition to CO_2, while the CER only requires CO_2. Power requirements for the cluster are met by a natural gas power plant (NGP) and photovoltaic system (PV). The CHR, SMR and NGP processes each have their own carbon capture units with a 90% capture efficiency, while a sequestration unit (SQU) stores any unutilized CO_2. Lastly, an air separation unit (ASU) supplies the DAC's oxygen (O_2) demand. Data on process specifics, namely, reference products, CAPEX parameters, and maximum capacities, are listed in Table 1, where the maximum capacity indicates the maximum allowable capacity of a process across the periods considered.

Table 1: Process reference products, CAPEX parameters and operational capacities

Resource	Reference Product (RP Unit)	CAPEX Parameter ($/RP Unit)	Maximum Capacity (RP Unit per period)
ASU	O_2 (t)	20.30	80,000
BEC	CO_2 (t)	34.00	3,000,000
CER	CH_3OH (t)	13.03	500,000
DAC	CO_2 (t)	102.06	1,000,000
CHR	CH_3OH (t)	11.64	500,000
CHR Capture	CO_2 (t)	6.98	60,000
NGP	Electricity (kWh)	10.00	20,000,000,000
NGP Capture	CO_2 (t)	12.49	750,000,000
PV	Electricity (kWh)	20.00	20,000,000,000
SQU	CO_2 (t)	9.02	1,250,000
SMR	H_2 (t)	13.09	125,000
SMR Capture	CO_2 (t)	1.08	1,250,000
WSE	H_2 (t)	623.20	125,000

The only inputs to the cluster are air, biomass, CO_2, natural gas, water, additives for DAC, and other utilities besides power. The given cluster was analyzed across three periods, where each period spans five years. The operational capacities and capital cost or CAPEX parameters remain fixed across all periods for all processes except BEC and DAC, whose capacities increase with their expected increase in deployment capacities. Specifically, the capture capacities of BEC increases from 1,000,000 tpp to 3,000,000 tpp, while that of DAC increases from 20,000 tpp to 1,000,000 tpp across the periods considered. Prices and process parameters for the BEC, CER, DAC, NGPP and SMR can be found in Table 2, while those for all other processes are obtained from Abraham et al. (2021). The NET parameters in Table 2 were acquired from Bhave et al. (2017) and Keith et al. (2018), while data for the CER, NGPP and SMR processes were found in Jouny et al. (2018), Biliyok and Yeung (2013), and Spath and Mann (2001) respectively.

Table 2: Process parameters (in Unit/RP Unit) and resource prices in ($/Unit)

Resource (Unit)	Price	BEC	CER	DAC	NGPP	SMR
Air (t)	-	-4.98	-	-1467.84	-0.01	-
BEC emissions (t)	-	4.72	-	-	-	-
Biomass (t)	60	-0.74	-	-	-	-
Calcium carbonate (t)	330	-	-	-0.02	-	-
Carbon dioxide (t)	40	1.00	-0.73	1.00	-	-
Hydrogen (t)	900	-	0.02	-	-	1.00
Methanol (t)	400	-	1.00	-	-	-
Natural Gas (t)	136	-	-	-0.12	-	-2.91
NGPP emissions (t)	-	-	-	-	0.01	-
Oxygen (t)	-	-	0.39	-0.35	-	-
Slurry (t)	-	-	-	-5.30	-	-
SMR emissions (t)	-	-	-	-	-	10.73
Treated air (t)	-	-	-	1474	-	-
Wastes (t)	-	-	-	0.70	-	0.20
Waste water (t)	-	-	-	21.58	-	-
Water (t)	0.02	-	-0.68	-3.11	-	-14.10
Cooling water (t)	0.03	-	-	-3.25	-0.11	-
Electricity (kWh)	-	574	-11532	-366	1.00	-316
MP Steam (t)	-	-	-	-	-	5.08
Process water (t)	0.02	-	-	-20.36	-	-4.80

3.2. Results

For illustrative purposes, the breakthroughs needed in process parameters were analyzed at inflation and discount rates of 10% and 5%, respectively. Under various scenarios, the optimization revealed different designs to meet methanol production demands over time. The activated processes in each scenario and period are shown in Figure 1.

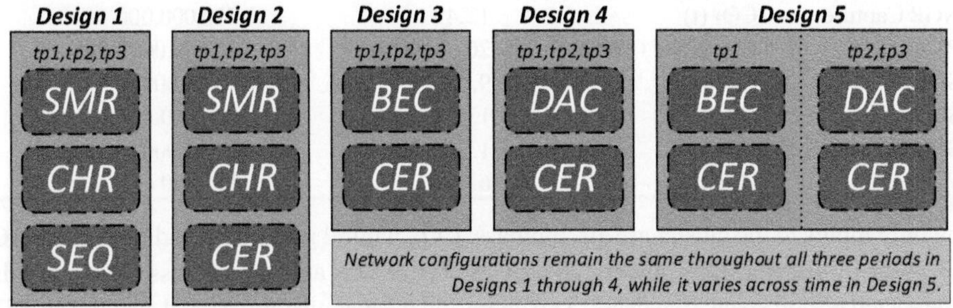

Figure 1: Activated processes for the designs analyzed

The optimization identifies methanol production via hydrogenation or CHR, where H_2 is provided by SMR and CO_2 by SMR capture, to be most profitable across time. Sequestration is a fundamental part of this design scenario, called D1, in storing the CO_2 captured from the CHR and SMR processes. Thus, when sequestration is unavailable, the cluster configuration changes to a new design, D2. Here, instead of being sequestered, the CO_2 captured from SMR unused in CHR, and the CO_2 captured from CHR itself are utilized in the CER or carbon electrolysis process. It is clear from these two cases, where the cluster design remains fixed across all periods considered, that the NETs are not an attractive CO_2 source, even as both methanol production routes activate.

To bring the NETs online, solely improving only their prospects, was thus not sufficient due to the high costs of the auxiliary processes supporting them. Of the two production routes, CER has a significantly higher power demand than CHR, considering even the additional units CHR must activate for H_2 production, carbon capture, and sequestration. Furthermore, with WSE being an expensive process, H_2 will continue to come from SMR, whose emissions, along with those from CHR, will always need to be captured and sequestered. With sequestration constrained, these captured emissions cannot leave the cluster and must be utilized in the CER process. In this way, methanol production via both routes prevents the activation of the NETs since there is no need to obtain CO_2 from the atmosphere as the cluster itself generates the required amount. Therefore, the CER process must become the sole methanol production route to integrate the NETs into the cluster, and to do so, the CER process requires a 72% reduction in its power requirement.

With the power efficiency of CER improved, design scenarios 3 and 4 aimed to activate either of the NETs as the sole source of CO_2. BEC met the CO_2 demand for all three periods with a 98% capital cost reduction in design D3. On the other hand, even with a 90% reduction in capital costs, DAC only fully supplied the second and third periods in design D4. DAC partially met the demands of the first period, however, due to its capacity limits, the cluster's CO_2 feed met the rest. When the model integrated both NETs, supplies of the first period were met by BEC, while DAC covered the remaining periods as in design D5. The capacity limitations of DAC prevent its activation in the first period of D5; however, in later periods when both NETs can meet the CO_2 demand, the DAC is more feasible due to its lower operating costs. The capacities across all three periods for each of the designs are summarized in Table 3.

Table 3: Cumulative process capacities across all periods for network configurations

Network	CHR ($t\ CH_3OH$)	CER ($t\ CH_3OH$)	BEC ($t\ CO_2$)	DAC ($t\ CO_2$)	NPV (Million $)
N1	1,500,000	-	-	-	734
N2	1,163,185	336,815	-	-	696
N3	-	1,500,000	1,092,275	-	772
N4	-	1,500,000	-	748,183	773
N5	-	1,500,000	364,092	728,184	774

To achieve such significant capital reductions is a challenge that requires a thorough understanding of the technology and parameters that define its efficiency such as selectivity and yield. Understanding these parameters will aid in identifying the pathways by which these cost reductions can be achieved. Thus, by incorporating these parameters into the multi-period model, it can therefore, determine the learning curves that can make these technologies competitive (Feriolia et al., 2009).

4. Conclusion

EIPs are an opportune means to integrate NETs with CCUS to derive greater collective benefits. The feasibility of integrating these technologies in EIPs was analyzed from a holistic perspective in terms of cash and resource flows as illustrated through the multi-period resource integration described here. The optimization determined that CER needs more energy efficiency, while both BEC and DAC require a reduction in capital costs to be deployed successfully. Thus, through the multi-period analysis, the proposed approach can analyze the deployment of emerging technologies and their varying parameters simultaneously considering operations in other periods during optimization, and without performing numerous iterations. Furthermore, the model can be extended to incorporate uncertainties of different parameters to create more resilient and sustainable systems.

References

E.J. Abraham, F. Ramadan, D.M. Al-Mohannadi, 2021, Synthesis of Sustainable Carbon Negative Eco-Industrial Parks, Frontiers in Energy Research, 9, 345.

D.M. Al-Mohannadi, P. Linke, 2016, On The Systematic Carbon Integration of Industrial Parks for Climate Footprint Reduction, Journal of Cleaner Production, 112, 5, 4053-4064.

R. Ahmed, S. Shehab, D.M. Al-Mohannadi, P. Linke, 2020, Synthesis of Integrated Processing Clusters, Chemical Engineering Science, 221, 115922.

A. Bhave, R.H.S. Taylor, P. Fennell, W.R. Livingston, N. Shah, N. Mac Dowell, J. Dennis, M. Kraft, M. Pourkashanian, M. Insa, J. Jones, N. Burdett, A. Bauen, C. Beal, A. Smallbone, J. Akroyd, 2017, Screening and Techno-economic Assessment of Biomass-Based Power Generation with CCS Technologies to Meet 2050 CO_2 Targets, Applied Energy, 190, 481–489.

C. Biliyok, H. Yeung, 2013, International Journal of Greenhouse Gas Control, 19, 396–405.

F. Feriolia, K. Schoots, B.C.C. van der Zwaanab, 2009, Use and Limitations of Learning Curves for Energy Technology Policy: A Component-learning Hypothesis, Energy Policy, 37, 7, 2525-2535.

T. Gasser, C. Guivarch, K. Tachiiri, C.D. Jones, P. Ciais, 2015, Negative Emissions Physically Needed to Keep Global Warming Below 2 °C, Nature Communications, 6, 1, 1–7.

IPCC, 2018, Global Warming of 1.5 °C.

M. Jouny, W. Luc, F. Jiao, 2018, General Techno-Economic Analysis of CO_2 Electrolysis Systems, Industrial and Engineering Chemistry Research, 57, 6, 2165–2177.

D.W. Keith, G. Holmes, D. St. Angelo, K. Heidel, 2018, A Process for Capturing CO_2 from the Atmosphere, Joule, 2, 8, 1573–1594.

M. Lameh, D.M. Al-Mohannadi, P. Linke, 2020, Graphical Analysis of CO_2 Emissions Reduction Strategies, Cleaner Engineering and Technology, 1, 100023.

M. Lameh, D.M. Al-Mohannadi, P. Linke, 2021, Minimum Marginal Abatement Cost Curves (Mini-MAC) for CO_2 Emissions Reduction Planning, Clean Technologies and Environmental Policy, https://doi.org/10.1007/s10098-021-02095-y

D. McLaren, 2012, A Comparative Global Assessment of Potential Negative Emissions Technologies, Process Safety and Environmental Protection, 90, 489–500.

R.S. Norhasyima, T.M.I. Mahlia, 2018, Advances in CO_2 Utilization Technology: A Patent Landscape Review, Journal of CO2 Utilization, 26, 323–335.

P.L. Spath, M.K. Mann, 2001, Life Cycle Assessment of Hydrogen Production via Natural Gas Steam Reforming.

R.R. Tan, K.B. Aviso, S. Bandyopadhyay, 2021, Pinch-Based Planning of Terrestrial Carbon Management Networks, Cleaner Engineering and Technology, 4, 100141.

Proceedings of the 14th International Symposium on Process Systems Engineering – PSE 2021+
June 19-23, 2022, Kyoto, Japan
http://dx.doi.org/10.1016/B978-0-323-85159-6.50128-7

Flexibility analysis of chemical processes considering overlaying uncertainty sources

Christian Langner[a,*], Elin Svensson[b], Stavros Papadokonstantakis[c], Simon Harvey[a]

[a] *Chalmers University of Technology, Gothenburg, Sweden*
[b] *CIT Industriell Energi AB, Gothenburg, Sweden*
[c] *TU Wien, Vienna, Austria*
* *christian.langner@chalmers.se*

Abstract

Chemical processes are often subject to uncertainty. Consequently, the evaluation of the flexibility of a process with respect to variations in inlet conditions is vital to identify bottlenecks in current process flowsheets or new flowsheet design proposals. The flexibility index is a well-established concept to perform flexibility analysis of chemical processes. In this paper, we propose novel reformulations of the flexibility index problem to account for overlaying uncertainty sources which interfere with each other. The aim of the paper is to identify and define overlaying uncertainty sources and to overcome shortcomings of existing approaches when calculating the flexibility index in such situations.

Keywords: Flexibility Analysis, Flexibility Index, Overlaying Uncertainty, Types of Uncertainty, Chemical Process Design.

1. Introduction

Flexibility analysis of chemical processes has been investigated since the 1980s when the flexibility index was introduced by Swaney and Grossmann (1985). Although established in the 1980s, the mathematical formulation of the flexibility index has also been applied in recent publications (e.g., da Silva et al. 2021). The flexibility index is defined as the ratio between the maximum feasible variation range (defined by operational constraints) and the expected variation range. Therefore, feasibility is guaranteed if the flexibility index is larger than or equal to 1.

Several extensions and reformulations have been suggested in literature to adapt the original formulation by Swaney and Grossmann (1985) to specific applications. Pulsipher and Zavala (2018) suggested to incorporate multivariate Gaussian random variables in the flexibility index problem to define expected variation ranges with ellipsoidal shape (compared to the hyperrectangular shape used traditionally) in order to capture correlations. In addition, Langner et al. (2021) suggested to study the geometrical shape of the distribution of operating points to explicitly define the expected variation range using linear boundary functions. Ochoa and Grossmann (2020) extended the original flexibility index problem to account also for uncertain parameters which cannot be measured and therefore cannot be subject to control actions during operation.

Traditionally, when formulating the flexibility index problem, the expected variation range is formulated for each uncertain parameter by accounting for the largest positive and/or negative deviation from a nominal operating point which has been observed (retrofit problem) or which is expected (greenfield problem) over a specific timeframe (e.g., lifetime of a plant). Consequently, the expected variation range is independent of time.

However, this is problematic in the case when sources of uncertainty interfere with each other, e.g., when the flexibility with respect to short-term operational disturbances is affected by an uncertain singular event (see e.g., Marton et al. 2021). Examples of such singular/rare events can be a switch in feedstock, a change of operational parameters required to comply with new emission legislation and/or a change in the production rate. All such events have in common that they can have a significant impact on the nominal operating conditions, i.e., the nominal operating point is likely to vary temporarily or even change permanently. On the other hand, it is very unlikely that short-term operational disturbances will disappear when the nominal operating point is subject to uncertainty. Consequently, in such cases we face overlaying sources of uncertainty which interfere with each other, meaning these singular/rare events divide the above-mentioned timeframe into intervals which need to be accounted for in the flexibility index problem.

This paper discusses possible approaches to account for overlaying uncertainty sources in the flexibility index problem and present the necessary reformulations of the flexibility index problem as originally reported by Swaney and Grossmann (1985).

2. Flexibility index and suggested reformulations

The formulation of the flexibility index problem reported by Swaney and Grossmann (1985) is given in Eq. (1) where *d* is the vector of design variables, *z* relates to the control variables, and the varying inlet conditions or uncertain parameters are denoted by θ.

$$\begin{aligned} FI &= \max \delta \\ s.t.\ & \max_{\theta \in T(\delta)} \min_{z} \max_{j \in J} f_j(d, z, \theta) \leq 0 \\ & T(\delta) = \{\theta_i | \theta_{i,N} - \delta\Delta\theta_i^- \leq \theta_i \leq \theta_{i,N} + \delta\Delta\theta_i^+\} \,\forall\, \theta_i \in \theta \\ & \delta \geq 0 \end{aligned} \tag{1}$$

The maximum feasible variation range is described by $T(\delta)$ which states that if $\delta = 1$, the maximum feasible and the expected variation range are similar. Hereafter, we include overlaying uncertainty sources (which interfere with each other) in the original formulation of the flexibility index (see Eq. (1)) and present the shortcomings. We then derive reformulations to the original flexibility index problem to overcome these shortcomings. For readability, the uncertainty sources are classified as shown in Table 1.

Table 1: Different classes of uncertainty based on the source or origin of the uncertainty

Conventional operational disturbances (included in the original flexibility index formulation, see Eq. (1))	Uncertainty class A
"Other" sources of uncertainty (i.e., nominal operating point varies or changes)	Uncertainty class B

2.1. Original flexibility index formulation and overlaying uncertainty sources

In line with the original formulation of the flexibility index problem, it may be intuitive to include (additional) uncertainty sources (of any kind and nature) in a similar fashion to that proposed for uncertainty class A by Swaney and Grossmann (1985). Thus, the vector

θ would represent all uncertain parameters (of class A and class B: $\theta_{class\ A}$ and $\theta_{class\ B}$) and $T(\delta)$ is formulated as in Eq. (1). This approach yields a single scalar which expresses the maximum feasible variation/change for each uncertain parameter in θ. Note that a physical uncertain parameter (e.g., an uncertain temperature) may be present in both sets, $\theta_{class\ A}$ and $\theta_{class\ B}$, while the expected variation range or change ($\Delta\theta^-$ and $\Delta\theta^+$) differs for each class. However, with such an approach it is not possible to gain information on the feasibility of operational short-term disturbances (class A) when the nominal operating point varies or changes (class B) since the uncertainty sources are analyzed independently of each other. Such information is, however, vital in design and planning processes and to overcome this problem, Eq. (1) needs to be formulated for different discrete nominal points (θ_N) and the resulting formulations can then be solved in an iterative scheme. This iterative scheme can be impractical and time-consuming; thus, we suggest reformulating Eq. (1).

2.2. Suggested reformulation of the flexibility index problem

In our approach, we aim to find the maximum feasible variation/change for uncertain parameters of class B which ensures that a pre-defined flexibility target of the uncertain parameters of class A (operational short-term disturbances) is feasible, e.g., the expected variations of the uncertain parameters of class A are exactly feasible. Thus, we distinguish between the two uncertainty classes and suggest reformulating Eq. (1) to Eq. (2).

$$
\begin{aligned}
&FI = \max \delta_B \\
&s.t.\ \max_{\theta \in T(\delta_A,\delta_B)} \min_{z} \max_{j \in J} f_j(d, z, \theta_{class\ A}, \theta_{class\ B}) \leq 0 \\
&T(\delta_A, \delta_B) = \begin{cases} \{\theta_i | \theta_{i,N} - \delta_A \Delta\theta_i^- \leq \theta_i \leq \theta_{i,N} + \delta_A \Delta\theta_i^+\}\ \forall\, \theta_i \in \theta_{class\ A} \\ \left.\begin{array}{l} \{\theta_k | \zeta_k - \delta_A \Delta\theta_{k,A}^- \leq \theta_k \leq \zeta_k + \delta_A \Delta\theta_{k,A}^+\} \\ \{\theta_k | \theta_{k,N} - \delta_B \Delta\theta_{k,B}^- \leq \zeta_k \leq \theta_{k,N} + \delta_B \Delta\theta_{k,B}^+\} \end{array}\right\} \forall\, \theta_k \in \theta_{class\ B} \end{cases} \\
&\delta_A = specified\ target, \delta_B \geq 0
\end{aligned}
\tag{2}
$$

Eq. (2) includes several reformulations compared to Eq. (1). When distinguishing between uncertain parameters of class A and of class B, the maximum feasible variation/change for each class is respected individually by defining a scalar δ for each class (δ_A, δ_B). As aforementioned, we suggest searching for the maximum feasible variation/change for uncertain parameters of class B which allows for a pre-defined flexibility target of the uncertain parameters of class A. Consequently, the constraint $\delta_A = specified\ target$ is included in Eq. (2) while searching for the maximum value of δ_B is formulated as the objective function. Furthermore, the uncertainty of the nominal value(s) for the uncertain parameters of class B is respected by defining the variables $\zeta_k\ \forall\, \theta_k \in \theta_{class\ B}$. Consequently, the first and the second line in $T(\delta_A, \delta_B)$ guarantee that expected short-term disturbances remain feasible when the nominal operating point varies or changes. The maximum feasible variation/change of the nominal operating point is found by including the third line in $T(\delta_A, \delta_B)$.

For solving Eq. (2), we suggest using the active constraint strategy proposed for solving Eq. (1) by Grossmann and Floudas (1987). This requires that an upper bound for the operational flexibility target value is pre-defined ($\delta_A = specified\ target$). This upper bound can be obtained in a first step by considering only the uncertain parameters of class A and thus formulating and solving Eq. (1). In a second step, the uncertain parameters of class B are added, and Eq. (2) can be formulated and solved.

If the expected variation range of operational uncertainty (class A) is itself expected to change (when the nominal operating point varies/changes), $\Delta\theta_{k,A}^{-}$ and $\Delta\theta_{k,A}^{+}$ can be defined as functions depending on the nominal operating point ζ_k (e.g., if the expected variation range of short-term disturbances is expected to be a percentual share of the nominal operating point, such as ± 5%).

3. Illustrative Example

Consider a process with a feasible operating region that can be described by a set of given constraints (Eq. (3a) to (3f)) where θ_1 and θ_2 correspond to two uncertain parameters and x_1 denotes an additional state variable.

$$\theta_1 - 2x_1 = 0 \tag{3a}$$
$$2x_1 - \left(67 - \frac{2}{3} * \theta_2\right) \leq 0 \tag{3b}$$
$$10 - 0.25\theta_2 - \theta_1 \leq 0 \tag{3c}$$
$$\theta_1 - (0.5\theta_2 + 5) \leq 0 \tag{3d}$$
$$2.5 + 0.05\theta_2 - 2x_1 \leq 0 \tag{3e}$$
$$\theta_1 - (22.5 - 0.05\theta_2) \leq 0 \tag{3f}$$

Let us further assume a nominal point $(\theta_{1,N}, \theta_{2,N}) = (12, 65)$ and due to operational disturbances, θ_1 and θ_2 are expected to vary in the range of (±4, ±8). Following the suggested two-step solution algorithm, Eq. (1) is formulated and solved for the illustrative example, and the flexibility index is calculated to be $FI_{Eq1} = \delta_{A,max} = 1.25$.

For illustrative purposes, we further assume that the nominal values of θ_1 and θ_2 are expected to change due to a singular event, but that the potential changes are not independent, i.e., ζ_1 is correlated with ζ_2. We assume that the maximum (expected) change of ζ_2 is $\Delta\theta_{2,B,max}^{-} = -40$ and the corresponding change of ζ_1 is given by $\zeta_1 = 23 - 0.17 * \zeta_2$. Solving Eq. (2) for $\delta_A = 1$ (expected operational disturbances are feasible), yields $\delta_B = 0.6$ meaning that ζ_2 may only decrease by $\Delta\theta_{2,B,feasible}^{-} = -24.0$ to ensure that the operational disturbances, (±4, ±8), can be handled by the process equipment also at the new operating point. The analysis is illustrated in Figure 1 in which the expected variation range of the operational disturbances (uncertainty class A) are shown as a black, hatched rectangle around the current nominal operating point, and the expected change of the operating point (uncertainty class B) is shown as solid black line. Additionally, the maximum feasible change of the nominal operating point is indicated by a grey arrow pointing from the current nominal operating point to the shifted operating point. The potential change of the nominal operating point is limited by the expected operational disturbances (visualized as grey, hatched rectangle around the shifted nominal point).

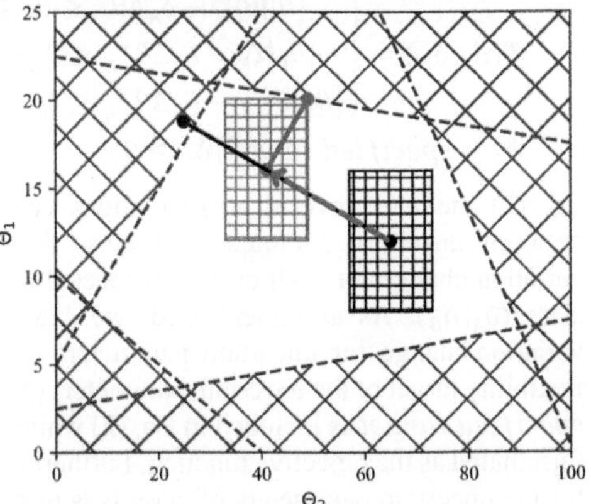

Figure 1: Visualization of flexibility analysis for illustrative example (operational disturbances overlaying with change of nominal operating point)

By means of an additional case, we now illustrate how the proposed approach can be used when the expected variation range of operational uncertainty (class A) is expected to change (when the nominal operating point varies/changes). An illustrative example, very similar to the previously presented example was developed, but in contrast to the previous example the operating variation does not remain constant but depends on the nominal point, i.e., $(\Delta\theta_{1,A}, \Delta\theta_{2,A}) = (\pm 0.3\zeta_1, \pm 0.3\zeta_2)$. The analysis of the additional case is shown in Figure 2.

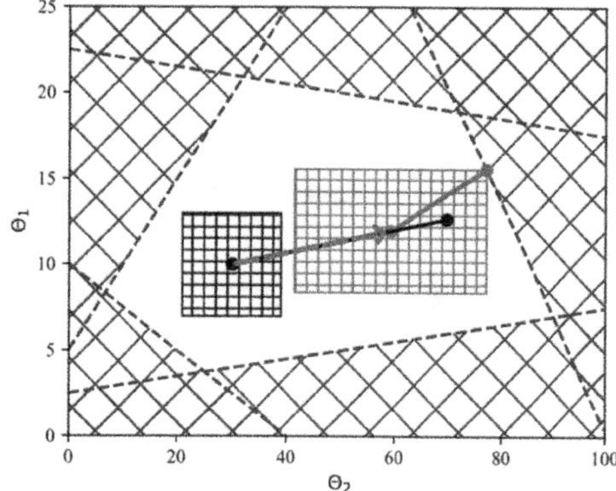

Figure 2: Visualization of flexibility analysis for additional case of illustrative example (operational disturbances depending on nominal point).
Solution of Eq (1): $FI_{Eq1} = \delta_{A,max} = 1.33$
Correlation between ζ_1 and ζ_2: $\zeta_1 = 8 + 0.06 * \zeta_2$
Solution of Eq. (2) for $\delta_A = 1$: $\delta_B = 0.73$

4. Industrial case study

To illustrate the practical application of the proposed reformulations, an industrial case study taken from Marton et al. (2021) was investigated. The case study involves three process streams which are part of two different process units of an oil refinery located in Sweden. The flow sheet of the case study is shown in Figure 3 and process data (including the variation range) is presented in Table 1 in Marton et al. (2021). For the analysis, it was assumed that the UA-value of heat exchangers HX 1-1 and 1-2 is 850 kW/K and 110kW/K for the exchanger HX 2. With the given design data and the variation data in Table 1 in Marton et al. (2021), the flexibility index was calculated to be $FI_{Eq1} = \delta_{A,max} = 1.38$ using Eq. (1). In Marton et al. (2021), it was also discussed that the refinery operating company is considering introducing biomass feedstock in the oil refinery, which would cause a substantial increase of the nominal flow rates of streams 1 and 2 (see Figure 3). Assuming a flow rate increase of streams 1 and 2 of 50-100% compared to current operation (numbers given in Figure 3), the reformulations suggested in this paper can be used to analyse if the process configuration would remain feasible (operational disturbances remain constant). Formulating and solving Eq. (2) yields $\delta_B = 0.5$ (for $\delta_A = 1$) for an expected increase in flow rates of streams 1 and 2 of 100%. Consequently, it can be concluded that the process configuration would be able to handle an increase of 50% in the flow rates while for any larger increase in flow rates the expected operational short-term uncertainty may not be feasible.

5. Influence of operational flexibility target value

The influence of the operational flexibility target value ($\delta_A = specified\ target$ in Eq. (2)) was investigated by means of sensitivity analyses. Eq. (2) was solved for different target values of δ_A for both cases of the illustrative example and the case study. We identified non-linear dependencies between δ_A and δ_B for the case study (due to non-linearities in the constraints describing the equipment) and the case when operational disturbances depend on the nominal point (percentual change itself is non-linear). For the first case of the illustrative example, we identified a linear dependency between δ_A and δ_B which is dependent on the limiting or active constraint (i.e., when the limiting/active constraint changes, the parameters of the linear dependency also change).

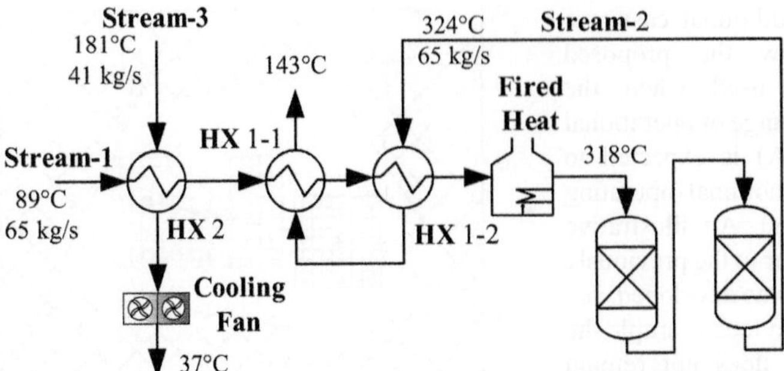

Figure 3: Flowsheet of heat exchanger network case study adapted from Marton et al. (2021).

6. Conclusion

This paper presented novel reformulations of the flexibility index problem to efficiently account for overlaying uncertainty sources which interfere with each other. We defined that overlaying uncertainty sources are present when the timeframe for which the flexibility analysis is aimed to be valid needs to be divided into intervals. We then established the need for the aforementioned reformulations by firstly classifying different (possibly overlaying) uncertainty sources and secondly presenting the shortcomings of the original flexibility index formulation when exposed to such overlaying uncertainty sources (i.e., iterative scheme). In this paper, we focused on the deterministic calculation of the flexibility index (i.e., based on expected variations). However, distinguishing between overlaying uncertainty sources should also be considered when operational disturbances and/or uncertainty of the nominal operating point are expressed via probability density functions. An illustrative example and an industrial case study were investigated and for both, the feasible change of the nominal operating point (due to a singular event) could be determined respecting short-term operational disturbances.

References

R. E. Swaney, I. E. Grossmann, 1985. An index for operational flexibility in chemical process design. Part I: Formulation and Theory. AIChE Journal 31 (4).

P. R. da Silva, M. E. Aragão, J. O. Trierweiler, and L. F. Trierweiler, 2021. A systematic approach for flexible cost-efficient hydrogen network design for hydrogen management in refineries, Chem. Eng. Res. Des., 172.

S. Marton, C. Langner, E. Svensson, and S. Harvey, 2021. Costs vs. flexibility of process heat recovery solutions considering short-term process variability and uncertain long-term development, Front. Chem. Eng.

I. E. Grossmann and C. A. Floudas, 1987. Active constraint strategy for flexibility analysis in chemical processes," Comput. Chem. Eng., 11 (6).

J. L. Pulsipher and V. M. Zavala, 2018. A mixed-integer conic programming formulation for computing the flexibility index under multivariate gaussian uncertainty," Comput. Chem. Eng., 119.

M. P. Ochoa and I. E. Grossmann, 2020. Novel MINLP formulations for flexibility analysis for measured and unmeasured parameters, Comput. Chem. Eng., 135.

C. Langner, E. Svensson, and S. Harvey, 2021. Flexibility analysis of chemical processes considering dependencies between uncertain parameters, Comput. Aided Chem. Eng., 50.

Proceedings of the 14th International Symposium on Process Systems Engineering – PSE 2021+
June 19-23, 2022, Kyoto, Japan
http://dx.doi.org/10.1016/B978-0-323-85159-6.50129-9

Flexible and Sustainable Methanol Production Including Option with Green Hydrogen

Nga Thi Quynh Do[a*], Stephane Haag[a], Frank Castillo-Weltter[a], Armin Gunther[b]

[a]*Air Liquide Innovation Campus, Gwinnerstraße 27-33, 60388 Frankfurt, Germany*
[b]*Air Liquide Engineering & Construction, Olof-Palme-Str. 35, 60439 Frankfurt, Germany*
**ngathiquynh.do@airliquide.com*

Abstract

The reduction of CO2 footprint, the valorisation of different carbon containing sources (stranded gas, biomass, plastic waste, high carbon-containing streams released by plants etc.) as well as the usage of renewable electricity are of increasing interest, especially in relation to global warming and the limitation of carbon containing natural resources. In this context, methanol is a key molecule; which can satisfy both environmental requirements and economic constraints; for energy storage, for clean fuels and as a building block for producing high value chemicals.

The utilization of hydrogen produced from electrolysis using renewable energy directly, the use of unconventional feedstock (CO2, off-gases etc.) with the changing of gas compositions and a higher focus on smaller units for methanol production are challenging and not only from an economical point of view but also regarding the catalyst degradation, the heat management, the by-product formation and the integration in an existing industrial complex. Therefore, the innovation philosophy has not only focused on finding a solution for the methanol synthesis loop but for the global process via new types of equipment (reactor, distillation, heat exchanger etc.), process intensification (layer management, intermediate product separation etc.), and smaller footprint (smaller equipment, new arrangement etc.) to optimize the CAPEX and OPEX.

In this contribution, an update of R&D methanol pilots is provided with some highlights on recent developments of the multistage reactor. These include the main pilot's features and capability, the campaign for validation of different scenarios i.e operating conditions, different design, model validation, by-product formation, dynamics, etc which specifically aims for off-gas and CO2 rich gases valorisation from the steel industry. The availability of the conventional pilot and the flexibility of the new developed methanol pilot at Air Liquide Innovation Campus Frankfurt paves a way for a physical and digital connection with advanced electrolysis pilots using renewable energy from the grid for H2 production and consequently to demonstrate a complete flexible and sustainable concept from power to X (i.e Fuel).

Keywords: Methanol; electrolysis; off-gas; carbon dioxide; hydrogen

1. Introduction

Carbon footprint reduction appears in the past few years as a key topic in multifaceted discussion in different industries and governments in reaching carbon neutrality. Until 2021, the 44 countries and the European Union have committed to meet a net-zero emissions target which accounts for around 70% of global CO2 emissions and GDP by 2050 (IEA, Net Zero by 2050). Supporting the sustainable development and climate objectives, Air Liquide pledges to reach carbon neutrality by 2050 by increasing the use of low-carbon electricity for operations, implementing innovative carbon capture technologies, optimizing supply chains and improving the efficiency of our production units and products portfolio (Figure 1).

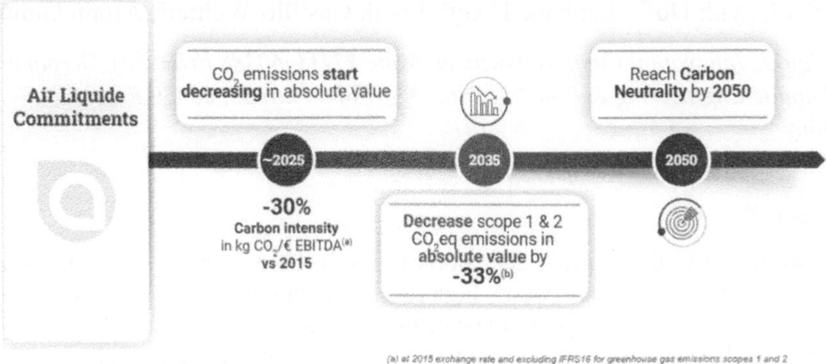

Figure 1: Air Liquide commitment and stepwise approach in reaching carbon neutrality until 2050 (Air Liquide Climate Objective)

Beside the direct electrification of renewable energy, it is believed that hydrogen from electrolysis is an excellent solution for the growth of renewable energy, enabling a novel way of renewable energy distribution to different industrial sectors i.e mobility, heat, chemical, steel… As renewable energy sources are widely dispersed and intermittent by nature, a storage and transportation solution is necessary to ensure the supply chain and the best green energy exploitation. Among different storage solutions, green hydrogen can be further combined with a C1 source i.e CO2, off-gas/flue gas with CO/CO2 content in producing methanol as a solution for carbon footprint reduction.

Air Liquide has a strong history in methanol production covering from R&D to various commercial products in its portfolio including the Lurgi Methanol and Lurgi MegaMethanolTM technologies. Since 1969, more than 68 licenses have been sold globally for a capacity of more than 55,5 million tonnes per year of methanol production. In a close collaboration with Engineering and Construction, R&D is well equipped with competency and pilots supporting different methanol research activities and benchmarking (N.T.Q. Do et al 2020; T. Oelmann et al, 2020). In the past years, different extensive studies on conventional based methanol and CO2-based methanol synthesis have been done at the Innovation Campus Frankfurt covering process development, new concept testing, catalyst validation, kinetics model and by-product model development (T. Svitnic et al, 2020) and strong focus recently is on off-gas valorisation and CO2 based methanol using green hydrogen (EU i3upgrade project funded by RFCS).

This paper aims to give an update on R&D methanol pilots with some highlights on recent developments of the multistage reactor development. These include the main pilot's features and capability, the campaign for validation of different scenarios i.e operating conditions, different design, model validation, byproduct formation, dynamics, etc which mainly aims for off-gas and CO2 rich gases valorization from the industry.

The availability of the conventional pilot and the flexibility of the new developed methanol pilot at Air Liquide Innovation Campus Frankfurt paves the way for a physical and digital connection with advanced electrolysis pilots using renewable energy from the grid for H2 production and consequently to demonstrate a complete flexible and sustainable concept from power to X (i.e Fuel).

2. Results and Discussion

2.1 Conventional Methanol Unit

Figure 2: Conventional MeOH pilot plan

The first methanol pilot was constructed more than 10 years ago featuring MegaMethanol set up with a water cooled reactor (WCR) and gas cooled reactor (GCR). The maximum methanol capacity of this pilot plant is about 6 kg/h. The unit is well equipped with a thermocouple for tracking temperature along the reactor length, control and analytical tools for composition analysis. It was used intensively to validate different concepts and catalyst testing in the past. Examples can be seen in figure 3 in which two catalyst testing concepts are presented.

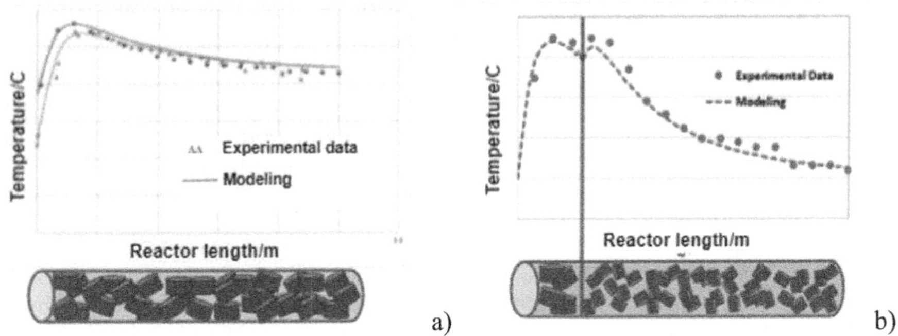

Figure 3: Concept testing at our first methanol pilot plant a) one layer catalyst testing b) two layers of catalyst testing

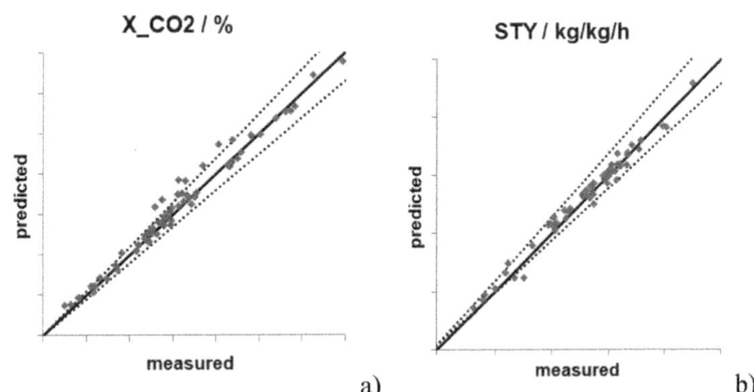

Figure 4: The fitting of modeling using CO2 kinetics and measure data a) CO2 conversion b) Space Time Yield (STY)

The temperature profile of one layer catalyst (figure 3a) and layer management (figure 3b) concept is shown in which one type of catalyst and two types of catalyst are installed inside the reactor correspondingly. There is an excellent agreement between experimental data and modeling of the two concepts which sets a good basis for scale up and commercialization (N.T.Q. Do et al 2020). One concrete example of the usage of this asset is the development of the layer management (LM) concept with Air Liquide Engineering & Construction and with Clariant as described in figure 3b. Within the LM concept, a different optimization strategy can be tailored for CAPEX (less catalyst volume, compact distillation) and OPEX (longer catalyst lifetime, less recycle ratio, heat management, less by-product formation) saving. This concept can also open for customized and disruptive design focusing on flexibility of feedstock, high H_2 efficiency and compactness of the whole methanol loop. Another example is an extensive test campaign with CO2 rich feed stocks to develop a brand new kinetic model for CO2 based methanol and a refined deactivation model for the catalyst under these conditions (see Figure 4).

2.2 Multistage Methanol Pilot Unit

Figure 5: Multistage MeOH Pilot plant

The new multistage methanol reactor (figure 5) has been built and successfully started in 2020 under the framework of an EU project funded by RFCS namely i3-upgrade (grant agreement No 800659) with the objective to convert off-gases from steel plant into methane and methanol. In this case it is very important to respond quickly to changes in load and in gas compositions, to be able to deal with high amounts of inert like methane and nitrogen, as well as to use very effectively the hydrogen available.

The reactor has several tubes with several stages which can be flexibly adjusted for different concept testing. The system is well equipped with thermocouple, hot gas sampling, and online-offline analysis. The throughput is up to 35 m^3N/h for feed gas and can produce methanol with capacity up to 20kg/h. The multistage reactor concept is promising to offer an optimal solution in the conversion of gases with high inert content since it allows very effective conversion rates at reduced recycle rates (down to <1), or even without recycling, and reduced costs (CAPEX & OPEX) for low reactive gases like CO2. As a first step toward validation, an experimental campaign has run in the multistage pilot for more than 1800 hours time on stream (TOS) to confirm for example byproduct content, temperature profiles and plant dynamics and to validate the process model setting as a basis for next step process design. The total byproduct value of the reactor under different pressure conditions can be seen in Table 1. This is crucial to ensure proper distillation column design and requested methanol grade.

Table 1: maximum temperature, hydrogen conversion and byproducts formation

Case	P/ bar	MUG/ Nm³/h	Tmax/°C	X_H2/%	By-products/wt-ppm
1	50	6.7	251	63.6	3808
2	70	6.7	261	72.7	3928
3	90	6.7	273	78.1	3909
4	110	6.7	279	81.9	3548

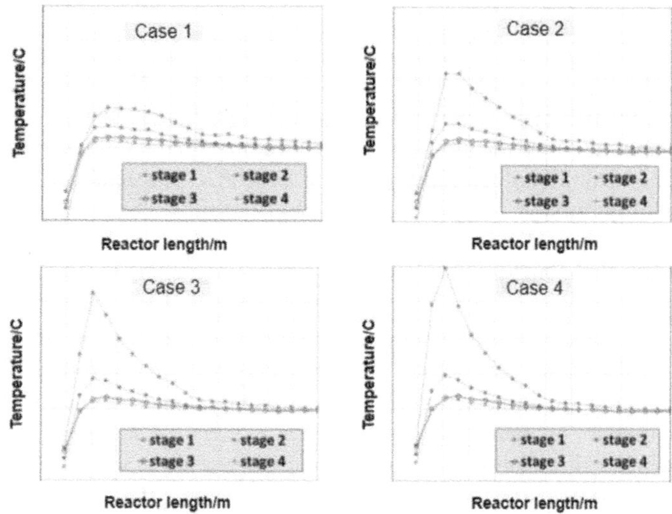

Figure 6: Temperature profile of 4 stages in 4 different cases studies as listed in table 1

The temperature profile decreases along with the stages and reaches a flat profile approaching the reactor end due to the reduction of exothermic reaction as the components approach equilibrium (figure 6) and also the cooling effect of the water jacket.

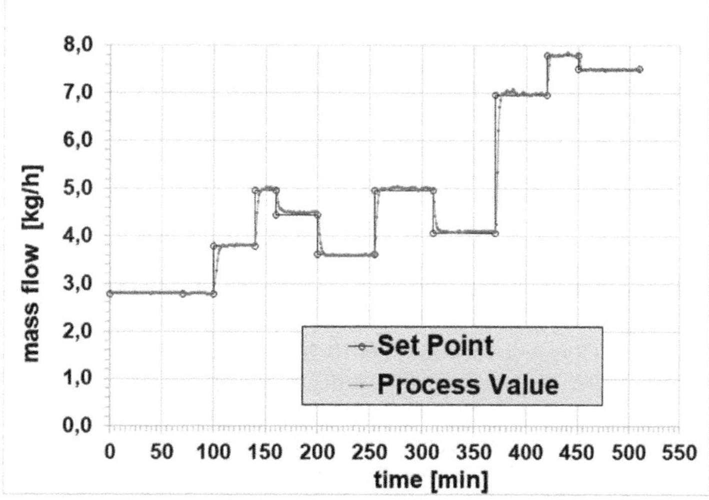

Figure 7: The load response of plant to set point

As renewable energy is very intermittent by nature. Additionally, offgas outlets in terms of composition and conditions can also vary depending on upstream feedstock and operation mode. Therefore, one of the challenges of integration from upstream fluctuation behavior to electrolysis and to hydrogen usage downstream like methanol is to know the bottle-neck(s) that determines the whole plant dynamics. This is to ensure the whole value chain operability and supply chain planning and optimization. Aiming to understand the dynamics, the campaign was done in the pilot by varying load in different steps and time intervals in a once-through setup. Results in figure 7 show a very fast response (less than 10 minutes) of the process value to the set point values. This is a huge advantage in comparison to the classical setup in which a much longer time is needed to respond to changes in load and in gas compositions. In the first step this indicates very good synergy in the coupling solution of electrolysis and this new multistage methanol reactor system. Moreover, it paves the way for innovative advanced process control schemes to respond properly to the availability of hydrogen and the CO and CO2 present in different streams for the methanol synthesis.

3. Conclusions and Outlook

The reduction of carbon footprint via the valorization of CO2 rich gas, off gas, and flue gases to fuel or further usable chemicals are of increasing interest for many industries. Combined with green hydrogen from electrolysis using renewable energy, this C-1 gas source can be used for producing clean methanol as a direct fuel source or building block for producing high value chemicals. To enable the synergy of the whole value chain from upstream (energy) to downstream (production, usage, storage), the innovation philosophy has not only focused on finding an optimal solution of one process unit but the whole chain. Having a stepwise approach, identification of determining process units is important for operability and process design. In this contribution, the strong focus on the methanol process can be realized. In addition to the conventional methanol pilot, the recent developments on new process concepts and the multistage reactor development has provided some detailed information based on the experimental campaign of about 2000 hours of TOS. The by-product formation, the temperature profile and peak temperature are in the common range and the fast response of the reactor can be achieved. The dynamic behaviour of the new pilot shows a promising synergy with electrolysis in valuing the renewable energy fluctuation. The flexibility in stage operation provides an opportunity in the development of tailor-made solutions for diverse carbon sources, especially focusing on a circular economy and on the valorisation of off-gases and of CO2 rich streams from industries and the distribution of renewable energy.

References

International Energy Agency, Net Zero by 2050 A Roadmap for the Global Energy Sector, July 2021.

Air Liquide Climate Objective (accessed on 10.2021), 2019.

N.T.Q. Do *et al.*, Layer Management for Methanol Process, Oil & Gas Magazine, June 2020.

T. Oelmann *et al.*, A new reactor concept for conversion of CO2 to Methanol, DGMK, Future of Chemicals and Fuels - Feedstocks and Process Technologies, October 2020.

T. Svitnik, *et al,* Data-driven approach for predictive modeling of by-product formation in methanol synthesis process, 30th Computer Aided Chemical Engineering, Volume 48, p 505-510, September 2020.

i3upgrade (https://www.i3upgrade.eu/), this project has received funding from the Research Fund for Coal and Steel, grant agreement No 800659; (accessed on 10.2021).

Proceedings of the 14th International Symposium on Process Systems Engineering – PSE 2021+
June 19-23, 2022, Kyoto, Japan
http://dx.doi.org/10.1016/B978-0-323-85159-6.50130-5

Optimization and Heat Exchanger Network Design of Diethyl Carbonate Two-step Synthesis Process from CO_2 and Propylene Oxide

Tsai-Wei Wu, I-Lung Chien*

Dept Chemical Engineering, National Taiwan University,
No.1, Sec. 4, Roosevelt Road, Da'an Dist.,10617 Taipei City, Taiwan;
ilungchien@ntu.edu.tw

Abstract

CO_2 has been deemed crucial as an alternative carbon source recently due to its low price and the urge to utilize it as a way to reduce its amount in the atmosphere. Diethyl carbonate (DEC) is a potential candidate for CO_2 conversion because it can serve as good fuel additive or solvent for lithium batteries. However, CO_2 conversion reaction often suffers from low conversion rate because of its very stable chemical activity. Not only catalyst development is essential, but the research from a process systems engineering (PSE) perspective is also necessary when considering the practical implementation in the future. In the previous work from our group (Chen & Chien, 2018), three processes of DEC synthesis from CO_2 and propylene oxide (PO) were proposed and compared. The results showed that the two-step process performed relatively better in CO_2 emission amount. The two step process includes PO reacting with CO_2 to produce propylene carbonate (PC) and PC reacting with ethanol to produce DEC. Nevertheless, after environmental evaluation throughout the two-step process, the positive net CO_2 emission amount indicated that it still couldn't be a strategy for CO_2 emission mitigation. In this study, the root cause of the high energy consumption of the process was reviewed, and it was found that the large excess ratio of the second step reaction led to massive energy consumption in the separation stage. Consequently, process optimization has been executed by sequential iterative procedure. Heat exchanger network according to pinch analysis along with thermally coupled configuration has been developed for the two-step DEC synthesis process, and the results showed that the new design can save at least 75% CO_2 emission amount for the process. The purpose of this work is to investigate the potentiality of the system to be a CO_2 emission reduction route.

Keywords: CO_2 Utilization; Diethyl Carbonate; Heat Exchanger Network; Optimization.

1. Introduction

Extreme climate all over the world due to the serious Greenhouse effect has caused many serious disasters nowadays. The reduction and utilization of CO_2 have become urgent research topics, and CO_2 valorisation can be a solution to consuming CO_2 profitably. Among the candidate products of CO_2 valorisation, DEC is a promising one for its wide applicability as fuel additive or solvent. In addition, no azeotropes exist in the system of DEC production process, which will be an advantage for the purification section.

Chen and Chien (2018) had investigated three routes for producing DEC by using CO_2 and PO as the feedstocks. Route 1 consists of three steps, which start from the production of PC, and the transesterification of which with methanol produces dimethyl carbonate

(DMC), leading to the final product DEC by reacting with ethanol. Route 2 has the same first step of producing PC, with the second step reacting PC with ethanol to produce DEC directly. Route 3 is a one-pot reaction of PO, CO_2 and ethanol, generating DEC with propylene glycol monoethyl ether (PEE) as by-product. After economic and environmental evaluations, route 2 was decided to be the process which exhibited larger potential for carbon dioxide utilization.

As a result, optimization, process intensification and heat exchanger network design were implemented in this study, in order to disclose the capability of reducing carbon emission through this application. Net CO_2 emission for route 2 in Chen and Chien (2018) was estimated to be 0.7 kg CO_2/kg DEC, and it is our target to reduce the value to less than 0 which can truly imply a reduction in carbon emission.

2. Process description and optimization

The process flowsheet of route 2 proposed by Chen and Chien (2018) is shown in Fig. 1, which demonstrates two reactors and four columns. CO_2 and PO are fed to a PFR first for the production of PC, which is purified in the following stripper. Subsequently, ethanol is fed into the system with PC in a CSTR for generating the desired product DEC. Ethanol excess ratio was set to be 8 to achieve a higher PC conversion, and this leads to high energy consumption to purify the unreacted ethanol for the following column. The last two columns are used for purifying DEC and the by-product PG.

Optimization by simple sequential iterative procedure has been carried out for choosing proper design parameters and operating conditions. Stripper pressure, stripper stage number, pressures, stage numbers and feed locations for the three purification columns were determined by the optimization procedure using total annual cost (TAC) as objective function. In this work, the overall TAC is calculated by Eq. (1), where TOC stands for total operating cost and TCC stands for total capital cost. The correlations for TAC calculation were from Luyben (2012).

$$\text{TAC} = \text{TOC} + \frac{\text{TCC}}{\text{payback period}} \tag{1}$$

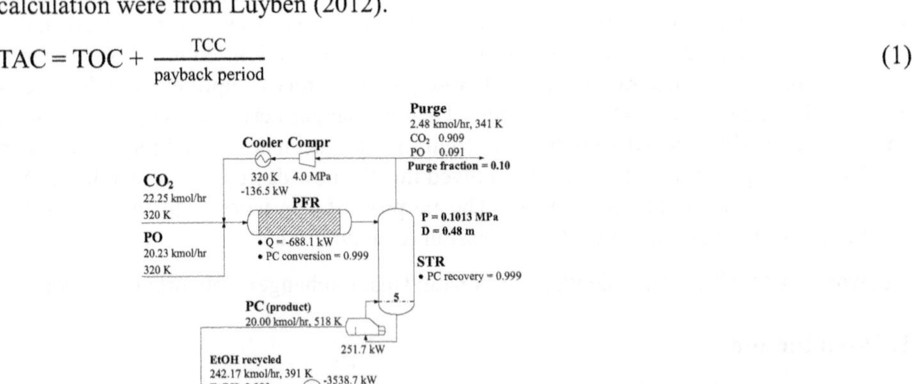

Fig. 1. DEC two-step production process flowsheet

After process optimization, in comparison to the base case in Fig. 1, pressures of stripper and C1 were adjusted lower to save reboiler duty and heat exchanger area. Number of stages in C3 has been increased considerably since PC and PG have close VLE curves which indicate more required stages for separation. Nevertheless, C1 remains to be the unit with the largest energy consumption.

3. CO_2 emission calculation

CO_2 emission amount throughout the process is calculated by the addition of CO_2 emission due to energy usage in each unit. In this process, steam of different grades for reboilers and electricity used in compressor were considered. The corresponding CO_2 emission amount of different utilities follows the calculation method proposed by Gadalla et al. (2005) and is listed in Table 1. The main correlation for calculating CO_2 emission amount is shown as Eq. (2), where Q_{Fuel} is the amount of fuel used; NHV is the net heating value of the fuel used in the boiler (LNG 51600 kJ/kg); C% is the carbon percentage of the fuel (75.4 for LNG); α is the molar weight ratio of CO_2/C (3.67).

$$[CO_2]_{Emiss} = (\frac{Q_{Fuel}}{NHV})(\frac{C\%}{100})\alpha \tag{2}$$

Table 1. Equivalent CO_2 emission amount

Utility	Equivalent CO_2 emission (kg/GJ)
Low-pressure steam, 0.5 MPa, 160 °C	72.86
Medium-pressure steam, 1.0 MPa, 184 °C	76.60
High-pressure steam, 4.2 MPa, 254 °C	91.14
Electricity	96.95
Cooling water	-

4. Process intensification and heat integration

4.1. Thermally-coupled process

Thermally-coupled columns are commonly used for columns with obvious remixing effect (Li et al., 2015; Wang et al., 2014), which leads to unnecessary energy consumption and can be observed on the figure of composition profile in columns. After reviewing the composition profile in the purification columns C1 – C3, it was found that C1 and C2 both had obvious remixing effect in DEC and PG components respectively. C2 and C3 was chosen to implement the thermally-coupled streams because high-pressure steam was used in these two columns, while medium-pressure steam was used in C1.

It can be observed that remixing effect has been almost eliminated after implementing thermally coupling to C2 and C3 as shown in Fig. 2. PG composition fluctuates less and the overall reboiler duty has been saved for 3.26%. Noted that optimization when implementing thermally coupling is necessary since vapor side draw flow rate and liquid side stream feed location are influential to the energy saving result. Optimized design parameters for the thermally-coupled columns can be seen in Fig. 3.

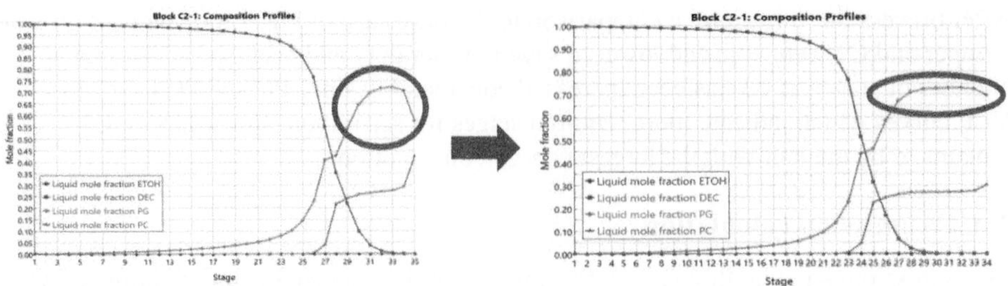

Fig. 2. Elimination of remixing effect in C2 after thermally coupling

4.2. Heat integration

By observing the energy consumption among each unit in Fig. 1, it is obvious that the most energy-consuming unit is C1 for ethanol purification. The ethanol purified specification was set to be 98 mol% for the sake of saving energy; however, the large excess ratio of ethanol to PC led to the significant amount of steam usage. Fortunately, this is an opportunity for using the top vapor in C1 as a heat source for the system. Final process flowsheet with thermally-coupled columns and heat integration is shown in Fig. 4. The top vapor stream of C1 was used to heat up the product stream of DEC reactor, and the top vapor streams of C2 and C3 joined the line to preheat the inlet stream fed to C1. The sequence of using different heat sources was determined by their temperature to guarantee the enough temperature difference for heat exchange. An auxiliary condenser is needed for C1, for the temperature of C1 top vapor stream is not high enough for complete heat exchange with reactor product stream. After optimization and heat integration, 60% of C1 reboiler duty can be reduced compared to the base case. A feed-effluent heat exchanger is further installed before the thermally-coupled columns C2 and C3.

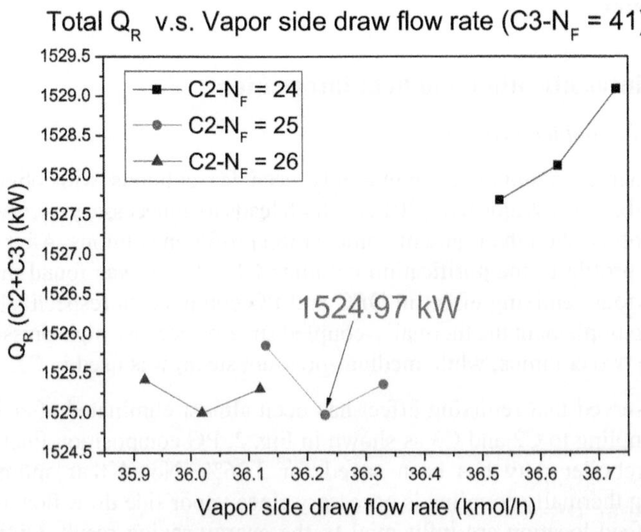

Fig. 3. Optimized design parameters for the thermally-coupled columns

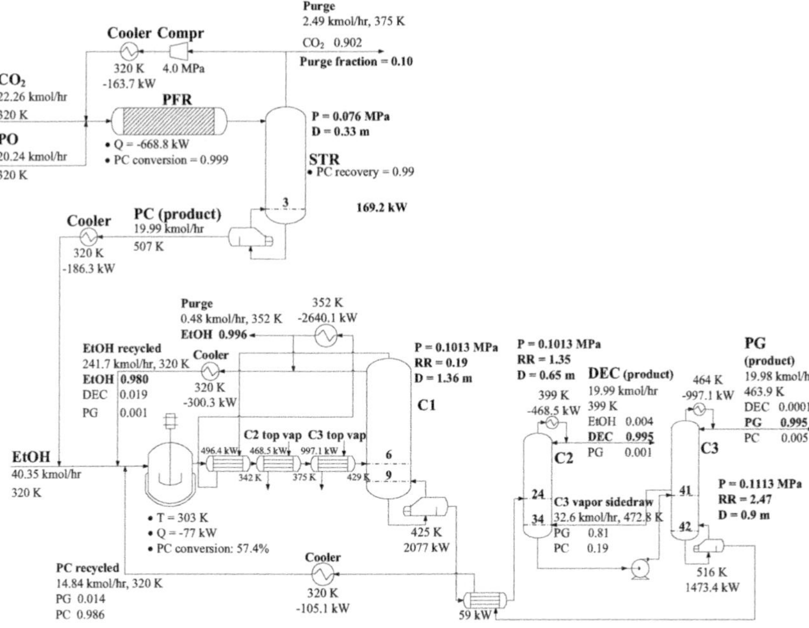

Fig. 4. Energy-saving process flowsheet

CO_2 emission amount of the base case (Fig. 1), optimized process and the final energy-saving process with heat integration (Fig. 4) is listed in Table 2. Optimization has successfully reduced the energy consumption in the both steps, and half of the CO_2 emission amount can be saved in this stage. After the implementation of thermal coupling and heat integration, significant CO_2 emission amount can be saved in the PC to DEC step along with the saving in energy consumption. A nearly zero value can be derived for the CO_2 net emission of the best process. Large excess ratio of ethanol and PC resulted in the failure of reducing CO_2 net emission to a negative value.

Table 2. CO_2 emission amount of the three processes

	Base case	Optimized	Optimized & Heat-integrated
CO_2 emission (kt/y)	Step A: 0.97	0.82	0.82
	Step B: 19.30	12.70	7.95
CO_2 consumption (kt/y)	7.04	7.04	7.04
Net CO_2 emission (kt/y)	13.22	6.57	1.82
DEC production (kt/y)	18.89	18.84	18.84
Net CO_2 emission (kg CO_2/kg DEC)	0.70	0.35	0.097
CO_2 (emission/consumption)	1.88	0.93	0.26

5. Conclusion

A CO_2 utilization process for producing DEC has been optimized and intensified by the implementation of thermally-coupled columns and heat integration in this study. In the base case, PC is generated by the reaction of PO and CO_2, subsequently, excess amount of ethanol is fed to a CSTR with PC to produce the desired product DEC. The largest disadvantage in the system is the large excess ratio of ethanol to PC, which leads to a unavoidable large reboiler duty in C1, accounting for up to 67% of CO_2 emission among the process. CO_2 emission amount was calculated to be 0.7 kg CO_2/kg DEC.

Sequential iterative procedure was used for the optimization of the base case. Results showed that CO_2 emission amount can be reduced to 0.35 kg CO_2/kg DEC by adjusting the operating pressure and design parameters in the system.

Thermal coupling was used as a strategy for process intensification. The remixing effect in C2 was almost eliminated and the overall heat duty can be saved for C2 and C3. Heat integration has also been investigated for the system, and four heat exchangers were installed to recover the heat from top distillate streams and a hot stream. The energy-saving process saves 86% of CO_2 net emission amount, leading to a nearly carbon neutral DEC production process.

With new development in catalyst in the future, it is expected that the conversion of PC to DEC can be enhanced, and the excess ratio of ethanol to PC can be reduced to a reasonable value. Additionally, green energy can be used for supplying the utilities used in this system, such as combined heat and power system or renewable energy. It is firm that researchers are going to explore in the field of green production, and there is high possibility that DEC production can be an approach dealing with CO_2 reduction and utilization in the near future.

References

Chen, M.K., & Chien, I. L., 2018, Potentials for CO_2 Utilization: Diethyl Carbonate Synthesis from Propylene Oxide, Computer Aided Chemical Engineering, 44133-138.

Gadalla, M. A., Olujic, Z., Jansens, P. J., Jobson, M., & Smith, R., 2005, Reducing CO_2 Emissions and Energy Consumption of Heat-Integrated Distillation Systems, Environmental Science & Technology, 39, 17, 6860-6870.

Li, L., Sun, L., Wang, J., Zhai, J., Liu, Y., Zhong, W., & Tian, Y., 2015, Design and Control of Different Pressure Thermally Coupled Reactive Distillation for Methyl Acetate Hydrolysis, Industrial & Engineering Chemistry Research, 54, 49, 12342-12353.

Luyben, W. L., 2012, Principles and Case Studies of Simultaneous Design: Wiley.

Wang, S.J., Cheng, S.H., Chiu, P.H., & Huang, K., 2014, Design and Control of a Thermally Coupled Reactive Distillation Process Synthesizing Diethyl Carbonate, Industrial & Engineering Chemistry Research, 53, 14, 5982-5995.

Proceedings of the 14th International Symposium on Process Systems Engineering – PSE 2021+
June 19-23, 2022, Kyoto, Japan
http://dx.doi.org/10.1016/B978-0-323-85159-6.50131-7

Characterization of Industrial Flaring under Uncertainty for the Design of Optimum Flare Recovery and Utilization Systems

Monzure-Khoda Kazi[a], Fadwa Eljack[a*], Saad Ali Al-Sobhi[a], Vasiliki Kazantzi[b], Nikolaos Kazantzis[c]

[a]Department of Chemical Engineering, College of Engineering, Qatar University, Doha P.O. Box-2713, Qatar
[b]Department of Business Administration, University of Thessaly, Larissa 41500, Greece
[c] Department of Chemical Engineering and Center for Resource Recovery and Recycling, Worcester Polytechnic Institute, 100 Institute Road, Worcester, MA 01609, USA
**Corresponding Author's E-mail: Fadwa.Eljack@qu.edu.qa*

Abstract

One of the main challenges in industrial applications is to optimally manage flare gases that are inevitably generated both in routine and non-routine process operations but can yet constitute valuable energy resources for process systems. A main challenge is to explore the best possible strategies for exploiting these valuable hydrocarbon streams and propose process design alternatives and operational solutions that achieve maximum recovery and use of flare gases at minimum total cost and considering the uncertainty variations associated with flaring incidents. This requires an understanding of the characteristics of flare streams that affect their recovery and reutilization potential as well as an examination of their impact on process system performance while recognizing that the inherently uncertain nature of flaring calls upon a probabilistic approach. In our study, we examine the impact of using a comprehensive probabilistic analysis framework for process flare streams' characterization on the design of an optimal recovery and utilization system. In particular, the work aims to explore the impact of uncertainty for key parameters on the design solutions, such as rate of flare occurrences that were assumed constant in other research works (Kazi et al., 2018). Suitable parametrized Monte Carlo (MC) simulations are employed for more accurate flare profile representations. A comparative study is conducted between the base case optimal design and values at risk solutions for cases where flaring variation increases may significantly affect the design features and economic performance of the process system. The proposed framework could inform decision makers' assessments of the impact of random variations in flaring profiles on process performance profile.

Keywords: Flare Management, Flaring Uncertainty, Monte Carlo, Flare Characterization.

1. Introduction

A dominant strategy in the circular economy era is material and energy recovery, recycling, and reuse, offering multiple economic, environmental, and social benefits when realized in an efficient manner. It has been shown that there are several flare management opportunities and enabling technologies for the recovery and utilization of flare streams from process industries that can significantly contribute to reducing the carbon footprint, increasing energy efficiency and enhancing economic process performance, thus supporting circular economy actions (Kamrava et al., 2015; Kazi et al., 2016; Kazi et al., 2015). In this respect, the main issue is to be able to explore the best possible strategies for scavenging these waste streams in a particular process system and suggest the optimal process design and operation alternatives for attaining their maximum recovery and utilization at the minimum possible annualized total cost. Moreover, a holistic strategy needs to be developed to consider the maximum potential plant-wide benefits under uncertainty variations associated with flaring.

The ability to adequately characterize streams set for flaring in terms of their energy supply potential is of paramount importance in order to recognize flaring perspectives, as potential waste energy carrier. From a process systems engineering point of view, flare stream characterization will facilitate the establishment of optimum designs for the flare recovery and utilization system. The challenge is that the flare occurrences, as well as flowrates and compositions of hydrocarbon streams flared from various process sites, constitute highly uncertain inputs to the design model of a recovery and utilization system in a controlled and safer manner (Kazi et al., 2019a, 2019b). Hence, their occurrence rates, and their energy content vary significantly over time and with respect to the process site(s) from which they are generated (Kazi et al., 2018; Kazi et al., 2015). Although challenging, the process energy utilization opportunities are broadened as available streams from multiple process sites can be mixed and segregated to obtain the optimum possible waste energy load. While flare streams' characterization is obviously source dependent, attaining their combined probabilistic profiles can help in directly identifying 'the big picture' of the design alternatives and providing insights into a more systematic design approach. Hence the framework suggested in this work encompasses a methodology to systematically examine the improvement of the integrated process performance regarding economics, energy consumption and most importantly the environmental impact for routine and non-routine flare gases during abnormal situations. In addition, the extent of variations in the uncertain inputs has been examined within the scope of their impact on the overall process performance profile through an appropriately developed probabilistic sensitivity analysis.

2. Problem statement

Given is a productive system with known design and operational data under certain utility requirements. Available is also a historical database of flaring events (flare causes, sources, frequencies, compositions, and duration) and specific regulatory limits on GHGs. A COGEN unit with a specific boiler type and known capital and operating expenditures is considered as an efficient flare mitigation tool. A systematic approach to maximize the use of available flare streams by optimally sizing the COGEN unit is developed with the aim to ultimately gain environmental and economic benefits, as well as to achieve efficient energy recovery and sustainability enhancement. The need to explore the impact of incorporating a flare mitigation system on process performance while considering the uncertainties of the flaring incidents is reflected in particular, whereas an examination on how the extent of variations in the uncertain inputs (flare frequency, amount etc.) impact performance outcomes (energy-related, environmental, economic) is performed.

3. Flare streams characterization and optimization model

Probability distributions of flare properties comprising input variables can capture the uncertainty and variability explicitly when incorporated into the optimization model taking into account all sources of uncertainty at the same time. Especially non-routine flaring events are constantly faced with uncertainty and variability, and thus can not be adequately represented in an optimization model. Monte Carlo (MC) techniques are utilized in this work to probabilistically characterize and interpret such incidents that can subsequently be employed as input variables in process optimization models. MC simulations provide a means to risk analysis by building models of possible outcomes after sampling a range of values for any uncertain variable. Producing probability distributions of all possible outcomes, MC techniques furnish the decision maker with a more realistic way of describing uncertainty in input variables that can propagate through the optimization modeling framework. They can also offer multiple insights from the whole process case scope and sensitivity analysis results.

In this study a previously developed multi-period optimization formulation is used, with the objective of minimizing total cost of the flare recovery and utilization system. The objective function is mathematically expressed as follows (Kazi et al., 2018):

Objective function:

$$\sum_{Min} \text{TAC} = \underbrace{C_{op} \times H_Y}_{\text{Annual Operating Cost}} + \underbrace{k_f \times (C_{Boiler} + C_{Turbine})}_{\text{Annual Fixed Cost}} - \underbrace{P_e \times H_Y}_{\text{Annual Income}} - \underbrace{E_o \times C_{tax}}_{\text{Carbon Tax Savings}} \quad (1)$$

$$\sum_{Min} \text{TAC} = \underbrace{C_{op} \times (\text{AOT} - \sum_{i=1}^{N} \boldsymbol{\alpha_i t_i})}_{\text{Annual Operating Cost}} + \underbrace{k_f \times (C_{Boiler} + C_{Turbine})}_{\text{Annual Fixed Costs}} - \underbrace{P_e \times (\text{AOT} - \sum_{i=1}^{N} \boldsymbol{\alpha_i t_i})}_{\text{Annual Income}} - \underbrace{\left(\sum_{i=1}^{N} e_{ji}^{U} - e_{ji} t_i\right) \times \mathbf{C_{tax}}}_{\text{Carbon Tax Savings}} \quad (2)$$

i = Flaring events (e.g., PRC trip, Acetylene reactor trip, CGC trip etc.)
k = Flaring locations (e.g., flare A, flare B, ... flare G)

Subjected to

$$\sum_{i=1}^{N} \alpha_i = 1 \quad (3)$$

$$\text{Where, } \alpha_i = \frac{n_i}{n_{tot}} = \frac{\text{Expected number of event } i \text{ per year}}{\text{Expected number of total events per year}} \quad (4)$$

$$t_i = \frac{m_{tot,i}}{m_i} = \frac{\text{Annual total mass flowrate of event } i}{\text{Mass flowrate of event } i \text{ at correspondin } k} \quad (5)$$

Eq. 1 represents the objective function of the optimization model expressed in terms of the total annualized cost (TAC) considering the operating costs related to fuels, boiler and turbine of the COGEN system, the annualized capital cost of the COGEN, the annualized income from any excess generated power, and the environmental cost in terms of CO2 tax savings for total emissions. Similarly, Eq. 2 refers to the TAC with the same four economic terms, but while considering the uncertain variable of operating time based on the flare duration fluctuations with the inclusion of α_i and t_i obtained from MC simulation results (see Eqs. 3-5) as explained in Kazi et al. (2018) (Kazi et al., 2018). The ultimate objective is to design an optimum COGEN unit (e.g., the size of the boiler and turbine) for flare minimization under uncertainty.

4. Results

4.1. Probabilistic characterization

To organize and visualize the data sets available for the ethylene process system under consideration, a MC simulation approach was adopted aiming to capitalize on the occurrence values of the random variables and characterize the flare streams with respect to the extent of their energy supply and utility potential. Therefore, a detailed statistical characterization of flare stream occurrences was performed first by using standard MC simulation techniques and probability distribution outcomes for flare flowrates that were generated for each uncertain incident as shown in Fig.1 for the off-spec production.

Flare distribution profiles can provide values for the whole range of flare flowrates associated with their probabilities, including maximum and minimum flowrate values or ranges of flow rates for different scenarios. For example, Fig. 1 demonstrates that the probability of the flare flow rate values for the off-spec production to reach up to 1.2 ×1[6] kg/yr is around 55%. Thus, if the probability/likelihood of each flaring incident per year is known, the expected flowrate value range of that incident can be estimated from its distribution profile. Next, these simulation results generated can be simultaneously fed to and propagated through the optimization model as random input variables, to generate a comprehensive set of solutions under different uncertainty scenarios. The set of solutions are obtained in the form of Pareto fronts representing heat and power combination points that dictate optimal designs of the COGEN system in the presence of flare uncertainties, as discussed in Kazi et al. (2018). Based on the results, the decision-maker can appropriately select, trade-off, and incorporate his design and operational preferences concerning the desired implementation goals and hierarchically implement and manage his preferred design solutions in a multi-objective decision-making approach.

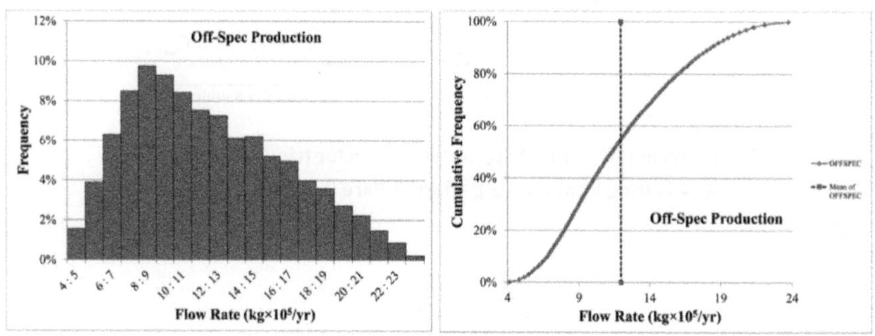

Figure 1. Frequency and cumulative distribution profiles of process upset during off-spec production

4.2. Sensitivity analysis

Next, sensitivity analysis was carried out to explore how the extent of variations in the uncertain inputs (frequencies, emissions, cost) impact performance outcomes. Initially the probability distribution for the simulated total flaring frequencies is depicted in Fig.2. Although it was found that the standard deviation of distribution is quite small in this case (0.0067), variations in the total amount of flowrates can be amplified, and hence greatly impact process performance outcomes such as, CO2 tax savings, and sizing the COGEN unit, as shown in Kazi et al. (2018).

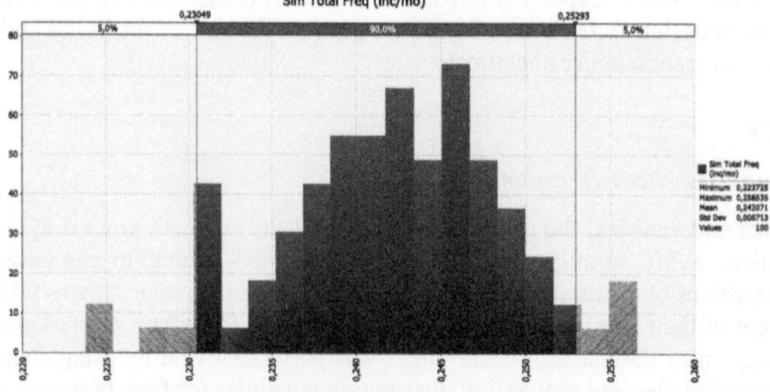

Figure 2. Simulated total frequencies (number of incidents/month)

The effect of the incident type on the simulated total Mean Time Between Incidents (MTBI) is next illustrated by employing the sensitivity analysis tool of the @Risk software, the results shown in Fig. 3. In particular, a dominant effect of incidents happening due to the off-spec production on total expected flaring events (due to the most frequent number of these incidents) was evident. The variability of the total amount of CO2 emissions generated in the ethylene production plant was also examined with respect to both incident type and time (year) of occurrence. In Fig. 4a it is shown that the highest variability in CO2 emissions was observed during the years 2005-2007, whereas the largest value is shown in 2012. All statistical reports are obtained to enable a full characterization of all the uncertain input variables for which probability distributions and variability analyses are produced.

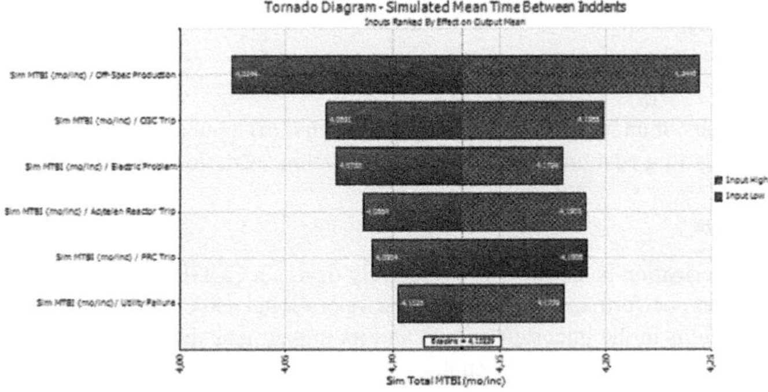

Figure 3. Impact of incident type on variability of total MTBI (mo/inc)

The analysis included examination of the impact of uncertainty in tax rates on expected total CO2 cost. Multiple scenarios with 0.9%, 1.2% and 1.5% annual tax rates were simultaneously examined, assuming a 0.5% annual tax rate increase. As seen in Fig. 4b, annual variability in expected CO2 cost exhibits the same pattern through the different scenarios, as expected, with a significantly accentuated effect for the 1.5% tax rate case. Uncertainty in economic and market conditions can thus be captured and propagated through the optimization model (Kazi et al., 2018). These uncertainty characteristics may influence and cause deviations from process objectives and hence need to be explicitly included in the model and explored for making more well-informed decisions at both the strategic (process design) and operational levels.

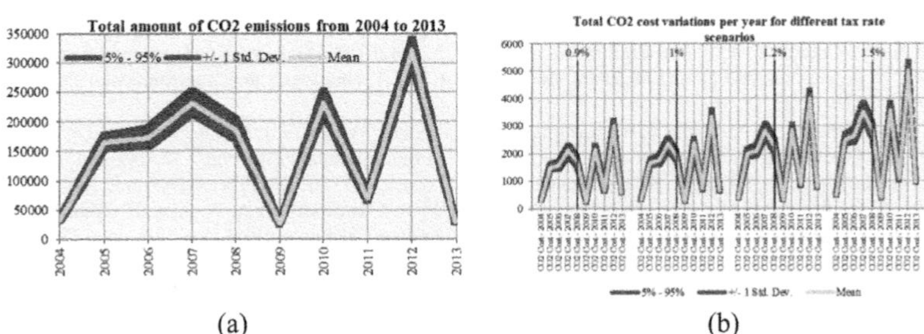

(a) (b)

Figure 4. (a) Variations of the total amount of CO2 Emissions through the decade (2004-2013) and (b) CO2 cost variations per year for different tax rate scenarios

4.3. Effects of uncertainties on process economics

Sensitivity analysis on the techno-economic and environmental factors was carried out in the light of a flaring uncertainty and it was observed that some of the components evaluated (i.e., CO2 tax savings) can significantly be influenced by mild changes in the flaring profiles (see Fig. 5a). The flare mitigation options may be over/under designed when evaluating the typical values for flare durations. Fig. 5b shows that, if uncertainties relating to flare incidents are incorporated, OPEX values may change for different sizes of the COGEN unit.

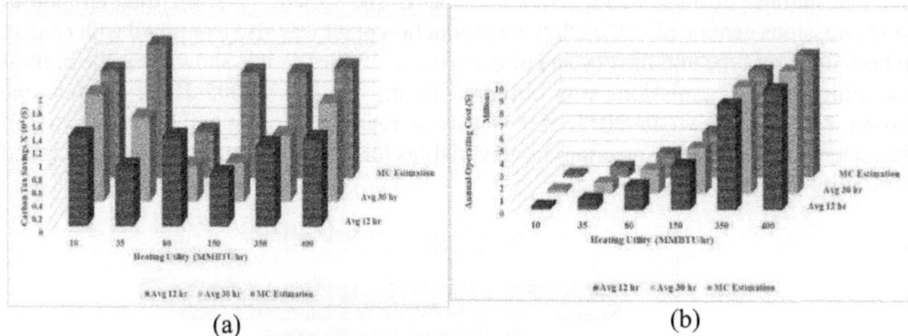

(a) (b)

Figure 5. Effects of uncertainties on economic factors: (a) annual CO2 tax savings and (b) annual operating cost under different flare duration scenarios from sources

5. Conclusions

Flaring characterization is essential to effectively design a COGEN system and improve integrated process performance at an economic, operational and environmental level. The extent of variations in the uncertain inputs and its impact was the focus of this work. In particular, the proposed framework enables: (1) integration of key data sets facilitating further elaboration (insightfully summarizing/visualizing input data of uncertain nature, describing basic features, statistically exploring dominant characteristics and trends that may have been overlooked), (2) probabilistic characterization of available flare streams as energy sources by insightfully generating real flaring profiles using standard MC techniques, (3) direct incorporation of the risk associated with the uncertain nature of the flaring events in the multi period optimization model, and (4) examination of the economic, environmental and energy-related trade-offs derived by optimizing the energy recovery and utilization system while providing valuable information to multiple end-users. Although the usual limitations of the existence of only scarce and case-dependant data hinders a more complete exploration of the system's behaviour, the conceptual sensitivity analysis framework for visualizing and describing the degree of impact of inherently uncertain parameters' variability on performance objectives is highlighted, aiming at generating real data-driven insights for enhancing the empirical understanding of efficient energy recovery and utilization systems.

References

Kamrava, S., Gabriel, K. J., El-Halwagi, M. M., & Eljack, F. T. (2015). Managing abnormal operation through process integration and cogeneration systems. Clean Technologies and Environmental Policy, 17, 119-128.

Kazi, M.-K., Eljack, F., Al-Sobhi, S. A., Kazantzis, N., & Kazantzi, V. (2019a). Application of i-SDT for safer flare management operation. Process Safety and Environmental Protection, 132, 249-264.

Kazi, M.-K., Eljack, F., Al-Sobhi, S. A., Kazantzis, N., & Kazantzi, V. (2019b). Process Dynamic Analysis and Control Strategy for COGEN option Used for Flare Utilization. In A. A. Kiss, E. Zondervan, R. Lakerveld & L. Özkan (Eds.), Computer Aided Chemical Engineering (Vol. 46, pp. 1255-1260): Elsevier.

Kazi, M.-K., Eljack, F., Amanullah, M., AlNouss, A., & Kazantzi, V. (2018). A process design approach to manage the uncertainty of industrial flaring during abnormal operations. Computers & Chemical Engineering, 117, 191-208.

Kazi, M.-K., Eljack, F., Elsayed, N. A., & El-Halwagi, M. M. (2016). Integration of Energy and Wastewater Treatment Alternatives with Process Facilities To Manage Industrial Flares during Normal and Abnormal Operations: Multiobjective Extendible Optimization Framework. Industrial & Engineering Chemistry Research.

Kazi, M.-K., Mohammed, F., AlNouss, A. M. N., & Eljack, F. (2015). Multi-objective optimization methodology to size cogeneration systems for managing flares from uncertain sources during abnormal process operations. Computers & Chemical Engineering, 76, 76-86.

Proceedings of the 14th International Symposium on Process Systems Engineering – PSE 2021+
June 19-23, 2022, Kyoto, Japan
http://dx.doi.org/10.1016/B978-0-323-85159-6.50132-9

DEVELOPMENT OF MICRO SCALE PRC USING LOW GRADE GEOTHERMAL THERMAL ENERGY

Ryosuke AKIMOTO [a], Yasuhiko SUZUKI[b], Yuki OGASAWARA[b], Masaru NAKAIWA[a] and Keigo MATSUDA[a*]

[a] Department of Chemistry and Chemical Engineering, Graduate School of Science and Engineering, Yamagata University, 4-3-16, Jonan, Yonezawa, Yamagata 992-8510, Japan

[b]Faculty of Chemistry and Chemical Engineering, Yamagata University, 4-3-16, Jonan, Yonezawa, Yamagata 992-8510, Japan

*Corresponding Author's E-mail: matsuda@yz.yamagata-u.ac.jp

ABSTRACT: In order to enhance the versatility, we proposed a design method in which a micro ORC of 10 kW class. The micro ORC is small scale power generation system for using renewable thermal energy such as hot springs. However, such thermal energy is of very low grade and involves temperature variations, so it is necessary to develop a versatile small power generation cycle. In this study, the design conditions of heat exchanger, expander, and pump were fixed for the micro ORC, and the power generation performance was investigated using six different working fluids for multiple heat source conditions. The heat source flow rate set to be 3,000 kg/h and the heat source temperature was 393 K. The heat sink flow rate set to be 18,000 kg/h and the temperature was 293 K. The pump discharge pressure was 1,500 kPa. As a result, Among the selected working fluids, butane showed the highest power generation performance of 12.9 kW. To predict the power generation performance of the micro ORC, we correlated the power generation of each working fluid with the thermophysical properties of the working fluid, but low correlation was obtained. Therefore, we introduced new parameter, Exergy Parameter Index (EPI), for predicting the power generation of a micro ORC. It was found to be a very reliable parameter for forecasting the power generation of a micro ORC.

Keywords: Power generation, Organic Rankine Cycle, Renewable energy

1. Introduction

Small ORCs are one-of-a-kind industrial products because the working fluid, evaporator, condenser, pump, and expander are designed to correspond to the heat source conditions. Therefore, it is not versatile and has a high cost. In order to design a small ORC, there are two ways of thinking about it: one is to create a one-of-a-kind device with the heat recovery rate as the objective function, and the other is to improve the power generation performance of the same device by changing the working fluid and pump discharge pressure. From the viewpoint of process enhancement, concepts such as miniaturization are necessary in the design of ORCs. Recently, several experimental studies of compact ORCs have been reported (Akimoto *et al.* 2021, Li *et al.* 2021 and Uusitaro *et al.* 2020 and). Many researchers have discussed the performance of power generation by changing the specification of the equipment for a given heat source. To the best of our knowledge, the same equipment specification of a small ORC for various heat sources has not been studied at all.

In this study, we proposed a micro ORC as a waste heat recovery technology for the 10 kW class, assuming that the pump, expander, and heat exchanger can work properly even if the working fluid was different. By considering the micro ORC, we could expect a low-cost and high-efficiency small-scale exhaust heat recovery technology. In this paper, the micro ORC design and its power generation performance was discussed. The micro ORC was adopted by a model-based approach. We investigated how the power generation performance of micro ORC was affected by the exchange of working fluid and the control of the pump discharge pressure. We also proposed an index to represent the operation and design methods that match the heat source conditions.

2. Modeling

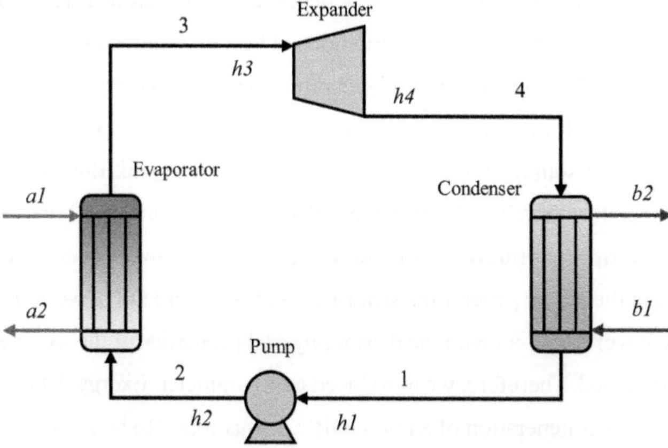

Fig. 1 Schematic diagram of the micro ORC

The schematic diagram of micro ORC with this study is shown in **Fig. 1**. Micro ORC consists of an evaporator, a condenser, an expander, a pump, and an injector of working fluid. The working fluid is supplied to the evaporator by the pump (1→2). In the evaporator, the working fluid is heated to the saturated vapor or superheated vapor by the heat source (2→3). The heated working fluid vapor is expanded through the expander to generate work (3→4). The expanded working fluid vapor is supplied to the condenser and condensed to the liquid by cooling water (4→1). Finally, the condensed the liquid is pumped back to the evaporator. **Table 1** shows the mass and

Table 1 Mass and Energy balance of each device

Device	Mass and energy balance equation
Evaporator	$\dot{m}_2 = \dot{m}_{a1}$ $\dot{m}_2(h_3 - h_2) = \dot{m}_{a1}(h_{a2} - h_{a1})$
Condenser	$\dot{m}_8 = \dot{m}_{b1}$ $\dot{m}_8(h_1 - h_8) = \dot{m}_{b1}(h_{b2} - h_{b1})$
Pump	$\dot{m}_1 = \dot{m}_2$ $W_p = \dot{m}_1(h_2 - h_1)$ $W_{p,net} = W_p / \eta_p$
Expander	$\dot{m}_4 = \dot{m}_5$ $W_{ex} = \dot{m}_4(h_5 - h_4)$ $W_{ex,net} = W_{ex}\,\eta_{ex}$

Table 2 Input parameter of design conditions for the micro ORC

Equipment	Design parameter	Value	Unit
Evaporators	Overall heat transfer coefficient	1,500	$W/(m^2 \cdot K)$
	Heat transfer area	4.0	m^2
	Minimum temperature approach	5.0	K
Condenser	Overall heat transfer coefficient	1,000	$W/(m^2 \cdot K)$
	Heat transfer area	15	m^2
	Minimum temperature approach	5.0	K
Pump	Efficiency	80	%
Expander	Isentropic efficiency	80	%
	Mechanical efficiency	80	%

Table 3 Input parameter of operation conditions for the micro ORC

Operation factor	Operation parameter	Value	Unit
Hot heat source	Flow rate	3,000	kg/h
	Temperature	393	K
	Pressure	200	kPa
Heat sink	Flow rate	18,000	kg/h
	Temperature	293	K
	Pressure	100	kPa
Pump	Discharge pressure	1,500	kPa

energy balance of each device. Operating conditions and design conditions of the micro ORC in this study are shown **Table 2** and **Table 3**. The working fluid was used propane, propylene, n-butane, isobutane, n-pentane, isopentane and R245fa.

3. Simulation results and discussion

Fig. 2 shows the power generation performance of each working fluid and relationship between the key parameters, boiling point and latent heat, and the net power generation under the conditions of heat source temperature of 393 K, pump discharge pressure of 1,500 kPa, and heat source flow rate of 3,000 kg/h. Among the selected working fluids, butane showed the highest power generation performance of 12.9 kW, and the lowest power generation is propane, its value is 2.75 kW. In Fig. 5a, for R245fa, n-butane, and isobutane, the latent heat + sensible heat at 1,500 kPa is related to the amount of electricity generated, while for propane and propylene, it is not. In addition, as shown in Fig.5b, the boiling point is not related to the net power generation for all the working fluids. These results show that the net power generation of the micro ORC cannot be estimated only by the physical properties such as latent heat, sensible heat, and boiling point. Since the condensation pressure varies depending on the working fluid, the pressure difference between the inlet and outlet of the expander is different for each working fluid. It is known that the greater the pressure difference, the greater the amount of power generated by the expander. For components such as propane and propylene, which have a low boiling point of 233K or lower and a high condensation pressure of 1,000 kPa or higher, the pressure difference between the inlet and outlet of the expander is less than 600 kPa, resulting in less power generation. Therefore, it cannot be inferred from the physical property values alone. The power generation by the heat engine can be evaluated by the energy input to the process and the driving force. It should be able to be expressed in terms of enthalpy and driving force. The enthalpy is the sum of sensible and latent heat, and the driving force is the pressure difference before and after the expander. In this study, this relationship is proposed as an innovative index to estimate the power generation performance. We define this index as exergy parameter index (EPI), which estimates the power

Heat source temperature: 393 K, Heat source flow rate: 3,000 kg/h, Pump discharge pressure : 1,500 kPa

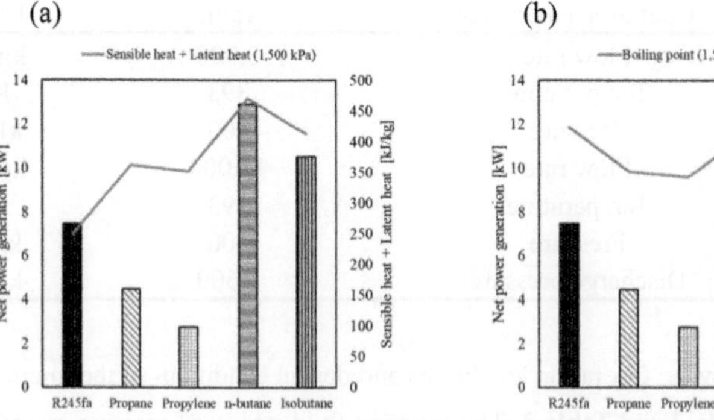

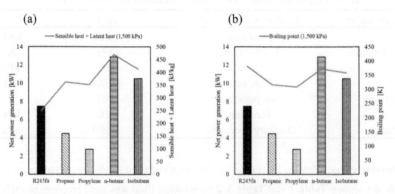

Fig. 2 The relationship between net power generation and: (a) Sensible + latent heat, (b) Boiling point (1,500 kPa)

generation performance of micro ORC using heat below 393 K. EPI is expressed by the following equation

$$EPI = \Delta P \cdot (h_{sensible} + h_{latent}) \quad (1)$$

where ΔP is pressure difference in the cycle, $h_{sensible}$ is sensible heat, and h_{latent} is latent heat. The pressure difference can be calculated as margin between the pump discharge pressure and the condensation pressure of the working fluid. $h_{sensible} + h_{latent}$ is heat required for the working fluid to become saturated vapor.

Fig. 3 show association between EPI and net power generation of micro ORCF. The EPI ranged between 1.22 and 5.91 each fluid. The larger the value of EPI, the higher the power tends to be generated: the EPI and power generation of n-butane were 5.91 (MPa·kg)/kJ and 12.9 kW, respectively. The EPI is good agreement with power generation performance each working fluids. Since the EPI considers not only the physical properties but also the mechanical parameters in the cycle, it could be predicted to the net power generation. It is clearly found that the EPI can be easy to estimate the net power generation for these conditions without any correction parameters. These findings will contribute to the spread of general-purpose small ORCs.

In this study, the EPI is a key index for predict the micro ORC performance and will be an index for future working fluid research, for example, objective function of materials informatics (MI).

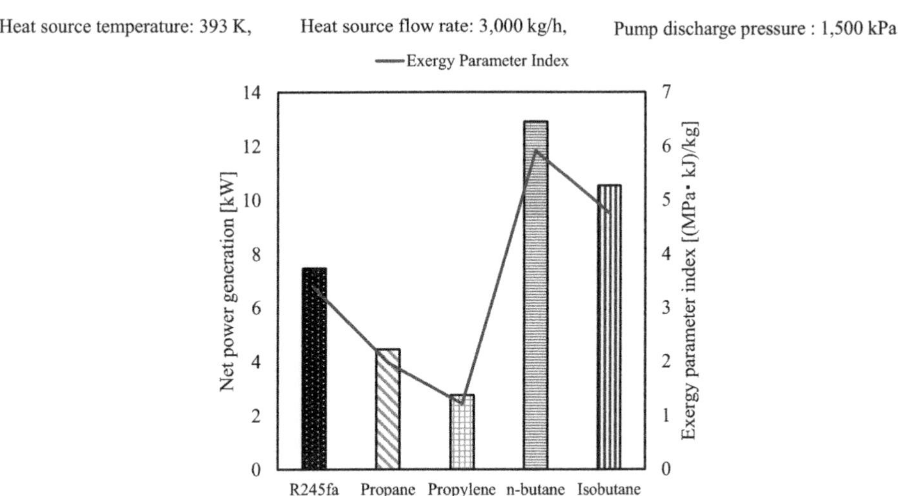

Fig. 3 The effect of net power generation on Exergy Parameter Index (EPI).

4. Conclusion

In this study, to improve the versatility of small scale ORCs and to clarify their design guidelines, a 10 kW class ORC (micro ORC) was developed on a model basis, an assumed that various working fluids operate in a single device, and the performance of each working fluid was investigated under fixed design conditions.

In the assumed ORC, n-butane showed the highest power generation performance among the selected working fluids. When the relationship between the power generation performance of each working fluid and the latent heat, sensible heat, and boiling point was investigated, no high correlation was found.

Therefore, we introduced a new parameter, Exergy Parameter Index, which can predict the power generation performance. It was defined the key parameter which considered sensible heat, latent heat and pressure difference in the cycle, and can be predict the power generation performance of the micro ORC. In this study, the EPI could design and operation conditions for the micro ORC. The micro ORC may not achieve appropriate performance due to variations in environmental conditions such as heat source temperature. These conditions will increase the power generation cost, resulting in negative economic efficiency. After that, the micro ORC should be designed to be sustainable from the perspective of rigorous tecno-economic analysis.

5. Reference

Akimoto, R., T. Yamaki, M. Nakaiwa, K. Matsuda. Applicability study of micro Kalina cycle for regional low grade geothermal heat in Japan. *Case Studies in Thermal Engineering*, **28**, 101506 (2021)

Li, Y. M., Hung, T. C., Wu, C. J., Su, T. Y., Xi, H., Wang, C. C. Experimental investigation of 3-kW organic Rankine cycle (ORC) system subject to heat source conditions: A new appraisal for assessment. *Energy*, **217**, 119342 (2021)

Uusitaro, A., Saaresti, T. T., Honkatukia, J., Dhanasegaran, R. Experimental study of small scale and high expansion ratio ORC for recovering high temperature waste heat. *Energy*, **208**, 118321 (2020)

Proceedings of the 14th International Symposium on Process Systems Engineering – PSE 2021+
June 19-23, 2022, Kyoto, Japan
http://dx.doi.org/10.1016/B978-0-323-85159-6.50133-0

Scenario Outcomes for Electric Power Generation Expansion Planning considering the State of Indiana as a Case Study

Abdul Ahmed[a], Kayla L. Richardson[b], Yufei Zhao[c], Cornelius M. Masuku[c]*

[a]*Chemical and Biological Engineering, Rensselaer Polytechnic Institute, Troy, NY 12180, USA.*
[b]*School of Electrical, Computer and Energy Engineering, Arizona State University, Tempe AZ 85287, USA.*
[c]*Davidson School of Chemical Engineering, Purdue University, West Lafayette, IN 47907, USA.*
cmasuku@purdue.edu

Abstract

This work assesses Indiana's electricity demands through the next few decades to identify an optimal combination. A mixed-integer linear programming mathematical modeling framework in which a combination of sources, generation technology, and capacity of future generation technologies are evaluated to minimize investment, operational and environmental costs is implemented. Our model is a modification of the implementation developed by Lara et al. (2018) with the data from databases such as the U.S. Energy Information Administration and other relevant agencies. Our model is implemented in Pyomo (Python optimization modeling objects), a free and accessible python-based software package for devising optimization models. While there may exist multiple combinations of energy sources that prove to be optimal when considering various sets of constraints, pertinent results are those that maximize the use of renewable energy sources while minimizing operational, environmental, and investment costs. This research aims to inform planning agencies of optimal energy infrastructure configurations for the State of Indiana, allowing for evaluations of the changes required to reach optimal operation with expected growing demand. The model and analysis of results can be applied to any other region (State or Country).

Keywords: Renewable Energy Integration; Mixed-Integer Linear programming; Optimization.

1. Main Text

In the advent of the current climate crisis, a transition to renewable energy systems has become widely apparent as a means to mitigate climate effects. In the past decade, within the United States, the use of renewable energy sources has risen. The desire to maximize the use of renewable energy sources stems from the fact that the alternative non-renewable, or traditional, power sources contribute more to the pollution of the environment (Lopez & Espiritu, 2011). However, energy data collected by the Energy Information Administration (EIA) shows that traditional energy sources, such as fossil fuels (petroleum, natural gas, and coal) and nuclear, continue to generate over 85% of total energy consumed in the U.S (U.S. EIA, 2021). Many factors, such as policy, public sentiment, and scientific advancements currently assist in driving the transition towards renewable energy systems. Many nations stand at this pivotal moment of restructuring. However, with this transition evolves a problem in terms of, what combinations of renewable and non-renewable technologies are most optimal to meet required energy demand?

Energy optimization models can be used to present this combination of energy sources. These models consider predictions of energy demand over several decades and determine which sources of energy best fulfil future energy needs. These models can then offer insight on creating a more sustainable energy system, presenting ideal evolutions of that energy system over multiple decades, without declaring how probable these evolutions are (Pfenninger et al., 2014). This work aims to formulate a multi-objective optimization modeling framework to evaluate the necessary changes in the energy systems infrastructure of the state of Indiana that meets EIA projected energy demand while minimizing environmental and capital costs. The research focuses on the increased use of renewable energy sources of solar and wind and the non-renewable, natural gas combined cycle. These three technologies are the expected drivers of future energy generation.

2. Research Methods

2.1. Collection of Data

In this research, we assessed the potential of solar and wind generative technologies to fulfil demand imposed by planned retirement, economic growth, and population growth, all while minimizing both environmental and capital costs. To do this, we created a linear program with an objective function of minimizing the implementation cost for a selected set of generative technologies. The model was informed with data retrieved primarily from the NREL (National Renewable Energy Laboratory) and the EIA (Energy Information Administration). The data consists of two primary types, cost, and performance. To drive the cost analysis aspect of the objective function, annual technology baseline (ATB) data for the U.S. of the year 2020 was retrieved from the NREL. This baseline data provided metrics of cost per performance for renewable and conventional generative technologies. The secondary data set consisted of supply curves of solar and wind for the U.S. Supply curve data for each technology consisted of the following: location (longitude and latitude), generative capacity potential, the area available, capacity factor, and distance to interconnect. Excluding transmission, all listed parameters were relevant to inform the model. In addition to these data sets, other data was prevalent in the formulation of the model. For instance, generator data, retrieved from the U.S. EIA, was used to determine the level of demand imposed by planned retirement for the ten-year time horizon (2020-2030). Relevant contributions included listings of planned retirements of coal generators and their respective nameplate capacities. The summations of these nameplate capacities served as the demand imposed by the planned retirement of the ten-year time horizon. For the twenty- and thirty-year time horizons, given the lack of data for planned retirement, linear extrapolation was applied to determine respective demand coefficients. Lastly, data from the EIA 2021 Annual Energy Outlook allowed the determination of time factored, and population factored growth in demand with applications of extrapolation techniques.

2.2. Treatment of Data

In the process of informing the computational model, the data is pre-processed with Python via Jupyter Notebook. As the focus of the research is the state of Indiana, a subset of supply data of Indiana was devised from the original supply curve data - representative of the whole United States. We employed a rigorous approach to accomplish this. Firstly, border and city location data were retrieved from online sources. This data mapped the border and cities of Indiana. With the Pandas package and data frames, border and city locations were unionized. A grouping of supply data, based on proximity, was then attached to the location data derived by the union of border and city locations. These locations were then mapped as nodes on a geospatial plot, providing an informative supply curve fitted to the state of Indiana. With this approach, we successfully elicited Indiana's supply data from that of the country.

To further refine the data, locations were sorted. The sorting convention was from greatest to least by the following ratio: potential generative capacity to the area of available land. High valued ratios are indicative of richer location quality. Quality, we define as the amount of generative potential per unit area of land. Following this definition, high qualities are desirable as they minimize the amount of land needed for system implementation, which reduces the associated cost of implementation. From this heuristic, a set of fifty nodes (locations) for solar and wind were developed, totaling one hundred decision variables of which selection proportions range from zero to one.

2.3. Mathematical Modeling

A mathematical model was constructed with Pyomo, a python-based optimization package. The optimization problem was solved with glpk as a solver. The data elicited from the model include generator location, generator type, and proportion of capacity selected per selected location. The framework of the mathematical model follows that of a linear program. The objective function is given as Equation (1). The objective function seeks to minimize the total implementation cost of the selected generative technologies and their respective capacities. C^t is the cost of implementing a selected configuration. C^t_{solar} is the average cost of solar per MW generative capacity for the time horizon of consideration. Likewise, C^t_{wind} is the average cost of wind per MW generative capacity for the time horizon of consideration and C^t_{ng} is the average cost of natural gas per MW generative capacity for the time horizon of consideration. The decision variables are x_i, the amount of solar capacity selected, and x_j, the amount of wind capacity selected. S represents solar capacities, W, wind capacities, and NG, natural gas capacities. The respective sets comprising selections for each decision variable are SS and WS. Lastly, t is used to represent the time horizons with subscripted variables dependent on time.

The first constraint is a peak demand constraint, Equation (2). This informs the selection of generative technologies and their respective capacities to ensure that the sum required load (load loss from the retirement and load expected as a result of population and economic growth) is met. In Equation (2), ED_t is the demand imposed by retirement, and the expected growth of population and economy for the planning horizon. Equation (3) confirms that the imposed demand for a given time horizon is equal to the sum of the demand imposed by retirement (R_t) within the horizon, and the contribution to demand from expected economic and population growth (E_t) within the horizon. Equation 4 proposes an intermittency constraint. In order to ensure that a proposed configuration is at least as reliable as the current energy infrastructure of Indiana, Equation 4 was developed to assess whether the realizable load (peak load multiplied by the capacity factor) is greater than or equal to the summation of the realizable load imposed by planned retirement and economic and population growth. CF^s, CF^w, and CF^{ng} are respectively the solar, wind, and natural gas capacity factors. CF^c is the coal capacity factor, and CF^{cc}

is the aggregated averaged capacity factor of solar, wind, and natural gas. The relevant sets are: CS, the Solar Capacity factor set; and CW, the Wind Capacity factor set. The last defined constraint is represented as Equation (5), the emissions constraint. This constraint allows for the assessment of scenarios of varying reliance on natural gas. Natural gas plays a pivotal role in integrative renewable energy systems. However, to limit the environmental effects of natural gas, this constraint controls emission tolerances accordingly. In Equation (5), x serves as the proportion of fulfilled demand occupied by natural gas.

$$\min C^t = \left(C^t_{solar}\sum_{i\in SS} S_i x_i\right) + \left(C^t_{wind}\sum_{j\in WS} W_j x_j\right) + \left(C^t_{ng}NG\right), \forall t \in \{10,20,30\} \tag{1}$$

$$\sum_{i\in SS} S_i x_i + \sum_{j\in WS} W_j x_j + NG \geq ED_t \quad \forall\, t \in \{10,20,30\} \tag{2}$$

$$ED_t = R_t + E_t, \quad t \in \{10,20,30\} \tag{3}$$

$$\sum_{i\in SS, a\in CS} S_i x_i CF^s_a + \sum_{j\in WS, a\in CW} W_j x_j CF^W_a + NG * CF^{ng} \geq (CF^c R + CF^{cc} E) \tag{4}$$

$$NG = xED_t \tag{5}$$

3. Results and Discussion

We initially considered the scenario of doubling current renewable generative capacity in the state of Indiana for a 5-year horizon. The objective was to determine the optimal configuration of counties achieving this specification. In our analysis, we observed that in 5 years, doubling renewable energy generative capacity reduces carbon emissions by 20%. Figure 1 compares the relative distribution of current generation technologies to what can be achieved from the considered scenario. The purpose of this illustration is to emphasize the motivation behind this study.

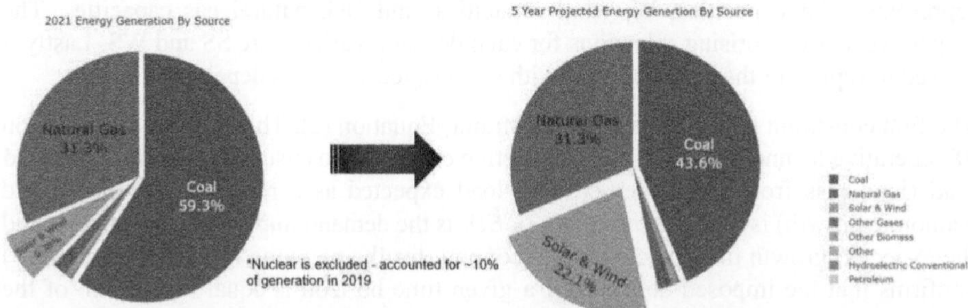

Figure 1: Comparison of relative distribution of current generation technologies to a 5-year projection when considering the scenario of doubling current renewable generative capacity.

The currently developed mathematical framework aimed to analyze three different time horizons, each incremented by a decade. As expected, the cost of implementing the determined optimal configuration rose each horizon. The driver of this rise was an increase in imposed demand as dictated by expected increases in planned retirement, economic growth, and population growth. Yet, this was somewhat balanced by the expected decreasing cost of implementing solar and wind generative technologies, resulting from developments in technology. Overall, spanning the three distinctive time horizons, a net increase in implementation cost is observed.

From the ten-year time horizon with a reliance on generation constituting 50 % natural gas, the calculated implementation cost was 28.2 billion USD. The distribution of solar to wind, based on contribution by generative capacity, is depicted in Figure 2. Each node is informative of both longitude and latitude. For the twenty-year time horizon of the same reliance factor, the calculated implementation cost was 84.1 billion USD. However, when the twenty-year model is fitted with data consisting of one hundred of the best (as defined by the heuristic in the treatment of data section) generative wind and solar sites, each, the computed implementation cost is 78.5 billion USD.

(a) (b) (c)

Figure 2: Nodes of selectable generation. (a) solar generation; (b) wind generation; (c)

selected configuration of wind and solar for a 10-year horizon with associated capacities. Yellow nodes are representative of solar, blue nodes representative of wind.

The configuration derived from this heuristic is more cost-effective as the higher consideration of wind allows for an overall increase in system reliability. Because of Equation (4), a larger selection of wind generative capacity reduces intermittency. This reduction in intermittency promotes a reduction in the net load of the selected configuration, which lowers the cost of implementing the optimized configuration. To significantly reduce costs, technological developments focused on increasing the reliability of wind and solar generators are warranted. The final analysis was the variation of the proportionality factor of natural gas deployed, x. This variation was carried out for the ten-year horizon. The first considered scenario was $x = 0.25$, the fulfilment of twenty-five percent of the imposed demand by natural gas. The cost of implementation increased to 38 billion USD. The second scenario was the complete minimization of environmental costs. Such is representative of absolute reliance on solar and wind. The cost of implementing the optimal configuration for this consideration is 51 billion USD. These sub scenarios are significant in portraying the relationship between capital costs of implementation and the amount of CO_2 emitted, with amounts of CO_2 emitted directly proportional to the demand fulfilled by natural gas.

The model developed for this study is very versatile to improvement. Future research could consider, for example, transmission which would require a more complex design and analysis of cost factors and energy retention. Another favorable consideration is time factorization, which is a means for better controlling intermittency. This consideration could entail the deployment of natural gas only when wind/solar is unavailable during the day. A third consideration is the implementation of storage technologies. Storage can act to negate solar and wind downtime. However, much research is necessary for the effective development and deployment of storage solutions.

4. Conclusions

This research assessed the capabilities of implementing solar, wind, and natural gas generative technologies to replace the retirement of many coal plants and meet the demand imposed by economic and population growth in the state of Indiana. In theory, the most practical way to reduce the effects of environmental degradation is a complete shift to renewable generation technologies. However, many factors impede this shift. Such factors include capital costs and intermittency. Of these two impeding factors, the most significant is that of intermittency. Due to the limited availability of wind and sunlight, energy infrastructures cannot exist solely by wind and solar. Thus, the practical solution has been the integration of renewable energy sources into current energy infrastructures. Such insertions also allow for the displacement of polluting generation sources, such as coal. However, because of intermittency, integrative systems suffer in reliability. Despite the localized nature of this study, the approaches, methods, and findings are well applicable to other regions of the U.S. and the world. The global energy situation is a complex subject, hence works such as this aim to produce informed and accurate conclusions to aid transitions when considering integrative energy infrastructures.

References

S. Akar, P. Beiter, W. Cole, D. Feldman, P. Kurup, E. Lantz, R. Margolis, D. Oladosu, T. Stehly, G. Rhodes, C. Turchi, L. Vimmerstedt (n.d.). *2020 annual technology baseline (ATB) cost and performance data for Electricity Generation Technologies.* NREL Data Catalog. Retrieved October 26, 2021, from https://data.nrel.gov/submissions/145.

C.L. Lara, D.S. Mallapragada, D.J. Papageorgiou, A. Venkatesh, I.E. Grossmann, 2018. Deterministic electric power infrastructure planning: Mixed-integer programming model and nested decomposition algorithm. *European Journal of Operational Research, 271*, 1037–1054.

N. Lopez, J.F. Espiritu, 2011. An approach to hybrid power systems integration considering different renewable energy technologies. *Procedia Computer Science, 6*, 463–468.

S. Pfenninger, A. Hawkes, J. Keirstead, 2014. Energy systems modeling for twenty-first century energy challenges. *Renewable and Sustainable Energy Reviews, 33*, 74–86.

U.S. Energy Information Administration, 2021. Annual Energy Outlook 2021. Accessed at: https://www.eia.gov/outlooks/aeo/pdf/AEO_Narrative_2021.pdf.

Proceedings of the 14th International Symposium on Process Systems Engineering – PSE 2021+
June 19-23, 2022, Kyoto, Japan
http://dx.doi.org/10.1016/B978-0-323-85159-6.50134-2

Requirements for the quality assessment of virtual commissioning models for modular process plants

Isabell Viedt[a*], Jonathan Mädler[a], Julius Lorenz[a], and Leon Urbas[a]

[a]*Chair of Process Control System and Process Systems Engineering Group, Technische Universität Dresden, 01062 Dresden, Germany*
isabell.viedt@tu-dresden.de

Abstract

Fast changing markets and higher demands for higher flexibility in the process industry in general, require modular concepts that decrease the necessary time-to-market. This requires process simulation in earlier engineering phases and make virtual commissioning of the modular process plants besides conventional commissioning essential. Quality constraints of the model for virtual commissioning also have to be considered to confidently trust the results and findings during virtual commissioning. A particular hard problem is the quality assurance of the third-party simulation models. Our currently investigated research hypothesis is that the VC application puts an emphasis on the factors efficiency, maintainability and compatibility as defined in the quality model approach for software quality assessment for a mapping towards process simulation. This paper addresses the necessary requirements for the quality assessment of simulation models for the purpose of virtual commissioning and presents factors, criteria and metrics for the assessment of virtual commissioning models. This paper extends the current framework for functional quality assessment of simulation models in smart equipment to the use case of virtual commissioning models and is a first step to the automated quality assessment for virtual commissioning models. Further, the need for model certification is discussed.

Keywords: Modular Plants; Process Operation; Quality Assessment; Quality Assurance; Virtual Commissioning.

1. Introduction

Fast changing markets and process conditions in the process industry create an increasing demand for flexibility of process plants. One approach for adapting to those demands are modular process plants (VDI, 2020). This standardized modular plant concept strives to be manufacturer independent for the configuration of process modules, which are called Process Equipment Assemblies (PEAs). Automation and orchestration requires standardized interfaces and communication protocols (Süß et al., 2016) which are described within the Module Type Package (MTP) (VDI/VDE/NAMUR, 2019). The orchestration of those plants is realized through the Process Orchestration Layer (POL) that supports the operator in the configuration of the modular process plants and allows service-based control (Bloch et al., 2018) with an emphasis on continuous processes. With modular process plants, new plant configuration and recipes must be tested before the start of production to assess feasibility and to identify possible optimizations (cf. Schenk et al., 2019). One possible strategy is the utilization of Virtual Commissioning (VC) which allows the feasibility and optimization assessment at an early stage of engineering. Since modular process plants will integrate different PEAs and components from different manufacturers, several third-party simulation models will be integrated the

VC framework. One defining aspect is therefore the quality assessment of those models to ensure trust in the quality of VC.

In this paper, section 2 describes current trends for virtual commissioning in modular process plants and further discusses current quality assessment approaches for simulation models. In section 3 the current approach to quality assessment of simulation models for virtual commissioning and the problems with the integration of third-party models is discussed. Quality factors, criteria and metrics specifically relevant for virtual commissioning models are shown. Section 4 presents the concept for the application of the quality assessment for virtual commissioning models to VC schemes. Further, current issues and research needs of applying quality assessment to virtual commissioning are addressed. The obtained requirements aim to be the basis for a future quality assessment framework implementation for virtual commissioning models in smart, modular plants.

2. State of the art

2.1. Virtual Commissioning for modular process plants

As with any process plant, the plant configurations of modular process plants must be validated before the start of production. Virtual commissioning (VC) is a good approach to cut cost, pre-qualify plant configurations and assess feasibility before real commissioning (Puntel-Schmidt et al., 2015). VC includes the testing of individual components, interlocks and functions of the automation system during development via simulation methods and models adapted to the respective purpose (Schenk et al., 2019). Therefore, models must consider actors and sensors in the plant, which are coupled with controllers in a Hardware-in-the-Loop (HIL), Software-in-the-Loop (SIL) or Model-in-the-Loop (MIL) architecture (cf. VDI/VDE 3693). Simulation models are either simple state machines or dynamic simulation models of varying fidelity (cf. VDI/VDE 3693).

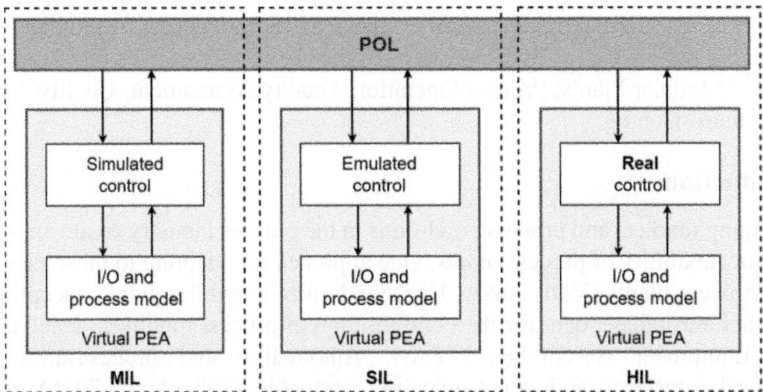

Figure 1: Test configurations for Virtual Commissioning (VC)

In modular plants, virtual commissioning can be used to safely test out new plant configuration and recipes regarding feasibility and optimization (cf. Schenk et al., 2019). Faults can therefore be detected and fixed in an early engineering phase which cuts cost and the overall time-to-market (Klose et al., 2019). Klose et al. (2021) suggest a digital twin applying the MTP for the integration of the simulation models. With this approach, the digital twins (DT) of the PEAs are integrated into a simulation or co-simulation environment and coupled to the POL. This considers the automation system including device and I/O-models, the controller in a SIL or MIL (cf. VDI/VDE 3693) scheme and a default material system (e.g. water run). To test service sequences, an OPC UA server can be utilized (Schenk et al., 2019). Furthermore, the water run models can be extended with physical property packages to ensure a better understanding of the service parameters and the process timing. Other than the interfaces for property packages, simulation control, and mass and energy flows, the interfaces for the information flow must be reconfigured to operate with the same service commands and data assemblies as the real PEA

2.2. Quality assessment for simulation models

Simulation models that are to be used in virtual commissioning of modular plants will be provided by PEA manufacturer. The partial models needed for VC are then integrated into a virtual commissioning framework, e.g. as co-simulation. To assure the quality of these simulation models assessment strategies are required. Currently used methods for that purpose focus mainly on accuracy of the model (Sargent, 2013). To integrate the quality assessment and control of simulation models into modern digital plants, a framework for what quality of a simulation models actually entails needs to be developed and implemented. A first approach to quality assessment of simulation models with pre-definition of quality attributes was proposed in Mädler et al. (2021).

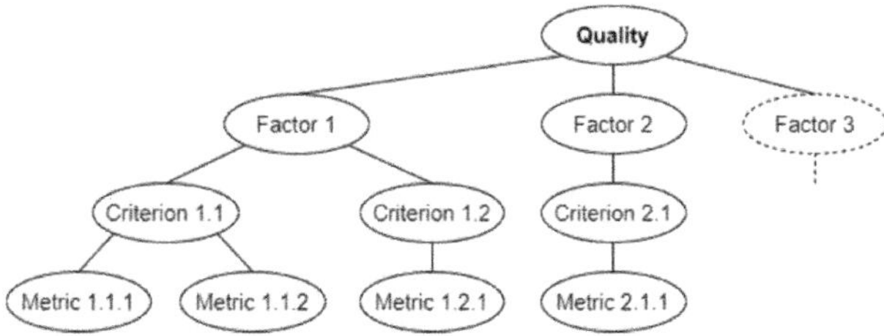

Figure 2: FCM model structure (McCall & Cavano, 1978)

With simulation models becoming an integral part of PEAs and plant equipment in general, simulation models can be considered a part of software. This allows the utilization of quality assessment strategies from software development. Current simulation model validation and verification methods (Sargent, 2013) are coupled with the approach of FCM (factors – criteria – metrics) models (McCall & Cavano, 1978) for structuring and executing quality assessment. One approach to FCM models, as mentioned in Mädler et al. (2021), is the ISO/IEC 25010 for the assessment of software product quality. The exemplary structure of a FCM model is shown in Fig. 2.

3. Requirements for third-party model integration

Virtual commissioning allows a pre-qualification of modular process plant configurations, recipes and interfaces while utilizing simulations models for the process in combination with models for the devices, I/O and controller representations. This means that not all models will be provided by the same manufacturer. Since model for virtual commissioning put an emphasis on the assembly of the VC framework from different partial models which varying depth and purpose, one important aspect to realizing the interchangeability of simulation models in VC and therefore individual PEAs is the integration of third-party models.

The quality model presented in Mädler et al. (2021) focuses on factors like functional suitability and reliability because the quality assessment is in this case intended for models for process simulation and optimization. For virtual commissioning, probably the most important aspect of models is the ability to combine the necessary partial models to a VC framework (Schenk et al., 2019). This makes the consideration of further quality factors necessary (cf. Mädler et al., 2021). As of now the framework only considers the quality factors functional suitability and reliability but with the extension of the use case to virtual commissioning model, the focus shifts to the factors compatibility, maintainability and performance efficiency. Other metrics like the validity domain of the model, as a metric for functional suitability, that specifically targets the design space of the model loses importance in the context of virtual commissioning.

3.1. Model compatibility

In this case the factor compatibility is defined through the quality criterion interoperability. The concept of interoperable models is not new and can be achieved through a standard for the interface to exchange information and models. They are used to integrate custom physical property packages, exchange mass, energy and information flows, and control the solution process of the simulation model. One approach is the CAPE-OPEN standard mostly for steady-state models (van Baten and Pons, 2014). Since CAPE-OPEN is an interoperability model and not a data model, the interoperability between different process modeling environments is not within the scope of CAPE-OPEN. This makes the CAPE-OPEN interface specification less appealing for dynamic process simulation since it does not initially enable co-simulation between third-party models on different simulation environments. Another standard is the functional mock-up interface (FMI) for dynamic models which allows import and export of both plant and controller models into and out of any simulation packages that support the specification (Blockwitz et al., 2012). Within FMI interfaces for both model exchange and co-simulation are covered. The co-simulation interface is intended for use with models where data is exchanged between subsystems only at discrete communication points and each subsystem is solved independently (Blockwitz et al., 2012). The model exchange interface is intended for use with models described by differential, algebraic and discrete equations with or without discontinuities where the system equations are solved simultaneously (Blockwitz et al., 2012).

3.2. Model maintainability

Besides the compatibility of the simulation for the VC framework, the maintainability (quality factor maintainability) of those models has to also be considered. Especially for virtual commissioning of modular plants different plant configurations have to be considered and tested. This means that the quality criterion reusability also needs to be considered to describe the maintainability of the models and the framework. With this it is important that different partial models can be reuse for different configuration of the MP to allow virtual commissioning. The models must be parameterizable to allow testing of recipes (Schenk et al., 2019) but also allow a reuse through a standardize interface (Fedorova et al., 2015). Furthermore, the transfer of models or model information into different simulation environments through XML allows a wider applicability (Fedorova et al., 2015), which is especially important for model exchange frameworks for virtual commissioning.

3.3. Performance efficiency

Another important quality factor to consider for models for VC applications is performance efficiency. In this context, the quality factor is defined by the quality criterion time-behaviour. For simulation models or digital twins used for virtual commissioning this means that real time and accelerated, hybrid continuous- and discrete-time simulation must be available to test recipes and interlocks as fast as possible in a virtual environment. To achieve synchronized, accelerated simulation, the POL must be able to operate in an accelerated mode as well.

4. Quality assessment for virtual commissioning models

The addition of three newly considered quality factors and their corresponding quality criteria and metric will make the quality assessment framework more holistic but also complex. This means that new metrics and assessment strategies have to be found to integrate the new factors. The proposed strategy shows that this means a shift from current quantitative assessment methods to more qualitative assessment metrics for the virtual commissioning models. Table 1 shows these additional quality factors, criteria and metrics which must be implemented into the framework in a next step.

Table 1: FCM model for the assessment of virtual commissioning models

Factor	Criterion	Metric
Compatibility	Interoperability	Interface standard adherence
		Interface standard compatibility
Maintainability	Reusability	Parameterizability
		Interface standard adherence
		Modeling environment transferability
Performance efficiency	Time-behaviour	Flexible simulation mode
		POL-compatible simulation mode

While a check for compliance with current interface standards for model exchange is easy to implement into an assessment framework, it is not easy to solve non-compliance of third-party models. Non-compliance with current standards will lead to workarounds and adjustments for successful application of virtual commissioning for modular plants. One strategy to ensure model compatibility could be a certification approach. Independent model certification has long been a topic of interest for modeling and simulation tasks but no concrete certification entities exist yet (Balci, 2010).

As virtual commissioning becomes increasingly important and security aspect will be necessary to consider, the factor of security as described in ISO/IEC 25010 will also need to be considered during systematic quality assessment of models, especially for virtual commissioning. This is especially important in the context of the criterion reusability.

5. Conclusion

With this paper, the first step towards systematic and potentially automated quality assessment for virtual commissioning models is taken. The requirements defined in this paper serve as a basis for the development of a quality assessment framework. The proposed concept outlines that the quality of models for virtual commissioning and the corresponding wish for potential automated assembly of the VC framework depends on additional quality factors in comparison to dynamic models used for process design. Interfaces for physical property packages, flows and simulation control must be developed further to allow tool independent usage and exchange of models. Furthermore, tools that potentially allow the transfers of models, or at least their information, for reuse in different environments also must be addressed. Depending on the use case and complexity of what VC is supposed to do in the future, new requirements to the models might arise and security concerns must be addressed. This paper extends the in Mädler et al. (2021) proposed framework for automated quality assessment of simulation models. As the use case for the simulation models shifts to virtual commissioning, new quality aspects need to be considered and others loses importance. The proposed extension of the framework now needs to be transferred to real world applications to assess the usability and integration of said concept. Since the proposed requirements and concept are only a first step, the new factors, criteria and metrics must be implemented into the MATLAB/Simulink framework and evaluated via case study.

References

O. Balci, 2010, Golden rules of verification, validation, testing, and certification of modeling and simulation applications, SCS M&S Magazine, 4, 4, 1-7H. Bloch, S. Hensel, M. Hoernicke, K. Stark, A. Menschner (neé Hahn), A. Fay, L. Urbas, T. Knohl, and J. Bernshausen, 2018, State-based control of process services within modular process plants, Procedia CIRP, 72, 1088–1093

T. Blockwitz, M. Otter, J. Akesson, M. Arnold, C. Clauss, H. Elmqvist, ..., and A. Viel, 2012, Functional mockup interface 2.0: The standard for tool independent exchange of simulation models, In ProceedingsISO/IEC, Systems and software engineering — Systems and software Quality Requirements and Evaluation (SQuaRE) — System and software quality models (ISO/IEC 25010:2011) (2011)

M. Fedorova, G. Tolksdorf, S. Fillinger, G. Wozny, M. Sales-Cruz, G. Sin, and R. Gani, 2015, Development of Computer Aided Modelling Templates for Model Re-use in Chemical and Biochemical Process and Product Design: Import and export of models. In Computer Aided Chemical Engineering, 37, 953-958

A. Klose, S. Merkelbach, A. Menschner, S. Hensel, S. Heinze, L. Bittorf, ..., and L. Urbas, 2019, Orchestration requirements for modular process plants in chemical and pharmaceutical industries, Chemical Engineering & Technology, 42, 11, 2282-2291

A. Klose, T. Schenk, R. Rosen, A. Botero, C. Schäfer, P. Da Silva Santos, S. Merkelbach, J. Lorenz, and L. Urbas, 2021, Virtuelle Inbetriebnahme modularer Prozessanlagen: Fallstudien zur Funktionsqualifizierung MTP-basierter Orchestrierung. atp magazin, 63, 04, https://doi.org/10.17560/atp.v63i04.2542

J. Mädler, I. Viedt, and L. Urbas, 2021, Applying quality assurance concepts from software development to simulation model assessment in smart equipment, Computer Aided Chemical Engineering, European Symposium on Computer Aided Process Engineering (ESCAPE), Istanbul

M. Oppelt, and L. Urbas, Otctober 2014, Integrated virtual commissioning an essential activity in the automation engineering process: From virtual commissioning to simulation supported engineering, In IECON 2014-40th Annual Conference of the IEEE Industrial Electronics Society, IEEE, 2564-2570

P. Puntel-Schmidt, and A. Fay, 2015, Levels of detail and appropriate model types for virtual commissioning in manufacturing engineering, IFAC-PapersOnLine, 48, 1, 922-927

T. Schenk, A. Botero Halblaub, R. Rosen, T. Heinzerling, J. Mädler, A. Klose, S. Hensel, and L. Urbas, 2019, Co-Simulation-based virtual Commissioning for modular process plants—Requirements, Framework and Support-Toolchain for a Virtual Automation Testing Environment. Automation 2019, 229–242

S. Süß, D. Hauf, A. Strahilov, and C. Diedrich, 2016, Standardized Classification and Interfaces of Complex Behaviour Models in Virtual Commissioning. Procedia CIRP, 52, 24-29

J. van Baten, and M. Pons, 2014, CAPE-OPEN: Interoperability in Industrial Flowsheet Simulation Software. Chemie Ingenieur Technik, 86, 7, 1052-1064

VDI, 2020, Modular plants - Fundamentals and planning modular plants (2776-1:2020-11)

VDI/VDE/NAMUR, 2019, Automation engineering of modular systems in the process industry – General concept and interface – Part 1 (2658-1:2019-10)

VDI/VDE, 2016, Virtual Commissioning – Model types and glossary (3693:2016-08)

Printed and bound by CPI Group (UK) Ltd, Croydon, CR0 4YY

03/10/2024

01040326-0014